Third Canadian Edition

nutrition

a functional approach

Janice Thompson
University of Bristol
University of New Mexico

Melinda Manore
Oregon State University

Judy Sheeshka
University of Guelph

PEARSON

Toronto

Vice-President, Editorial Director: Gary Bennett
Senior Acquisitions Editor: Lisa Rahn
Marketing Manager: Jenna Wulff
Senior Developmental Editor: Paul Donnelly
Project Manager: Richard di Santo
Production Editor: Kelly Keeler, Element LLC
Copy Editor: Cat Haggert
Proofreader: Jeff Georgeson
Photo and Permissions Researchers: Stephen Merland and Jillian Santos, PreMedia Global
Compositor: Element LLC
Art Director: Julia Hall
Interior and Cover Designer: Anthony Leung
Cover Image: Chris Cole/Gettyimages

10 9 8 7 6 5 4 3 2 1 CKV

Library and Archives Canada Cataloguing in Publication

Thompson, Janice, 1962–
    Nutrition : a functional approach / Janice Thompson, Melinda Manore, Judy Sheeshka.—3rd Canadian ed.

Includes index.
ISBN 978-0-321-74887-4

    1. Nutrition—Textbooks. I. Manore, Melinda, 1951– II. Sheeshka, Judy Diane, 1952– III. Title.

QP141.T46 2013   613.2   C2013-900084-4

ISBN 978-0-321-74887-4

About the Authors

Janice Thompson earned a Ph.D at Arizona State University in exercise science with an emphasis in exercise physiology and nutrition. She is currently Bristol University's Head of the Centre of Exercise, Nutrition, and Health Sciences and Professor of Public Health Nutrition. Her research focuses on designing and assessing the impact of nutrition and physical activity interventions to reduce the risks for obesity, cardiovascular disease, and type 2 diabetes in high-risk populations. She also teaches nutrition and research methods courses and mentors graduate research students.

Melinda Manore earned a Ph.D. in human nutrition with a minor in exercise physiology at Oregon State University (OSU). She is the past chair of the Department of Nutrition and Food Management at OSU, and is currently a professor in the Department of Nutrition and Exercise Sciences. Prior to her tenure at OSU, she taught at Arizona State University for 17 years. Melinda's area of expertise is nutrition and exercise, especially the role of diet and exercise in health, exercise performance, weight control, and micronutrient needs. She focuses on the nutritional needs of active women and girls.

Judy Sheeshka is Professor and Discipline Head of Dietetics at Victoria University in Melbourne Australia. She previously spent 21 years in Applied Human Nutrition at the University of Guelph in Guelph, Ontario. Her research interests focus on nutrition policy, and she recently examined consumers' views of menu labelling, policy on advertising foods and beverages to children, and consumers' understanding of the Nutrition Facts Panel on packaged foods. She also has a strong interest in food security issues from the perspective of individuals experiencing food insecurity and hunger.

Welcome to *Nutrition: A Functional Approach*, Third Canadian Edition!

Why We Wrote the Book

Nutrition gets a lot of press. Pick up a magazine and you'll read the latest debate over which type of diet is best for weight loss; turn on the TV and you'll hear a celebrity describe how she lost 50 pounds without exercising; scan the headlines or read some blogs and you'll discover the politics surrounding the creation of new enhanced "designer" foods. How can you evaluate these sources of nutrition information and find out whether the advice they provide is reliable? How do you navigate through seemingly endless recommendations and come up with a way of eating that's right for *you*—one that supports your physical activity, allows you to maintain a healthful weight, and helps you avoid chronic diseases?

We Wrote This Book to Help You Answer These Questions

Nutrition: A Functional Approach began with our conviction that both students and instructors would benefit from an accurate and clear textbook that links nutrients to their functional benefits. As authors and instructors, we know that students have a natural interest in their bodies, their health, their weight, and their success in sports and other activities. By demonstrating how nutrition relates to these interests, ***Nutrition: A Functional Approach*** empowers students to reach their personal health and fitness goals. Throughout the text, material is presented in a lively narrative that continually links the facts to students' circumstances, lifestyles, and goals. Information on current events and research keeps the inquisitive spark alive, illustrating that nutrition is truly a "living" science and a source of considerable debate. The content of ***Nutrition: A Functional Approach*** is appropriate for non-nutrition majors, but also includes information that will challenge students who have a more advanced understanding of chemistry and math. We present the "science side" in a contemporary narrative style that's easy-to-read and understand, with engaging features that reduce students' fears and encourage them to apply the material to their lives. Also, because this book is not a derivative of a major's text, the writing and the figures are cohesive and always level-appropriate.

As educators, we are familiar with the myriad challenges of presenting nutrition information in the classroom, and we have included the most comprehensive ancillary package available to assist instructors in successfully meeting these challenges. We hope to contribute to the excitement of teaching and learning about nutrition: a subject that affects all of us, a subject so important and relevant that correct and timely information can make the difference between health and disease.

New in the Third Canadian Edition

Key goals for this edition included providing the most up-to-date and accurate nutrition information currently available and optimizing students' ability to learn this information and apply it to their daily lives. To achieve this we have made some dramatic changes to our organization and material presentation. The text is now shorter by one chapter, going from 16 chapters in the second edition to 15 chapters in this edition. We added several exciting new features, updated and integrated current information from recent scientific studies, and significantly enhanced the already excellent art program to ensure that *Nutrition: A Functional Approach* would be the most up-to-date and easiest-to-use, comprehensive resource for nutrition students currently available.

Fifteen **In Depth** "mini-chapters" appear in this edition. These practical, topical, and graphically lively presentations follow every chapter in the text, many with a dedicated focus on the links between nutrition and disease. In addition we included numerous new elements in this edition aimed at making nutritional information more relevant to students' everyday lives. New features include **Eating Right All Day**, a visual guide to suggested meal options tied to specific chapter content on micro- and macronutrients and key body systems; **Quick Tips**, brief lists appearing frequently throughout the text which, taken all together, provide an extensive array of simple suggestions and ideas for incorporating better eating habits into each student's day; **What About You?**, a varied self-assessment feature that emphasizes active learning and content integration; and **Hot Topics**, informative snapshots of current issues that students are undoubtedly encountering in sometimes less-reliable sources of popular information. Also note that **References** now appear at the back of the text.

Additionally, this edition introduces four new full-page **NutriTools** activity overviews linked to the chapters on designing healthful diets (Build-a-Meal), carbohydrates (Build-a-Sandwich), fats (Build-a-Pizza), and antioxidants (Build-a-Salad), which tie-in with NutriTools content available on MasteringNutrition™.

The Visual Walkthrough at the front of this text provides an overview of these and other important features in the third Canadian edition. For specific changes to each chapter, please see below.

Chapter 1

- Updated the Nutrition Debate on nutrigenomics and moved the feature into the chapter.
- Added an In Depth mini-chapter on alcohol.
- Revised content on the evolution of nutrition as a science, and on the research of the role of nutrition in chronic diseases.
- Incorporated content on pellagra into the Nutrition Myth or Fact? feature box.
- Created a Quick Tips box covering information on evaluating media hype.

Chapter 2

- Captured information on probiotics in a new Nutrition Debate.
- Discussed phytochemicals in the In Depth mini-chapter.
- Added new content on structure-function food label claims and added a new table with the claims currently permitted in Canada.
- Brought the Mediterranean Diet Pyramid up to date.
- Inserted a Quick Tips box on the nutritional costs of eating out.

Chapter 3

- Included colon cleansing in a new Nutrition Debate.
- Covered the etiology of peptic ulcers in a new Nutrition Myth or Fact? box.
- Revised the neuromuscular regulation of digestion and updated the terminology for GER and GERD.
- Developed a Quick Tips section on traveller's diarrhea, and inserted the Bristol Stool Chart.
- Added an In Depth mini-chapter on disorders related to specific foods.
- Incorporated information on Canada's Food Allergen program.
- Captured extreme dieting and colon cleansing in Find the Quack.

Chapter 4

- Discussed the connections between nutrition and diabetes in the In Depth mini-chapter.
- Included the most current information on artificial sweeteners.
- Shifted material on lactose intolerance to the In Depth mini-chapter following Chapter 3.
- Provided hypoglycaemia content in a Hot Topic box.
- Updated the Shopper's Guide content on complex carbohydrates and integrated the content into the text's narrative.
- Expanded content on insulin insensitivity and pre-diabetes.
- Added a new Eating Right All Day feature focusing on carbohydrates.
- Created a new Hot Topic on insulin pumps.

Chapter 5

- Revised the Nutrition Debate on fat blockers.
- Featured the links between nutrition and cardiovascular disease in the In Depth mini-chapter.
- Incorporated the discussion of chitosan and fat blockers (previously in Chapter 3) into the Nutrition Debate.
- Presented a new Hot Topic on nuts.
- Updated the Highlight on Dr. Alejandro Marangoni and alternatives to trans fats.
- Reworked the Shopper's Guide material on dietary fats into the text's narrative.
- Highlighted dietary fats in the new Eating Right All Day feature.
- Added a new Quick Tips feature on shopping for foods low in saturated and *trans* fats.

Chapter 6

- Created a new Nutrition Debate on the connections between meat consumption and global warming.
- Showcased vitamins and minerals within an In Depth mini-chapter.
- Revised content on vegetarian diets, including flexitarian diets.
- Discussed amino acid supplements in a new Hot Topic.
- Updated content on disorders related to inadequate protein intake.
- Incorporated new material on plant protein sources.

Chapter 7

- Focused chapter-opening scenario on vitamin water.
- Revised the Nutrition Debate on sports beverages, and shifted this feature into the chapter.
- Featured dehydration and fluid-balance disorders in the In Depth mini-chapter.
- Updated content in Figure 7.7 for calculations on water intake and output for the average adult female.
- Increased coverage of fluid-related disorders to include heat-related illnesses.
- Provided an overview of exercise-related hyponatremia in the Nutrition Myth or Fact? box.
- Moved material on potassium sources from the Shopper's Guide into the chapter.

- Expanded the food source graph figures to display 100% AI or RDA to contextual-ize serving size vs. daily needs.
- Added a new Eating Right All Day focusing on sodium.
- Updated Nutrition Myth or Fact? on the safety of bottled water versus tap water.

Chapter 8

- Incorporated a new Nutrition Debate on antioxidants.
- Created an In Depth mini-chapter that showed the links between nutrition and cancer.
- Provided the most up-to-date coverage of beta-carotene.
- Presented coverage of vitamin A and acne in a new Hot Topic.
- Updated content on the contribution of minerals to antioxidant enzyme systems.
- Shifted the Shopper's Guide content on vitamin E, vitamin A, and beta-carotene sources into the text and the Quick Tips features.
- Featured damage from tobacco use and nutritional links in the In Depth mini-chapter.
- Added a new Eating Right All Day focusing on antioxidants.
- Repositioned Nutrition Debate content on vitamin and mineral supplements into the Chapter 10 In Depth mini-chapter.

Chapter 9

- Revised chapter-opening scenario to focus on bone health and falls.
- Inserted a new Nutrition Debate on vitamin D deficiency.
- Focused the In Depth mini-chapter on the links between nutrition and osteoporosis.
- Updated Table 9.3 on the factors affecting vitamin D synthesis.
- Integrated calcium and vitamin D sources from the Shopper's Guide into the text.
- Created a new Eating Right All Day focusing on calcium.
- Moved the discussion on Sprinkles to the In Depth mini-chapter on global nutri-tion following Chapter 13.
- Added a new section on bone loss during cancer treatment.
- Captured new medications to reduce bone loss.

Chapter 10

- Revised the efficacy of zinc lozenges in fighting colds in the Nutrition Debate.
- Added an In Depth mini-chapter on dietary supplements and natural health products.
- Highlighted the role of vitamin B_6 and PMS in a new Hot Topic.
- Relocated the material on iron sources from the Shopper's Guide into the text.
- Provided a new Quick Tips box on retaining vitamins in foods.
- Developed a new Eating Right All Day focusing on iron.

Chapter 11

- Changed the chapter-opening scenario to focus on "fat talk."
- Replaced discussion of near infrared reactances with DEXA in the body composi-tion assessment section.

- Relocated information on the nutrition paradox to the In Depth mini-chapter on global nutrition following Chapter 13.

- Updated information on leptin, ghrelin, peptide YY, and uncoupling proteins in brown adipose tissue.

- Developed a new In Depth mini-chapter on the links between nutrition and obesity.

- Updated information on bariatric surgery, such as evidence of remission of Type 2 diabetes, new techniques, and loss of excess weight following various procedures.

- Inserted a new Nutrition Debate on the appropriateness of bariatric surgery for adolescents.

- Revised content on healthful body weight.

- Highlighted the relationship between cultural and economic factors and body weight.

- Expanded content on behavioural modification regarding weight loss.

- Increased coverage of low-carbohydrate diets.

- Discussed dietary supplements for weight loss in a new Hot Topic feature.

- Added new Quick Tips boxes on portion sizes, overcoming barriers to weight loss, and modifying behaviour.

Chapter 12

- Included the Physical Activity Guidelines released in 2011 by the Canadian Society for Exercise Physiology in consultation with the Public Health Agency of Canada.

- Featured physical activity advice for 18- to 64-year-olds in a new Quick Tips box.

- Provided a new Nutrition Debate on addiction to exercise.

- Captured content on night-eating syndrome.

- Added a new What About You? on disordered eating.

- Shifted content on deceptive practices in marketing ergogenic aids into a new Hot Topic.

- Brought fluid/dehydration content up to date.

- Discussed muscle dysmorphia in men in a new Hot Topic.

Chapter 13

- Updated the content on genetically modified organisms and moved it from the Nutrition Debate feature into the chapter.

- Created a new In Depth mini-chapter on global nutrition.

- Developed a new Figure 13.1 on food safety issues "from farm to table."

- Added a new Nutrition Myth or Fact? on mad cow disease.

- Inserted a new figure on acute and long-term effects of malnutrition across the life cycle.

- Discussed the use of bisphenol A (BPA) in canned foods in a new Hot Topic.

- Added a new Quick Tips feature on reducing exposure to pesticides.

- Captured up-to-date information on organic foods and their regulation in Canada.

- Relocated content from Chapter 9 on Sprinkles into the new In Depth mini-chapter on global nutrition, with a new focus on treating iron deficiency.

Chapter 14

- Incorporated a new discussion on whether mothers can breastfeed their adopted babies in a new Hot Topic.

- Updated recommendations for weight gain during pregnancy.

- Revised Canadian statistics on breastfeeding and complications.

- Captured a new Nutrition Debate on whether formula-feeding should be penalized with high taxes.

- Focused the new In Depth mini-chapter on fetal origins theory.

- Included a new chart with food safety information for pregnant women.

- Added new WHO growth charts adapted for Canada.

- Updated the recommendations for vitamin D supplementation for infants.

- Provided a new figure on the fetal origins of adult diseases in the In Depth mini-chapter.

Chapter 15

- Featured energy drinks in a new chapter-opening scenario.

- Inserted a provocative discussion about breakfast as the most important meal of the day in the new Nutrition Myth or Fact? feature.

- Revised vitamin D recommendations.

- Discussed whether senior supplements were a marketing ploy in a new Hot Topic.

- Included the nine D's of geriatric weight loss.

- Inserted information on medication and nutrient interactions.

- Incorporated advice on stocking a first kitchen in a new Quick Tips box.

- Showcased a new Nutrition Debate on restricting the sale of energy drinks to children.

- Added a new In Depth mini-chapter on longevity diets.

- Presented new content on childhood food insecurity.

- Offered new content on bone density issues for adolescents.

Content Is Applied to Life

Because students are most interested in how nutrition applies to their own lives, we developed several learning tools throughout the book to illustrate real-life implications of nutrition. For instance, to teach students the effect of vitamins and minerals in the body, we organized the micronutrients chapters according to their function. We also developed nutrition debates, math activities, and nutrition label activities that encourage students to put that information into practice.

Functional Organization

Students have traditionally learned about micronutrients by memorizing each one along with their deficiency symptoms and toxicity syndromes. With this traditional approach, we found that students quickly forget this information, and that they didn't really understand why micronutrients are so important. To address this challenge, we decided to illustrate the immediate health issues and physiological functions of vitamins and minerals by discussing them within the context of fluid and electrolyte balance, antioxidant function, bone health, and energy metabolism and blood formation. We discovered, through our own experience teaching and through extensive class testing, that this functional approach helps students to think about these micronutrients on a conceptual level, enabling them to answer the questions "Why are vitamins and minerals important?" and "What do they do?" This approach also promotes better retention of the material and application to real life.

You Do the Math

You Do the Math boxes show students how to perform nutritional calculations, such as determining their own body mass index (BMI). Knowledge of these calculations helps students determine their own nutritional needs.

Nutrition Label Activities

Nutrition Label Activities teach students how to read and evaluate labels from real food products so they can make educated choices about the foods they eat. Students can use the skills they learn when they do their food shopping.

Teaching How to Evaluate Nutrition Information

One of our goals with *Nutrition: A Functional Approach,* **Third Canadian Edition,** is to teach students how to evaluate the nutrition information they encounter every day. To that end, each chapter discusses how to find and evaluate reliable sources for nutrition facts, and provides references students can trust for answers to common nutrition questions. In addition, the following features help to debunk some commonly held myths about nutrition.

Test Yourself Questions

A brief **Test Yourself** quiz at the beginning of each chapter piques students' interest in the topics to be covered by raising and dispelling common myths about nutrition. The answers to these questions can be found at the end of each chapter.

Nutrition Myth or Fact

Nutrition Myth or Fact boxes provide the facts behind the hype on many current nutrition and dietary issues. They dispel common misconceptions and teach students how to critically evaluate information on the internet, in the mass media, and from their peers.

Nutrition Debates

Nutrition Debates contain in-depth coverage of current events and hot topics, such as vitamin and mineral supplementation. By presenting both sides of the argument, these debates encourage students to think critically about controversial issues and become more informed and discriminating consumers of nutrition and health information.

Captivating Student Interest

To capture students' interest and to motivate them to read on, we created chapter-opening scenarios and Highlight boxes that stimulate students' curiosity, as well as mini-chapters that delve deeper into specific topics. We also included appealing and informative illustrations and photos that draw students into the text and create an engaging learning environment.

Chapter-Opening Scenarios

Chapter-Opening Scenarios begin each chapter with a real-life story that teaches students about the sometimes life-altering effects of diet and exercise. These scenarios grab students' attention and motivate them to delve deeper into the chapter material.

Highlight Boxes

Highlight boxes provide further insight into topics that students will recognize from the mass media and popular culture, such as mad cow disease or sports beverages. These boxes discuss the nutritional facts and theories behind these often complex issues.

In Depth Mini-chapters

In Depth Mini-chapters are practical, topical, and graphically lively presentations that appear after every chapter in the text. Many offer a dedicated focus on the links between nutrition and disease.

Art, Photos, and Tables

The **art program** was designed to walk students through the body's processing of nutrients. Insets are provided on digestion diagrams to illustrate context, so students understand where in the body a given process is located. The photos were chosen to provide illustration for conditions created by nutrient deficiencies, as well as to show students foods that they may not immediately think of as good sources for specific nutrients. Tables integrate nutrition information, and special figures act as "shopper's guides," indicating foods that are good sources of Dietary Reference Intakes of specific vitamins and minerals.

Support for the Student

In writing *Nutrition: A Functional Approach,* **Third Canadian Edition,** we worked to develop pedagogical features that would benefit students by helping them learn and remember all the information in the chapter. These features help students review the material they just learned, find more information, check their understanding of the material, and stay focused on the most important points.

Chapter Objectives

Chapter objectives help students stay focused by listing the most important concepts in the chapter. After reading the chapter, students can go back and review the objectives to make sure that they understand each point.

Recaps

Recap paragraphs appear throughout each chapter, and rephrase what students just learned in preceding sections. They provide a quick summary and use new wording to help students remember the concept (not just the words) before moving on to the next topic.

Test Yourself Answers

Test Yourself Answers to each chapter's Test Yourself questions are located at the end of the textbook, pages AN-1 to AN-11. Using the Test Yourself answers enables students to evaluate their responses to these questions about nutrition.

Chapter Summaries

Chapter summaries provide quick reviews of the major points and topics covered in each chapter. By reading through the chapter summaries, students can determine whether they have understood information about the chapter's main concepts.

Review Questions

Review questions at the end of each chapter allow students to assess their retention and understanding of the material they have covered in the chapter. Answers to multiple choice review questions appear at the end of the book (pages AN-1 to AN-11); answers to the short answer questions are found on the MasteringNutrition site in the Study Area.

Web Links and References

Web Links at the end of each chapter provide students with connections for further information and study. The comprehensive references for each chapter appear at the end of the book.

Acknowledgments

This book would not have been possible without the information retrieval skills of my research assistants, Carolyn Bowman, Megan Skinner, Eliana Witchell, Lauren Tucker, Maxine Fung, Kelly Matheson, Jessica Wegener, Alison Campbell, and June Matthews. Their creativity and assistance was much appreciated. I am also very grateful for the assistance of food safety experts Mary Alton Mackey and Dr. Bonnie Lacroix in rewriting sections of Chapter 13.

I am very grateful to the outstanding researchers who agreed to be interviewed and featured in this book: Dr. Linda McCargar at the University of Alberta, Dr. Susan Whiting at the University of Saskatchewan, Dr. Alejandro Marangoni at the University of Guelph, and Dr. Stanley Zlotkin and Dr. Deborah O'Connor at the University of Toronto and the Hospital for Sick Children.

The talented staff at Pearson Canada need to be acknowledged for their dedication to this project, their writing and editorial skills, and their patience. Developmental Editor Paul Donnelly was invaluable in providing guidance about the content and in eliciting great feedback from the peer reviewers. Copy Editor Cat Haggert provided her exceptional editing skills. Project Manager Richard di Santo efficiently oversaw the production process with Kelly Keeler's invaluable assistance, and Media Developer Maureen de Sousa worked tirelessly on MasteringNutrition. I am indebted to Lisa Rahn, Acquisitions Editor, for her support and dedication to the preparation of the third Canadian edition.

Additionally, I am grateful to the following people for their valued input and assistance in reviewing this book:

Nooshin Alizadeh-Pasdar
University of British Columbia

Sebastien Boyas
University of Ottawa

Karen Davidson
Langara College

Natalie Hamilton
Seneca College

Vineet Johnson
Capilano University

Kathy Keiver
University of the Fraser Valley

Lynn Lafave
Mount Royal University

Jeffrey Lalonde
Queen's University

Shelly Lang
Mohawk College

Paul LeBlanc
Brock University

Janet Le Patourel
Langara College

Jane Mackie
Trent University

Milly Ryan-Harshman
University of Ontario Institute of Technology

Jake Sandison
Loyalist College

Lynneth Stuart-Hill
University of Victoria

Norman Temple
Athabasca University

Apollinaire Tsopmo
Carleton University

Amandio Vieira
Simon Fraser University

Christine Wellington
University of Windsor

—Judy Sheeshka, August 2012

Brief Contents

Contents

IN DEPTH: Alcohol 30

Chapter 3

The Human Body: Are We Really What We Eat?

72

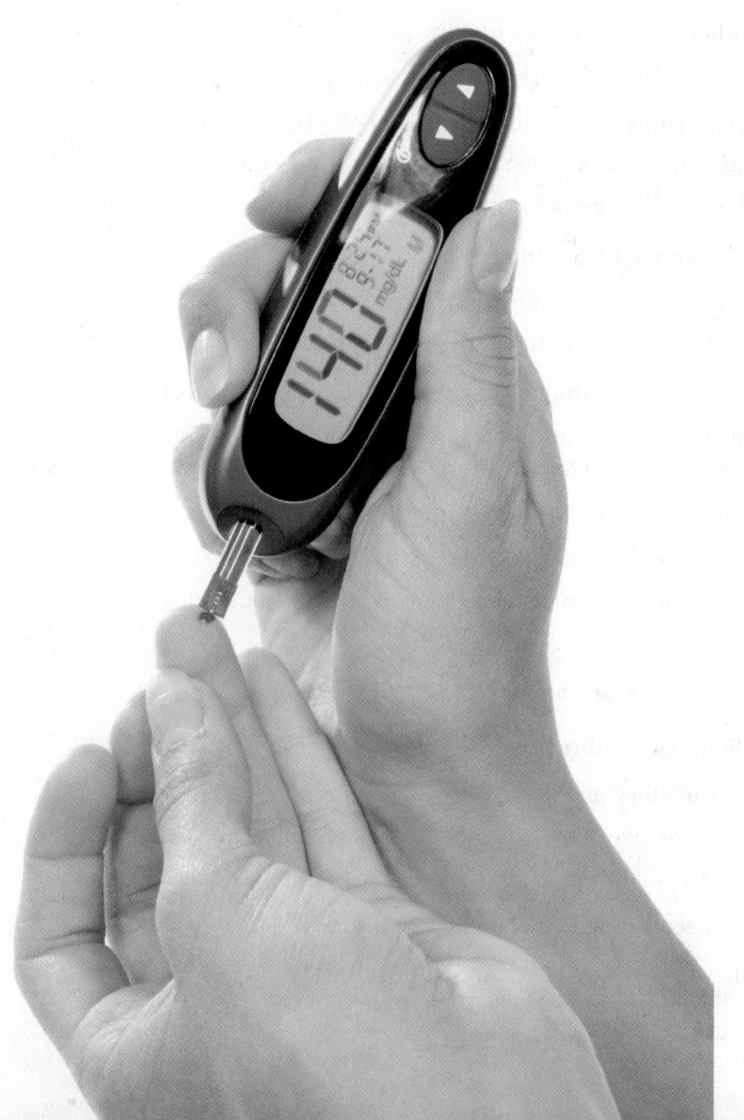

Chapter 5
Fats: Essential Energy-Supplying Nutrients

146 Rocky Road

Highlight:

Is there an Alternative to Trans fatty Acids?

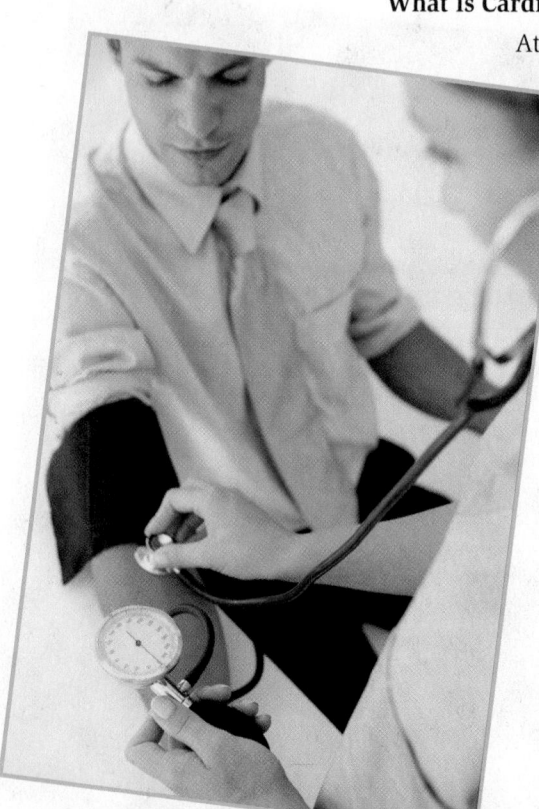

Chapter 7

Nutrients Involved in Fluid and Electrolyte Balance
226

Chapter 8

Nutrients Involved in Antioxidant Function

254

279

IN DEPTH: **Cancer**

Chapter 9

Nutrients Involved in Bone Health · 286

IN DEPTH: Osteoporosis 314

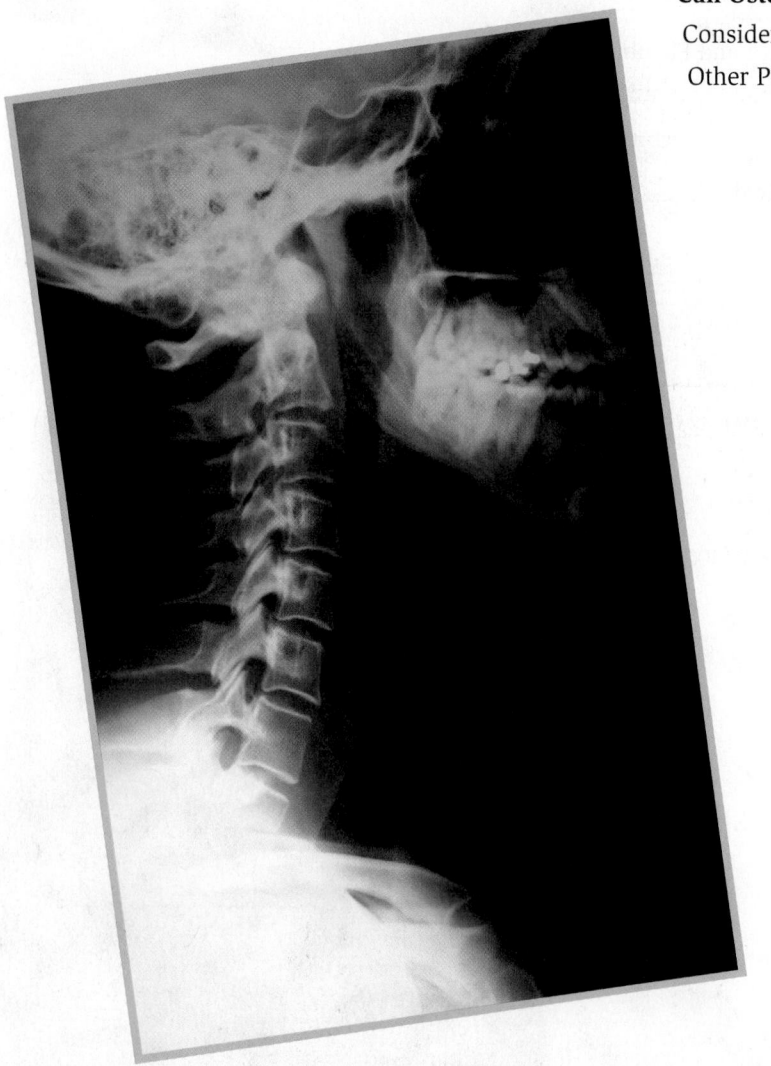

Chapter 10
Nutrients Involved in Energy Metabolism and Blood Health *322*

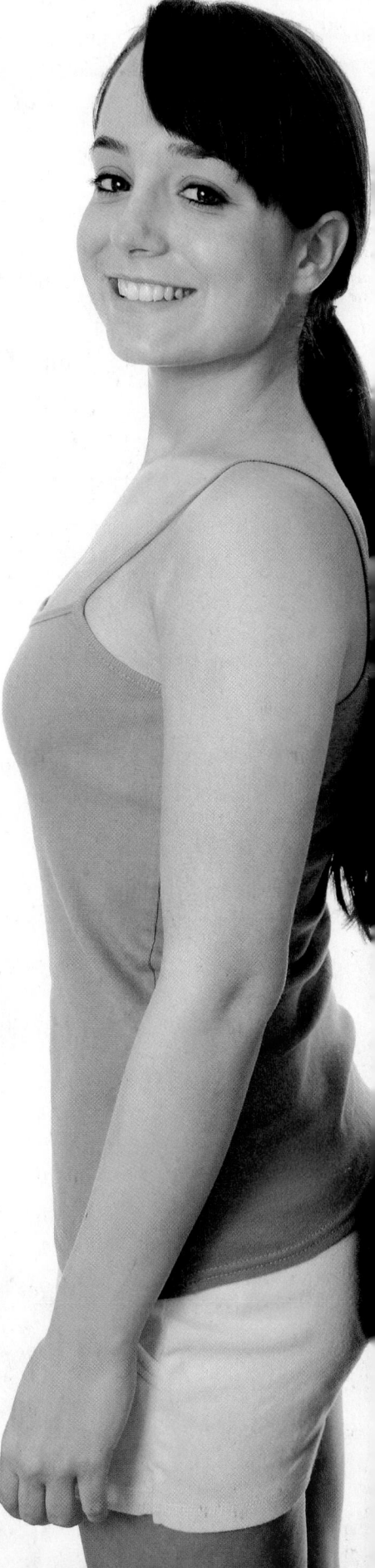

IN DEPTH: **Obesity**　　　　　　　　　395

Chapter 13

Food Safety and Technology: Impact on Consumers

446

IN DEPTH: **Global Nutrition** 482

Chapter 14

Nutrition Through the Life Cycle: Pregnancy and the First Year of Life

492

Help your students **make connections** to good nutrition

Help students make
important nutrition connections

Vitamins and Minerals: Micronutrients with Macro Powers

WANT TO FIND OUT...

- how a few fortunate accidents led to the discovery of micronutrients?
- why large doses of certain micronutrients could kill you—and which ones?
- whether micronutrient supplements have the same health benefits as nutrients found in whole foods?

READ ON. Have you heard the one about the college student on the junk-food diet who developed scurvy, a disease caused by inadequate intake of vitamin C? This "urban legend" seems to circulate on most college campuses every year, but that might be because there's some truth behind it. Away from their families, many college students do adopt diets that are deficient in one or more micronutrients. For instance, some students adopt a vegan diet with insufficient iron, whereas others stop choosing foods rich in calcium and vitamin D. Why

216

Thompson, Manore, and Sheeshka build on students' natural interest in nutrition by demonstrating in a clear, conversational style how key nutritional information relates to their health, and how to debunk commonly held misconceptions.

NEW! In Depth mini chapters

In Depth mini chapters have been added to the Third Edition, with every main chapter now followed by a corresponding In Depth treatment of key concepts.

- **NEW! The New In Depth** structure presents compelling content that focuses on the important connections between nutrition, health, and disease.

- **The In Depth on Vitamins and Minerals** gives instructors flexibility with micronutrient material by presenting it in the traditional way, to serve as a quick overview prior to the first functional chapter.

What About You?

Do You Eat in Response to External or Internal Cues?

Whether you're trying to lose weight, gain weight, or maintain your current weight, you might find it intriguing to keep a log of the reasons behind your decisions about what, when, where, and why you eat. Are you eating in response to internal sensations telling you that your body needs food, or in response to your emotions, your situation, or a prescribed diet? Keeping a "cues" log for one full week would give you the most accurate picture of your eating habits, but even logging two days of meals and snacks should increase your cue awareness.

Each day, every time you eat a meal, snack, or beverage other than water, make a quick note of the following:

- When you eat: Many people eat at certain times (for example, 6 p.m.) whether they are hungry or not.
- What you eat, and how much: Do you choose a cup of yogurt and a 180 mL (6 fl. oz.) glass of orange juice or a candy bar and a 500 mL (approx. 18 fl. oz.) cola?
- Where you eat: At home, watching television; on the subway; and so on.
- With whom you eat: Are you alone or with others? If with others, are they also eating? Have they offered you food?
- Your emotions: Some people overeat when they are happy, others when they are anxious, depressed, bored, or frustrated. Still others eat as a way of denying feelings they don't want to identify and deal with. For some, food becomes a substitute for emotional fulfillment.
- Your sensations—what you see, hear, or smell: Are you eating because you just saw a TV commercial for pizza, or smelled homemade cookies?

- Any dietary restrictions: Are you choosing a particular food because it is allowed on your current diet plan? Or are you hungry for a meal but drinking a diet soft drink to stay within a certain energy allowance ? Are you restricting yourself because you feel guilty about having eaten too much at another time?
- Your physiologic hunger: Finally, rate your hunger on a scale from 1 to 5 as follows:

  1 = you feel uncomfortably full or even stuffed
  2 = you feel satisfied but not uncomfortably full
  3 = neutral; you feel no discernible satiation or hunger
  4 = you feel hungry and want to eat
  5 = you feel strong physiologic sensations of hunger and need to eat

After keeping a log for two or more days, you might become aware of patterns you'd like to change. For example, maybe you notice that you often eat when you are not actually hungry but are worried about homework or personal relationships. Or maybe you notice that you can't walk past the snack bar without going in. This self-awareness may prompt you to change those patterns. For instance, instead of stifling your worries with food, you could write down exactly what you are worried about, including steps you can take to address your concerns. And the next time you approach the snack bar, you could check with your gut: are you truly hungry? If so, then purchase a healthful snack, maybe a piece of fruit or a bag of unsalted peanuts. If you're not really hungry, then take a moment to acknowledge the strength of this visual cue—and then walk on by.

NEW! Quick Tips

This feature provides helpful suggestions for incorporating better nutrition into daily life, in a succinct list. Examples include shopping advice, cooking suggestions, food preparation tips, eating out ideas, exercise-related topics, food sources, and other creative ways to apply what readers have learned.

QUICK TIPS

Hunting for Fibre

- Select breads made with whole grains, such as wheat, oats, barley, and rye. Two slices of whole-grain bread provide 4–6 grams of fibre.
- Switch from a low-fibre breakfast cereal to one that has at least 4 grams of fibre per serving.
- For a mid-morning snack, stir 1–2 tablespoons of whole ground flaxseed meal (4 grams of fibre) into a cup of low-fat or non-fat yogurt. Or choose an apple or a pear, with the skin left on (approximately 5 grams of fibre).
- Instead of potato chips with your lunch-time sandwich, have a side of carrot sticks or celery sticks (approximately 2 grams of fibre per serving).

- Eat legumes every day, if possible (approximately 6 grams of fibre per serving). Have them as your main dish, as a side, or in soups, chili, and other dishes.
- Don't forget the vegetables! A cup of cooked leafy greens provides about 4 grams of fibre, and a salad is rich in fibre.
- For dessert, try fresh, frozen, or dried fruit or a high-fibre granola cereal with sweetened soy milk.
- When shopping, choose fresh fruits and vegetables whenever possible. Buy frozen vegetables and fruits when fresh produce is not available. Check frozen selections to make sure there is no sugar or salt added.
- Be careful when buying canned fruits, vegetables, and legumes, as they may be high in added sugar or sodium. Select versions without added sugar or salt, or rinse before serving.

NEW! What About You?

This self-assessment feature includes checklists, questionnaires and other engaging formats that present brief, targeted activities emphasizing active learning and applied thinking skills.

NEW! Eating Right All Day

Eating Right All Day visually highlights tasty suggestions students can use to improve their daily meals. The breakfast/lunch/dinner/snack format features appealing examples of satisfying everyday meals that are also good sources of nutrients.

Eating Right All Day

Breakfast
Whole-grain waffle with jam instead of a ham & cheese omelette!

Lunch
Spinach salad instead of pastrami submarine sandwich!

Dinner
Veggie pizza instead of pepperoni!

Snack
Unsalted almonds instead of corn chips!

Make connections through media

MasteringNutrition®

MasteringNutrition is a course management system that makes it easy to organize your class, personalize your students' educational experience, and push their learning to the next level.

Designed to help you maximize class time, MasteringNutrition offers customizable, easy-to-assign, and automatically graded assessments and pedagogical tools that motivate students to learn outside of class and arrive prepared for lecture.

Developed by science educators for students and professors, the Mastering platform has over one million active registrants and a proven history with over 9 years of student use in 30 countries.

Animations

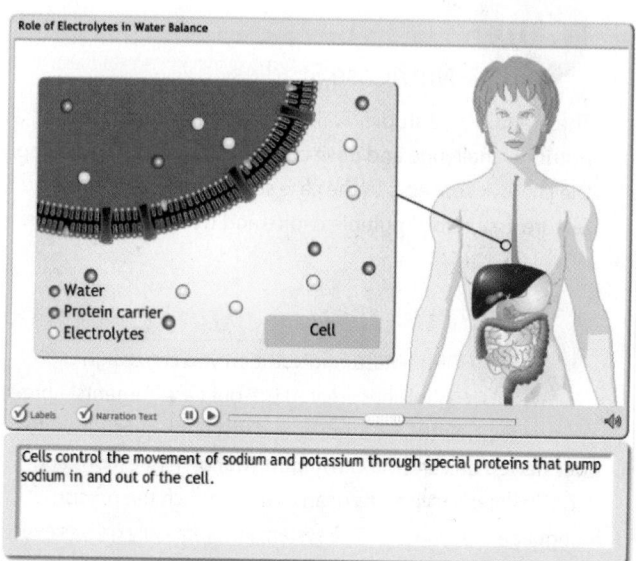

Cells control the movement of sodium and potassium through special proteins that pump sodium in and out of the cell.

See It
NutriTools

Students can experiment with NutriTools—Build-a-Salad, Build-a-Pizza, Build-a-Meal, and more—to combine different food options and thereby learn how to create healthier meals. NutriTools activities offer assignable questions.

Read It

Pearson eText

Highlight function allows students to highlight whatever they want to remember.

Google®-based search function.

Zoom lets students zoom in and out for better viewing.

Hyperlinks link to quizzes, activities, and animations.

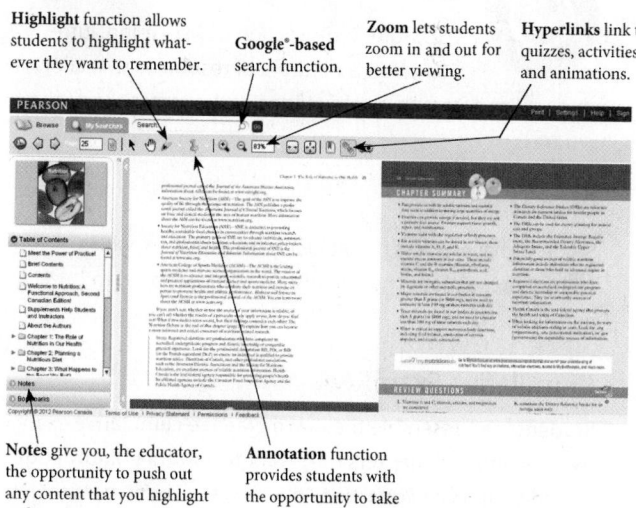

Notes give you, the educator, the opportunity to push out any content that you highlight and notes to your class.

Annotation function provides students with the opportunity to take notes.

Pre-Lecture Quiz

Ensure that students come to lecture prepared by assigning a Pre-Lecture Quiz featuring multiple choice, fill-in-the-blank, and short answer questions based on chapter content.

Hear It

NutriCase Studies

These audio case studies walk listeners through a real life nutrition challenge and pose compelling questions that apply the chapter concepts to the case study. NutriCase Studies feature assignable multiple choice and true-false questions.

Assign It

With MasteringNutrition you can assign publisher-created pre-built assignments—pre-lecture tests, NutriCase Studies, and test bank questions—to get started quickly. You can import your own questions and edit any of our questions or answers to match the precise language that you use. The system automatically grades every assignment that features machine-graded questions (multiple choice and fill-in-the-blank), and students' results appear in the gradebook. Note that instructor-graded questions (short answer and essay questions) must be graded by the professor.

Study It

The Study Tools section of MasteringNutrition offers a plethora of resources that allow students to assess their knowledge of the material and their progress.

Prep Materials

Students have access to Get Ready for Nutrition, which features extra math and chemistry content related to nutrition.

Cumulative Exam

Students can assemble their own practice cumulative exam by selecting the chapters they want to test their knowledge and the number of questions per chapter. The system then draws on a variety of questions. Note that these questions are different than the ones offered in the test bank to which you have access. MasteringNutrition automatically grades answers, so students can get feedback and check their understanding right away.

Study on the Go

This QR code appears at the end of every chapter and provides learning resources that students can use with their smartphone to study-on-the-go. Students can access self-review quizzes, flashcards, and more!

If students don't have an app to scan the QR code, they can download it for free by visiting one of the sites below on their smartphones. After installation, the phone will scan the code, and link to Pearson's Study on the Go content.

ScanLife: http://getscanlife.com

NeoReader: http://get.neoreader.com

QuickMark: http://www.quickmark.com.tw

Grade It

Gradebook

Get easy-to-interpret insights into students performance using the gradebook. MasteringNutrition automatically grades every assignment that features machine-grade questions. At a glance, you can see vulnerable students and challenging assignments. The gradebook's diagnostics provide unique insight into the class, and student performance. Charts summarize the most difficult problems, students-at-risk, grade distribution, and score improvement over the duration of the course.

Access It

Instructor Resources

You can access all of the resources that accompany *Nutrition: A Functional Approach*, Third Canadian Edition—the Instructor's Manual, PowerPoints, Image Library, PRS Questions, Test Item File, and MyTest—from MasteringNutrition.

A Healthy Approach to Diet Analysis

Accessible via MasteringNutrition, MyDiet-Analysis offers an accurate, reliable, easy-to-use program that helps students assess their lifestyles. Featuring a database of nearly 20 000 foods, the program assists in the tracking of diet and activity levels. Students can generate and submit reports electronically.

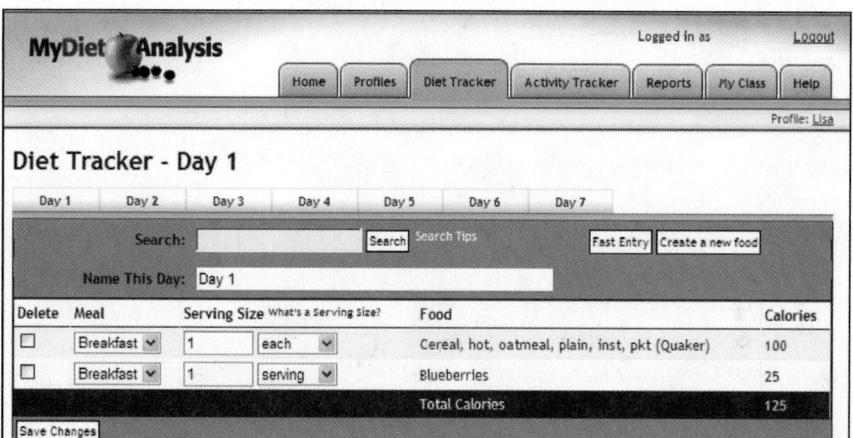

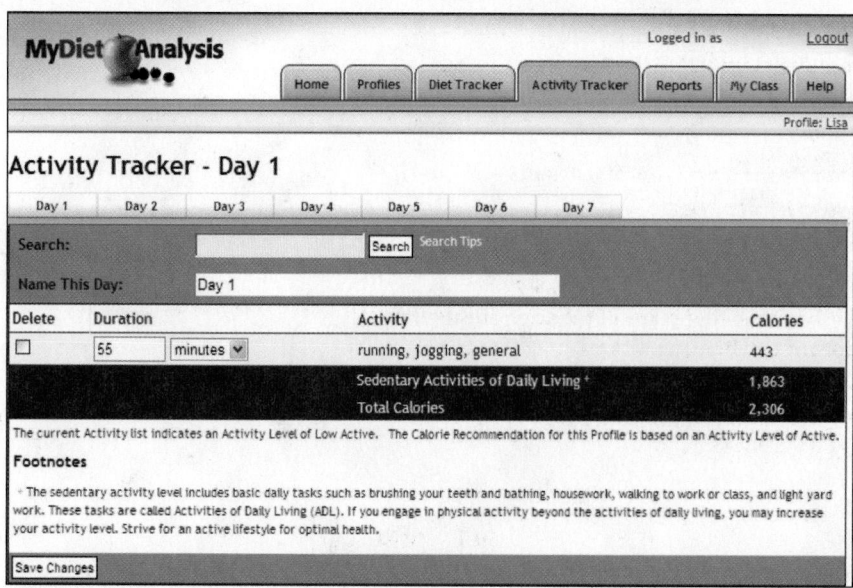

The Role of Nutrition in Our Health

1

Dylan hadn't expected that university life would make him feel so tired. After classes, he just wanted to go back to his residence room and sleep. Plus, he had been having difficulty concentrating and was worried that his first-semester grades would be far below those he'd achieved in high school. Scott, his roommate, had little sympathy. "It's all that junk food you eat!" he insisted. "Let's go down to the organic market for some real food." Dylan dragged himself to the market with Scott but rested at the juice counter while his roommate went shopping. A middle-aged woman wearing a white lab coat approached him and introduced herself as the market's staff nutritionist. "You're looking a little pale," she said. "Anything wrong?" Dylan explained that he had been feeling tired lately. "I don't doubt it," the woman answered. "I can see from your skin tone that you're anemic. You need to start taking an iron supplement." She took a bottle of pills from a shelf and handed it to him. "This one is the easiest for you to absorb, and it's on special this week. Take it twice a day, and you should start feeling better in a day or two." Dylan purchased the supplement and began taking it that night with the meal his roommate had prepared. He took it twice the next day as well, just as the nutritionist had recommended, but didn't feel any better. After two more days, he visited the university health clinic, where a nurse drew some blood for testing. When the results of the blood tests came in, the physician told him that his thyroid gland wasn't making enough of the hormone that he needed to keep his body functioning properly. She prescribed a medication and congratulated Dylan for catching the problem early. "If you had waited," she said, "it would only have gotten worse, and you could have

3

become seriously ill." Dylan asked if he should continue taking his iron supplements. The physician looked puzzled. "Where did you get the idea that you needed iron supplements?"

Like Dylan, you've probably been offered nutrition-related advice from well-meaning friends and self-professed "experts." Perhaps you found the advice helpful, or maybe, as in Dylan's case, it turned out to be all wrong. Where can you go for reliable advice about nutrition? What exactly *is* nutrition, and why does what we eat have such an influence on our health? In this chapter, we'll begin to answer these questions, and you'll gain a deeper understanding as you work through the rest of this book. Our goal is that, by the time you finish this course, you'll be the expert on your own nutritional needs!

What Is Nutrition?

If you think that the word *nutrition* means pretty much the same thing as *food*, you're right—partially. But the word has a broader meaning, which will gradually become clear as you make your way in this course. Specifically, **nutrition** is the science that studies food and how food nourishes our body and influences our health. It encompasses how we consume, digest, metabolize, and store nutrients and how these nutrients affect our body. Nutrition also involves studying the factors that influence our eating patterns, making recommendations about the amount we should eat of each type of food, attempting to maintain food safety, and addressing issues related to the global food supply. You can think of nutrition, then, as the discipline that encompasses everything about food.

Nutrition is a relatively new scientific discipline. Although food has played a defining role in the lives of humans since the evolution of our species, the importance of nutrition to our health has been formally recognized and studied over only the past 100 years or so. Early research in nutrition focused on making the link between nutrient deficiencies and illness. For instance, the cause of scurvy, which is a vitamin C deficiency, was discovered in the mid-1700s. At that time, however, vitamin C had not been identified—what was known was that some ingredient found in citrus fruits could prevent scurvy. Another example of early discoveries in nutrition is presented in the Nutrition Myth or Fact? box about a disease called pellagra.

Nutrition research continued to focus on identifying and preventing deficiency diseases through the first half of the twentieth century. Then, as the higher standard of living after World War II led to an improvement in the Canadian diet, nutrition research began pursuing a new objective: supporting wellness and preventing and treating **chronic diseases**—that is, diseases that come on slowly and can persist for years, often despite treatment. Chronic diseases of particular interest to nutrition researchers include obesity, heart disease, type 2 diabetes, and various cancers. This new research has raised as many questions as it has answered, and we still have a great deal to learn about the relationship between nutrition and chronic disease.

In the closing decades of the twentieth century, an exciting new area of nutrition research began to emerge. Reflecting our growing understanding of genetics, *nutrigenomics* seeks to uncover links between our genes, our environment, and our diet. The Nutrition Debate on page 25 describes this new field of research in detail.

◀ Nutrition is the science that studies all aspects of food.

nutrition The science that studies food and how food nourishes our body and influences our health.

chronic diseases Diseases that come on slowly and can persist for years, often despite treatment.

How Does Nutrition Contribute to Health?

Think about it: if you eat three meals a day, by this time next year, you'll have had more than a thousand chances to influence your body's makeup! As you'll learn in this text, you are what you eat: the substances you take into your body are broken down and reassembled into your brain cells, bones, muscles—all of your tissues and organs. The foods you eat also provide your body with the energy it needs to function properly.

NUTRITION MYTH OR FACT?
Is Pellagra an Infectious Disease?

In the first few years of the twentieth century, Dr. Joseph Goldberger successfully controlled outbreaks of several fatal infectious diseases, from yellow fever in Louisiana to typhus in Mexico. So it wasn't surprising that, in 1914, the Surgeon General of the United States chose him to tackle another disease, thought to be infectious, that was raging throughout the South. Called *pellagra,* the disease was characterized by a skin rash, diarrhea, and mental impairment. At the time, it afflicted more than 50 000 people each year, and in about 10% of cases it resulted in death.

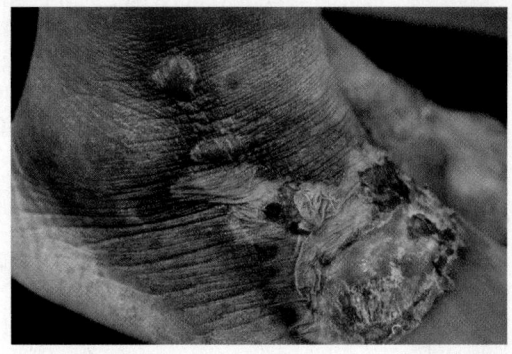

⬆ Pellagra is often characterized by a scaly skin rash.

Goldberger began studying the disease by carefully observing its occurrence in groups of people. He asked, if it is infectious, then why would it strike children in orphanages and prison inmates yet leave their nurses and guards unaffected? Why did it overwhelmingly affect impoverished millworkers and sharecroppers while leaving their affluent (and well-fed) neighbours healthy? Could a dietary deficiency cause pellagra?

To confirm his hunch, he conducted a series of trials in which he fed afflicted orphans and prisoners, who had been consuming a limited, corn-based diet, a variety of nutrient-rich foods, including meats. They recovered. Moreover, orphans and inmates who did not have

pellagra and ate the new diet did not develop the disease. Finally, Goldberger recruited 11 healthy prison inmates, who, in return for a pardon of their sentence, agreed to consume a corn-based diet. After five months, 6 of the 11 developed pellagra.

Still, many skeptics were unable to give up the idea that pellagra was an infectious disease. To prove that pellagra was not spread by germs, Goldberger and his colleagues deliberately injected themselves with and ingested patients' scabs, nasal secretions, and other bodily fluids. He and his team remained healthy.

Although Goldberger could not identify the precise component in the new diet that cured pellagra, he eventually found an inexpensive and widely available substance, brewer's yeast, that when added to the diet prevented or reversed the disease. Shortly after Goldberger's death in 1937, scientists identified the nutrient that is deficient in the diet of pellagra patients: niacin, one of the B-vitamins, which is plentiful in brewer's yeast.

Source: Based on Howard Markel, "The New Yorker Who Changed the Diet of the South," *New York Times*, 12 August 2003, p. D5.

In addition, we know that proper nutrition can help us improve our health, prevent certain diseases, achieve and maintain a desirable weight, and maintain our energy and vitality. Let's take a closer look at how nutrition supports health and wellness.

Nutrition Is One of Several Factors Contributing to Health

Health can be defined in many ways. Traditionally health was considered simply the absence of disease. However, as we have learned more about our health and what it means to live a healthy lifestyle, our definition of health has expanded. The World Health Organization defines it as "A state of complete physical, mental, and social well-being and not merely the absence of disease or infirmity."* Health is now considered to be a multidimensional process, one that includes physical, emotional, social, occupational, and spiritual health **(Figure 1.1)**. Health is not an endpoint in our lives, but is an active process we work on every day.

In this book we focus on two critical aspects of physical health: nutrition and physical activity. The two are so closely related that you can think of them as two sides of the same coin: our overall state of nutrition is influenced by how much energy we expend doing daily activities, and our level of physical activity has a

health A multidimensional, lifelong process that includes physical, emotional, social, occupational, and spiritual health.

*Preamble to the Constitution of the World Health Organization as adopted by the International Health Conference, New York, 19–22 June, 1946; signed on 22 July 1946 by the representatives of 61 States (Official Records of the World Health Organization, no. 2, p. 100) and entered into force on 7 April 1948.

Physical health includes nutrition and physical activity

Spiritual health includes spiritual values and beliefs

Emotional health includes positive feelings about oneself and life

Social health includes family, community, and social environment

Occupational health includes meaningful work or vocation

◀ **Figure 1.1** Many factors contribute to health. Primary among these are a nutritious diet and regular physical activity.

major impact on how we use the nutrients in our food. We can perform more strenuous activities for longer periods of time when we eat a nutritious diet, whereas an inadequate or excessive food intake can make us lethargic. A poor diet, inadequate or excessive physical activity, or a combination of these also can lead to serious health problems. Finally, several studies have suggested that healthful nutrition and regular physical activity can increase feelings of well-being and reduce feelings of anxiety and depression. In other words, wholesome food and physical activity just feel good!

A Healthful Diet Can Prevent Some Diseases and Reduce Your Risk for Others

Nutrition appears to play a role—from a direct cause to a mild influence—in the development of many diseases **(Figure 1.2)**. As you read in the Nutrition Myth or Fact? box on pellagra, nutrient deficiencies can cause serious, even life-threatening, illnesses; such diseases as scurvy, goitre, and rickets are other examples. Early nutrition research focused on identifying the missing nutrient behind such diseases and on developing guidelines for nutrient intakes that are high enough to prevent them. Over the years, nutrition scientists successfully lobbied for the fortification of foods with the nutrients of greatest concern. These measures, along with a more abundant and reliable food supply, have almost completely wiped out the majority of nutrient-deficiency diseases in developed countries. However, they are still major problems in many developing nations. Some of the nutritional issues affecting developing nations will be discussed in the In Depth section following Chapter 13.

It probably won't surprise you to learn that the primary link between poor nutrition and mortality is obesity. That is, obesity is fundamentally a consequence of eating more calories than are expended. At the same time, obesity is a well-established risk factor for heart disease, stroke, and type 2 diabetes.

In Canada, the United States, New Zealand, and the United Kingdom, the prevalence of obesity, type 2 diabetes mellitus, and some cancers have dramatically increased over the past 20 years (Raine, 2004). Statistics Canada (2011b) data show that the percentage of Canadian adults who were obese was higher in 2008 than in 1978–79. Overall, 17.5% of adults were obese, compared to 13.8% in the 1978–79 Canada Health Survey. Another 33.1% were categorized as being overweight,

▶ **Figure 1.2** The relationship between nutrition and human disease. Notice that whereas nutritional factors are only marginally implicated in the diseases of the top row, they are strongly linked to the development of the diseases in the middle row and truly causative of those in the bottom row.

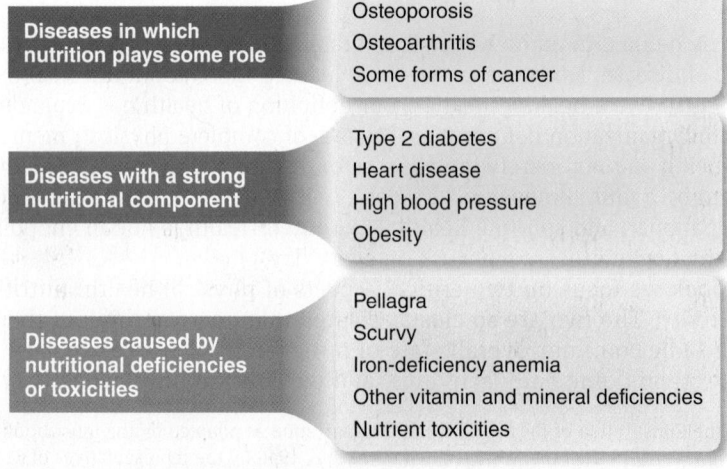

Diseases in which nutrition plays some role
Osteoporosis
Osteoarthritis
Some forms of cancer

Diseases with a strong nutritional component
Type 2 diabetes
Heart disease
High blood pressure
Obesity

Diseases caused by nutritional deficiencies or toxicities
Pellagra
Scurvy
Iron-deficiency anemia
Other vitamin and mineral deficiencies
Nutrient toxicities

meaning that half (50.6%) of Canadians aged 18 and older were either overweight or obese. As well, 20.0% of adolescents aged 12 to 17 years were obese or overweight (Statistics Canada, 2011a). Chapter 11 examines overweight and obesity, and the health risks of these conditions for adults, in more detail. The implications of this trend for the health of children and adolescents are also discussed in more detail in Chapter 15.

We know that obesity and its accompanying conditions are significantly affected by nutrition and activity: regularly consuming foods that are high in total energy (kilocalories or kilojoules), total fat, and saturated fat and low in fibre is associated with an increased risk for obesity, heart disease, type 2 diabetes, and possibly some forms of cancer. The imbalance of consuming too much food and being sedentary (inactive) also greatly increases our risk for these diseases. Throughout this text, we will discuss in more detail how nutrition and physical activity affect the development of obesity and other chronic diseases.

Nutrition appears to play a role in many diseases. Its role can vary from mild influence, to a strong association, to directly causing a disease **(Figure 1.2)**. For instance, **undernutrition**—meaning a diet that lacks energy or specific essential nutrients—is known to cause deficiency diseases such as anemia and scurvy. **Essential nutrients** are ones that can't be manufactured by the human body at all, or in amounts sufficient to meet the body's needs, and must either come from food in the diet or nutrient supplements. **Overnutrition**—a diet that has an imbalance of fats, carbohydrates, and proteins or simply too much energy—has a strong association with diseases such as type 2 diabetes and heart disease, and it appears to play a role in some forms of cancer. Thus, **malnutrition**, or "bad" nutrition, refers to both under- and overnutrition. As more nutrition research is completed, we will continue to uncover relationships between various forms of malnutrition and various types of diseases.

RECAP Nutrition is the science that studies food and how food affects our body and our health. Nutrition is an important component of wellness and is strongly associated with physical activity. One goal of a healthful diet is to prevent nutrient-deficiency diseases, such as scurvy and pellagra; a second goal is to lower the risk for chronic diseases, such as type 2 diabetes and heart disease.

What Are Nutrients?

A glass of milk or a spoonful of peanut butter may seem to be made up of only one substance, but in reality most foods are a combination of many different chemicals. Some of these chemicals are not useful to the body, whereas others are critical to human growth and function. These latter chemicals are referred to as **nutrients.** The following are the six groups of nutrients found in the foods we eat **(Figure 1.3)**:

- carbohydrates
- fats and oils (two types of lipids)
- proteins
- vitamins
- minerals
- water

The term *organic* is commonly used to describe foods that are grown without the use of synthetic pesticides. When scientists describe individual nutrients as **organic**, however, they mean that these nutrients contain both carbon and hydrogen, fundamental units of matter that are common to all living organisms. Carbohydrates, lipids, proteins, and vitamins are organic. Minerals and water are not. Organic and inorganic nutrients are equally important for sustaining life but differ in their structures, functions, and basic chemistry.

Alcohol is a chemical commonly consumed in beverages and which may also be added to some foods as a flavouring or preservative. However, it is not considered a nutrient because it is not critical for body functioning or the building or repairing

undernutrition A diet that lacks energy or specific essential nutrients.

essential nutrients Nutrients that must come from food or nutrient supplements because they are not manufactured by the body at all or in amounts sufficient to meet the body's needs.

overnutrition A diet that has an imbalance of fats, carbohydrates, and proteins or simply too much energy.

malnutrition Any condition associated with under- or overnutrition.

nutrients Chemicals found in foods that are critical to human growth and function.

organic A substance or nutrient that contains the elements carbon and hydrogen.

Carbohydrates are the primary source of fuel for our body, particularly for our brain.

▶ **Figure 1.3** The six groups of essential nutrients found in the foods we consume.

SIX GROUPS OF ESSENTIAL NUTRIENTS

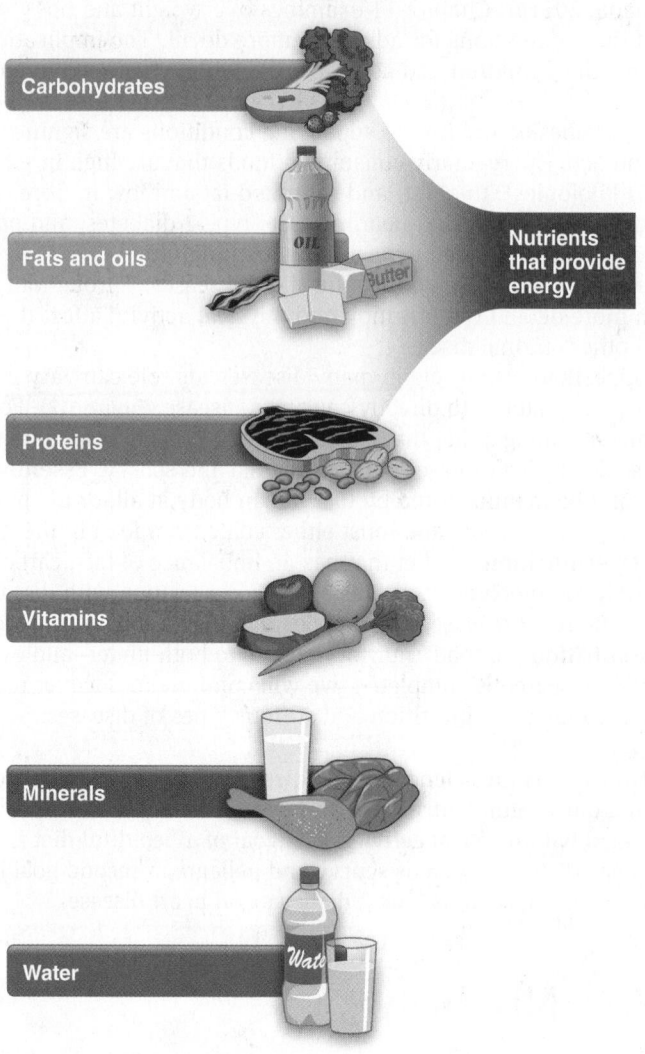

of tissues. In fact, alcohol is considered to be both a drug and a toxin. We discuss alcohol *In Depth* on pages 29–36.

Macronutrients Provide Energy

Carbohydrates, fats, and proteins are the only nutrients that provide energy. By this we mean that our body breaks down these nutrients and reassembles their components into a fuel that supports physical activity and basic functioning. Although taking a multivitamin might be beneficial in other ways, it will not provide you with the energy for a 20-minute session on the stairclimber! The energy nutrients are also referred to as **macronutrients**. *Macro* means "large," and our body needs relatively large amounts of these nutrients to support normal function and health.

We express energy in units of kilojoules (kJ) or kilocalories (kcal). Refer to the Highlight Box "What Is a Calorie?" for an explanation of energy and these units of measurement. Both carbohydrates and proteins provide 17 kilojoules (4 kcal) per gram, while fats provide 37 kilojoules (9 kcal) per gram. Thus, for every gram of fat we consume, we obtain more than twice the energy as compared with a gram of carbohydrate or protein. Refer to the You Do the Math box to learn how to calculate the energy contribution of carbohydrate, fat, and protein in a given food.

macronutrients Nutrients that our body needs in relatively large amounts to support normal function and health. Carbohydrates, fats, and proteins are macronutrients.

HIGHLIGHT
What Is a Calorie?

Confused by the terms *energy*, *kilocalorie*, and *Calorie*? Should these terms be used interchangeably? What do they really mean? The brief review provided in this highlight should broaden your understanding. First, some precise definitions:

- *Energy* is defined as the capacity to do work. We derive energy from the energy-containing nutrients in the foods we eat; namely, carbohydrates, fats, and proteins.

- A *kilocalorie* (kcal), or *Calorie* (Cal), is the amount of heat required to raise the temperature of one kilogram of water by one degree Celsius. It is a unit of measurement we use to quantify the amount of energy in food that can be supplied to the body. For instance, we say

that energy found in 1 gram of carbohydrate is equal to 4 kcal, or 4 Cal.

- In Canada, we use the *International System of Units (SI)*. The exact conversion is: 1 kcal (or 1 Cal) = 4.184 *kilojoules (kJ)*. For approximate calculations, you can use 1 kcal = 4.2 kJ. In general, energy measured in kJ should be rounded to the nearest 10 kJ.

It is most appropriate to use the term energy when you are referring to the general concept of energy intake or energy expenditure. If you are discussing the specific units related to energy, use either kilojoules or kilocalories. The food labels in Canada use Calorie (upper case "C"); we have chosen to use kilojoules as the unit of measurement throughout this book.

Carbohydrates Are a Primary Fuel Source

Carbohydrates are the primary source of fuel for our body, particularly for our brain and during physical exercise **(Figure 1.4)**. *Carbo* refers to carbon, and *hydrate* refers to water. You may remember that water is made up of hydrogen and oxygen. Thus, carbohydrates are composed of chains of carbon, hydrogen, and oxygen.

Carbohydrates encompass a wide variety of foods; rice, wheat, and other grains as well as vegetables are carbohydrates, and fruits contain natural sugars that are carbohydrates. Carbohydrates are also found in legumes (including lentils, dry beans, and peas), milk and other dairy products, seeds, and nuts. Carbohydrates and their role in health are the subject of Chapter 4.

Also, have you ever heard that alcohol provides "empty calories"? Alcohol contributes 29 kJ (7 kcal) per gram. You can calculate the percentage of kJ (kcal) from alcohol in your daily diet, but remember that it is not considered an energy nutrient.

These calculations will be very useful throughout this course as you learn more about how to design a healthful diet and how to read labels to assist you in meeting

carbohydrates One of three macronutrients, a compound made up of carbon, hydrogen, and oxygen that is derived from plants and provides energy.

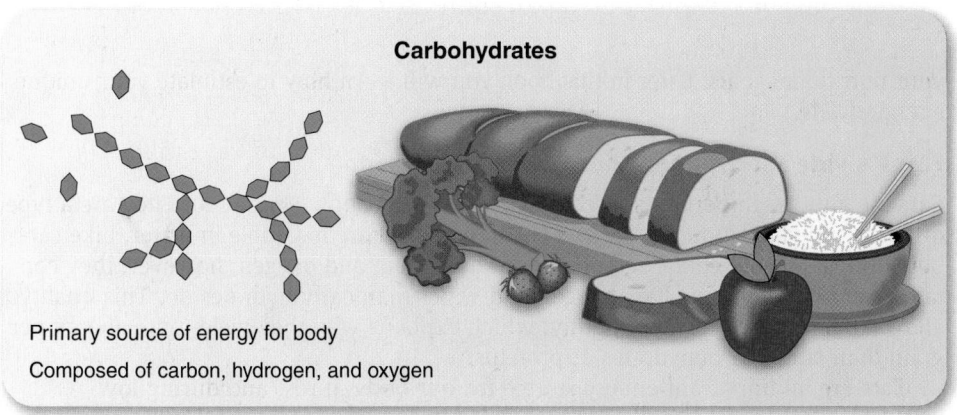

Carbohydrates

Primary source of energy for body

Composed of carbon, hydrogen, and oxygen

Figure 1.4 Carbohydrates are a primary source of energy for our body and are found in a wide variety of foods.

YOU DO THE MATH

Calculating the Energy Contribution of Carbohydrates, Fats, and Proteins

The energy in food is used for everything from maintaining normal body functions—such as breathing, digesting food, and repairing damaged tissues and organs—to enabling you to perform physical activity and even to read this text. So how much energy is produced from the foods you eat?

Carbohydrates are the main energy source for your body and should make up the largest percentage of your nutrient intake, about 45%–65%; they provide 17 kJ (4 kcal) of energy per gram of carbohydrate consumed. Proteins also provide 17 kJ (4 kcal) of energy per gram, but they should be limited to no more than 10%–35% of your daily energy intake. Fats provide the most energy, 37 kJ (9 kcal) per gram. Fats should make up approximately 20%–35% of your total energy intake per day. To figure out whether you're taking in the appropriate percentages of carbohydrates, fats, and proteins, you will need to use a little math.

1. Let's say you have completed a personal diet analysis, and you consume 10 460 kJ (2500 kcal) per day. From your diet analysis, you also find that you consume 300 g of carbohydrates, 90 g of fat, and 123 g of protein.

2. To calculate your percentage of total energy that comes from carbohydrate, you must do two things:

   a. Take your total grams of carbohydrate and multiply by the energy value for carbohydrate to give you how many kJ (kcal) of carbohydrate you have consumed.

   > 300 g of carbohydrate × 17 kJ (4 kcal) per gram
   > = 5020 kJ (1200 kcal) of carbohydrate

   b. Take the number of kcal of carbohydrate you have consumed, divide this number by the total number of kJ (kcal) you consumed, and multiply by 100. This will give you the percentage of the total energy you consume that comes from carbohydrate.

   > (5020 kJ ÷ 10 460 kJ) × 100
   > = 48% of total energy comes from carbohydrate

or

> (1200 kcal ÷ 2500 kcal) × 100
> = 48% of total energy comes from carbohydrate

3. To calculate your percentage of total energy that comes from fat, you follow the same steps but incorporate the energy value for fat:

   a. Take your total grams of fat and multiply by the energy value for fat to find the kJ (kcal) of fat you consumed.

   > 90 g of fat × 37 kJ (9 kcal) per gram
   > = 3330 kJ (810 kcal) of fat

   b. Take the number of kcal of fat you have consumed, divide this number by the total number of kcal you consumed, and multiply by 100 to get the percentage of total energy you consume that comes from fat.

   > (3330 kJ ÷ 10 420 kJ) × 100
   > = 32% of total energy comes from fat

or

> (810 kcal ÷ 2500 kcal) × 100
> = 32% of total energy comes from fat

Now try these steps to calculate the percentage of the total energy you consume that comes from protein. The sum of your percentages for carbohydrate, fat, and protein should add up to 100%. These calculations will be very useful throughout this course as you learn more about how to plan a nutritious diet and how to read labels to assist you in meeting your nutrition goals. Later in this book, in Chapter 11, you will learn how to estimate your unique energy needs and determine the ideal amount of energy you need from carbohydrate, fat, and protein.

your nutritional goals. Later in this book you will learn how to estimate your unique energy needs.

Fats Provide Energy and Other Essential Nutrients

fats An important energy source for our body at rest and during low-intensity exercise.

Fats are another important source of energy for our body **(Figure 1.5)**. They are a type of *lipids*, a diverse group of organic substances that are insoluble in water. Like carbohydrates, fats are composed of carbon, hydrogen, and oxygen; however, they contain proportionally much less oxygen and water than carbohydrates do. This quality allows them to pack together tightly, which explains why they yield more energy per gram than either carbohydrates or proteins.

Fats are an important energy source for our body at rest and during low-intensity exercise. Our body is capable of storing large amounts of fat as adipose tissue. These fat stores can then be broken down for energy during periods when we are not eating—for example, while we are asleep. Foods that contain fats are

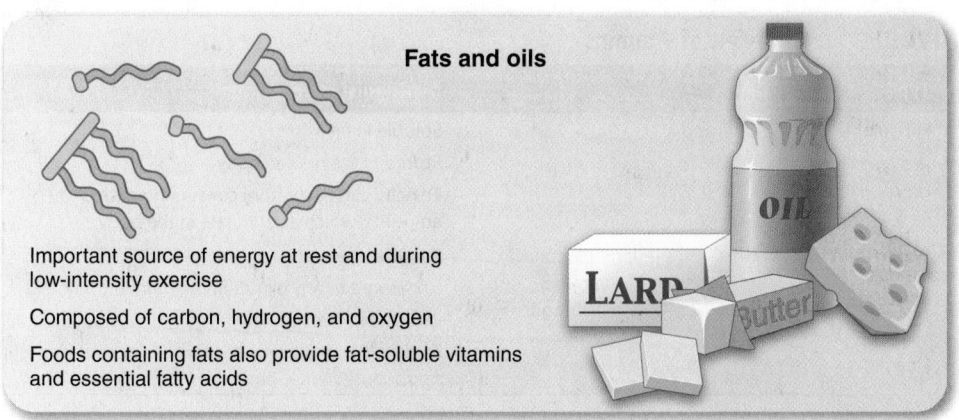

Figure 1.5 Fats are an important energy source during rest and low-intensity exercise. Foods containing fats also provide other important nutrients.

also essential for the transportation into our body of certain vitamins that are soluble only in fat.

Dietary fats come in a variety of forms. Solid fats include such things as butter, lard, and margarine. Liquid fats, referred to as *oils*, include vegetable oils, such as canola and olive oils. Cholesterol is a form of lipid that our body can make independently, and it can be consumed in the diet. Chapter 5 provides a thorough discussion of lipids.

Proteins Support Tissue Growth, Repair, and Maintenance

Proteins also contain carbon, hydrogen, and oxygen, but they are different from carbohydrates and fats in that they contain the element *nitrogen* **(Figure 1.6)**. Within proteins, these four elements assemble into small building blocks known as amino acids. We break down dietary proteins into amino acids and reassemble them to build our own body proteins—for instance, the proteins in our muscles and blood.

Although proteins can provide energy, they are not a primary source of energy for our body. Instead, the main role of proteins is in building new cells and tissues. Proteins are also important in regulating the breakdown of foods and our fluid balance.

Proteins are found primarily in meats and dairy products, but seeds, nuts, and legumes are also good sources, and we obtain small amounts from vegetables and whole grains. Proteins are the subject of Chapter 6.

proteins The only macronutrient that contains nitrogen; the basic building blocks of proteins are amino acids.

Fats are an important source of energy for our body, especially when we are at rest.

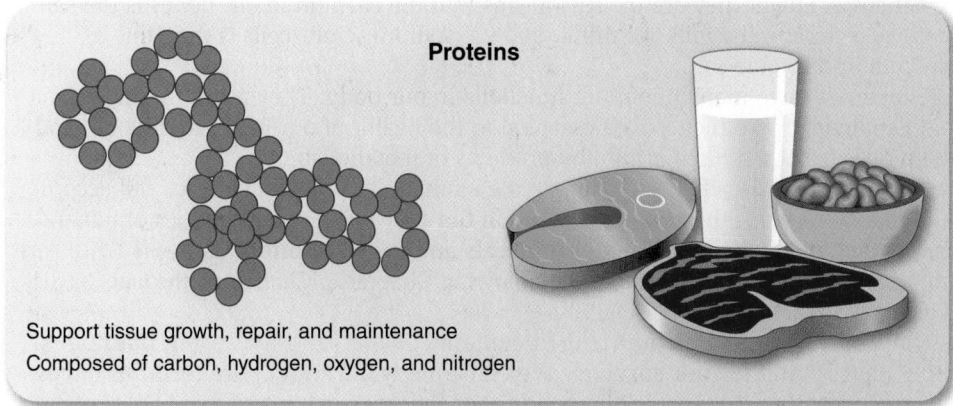

Figure 1.6 Proteins contain nitrogen in addition to carbon, hydrogen, and oxygen. Proteins support the growth, repair, and maintenance of body tissues.

◆ Fat-soluble vitamins are found in a variety of fat-containing foods, including dairy products.

TABLE 1.1 **Overview of Vitamins**		
Type	**Names**	**Distinguishing Features**
Fat-soluble	A, D, E, and K	Soluble in fat
		Stored in the human body
		Toxicity can occur from consuming excess amounts, which accumulate in the body
Water-soluble	C, B-vitamins (thiamin, riboflavin, niacin, vitamin B_6, vitamin B_{12}, pantothenic acid, biotin, and folate)	Soluble in water
		Not stored to any extent in the human body
		Excess excreted in urine
		Toxicity generally only occurs as a result of vitamin supplementation

micronutrients Nutrients needed in relatively small amounts to support normal health and body functions. Vitamins and minerals are micronutrients.

vitamins Organic compounds that assist in regulating body processes.

metabolism The process by which large molecules, such as carbohydrates, fats, and proteins, are broken down via chemical reactions into smaller molecules that can be used as fuel, stored, or assembled into new compounds the body needs.

fat-soluble vitamins Vitamins that are not soluble in water but are soluble in fat. These include vitamins A, D, E, and K.

water-soluble vitamins Vitamins that are soluble in water. These include vitamin C and the B-vitamins.

minerals Inorganic substances that are not broken down during digestion and absorption and are not destroyed by heat or light. Minerals assist in the regulation of many body processes and are classified as major minerals or trace minerals.

major minerals Minerals that must be consumed in amounts of 100 mg/day or more and that are present in the body at the level of 5 g or more.

Micronutrients Assist in the Regulation of Body Functions

Vitamins and minerals are referred to as **micronutrients**. That's because we need relatively small amounts of these nutrients to support normal health and body functions.

Vitamins are organic compounds that help regulate our body's functions. Contrary to popular belief, vitamins do not contain energy (kJ or kcal); however, they are essential to energy **metabolism**, the process by which the macronutrients are broken down into the smaller molecules that our body can absorb and use. So vitamins assist with releasing and using the energy in carbohydrates, fats, and proteins. They are also critical in building and maintaining healthy bone, muscle, and blood; supporting our immune system, so that we can fight infection and disease; and ensuring healthy vision.

Vitamins are classified as two types: **fat-soluble vitamins** and **water-soluble vitamins (Table 1.1)**. This classification affects how vitamins are absorbed, transported, and stored in our body. Both types of vitamins are essential for our health and are found in a variety of foods. Learn more about vitamins in the **In Depth** examination following Chapter 6. Chapters 7 through 10 discuss individual vitamins in detail.

Minerals are inorganic substances because they do not contain carbon and hydrogen. In fact, minerals are not compounds made up of smaller components; instead, they are fundamental units of matter themselves. Some important dietary minerals are sodium, potassium, calcium, magnesium, and iron. Since minerals are already in the most fundamental form possible, they cannot be broken down during digestion or when our body uses them to promote normal function; they are also not destroyed by heat or light. Thus, all minerals maintain their structure, no matter what environment they are in. This means that the calcium in our bones is the same as the calcium in the milk we drink, and the sodium in our cells is the same as the sodium in our table salt.

Minerals have many important functions in our body. They assist in fluid regulation and energy production, are essential to the health of our bones and blood, and help rid our body of the harmful by-products of metabolism.

Minerals are classified according to the amounts we need in our diet and according to how much of the mineral is found in our body. The two categories of minerals in our diet and body are the **major minerals** and the **trace minerals (Table 1.2)**. Learn more about minerals in the **In Depth** following Chapter 6. Chapters 7 through 10 discuss individual minerals in detail.

Water is an inorganic nutrient (it contains oxygen and hydrogen, but not carbon) that is vital for our survival. We consume water in its pure form; in juices, soups, and other liquids; and in solid foods, such as fruits and vegetables. Adequate water intake ensures the proper balance of fluid both inside and outside

TABLE 1.2 Overview of Minerals

Type	Names	Distinguishing Features
Major minerals	Calcium, phosphorus, sodium, potassium, chloride, magnesium, sulphur	Needed in amounts greater than 100 mg/day in our diets Amount present in the human body is greater than 5 g (or 5000 mg)
Trace minerals	Iron, zinc, copper, manganese, fluoride, chromium, molybdenum, selenium, iodine	Needed in amounts less than 100 mg/day in our diets Amount present in the human body is less than 5 g (or 5000 mg)

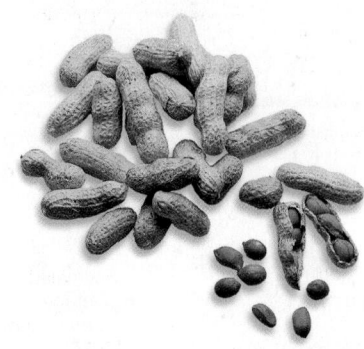

⬆ Peanuts are a good source of magnesium and phosphorus, which play important roles in the formation and maintenance of our skeleton.

our cells, and it assists in the regulation of nerve impulses, muscle contractions, nutrient transport, and the excretion of waste products. Because of the key role that water plays in our health, Chapter 7 focuses on water and its function in our body.

RECAP The six essential nutrient groups found in foods are carbohydrates, fats, proteins, vitamins, minerals, and water. Carbohydrates, fats, and proteins are macronutrients. Often referred to as energy nutrients, they provide our body with energy. Carbohydrates and fats are our main energy sources; proteins primarily support tissue growth, repair, and maintenance. Vitamins and minerals are micronutrients. Vitamins are organic compounds that assist in breaking down the macronutrients for energy and in maintaining many other functions. Minerals are inorganic units of matter that play critical roles in virtually all aspects of human health and function. Water is critical for our survival and is important for regulating nervous impulses, muscle contractions, nutrient transport, and the excretion of waste products.

How Much of Each Nutrient Do Most People Need?

Now that you know what the six classes of nutrients are, you're probably wondering how much of each you need each day. That depends on your gender, your age, your activity level, and many other factors. In Chapter 2, you'll learn how to plan a healthful diet that's just right for you. To get ready, you need to become familiar with the current standard intake recommendations that apply to most healthy people.

Use the Dietary Reference Intakes to Check Your Nutrient Intake

The United States and Canada share a set of standards defining the recommended intake values for various nutrients. These are called the **Dietary Reference Intakes (DRIs) (Figure 1.7)**. The DRIs are dietary standards for healthy people only; they do not apply to people with diseases or to those who are suffering from nutrient deficiencies. For each nutrient (such as vitamin C or iron), the DRIs identify the amount needed to prevent deficiency diseases in healthy individuals, as well as the amount that may reduce the risk for chronic diseases in healthy people. The DRIs also establish an upper level of safety for nutrient intake.

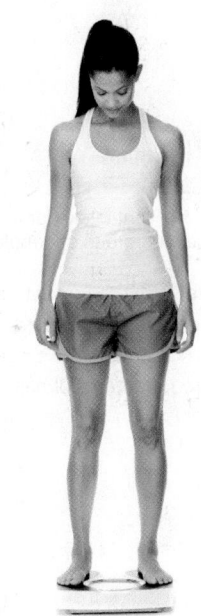

⬆ Knowing your daily Estimated Energy Requirement (EER) is a helpful way to maintain a healthy body weight.

trace minerals Minerals that must be consumed in amounts of less than 100 mg/day and that are present in the body at the level of less than 5g.

Dietary Reference Intakes (DRIs) A set of nutritional reference values for the United States and Canada that applies to healthy people.

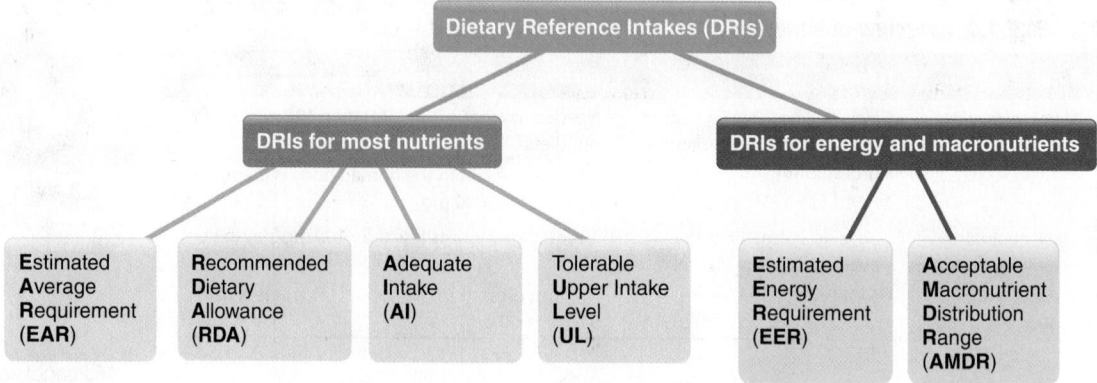

Figure 1.7 The Dietary Reference Intakes (DRIs) for all nutrients. Note that the Estimated Energy Requirement (EER) applies only to energy, and the Acceptable Macronutrient Distribution Range (AMDR) applies only to the macronutrients and alcohol.

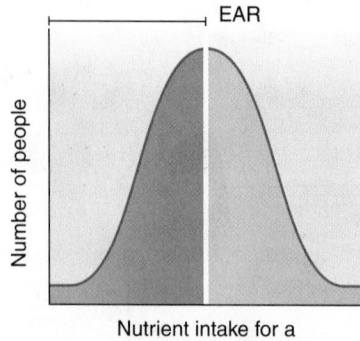

Figure 1.8 The Estimated Average Requirement (EAR) represents the average daily nutrient intake level that meets the requirements of half the healthy individuals in a given group.

Estimated Average Requirement (EAR) The average daily nutrient intake level estimated to meet the requirement of half the healthy individuals in a particular life stage or gender group.

Recommended Dietary Allowance (RDA) The average daily nutrient intake level that meets the nutrient requirements of 97%–98% of healthy individuals in a particular life stage and gender group.

Adequate Intake (AI) A recommended average daily nutrient intake level based on observed or experimentally determined estimates of nutrient intake by a group of healthy people.

The DRIs for most nutrients consist of four values:

- Estimated Average Requirement (EAR)
- Recommended Dietary Allowance (RDA)
- Adequate Intake (AI)
- Tolerable Upper Intake Level (UL)

For total energy and the macronutrients, different standards are used. We'll identify those shortly.

The Estimated Average Requirement Guides the Recommended Dietary Allowance

The **Estimated Average Requirement (EAR)** represents the average daily intake level estimated to meet the requirement of half the healthy individuals in a particular life stage and gender group (IOM 2003). **Figure 1.8** is a graph representing this value. As an example, the EAR for phosphorus for women between the ages of 19 and 30 years represents the average daily intake of phosphorus that meets the requirement of half the women in this age group. Scientists use the EAR to define the Recommended Dietary Allowance (RDA) for a given nutrient. Obviously, if the EAR meets the needs of only half the people in a group, then the recommended intake will be higher.

The Recommended Dietary Allowance Meets the Needs of Nearly All Healthy People

The **Recommended Dietary Allowance (RDA)** represents the average daily nutrient intake level that meets the requirements of 97%–98% of healthy individuals in a particular life stage and gender group **(Figure 1.9)** (IOM, 2003). For example, the RDA for phosphorus is 700 mg per day for women between the ages of 19 and 30 years. This amount of phosphorus will meet the nutrient requirements of almost all women in this age category.

Again, scientists use the EAR to establish the RDA. In fact, if an EAR cannot be determined for a nutrient, then this nutrient cannot have an RDA. When this occurs, an Adequate Intake value is determined for the nutrient.

The Adequate Intake Is Based on Estimates of Nutrient Intakes

The **Adequate Intake (AI)** value is a recommended average daily nutrient intake level assumed to be adequate. It is based on observations or experiments involving healthy people, and it is used when an RDA cannot be determined (IOM, 2003). For nutrients having an AI value, including vitamin D, vitamin K, fluoride, and others, more research needs to be done, so that an EAR, and subsequently an RDA, can be established.

In addition to RDA and AI values for nutrients, an upper level of safety for nutrients, or Tolerable Upper Intake Level, has also been established.

The Tolerable Upper Intake Level Is the Highest Level That Poses No Health Risk

The **Tolerable Upper Intake Level (UL)** is the highest average daily nutrient intake level likely to pose no risk of adverse health effects to almost all individuals in a particular life stage and gender group (IOM, 2003). This does not mean that we should consume this intake level or that we will receive more benefits from a nutrient by meeting it. Rather, as our intake of a nutrient increases in amounts above the UL, the potential for toxic effects and health problems increases. Use the UL value to help you determine the highest average intake level that is deemed safe to consume.

The Estimated Energy Requirement Is the Intake Predicted to Maintain a Healthy Weight

The **Estimated Energy Requirement (EER)** is defined as the average dietary energy intake that is predicted to maintain energy balance in a healthy adult. The EER can be individualized according to a person's level of activity, age, gender, weight, and height, along with other factors (IOM, 2002). The EER for an active person is higher than the EER for an inactive person, even if all the other factors (age, gender, and so on) are the same.

The Acceptable Macronutrient Distribution Range Is Associated with Reduced Risk for Chronic Diseases

The **Acceptable Macronutrient Distribution Range (AMDR)** defines a range of macronutrient intakes that provides adequate levels of essential nutrients and is associated with a reduced risk for chronic disease (IOM, 2002). The AMDR is expressed as a percentage of total energy. The AMDR also has a lower and an upper boundary; if we consume nutrients below or above this range, we increase our risk of either a deficiency or chronic disease. The AMDRs for carbohydrate, fat, and protein are listed in **Table 1.3**.

Diets Based on the DRIs Promote Health

The primary goal of dietary planning is to develop an eating plan that is nutritionally adequate, meaning that the chances of consuming too little or too much of any nutrient are very low. By eating foods that give you nutrient intakes that meet the DRI values, you help your body maintain a healthful weight, support your daily physical activity, prevent nutrient deficiencies and toxicities, and reduce your risk for chronic disease.

Throughout this text, the DRI values are reviewed with each nutrient as it is introduced. They are also listed together in tables on the inside cover and pages at the back of this book. Find your life stage group and gender in the left-hand column; then simply look across to see each nutrient's value for you. Using the DRI values in conjunction with diet-planning tools, such as *Eating Well with Canada's Food Guide*, will ensure that you have a healthful and adequate diet. Chapter 2 provides details on how you can use these tools.

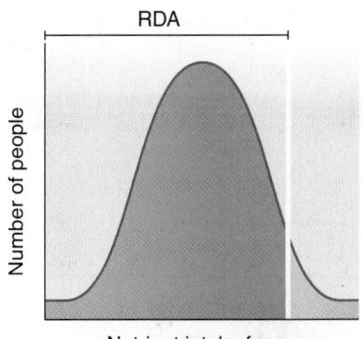

Number of people

Nutrient intake for a defined group of people

Figure 1.9 The Recommended Dietary Allowance (RDA) represents the average daily nutrient intake level that meets the requirements of almost all (97%–98%) healthy individuals in a given life stage or gender group.

Tolerable Upper Intake Level (UL) The highest average daily nutrient intake level likely to pose no risk of adverse health effects to almost all individuals in a particular life stage and gender group.

Estimated Energy Requirement (EER) The average dietary energy intake that is predicted to maintain energy balance in a healthy adult.

Acceptable Macronutrient Distribution Range (AMDR) The range of macronutrient intakes that provides adequate levels of essential nutrients and is associated with a reduced risk for chronic disease.

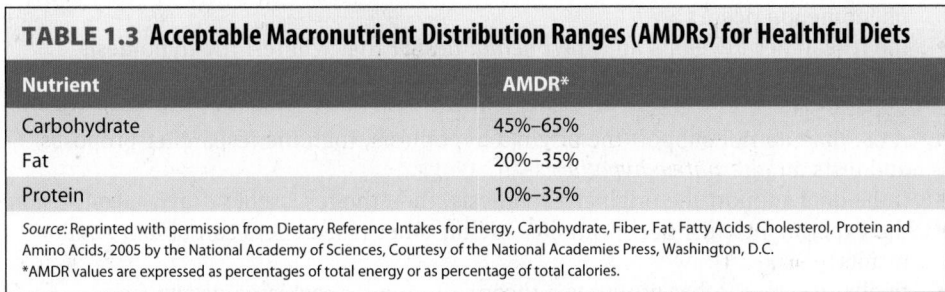

TABLE 1.3 Acceptable Macronutrient Distribution Ranges (AMDRs) for Healthful Diets

Nutrient	AMDR*
Carbohydrate	45%–65%
Fat	20%–35%
Protein	10%–35%

Source: Reprinted with permission from Dietary Reference Intakes for Energy, Carbohydrate, Fiber, Fat, Fatty Acids, Cholesterol, Protein and Amino Acids, 2005 by the National Academy of Sciences, Courtesy of the National Academies Press, Washington, D.C.
*AMDR values are expressed as percentages of total energy or as percentage of total calories.

RECAP The Dietary Reference Intakes (DRIs) are nutrient standards established for healthy people in a particular life stage and gender group. The Estimated Average Requirement (EAR) identifies the level of intake that meets the requirements of half the healthy individuals in a group. The Recommended Dietary Allowance (RDA) identifies the intake level that meets the requirements of 97%–98% of healthy individuals in a group. The Adequate Intake (AI) is used when there is not enough information to set an RDA. The Tolerable Upper Intake Level (UL) is the highest daily nutrient intake level that likely poses no risk for adverse health effects. The Estimated Energy Requirement (EER) is the average daily energy intake that is predicted to maintain energy balance in a healthy adult. The Acceptable Macronutrient Distribution Range (AMDR) defines ranges of macronutrient intake that provide adequate levels of essential nutrients and are associated with reduced risk for chronic disease.

Research Study Results: Who Can We Believe?

"Eat more carbohydrates! Fats cause obesity!"

"Eat more protein and fat! Carbohydrates cause obesity!"

Do you ever feel overwhelmed by the abundant and often conflicting advice in media reports related to nutrition? If so, you are not alone. In addition to the "high-carb, low-carb" controversy, we've been told that calcium supplements are essential to prevent bone loss and that calcium supplements have no effect on bone loss; that high fluid intake prevents constipation and that high fluid intake has no effect on constipation; that coffee and tea can be harmful and that both can be beneficial! How can you navigate this sea of changing information? What constitutes valid, reliable evidence, and how can you determine whether research findings apply to you?

To become a more informed critic of product claims and nutrition news, you need to understand the research process and how to interpret the results of different types of studies. Let's have a look.

Research Involves Applying the Scientific Method

When confronted with a claim about any aspect of our world, from "The Earth is flat" to "Carbohydrates cause obesity," scientists, including nutritionists, must first consider whether the claim can be tested. In other words, can evidence be presented to substantiate the claim and, if so, what data would qualify as evidence? Scientists worldwide use a standardized method of looking at evidence, called the *scientific method*. This method usually includes the following steps, which are described in more detail below and summarized in **Figure 1.10**:

- the researcher makes an *observation* and a description of a phenomenon
- the researcher proposes a *hypothesis,* or an educated guess, to explain why the phenomenon occurs
- the researcher develops an *experimental design* that will test the hypothesis
- the researcher *collects and analyzes data* that will either support or reject the hypothesis
- if the data do not support the original hypothesis, then the researcher proposes and tests an *alternative hypothesis*
- if the data support the original hypothesis, then the researcher draws a *conclusion*
- the experiment must be *repeatable,* so that other researchers can obtain similar results
- finally, the researcher proposes a *theory* offering a conclusion drawn from repeated experiments that have supported the hypothesis time and time again

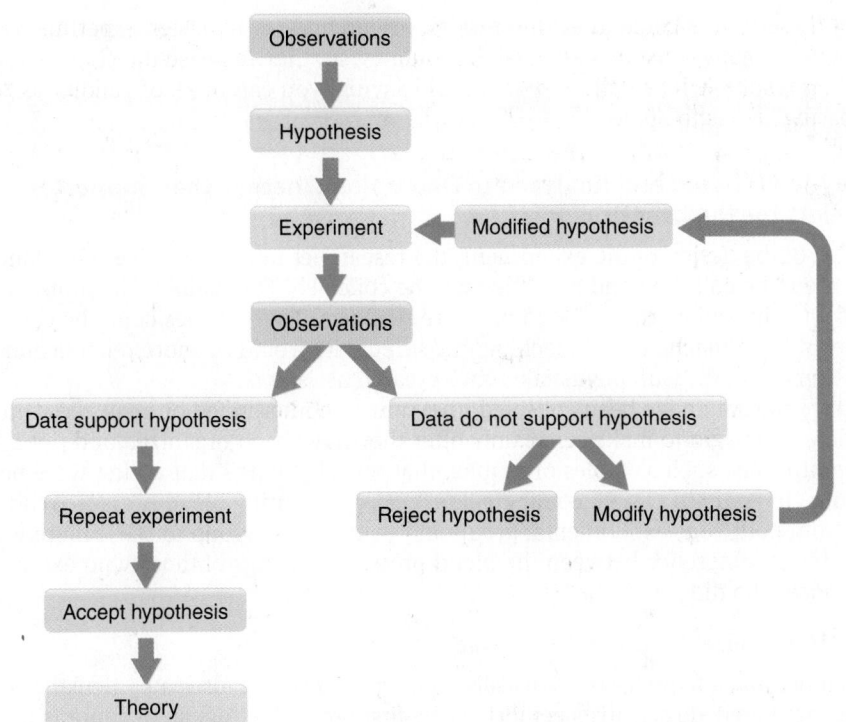

◀ **Figure 1.10** The scientific method, which forms the framework for scientific research. The researcher makes an observation regarding a phenomenon. This leads the researcher to ask a question. A hypothesis is generated to explain the observations. The researcher conducts an experiment to test the hypothesis. Observations are made during the experiment, and data are generated and documented. The data may either support or refute the hypothesis. If the data support the hypothesis, more experiments are conducted to test and confirm support for the hypothesis. A hypothesis that is supported after repeated testing may be called a theory. If the data do not support the hypothesis, the hypothesis is either rejected or modified and then retested.

Observation of a Phenomenon Initiates the Research Process

The first step in the scientific method is to observe and describe a phenomenon. Let's say you are working in a healthcare office that caters to older clients. You have observed that many of them have high blood pressure, but some have normal blood pressure. After talking with a large number of clients, you notice a pattern in that those who report being more physically active are also those with lower blood pressure readings. This observation leads you to question a possible relationship between physical activity and blood pressure. Your next step would be to develop a *hypothesis*, a possible explanation for your observation.

A Hypothesis Is a Possible Explanation for an Observation

A **hypothesis** is sometimes referred to as a research question. In our example, your hypothesis could be "Adults over age 65 with high blood pressure who begin and maintain a program of 45 minutes of aerobic exercise daily will experience a decrease in blood pressure." Your hypothesis must be written so that it can be supported or rejected. In other words, it must be testable.

hypothesis An educated guess as to why a phenomenon occurs.

An Experiment Is Designed to Test the Hypothesis

An *experiment* is a scientific study that is conducted to test a hypothesis. A well-designed experiment should have several key elements:

- The *sample size,* or the number of people being studied, should be adequate to ensure that the results obtained are not due to chance alone. For example, would you be more likely to believe a study that tested 5 people or 500?
- Having a *control group* is essential for comparing treated to untreated individuals. A control group consists of people who are as much like the treated group as possible, except with respect to the *variable* being tested. For instance, in your study, 45 minutes of daily aerobic exercise would be the variable; the experimental group would consist of people over age 65 with high blood pressure who exercise; and the control group would consist of similar people who do not exercise. Using a control group helps a researcher judge whether a particular treatment has worked.
- A good experimental design also attempts to control for other variables that may coincidentally influence the results. For example, what if someone in your study was on a diet, smoked, or took blood pressure–lowering medication? Since any

of these factors could affect the results, researchers try to design experiments that have as many *constants* as possible. In doing so, they increase the chance that their results will be valid. To use an old saying, you can think of validity as "comparing apples to apples."

Data Are Collected and Analyzed to Determine Whether They Support or Reject the Hypothesis

As part of the design of the experiment, the researcher must determine what kind of data are to be collected and how they will be collected. For example, in your study the data being collected are blood pressure readings. These values could be collected by people or a machine, but machine measurements would be more reliable and consistent than measurements taken by research assistants.

Once the data have been collected, they must be interpreted or analyzed. Often, the data will begin to make sense only after they have been organized and put into different forms, such as tables or graphs, that reveal patterns that at first were not obvious. In your study, you could create a graph comparing blood pressure readings from both your experimental group and your control group to see if there was a significant difference between the blood pressure readings of those who exercised and those who did not.

Most Hypotheses Need to Be Refined

Remember that a hypothesis is basically a guess as to what causes a particular phenomenon. Rarely do scientists get it right the first time. The original hypothesis is often refined after the initial results are obtained, usually because the answer to the question is not clear and leads to more questions. When this happens, an alternative hypothesis is proposed, a new experiment is designed, and the new hypothesis is tested.

An Experiment Must Be Repeatable

One research study does not prove or disprove a hypothesis. Ideally, multiple experiments are conducted over many years to thoroughly test a hypothesis. Indeed, repeatability is a cornerstone of scientific investigation. Supporters and skeptics alike must be able to replicate an experiment and arrive at similar conclusions, or the hypothesis becomes invalid. Have you ever wondered why the measurements used in scientific textbooks are always in the metric system? The answer is repeatability. Scientists use the metric system because it is universal, thus allowing repeatability in any research facility worldwide.

Unfortunately, media reports on the findings of a research study that has just been published rarely include a thorough review of the other studies conducted on that topic. Thus, you should never accept one report in a newspaper or magazine as absolute fact on any topic.

A Theory May Be Developed Following Extensive Research

theory A conclusion drawn from repeated experiments.

If the results of multiple experiments consistently support a hypothesis, then scientists may advance a **theory**. A theory represents a scientific consensus (agreement) as to why a particular phenomenon occurs. Although theories are based on data drawn from repeated experiments, they can still be challenged and changed as the knowledge within a scientific discipline evolves. For example, at the beginning of this chapter we said that the prevailing theory held that pellagra was an infectious disease. Many different types of experiments were conducted before their results finally confirmed that the disease is due to niacin deficiency. We continue to apply the scientific method to test hypotheses and challenge theories today.

RECAP The scientific method begins with observation of a phenomenon. The researcher then proposes a hypothesis, and designs and conducts an experiment, collecting and analyzing data that support or refute the hypothesis. If the data are rejected, then an alternative hypothesis is proposed and tested. If the data support the original hypothesis, then a conclusion is drawn. A hypothesis that is supported after repeated experiments may be called a theory.

Various Types of Research Studies Tell Us Different Stories

You have just learned how the scientific method is applied to test a hypothesis. Depending on how the research study is designed, we can gather information that tells us different stories. Let's take a look at the types of research conducted and see what they tell us.

Epidemiological Studies Inform Us of Existing Relationships

Epidemiological studies are also referred to as observational studies. They involve assessing nutritional habits, disease trends, or other health phenomena of large populations and determining the factors that may influence these phenomena. However, these studies can indicate only relationships between factors, not specifically a cause-and-effect relationship. Let's say that an epidemiological study finds that the blood pressure values of physically active older adults are lower than those of inactive older adults. These results do not indicate that regular physical activity reduces blood pressure or that inactivity causes high blood pressure. All these results can tell us is that there is a relationship between higher physical activity and lower blood pressure in older people.

Model Systems

Humans are not very good experimental models because it is difficult to control all of the variables that affect our lives. Humans also have long life spans, so it would take a long time to determine the results of certain nutritional interventions. For this reason, laboratory studies generally involve experiments with animals. Animals with short reproduction times can be studied when researchers need to look at the effects of specific treatments over many generations. Animal studies are also used to conduct research that is not acceptable to conduct on humans. For instance, it is possible to study nutritional deficiencies in animals by causing a deficiency and studying its adverse health effects over the life span of the animal. In many cases, animal studies provide preliminary information that can assist us in designing and implementing human studies.

One drawback to animal studies is that the results may not apply directly to humans. Another drawback is the ethical implications of these studies, especially when the research reduces the animals' quality of life.

Human Studies

The two primary types of studies conducted with humans are case control studies and clinical trials. *Case control studies* are epidemiological studies done on a smaller scale. They involve comparing a group of individuals with a particular condition (for instance, adults over age 65 with high blood pressure) to a similar group without this condition. This comparison allows the researcher to identify factors other than the defined condition that differ between the two groups. By identifying these factors, researchers can gain a better understanding of things that may cause or help prevent the condition. For instance, in your experiment, you may find that older adults with low blood pressure not only are more physically active but also eat more fruits and vegetables and less sodium.

Clinical trials are tightly controlled experiments in which an intervention is made to determine its effect on a certain condition. Interventions may include medications, nutritional supplements, controlled diets, and exercise programs. The experimental group is given the intervention, but the control group is not. The responses are then compared. In your experiment, you could assign the experimental group to an exercise program and the control group to a program in which no exercise is done. After the intervention phase, you could compare the blood pressures of the people who exercised and those who did not. If the blood pressure of the experimental group decreased and the blood pressure of the control group did not, and if the amount of the decrease was statistically significant, then you could propose that the exercise program caused a decrease in blood pressure.

Epidemiological studies indicate relationships between factors, such as between exercise and blood pressure in older adults, but cannot prove cause and effect.

Among clinical trials, the type considered most likely to produce valid, reliable data is the *double-blind, placebo-controlled study*. In a double-blind study, neither the researchers nor the participants know which group is really getting the treatment. Blinding helps prevent the researchers from seeing only the results they want to see. A *placebo* is an imitation treatment that has no scientifically recognized therapeutic value—for instance, a sugar pill that looks, feels, smells, and tastes identical to the medication being tested. In a double-blind, placebo-controlled study, neither the researchers providing the treatment nor the study participants receiving it know whether the treatment being administered is the one being tested or a placebo.

Another important variable that cannot be overlooked in clinical trials is the effect of participation in the study on the participants' state of mind. This is known as the *psychosomatic effect* or *placebo effect*. Sometimes, just knowing they're in a study causes participants to experience physiologic changes, which they may interpret as therapeutic. For example, the older people in your blood pressure study may subconsciously be more relaxed and content because they feel validated and important. They may therefore show a decrease in blood pressure. Similarly, someone who takes an "herbal supplement," believing that it will help relieve insomnia, may fall asleep more easily because of that belief, even if the pill is actually a placebo.

QUICK TIPS

Detecting Media Hype

▶ Consider the source of the information. Who is reporting it? Is it an article in a newspaper, in a magazine, or on the Internet? Who wrote it? If the report is made by a person or group who may financially benefit from your buying the products, you should be skeptical of the reported results. Also, many people who write for popular magazines and newspapers are not trained in science and are capable of misinterpreting research results.

▶ Find out who conducted the research and who paid for it. Was the study funded by a company that stands to profit from certain results? Are the researchers receiving goods, personal travel funds, speaking fees, or other perks from the research sponsor, or do they have investments in companies or products related to their study? If the answer to these questions is yes, there exists a conflict of interest between the researchers and the funding agency. This conflict of interest may seriously compromise the researchers' ability to conduct unbiased research and report the results in an accurate and responsible manner.

▶ Evaluate the content. Is the report based on reputable research studies? Did the research follow the scientific method, and were the results reported in a reputable scientific journal? Ideally, the journal is peer-reviewed; that is, the articles are critiqued by other specialists working in the same scientific field. A reputable report should include the reference, or source of the information, and should identify researchers by name. This allows the reader to investigate the original study and determine its merit. Some reputable nutrition journals are identified later in this chapter.

▶ Watch for red flags. Is the report based on testimonials about personal experiences? These should make you suspicious, as testimonials are fraught with bias. Are sweeping conclusions made from only one study? Remember that one study cannot answer all of our questions or prove any hypothesis. View the findings from individual studies in their proper perspective. Are the claims made in the report too good to be true? For instance, does the report say the treatment can quickly cure a chronic disease or improve a multitude of conditions? If something sounds too good to be true, it probably is. In short, testimonials, sweeping conclusions, and claims about curing diseases or treating many conditions are red flags that should prompt you to question the validity of the report.

Use Your Knowledge of Research to Help You Evaluate Media Reports

How can all of this research information assist you in becoming a better consumer and critic of media reports? By having a better understanding of the research process and types of research conducted, you are more capable of discerning the truth or fallacy within media reports. Keep the Quick Tips points in the box at the left in mind when examining any media report.

Throughout this text, we provide you with information to assist you in becoming a more educated consumer regarding nutrition. You will learn about labelling guidelines, the proper use of supplements, and whether various nutrition topics are myths or facts. We'll also test your knowledge at the end of every chapter with a feature called "Find the Quack." As you may know, *quackery* is the misrepresentation of a product, program, or service for financial gain. For example, a high-priced supplement may be marketed as uniquely therapeutic, when, in fact, it is only as effective as much less expensive remedies commonly available. Many manufacturers of such products describe them as "patented," but this means only that the product has been registered with a government patent office, for a fee. It provides no guarantee of the product's effectiveness or its safety. After considering the information presented in each Find the Quack feature, you'll have a chance to decide for yourself: Is this a legitimate product or service, or is it quackery? Armed with the information in this book, plus plenty of opportunities to test your knowledge, you will become more confident when trying to evaluate nutrition claims.

RECAP Epidemiological studies involve large populations, model studies involve animals, and human studies include case control studies and clinical trials. Each type of study can be used to gather a different kind of data. When evaluating media reports, consider who is reporting the information, who conducted and paid for the research, whether the research was published in a reputable journal, and whether it involves testimonials or makes claims that sound too good to be true. Quackery is the misrepresentation of a product, program, or service for financial gain.

◆ To become a more educated consumer and informed critic of nutrition reports in the media, you need to understand the research process and how to interpret study results.

Nutrition Advice: Who Can You Trust?

Earlier in this chapter, you learned that one of the major nutrition concerns in Canada is our high risk for certain chronic diseases. One result of this concern has been the publication of an almost overwhelming quantity of nutrition information on television shows, websites, newspapers, magazines, journals, and many other forums. In addition to this information overload, we continually discover that the nutrition messages from these supposedly "expert" sources are confusing, dissimilar, or even contradictory. On certain issues, even nutrition scientists and physicians cannot seem to agree! If you are wondering how to determine whether an "expert" is trustworthy, the following discussion should help.

Trustworthy Experts Are Educated and Credentialed

The number of health professionals who provide reliable nutrition information is considerable, so it's not possible to identify them all in this chapter. The following are the most important professionals providing reputable nutrition information:

- Registered Dietitian—A registered dietitian (RD) is a health professional with a baccalaureate (bachelor's) degree in foods and nutrition from a university program accredited by the Dietitians of Canada (DC). After finishing this undergraduate degree, the individual needs to complete a dietetic internship or equivalent practicum experience. (At some universities, the dietetic internship is integrated into the undergraduate degree program or into a master's degree program.) The final steps are to successfully complete the Canadian Dietetic Registration Examination and to become registered with a provincial regulatory body. As is the case for other health professionals, provincially mandated colleges or registration boards ensure public safety. These colleges monitor the competence of members, protect the public from unsafe or unethical dietetic practice, respond to complaints from the public, and discipline members when necessary. The title *dietitian* is legally protected in each province so that only qualified practitioners with the appropriate education can use it. Look for the professional designation RD, PDt, or RDt (or the French equivalent Dt.P). To find registered dietitians in your community, check the Dietitians of Canada website, www.dietitians.ca.

- Nutritionist—The title *nutritionist* (e.g., a public health nutritionist) is protected for dietitians in some provinces but not in most, so people with different levels of training and knowledge can call themselves a nutritionist. Unqualified people sometimes use the terms *registered* or *certified* with a variation of *nutrition* as a

⬆ Your medical doctor may have limited experience and training in the area of nutrition but can refer you to a registered dietitian (RD) to assist you in meeting your dietary needs.

title. To make sure a person is a qualified nutrition professional, contact the Dietitians of Canada or the provincial regulatory body in your area.

- Professional with an advanced degree (a master's degree [MSc, MAN, MHSc, MScFN, MScAHN] or doctoral degree [PhD]) in nutrition—There are many individuals who are educated and experienced in nutrition and hold an advanced degree. Some of these individuals teach at community colleges and universities or work in fitness and health settings. Not all of these individuals are registered dietitians. Such individuals who do not have a registered dietitian designation (RD, PDt, RDt, or Dt.P) are very knowledgeable about nutrition and health, but they are not qualified to provide clinical dietary counselling or treatment for individuals with diseases or illnesses.
- Medical doctor—A medical doctor, also called a physician or MD, is educated, trained, and licensed to practise medicine in Canada. This individual typically has limited experience and training in the area of nutrition. However, if you become ill, the medical doctor is usually one of the first health professionals you'll see for an accurate medical diagnosis. If you require a dietary plan to treat an illness or disease, most medical doctors will refer you to an RD to assist you in meeting your dietary needs.

Remember that, as an educated consumer, it is important to seek out individuals who can provide you with reliable nutrition information. Even highly educated and credentialed people have limits to their knowledge and can make mistakes. Seeking a second opinion about nutrition information that affects your health is strongly advised.

Government Sources of Information Are Trustworthy

Federal, provincial or territorial, and municipal government health agencies have been restructured quite a bit in the past 20 years to better address the health problems related to malnutrition in Canada. These agencies are funded with taxpayer dollars, and some also provide financial support for research in the areas of nutrition and health. A few of the main government agencies affiliated with Health Canada include:

Office of Nutrition Policy and Promotion, Health Products and Food Branch, Health Canada
This office conducts reviews of nutrition policy and recommendations. For example, guidelines for determining healthy weights, infant feeding recommendations, nutrition labelling guidelines, and *Eating Well with Canada's Food Guide* are all available at this website. Visit www.hc-sc.gc.ca/fn-an/nutrition/index-eng.php to learn more about food and nutrition policy in Canada.

Natural Health Products Directorate, Health Products and Food Branch, Health Canada
The mission of this directorate is "to ensure that all Canadians have ready access to natural health products that are safe, effective, and of high quality, while respecting freedom of choice and philosophical and cultural diversity." To learn more about the regulation of natural health products in Canada, visit www.hc-sc.gc.ca/dhp-mps/prodnatur/index-eng.php.

Canadian Food Inspection Agency, Bureau of Food Safety and Consumer Protection
The Canadian food supply is inspected by this agency, which reports to Ministry of Agriculture. Food recalls, mad cow disease, biotechnology, and food package labelling requirements for manufacturers are some of the topics that you can find at www.inspection.gc.ca.

Public Health Agency of Canada
The federal government created this national agency, with a Chief Public Health Officer for Canada, in the wake of the Walkerton, Ontario, experience with a deadly microorganism (E. coli 0157:H7) in its water supply, the SARS crisis, and the avian flu outbreak in British Columbia. Its mandate is to prevent disease and injury and to promote health by monitoring trends in chronic infectious and non-infectious diseases and by conducting research. Learn more about this agency at www.phac-aspc.gc.ca.

U.S. Sources
The United States government and large national not-for-profit health agencies have the resources to organize and disseminate the most recent and reliable information

on nutrition and health. Among the most recognized and respected of these agencies are the National Institutes of Health and the Centers for Disease Control and Prevention.

The **National Institutes of Health (NIH)** is the world's leading medical research centre and the focal point for medical research in the United States. The mission of the NIH is to uncover new knowledge that leads to better health for everyone. The NIH has many institutes and centres that investigate a broad array of nutrition-related health issues. These include:

- National Cancer Institute (NCI)
- National Heart, Lung, and Blood Institute (NHLBI)
- National Institute of Diabetes and Digestive and Kidney Diseases (NIDDK)
- National Center for Complementary and Alternative Medicine (NCCAM)

NIH headquarters are located in Bethesda, Maryland.

The **Centers for Disease Control and Prevention (CDC)** is the leading federal agency in the United States to protect the health and safety of people. The CDC is located in Atlanta, Georgia, and works in the areas of health promotion, disease prevention and control, and environmental health. Among its many activities, the CDC supports two large national surveys that monitor the health, lifestyle behaviours, and food and nutrient intakes of Americans—the Behavioral Risk Factor Surveillance System (BRFSS) and the National Health and Nutrition Examination Survey (NHANES). Unfortunately, we have no similar nutrition and food-monitoring systems in Canada to track changes in what people are eating and trends in nutrition issues over time.

Professional Organizations Provide Reliable Nutrition Information

There are a number of professional organizations whose members are qualified nutrition professionals, scientists, and educators. These organizations publish cutting-edge nutrition research studies and educational information in journals that are accessible in most university and medical libraries. Some of these organizations include:

- Dietitians of Canada (DC)—This is the national professional organization for dietitians in Canada, and membership is voluntary. DC promotes dietitians as credible sources of nutrition advice, organizes an annual national Nutrition Month campaign, and represents the profession when policy issues related to health and nutrition are being discussed in the public domain. It publishes the *Canadian Journal of Dietetic Practice and Research.*
- Canadian Society for Nutrition—The Society represents nutritional scientists in academia, government, industry, hospitals, and research institutes. The purpose of the CSNS is to acquire, share, and encourage the use of knowledge in the science of nutrition.
- Canadian Society of Nutrition Management (CSNM)—This is the professional association for nutrition managers, who complete two-year accredited programs in food and nutrition management.
- International Society for Behavioral Nutrition and Physical Activity (ISBNPA)—This professional organization was formed in 2000 to bring together researchers interested in nutrition and physical activity. Goals include increasing our understanding of the determinants of healthy eating and physical activity behaviours and developing successful intervention programs.
- The Academy of Nutrition and Dietetics (formerly called the American Dietetic Association or ADA)—This is the largest organization of food and nutrition professionals in the United States. The mission of this organization is to promote nutrition, health, and well-being. It publishes the *Journal of the Academy of Nutrition and Dietetics.*
- The American Society for Nutrition (ASN)—The goal of the ASN is to improve the quality of life through the science of nutrition. The ASN publishes a professional journal called the *American Journal of Clinical Nutrition.*

National Institutes of Health (NIH) The world's leading medical centre and the focal point for medical research in the United States.

Centers for Disease Control and Prevention (CDC) The leading federal agency in the United States that protects the health and safety of people. Its mission is to promote health and quality of life by preventing and controlling disease, injury, and disability.

⬆ Lifestyle behaviours, such as eating an unhealthful diet, can increase your risk for chronic disease.

- The Society for Nutrition Education and Behavior (SNEB)—The SNEB is dedicated to promoting healthy, sustainable food choices in communities through nutrition research and education. The primary goals of the SNEB are to educate individuals, communities, and professionals about nutrition education and to influence policy makers about nutrition, food, and health. The professional journal of the SNEB is the *Journal of Nutrition Education and Behavior.*
- The American College of Sports Medicine (ACSM)—The ACSM is the leading sports medicine and exercise science organization in the world. Many members are nutrition professionals who combine their nutrition and exercise expertise to promote health and athletic performance. *Medicine and Science in Sports and Exercise* is the professional journal of the ACSM.

RECAP Registered dietitians are professionals who have completed an accredited undergraduate program and dietetic internship or comparable practical experience. Look for the professional designation RD, PDt, or RDt (or the French equivalent Dt.P) to ensure an individual is qualified to provide nutrition advice. Dietitians of Canada and other professional associations are excellent sources of reliable nutrition information. Health Canada is the lead federal agency responsible for protecting people's health.

Nutrition DEBATE

Nutrigenomics: Personalized Nutrition or Pie in the Sky?

Agouti mice are normally yellow, obese, and prone to cancer and diabetes. When agouti mice breed, these traits are passed on to their offspring. Look at the picture of the agouti mice on this page; do you see a difference? The mouse on the right is obviously brown and of normal weight, but what you can't see is that it did not inherit its parents' susceptibility to disease. What caused this dramatic difference?

In 2000, researchers found that, when they changed the mother's diet just before conception, they could "turn off" the agouti gene, and any offspring born to that mother would appear normal (Watters, 2006). As you might know, a *gene* is a segment of DNA, a substance in cells that is responsible for passing on traits from parents to offspring. The diet that the researchers fed the mother was high in a chemical that attached to the agouti gene and disabled it (Watters, 2006). This study was one of the first to link a change in diet to a genetic modification, and it led to the emerging science of *nutrigenomics*.

What Is Nutrigenomics

Nutrigenomics is a scientific discipline studying the interactions between genes, the environment, and nutrition (NCMHD Center of Excellence for Nutritional Genomics, 2007; Johnson and Kaput, 2003). A key theory behind nutrigenomics is that our genes may respond to factors in our diet.

Nutrigenomics proposes that foods can act as a switch in body cells, turning on some genes and turning off others. When a gene is activated, it instructs the cell to create a protein that will show up as a characteristic or an ability, such as yellow fur or a tendency to store fat. When a gene is switched off, the cell will not create that protein, and the organism's form or function will differ. In addition, scientists are discovering that diet can affect gene expression not only in the exposed organism but also in his or her offspring (Watters, 2006; NCMHD

Center of Excellence for Nutritional Genomics, 2007; Johnson and Kaput, 2003). It's an intriguing theory—but is there any evidence to support it?

Evidence for Nutrigenomics

Several observations support the theory. For example, nutrition researchers have long noted that some people will lose weight on a specific diet and exercise program, whereas others following the same program will not (Johnson and Kaput, 2003; Grierson, 2003). The varying results are now thought to depend to a certain extent on how the foods in that diet affect the study participants' genes. Evidence from population studies also supports nutrigenomics. For example, when different ethnic groups are exposed to a Western diet, the percentage of type 2 diabetes increases in some populations significantly more than in others (NCMHD Center of Excellence for Nutritional Genomics, 2007).

Evidence of nutrigenomics' influencing future generations includes the breakthrough study of agouti mice, as well as data that suggest a link between the availability of food and diabetes. Researchers have found that, when one generation experiences a food surplus during critical periods of reproductive development, their offspring are more likely to develop diabetes (Watters, 2006).

Promises and Challenges of Nutrigenomics

One promise of nutrigenomics is that it can help people improve their health through diet alone (Johnson and Kaput, 2003). For example, some researchers are studying how leafy green vegetables may turn on an important gene that suppresses cancerous tumours (Wallace, 2007).

Another promise of nutrigenomics is personalized nutrition. In the world of nutrigenomics, you would provide a tissue sample for genetic analysis. Then your healthcare provider would tailor a diet to your genetic makeup. This "per-

sonalized diet" would identify foods you should eat and foods you should avoid to turn on beneficial genes and turn off genes that may be detrimental.

One challenge in making nutrigenomic therapies a reality is determining what foods turn on or off specific genes in specific people. Genetic pathways are extremely complicated, and turning on a gene may have a beneficial effect on one body function but a harmful effect on another. Individual factors, such as age, gender, and lifestyle, also may affect how different foods interact with these different genes. Even emotional and social factors may play a role (Kaput and Rodriguez, 2004). In addition, dietary intervention to prevent or treat chronic diseases would be challenging because multiple genes may be involved: for instance, scientists have determined that hundreds of genes are linked to type 2 diabetes.

Even by themselves, food interactions are extremely complicated because, in any one meal, we consume hundreds of compounds. Think about all the ingredients in just one food item, such as pancakes. Each one of these ingredients may directly or indirectly affect the expression of many different genes in many different ways (Kaput and Rodriguez, 2004). Which of the ingredients consumed affect what gene and how? It will be years before researchers are capable of mapping out these complex interactions.

With only a change in diet, inbred agouti mice (left) gave birth to young mice (right) that differed not only in their appearance but also in their susceptibility to disease.

Chapter Review

Test Yourself ANSWERS

1. False. Calories are a measure of the energy in foods, not their fat content exclusively. More precisely, a kilocalorie is the amount of heat required to raise the temperature of 1 kilogram of water by 1 degree Celsius.

2. True. Carbohydrates and fats are the primary energy sources for our body.

3. True. The RDA does meet the needs of almost all healthy people of a given age and gender.

4. False. The term *nutritionist* is not protected in Canada and can be used by people with little formal training in nutrition. The term *registered dietitian* is a protected term and can only be used by people who have completed an accredited undergraduate program and dietetic internship or have comparable practical experience.

Find the Quack

Since she was a little girl, Kwan Yu has imagined her wedding day with the same essential detail: walking down the aisle in her mother's wedding dress. Now her wedding is just six months away and, to fit into that dress, she'll need to lose a whole dress size. It's not surprising, then, that when she sees a weight-loss booth at a bridal show, Kwan Yu stops in. A slender young woman introduces herself as Amy and listens closely as Kwan Yu explains why she simply must lose 13.6 kg or 30 pounds in the next six months. Amy smiles reassuringly: "You've come to the right place! Your goal of losing 30 pounds in six months is closer than you ever imagined with Mini Mix, my patented minimizer-formula weight-loss powder. Mixed with 250 mL or 8 fl. oz. of skim milk, it's a complete low-calorie breakfast, and it curbs your appetite for the rest of the day! It's full of vitamins and minerals, so you won't need to worry when you just don't feel like eating anything else all day—Mini Mix meets your nutritional needs for up to 24 hours!" Kwan Yu notices the price on the stack of cans of the powder: $49 for a can that says it's "a 30-day supply." She quickly calculates: $300 seems like a lot of money for six months' worth of powdered vitamins. How can she tell whether the product is legit? While she is trying to decide, another customer approaches the booth, and Amy begins to chat with her. Kwan Yu uses the opportunity to look around the booth. She notices on the wall a framed certificate. Beneath Amy's name is the title Certified Nutrition Consultant, and beneath that is the name of a professional-sounding association of "Nutrition Consultants." Kwan Yu then picks up a can of Mini Mix. On the label, she reads the following:

- Consumed as recommended with 8 ounces of skim milk, Mini Mix provides 100% of the recommended intake of 1 day's micronutrient needs for just 630 kJ (150 kcal).

- One scoop of Mini Mix powder also contains a precise blend of natural appetite suppressants from around the world, including willow bark from Germany and guarana from Brazil. Mini Mix also contains all-natural vanilla or chocolate flavouring.

- Drinking one Mini Mix shake per day will curb your appetite for the rest of the day. Because you won't feel hungry, you won't be tempted to overeat. You'll lose weight quickly and keep it off for life!

1. The certificate on the wall of the Mini Mix booth states that Amy is a certified nutrition consultant. Does this mean that Amy has graduated from an educational institution with a degree in nutrition? If not, what does it mean?

2. The Mini Mix label says that the product "provides 100% of the recommended intake of 1 day's micronutrient needs for just 630 kJ (150 kcal)." Amy claims, "It's full of vitamins and minerals, so you won't need to worry when you just don't feel like eating anything else all day—Mini Mix meets your nutritional needs for up to 24 hours!" Are these claims essentially identical? Could they be true? Why or why not?

3. Mini Mix contains "willow bark from Germany and guarana from Brazil." Look up these plants on a reputable online encyclopedia, such as *Britannica*. What substances do they contain?

4. Mini Mix costs $49 for a 30-day supply. Should Kwan Yu purchase a can? Why or why not?

Answers can be found in the study area of MasteringNutrition.

Review Questions

1. Vitamins A and C, thiamin, calcium, and magnesium are considered
   a. water-soluble vitamins.
   b. fat-soluble vitamins.
   c. energy nutrients.
   d. micronutrients.

2. The term *malnutrition* refers to
   a. undernutrition due to not consuming enough energy from food.
   b. overnutrition due to eating too much food.
   c. undernutrition resulting from inadequate nutrient intakes.
   d. all of the above.

3. Ten grams of fat
   a. contains 170 kJ (40 kcal) of energy.
   b. constitutes the Dietary Reference Intake for an average adult male.
   c. contains 370 kJ (90 kcal) of energy.
   d. constitutes the Tolerable Upper Intake Level for an average adult male.

4. Which of the following statements about hypotheses is true?
   a. Hypotheses can be tested by clinical trials.
   b. "Many inactive people have high blood pressure" is an example of a hypothesis.
   c. If the results of multiple experiments consistently support a hypothesis, it is confirmed as fact.
   d. "A high-protein diet increases the risk for porous bones" is an example of a hypothesis.

5. Choose the incorrect statement about vitamins.
   a. Vitamins A, D, E, and K are fat-soluble vitamins.
   b. Water-soluble vitamins can never be toxic.
   c. Fat-soluble vitamins are stored in the human body.
   d. Vitamins are organic compounds.

6. Carbohydrates, fats, and proteins have all the below in common *except* they
   a. contain carbon, hydrogen, and oxygen.
   b. break down and reassemble into a fuel that is used by the body.
   c. are all primary sources of energy.
   d. are referred to as macronutrients.

7. Which DRI value is based on the average daily nutrient intake level that meets the nutrient requirements of most healthy individuals in a given life stage and gender group?
   a. Adequate Intake
   b. Estimated Average Requirement
   c. Tolerable Upper Intake Level
   d. Recommended Dietary Allowance

8. Which of the following is *not* a function of minerals in the body?
   a. Assist in fluid regulation.
   b. Help rid the body of harmful metabolism by-products.
   c. Produce energy.
   d. Help maintain bone and blood health.

9. Choose the correct statement.
   a. Minerals are organic substances.
   b. All vitamins are fat-soluble.
   c. Proteins contain only hydrogen, oxygen, and carbon.
   d. Fats are insoluble in water.

10. Explain the difference between a trace mineral and a major mineral.

11. Compare the Estimated Average Requirement to the Recommended Dietary Allowance.

12. Your uncle has learned that you are taking a nutrition course and asks, "How can I find reliable nutrition information?" How would you answer?

13. Your mother, who is a self-described "chocolate addict," phones you. She has read in the newspaper a summary of a research study suggesting that the consumption of a moderate amount of bittersweet chocolate reduces the risk of heart disease in older women. You ask her who funded the research. She says she doesn't know and asks you why it would matter. Explain why such information is important.

14. Intrigued by the idea of a research study on chocolate, you obtain a copy of the full report. In it, you learn that
    • twelve women participated in the study;
    • the women's ages ranged from 65 to 78;
    • the women had all been diagnosed with high blood pressure;
    • they all described themselves as sedentary; and
    • six of the twelve smoked at least half a pack of cigarettes a day, but the others did not smoke.

    Your mother is 51 years old, walks daily, and takes a weekly swim class. Her blood pressure is on the upper end of the normal range. She does not smoke. Identify at least three aspects of the study that would cause you to doubt its relevance to your mother.

Case Study

Now that you have had the chance to learn the basics in regards to the importance and role of nutrition in our health, let's meet Cory, a 19-year old male. Cory is living away from home for the first time and he is finding it difficult to balance his energy intake with his energy expenditure. Cory finds that he is eating slightly more than in the past and that he is less physically active.

After recording his intake for three days, Cory discovers he is consuming, on average, 12 130 kJ (2900 kcal) per day. Carbohydrates, fat, and protein are present in the amounts of 486 grams, 77 grams, and 65 grams, respectively.

a. Calculate the percentage of total energy that comes from carbohydrate, fat, and protein. (Hint: the sum of the percentages should total 100%).

b. Refer to the Acceptable Macronutrient Distribution Ranges (AMDR). Do Cory's nutrient intakes fall within the ranges?

c. Based on the above information, including your energy intake calculations, is Cory's diet classified as undernutrition or overnutrition? What risks are associated with this diet?

d. The importance of micronutrients, both vitamins and minerals, is often overlooked. To demonstrate to Cory the importance of consuming adequate levels of vitamins and minerals, list two beneficial roles of each. What foods are generally good sources of both micronutrients?

e. List three people or places you would advise Cory to go to for nutrition advice. Give reasons for your choices.

Answers to Review Questions can be found at the back of this text.

Web Resources

www.hc-sc.gc.ca/fn-an/nutrition/index-eng.php
Health Canada

Search this site for food and nutrition guidelines and policies and for reports and statistics on the health of Canadians.

www.dietitians.ca
Dietitians of Canada (DC)

Ask nutrition and diet questions or get the names of qualified dietitians in your community from this national professional organization.

www.eatright.org
Academy of Nutrition and Dietetics

The professional organization of dietitians in the United States (formerly called the American Dietetic Association).

www.cdc.gov
Centers for Disease Control and Prevention (CDC)

Visit this site for additional information about the leading federal agency in the United States that protects the health and safety of people.

www.cdc.gov/nchs
National Center for Health Statistics

Go to this site to learn more about the National Health and Nutrition Examination Survey (also referred to as NHANES) and other U.S. national health surveys.

www.nih.gov
National Institutes of Health (NIH)

Find out more about the National Institutes of Health, an agency under the U.S. Department of Health and Human Services.

www.nutrition.org
The American Society for Nutrition (ASN)

Learn more about the American Society for Nutrition and its goal to improve quality of life through the science of nutrition.

www.sneb.org
Society for Nutrition Education and Behavior (SNEB)

Go to this site for further information about the Society for Nutritional Education and Behavior and its goals to educate individuals, communities, and professionals about nutrition education and influence policy makers about nutrition, food, and health.

www.acsm.org
American College of Sports Medicine (ACSM)

Obtain information about the leading sports medicine and exercise science organization in the world.

MasteringNutrition®

Assignments

Animation Dietary Reference Intakes (DRI) Determination • Alcohol Absorption

Activities NutriTools

Study Area

Practice Tests • Study Tools • Diet Analysis • eText

Study on the Go

Scan this code with your smartphone

At the end of every chapter, you will find a QR code like the one here that provides access to Study on the Go, linking you to extra resources including quizzes and glossary flashcards. You can link to Study on the Go content through your smartphone, allowing you to study whenever and wherever you wish. Go to one of the sites below to see how to download an app to your smartphone for free. Once the app is installed, the phone will scan the code and link to a website containing *Nutrition: A Functional Approach's* Study on the Go content.

ScanLife

http://getscanlife.com

NeoReader

http://get.neoreader.com

QuickMark

http://www.quickmark.com.tw

Alcohol

READ ON.
No one should have to spend his 19th birthday in an emergency room, but that's what happened to Todd the night he turned 19. His friends took him off campus to celebrate, and, with their encouragement, he attempted to drink 19 shots before the bar closed at 2:00 a.m. Fortunately for Todd, when he passed out and couldn't be roused, his best friend noticed his cold, clammy skin and erratic breathing and drove him to the local emergency room. There, his stomach was pumped and he was treated for alcohol poisoning. He regained consciousness but felt sick and shaky for several more hours. Not everyone is so lucky.

Some people with alcohol poisoning never wake up.

What makes excessive alcohol intake so dangerous, and why is moderate alcohol consumption often considered healthful? How can you tell if someone is struggling with alcohol addiction, and what can you do to help? What if that someone is you? We explore these questions *In Depth* here.

Alcohols are chemical compounds structurally similar to carbohydrates, with one or more hydroxyl (OH) group. **Ethanol** is the specific type of alcohol found in beer, wine, and distilled spirits, such as whiskey and vodka. It is a by-product of the *fermentation* process, in which yeast breaks down grains, fruits, or vegetables. Throughout this discussion, the common term *alcohol* will be used to represent the specific compound *ethanol*.

◆ **Figure 1** What does one drink look like? A drink is equivalent to 43 mL (1.5 fl. oz.) of distilled spirits, 142 mL (5 fl. oz.) of wine, 280 mL (10 fl. oz.) of wine cooler, or 341 mL (12 fl. oz.) of beer.

What Do We Know About Moderate Alcohol Intake?

Alcohol intake is usually described as "drinks per day." A **drink** is defined as the amount of a beverage that provides 14 mL (0.5 fl. oz.) of pure alcohol. For example, 341 mL (12 fl. oz.) of beer, 280 mL (10 fl. oz.) of a wine cooler, 142 mL (5 fl. oz.) of wine, and 43 mL (1.5 fl. oz.) of 80 proof whiskey, scotch, gin, or vodka are each equivalent to one drink **(Figure 1)**. **Proof** is a measure of the alcohol content of a liquid; 100 proof liquor is 50% alcohol by volume, 80 proof liquor is 40% alcohol by volume, and so on.

Canada has a new set of national low-risk alcohol drinking guidelines that have been endorsed by the federal, provincial, and territorial governments, as well as many Canadian health organizations. These guidelines are shown in **Table 1**.

As we discuss here, there are both health benefits and concerns related to moderate alcohol intake. When deciding if or how much alcohol to drink, you need to weigh the pros and cons of alcohol consumption as they relate to your own health history.

Benefits of Low Alcohol Intake

In most people, alcohol intake offers some psychological benefits; it can reduce stress and anxiety while improving self-confidence. It can also have nutritional benefits: in the elderly, small amounts of alcohol can improve appetite and dietary intake (Dufour et al., 1992).

In addition, low-risk alcohol consumption has been linked to lower rates of heart disease for middle-aged people. Alcohol increases levels of the "good" type of cholesterol (HDL) while lowering the concentration of "bad" cholesterol (LDL); it also reduces the risk for abnormal clot formation in the blood vessels (Gunzerath et al., 2004). Recently, there has been a lot of interest in

resveratrol, which is a powerful antioxidant found in red wines and foods such as grapes and nuts. Some researchers, based on experiments with mice, are proposing that resveratrol may be able to lower our risk for certain chronic diseases, such as diabetes, heart disease, and liver disease. However, if resveratrol is found to be effective in promoting human health, the amount needed would be so high that it would have to be given as a purified supplement, not in the form of red wine.

alcohol Chemically, a compound characterized by the presence of a hydroxyl group; in common usage, a beverage made from fermented fruits, vegetables, or grains and containing ethanol.

ethanol A specific alcohol compound (C_2H_5OH) formed from the fermentation of dietary carbohydrates and used in a variety of alcoholic beverages.

drink The amount of an alcoholic beverage that provides approximately 17 mL or 13.5 grams of pure ethanol.

proof A measure of the alcohol content of a liquid; 100 proof liquor is 50% alcohol by volume, 80 proof liquor is 40% alcohol by volume, and so on.

resveratrol A potent phenolic antioxidant found in red wine as well as grapes and nuts.

TABLE 1 Canada's Low-Risk Alcohol Drinking Guidelines

Guideline 1 (Your limits)

Reduce your long-term health risks by drinking no more than:

- 10 drinks a week for women, with no more than 2 drinks a day most days
- 15 drinks a week for men, with no more than 3 drinks a day most days

Plan non-drinking days every week to avoid developing a habit.

Guideline 2 (Special occasions)

Reduce your risk of injury and harm by drinking no more than three drinks (for women) and four drinks (for men) on any single occasion.

Plan to drink in a safe environment. Stay within the weekly limits outlined in Guideline 1.

Guideline 3 (When zero's the limit)

Do not drink when you are:

- driving a vehicle or using machinery and tools;
- taking medicine or other drugs that interact with alcohol;
- doing any kind of dangerous physical activity;
- living with mental or physical health problems;
- living with alcohol dependence;
- pregnant or planning to be pregnant;
- responsible for the safety of others; or
- making important decisions.

Guideline 4 (Pregnant? Zero is safest)

If you are pregnant, planning to become pregnant, or before breastfeeding, the safest choice is to drink no alcohol at all.

Guideline 5 (Delay your drinking)

Alcohol can harm the way the body and brain develop. Teens should speak with their parents about drinking. If they choose to drink, they should do so under parental guidance; never more than 1–2 drinks at a time, and never more than 1–2 times per week. They should plan ahead, follow local alcohol laws and consider the Safer drinking tipslisted in this brochure.

Youth in their late teens to age 24 years should never exceed the daily and weekly limits outlined in Guideline 1 (Your limits).

Source: Canadian Centre on Substance Abuse (2012). Retrieved on Aug. 1, 2012 from www.ccsa.ca/eng/priorities/alcohol/Canada-low-risk-alcohol-drinking-guidelines/pages/default.aspx.

Notice that this definition of low-risk drinking is based on a maximum daily and a maximum weekly intake; a person who does not drink any alcohol on weekdays but downs a six-pack of beer most Saturday nights would NOT be classified as a "low-risk drinker"! These guidelines also identify groups of individuals who should not consume alcohol at all, including women who are or may become pregnant and children. In addition, people with a history of alcoholism and those taking medications that interact with alcohol should not drink at all, nor should individuals driving, operating machinery, or engaged in other tasks that require attention and coordination.

Alcohol can interfere with and increase the risks of using various over-the-counter and prescription medications.

Concerns About Alcohol Intake

Not everyone responds to alcohol in the same manner. A person's age, genetic makeup, state of health, and use of medications can influence both immediate and long-term responses to alcohol intake, even at moderate levels. For example, some women appear to be at increased risk for breast cancer when consuming low to moderate amounts of alcohol. As few as two drinks per day can increase the risk for hypertension (high blood pressure) in some people, especially if they consume the alcohol without food (Stranges et al., 2004). Moderate use of alcohol has also been linked to a higher rate of bleeding in the brain, resulting in what is termed *hemorrhagic stroke* (Meister et al., 2000).

Alcohol has a relatively high caloric content (29 kJ or 7 kcal/g). Only fat (37 kJ or 9 kcal/g) has more Calories per gram. If you're watching your weight, you might be interested to know that a serving of wine is about 420 kJ (100 kcal), beer is about 630 kJ (150 kcal), and a typical margarita is over 1260 kJ (300 kcal)! What's more, unlike solid foods, alcoholic beverages fail to trigger the satiety, or "fullness," response (Caton et al., 2004). So it's not surprising that regularly consuming alcohol makes it difficult to avoid weight gain. Alcohol intake may also reduce your inhibitions, leading you to overeat!

The potential for drug–alcohol interactions is well known; many medications carry a warning label advising consumers to avoid alcohol while taking the drug. These include common over-the-counter pain remedies, such as acetaminophen, aspirin, and ibuprofen, which, when consumed with alcohol, are associated with gastrointestinal bleeding. Alcohol magnifies the effect of certain painkillers, sleeping pills, antidepressants, and anti-anxiety medications and can lead to loss of consciousness. In people with diabetes using insulin injections or oral medications to lower blood glucose (blood sugar), alcohol can exaggerate the drug's effect, leading to an inappropriately low level.

As you can see, there are both benefits and risks to alcohol consumption, even at low to moderate amounts. Experts agree that people who are currently consuming alcohol in moderation and who have low or no risk for alcohol addiction or medication interaction can safely continue their current level of use. Adults who abstain from alcohol, however, should not start drinking just for the possible health benefits. Individuals who have a personal or family history of alcoholism or fall into any other risk category should consider totally abstaining from alcohol use.

What Happens to Alcohol in the Body?

Most of the alcohol someone drinks is absorbed directly into the bloodstream from both the stomach and the small intestine; it does not have to be broken down first. Consuming foods with some fat, protein, and fibre slows the absorption of alcohol and can reduce *blood alcohol concentration* (*BAC*) by as much as 50% compared to peak BAC when drinking on an empty stomach. Carbonated alcoholic beverages are absorbed very rapidly, which explains why champagne and other sparkling wines are so quick to generate an alcoholic "buzz." Women often absorb 30%–35% more of a given alcohol intake than do men of the same size, which may explain why women often show a greater response to alcohol compared to men.

A small amount of the alcohol in the stomach is broken down before it is absorbed. The rest travels in the bloodstream to the liver, where it is broken down at a fairly steady rate. On average, a healthy adult metabolizes the equivalent of one drink per hour. If someone drinks more than that, such as two or three alcoholic drinks in an hour, the liver is unable to "keep up." The excess alcohol is released back into the bloodstream, and then is distributed to all body fluids and tissues, including the brain. Anytime you consume more than one alcoholic beverage per hour, you are exposing every tissue in your body to the toxic effects of alcohol.

Despite what you may have heard, there is no effective intervention to speed up the breakdown of alcohol (Table 2). The key to keeping your BAC below the legal limit is to drink alcoholic beverages while eating a meal or large snack; to drink very slowly, no more than one drink per hour; and to limit your total consumption of alcohol on any one occasion.

It also helps to fully quench your thirst with a non-alcoholic beverage *before* having your first alcoholic drink, and to make every other beverage non-alcoholic. More tips for controlling your alcohol intake are in the Quick Tips feature on the next page.

A person who steadily increases his or her alcohol consumption over time becomes more tolerant of a given intake of alcohol. Chronic drinkers experience *metabolic tolerance*, a condition in which the liver becomes more efficient in its breakdown of alcohol. This means that the person's BAC rises more slowly after consuming a certain number of drinks. In addition, chronic drinkers develop what

is called *functional tolerance*, meaning that they show few, if any, signs of impairment or intoxication even at high BACs. As a result, these individuals may need to consume twice as much alcohol as when they first started drinking to reach the same state of euphoria.

Effects of Alcohol Abuse on Personal Health

Alcohol is a drug. It exerts a narcotic effect on virtually every part of the brain, acting as a sedative and depressant. Excessive intake of this drug, whether occasional or chronic, is generally referred to as **alcohol abuse** and can lead to alcoholism.

Binge drinking, the consumption of five or more alcoholic drinks on one occasion (within a 3- to 5-hour span, for example) for men, or four or more for women, occurs in about 15% of U.S. adults and in youth as young as 12 years of age (NIAAA, 2004). Binge drinking by university students and other young adults (or even underage adolescents) increases the risk for potentially fatal falls, drownings, and automobile accidents. Acts of physical violence, including vandalism and physical and sexual assault, are also associated with binge drinking. The physiologic consequences also carry over beyond the actual binge: hangovers, which are discussed shortly, are practically inevitable, given the amount of alcohol consumed.

Alcoholism (also called *chronic alcohol dependence*) is a disease characterized by chronic dependence on alcohol, with the following symptoms:

- craving: a strong need or urge to drink alcoholic beverages;

alcohol abuse The excessive consumption of alcohol, whether chronically or occasionally.

binge drinking The consumption of five or more alcoholic drinks on one occasion for men, or four or more for women.

alcoholism A disease state characterized by chronic dependence on alcohol.

TABLE 2 Myths About Alcohol Metabolism	
The Claim	**The Reality**
Physical activity, such as walking around, will speed up the breakdown of alcohol.	Muscles don't metabolize alcohol; the liver does.
Drinking a lot of coffee will keep you from getting drunk.	Coffee does not cause alcohol to be excreted in the urine.
Using a sauna or steam room will force the alcohol out of your body.	Very little alcohol is lost in the sweat; the alcohol will remain in your bloodstream.
Herbal and nutritional products are available that speed up the breakdown of alcohol.	There is no scientific evidence that commercial supplements will increase the rate of alcohol metabolism; they will not lower blood alcohol levels.

- loss of control: the inability to stop once drinking has begun;
- physical dependence: the presence of nausea, sweating, shakiness, and other signs of withdrawal after stopping alcohol intake; and
- tolerance: the need to drink larger and larger amounts of alcohol to get the same "high," or pleasurable sensations, associated with alcohol intake.

Alcohol Hangovers

Alcohol hangover is a common and extremely unpleasant consequence of drinking too much alcohol. It lasts up to 24 hours, and its symptoms include headache, fatigue, dizziness, muscle aches, nausea and vomiting, sensitivity to light and sound, and extreme thirst. Some people also experience depression, anxiety, irritability, and other mood disturbances.

Some of the symptoms occur because of alcohol's effect as a *diuretic*, a compound that increases urine output. Alcohol inhibits the release of

QUICK TIPS

Taking Control of Your Alcohol Intake

▶ Think about WHY you are planning to drink. Is it to relax and socialize, or are you using alcohol to release stress? If the latter, try some stress-reduction techniques that don't involve alcohol, such as exercise, yoga, meditation, or simply talking with a friend.

▶ Make sure you have a protein-containing meal or snack before your first alcoholic drink; having food in the stomach delays its emptying. This gives more of the alcohol a chance to be broken down and means that less is available to be absorbed into the bloodstream.

▶ Before you drink alcohol, have a large glass of water, iced tea, or a soft drink. Once your thirst has been satisfied, your rate of fluid intake will drop. After that, rotate between alcoholic and non-alcoholic drinks.

▶ Dilute hard liquor with large amounts of diet soft drinks, water, or juice. Remember, a glass of pure orange juice doesn't look any different from one laced with vodka, so no one will even know what it is you are or are not drinking! These diluted beverages are cheaper and lower in Calories, too!

▶ Whether or not your drink is diluted, sip slowly to allow your liver time to keep up with your alcohol intake.

▶ If your friends pressure you to drink, volunteer to be the designated driver. You'll have a "free pass" for the night in terms of saying no to alcoholic drinks.

▶ Decide in advance what your alcohol intake will be, and plan some strategies for sticking to your limit. If you are going to a bar, for example, take only enough money to buy two beers and two soft drinks. If you are at a party, stay occupied dancing, sampling the food, or talking with friends, and stay as far away from the keg as you can.

▲ Binge drinking or excessive drinking can lead to a number of negative consequences.

▲ Is it wine or juice? The only way to tell if this glass holds an alcoholic or a non-alcoholic drink is to take a sip! At a party, fruit juices and soft drinks can be socially acceptable substitutes for alcoholic drinks.

the hormones that normally regulate urine production, so the body loses excessive fluid and minerals, such as sodium. This results in headache, thirst, dizziness, and light-headedness. The strategies suggested earlier—quenching your thirst with a non-alcoholic beverage before drinking alcohol and switching between alcoholic and non-alcoholic drinks—can help you avoid dehydration.

Alcohol irritates the lining of the stomach and increases the production of stomach acid. This may account for the abdominal pain, nausea, and vomiting seen in most hangovers.

Alcohol also disrupts normal body metabolism, leading to low levels of blood glucose and elevated levels of blood acidity. These disturbances contribute to the characteristic fatigue, weakness, and mood changes seen after excessive alcohol intake. Finally,

alcohol disrupts various biological rhythms, such as sleep patterns and cycles of hormone secretion, leading to a jet lag type of effect.

While many folk remedies, including various herbal products, are claimed to prevent or reduce hangover effects, few have been proven effective. Drinking water or other non-alcoholic beverages will minimize the risk for dehydration, while the consumption of toast or dry cereal will bring blood glucose levels back to normal. Getting adequate sleep can counteract the fatigue, and the use of antacids may reduce nausea and abdominal pain. Although

alcohol hangover A consequence of drinking too much alcohol; symptoms include headache, fatigue, dizziness, muscle aches, nausea and vomiting, sensitivity to light and sound, extreme thirst, and mood disturbances.

acetaminophen, aspirin, and ibuprofen might be useful for headaches, they may worsen stomach pain, increase the risk for gastrointestinal bleeding, and over time increase the risk for liver damage.

Reduced Brain Function

Alcohol is well known for its ability to alter behaviour, mainly through its effects on the brain. Even at low intakes, alcohol impairs reasoning and judgment (Table 3). For university students, the academic consequences of drinking include falling behind in classes, doing poorly on exams and papers, missing classes, and getting lower grades overall (Naimi et al., 2003). Alcohol also interferes with normal sleep patterns, alters sight and speech, and leads to loss of fine and gross motor skills, such as handwriting, hand–eye coordination, and balance. Many people who drink experience unexpected mood swings, intense anger, or unreasonable irritation. Others react in the opposite direction, becoming sad, withdrawn, and lethargic. When teens or young adults chronically consume excessive amounts of alcohol, they may permanently damage brain structure and function (NIAAA, 2007). Intellectual functioning and memory can be lost. In addition, early exposure to alcohol increases the risk for future alcohol addiction and may contribute to life-long deficits in memory, motor skills, and muscle coordination (Oscar-Berman and Marinkovic, 2003; Brown et al., 2000).

Alcohol Poisoning

At very high intakes of alcohol, a person is at risk for **alcohol poisoning**, a metabolic state that occurs in response to binge drinking. At high BACs, the respiratory centre of the brain is depressed and cardiac function shuts down, leading to loss of consciousness, heart failure, and death. Like Todd in our opening story, many binge drinkers lose consciousness before alcohol poisoning becomes fatal, but emergency care is often essential.

TABLE 3 Effects of Blood Alcohol Concentration (BAC) on Brain Activity

Blood Alcohol Concentration	Typical Response
0.02%–0.05%	Feeling of relaxation, euphoria, relief
0.06%–0.10%	Impaired judgment, fine motor control, and coordination; loss of normal emotional control; legally drunk in many parts of Canada
0.11%–0.15%	Impaired reflexes and gross motor control; staggered gait; legally drunk in all provinces and territories; slurred speech
0.16%–0.20%	Impaired vision; unpredictable behaviour; further loss of muscle control
0.21%–0.35%	Total loss of coordination; nearly unconscious
0.40% and above	Loss of consciousness; coma; suppression of respiratory response; death

If someone passes out after a night of hard drinking, he or she should never be left alone to "sleep it off." Instead, the person should be placed on his or her side to prevent aspiration if vomiting occurs. The person should also be watched carefully for cold and clammy skin, a bluish tint to the skin, or slow, irregular breathing. If any of these signs become evident, or there is any reason to believe he or she has alcohol poisoning, seek emergency healthcare immediately.

Reduced Liver Function

In addition to its effects on the brain, alcohol can damage the liver, which is the main site of alcohol metabolism. Liver cells are damaged or destroyed during periods of excessive alcohol intake; the longer the alcohol abuse, the greater the damage to the liver. **Fatty liver**, a condition in which abnormal amounts of fat build up in the liver, is an early yet reversible sign of alcohol-related liver damage. **Alcoholic hepatitis** causes loss of appetite, nausea and vomiting, abdominal pain, and jaundice (a yellowing of the skin and eyes, reflecting loss of liver function). **Cirrhosis of the liver** is often the result of long-term alcohol abuse; liver cells are scarred, blood flow through the liver is impaired, and liver function declines (Figure 2).

---

alcohol poisoning A potentially fatal condition in which an overdose of alcohol results in cardiac and/or respiratory failure.

fatty liver An early and reversible stage of liver disease often found in people who abuse alcohol and characterized by the abnormal accumulation of fat within liver cells; also called alcoholic steatosis.

alcoholic hepatitis Inflammation of the liver caused by alcohol; other forms of hepatitis can be caused by a virus or toxin.

cirrhosis of the liver Endstage liver disease characterized by significant abnormalities in liver structure and function; may lead to complete liver failure.

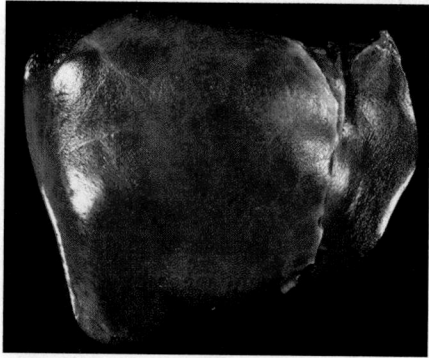
(a)

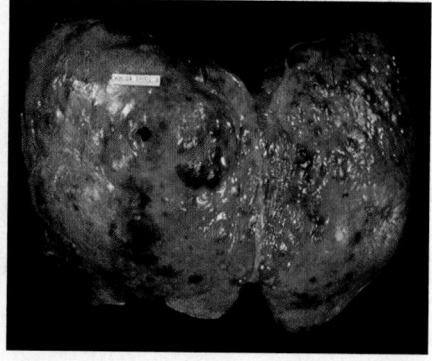
(b)

Figure 2 Cirrhosis of the liver, caused by chronic alcohol abuse. **(a)** A healthy liver. **(b)** A liver damaged by cirrhosis.

Increased Risk for Chronic Disease

Heavy drinking has been associated with a number of diseases. For example, it damages the pancreas, which produces insulin, a hormone essential for blood glucose regulation. It also decreases the body's ability to respond properly to insulin. The result is chronically elevated blood glucose levels and an increased risk for diabetes. Research has strongly linked heavy alcohol intake to increased risk for cancer of the mouth and throat, esophagus, liver, colon, rectum, and female breast (Butt et al., 2011). So, although moderate drinking may provide some health benefits, it is clear that chronically high intakes of alcohol damage a number of body organs and systems, increasing a person's risk for chronic disease and death.

Malnutrition

As alcohol intake increases to 30% or more of total energy intake, appetite is lost and the intake of healthful foods declines. Over time, the diet becomes deficient in protein, fats, carbohydrates, vitamins A and C, and minerals such as iron, zinc, and calcium. Even if food intake is maintained, the toxic effects of alcohol damage many digestive organs, including the stomach, small intestine, pancreas, and liver. The digestion of foods and absorption of nutrients become inadequate, leading to malnutrition and inappropriate weight loss.

Fetal and Infant Health Problems

Alcohol is a known **teratogen** (a substance that causes fetal harm) that readily crosses the placenta into the fetal bloodstream. Since the immature fetal liver cannot effectively break down the alcohol, it accumulates in the fetal blood and tissues, increasing the risk for various birth defects. The effects of maternal alcohol intake are dose-related: the more the mother drinks, the greater the potential harm to the fetus. Drinking early in the pregnancy—even before the woman realizes she is pregnant—can cause particularly severe harm.

Fetal Alcohol Spectrum Disorder (FASD) is an umbrella term used to describe the range of complications that develop when a woman consumes alcohol while pregnant. There are no national statistics on the prevalence of FASD in Canada and it appears to vary greatly across communities (Chudley et al., 2005). The diagnosis of *Alcohol Related Birth Defects* (ARBD) is made when an infant is born with one or more congenital defects, including malformations of the heart, bone, kidney, eyes, or ears as the result of prenatal exposure to alcohol. Alcohol consumption during pregnancy can also result in *Alcohol*

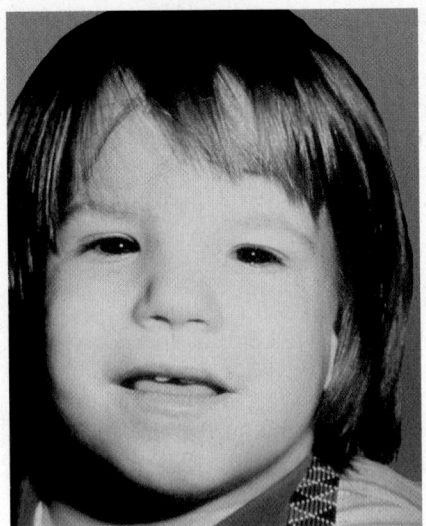

Figure 3 A child with fetal alcohol syndrome (FAS). The facial features typical of children with FAS include a short nose with a low, wide bridge; drooping eyes with an extra skinfold; and a flat, thin upper lip. These external traits are typically accompanied by behavioural problems and learning disorders. The effects of FAS are irreversible.

Related Neurodevelopmental Disorders (ARND), which lead to central nervous system damage, learning impairments, and behavioural problems throughout life including hyperactivity, attention deficit disorder, or other related disorders.

Fetal alcohol syndrome (FAS) is the most severe of these conditions and is characterized by malformations of the face, limbs, heart, and nervous system. The characteristic facial features persist throughout the child's life (**Figure 3**). Newborn and infant death rates are abnormally high, and those who do survive may suffer from emotional, behavioural, social, learning, and developmental problems throughout life. FAS is one of the most common causes of developmental disability in Canada (PHAC, 2008) and the only one that is completely preventable. There are three categories of FAS diagnosis: FAS

teratogen A compound known to cause fetal harm or danger.

fetal alcohol syndrome (FAS) A set of serious, irreversible alcohol-related birth defects characterized by certain physical and mental abnormalities.

Excessive alcohol intake greatly increases the risks for car accidents and other traumatic injuries.

with a confirmed history of alcohol exposure, FAS without a confirmed history of alcohol exposure during pregnancy, and partial FAS (Chudley et al., 2005). The term "fetal alcohol effects" or "FAE" is no longer used in Canada or by the Institute of Medicine (Chudley et al., 2005).

There is no known safe level of alcohol consumption for pregnant women. Women who are pregnant, think they may be pregnant, or are trying to become pregnant should abstain from all alcoholic beverages.

Women who are breastfeeding should also abstain from alcohol, since it easily passes into the breast milk at levels equal to blood alcohol concentrations. If consumed by the infant, the alcohol in breast milk can slow motor development, depress the central nervous system, and increase sleepiness in the child. Alcohol also reduces the mother's ability to produce milk, putting the infant at risk for malnutrition.

Web Resources

www.aa.org
Alcoholics Anonymous, Inc.

This site provides links to AA groups in Canada and the United States and provides information on the AA program.

www.al-anon.alateen.org
Al-Anon Family Groups

This site provides links to Al-Anon and Alateen groups in Canada and the United States, which provide support for spouses, children, and other loved ones of people addicted to alcohol.

www.ccsa.ca
Canadian Centre on Substance Abuse

This site provides links to research reports on alcohol and other substance abuse in Canada.

www.camh.net
Centre for Addiction and Mental Health

This site provides education and resources for help with addictions and mental illness.

www.niaaa.nih.gov
National Institute on Alcohol Abuse and Alcoholism

Visit this website for information on the prevalence, consequences, and treatments of alcohol-related disorders. Information for healthcare providers, people struggling with alcohol abuse, and family members is available free of charge.

www.collegedrinkingprevention.gov
College Drinking: Changing the Culture

The NIAAA developed this website specifically for college students seeking information and advice on the subject of college drinking. Services include self-assessment questionnaires, answers to frequently asked questions, news articles, research, and links to support groups.

www.madd.ca
Mothers Against Drunk Driving Canada

Links to local chapters, statistics related to drunk driving, and prevention strategies are easily accessed from this site.

Designing a Healthful Diet

2

CHAPTER OBJECTIVES

After reading this chapter you will be able to:

1. Describe the four characteristics of a nutritious diet, pp. 40–44.

2. Interpret the Nutrition Facts table on a food label, pp. 42–44.

3. Use the food groups and recommended number of servings of each in *Eating Well with Canada's Food Guide* to plan a nutritious diet, pp. 50–56.

4. Name at least four ways to apply guidelines for healthy eating when eating out, p. 63.

Test Yourself

1. (T) (F) A nutritious diet can include most foods.

2. (T) (F) Food labels are the most commonly used tool for choosing healthy foods.

3. (T) (F) The portion sizes used in *Eating Well with Canada's Food Guide* are based on the "average" portion sizes eaten by Canadians.

4. (T) (F) Manufacturers must list the ingredients in packaged food in descending order by weight.

5. (T) (F) Manufacturers can claim that eating their food products helps prevent diseases like cancer.

Test Yourself answers can be found at the end of the chapter.

Shivani and her parents moved to Canada from India when she was six years old. Although she was delicate in comparison to her Canadian peers, Shivani was healthy and energetic, excelling in school and riding her new bike in her suburban neighbourhood. By the time Shivani entered high school, her weight had caught up to that of her Canadian classmates. Now in her first year of university, she has joined the 23% of 18 and 19 year olds in Canada who are overweight or obese (Stats Canada, 2011) Shivani explains, "In India, the diet is mostly rice, lentils, and vegetables. Many people are vegetarians, and many others eat meat only once or twice a week, and very small portions. Desserts are only for special occasions. When we moved to Canada, I wanted to eat like all the other kids: hamburgers, french fries, soft drinks, and sweets. I gained a lot of weight on that diet, and now my doctor says my cholesterol level, my blood pressure, and my blood sugar level are all too high. I wish I could start eating like my relatives back in India again, but they don't serve rice and lentils at the residence cafeteria."

What influence does diet have on health? What exactly qualifies as a "poor diet," and what makes a diet healthful? Is it more important to watch how much we eat or what kinds of foods we choose? Is low-carb better, or low-fat?

The truth is, there's no one way to eat that's right for everyone. We're individuals with unique preferences, needs, and cultural influences. You may love broccoli, whereas your roommate can't stand it. A person with diabetes may need to eat less added sugar than a person without diabetes. People following certain religious practices may avoid specific meats and dairy products. Thus, there are literally millions of ways to design a healthful diet to fit individual needs.

A healthful diet can help prevent disease.

healthful diet A diet that provides the proper combination of energy and nutrients and is adequate, moderate, balanced, and varied.

adequate diet A diet that provides enough of the energy, nutrients, and fibre needed to maintain a person's health.

moderation Eating any foods in moderate amounts—not too much and not too little.

balanced diet A diet that contains the combinations of foods that provide the proper proportions of nutrients.

Given all this potential confusion, it's a good thing there are nutritional tools to guide us in designing our own healthful diet. In this chapter, we'll discover these tools, including *Eating Well with Canada's Food Guide*. Before we explore the question of how to design a healthful diet, however, we should first make sure we understand what a healthful diet *is*.

What Is a Healthful Diet?

A **healthful diet** provides the proper combination of energy and nutrients. It has four characteristics: it is adequate, moderate, balanced, and varied. No matter if you are young or old, overweight or underweight, healthy or ill, if you keep these characteristics in mind, you will be able to select foods that provide you with the optimal combination of nutrients and energy each day.

A Healthful Diet Is Adequate

An **adequate diet** provides enough of the energy, nutrients, and fibre to maintain a person's health. A diet may be inadequate in only one area, or many areas. For example, many people in Canada do not eat enough vegetables and therefore are not consuming enough of the fibre and micronutrients vegetables provide. However, their intake of protein, fat, and carbohydrate may be adequate. In fact, some people who eat too few vegetables are overweight or obese, which means that they are eating a diet that, although inadequate in one area, exceeds their energy needs. On the other hand, a generalized state of undernutrition can occur if an individual's diet contains an inadequate level of several nutrients for a long period of time.

A diet that is adequate for one person may not be adequate for another. For example, the energy needs of a young woman who is lightly active are approximately 7100 kJ to 8400 kJ (1700 to 2000 kcal) each day, whereas a highly active male athlete may require more than 16 800 kJ (4000 kcal) each day to support his body's demands. These two individuals differ greatly in their activity level and in their quantity of body fat and muscle mass, which means they require very different levels of fat, carbohydrate, protein, and other nutrients to support their daily needs.

A Healthful Diet Is Moderate

Moderation is one of the keys to a healthful diet. **Moderation** refers to eating any foods in moderate amounts—not too much and not too little. If we eat too much or too little of certain foods, we cannot reach our health goals. For example, some people drink as much as 1875 mL (60 fluid ounces as three, 20 oz. bottles) of soft drinks on some days. Drinking this much contributes an extra 3200 kJ or 765 kcal of energy to a person's diet. To allow for this extra energy and avoid weight gain, most people would need to reduce their food intake significantly. This could mean eliminating many healthful food choices. In contrast, people who drink mostly water or other beverages that contain little or no energy can consume more nourishing foods that will support their health. Excess intake of sweets and fats are associated with overweight and obesity and high salt intake is associated with high blood pressure and heart disease.

A Healthful Diet Is Balanced

A **balanced diet** contains the combinations of foods that provide the proper proportions of nutrients. As you will learn in this course, the body needs many types of foods in varying amounts to maintain health.

A diet that is adequate for one person may not be adequate for another. A woman who is lightly active may require fewer kilojoules or kilocalories of energy per day than a highly active male.

For example, fruits and vegetables are excellent sources of fibre, vitamin C, potassium, and magnesium. In contrast, meats are not good sources of fibre and these nutrients. However, meats are excellent sources of protein, iron, zinc, and copper. By eating the proper balance of all healthful foods, including fruits, vegetables, and meats or meat substitutes, we can be confident that we're consuming the balanced nutrition we need to maintain health.

A Healthful Diet Is Varied

Variety refers to eating many different foods from the different food groups on a regular basis. With thousands of healthful foods to choose from, trying new foods is a fun and easy way to vary your diet. Eat a new vegetable each week or substitute one food for another, such as raw spinach on your turkey sandwich in place of iceberg lettuce. Selecting a variety of foods increases the likelihood that you will consume the multitude of nutrients your body needs. As an added benefit, eating a varied diet prevents boredom and helps you avoid the potential of getting into a "food rut." Later in this chapter, we'll provide suggestions for eating a varied diet.

variety Eating a lot of different foods each day.

RECAP A healthful diet provides adequate nutrients and energy, and it includes sweets, fats, and salty foods in moderate amounts only. A healthful diet includes an appropriate balance of nutrients and a wide variety of foods.

What Tools Can Help Me Design a Healthful Diet?

Many people feel it is impossible to eat a healthful diet. They may mistakenly believe that the foods they would need to eat are too expensive or not available to them, or they may feel too busy to do the necessary planning, shopping, and cooking. Some people rely on dietary supplements to get enough nutrients instead of focusing on eating a variety of foods. But is it really that difficult to eat healthfully?

Although designing and maintaining a healthful diet is not as simple as eating whatever you want, most of us can improve our diets with a little practice and a little help. Let's look at some tools for designing a healthful diet.

The serving size on a nutrition label may not be the same as the amount you eat.

Canada's Food Labels

A new set of labelling regulations became mandatory for all prepackaged foods in Canada on December 12, 2007. These regulations specify which foods need a food label, provide detailed descriptions of the information that must be included on the food label, and outline the food products that are exempt from carrying nutrition information on their food labels. The latter are shown in **Table 2.1**.

Choosing a smaller-size drink of pop, or switching to diet pop, helps to maintain a healthy body weight. Better yet—drink water to quench your thirst!

TABLE 2.1 Examples of Foods Exempt from Carrying Nutrition Information

- foods such as spices and coffee, where the amounts of nutrients required on the label would be "0"
- alcoholic drinks (with an alcohol content of more than 0.5%)
- fresh vegetables or fruits, with no added ingredients
- fresh meats
- foods sold at roadside stands, craft shows, flea markets, fairs, or farmers' markets by the person who prepared and processed them
- individual servings of food sold for immediate consumption, such as salads and sandwiches, that have not been treated or packaged to extend their durable life
- one-bite candies or desserts
- prepackaged individual portions of food intended to be served with meals or snacks by a restaurant or other commercial enterprise
- some cow and goat milk products sold in refillable glass containers

Source: Canada Gazette, Vol. 137, No. 1, January 1, 2003, "Food and Drug Act: Regulations Amending the Food and Drug Regulations," B.01.401, http://canadagazette.gc.ca/partII/2003/20030101/html/sor11-e.html (accessed January 2006). Reproduced with the permission of the Minister of Public Works and Government Services Canada, 2012.

In this chapter you will learn how to read food labels, a skill that can help you meet your nutritional goals.

Food labels allow food manufacturers to communicate directly with purchasers and consumers to compare similar products. The food label has three main purposes (Health Canada, 2003):

- To give basic product information, including a list of ingredients, product weight or net quantity, best-before or expiry dates, grade or quality, country of origin, and the name and address of the manufacturer, dealer, or importer. Some manufacturers also include 1-800 phone numbers or website addresses for consumers to contact them directly with product-related questions.
- To provide health, safety, and nutrition information. This includes nutrition information such as the amount and type of fats, proteins, carbohydrates, vitamins, and minerals present in a specified serving size (in the Nutrition Facts table). The label may also give instructions for safe storage and handling of the product.
- To provide a means for marketing or promoting the product by label claims such as "low fat," "cholesterol free," "high source of fibre," "product of Canada," "no preservatives added," and so on.

Food Labels Can Have Four Main Components

The labels on packaged foods can have four main parts, as shown in **Figure 2.1**.

1. *Ingredient list:* The ingredients must be listed in descending order by weight. This means that the first product listed in the ingredient list is the predominant ingredient, by weight (not volume amount), in that food. This information is essential for people with food allergies. Such individuals need to see whether a food contains an ingredient they are allergic to, such as wheat or peanuts. But it can

Nutrient content claims

Health claims

Ingredient list

Nutrition Facts table

Nutrition Facts		
Per 1/2 cup (30 g)		
Amount	Cereal	With 1/2 cup 1% milk
Calories	110	170
		% Daily Value
Fat *1 g	2 %	3 %
Saturates 0 g + Trans 0 g	0 %	5 %
Polyunsaturates 0.4 g		
Omega-6 0.4 g		
Omega-3 0 g		
Monounsaturates 0.2 g		
Cholesterol 0 mg		
Sodium 270 mg	11 %	14 %
Carbohydrate 23 g	8 %	10 %
Fibre 13 g	52 %	52 %
Soluble Fibre 0.5 g		
Insoluble Fibre 12 g		
Sugars 5 g		
Protein 3 g		
Vitamin A	0 %	6 %
Vitamin C	0 %	0 %
Calcium	2 %	15 %
Iron	30 %	30 %
Vitamin D	0 %	20 %
Thiamine	45 %	50 %
Riboflavin	6 %	20 %
Niacin	6 %	10 %
Vitamin B₆	10 %	15 %
Folate	8 %	10 %
Vitamin B₁₂	0 %	20 %
Pantothenate	6 %	10 %
Phosphorus	20 %	30 %
Magnesium	30 %	40 %
Zinc	20 %	25 %
* Amount in cereal		

Information of food manufacturer, packer, or distributor

Figure 2.1 The four main parts of a food label and the contact information. (Courtesy of President's Choice®, www.presidentschoice.ca.)

be very useful in many other situations as well; for example, when you are looking for foods that are lower in fat or sugar, or attempting to identify foods that contain whole wheat instead of white flour. The ingredient list has been mandatory on packaged foods for many years.

2. *Nutrition Facts table:* The **Nutrition Facts table** is required on all products except those listed in Table 2.1. The amount of energy and 13 core nutrients (fat, saturated fat, trans fat, cholesterol, sodium, carbohydrate, fibre, sugar, protein, vitamin A, vitamin C, calcium, and iron) in 1 serving of the food must be provided. Canada was the first country to require the amount of trans fat to be listed on product labels.

   In the Nutrition Facts table and nutrient content claims (discussed next), the energy content is given as **Calories**. (Recall that 1 Calorie is equal to 1 kilocalorie and both are equivalent to 4.184 kilojoules.) Manufacturers have the option of adding the energy content in kilojoules (kJ) in parentheses.

   Manufacturers also have the option of stating the amounts of additional nutrients in an expanded format: potassium, soluble and insoluble fibre, sugar alcohol, starch, and the following vitamins and minerals: vitamin D, vitamin E, vitamin K, thiamin, riboflavin, niacin, vitamin B_6, folate, vitamin B_{12}, biotin, pantothenic acid, phosphorus, iodide, magnesium, zinc, selenium, copper, manganese, chromium, molybdenum, and chloride.

   For foods made specifically for children under the age of two years, a simplified version of the Nutrition Facts table is used. The amount of Calories and 10 nutrients are listed, but the saturated and trans fats and cholesterol content are not required. **Figure 2.2** compares the standard format, the expanded format, and the simplified form used for children under the age of two years.

3. *Nutrient content claims:* These are claims about the amount of a nutrient in a food; for example, "reduced in fat," "high in fibre," "cholesterol free," and "source of iron." The nutrient content claims have been revised so that they are based on standardized serving sizes for similar products. Before these terms can be used on a label or in an advertisement, the exact amount of a nutrient in 1 serving has to be determined and has to meet set criteria (see **Table 2.2** for examples of these).

   These nutrient content claims are usually on the front of food packages, where consumers can easily see them. Any of the following words may indicate a nutrient content claim:

- free
- less
- reduced
- very high
- source of
- good source of
- low
- more
- lower
- light or lite
- high source of
- excellent source of

TABLE 2.2 Examples of Common Nutrient Content Claims

- Claims of "free" mean that the number of kJ (kcal) or the amount of a nutrient is nutritionally insignificant in a specified amount of food. For example, to be "sodium free," a product has to contain less than 5 mg of sodium per serving. "Free of sugar" means that a product has less than 50 mg of sugar and fewer than 17 kJ (5 kcal) per serving. Other wording can be used instead of "free of sugar": "no sugar," "0 sugar," "contains no sugar," and "sugar free" all mean the same thing on a label.

- "Low" means there is a small amount of a nutrient present in 1 serving. For example, "low fat" indicates the product contains 3 g of fat or less per serving.

- "Reduced" indicates that there is at least 25% less of a nutrient in 1 serving, compared to the "original" product or a similar product. For example, Christie's Ritz 25% Less Fat™ crackers have 25% less fat than the original Ritz™ crackers. Kellogg's Frosted Flakes 1/3 Less Sugar™ cereal has 33% less sugar than the original Frosted Flakes™ product.

- "Source" means that there is a significant amount of a nutrient in 1 serving. For example, a product must contain 2 or more grams of dietary fibre to be called a "source of fibre."

Source: Health Canada. 2003. Frequently Asked Questions About Nutrition Labelling. http://hc-sc.gc.ca/fn-an/label-etiquet/nutrition/educat/te_quest-eng.php#18. (accessed September 2008).

Nutrition Facts table The table on a food package label that gives the amount of energy and a minimum of 13 key nutrients in one serving of the food.

Calorie 1 Calorie = 1 kcal = 4.184 kilojoules.

Nutrition Facts

Serving Size 125 mL (35 g)
Servings Per Container 13

Amount Per Serving

Calories 90	Calories from fat 9
	Calories from Saturated + Trans 0

	% Daily Value*
Total Fat 1 g	**2 %**
Saturated 0 g + Trans 0 g	**0 %**
Omega-6 Polyunsaturated 0.5 g	
Omega-3 Polyunsaturated 0 g	
Monounsaturated 0.2 g	
Cholesterol 0 mg	**0 %**
Sodium 300 mg	**12 %**
Potassium 410 mg	**12 %**
Total Carbohydrate 27 g	**9 %**
Dietary Fibre 12 g	**48 %**
Soluble Fibre 0 g	
Insoluble Fibre 11 g	
Sugars 6 g	
Sugar Alcohols 0 g	
Starch 9 g	
Protein 4 g	

Vitamin A	0 %	Vitamin C	0 %
Calcium	2 %	Iron	35 %
Vitamin D	0 %	Vitamin E	6 %
Vitamin K	10 %	Thiamine	55 %
Riboflavin	4 %	Niacin	25 %
Vitamin B$_6$	10 %	Folate	10 %
Vitamin B$_{12}$	0 %	Biotin	30 %
Pantothenate	8 %	Phosphorus	30 %
Iodide	0 %	Magnesium	50 %
Zinc	25 %	Selenium	6 %
Copper	20 %	Manganese	10 %
Chromium	10 %	Molybdenum	10 %
Chloride	10 %		

* Percent Daily Values are based on a 2,000 Calorie diet. Your daily values may be higher or lower depending on your Calorie needs:

		Calories:	2,000	2,500
Total Fat	Less than		65 g	80 g
Saturated + Trans	Less than		20 g	25 g
Cholesterol	Less than		300 mg	300 mg
Sodium	Less than		2,400 mg	2,400 mg
Potassium			3,500 mg	3,500 mg
Total Carbohydrate			300 g	375 g
Dietary Fibre			25 g	30 g

Calories per gram:
Fat 9   Carbohydrate 4   Protein 4

Nutrition Facts

Per 125 mL (87 g)

Amount	% Daily Value
Calories 80	
Fat 0.5 g	**1 %**
Saturated 0 g + Trans 0 g	**0 %**
Cholesterol 0 mg	
Sodium 0 mg	**0 %**
Carbohydrate 18 g	**6 %**
Fibre 2 g	**8 %**
Sugars 2 g	
Protein 3 g	

Vitamin A	2 %	Vitamin C	10 %
Calcium	0 %	Iron	2 %

Nutrition Facts

Per 1 jar (128 mL)

	Amount
Calories	110
Fat	0 g
Sodium	10 mg
Carbohydrate	27 g
Fibre	4 g
Sugars	18 g
Protein	0 g

% Daily Value			
Vitamin A	6 %	Vitamin C	45 %
Calcium	2 %	Iron	2 %

(a)   **(b)**   **(c)**

Figure 2.2 Label formats. **(a)** Standard format; **(b)** additional information (expanded); **(c)** format for foods for children less than two years of age.
Source: Compendium of Templates for Nutrition Facts Tables. Health Canada, 2003. Minister of Public Works and Government Services Canada, 2012.

Manufacturers can decide whether they want to have nutrient content claims on their products. Some of the more important changes to nutrient content claims include:

- Claims for saturated fatty acids include a restriction on levels of both saturated and trans fatty acids. In other words, for a label to indicate that a product is low in trans fats, the product must also be low in saturated fats.
- The claim "[product name] is fat free" is allowed only if accompanied by the statement "low fat" or "low in fat" (3 g of fat or less per serving).
- The nutrient content claim "light" is allowed only on foods that meet the criteria for either "reduced in fat" or "reduced in Calories." There must be a statement that explains what makes the food light (i.e., "low in fat" or "low in Calories").
- "Light" can also be used to describe a characteristic of a food, such as "light tasting" and "lite in colour."
- Terms related to the carbohydrate content of foods, such as "low carb," "low carbohydrate," and "carbohydrate reduced," are not allowed.
- Claims related to the glycemic index (see Chapter 4) are also not permitted, as they are considered drug claims. Examples include "rapid absorption," "does not raise blood sugar," "non-glycemic," and "low glycemic index."
- The only nutrient content claims that are permitted for foods for children under two years of age are "source of protein," "excellent source of protein," "more protein," "no added salt," and "no added sugar."

4. *Health claims:* These are defined by the Canadian Food Inspection Agency (CFIA, 2011) as "any representation in labelling or advertising that states, suggests, or implies that a relationship exists between consumption of a food, or an ingredient in the food, and health." There are three main types of health claims: disease risk reduction and therapeutic claims; function claims; and general health claims (CFIA, 2011). Our focus here is on the first category, disease risk reduction and therapeutic claims; at the present time, there are no therapeutic claims approved and there are seven disease risk reduction claims approved.

According to Health Canada (2011), a **disease risk reduction claim** "is generally a statement that links a food or a constituent of a food to reducing the risk of developing a diet-related disease or condition, (e.g., osteoporosis, hypertension) in the context of the total diet." **Table 2.3** outlines the disease risk reduction claims that are currently allowed on Canadian food labels. Health claims involving fat and cancer as well as dietary fibre and cancer are currently permitted in the United States but not in Canada.

Disease risk reduction claim A statement that links a food or a food ingredient with reduced risk of disease or a condition in the context of a total diet.

How to Read and Use the Nutrition Facts Table on Foods

Figure 2.3 shows an example of a bilingual Nutrition Facts table with additional information (i.e., the expanded format). There is a variety of information in this table that is useful when planning a nutritious diet.

You can use this information to learn more about an individual food, and you can also use it to compare one food to another. Let's start at the top of the table and examine how to use this information.

1. *Serving size and servings per container:* Describes the serving size in a common metric measure (e.g., millilitres) and a weight (e.g., grams). Keep in mind that the serving size listed on the package may not be the same as 1 serving according to *Canada's Food Guide.* It also may not be the same as the amount *you* eat! You must factor in how much of the food you eat when determining the amount of nutrients that this food contributes to your actual intake.
2. *Calories, Calories from fat, and Calories from saturated + trans fats per serving:* Describes the total number of Calories. In this example, 1 serving of the food has 90 Calories (380 kJ), with 9 of those Calories coming from fat. This means that 10% of the Calories in this product come from fat (9 ÷ 90 = 10%), making it relatively low in fat. Notice in the list of nutrients that saturated and trans fats are summed together, and if manufacturers choose to list the amount of omega-3

TABLE 2.3 Disease Risk Reduction Claims Permitted on Food Labels

Psyllium Products and Blood Cholesterol Lowering

Primary statement:

"[serving size from Nutrition Facts table in metric or common household measures] of (Brand name) [name of food] with psyllium supplies/provides X% of the daily amount of the fibres shown to help reduce/lower cholesterol."

For example:

"1 cup (30 g) of Brand X cereal with psyllium supplies 50% of the daily amount of fibres shown to help lower cholesterol."
The "daily amount" referred to in the primary statement is 7 grams psyllium fibre.

Oat Products and Blood Cholesterol Lowering

Primary statement:

"[serving size from Nutrition Facts table in metric and common household measures] of (Brand name) [name of food] [with name of eligible fibre source] supplies/provides [X% of the daily amount] of the fibres shown to help reduce/lower cholesterol."

For example:

If the eligible fibre source is a food itself: "1 cup (X g) of Quaker Oatmeal supplies X% of the daily amount of the fibres shown to help reduce cholesterol"
If the eligible fibre source is an ingredient: "1 muffin (X g) with oat bran provides X% of the daily amount of the fibres shown to help lower cholesterol"
The "daily amount" referred to in the primary statement is 3 grams beta-glucan oat fibre.

Plant Sterols (Phytosterols) and Blood Cholesterol Lowering

Primary statement:

"[serving size from Nutrition Facts table in metric and common household measures] of [naming the product] provides X% of the daily amount of plant sterols shown to help reduce/lower cholesterol in adults."

Two additional statements that could be used in combination or alone:

1. "Plant sterols help reduce [or help lower] cholesterol."
2. "High cholesterol is a risk factor for heart disease."

The "daily amount" referred to in the primary statement is 2 grams.

Calcium and Osteoporosis

"A healthy diet with adequate calcium and vitamin D, and regular physical activity, help to achieve strong bones and may reduce the risk of osteoporosis. (Naming the food) is an excellent source of calcium and vitamin D."
There are five other slight variations in wording allowed for this claim.

Fruits, Vegetables and Cancer

"A healthy diet rich in a variety of vegetables and fruit may help reduce the risk of some types of cancer."
The following are excluded from this claim: potatoes, yams, cassava, plantain, corn, mushrooms, mature legumes and their juices, jams and jellies, olives, and powdered fruits and vegetables.

Dietary Fat, Saturated Fat, Cholesterol, Trans Fatty Acids and Coronary Heart Disease

"A healthy diet low in saturated and trans fats may reduce the risk of heart disease. (Naming the food) is low in saturated and trans fats."

Sodium and Hypertension

"A healthy diet containing foods high in potassium and low in sodium may reduce the risk of high blood pressure, a risk factor for stroke and heart disease. (Naming the food) is a good source of potassium and is low in sodium."
There are five other slight variations in wording allowed for this claim.

Source: Health Claim Assessments. Health Canada, 2010. Minister of Public Works and Government Services Canada, 2012.

Percent daily values (%DV)
Information on a Nutrition Facts table that identifies how much a serving of food contributes to your overall intake of nutrients listed on the label; based on an energy intake of 2000 Calories (8400 kJ) per day.

polyunsaturated fatty acids, they must also list the amount of omega-6 polyunsaturated fatty acids. Monounsaturated fatty acids are listed separately.

3. *Percent daily values (%DV):* **Percent daily values (%DV)** information tells you how much a serving of food contributes to your overall intake of the various nutrients listed on the label. The amounts of fat, saturated fat, and trans fat, sodium, carbohydrate, and fibre in 1 serving are stated in grams or milligrams, as well as a %DV. The remaining nutrients are listed as a %DV only. The %DV is based on recommendations for a healthy adult 2000-Calorie (8400 kJ) diet and is an easy way of determining the relative amount (i.e., a little or a lot) of a nutrient in 1 serving. For example, using a 2000-Calorie diet with 30% of its Calories as fat, the daily value for fat would be 65 grams. A product with

Nutrition Facts Valeur nutritive	
Serving Size 125 mL (35 g) / Portion 125 mL (35 g) Servings Per Container 13 Portions par contenant 13	
Amount Per Serving / Teneur par portion	
Calories / Calories 90 (380 kJ) Calories from fat / Calories des lipides 9 Calories from Saturated + Trans 0 Calories des lipides saturés et trans 0	
% Daily Value / % valeur quotidienne*	
Total Fat / Lipides 1 g	**2 %**
Saturated / saturés 0 g + Trans / trans 0 g	**0 %**
Polyunsaturated / polyinsaturés 0.5 g	
Omega-6 / oméga-6 0.5 g	
Omega-3 / oméga-3 0 g	
Monounsaturated / monoinsaturés 0.2 g	
Cholesterol / Cholestérol 0 mg	**0 %**
Sodium / Sodium 300 mg	**12 %**
Potassium / Potassium 410 mg	**12 %**
Total Carbohydrate / Glucides 27 g	**9 %**
Dietary Fibre / Fibres alimentaires 12 g	**48 %**
Soluble Fibre / Fibres solubles 0 g	
Insoluble Fibre / Fibres insolubles 11 g	
Sugars / Sucres 6 g	
Sugar Alcohols / Polyalcools 0 g	
Starch / Amidon 9 g	
Protein / Protéines 4 g	
Vitamin A / Vitamine A	**0 %**
Vitamin C / Vitamine C	**0 %**
Calcium / Calcium	**2 %**
Iron / Fer	**35 %**

	% Daily Value / % valeur quotidienne*
Vitamin D / Vitamine D	0 %
Vitamin E / Vitamine E	6 %
Vitamin K / Vitamine K	10 %
Thiamine / Thiamine	55 %
Riboflavin / Riboflavine	4 %
Niacin / Niacine	25 %
Vitamin B$_6$ / Vitamine B$_6$	10 %
Folate / Folate	10 %
Vitamin B$_{12}$ / Vitamine B$_{12}$	0 %
Biotin / Biotine	30 %
Pantothenate / Pantothénate	8 %
Phosphorus / Phosphore	30 %
Iodide / Iodure	0 %
Magnesium / Magnésium	50 %
Zinc / Zinc	25 %
Selenium / Sélénium	6 %
Copper / Cuivre	20 %
Manganese / Manganèse	10 %
Chromium / Chrome	10 %
Molybdenum / Molybdène	10 %
Chloride / Chlorure	10 %

* Percent Daily Values are based on a 2,000 Calorie diet. Your daily values may be higher or lower depending on your Calorie needs:

		Calories:	2,000	2,500
Total Fat	Less than		65 g	80 g
Saturated + Trans	Less than		20 g	25 g
Cholesterol	Less than		300 mg	300 mg
Sodium	Less than		2,400 mg	2,400 mg
Potassium			3,500 mg	3,500 mg
Total Carbohydrate			300 g	375 g
Dietary Fibre			25 g	30 g

Calories per gram:
Fat 9   Carbohydrate 4   Protein 4

* Pourcentage de la valeur quotidienne selon un régime alimentaire de 2 000 Calories. Vos valeurs quotidiennes personnelles peuvent être plus ou moins élevées selon vos besoins énergétiques :

		Calories :	2 000	2 500
Lipides	moins de		65 g	80 g
saturés + trans	moins de		20 g	25 g
Cholestérol	moins de		300 mg	300 mg
Sodium	moins de		2 400 mg	2 400 mg
Potassium			3 500 mg	3 500 mg
Glucides			300 g	375 g
Fibres alimentaires			25 g	30 g

Calories par gramme :
Lipides 9   Glucides 4   Protéines 4

Figure 2.3 Bilingual Nutrition Facts table with additional information.

Source: Compendium of Templates for Nutrition Facts–Label Formats. Health Canada, 2003. Minister of Public Works and Government Services Canada, 2012.

13 grams of fat in 1 serving has a % daily value of $13/65 \times 100 = 20\%$. In other words, 1 serving of this food would provide 20% of the daily value (DV) for fat. Foods that contain less than 5% DV of a nutrient are considered low in that nutrient, while foods that contain more than 15% DV are considered high in that nutrient. If you are trying to consume more calcium in your diet, selecting foods that contain more than 15% DV for calcium are good choices. In contrast, if you are trying to consume lower-fat foods, selecting foods that contain less than 5% or 10% of the fat DV will help you reach your goals. By comparing the %DV between foods for any nutrient, you can quickly decide which food is higher or lower in that nutrient without having to know anything about how many Calories you need.

You may be asking yourself, "How do the %DV relate to the Recommended Dietary Allowances (RDA) and the Dietary Reference Intakes (DRIs) we discussed in Chapter 1?" Remember that the DRI is an umbrella term that applies to a group of nutrient standards, including the RDA, Estimated Average Requirement (EAR), Adequate Intake (AI), Tolerable Upper Intake Level (UL), and Acceptable Macronutrient Distribution Ranges (AMDR). Many of these values are specific to life-stage and gender. In contrast, the %DV is used as a food labelling tool, and its value is determined by using two additional standardized values, the

TABLE 2.4 Standards Used to Calculate the % Daily Value (2000 Calories or 8400 kJ)

Vitamin or Mineral Nutrient	Units	Persons 2 Years of Age or Older	Infants and Children Less than 2 Years Old
(a) Recommended Daily Intake			
Vitamin A	RE[a]	1000	400
Vitamin D	µg[b]	5	10
Vitamin E	mg[c]	10	3
Vitamin C	mg	60	20
Thiamin, thiamine, or vitamin B₁	mg	1.3	0.45
Riboflavin, or vitamin B₂	mg	1.6	0.55
Niacin	NE[d]	23	8
Vitamin B₆	mg	1.8	0.7
Folacin, or folate	µg	220	65
Vitamin B₁₂	µg	2	0.3
Pantothenic acid, or pantothenate	mg	7	2
Vitamin K	µg	80	30
Biotin	µg	30	8
Calcium	mg	1100	500
Phosphorus	mg	1100	500
Magnesium	mg	250	55
Iron	mg	14	7
Zinc	mg	9	4
Iodide	µg	160	55
Selenium	µg	50	15
Copper	mg	2	0.5
Manganese	mg	2	1.2
Chromium	µg	120	12
Molybdenum	µg	75	15
Chloride	mg	3400	1000

Nutrient	Amount
(b) Reference Standards	
Fat	65 g
The sum of saturated fatty acids and trans fatty acids	20 g
Cholesterol	300 mg
Carbohydrate	300 g
Fibre	25 g
Sodium	2400 mg
Potassium	3500 mg

[a] RE = retinol equivalents [b] µg = micrograms [c] mg = milligrams [d] NE = niacin equivalents.
Source: Canadian Food Inspection Agency. Reproduced or adapted with the permission of the Minister of Pubic Works and Government Services Canada, 2012.

Recommended Daily Intakes (RDI) for vitamins and minerals and the **reference standards** for nutrients other than vitamins and minerals. **Table 2.4** lists the RDIs and reference standards used as the basis of the %DV for labelling purposes. Refer to the You Do the Math box (on the next page) to learn how to use the %DV to calculate specific amounts of nutrients.

4. *Footnote* (or lower part of the Nutrition Facts table): The lower part of the table includes a footnote that appears only on the expanded format. This footnote tells you that the %DV are based on a 2000-Calorie (8400 kJ) diet and that your needs may be higher or lower based on your individual energy needs. The remainder of the footnote includes a table with values that illustrate the differences in recommendations between a 2000-Calorie (8400 kJ) and 2500-Calorie (10 500 kJ) diet; for instance, someone eating 2000 Calories should strive to eat less than 65 grams of fat per day, while a person eating 2500 Calories should eat less than 80 grams of fat per day.

Recommended Daily Intakes (RDI) The amounts of vitamins and minerals used to calculate the % daily values.

reference standards The amounts of nutrients other than vitamins and minerals used to calculate the % daily values.

YOU DO THE MATH

Using the % Daily Values (%DV) to Calculate Specific Amounts of Calcium and Iron

The %DV can be used to calculate specific amounts of any nutrient listed on the label. Let's say you are a male who is 23 years of age. You are interested in meeting the DRI standards for both calcium and iron, and you are curious about how much of the food shown in Figure 2.3 contributes to your daily intake of these two nutrients. We will use Table 2.4 and Figure 2.3 to assist us in these calculations.

a. *Calcium:* The %DV for calcium listed on the label is 2%. As you can see in Table 2.4, the RDI for calcium is 1100 mg. By multiplying the %DV by 1100 mg, you will get the total amount of calcium (in milligrams) in 1 serving of this food:

$$2\% = 0.02$$
$$0.02 \times 1100 \text{ mg} = 22 \text{ mg}$$

How do we know how much this food contributes to your calcium requirement as described by the DRI standards? The RDA for calcium for a man 23 years of age is 1000 mg. By dividing the amount of calcium in milligrams in 1 serving of this food by the AI for calcium (1000 mg) and multiplying by 100, you will get the percentage of your RDA for calcium from this food:

$$22 \text{ mg} \div 1000 \text{ mg} \times 100 = 2.2\% \text{ of your RDA for calcium}$$

b. *Iron:* The %DV for iron listed on the label is 35%. As you can see in **Table 2.4**, the RDI for iron is 14 mg. By multiplying the %DV by 14 mg, you will get the total amount of iron (in milligrams) in 1 serving of this food:

$$35\% = 0.35$$
$$0.35 \times 14 \text{ mg} = 4.9 \text{ mg}$$

How do we know how much this food contributes to your iron requirement as described by the DRI standards? The Recommended Dietary Allowance (RDA) for iron for a man 23 years of age is 8 mg. By dividing the amount of iron in milligrams in 1 serving of this food by the RDA for iron (8 mg) and multiplying by 100, you will get the percentage of your RDA for iron from this food:

$$4.9 \text{ mg} \div 8 \text{ mg} \times 100 = 61\% \text{ of your RDA for iron}$$

These calculations are very helpful when you need to determine how well a food meets your individual nutrient needs based on your gender and age. The %DV are a helpful guide in determining whether a food is high or low in a given nutrient, and the calculations just shown can further assist you when you do not eat a 2000-Calorie (8400 kJ) diet or you want to determine how well your diet is meeting the DRI standards.

By comparing labels from different foods, you can start planning a more nutritious diet today. Try looking at the two labels in **Figure 2.4** to decide which food is a better choice. First, decide which nutrients are most important to you. Let's assume you are trying to eat foods with more dietary fibre and iron. The label on the left shows that Cereal A contains 1 gram of dietary fibre and 30% of the DV for iron per serving. The label on the right shows that Cereal B contains 6 grams of dietary fibre and 60% of the DV for iron per serving. For these two nutrients, Cereal B, on the right, would clearly be the more nutritious choice.

Notice that Cereal B is a denser cereal, though. One serving of Cereal B is 25 biscuits, or approximately 1 cup; this weighs 55 grams and contains 270 Calories when served with 125 mL (1/2 cup) of 2% milk. One serving of Cereal A is 250 mL (1 cup) of flakes, which weighs 30 grams and contains 180 Calories when served with 125 mL (1/2 cup) of 2% milk. Part of the reason that Cereal B has more energy and nutrients for the same 250 mL (1 cup) amount is that it is denser—biscuits are more compact than flakes.

Health Canada (2008) has an interactive nutrition label and quiz on their website, to help you learn the parts of the food label and interpret the information. Visit their website at www.hc-sc.gc.ca/fn-an/label-etiquet/nutrition/cons/interactive-eng.php.

Nutrition Facts

Serving 1 cup (30 g)
Cereal A

Amount	Cereal Only	With 1/2 cup 2% milk
Calories	120	180
		% Daily Value
Fat 0 g*	0%	4%
Saturated 0 g + Trans 0 g	0%	8%
Cholesterol 0 g	0%	3%
Sodium 160 mg	7%	10%
Potassium 30 mg	1%	6%
Carbohydrate 30 g	10%	12%
Fibre 1 g	4%	4%
Sugars 8 g		
Starch 21 g		
Protein 3 g		
Vitamin A	0%	8%
Vitamin C	0%	0%
Calcium	10%	20%
Iron	30%	30%
Vitamin D	0%	25%
Thiamin	45%	50%
Riboflavin	35%	50%
Niacin	8%	15%
Vitamin B₆	10%	15%
Folate	10%	10%
Vitamin B₁₂	0%	25%
Pantothenate	6%	15%
Phosphorus	10%	20%
Magnesium	10%	15%
Zinc	6%	10%
*Amount in cereal		

Nutrition Facts

Serving 25 biscuits (55 g)
Cereal B

Amount	Cereal Only	With 1/2 cup 2% milk
Calories	210	270
		% Daily Value
Fat 1 g*	2%	6%
Saturated 0.4 g + Trans 0 g	2%	9%
Cholesterol 0 g	0%	3%
Sodium 5 mg	0%	3%
Potassium 200 mg	6%	11%
Carbohydrate 49 g	16%	18%
Fibre 6 g	24%	24%
Sugars 15 g		
Starch 28 g		
Protein 5 g		
Vitamin A	0%	8%
Vitamin C	0%	0%
Calcium	0%	15%
Iron	60%	60%
Vitamin D	0%	25%
Thiamin	80%	90%
Riboflavin	2%	15%
Niacin	10%	15%
Vitamin B₆	20%	20%
Folate	15%	15%
Vitamin B₁₂	0%	25%
Pantothenate	15%	20%
Phosphorus	0%	10%
Magnesium	20%	30%
Zinc	20%	25%
*Amount in cereal		

Figure 2.4 Labels from two breakfast cereals. Note that there is less dietary fibre and iron in Cereal A than in Cereal B, but the serving size and energy content of Cereal B are higher.

™ The Health Check logo, Health Check word mark, and Heart and Stroke Foundation word mark are trademarks of the Heart and Stroke Foundation of Canada used under license.

ᴹᶜ Le logo Visez santé, les mots servant de marque Visez santé et les mots servant de marque Fondation des maladies du cœur et de l'AVC sont des marques de commerces de la Fondation des maladies du cœur et de l'AVC du Canada utilisées sous licence.

Logo Programs Can Help Consumers Make Healthier Choices in Grocery Stores

To help Canadians quickly tell if a food is a nutritious choice, the Heart and Stroke Foundation of Canada launched Health Check™, a non-profit food information program to promote healthy eating. The program logo, including the words *Heart and Stroke Foundation,* appears on over 1500 food products that have met specific nutrient content criteria developed by the Canadian Heart and Stroke Association and designed to be consistent with *Canada's Food Guide.* Manufacturers voluntarily participate in the program and pay a one-time evaluation fee, plus an annual licensing fee, to have their products assessed. Some nutrient content criteria were not in keeping with new Health Canada guidelines (e.g., trans fat guidelines) and the new *Food Guide*; as a result, criteria for fat, trans fat, sugar, sodium, and fibre have been revised (Health Check, 2008). For example, a 10 gram serving of margarine must be non-hydrogenated, contain 2 g or less saturated and trans fat combined, have 2% or less of total fat as trans fat, and have 140 mg or less sodium. A limited number of family restaurants also participate in the Health Check™ program, including Boston Pizza™, Swiss Chalet™, and Druxy's™.

There are other programs using logos to help consumers make healthier choices, but they use different nutritional criteria. These criteria are developed by the manufacturer, rather than a non-profit health organization, and they vary in their emphasis. For example, the President's Choice® line of products has over 400 products in their Blue Menu™ program.

RECAP Reading food labels is a necessary skill when planning a nutritious diet. Food labels must list the ingredients in a food, in descending order by weight, and include a Nutrition Facts table. The Nutrition Facts table provides specific information about Calories (kJ), macronutrients, and select vitamins, minerals, and other components (such as dietary fibre). The %DV is useful to compare food products or to tell if the product contains a little or a lot of a specific nutrient. Nutrient content claims and seven specific disease risk reduction claims are also allowed.

Dietary Guidance in Canada

The Canadian government first issued nutrition advice to Canadians in 1942. The world was at war, some foods were rationed or hard to get (e.g., milk), and many people didn't have enough money to buy the food they needed. The government felt it should give people guidance on how to eat to stay healthy in spite of food shortages. *Canada's Official Food Rules* (1942) listed the amounts of "health protective foods" to be eaten every day.

Over the years, as the Canadian food supply changed, people changed their eating habits, and as new scientific information became available, nutrition advice also changed. *Canada's Official Food Rules* (1942) became *Canada's Food Rules* (1944, revised in 1949), then *Canada's Food Guide* (1961, with two subsequent revisions in 1977 and 1982), then *Canada's Food Guide to Healthy Eating*, released in 1992, and finally, in February 2007, *Eating Well with Canada's Food Guide.*

While the original purpose of nutrition advice was to prevent nutrition deficiencies, few people today have malnutrition because they don't get enough food. In fact, many Canadians are overweight or obese and at risk for diseases that are linked to diets containing too much energy or fat. Today's nutrition advice for Canadians is designed (1) to reduce the risk of chronic disease and obesity, and (2) to help people get all the nutrients they need for good health. This advice focuses on how much to eat *and* the kinds of food to eat. Unlike previous versions of *Canada's Food Guide*, which were double-sided tear-sheets, the newest version is a six-page fold-out booklet, to provide consumers with age- and gender-specific advice. It is available in 10 languages in addition to French and English: Arabic, Simplified Chinese, Farsi (Persian), Korean, Punjabi, Russian, Spanish, Tagalog, Tamil, and Urdu.

What Does *Eating Well with Canada's Food Guide* Tell You?

The cover of *Canada's Food Guide* (Figure 2.5) shows four arcs of a rainbow, representing the four food groups. The outermost arc is green, and contains the Vegetables

<u>Calories</u> — 1 calorie = 1 kCal = 4.184 kilojoules

(45) — 10% of calories comes from fat
    ↳ example: 90 calories (380 kJ), 9 calories from fat
    ↳ example: 2000 calorie (8400 kJ) diet with 30%
            of it as fat, daily value for fat
            would be <u>65 grams</u>.
            If a product had 13 grams of fat in 1 serving
            it has a % daily value of $13/65 \times 100 = \underline{20\%}$

> Foods that contain less then 5% DV of a nutrient are
> considered low in that nutrient, while foods that contain
> more than 15% DV are considered high in that nutrient

RDI (Recommended Daily Intakes) — TABLE 2.4 (48)
You Do the Math — (Pg. 49).
    ↳ by multiplying the % DV by the RDI
        — example: + Calcium has 2% DV and the RDI
                for calcium is 1100 mg :
                | $0.02 \times 1100 = 22\,mg$ |
                + DRI standards: a 23 year old male
              has an RDA for calcium is 1000 mg.
              | $22\,mg \div 1000\,mg \times 100 = 2.2\%$ of RDA for |
                                      Calcium

        — example: + IRON has 35% DV and 14 mg RDI
                | $0.35 \times 14\,mg = 4.9\,mg$ |
                + DRI standard for iron in a 23 year old male
              has a RDA of 8 mg
              | $4.9\,mg \div 8\,mg \times 100 = 61\%$ RDA for Iron |

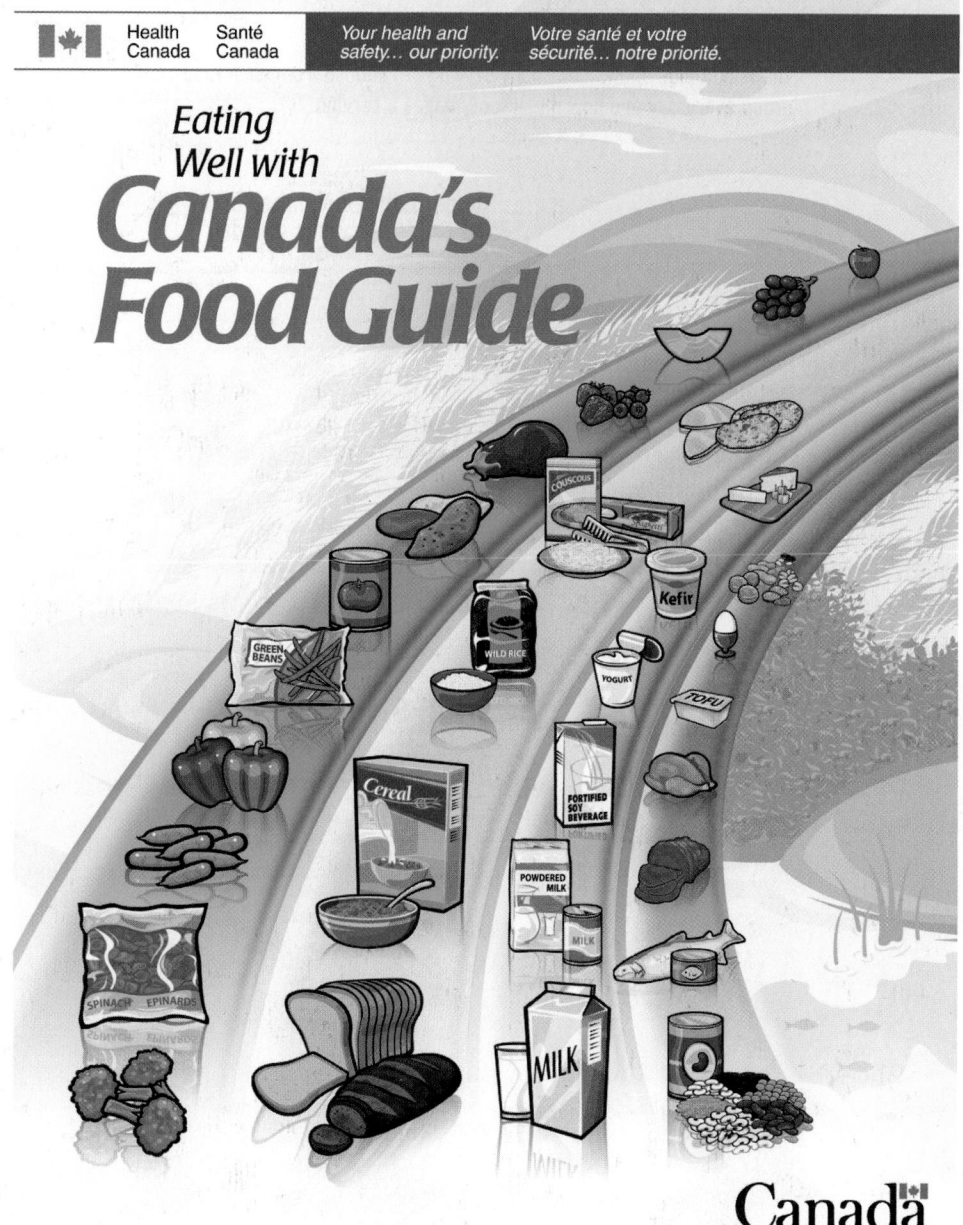

🔺 **Figure 2.5** *Eating Well with Canada's Food Guide* cover. The four arcs of the rainbow represent the four food groups.

Source: Eating Well with Canada's Food Guide, http://www.hc-sc.gc.ca/fn-an/food-guide-aliment/index-eng.php. © Her Majesty the Queen in Right of Canada, represented by the Minister of Health Canada, 2007. HC Pub.:4651, Cat.:H164-38/1-2007E, ISBN:0-662-44467-1.

and Fruits food group. The next largest arc is yellow, and contains the Grain Products. Note that in the previous version of *Canada's Food Guide*, these two food groups were in reverse order. The next arc is blue, and contains the Milk and Alternatives food group, and the smallest, inner-most arc is red, representing the Meat and Alternatives group.

The first panel inside the booklet shows the recommended number of *Food Guide* servings per day (**Figure 2.6**). There are three age categories for children: 2–3 years; 4–8 years; and 9–13 years. Within each age category, the number of recommended servings for boys and girls is the same for each of the four food groups. In the teen years, ages 14 to 18, females and males have different recommended daily amounts, except for Milk and Alternatives. There are two age categories for adults,

Figure 2.6 *Eating Well with Canada's Food Guide* recommended number of *Food Guide* servings per day from each of the four food groups. *Source:* Recommended Number of Food Guide Servings Per Day, http://www.hc-sc.gc.ca/fn-an/food-guide-aliment/basics-base/quantit-eng.php, Health Canada, 2007. Reproduced with the permission of the Minister of Public Works and Government Services Canada, 2012.

How to use Canada's Food Guide

The Food Guide shows how many servings to choose from each food group every day and how much food makes a serving.

Recommended Number of Food Guide Servings per day			
Children 2–3 years old	Children 4–13 years old	Teens and Adults (Females)	(Males)
Vegetables and Fruit Fresh, frozen and canned.			
4	5-6	7-8	7-10
Grain Products			
3	4-6	6-7	7-8
Milk and Alternatives			
2	2-4	Teens 3-4 / Adults (19-50 years) 2 / Adults (51+ years) 3	Teens 3-4 / Adults (19-50 years) 2 / Adults (51+ years) 3
Meat and Alternatives			
1	1-2	2	3

19–50 years and 51+ years, and both list the recommended number of servings from each food group for men and women separately.

This is the first time that *Canada's Food Guide* has tailored *Food Guide* servings per day to nine different age and sex groups, to help ensure that consumers who follow the guide are eating the recommended amounts of various nutrients each day while preventing obesity.

What Is One *Food Guide* Serving in *Eating Well with Canada's Food Guide*?

What is considered 1 *Food Guide* serving in *Eating Well with Canada's Food Guide*? The middle panel in *Canada's Food Guide* (**Figure 2.7**) shows examples of serving sizes for foods in each group.

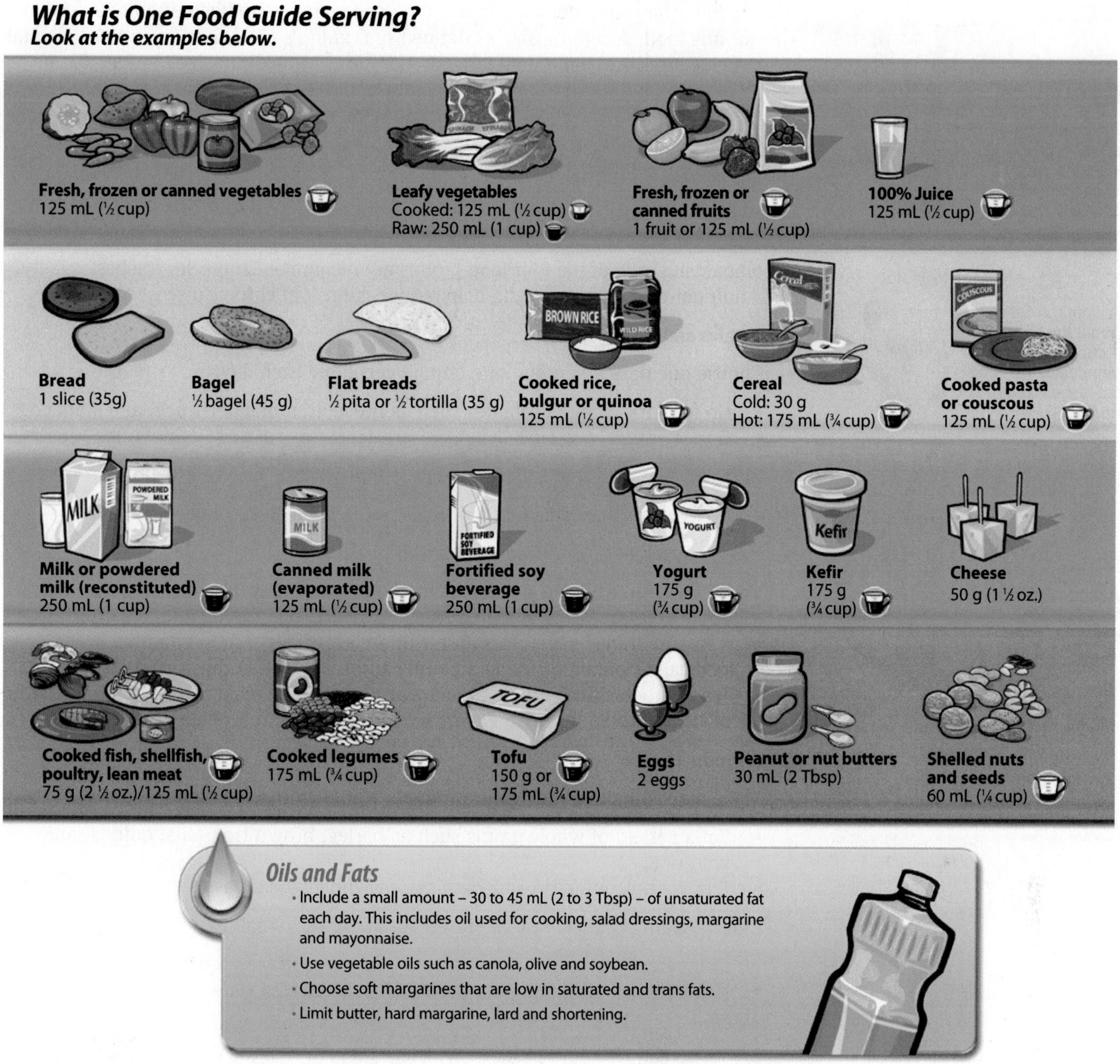

What is One Food Guide Serving?
Look at the examples below.

Fresh, frozen or canned vegetables
125 mL (½ cup)

Leafy vegetables
Cooked: 125 mL (½ cup)
Raw: 250 mL (1 cup)

Fresh, frozen or canned fruits
1 fruit or 125 mL (½ cup)

100% Juice
125 mL (½ cup)

Bread
1 slice (35g)

Bagel
½ bagel (45 g)

Flat breads
½ pita or ½ tortilla (35 g)

Cooked rice, bulgur or quinoa
125 mL (½ cup)

Cereal
Cold: 30 g
Hot: 175 mL (¾ cup)

Cooked pasta or couscous
125 mL (½ cup)

Milk or powdered milk (reconstituted)
250 mL (1 cup)

Canned milk (evaporated)
125 mL (½ cup)

Fortified soy beverage
250 mL (1 cup)

Yogurt
175 g
(¾ cup)

Kefir
175 g
(¾ cup)

Cheese
50 g (1 ½ oz.)

Cooked fish, shellfish, poultry, lean meat
75 g (2 ½ oz.)/125 mL (½ cup)

Cooked legumes
175 mL (¾ cup)

Tofu
150 g or
175 mL (¾ cup)

Eggs
2 eggs

Peanut or nut butters
30 mL (2 Tbsp)

Shelled nuts and seeds
60 mL (¼ cup)

Oils and Fats
- Include a small amount – 30 to 45 mL (2 to 3 Tbsp) – of unsaturated fat each day. This includes oil used for cooking, salad dressings, margarine and mayonnaise.
- Use vegetable oils such as canola, olive and soybean.
- Choose soft margarines that are low in saturated and trans fats.
- Limit butter, hard margarine, lard and shortening.

Figure 2.7 *Eating Well with Canada's Food Guide* suggested serving sizes. The amount shown for each food represents one food guide serving.
Source: Eating Well with Canada's Food Guide. Health Canada, 2011. Minister of Public Works and Government Services Canada, 2012.

A serving of vegetables is 250 mL (1 cup) of raw leafy vegetables such as uncooked spinach or 125 mL (1/2 cup) of chopped fresh, frozen, or canned vegetables such as broccoli or squash. A serving from the Grain Products group is defined as 1 slice of bread, 1/2 of a regular pita or hamburger bun, or 30 g (1 oz.) of cold cereal. Fortified soy beverages (250 mL or 1 cup) and Kefir (175 g or ¾ cup) are now included in the Milk and Alternatives food group. A serving of cooked lean meat, fish, shellfish, or poultry is 75 g (2.5 oz.), which is approximately the size of a deck of cards. A serving of meat alternatives could be 2 eggs, 30 mL (2 Tbsp) peanut butter, 150 grams or 175 mL (3/4 cup) tofu, 175 mL (3/4 cup) cooked legumes, or 60 mL (1/4 cup) nuts and seeds. Although it may seem unnatural or inconvenient to measure our food servings, understanding the size of a serving is critical to planning a nutritious diet.

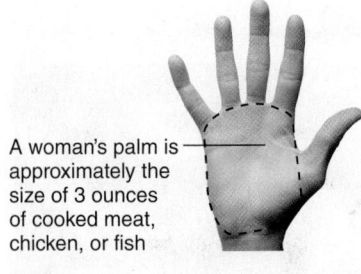

A woman's palm is approximately the size of 3 ounces of cooked meat, chicken, or fish

(a)

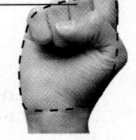

A woman's fist is about the size of 1 cup of pasta or vegetables (a man's fist is the size of about 2 cups)

(b)

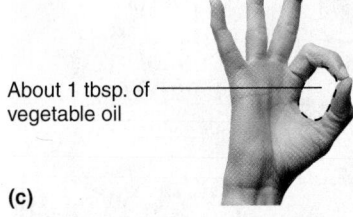

About 1 tbsp. of vegetable oil

(c)

Figure 2.8 Use your hands to help you estimate the serving sizes of common foods.

It is important to understand that there is no standardized definition of a serving size for any food. A serving size as defined in *Canada's Food Guide* may not be equal to a serving size listed on a food label. In addition, a "medium-sized" vegetable or fruit may be much smaller than the vegetables and fruit that we buy. Try the Nutrition Label Activity to see how well you know the recommended portion sizes in *Eating Well with Canada's Food Guide*. See **Figure 2.8** for some tips on estimating serving sizes using your hands.

Make Each *Food Guide* Serving Count....Wherever You Are—At Home, at School, at Work, or When Eating Out!

Accompanying each of the four food groups are recommendations for the best quality, most nutrient-rich food choices to help reduce the risk of chronic disease and obesity.

Vegetables and Fruit

- Choose one dark green and one orange vegetable each day.

  - Go for dark-green vegetables such as broccoli, romaine lettuce, and spinach.
  - Go for orange vegetables such as carrots, sweet potatoes, and winter squash.

- Choose vegetables and fruit prepared with little or no added fat, sugar, or salt.

  - Enjoy vegetables steamed, baked, or stir-fried instead of deep-fried.

- Have vegetables and fruit more often than juice.

Vegetables and Fruit are grouped together because they are good sources of carbohydrate, dietary fibre, vitamins A and C, folate, potassium, and magnesium. Dark-green and orange vegetables and fruit are especially rich in vitamins A and C. These foods also contain differing amounts and types of naturally occurring chemicals called phytochemicals that enhance our health. A detailed explanation of phytochemicals is presented in the **In Depth** section following this chapter.

Grain Products

- Make at least half of your grain products whole grain each day.

  - Eat a variety of whole grains such as barley, brown rice, oats, quinoa, and wild rice.
  - Enjoy whole-grain breads, oatmeal, or whole wheat pasta.

- Choose grain products that are lower in fat, sugar, or salt.

  - Compare the Nutrition Facts table on labels to make wise choices.
  - Enjoy the true taste of grain products. When adding sauces or spreads, use small amounts.

Bread, cereal, rice, and pasta are clustered together in the Grain Products food group because they provide complex carbohydrates and dietary fibre, and are good sources of the nutrients riboflavin, thiamin, niacin, iron, folate, zinc, protein, and magnesium. Whole-grain products are especially good sources of dietary fibre and the nutrients listed, while enriched products have some of the nutrients lost in processing added back into the final product.

Milk and Alternatives

- Drink skim, 1%, or 2% milk each day.

  - Have 500 mL (16 fl. oz. or 2 cups) of milk every day for adequate vitamin D.
  - Drink fortified soy beverages if you do not drink milk.

- Select lower-fat milk alternatives.

  - Compare the Nutrition Facts table on yogurts or cheeses to make wise choices.

The Milk and Alternatives food group contains foods that are good sources of calcium, phosphorus, riboflavin, protein, and vitamin B_{12}. In addition, many of these foods are also fortified with vitamins D and A. Lower-fat products have the same levels of these nutrients as their full-fat counterparts, with only the fat removed. If you don't consume milk products, you will need to replace them with other foods that provide calcium, such as calcium-fortified orange juice and soy milk, turnip greens, broccoli, kale, black-eyed peas, or sardines. A diet that lacks adequate amounts of calcium may put you at risk for excessive bone loss and its related health consequences (see Chapter 9).

Meat and Alternatives

- Have meat alternatives such as beans, lentils, and tofu often.
- Eat at least 2 *Food Guide* servings of fish each week.

  - Choose fish such as char, herring, mackerel, salmon, sardines, and trout.

- Select lean meat and alternatives prepared with little or no added fat or salt.

  - Trim the visible fat from meats. Remove the skin on poultry.
  - Use cooking methods such as roasting, baking, or poaching that require little or no added fat.
  - If you eat luncheon meats, sausages, or prepackaged meats, choose those lower in salt (sodium) and fat.

When grocery shopping, try to select a variety of fruits and vegetables.

The Meat and Alternatives food group consists of foods that are good sources of protein, phosphorus, vitamin B_6, vitamin B_{12}, zinc, magnesium, iron, niacin, riboflavin, and thiamin. Dried peas, beans, and lentils are called legumes and are promoted because they are high in dietary fibre and low in fat. Meats, particularly processed meat products, and poultry can be high in saturated fats; leaner cuts of meat, low-fat processed meat products, skinless poultry, and fish are recommended.

In the previous version of *Canada's Food Guide* (1992), there was a paragraph about "Other Foods"—foods and beverages that were not part of any food group. They included foods that were high in fat, sugar, or salt; beverages such as tea, coffee, and soft drinks; and seasonings and condiments. The new *Eating Well with Canada's Food Guide* encourages consumers to eat well by:

Eating a diet rich in whole-grain foods like whole wheat bread and brown rice can enhance your overall health.

Limiting foods and beverages high in Calories, fat, sugar, or salt (sodium) such as cakes and pastries, chocolate and candies, cookies and granola bars, doughnuts and muffins, ice cream and frozen desserts, french fries, potato chips, nachos and other salty snacks, alcohol, fruit flavoured drinks, soft drinks, sports and energy drinks, and sweetened hot or cold drinks.

Guidance on choosing appropriate amounts of healthier oils and fats is also provided in *Canada's Food Guide*:

- Include a small amount—30 to 45 mL (2 to 3 Tbsp)—of unsaturated fat each day. This includes oil used for cooking, salad dressings, margarine, and mayonnaise.
- Use vegetable oils such as canola, olive, and soybean.
- Choose soft margarines that are low in saturated and trans fats.
- Limit butter, hard margarine, lard, and shortening.

Advice for Different Ages and Stages

On the back of the *Food Guide* is a panel that provides specific advice for children, women of childbearing age, and men and women over 50. Parents are advised not to limit the fat intake of young children who need energy to support their growth and development. All women of childbearing age are advised to take a multivitamin supplement containing folic acid every day, and to ensure that they also have iron in their multivitamin supplement if they become pregnant. Finally, men and women over the age of 50 are advised to consume the recommended servings of food groups and take a daily vitamin D supplement of 10 μg (400 IU). This is the first time that *Canada's Food Guide* has recommended that certain groups supplement their food intakes with specific vitamins and minerals.

Eat Well and Be Active Today and Every Day!

The last panel of the *Food Guide* (**Figure 2.9**) encourages people to think about their activity levels in addition to their food intakes. **Table 2.5** lists some ways that you can incorporate *Canada's Food Guide* into your daily life.

Being physically active for at least 30 minutes each day can reduce your risk for chronic diseases.

▶ **Figure 2.9** *Eating Well with Canada's Food Guide* activity recommendations for better health and a healthy body weight.
Source: Eating Well with Canada's Food Guide. Health Canada, 2011. Minister of Public Works and Government Services Canada, 2012.

Advice for different ages and stages...

Children

Following *Canada's Food Guide* helps children grow and thrive.

Young children have small appetites and need calories for growth and development.

- Serve small nutritious meals and snacks each day.
- Do not restrict nutritious foods because of their fat content. Offer a variety of foods from the four food groups.
- Most of all... be a good role model.

Women of childbearing age

All women who could become pregnant and those who are pregnant or breastfeeding need a multivitamin containing **folic acid** every day. Pregnant women need to ensure that their multivitamin also contains **iron**. A health care professional can help you find the multivitamin that's right for you.

Pregnant and breastfeeding women need more calories. Include an extra 2 to 3 Food Guide Servings each day.

Here are two examples:
- Have fruit and yogurt for a snack, or
- Have an extra slice of toast at breakfast and an extra glass of milk at supper.

Men and women over 50

The need for **vitamin D** increases after the age of 50.

In addition to following *Canada's Food Guide*, everyone over the age of 50 should take a daily vitamin D supplement of 10 µg (400 IU).

How do I count Food Guide Servings in a meal?

Here is an example:

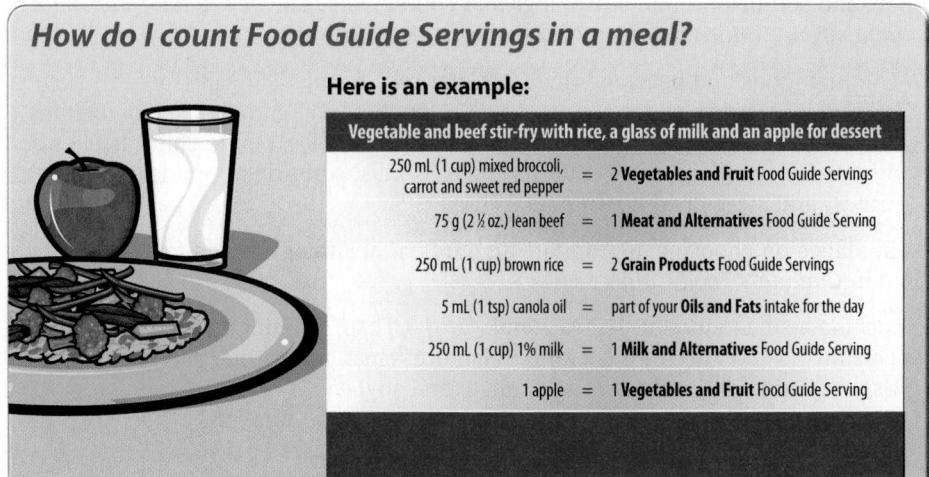

Vegetable and beef stir-fry with rice, a glass of milk and an apple for dessert		
250 mL (1 cup) mixed broccoli, carrot and sweet red pepper	=	2 **Vegetables and Fruit** Food Guide Servings
75 g (2 ½ oz.) lean beef	=	1 **Meat and Alternatives** Food Guide Serving
250 mL (1 cup) brown rice	=	2 **Grain Products** Food Guide Servings
5 mL (1 tsp) canola oil	=	part of your **Oils and Fats** intake for the day
250 mL (1 cup) 1% milk	=	1 **Milk and Alternatives** Food Guide Serving
1 apple	=	1 **Vegetables and Fruit** Food Guide Serving

Get Personalized *Food Guide* Information!

For the first time, consumers can visit *Canada's Food Guide* online at www.hc-sc. gc.ca/fn-an/food-guide-aliment/index-eng.php and take a guided tour of the new guide or use interactive tools. Try filling in your own age, sex, food preferences, and favourite ways to be active in *My Food Guide,* to get your own customized version of *Canada's Food Guide.*

RECAP *Eating Well with Canada's Food Guide* can be used to plan a nutritious diet—one that provides adequate nutrients and energy and includes foods that are less nutritious in moderate amounts only, to prevent obesity. Following the advice in *Canada's Food Guide* will ensure your diet includes an appropriate balance of foods from the four food groups, and a wide variety of foods. The recommended number of servings from the four food groups—Vegetables and Fruit; Grain Products;

TABLE 2.5 Ways to Incorporate *Eating Well with Canada's Food Guide* into Your Daily Life

If You Normally Do This	Try Doing This Instead
Watch television when you get home at night	Do 30 minutes of stretching or lifting of hand weights in front of the television
Drive to the store down the block	Walk to and from the store
Go out to lunch with friends	Take a 15- or 30-minute walk with your friends at lunchtime 3 days each week
Eat white bread with your sandwich	Eat 100% whole wheat bread or some other bread made from whole grains
Eat white rice or fried rice with your meal	Eat brown rice or even try wild rice
Choose cookies or a candy bar for a snack	Choose a fresh nectarine, peach, apple, orange, or banana for a snack
Order french fries with your hamburger	Order a green salad with low-fat salad dressing on the side
Spread butter or margarine on your white toast each morning	Spread fresh fruit compote on whole-grain toast
Order a bacon double cheeseburger at your favourite restaurant	Order a turkey burger or grilled chicken sandwich without the cheese and bacon, and add lettuce and tomato
Drink regular soft drinks to quench your thirst	Drink iced tea, ice water with a slice of lemon, seltzer water, or diet soft drinks
Eat regular potato chips and pickles with your favourite sandwich	Eat carrot slices and crowns of fresh broccoli and cauliflower dipped in low-fat or non-fat ranch dressing

Milk and Alternatives; and Meat and Alternatives—depends upon your age and sex. It is important to realize that the serving sizes of foods listed in *Canada's Food Guide* may be smaller than the amounts we normally eat or are served. Use the interactive tool provided on Health Canada's website to create your own customized *My Food Guide*.

Eating Well with Canada's Food Guide: First Nation, Inuit and Métis

For the first time, Health Canada has produced a food guide specifically for Aboriginal peoples: *Eating Well with Canada's Food Guide: First Nation, Inuit and Métis* **(Figure 2.10).**

NUTRITION LABEL ACTIVITY
How Realistic Are the Serving Sizes Listed on Food Labels?

Many people read food labels to determine the energy (caloric) value of foods, but it is less common to pay close attention to the actual serving size that corresponds to the listed caloric value. To test how closely your "naturally selected" serving size matches the actual serving size of certain foods, try these label activities:

- Choose a breakfast cereal that you commonly eat. Pour the amount of cereal you would normally eat into a bowl. Before adding milk, use a measuring cup to measure the amount of cereal you poured. Now read the label of the cereal to determine the serving size, for example, 125 mL or 250 mL (1/2 cup or 1 cup) and the caloric value listed on the label. How do your "naturally selected" serving size and the label-defined serving size compare?

- At your local grocery store, locate various boxes of snack crackers. Look at the number of crackers and total Calories per serving listed on the labels of crackers such as regular Triscuits, reduced-fat Triscuits, Vegetable Thins, and Ritz crackers. How do the number of crackers and total Calories per serving differ for the serving size listed on each box? How do the serving sizes listed in the Nutrition Facts Panel compare to how many crackers you would usually eat?

These activities are just two examples of ways to understand how nutrition labels can help you make balanced and healthful food choices. As many people do not know what constitutes a serving size, they are inclined to consume too much of some foods (such as snack foods and meat) and too little of other foods (such as fruits and vegetables).

▶ **Figure 2.10** *Eating Well with Canada's Food Guide: First Nation, Inuit and Métis.*
Source: Eating Well with Canada's Food Guide: First Nations, Inuit and Métis. Health Canada, 2007. Reproduced with the permission from the Minister of Health.

Eating Well with
Canada's Food Guide
First Nations, Inuit and Métis

Notice that this version of *Canada's Food Guide* uses a circle rather than a rainbow format, and the centre of the circle illustrates various traditional ways in which Aboriginal peoples are physically active. Foods enjoyed by these cultural groups, such as bannock, fiddleheads, seaweed, and traditional game meats, are included within the four food groups.

Other Food Guides

The Mediterranean Diet, which is itself a variation on the old U.S. Pyramid model, has enjoyed considerable popularity. Does it deserve its reputation as a healthy diet? Check out the Hot Topic box to learn more about the Mediterranean Diet.

Choose Foods High in Nutrient Density

As a general guideline, you should choose foods rich in nutrients—foods that have a high nutrient density. This means eating foods that give you the highest amount of nutrients for the least amount of energy (or kcal). As an example,

◀ Nutrient-packed foods—such as kale, which is an excellent source of calcium—should be part of a well-rounded diet.

YOU DO THE MATH

How Much Exercise Is Needed to Combat Increasing Food Portion Sizes?

Although the causes of obesity are complex and result from different factors, most researchers agree that one reason obesity rates are rising is a combination of increased energy intake due to expanding portion sizes and a reduction in overall daily physical activity. This box explores how portion sizes have increased over the past 30 years and how much physical activity you would need to expend the excess energy provided by these larger portion sizes.

The photos in **Figure 2.11** show foods whose portion sizes have increased substantially. A few decades ago, a bagel had a diameter of approximately 7.6 cm (3 in.) and contained 590 kJ (140 kcal). Today, a bagel is about 15.2 cm (6 in.) in diameter and contains 1470 kJ (350 kcal). Similarly, 30 years ago, a cup of coffee was 250 mL (8 fl. oz.) and, if consumed without milk and sugar, contained about 2 kcal. Today, a standard coffee mocha is twice that size and contains 1470 kJ (350 kcal); this excess energy comes from sugar, milk, and flavoured syrup.

On her morning break at work, Judy routinely consumes a bagel and a coffee drink like the ones described here. How much physical activity would Judy need to do to "burn" this excess energy? Let's do some simple math to answer this question.

1. Calculate the excess energy Judy consumes from both of these foods:

   a. Bagel: 1470 kJ (350 kcal) in larger bagel—590 kJ (140 kcal) in smaller bagel = 880 kJ (210 kcal) extra

   b. Coffee: 1470 kJ (350 kcal) in large coffee mocha—8 kJ (2 kcal) in small regular coffee = 1462 kJ (348 kcal) extra

   Total excess energy for these two larger portions = 2340 kJ (558 kcal)

2. Judy has started walking each day in an effort to lose weight. Judy currently weighs 91 kg (200 lb). Based on her relatively low fitness level, Judy walks at a slow pace (approximately 3.2 km per hour); it is estimated that walking at this pace expends 11 kJ per kg (1.2 kcal per pound) of body weight per hour. How long does Judy need to walk each day to expend 2340 kJ (558 kcal)?

   a. First, calculate how much energy Judy expends if she walks for a full hour by multiplying her body weight by the energy cost of walking per hour: 11 kJ/kg body weight × 91 kg = 1000 kJ or

   1.2 kcal/lb body weight × 200 lb = 240 kcal

   b. Next, you need to calculate how much energy she expends each minute she walks by dividing the energy cost of walking per hour by 60 minutes:

   1000 kJ/hour ÷ 60 minutes/hour = 17 kJ/minute

   240 kcal/hour ÷ 60 minutes/hour = 4 kcal/minute

   c. To determine how many minutes she would need to walk to expend 2340 kJ (558 kcal), divide the total amount of energy she needs to expend by the energy cost of walking per minute:

   2340 kJ ÷ 17 kJ/minute = 138 minutes

   558 kcal ÷ 4 kcal/minute = 139.5 minutes*

Thus, Judy would need to walk for approximately 140 minutes, or about 2 hours and 20 minutes, to expend the excess energy she consumes by eating the larger bagel and coffee. If she wanted to burn off all of the energy in her morning snack, she would have to walk even longer, especially if she enjoyed her bagel with cream cheese!

Now use your own weight to determine how much walking you would have to do if you consumed the same foods:

a. 11 kJ/kg (1.2 kcal/lb) × (your weight in kilograms or pounds) _____ kJ/hour (kcal/hour)

   (If you walk at a brisk pace, use 22 kJ/kg or 2.4 kcal/lb.)

b. _____ kJ/hour (kcal/hour) ÷ 60 minutes/hour = _____ kJ/minutes (kcal/minute)

c. 2340 extra kJ (558 extra kcal) in bagel and coffee ÷ _____ kJ/minutes (kcal/minutes) = _____ minutes

For more information about large portion sizes and the physical activities necessary to avoid weight gain, see Web Resources at the end of this chapter.

20 Years Ago　　　　　**Today**

7.6 cm diameter, 590 kJ (140 kcal)　　15.2 cm diameter, 1470 kJ (350 kcal)

(a) Bagel

250 mL, 2 kcal　　　　500mL, 1470 kJ (350 kcal)

(b) Coffee

Figure 2.11 Examples of increases in food portion sizes over the past 20 years. **(a)** A bagel has increased in diameter from 7.6 cm (3 in.) to 15.2 cm (6 in.); **(b)** a cup of coffee has increased from 250 mL (8 fl. oz.) to 500 mL (16 fl. oz.) and now commonly contains Calorie-dense flavoured syrup as well as steamed whole milk.

* slight differences are due to rounding of kJ.

The Mediterra-nean Diet

A Mediterranean-style diet has received significant attention in recent years, as the rates of cardiovascular disease in many Mediterranean countries are substantially lower than the rates in the United States. These countries include Portugal, Spain, Italy, France, Greece, Turkey, and Israel. Each country has unique dietary patterns; however, they share the following characteristics:

- Meat is eaten monthly, and eggs, poultry, fish, and sweets are eaten weekly, making the diet low in saturated fats and refined sugars.
- The fat used predominantly for cooking and flavour is olive oil, making the diet high in monounsaturated fats.
- Foods eaten daily include grains, such as bread, pasta, couscous, and bulgur; fruits; beans and other legumes; nuts; vegetables; and cheese and yogurt. These choices make this diet high in fibre and rich in vitamins and minerals.

Figure 2.12 illustrates the Mediterranean Diet Pyramid. Its similarities to *Canada's Food Guide* include suggestions for daily physical activity and a daily intake of breads, cereals, other grains, fruits, and vegetables. It is different from *Canada's Food Guide* in that it includes the daily consumption of beans, other legumes, and nuts and the infrequent consumption of meat, fish, poultry, and eggs. Cheese and yogurt, rather than milk, are the primary dairy sources. A unique feature of the Mediterranean Diet is the consumption of wine and olive oil daily.

TABLE 2.6 A Comparison of One Day's Meals that Contain Foods High in Nutrient Density to Meals that Contain Foods Low in Nutrient Density

Meals with Foods High in Nutrient Density	Meals with Foods Low in Nutrient Density
Breakfast:	**Breakfast:**
250 mL (1 cup) cooked oatmeal with 125 mL (4 fl. oz.) skim milk	250 mL (1 cup) puffed rice cereal with 125 mL (4 fl. oz.) whole milk
1 slice whole wheat toast with 5 mL (1 tsp) butter	1 slice white toast with 5 mL (1 tsp) butter
175 mL (6 fl. oz.) grapefruit juice	175 mL (6 fl. oz.) grape drink
Snack:	**Snack:**
1 peeled orange	355 mL (12 fl. oz.) can orange pop
250 mL (1 cup) non-fat yogurt	45 g (11/2 oz.) cheddar cheese
Lunch:	**Lunch:**
Turkey sandwich:	Hamburger:
90 g (3 oz.) turkey breast	90 g (3 oz.) cooked regular ground beef
2 slices whole-grain bread	1 white hamburger bun
10 mL (2 tsp) Dijon mustard	10 mL (2 tsp) Dijon mustard
3 slices fresh tomato	15 mL (1 Tbsp) tomato ketchup
2 leaves red leaf lettuce	2 leaves iceberg lettuce
250 mL (1 cup) baby carrots with broccoli crowns	1 snack-sized bag potato chips
500 mL (16 fl. oz.) cola soft drink	
Snack:	**Snack:**
1/2 whole wheat bagel	3 chocolate sandwich cookies
15 mL (1 Tbsp) peanut butter	355 mL (12 fl. oz.) can diet pop
1 medium apple	10 Gummi Bears candy
Dinner:	**Dinner:**
Spinach salad:	Green salad:
250 mL (1 cup) spinach leaves	250 mL (1 cup) iceberg lettuce
60 mL (1/4 cup) diced tomatoes	60 mL (1/4 cup) diced tomatoes
60 mL (1/4 cup) green pepper	5 mL (1 tsp) green onions
125 mL (1/2 cup) kidney beans	60 mL (1/4 cup) bacon bits
15 mL (1 Tbsp) fat-free Italian dressing	15 mL (1 Tbsp) regular ranch dressing
90 g (3 oz.) broiled chicken breast	90 g (3 oz.) beef round steak, breaded and fried
125 mL (1/2 cup) cooked brown rice	125 mL (1/2 cup) cooked white rice
125 mL (1/2 cup) steamed broccoli	125 mL (1/2 cup) kernel corn
250 mL (8 fl. oz.) skim milk	250 mL (8 fl. oz.) iced tea

Note: The conversions between Imperial and metric measures used here are not exact, but are common conversions used in recipes and on food products in Canada. The exact conversions are slightly different in the United States (e.g., 1 fl. oz. = 29.57 mL; 8 fl. oz. = 1 cup = 237 mL) and in Canada (1 fl. oz. = 28.41 mL; 8 fl. oz. = 1 cup = 227 mL). As a result, U.S. volume measures are slightly larger (approximately 4%) than Canadian measures.

three Oreo cookies provide the same number of Calories as a medium banana and 125 mL (1/2 cup) of fresh blackberries. Yet as you might guess, the density of nutrients in the fruit is far superior, giving you more true nourishment per kcal **(Figure 2.13)**.

A helpful analogy for selecting nutrient-dense foods is shopping for clothes on a tight budget. If you had only $40 in your clothing budget, you would most likely buy two pairs of pants on sale for $20 each instead of one pair of pants for $40. Because you can only "afford" a certain number of Calories each day to maintain a healthy weight, it makes sense to maximize the nutrients you can get for each Calorie you consume. **Table 2.6** provides a comparison of one day of meals that are high in nutrient density to meals that are low in nutrient density. This example can assist you in selecting the most nutrient-rich foods when planning your meals.

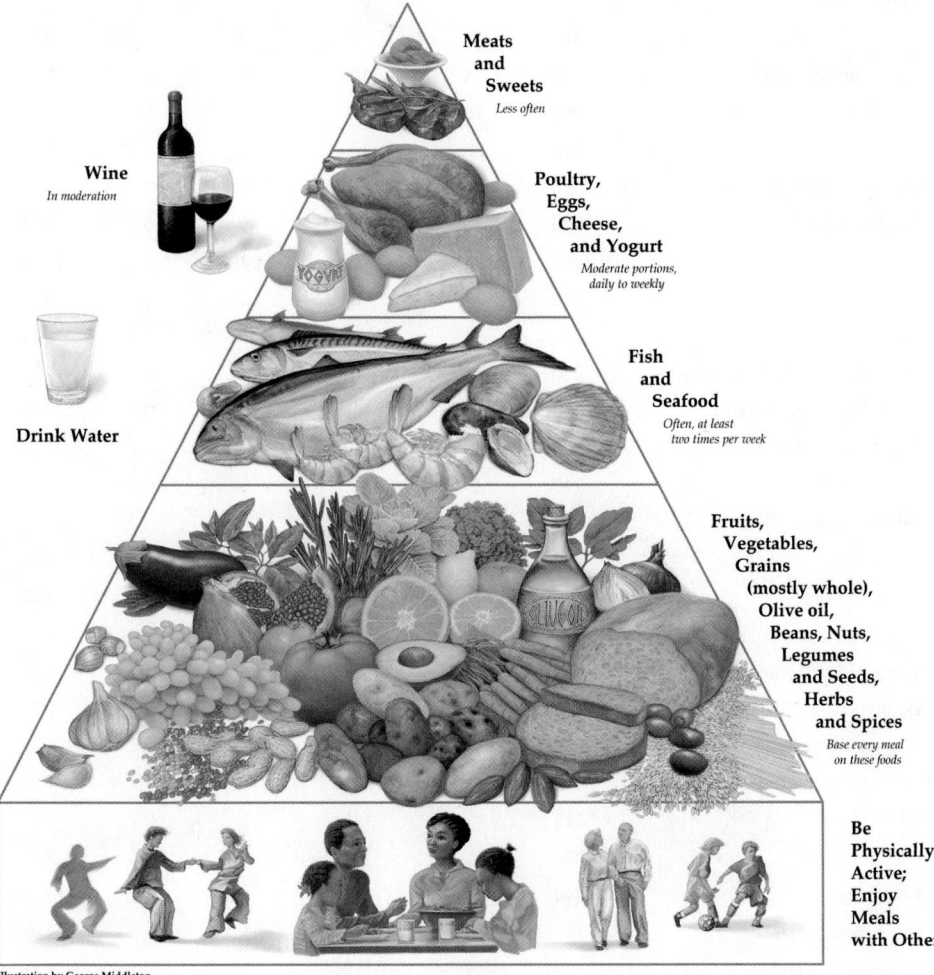

Mediterranean Diet Pyramid
A contemporary approach to delicious, healthy eating

Meats
and
Sweets
Less often

Wine
In moderation

Poultry,
Eggs,
Cheese,
and Yogurt
*Moderate portions,
daily to weekly*

Drink Water

Fish
and
Seafood
*Often, at least
two times per week*

Fruits,
Vegetables,
Grains
(mostly whole),
Olive oil,
Beans, Nuts,
Legumes
and Seeds,
Herbs
and Spices
*Base every meal
on these foods*

Be
Physically
Active;
Enjoy
Meals
with Others

Illustration by George Middleton

© 2009 Oldways Preservation and Exchange Trust • www.oldwayspt.org

Figure 2.12 The Mediterranean Diet Pyramid. Interestingly, the Mediterranean Diet is not lower in fat; in fact, about 40% of the total energy in this diet is derived from fat, which is much higher than the dietary fat recommendations made in Canada and the United States. However, the majority of fat in the Mediterranean Diet is from plant oils, which are more healthful sources than the animal fats found in the North American diet, making the Mediterranean Diet more protective against cardiovascular disease.

(a)

(b)

Figure 2.13 Examples of foods that are low and high in nutrient density. **(a)** Three chocolate sandwich cookies; **(b)** The combination of one medium banana and 125 mL (1/2 cup) fresh blackberries. Each bowl of food provides approximately 600 kJ (145 kcal). The cookies provide 230 kJ (56 kcal) from fat (6.2 grams), 1 gram of fibre, and very few vitamins and minerals. The fruit combination provides almost 7 grams of fibre, 32 kJ (8 kcal) from fat (0.85 grams), and a significant amount of other nutrients, such as potassium (608 mg), vitamin A (21 RE), and vitamin C (26 mg). For our limited daily energy budget, the fruit is richer in nutrients (more nutrient-dense) and a more healthful choice. (Calculated using USDA Nutrient Database for Standard Reference, Release 15, September 2002.)

Can Eating Out Be Part of a Healthful Diet?

How much of your food budget do you spend each week on restaurant meals? According to Statistics Canada, Canadian households spent an average of $143 weekly for food in 2010; 28% of their food dollars were on restaurant meals and 72% was spent on food purchased from stores (Statistics Canada, 2012).

The Hidden Costs of Eating Out

Table 2.7 lists some of the foods served at Tim Hortons and Burger King restaurants. As you can see, a regular Burger King hamburger has only 1090 kJ or 260 kcal, whereas the WHOPPER with Cheese has 3180 kJ (760 kcal). A meal of the WHOPPER with Cheese, large french fries, and a large Coke provides 6360 kJ (1520 kcal). This meal has almost enough energy to support an entire day's needs for a small, lightly active woman! Similar meals at other fast-food chains are also very high in Calories, not to mention total fat and sodium.

TABLE 2.7	Nutritional Value of Selected Fast Foods in Canada					
Menu Item	Total kcal	Fat (% of kcal)	Total Fat (grams)	Saturated Fat (grams)	Trans fat (grams)	Sodium (mg)
Tim Hortons						
Turkey Bacon Club Sandwich	370	17	7	2	0	1410
Egg Salad Sandwich	360	33	13	3	0	760
Ham & Swiss Sandwich	390	28	12	5	0.2	1450
Bagel BELT	460	29	15	6	0.2	1000
English Muffin, Egg, Sausage, Cheese	430	52	25	10	0.2	940
Maple Oatmeal	220	10	2.5	0.5	0	220
Chili	300	57	19	7	1	1320
Boston Cream Donut	250	29	8	3.5	0.1	260
Maple Dip Donut	210	34	8	3.5	0.1	190
Oatmeal Raisin Spice Cookie	220	33	8	5	0.1	200
Iced Cappuccino (10 oz.)	250	40	11	6	0.4	50
Café Mocha (10 oz.)	190	38	8	7	0.3	170
Hot Chocolate (10 oz.)	240	23	6	5	0.2	360
Burger King						
Hamburger	260	38	11	4	0.4	500
Cheeseburger	300	42	14	6	0.5	710
WHOPPER	670	54	40	11	1	910
WHOPPER with cheese	760	56	47	16	1.5	1320
Double WHOPPER	910	57	58	19	2	980
Original Chicken	680	57	43	8	0.4	1430
Tendergrill Chicken	370	39	16	2.5	0.1	910
Fries, small	220	45	11	2	0.2	500
Fries, medium	350	44	17	3.5	0.4	790
Fries, large	440	45	22	4.5	0.5	1000
Onion rings, small	150	48	8	1.5	0.1	290
Onion rings, medium	320	48	17	2.5	0.1	620
Onion rings, large	410	46	21	3.5	0.1	790

Source: Tim Hortons Nutrition Guide, www.timhortons.com/ca/pdf/nutrition-guide-can.pdf; and Burger King Canada, http://en.burgerking.ca/cms/en/us/cms_out/ digital_assets/files/pages/NutritionInformation.pdf (accessed March 2012).

Foods served at fast-food chains are often high in Calories, total fat, and sodium.

Eating out can be a part of a healthful diet, if you are careful to choose wisely.

Fast-food restaurants are not alone in serving large portions. Most sit-down restaurants also serve large meals, which may include bread with butter, a salad with dressing, sides of potatoes and other vegetables, and free refills of sugar-filled drinks. Combined with a high-fat appetizer, such as potato skins, fried onions, fried mozzarella sticks, or buffalo wings, it is easy to eat more than 8400 kJ or 2000 kcal at one meal.

Does this mean that eating out cannot be a part of a healthful diet? Not necessarily. By becoming an educated consumer and making wise meal choices, you can enjoy both a healthful diet and the social benefits of eating out.

The Healthful Way to Eat Out

Most restaurants, even fast-food restaurants, offer lower-fat menu items. For instance, eating a regular Burger King hamburger, a small order of french fries, and a diet beverage or water provides 2000 kJ or 480 kcal and 22 g of fat. To provide some

About 1,430 kcal	About 610 kcal

McDonald's Big Mac
  hamburger
French fries, extra large
3 tbsp. ketchup
Apple pie

Subway cold cut trio 6"
  sandwich
Granola bar, hard, with
  chocolate chips,
  1 bar (24 g)
1 fresh medium apple

◆ **Figure 2.14** The energy density of two fast-food meals. The meal on the left is higher in total energy and fat, while the meal on the right is lower in energy and fat and is the preferred choice for someone trying to lose weight.

vegetables for the day, you can add a side salad with low-fat or non-fat salad dressing. Other fast-food restaurants also offer smaller portions, sandwiches made with whole-grain bread, grilled chicken or other lean meats, and side salads. Many sit-down restaurants offer "lite" menu items, such as grilled chicken and a variety of vegetables, which are usually a much better choice than foods from the regular menu. See the energy density of two fast-food meals, shown in **Figure 2.14**.

Here are some other suggestions on how to eat out in moderation. Practice some of these Quick Tips every time you eat out.

QUICK TIPS

Eating Right When You're Eating Out

▸ Avoid all-you-can-eat buffet-style restaurants.
▸ Avoid appetizers that are breaded, fried, or filled with cheese or meat, or skip the appetizer completely.
▸ Order a healthful appetizer as an entrée instead of a larger meal.
▸ Order your meal from the children's menu.
▸ Share an entrée with a friend.
▸ Order broth-based soups instead of cream-based soups.
▸ Order any meat dish grilled or broiled, and avoid fried or breaded meat dishes.
▸ If you order a meat dish, select lean cuts of meat.
▸ Order a meatless dish filled with vegetables and whole grains. Avoid dishes with cream sauces and a lot of cheese.
▸ Instead of a beef burger, order a chicken burger, fish burger, or veggie burger.
▸ Order a salad with low-fat or non-fat dressing served on the side.
▸ Order steamed vegetables on the side instead of potatoes or rice. If you order potatoes, make sure to get a baked potato (with very little butter or sour cream, on the side).
▸ Order beverages with few or no Calories, such as water, tea, or diet drinks. Avoid coffee drinks made with syrups, as well as those made with cream, whipping cream, or whole milk.
▸ Don't feel you have to eat everything you're served. If you feel full, take the rest home for another meal.

▸ Skip dessert or share one dessert with a lot of friends, or order fresh fruit for dessert.
▸ Watch out for those "yogurt parfaits" offered at some fast-food restaurants. Many are loaded with sugar, fat, and Calories.

◆ When ordering your favourite coffee drink, avoid flavoured syrups, cream, and whipping cream and request reduced-fat or skim milk instead.

Nutrition DEBATE
Can Probiotics Improve Our Health?

When you see the word "probiotics" on products, what first comes to mind? Do you know what they are? Do you gravitate towards products that advertise themselves to be probiotic? Do you believe their claims?

Probiotics are defined by the Food and Agriculture Organization of the United Nations and the World Health Organization as "Live microorganisms, which when administered in adequate amounts, confer a health benefit on the host" (FAO, 2001). This definition means a number of things. First, probiotic microorganisms (specific genus, species, and strains such as *Bifidobacterium animalis* DN 117-001) must be tested to prove that they have health benefits for humans. Second, studies must identify the proper number of microorganisms required to safely provide health benefits. Third, the microorganisms must still be alive by the end of the shelf life of the product for people to get the health benefits (Reid et al., 2008).

Let's consider designer yogurts with added probiotics. People have been consuming yogurt for thousands of years. Yogurt contains live bacteria, called *probiotics* ("pro-life"), which are known to benefit human health. These helpful bacteria reproduce in the food naturally during the production process. Probiotics are also available in supplement form.

How do probiotics work? When a person consumes a product containing probiotics, the bacteria adhere to the intestinal wall for a few days, exerting their beneficial effects. Although their exact actions are currently being researched, it is believed that some crowd out harmful bacterial, viral, and fungal species; some produce nutrients and other helpful substances; and others influence the immune system (Saier and Mansour, 2005). They may be beneficial for conditions such as some forms of

diarrhea, irritable bowel syndrome, inflammatory bowel disease, lactose intolerance, and certain types of infections (Saier and Mansour, 2005; Doron and Gorbach, 2006; Ezendam and van Loveren, 2006).

It is important to remember that, to be effective, foods containing probiotics must provide an adequate number of bacteria, thought to be 1 to 10 billion (Sanders et al., 1996). In the United States, the National Yogurt Association has created a "Live Active Culture" seal to be placed on yogurt containers to indicate that the yogurt has an adequate amount of active bacteria per gram. Canada does not currently have this kind of seal. Also, because they can survive in the body for only a limited period of time, probiotics should be consumed daily, and they must be stored properly (usually refrigerated) and consumed within a relatively brief period of time.

Some food manufacturers are employing researchers to find and cultivate strains of probiotic bacteria that have specific health benefits. For example, Activia, a yogurt made by Danone, contains a probiotic species said to promote regular bowel movements by reducing the time stool stays in the colon. The longer fecal matter remains in the colon, the more water is removed from it, and the harder it gets, so reduced transit time means softer bowel movements. Is this claim valid?

In January of 2008 in the United States, a class action lawsuit was filed against Dannon Co. Inc. (Danone in Canada; part of the larger French company, Groupe Danone) claiming it made false probiotic claims for its products (CTV. ca, 2008). Dannon advertised that its products, Activia yogurt and DanActive, had been clinically proven to give health benefits. Those filing the suit claimed that some of

Dannon's studies on their products actually showed that there was no conclusive evidence of health benefits from these products and that Dannon was fully aware of the failed studies before their $100 million campaign add on probiotics. Dr. Gregor Reid, a leading researcher in Canadian probiotics as well as the Chair of the United Nations/World Health Organization Expert Panel and Working Group on Probiotics, defended Dannon, saying it had actually conducted a number of successful studies on their probiotic products. Four studies published in peer-reviewed journals found that consuming three, 4-oz. (125 mL) servings of Activia a day for 10 to 14 days sped up stool transit time by 10% to 40%. This effect was seen in both men and women. Convinced? If constipation were a problem for you, would you eat Activia three times a day?

For trustworthy information about probiotics, visit the Canadian Research & Development Centre for Probiotics: www.crdc-probiotics.ca.

◀ Consuming Activia yogurt may improve bowel function.

Chapter Review

Test Yourself ANSWERS

1. True. A nutritious diet can include most foods.

2. True. Most Canadians report that they look at food labels when they are shopping, to make healthy choices.

3. False. The portion sizes used in *Eating Well with Canada's Food Guide* are not based on the "average" portion sizes eaten by Canadians; they are recommended portion sizes. Most Canadians have portion sizes that are larger than those in the *Food Guide*.

4. True. Manufacturers must list the ingredients in packaged food in descending order by weight, not by volume or amount.

5. False. Manufacturers can claim that eating their foods or food products contain ingredients that are associated with reduced risks of some diseases, in the context of a healthy diet. However, they are not permitted to suggest that eating their product can prevent or treat a disease.

Find the Quack

Amanpreet is a 19-year-old first-year university student. Everyone in Amanpreet's family is either overweight or obese, but now that she is away from home and living at an out-of-province school Amanpreet has become determined to break out of her "family pattern" and lose weight. In a fashion magazine she reads about a grapefruit diet called the Mayo Clinic Diet. Amanpreet figures that any diet with a medical clinic behind it must be reputable, so she decides to try it. The diet requires that Amanpreet eat two eggs and two slices of bacon every morning with a 250 mL (8 fl. oz.) glass of grapefruit juice or half a grapefruit; eat a salad, red meat or poultry, and another serving of grapefruit at lunch; and eat a salad, red meat or poultry, and another serving of grapefruit at dinner. No snacks between meals are allowed. The diet is to be followed for 8 weeks: 12 days on the diet followed by 2 days off, then resumption of the diet again.

The magazine article makes the following claims:

- The consumption of grapefruit or grapefruit juice is absolutely essential because the grapefruit "is a catalyst that starts the fat-burning process."

- The consumption of bacon and eggs at breakfast and salad at lunch and dinner is also absolutely essential because these foods combine to promote fat burning.

- Anyone following the diet will lose 24 kg or 52 lb. in eight weeks. No weight loss will occur during the first four days, but the average weight loss for the remainder of the eight-week period will be 0.5 kg or 1 lb. a day.

- The diet is safe and healthful if followed as described for eight weeks.

1. Although you have not yet studied digestion and the absorption of food, do you believe the article's claim that there is something unique about grapefruit that catalyzes (initiates and speeds up) fat burning? Why or why not?

2. If the loss of 0.5 kg or 1 lb. of body weight requires the body to expend 14 600 kJ or 3500 kcal more than it takes in, do you think it is possible for anyone trying the grapefruit diet to lose 24 kg (52 lb.) in 56 days, without any prescribed physical activity and the daily consumption of two eggs, two strips of bacon, three servings of grapefruit, two salads, and two servings of meat or poultry? Why or why not?

3. What two food groups are entirely missing from this diet? Do you think this is problematic for some dieters? Why or why not?

4. Do you believe that this grapefruit diet, which the article refers to as the Mayo Clinic Diet, is truly endorsed by the Mayo Clinic—the medical institution based in Rochester, Minnesota, and known internationally for its high-quality healthcare? Go online and, using your favourite search engine, type in the search terms "grapefruit diet" and "Mayo Clinic." What do you discover?

Answers can be found in the study area of MasteringNutrition.

 **NutriTools** Visit MasteringNutrition to access interactive animations, including:

- What's Missing on This Label?

Review Questions

1. The Nutrition Facts table identifies which of the following?
   a. All of the nutrients and Calories in the package of food.
   b. The Recommended Dietary Allowance for each nutrient found in the package of food.
   c. A footnote identifying the Tolerable Upper Intake Level for each nutrient found in the package of food.
   d. The % daily values of select nutrients in a serving of the packaged food.

2. An adequate diet
   a. provides enough energy to meet minimum daily requirements.
   b. provides enough of the energy, nutrients, and fibre to maintain a person's health.
   c. provides a sufficient variety of nutrients to maintain a healthy weight and to optimize our body's metabolic processes.
   d. contains combinations of foods that provide healthful proportions of nutrients.

3. Which of the following are required on labels for foods intended for infants and children less than two years of age?
   a. Saturated and trans fats
   b. Starch and fibre
   c. Cholesterol and trans fats
   d. Protein and iron

4. The Health Check™ symbol on a package tells you that the food
   a. meets a set of criteria by the Canadian Heart and Stroke Association for a "heart-healthy" choice.
   b. has been approved by the Canadian Diabetes Association for diets for people with diabetes.
   c. meets Health Canada's criteria for a nutritious food choice.
   d. is part of *Canada's Food Guide* for people with high blood pressure.

5. What does it mean to choose foods for their nutrient density?
   a. Dense foods such as peanut butter or chicken are more nutritious choices than transparent foods such as mineral water or gelatine.
   b. Foods with a lot of nutrients relative to their energy content, such as fish, are more nutritious choices than foods with less nutrients, such as candy.
   c. Energy-dense foods such as cheesecake should be avoided.
   d. Fat makes foods dense, and thus foods high in fat should be avoided.

6. Choose the correct statement.
   a. Percent daily values indicate the amount a nutrient should contribute to your overall energy intake per day.
   b. Ingredients must be listed in ascending order by weight.
   c. If Omega-3 polyunsaturated fats are listed, omega-6 polyunsaturated fats must be listed as well.
   d. Health claims relate to the amount of nutrient in a food.

7. List ways to make eating out healthy. Hint: Think of what you order when you're out to dinner and describe ways you could tweak the meal to make it healthy and lower the number of Calories consumed.

8. How can Percent Daily Values aid in making healthy food choices?

9. Defend the statement that no single diet can be appropriate for every human being.

10. Describe the main characteristics of a traditional Mediterranean Diet.

11. Your little sister, Laura, comes home in tears because her elementary school has removed the vending machine with all of her favourite recess snacks. Laura is a healthy, active Grade 4 student who always brings a packed lunch with nutrient-dense foods like sandwiches, vegetables, and fruit. She whines that removing vending machines isn't fair. Do you agree with the school's decision to remove the vending machines?

12. Vending machines are a source of extra income for many schools as the schools may receive a percentage of the profits from sales. Is this situation a conflict of interest for schools? While schools cannot control what students choose to eat, should they be held accountable for making these nutrient-void snacks so readily available? If you were on the committee deciding the fate of elementary school vending machines, what side would you be on, and what would your arguments be?

Case Study

Now that you've had the opportunity to learn about nutritious diet planning, let's discuss Katie, a 20-year-old university student who lives in an apartment with one roommate. Since moving away from home, Katie has found it difficult to eat regular, nutritious meals. She often finds herself in the grocery store lost at the thought of having to make decisions about which product to purchase. The choices are seemingly endless!

Questions:
   a. What tools are available directly on the product package to aid Katie in making healthful food choices?

b. Katie decides to purchase a large meat lasagna to last her several meals. The whole meat lasagna is 1.2 kg (1200 g). One portion (300 g) contains 390 Calories and 13 grams of fat.

  i. If Katie eats one-half of the meat lasagna at dinner, how many grams of fat did she consume?

  ii. If Katie's recommended intake of fat is 65 grams, what is her percent daily value of fat from the meat lasagna?

c. According to *Canada's Food Guide*, how many servings from each food group should she aim to consume each day? List several healthful food choices found at the grocery store for each group (remember to think about why they are healthy choices).

d. List several foods that you would advise Katie to purchase sparingly.

Answers to Review Questions can be found at the back of this text.

Web Resources

www.dietitians.ca
Dietitians of Canada

Click on "Your Health" and then "Assess Yourself" and "EATracker" to see if your eating and physical activity patterns are on track!

www.hc-sc.gc.ca/fn-an/label-etiquet/nutrition/cons/interactive_e.html
Health Canada's Interactive Nutrition Label

This is an interactive site to help you learn about the new food label. When you think you know the parts of the label, take the interactive quiz!

www.5to10aday.com
5-to-10-a-Day for Better Health

Visit this site to learn more about The Mix it up! Campaign, a social marketing initiative aimed at helping Canadians of all ages eat more fruits and vegetables as part of a healthy diet and active lifestyle to better their health.

www.healthcheck.org
Heart and Stroke Foundation of Canada's Health Check

Developed by the Heart and Stroke Foundation, Health Check™ is a non-profit food information program to promote healthy food choices. Over 1500 food products in Canada carry the Health Check™ logo and explanatory messages on the website describe how the food products fit in a healthy diet.

www.mcdonalds.ca/ca/en/food/nutrition_calculator.html
McDonald's Canada

Log on to the nutrition calculator and select different beverages and foods to see their nutrient contents.

www.bk.com
Burger King

Trying selecting various food and beverage items from the Menu tab to see the amounts of energy and nutrients they contain.

www.inspection.gc.ca
Canadian Food Inspection Agency

If you are interested in more information about the new food labels in Canada, health claims, and so on, this is the place to find it.

www.hc-sc.gc.ca/ahc-asc/branch-dirgen/hpfb-dgpsa/onpp-bppn/index-eng.php
Office of Nutrition Policy and Promotion, Health Canada

Learn more about *Eating Well with Canada's Food Guide* and other Canadian nutrition policies.

www.oldwayspt.org
Oldways Preservation and Exchange Trust

Find variations of ethnic and cultural food pyramids.

www.crdc-probiotics.ca
The Canadian Research & Development Centre for Probiotics

Visit this centre to learn more about Canadian research on probiotics.

MasteringNutrition®

Assignments
Animation Reading Labels
Activities NutriTools

Study Area
Practice Tests • Diet Analysis • eText

Phytochemicals

WANT TO FIND OUT...

- **what's behind all the fuss about phytochemicals?**

- **why stressing your cells can be a good thing?**

- **why you can't put fruits and veggies into a pill?**

READ ON

Imagine a patient seeing his physician for his annual physical exam. The physician measures his blood pressure and finds it slightly elevated. At the close of the visit, she hands the patient a prescription: *one apple, 2 servings of dark-green leafy vegetables, a half cup of oatmeal, and 2 cups of soy milk daily.* The patient accepts the prescription gratefully, assuring his physician as he says goodbye, "I'll stop at the market on my way home!"

Sound unreal? As researchers provide more evidence of the link between nutrition and health, scenarios like this might become familiar. Here we explore *In Depth* some of the reasons that certain chemicals that occur naturally in plant foods are thought to promote health. Who knows? When you finish reading, you might find yourself writing up your own health-promoting grocery list!

What Are Phytochemicals?

Phyto- means "plant," so **phytochemicals** are plant chemicals. These naturally occurring compounds are believed to protect plants from a variety of injurious agents, including insects, microbes, the oxygen they produce, and the UV light they capture and transform into the nutrients we need. Although more than 5000 different phytochemicals have already been identified, researchers believe there are thousands more (Liu, 2003). Any one food can contain hundreds. **Figure 1** shows some groups of only a few of the most common.

Phytochemicals are not considered nutrients—that is, substances necessary for sustaining life. Even for carotenoids, a well-studied class of phytochemicals, the Food and Nutrition Board of the Institute of Medicine concluded in 2000 that there is not enough evidence to establish a daily recommended intake (Food and Nutrition Board IOM, 2000). So, whereas a total lack of vitamin C or iron is incompatible with life, a total lack of

---

phytochemicals Compounds found in plants that are believed to have health-promoting effects in humans.

diseases of aging Conditions that typically occur later in life as a result of lifelong accumulated risk, such as exposure to high-fat diets, a lack of physical activity, and excess sun exposure.

metabolites The form that nutrients take when they have been used by the body. For example, lactate is a metabolite of carbohydrate that is produced when we use carbohydrate for energy.

lutein or allylic sulphur compounds is not known to be fatal. On the other hand, eating an abundance of phytochemical-rich foods has been shown to reduce the risk for cardiovascular disease, cancer, diabetes, Alzheimer's disease, cataracts, and age-related functional decline (Liu, 2003; Food and Nutrition Board IOM, 2000; Chun et al., 2007).

The evidence supporting this observation of a reduced disease risk stems mainly from large epidemiological studies in which people report their usual food intake to researchers, who then look for relationships between specific dietary patterns and common diseases. These large studies often find that the reduced disease risk from high intakes of plant foods cannot be attributed solely to differences in intake of macronutrients and micronutrients. This suggests that other compounds in plant foods may be reducing the risk for disease.

As we noted in Chapter 1, epidemiological studies can only reveal *associations* between general patterns of food intake and health conditions; they cannot prove that a food or dietary pattern directly *causes* a health outcome. To better understand how phytochemicals influence health and disease, researchers have turned to biochemical, cellular, and animal studies.

How Do Phytochemicals Reduce Our Risk for Disease?

For decades, laboratory experiments have shown that, at least in the test tube, many phytochemicals have antioxidant properties. As you will learn in Chapter 8, antioxidants can neutralize certain unstable, highly reactive compounds, called *free radicals*, that damage our cells. Free radicals are an unavoidable by-product of normal metabolism, but they are also produced in response to radiation, air pollution, industrial chemicals, tobacco smoke, infections, and even intense exercise.

The health effects of this damage, also known as oxidative damage,

typically don't arise until later in life. Many **diseases of aging,** such as cardiovascular disease, cancer, cataracts, arthritis, and certain neurologic disorders, have been linked to oxidative damage that accumulates over years. It's no surprise, therefore, that antioxidant-rich foods reduce the risk for these conditions.

Unfortunately, biology is not fully explained by a few simple chemical reactions. In fact, the latest research evidence on phytochemicals suggests that their health-promoting properties are largely unrelated to the antioxidant activity measured in the test tube (Melton, 2006; Linus Pauling Institute, 2005). This is in part because phytochemicals can be modified during digestion and after absorption, so that cells are exposed to **metabolites** that are structurally different from the phytochemicals found in foods (Linus Pauling Institute, 2005). Clearly, the test tube cannot explain what is happening inside the body.

Fortunately, researchers have also done cellular and animal studies, which have revealed that phytochemicals have many health-promoting functions independent of their antioxidant properties. For example, phytochemicals are thought to

- reduce inflammation (Beauchamp et al., 2005), which is linked to the development of Alzheimer's disease and cardiovascular disease and is symptomatic of arthritis.
- protect against cancer by slowing tumour cell growth, instructing cancer cells to die, and enhancing the activity of enzymes that detoxify cancer-promoting agents, called carcinogens (Liu, 2004).

⬆ Apricots contain carotenoids, a type of phytochemical.

Phytochemical	Health Claims	Food Source	
Carotenoids: alpha-carotene, beta-carotene, lutein, lycopene, zeaxanthin, etc.	Diets with foods rich in these phytochemicals may reduce the risk for cardiovascular disease, certain cancers (e.g., prostate), and age-related eye diseases (cataracts, macular degeneration).	Red, orange, and deep-green vegetables and fruits, such as carrots, cantaloupe, sweet potatoes, apricots, kale, spinach, pumpkin, and tomatoes	
Flavonoids:[1] flavones, flavonols (e.g., quercetin), catechins (e.g., epigallocatechin gallate or EGCG), anthocyanidins, isoflavonoids, etc.	Diets with foods rich in these phytochemicals are associated with lower risk for cardiovascular disease and cancer, possibly because of reduced inflammation, blood clotting, and blood pressure and increased detoxification of carcinogens or reduction in replication of cancerous cells.	Berries, black and green tea, chocolate, purple grapes and juice, citrus fruits, olives, soybeans and soy products (soy milk, tofu, soy flour, textured vegetable protein), flaxseed, whole wheat	
Phenolic acids:[1] ellagic acid, ferulic acid, caffeic acid, curcumin, etc.	Similar benefits as flavonoids.	Coffee beans, fruits (apples, pears, berries, grapes, oranges, prunes, strawberries), potatoes, mustard, oats, soy	
Phytoestrogens:[2] genistein, diadzein, lignans	Foods rich in these phytochemicals may provide benefits to bones and reduce the risk for cardiovascular disease and cancers of reproductive tissues (e.g., breast, prostate).	Soybeans and soy products (soy milk, tofu, soy flour, textured vegetable protein), flaxseed, whole grains	
Organosulphur compounds: allylic sulphur compounds, indoles, isothiocyanates, etc.	Foods rich in these phytochemicals may protect against a wide variety of cancers.	Garlic, leeks, onions, chives, cruciferous vegetables (broccoli, cabbage, cauliflower), horseradish, mustard greens	

[1] Flavonoids, phenolic acids, and stilbenes are three groups of phytochemicals called phenolics. The phytocemical Resveratrol is a stilbene. Flavonoids and phenolic acids are the most abundant phenolics in our diet.
[2] Phytoestrogens include phytochemicals that have mild or anti-estrogenic action in our body. They are grouped together based on this similarity in biological function, but they also can be classified into other phytochemical groups, such as isoflavonoids.

Figure 1 Health claims and food sources of phytochemicals.

- protect against infections indirectly by enhancing immune function and directly by acting as antibacterial and antiviral agents (Liu, 2004).

- reduce the risk for cardiovascular disease by lowering blood lipids, blood pressure, and blood clotting (Liu, 2003).

It is not yet known which of these roles is most important in reducing disease risk. Many other issues are also not well understood yet, such as which phytochemicals are needed and how much.

Is There an RDA for Phytochemicals?

Most well-controlled studies research only one phytochemical or food at a time. When the results are published, we read about them in the popular press: one day we're advised to eat tomatoes, another day blueberries, and then pomegranates. But these individual findings can be misleading. As scientists begin to "map" more and more phytochemicals, they're making the following discoveries:

- Phytochemicals interact with each other in the body to produce a synergistic effect, which is greater than the sum of the effects of individual phytochemicals (Liu, 2003). This may explain why whole tomatoes were found to reduce prostate cancer in rats, whereas a phytochemical called lycopene that is present in tomatoes, when given alone, did not (Boileau et al., 2003).
- Phytochemicals interact with macronutrients and vitamins and minerals. For example, the anticancer effect of garlic is enhanced by vitamin A, selenium, and certain fats (Milner, 2001).

⬆ Choose whole foods as sources of phytochemicals, rather than supplements, whenever possible.

Web Resources

www.aicr.org
American Institute for Cancer Research

Search for "phytochemicals" to learn about the AICR's stance on and recommendations about phytochemicals and their roles in cancer prevention.

lpi.oregonstate.edu
Linus Pauling Institute

This extensive website covers not only phytochemicals but also nutrients and other cutting-edge health and nutrition topics.

HOT TOPIC

Will a PB&J Keep the Doctor Away?

Whole-grain bread, natural peanut butter, and grape jelly: how could a food that tastes so good be good for the body, too? We've known for decades about the fibre, micronutrients, and healthful fats a PB&J provides. But recently, research has revealed that the comforting PB&J is a good source of resveratrol, a phytochemical being studied in labs worldwide. Research has linked resveratrol to protective effects against cancer, heart disease, obesity, viral infections, and neurologic diseases, such as Alzheimer's disease; however, so far, the effects have been demonstrated only in mice (Baur et al., 2006; Lagouge et al., 2006).

A flavonoid, resveratrol is found in the skins of dark grapes, in dark grape juice, in most red wines, and in dark berries, such as blueberries and cranberries. However, fruits are not the only source: resveratrol also happens to be plentiful in peanuts, including peanut butter. Still, no one knows what an effective "dose" of resveratrol looks like, or whether the amounts in a PB&J qualify. We also don't yet know whether high doses, such as those found in supplements, can be harmful.

If you decide to add resveratrol to your diet, we hope you'll bypass supplements in favour of the humble PB&J. Although the jury is still out on the benefits of its resveratrol content, it makes a highly nutritious meal or snack, doesn't need refrigeration, is inexpensive, and tastes great.

Phytochemicals can act in different ways under different circumstances in the body. For example, phytoestrogens in soy appear to reduce the incidence of breast cancer in healthy women, but they may enhance cancer development when the disease is already present (Rice and Whitehead, 2006). For these reasons, no RDA for phytochemicals can safely be established for any life-stage group.

In addition, although epidemiological studies suggest that the more phytochemicals we consume, the better our health, this benefit appears to be limited to the phytochemicals consumed in foods. That is, phytochemicals appear to be protective in the low doses commonly provided by foods, but they may have very different effects as supplements. This may be due to their mode of action: scientists now believe that, instead of *protecting* our cells, phytochemicals might benefit our health by *stressing* our cells, causing them to rev up their internal defence systems (Melton, 2006). Cells are very well equipped to deal with minor stresses, but not with excessive stress, which may explain why clinical trials with phytochemical supplements rarely show the same benefits as high intakes of plant foods (Melton, 2006; Meyskens and Szabo, 2005).

So, are phytochemical supplements harmful? Generally speaking, taking high doses of anything is risky. A basic principle of toxicology is that any compound can be toxic if the dose is high enough. Dietary supplements are no exception to this rule. For example, clinical trials found that supplementing with 20 to 30 mg/day of beta-carotene for four to six years increased lung cancer risk by 16% to 28% in smokers (The Alpha-Tocopherol, Beta-Carotene Cancer Prevention Study Group, 1994; Omenn et al., 1996). Based on these and other results, experts recommend against beta-carotene supplementation (US Preventive Services Task Force, 2003).

In short, whereas there is ample evidence to support the health benefits of diets rich in fruits, vegetables, legumes, whole grains, and nuts, no recommendation for precise amounts can be given, and phytochemical supplements should be avoided. The best advice for optimal health is to consume a plant-based diet consisting of as many whole foods as possible.

The Human Body: Are We Really What We Eat?

3

H

ow would it change your life to have to read a label before you put any kind of food in your mouth? Would you be less likely to accept invitations to go out to eat with friends? Would you take chances with your health and simply eat whatever you wanted? Imagine what it would be like to have your meals and drinks be such important decisions, and you'll start to see what people with celiac disease have to deal with every day.

According to the Canadian Digestive Health Foundation, an estimated 20 million Canadians suffer from digestive disorders each year, and digestive diseases account for 10% of all hospitalizations. The particular condition that has been dramatically increasing in recent years is celiac disease, where a person is intolerant to gluten, a wheat protein found in a wide assortment of food products. What is unique about celiac disease is that the only successful treatment for managing its symptoms is a lifelong gluten-free diet. This means reading every single label for each and every food you decide to eat, for the rest of your life. It's not always easy, either— did you know that there can be gluten in soy sauce, herbs and spices, and even vitamins? What about the peanut butter jar in your house—if there are any bread crumbs on the knife you're using to spread it on your toast, they could end up in the jar. Celiac sufferers might need their very own peanut butter jar, just for them.

Celiac disease certainly isn't the only digestive disorder, and many of these conditions require dietary changes to help manage and treat their effects on our bodies. In this chapter we

Food stimulates our senses.

Hunger is a physiologic stimulus that prompts us to find food and eat.

hunger A physiologic sensation that prompts us to eat.

appetite A psychological desire to consume specific foods.

anorexia An absence of appetite.

hypothalamus A region of forebrain above the pituitary gland, where visceral sensations, such as hunger and thirst, are regulated.

address some of these disorders, all of which are related to the digestion, absorption, and elimination of food. We begin with a look at why we want to eat, and how appetite and hunger can be affected. Then we introduce the gastrointestinal system and explore what happens to the food we eat. We find out if we really "are what we eat"!

Why Do We Want to Eat What We Want to Eat?

You've just finished eating at your favourite Thai restaurant. As you walk back to the block where you parked your car, you pass a bakery window displaying several cakes and pies, each of which looks more enticing than the last, and through the door wafts a complex aroma of coffee, cinnamon, and chocolate. You stop. You know you're not hungry, but you go inside and buy a slice of chocolate torte and an espresso anyway. Later that night, when the caffeine from the chocolate and espresso keeps you awake, you wonder why you succumbed.

Two mechanisms prompt us to seek food: hunger and appetite. **Hunger** is a physiologic drive for food that occurs when our body senses that we need to eat. The drive is *nonspecific;* when you're hungry, a variety of foods could satisfy you. If you've recently finished a nourishing meal, then hunger probably won't compel you toward a slice of chocolate torte. Instead, the culprit is likely to be **appetite**, a psychological desire to consume *specific* foods. It is aroused when environmental cues— such as the sight of chocolate cake or the smell of coffee—stimulate your senses, triggering pleasant emotions and memories.

People commonly experience appetite in the absence of hunger. That's why you can crave cake and coffee even after eating a full meal. On the other hand, it is possible to have a physiologic need for food yet have no appetite. This state, called **anorexia**, can accompany a variety of illnesses from infectious diseases to mood disorders. It can also occur as a side effect of certain medications, such as the chemotherapy used in treating cancer patients. Although the following sections describe hunger and appetite as separate entities, ideally the two states coexist: we seek specific, appealing foods to satisfy a physiologic need for nutrients.

The Hypothalamus Prompts Hunger in Response to Various Signals

Because hunger is a physiologic stimulus that drives us to find food and eat, we often feel it as a negative or unpleasant sensation. The primary organ producing that sensation is the brain. That's right—it's not our stomach but our brain that tells us when we're hungry. The region of brain responsible for prompting us to seek food is called the **hypothalamus (Figure 3.1)**. It's located above the pituitary gland in the forebrain, a region that regulates many types of involuntary activity. The hypothalamus triggers feelings of either hunger or satiation (fullness) by integrating signals from three sources: nerve cells, chemicals called *hormones,* and the amount and type of food we eat. Let's review these three types of signals.

The Role of Nerve Cells

One important signal comes from nerve cells lining the stomach and small intestine that detect changes in pressure according to whether the organ is empty or distended with food. The cells relay these data to the hypothalamus. For instance, if you have not eaten for many hours and your stomach and small intestine do not contain food, these data are sent to the hypothalamus, which in turn prompts you to experience the sensation of hunger.

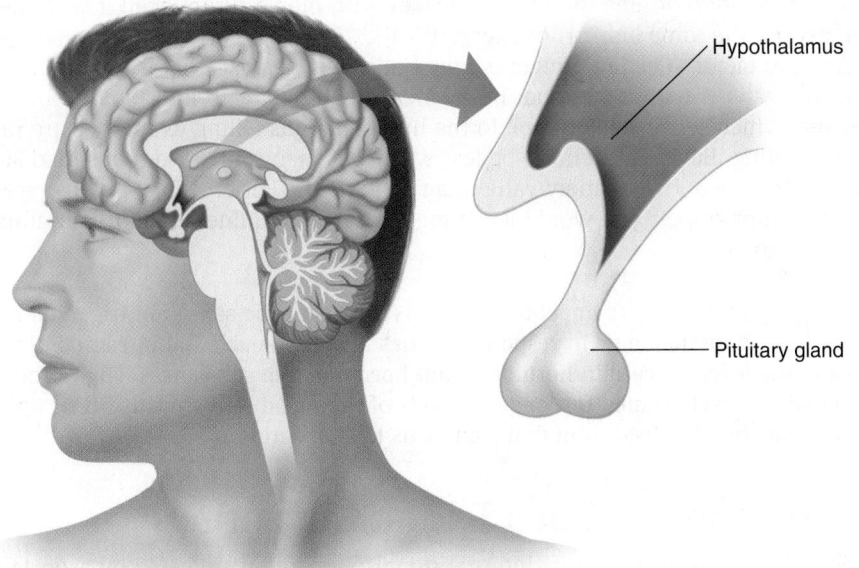

Figure 3.1 The hypothalamus triggers hunger by integrating signals from nerve cells throughout the body, as well as from messages carried by hormones.

Hypothalamus

Pituitary gland

The Role of Hormones

Hormones are chemical messengers that are secreted into the bloodstream by one of the many *glands* of the body. The presence of different hormones in the blood helps regulate body functions. Insulin and glucagon are two hormones responsible for maintaining blood glucose levels. Glucose is our body's most readily available fuel supply. It's not surprising then that its level in the blood is an important signal affecting hunger. When we have not eaten for a while our blood glucose levels fall, prompting a change in the level of insulin and glucagon. This chemical message is relayed to the hypothalamus, which then prompts us to eat to supply our body with more glucose.

After we eat, the hypothalamus picks up the sensation of a distended stomach, other signals from the gut, and a rise in blood glucose levels. When it integrates these signals, you have the experience of feeling full, or *satiated*. However, as we have noted, even though our brain sends us clear signals about hunger, most of us become adept at ignoring them and eat when we are not truly hungry.

In addition to insulin and glucagon, a variety of other hormones and hormone-like substances signal the hypothalamus to cause us to feel hungry or satiated. Examples of hormones and hormone-like substances that stimulate food intake include neuropeptide Y and galanin, while those that create feelings of satiety include leptin, cholecystokinin (CCK), and serotonin (Bell and Rolls, 2001).

The effects of CCK on satiety are known to be short-lived, whereas the appetite-suppressing effects of the intestine's release of the hormone PYY_{3-36} may continue for 24 hours (Batterham et al., 2002). In addition to hormones, gastric and gut peptides—chains of amino acids that are intermediate products of protein digestion—are also known to work with hormones and hormone-like substances in regulating appetite. The gastric peptide ghrelin stimulates the secretion of neuropeptide Y, which in turn causes people to feel hungry and to eat. Ghrelin appears to be activated two hours after eating and to be associated with insulin concentrations, but the mechanisms are not yet known (Blom et al., 2005). This is an area of intensive research, and the findings may one day enable us to use therapeutic measures to treat overeating and obesity.

The Role of the Amount and Type of Food

Although the reason behind this observation is not understood, researchers have long recognized that foods containing protein have the highest satiety value (Orr and Davy, 2005). This means that a ham and egg breakfast will cause us to feel satiated

hormone A chemical messenger secreted into the bloodstream by one of the many glands of the body, which acts as a regulator of physiologic processes at a site remote from the gland that secreted it.

for a longer period of time than will pancakes with maple syrup, even if both meals have exactly the same amount of energy (kcal).

Another factor affecting hunger is how bulky the meal is—that is, how much fibre and water is within the food. Bulky meals tend to stretch the stomach and small intestine, which sends signals back to the hypothalamus telling us that we are full, so we stop eating. Beverages tend to be less satisfying than semi-solid foods, and semi-solid foods have a lower satiety value than solid foods. For example, if you were to eat a bunch of grapes, you would feel a greater sense of fullness than if you drank a glass of grape juice.

RECAP In contrast to appetite, hunger is a physiologic sensation triggered by the hypothalamus in response to cues about stomach and intestinal disten-sion and the levels of certain hormones and hormone-like substances. High-protein foods make us feel satiated for longer periods of time, and bulky meals fill us up quickly, causing the distension that signals us to stop eating.

Environmental Cues Trigger Appetite

Whereas hunger is prompted by internal signals, appetite is triggered by aspects of our environment. The most significant factors influencing our appetite are sensory data, social and cultural cues, and learning (**Figure 3.2**).

The Role of Sensory Data

Foods stimulate our five senses. Foods that are artfully prepared, arranged, or decorat-ed, with several different shapes and colours, appeal to our sense of sight. The aromas of foods such as freshly brewed coffee and baked goods can also be powerful stimu-lants. Much of our ability to taste foods actually comes from our sense of smell. This is why foods are not as appealing when we have a stuffy nose due to a cold. Certain tastes, such as sweetness, are almost universally appealing, while others, such as the astringent taste of some foods (for instance, spinach and kale), are quite individual. Texture, or "mouth feel," is also important in food choices, as it stimulates nerve endings sensitive to touch in our mouth and on our tongue. Even our sense of hearing can be stimulated by foods, from the fizz of cola to the crunch of pretzels.

Social and Cultural Cues	Sensory Data					Learned Factors
Special occasions	Sight	Smell	Taste	Texture	Sound	Family
Certain locations and activities						Community
Being with others						Religion
Time of day						Culture
Environmental sights and sounds associated with eating						New learning from exposure to new cultures, new friends, nutrition education, and so on
Emotions prompted by external events such as interpersonal conflicts, personal failures or successes, financial and other stressors, and so on						

Figure 3.2 Appetite is a drive to consume specific foods, such as popcorn at the movies. It is aroused by social and cultural cues and sensory data and is influenced by learning.

The Role of Social and Cultural Cues

In addition to sensory cues, our brain's association with certain social events, such as birthday parties and holiday gatherings, can stimulate our appetite. At these times, our culture gives us permission to eat more than usual or to eat special festive foods. Even when we feel full, these cues can motivate us to accept a second helping.

For some people, being in a certain location, such as at a baseball game or a movie theatre, can trigger appetite. Others may be influenced by activities such as watching television or at certain times of the day associated with mealtimes. Many people feel an increase or a decrease in appetite according to whom they are with; for example, they may eat more when at home with family members and less when out on a date.

In some people, appetite masks an emotional response to an external event. For example, a person might experience a desire for food rather than a desire for emotional comfort after receiving a failing grade or arguing with a close friend. Many people crave food when they're frustrated, worried, or bored or when they're at a gathering where they feel anxious or awkward. Others subconsciously seek food as a "reward." For example, have you ever found yourself heading out for a burger and fries after handing in a term paper?

The Role of Learning

Pigs' feet, anyone? What about blood sausage, stewed octopus, or snakes? These are delicacies in various cultures. Would you eat grasshoppers? If you'd grown up in certain parts of Africa or Central America, you might. That's because your preference for particular foods is largely a learned response. The culture in which you are raised teaches you what plant and animal products are appropriate to eat. If your parents fed you cubes of plain tofu throughout your toddlerhood, then you are probably still eating tofu.

That said, early introduction to foods is not essential: we can learn to enjoy new foods at any point in our lives. For instance, many immigrants adopt a diet typical of their new home, especially when their traditional foods are not readily available. This happens temporarily when we travel: the last time you were away from home, you probably sampled a variety of dishes that are not normally part of your diet.

Food preferences also change when people learn what foods are most healthful. Since reading Chapter 1, has your diet changed at all? Chances are, as you learn more about the health benefits of specific types of carbohydrates, fats, and proteins, you'll start incorporating more of these foods in your diet.

We can also "learn" to dislike foods we once enjoyed. For example, if we experience an episode of food poisoning after eating undercooked scrambled eggs, we might develop a strong distaste for all types of eggs. Many adults who become vegetarians do so after learning about the treatment of animals in slaughterhouses: they might have eaten meat daily when young but no longer have any appetite for it.

Now that you understand the differences between appetite and hunger, as well as the influence of learning on food choices, you might be curious to investigate your own reasons for eating what and when you do. If so, check out the self-assessment box What About You: Do You Eat in Response to External or Internal Cues?

⬆ Food preferences are influenced by the family and culture you are raised in.

RECAP In contrast to hunger, appetite is a psychological desire to consume specific foods. It is triggered when external stimuli arouse our senses, and it often occurs in combination with social and cultural cues. Our preference for certain foods is largely learned from the culture in which we were raised, but our food choices can change with exposure to new foods or through new learning experiences.

What About You?

Do You Eat in Response to External or Internal Cues?

Whether you're trying to lose weight, gain weight, or maintain your current weight, you might find it intriguing to keep a log of the reasons behind your decisions about what, when, where, and why you eat. Are you eating in response to internal sensations telling you that your body needs food, or in response to your emotions, your situation, or a prescribed diet? Keeping a "cues" log for one full week would give you the most accurate picture of your eating habits, but even logging two days of meals and snacks should increase your cue awareness.

Each day, every time you eat a meal, snack, or beverage other than water, make a quick note of the following:

▶ When you eat: Many people eat at certain times (for example, 6 p.m.) whether they are hungry or not.

▶ What you eat, and how much: Do you choose a cup of yogurt and a 180 mL (6 fl. oz.) glass of orange juice or a candy bar and a 500 mL (approx. 18 fl. oz.) cola?

▶ Where you eat: At home, watching television; on the subway; and so on.

▶ With whom you eat: Are you alone or with others? If with others, are they also eating? Have they offered you food?

▶ Your emotions: Some people overeat when they are happy, others when they are anxious, depressed, bored, or frustrated. Still others eat as a way of denying feelings they don't want to identify and deal with. For some, food becomes a substitute for emotional fulfillment.

▶ Your sensations—what you see, hear, or smell: Are you eating because you just saw a TV commercial for pizza, or smelled homemade cookies?

▶ Any dietary restrictions: Are you choosing a particular food because it is allowed on your current diet plan? Or are you hungry for a meal but drinking a diet soft drink to stay within a certain energy allowance ? Are you restricting yourself because you feel guilty about having eaten too much at another time?

▶ Your physiologic hunger: Finally, rate your hunger on a scale from 1 to 5 as follows:

1 = you feel uncomfortably full or even stuffed

2 = you feel satisfied but not uncomfortably full

3 = neutral; you feel no discernible satiation or hunger

4 = you feel hungry and want to eat

5 = you feel strong physiologic sensations of hunger and need to eat

After keeping a log for two or more days, you might become aware of patterns you'd like to change. For example, maybe you notice that you often eat when you are not actually hungry but are worried about homework or personal relationships. Or maybe you notice that you can't walk past the snack bar without going in. This self-awareness may prompt you to change those patterns. For instance, instead of stifling your worries with food, you could write down exactly what you are worried about, including steps you can take to address your concerns. And the next time you approach the snack bar, you could check with your gut: are you truly hungry? If so, then purchase a healthful snack, maybe a piece of fruit or a bag of unsalted peanuts. If you're not really hungry, then take a moment to acknowledge the strength of this visual cue—and then walk on by.

Are We Really What We Eat?

You've no doubt heard over and over again the saying "You are what you eat." Is this scientifically true? To answer that question, and to better understand how we digest and process foods, we'll need to look at how our body is organized **(Figure 3.3)**.

Atoms Bond to Form Molecules

Like all substances on earth, our body is made up of atoms. Atoms are tiny units of matter that cannot be broken down by natural means. Atoms almost constantly bind to each other in nature. When they do, they form groups called molecules. For example, a molecule of water is composed of two atoms of hydrogen and an atom of oxygen, which is abbreviated H_2O.

Every bite of food we eat is composed of molecules. The actions of digestion break food down into molecules small enough to be absorbed easily through the gastrointestinal wall and transported in the bloodstream to every part of the body. We use these molecules to help build body structures, to assemble whatever chemicals we need, and to provide the energy we must have to live.

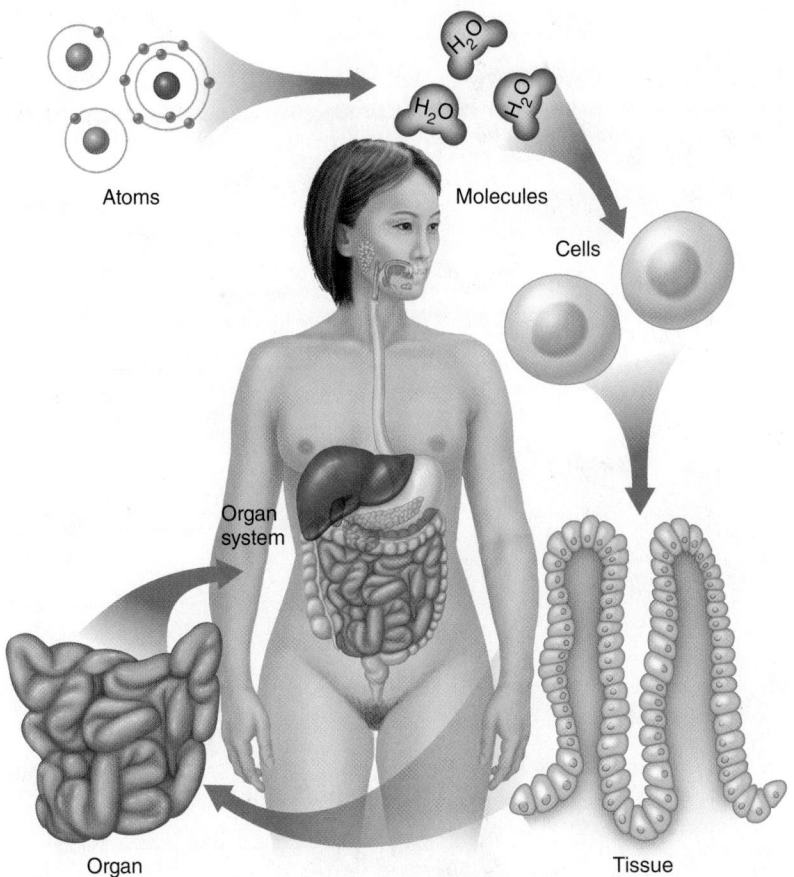

Atoms

Molecules

Cells

Organ system

Organ

Tissue

Figure 3.3 The organization of the human body. Atoms bind together to form molecules, and the body's cells are composed of molecules of the food we eat. Cells join to form tissues, one or more types of which form organs, such as the small intestine. Body systems, such as the gastrointestinal system, are made up of several organs, each of which performs a discrete function within that system.

Molecules Join to Form Cells

Cells are the smallest units of life. That is, cells can grow, reproduce, and perform certain basic functions, such as taking in nutrients, transmitting impulses, producing chemicals, and excreting wastes. The human body is composed of billions of cells, many of which have short life spans and must be replaced continually. To support this demand for new cells, we need a ready supply of nutrient molecules to serve as building blocks. All cells, whether of the skin, bones, or brain, are made of the same basic nutrient molecules, which are derived from the foods we eat.

Cells Are Encased in a Functional Membrane

Cells are encased by a thin covering called a **cell membrane (Figure 3.4)**. This membrane defines the cell's boundaries: it encloses the cell's contents and acts as a gatekeeper, either allowing or denying the entry and exit of molecules, such as nutrients and wastes.

Cell membranes are composed of two layers of molecules called phospholipids, which consist of a long lipid "tail" that repels water, bound to a round phosphate "head" that interacts with water. Located throughout the membrane are molecules of another lipid, cholesterol, which helps keep the membrane flexible. The membrane is also studded with various proteins, which assist in the gatekeeper function, allowing the transport of nutrients and other substances across the cell membrane.

Cells Contain Organelles, Which Support Life

The cell membrane encloses the semi-liquid **cytoplasm** (Figure 3.4), which includes a variety of **organelles**. These tiny structures accomplish some surprisingly sophisticated functions. A full description of all the organelles and their

cell The smallest unit of matter that exhibits the properties of living things, such as growth, reproduction, and metabolism.

cell membrane The boundary of an animal cell that separates its internal cytoplasm and organelles from the external environment.

cytoplasm The interior of an animal cell, not including its nucleus.

organelle A tiny "organ" within a cell that performs a discrete function necessary to the cell.

◗ **Figure 3.4** A representative cell of the small intestine, showing the cell membrane, cytoplasm, and a variety of organelles. The cell membrane is a double layer of phospholipid molecules, aligned such that the lipid tails form a water-repellent interior, whereas the phosphate heads interact with the fluids inside and outside the cell. The fluid inside the cell is the cytoplasm. Within it are a variety of organelles.

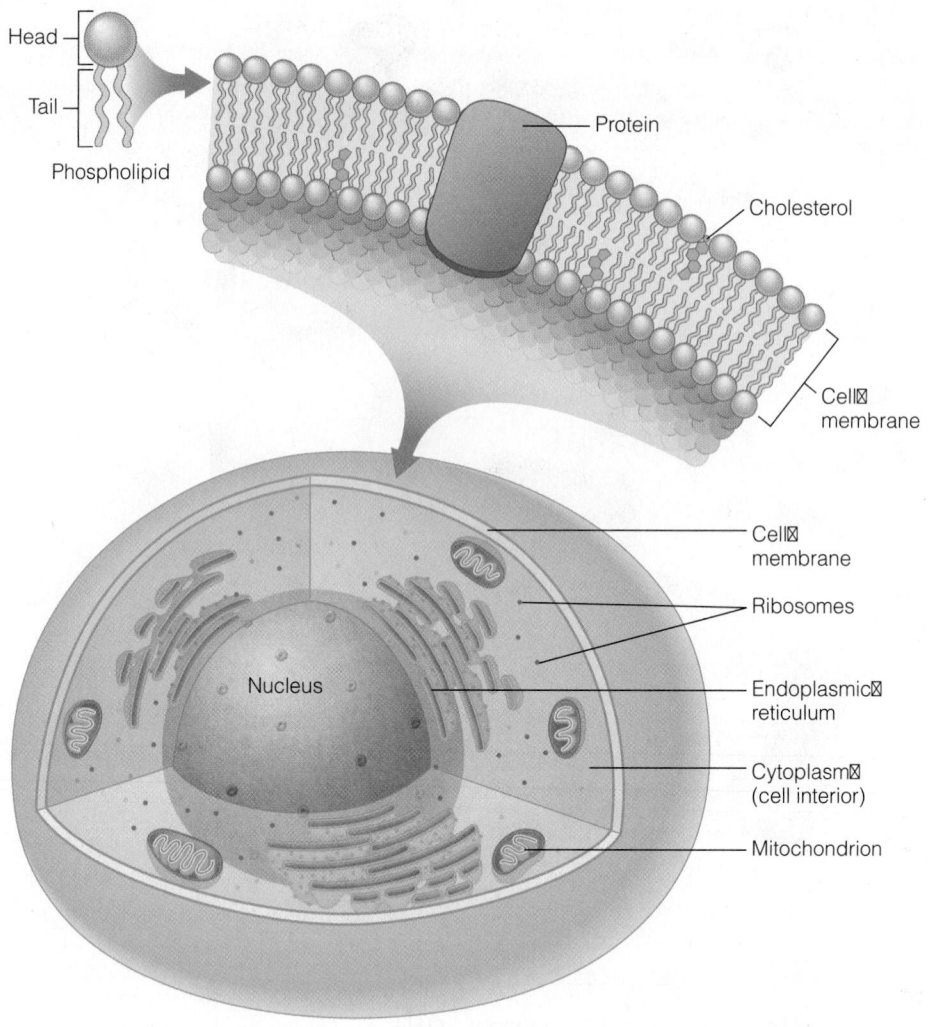

roles is beyond the scope of this book. In terms of nutrition, the most important are the following:

- *Nucleus.* The nucleus is where our genetic information, in the form of deoxyribonucleic acid (DNA), is located. The cell nucleus is darkly coloured because DNA is a huge molecule that is tightly packed within it. A cell's DNA contains the instructions that the cell uses to make certain proteins.
- *Ribosomes.* Ribosomes use the instructions from DNA to assemble proteins.
- *Endoplasmic reticulum (ER).* Proteins assembled on the ribosomes enter this network of channels and are further processed and packaged for transport. The ER is also responsible for the breakdown of lipids and for storage of the mineral calcium.
- *Mitochondria.* Often called the cell's powerhouses, mitochondria produce the energy molecule adenosine triphosphate (ATP) from basic food components. ATP can be thought of as a stored form of energy that can be drawn upon as we need it. Cells that have high energy needs—such as muscle cells—contain more mitochondria than do cells with lower energy needs.

Cells Join to Form Tissues, Organs, and Systems

tissue A grouping of like cells that performs a function; for example, muscle tissue.

organ A body structure composed of two or more tissues and performing a specific function; for example, the esophagus.

Cells of a single type, such as muscle cells, join to form functional sheets or twisted strands of cells called **tissues**. We'll cover some of the unique tissues of the gastrointestinal tract later in this chapter. In general, several types of tissues join together to form **organs**, which are sophisticated structures that perform a unique body function. The stomach and the small intestine are examples of organs.

Organs are further grouped into **systems** that perform integrated functions. The stomach, for example, is an organ that is part of the gastrointestinal system. It holds and partially digests a meal, but it can't perform all the system functions—digestion, absorption, and elimination—by itself. These functions require the cooperation of several organs. In the next section, we'll see how the organs of the gastrointestinal system work together to accomplish digestion and the absorption of foods and elimination of waste products.

RECAP Atoms join to form molecules. Cells, the smallest units of life, are encased in a membrane and contain functional units called organelles. Different cell types give rise to different tissue types and ultimately to all of the different organs of the body. A system is a group of organs that together accomplish a discrete body function, such as digestion.

What Happens to the Food We Eat?

When we eat, the food is digested, then the useful nutrients are absorbed, and finally the waste products are eliminated. But what does each of these processes really entail? In the simplest terms, **digestion** is the process by which foods are broken down into their component molecules, either mechanically or chemically. **Absorption** is the process of taking these products of digestion through the wall of the small intestine for entry into the bloodstream or lymph system (described on pp. 86–91). **Elimination** is the process by which the undigested and unabsorbed portions of food and waste products are removed from the body.

Digestion, absorption, and elimination occur in the **gastrointestinal (GI) tract**, the organs that work together to process foods. The GI tract is a long muscular tube: if held out straight, an adult GI tract would be approximately 4.5 metres (about 15 feet) in length. Food within this tube is digested into molecules small enough to be absorbed by the cells lining the GI tract and thereby passed into the bloodstream.

The GI tract begins at the mouth and ends at the anus **(Figure 3.5)**. It is composed of several distinct organs, including the mouth, esophagus, stomach, small intestine, and large intestine. The flow of food between these organs is controlled by muscular **sphincters**, which are tight rings of muscle that open when a nerve signal indicates that food is ready to pass into the next section. Surrounding the GI tract are several accessory organs, including the salivary glands, liver, pancreas, and gallbladder, each of which has a specific role in digestion and the absorption of nutrients.

Now let's take a look at the role of each of these organs in processing the food we eat. Imagine that you ate a turkey sandwich for lunch today. It contained two slices of bread spread with mayonnaise, some turkey, two lettuce leaves, and a slice of tomato. Let's travel along with the sandwich and see what happens as it enters your GI tract and is digested and absorbed into your body.

Digestion Begins in the Mouth

Believe it or not, the first step in the digestive process is not your first bite of that sandwich. It is your first thought about what you want for lunch and your first whiff of turkey and freshly baked bread as you stand in line at the deli. In this **cephalic phase** of digestion, hunger and appetite work together to prepare the GI tract to digest food. The nervous system stimulates the release of digestive juices in preparation for food entering the GI tract, and sometimes we experience some involuntary movement commonly called "hunger pangs."

Now let's stop smelling that sandwich and take a bite and chew! Chewing moistens the food and breaks it down into pieces small enough to swallow **(Figure 3.6)**. Thus, chewing starts the mechanical digestion of food. The tough coating surrounding the lettuce fibres and tomato seeds is also broken open, facilitating digestion. This is especially important when we're eating foods that are high in fibre, such as grains, fruits, and vegetables. Chewing also mixes everything in your sandwich together: the protein in the turkey; the carbohydrates in the bread, lettuce, and tomato; the fat in the mayonnaise; and the vitamins, minerals, and water in all of the foods.

system A group of organs that work together to perform a unique function; for example, the gastrointestinal system.

digestion The process by which foods are broken down into their component molecules, either mechanically or chemically.

absorption The physiologic process by which molecules of food are taken from the gastrointestinal tract into the bloodstream or lymph system.

elimination The process by which undigested and unabsorbed portions of food and waste products are removed from the body.

gastrointestinal (GI) tract A long, muscular tube consisting of several organs: the mouth, esophagus, stomach, small intestine, and large intestine.

sphincter A tight ring of muscle separating some of the organs of the GI tract and opening in response to nerve signals indicating that food is ready to pass into the next section.

cephalic phase The earliest phase of digestion, in which the brain thinks about and prepares the digestive organs for the consumption of food.

Digestion of a sandwich starts before you even take a bite.

▶ **Figure 3.5** An overview of the gastrointestinal (GI) tract. The GI tract begins in the mouth and ends at the anus and is composed of numerous organs.

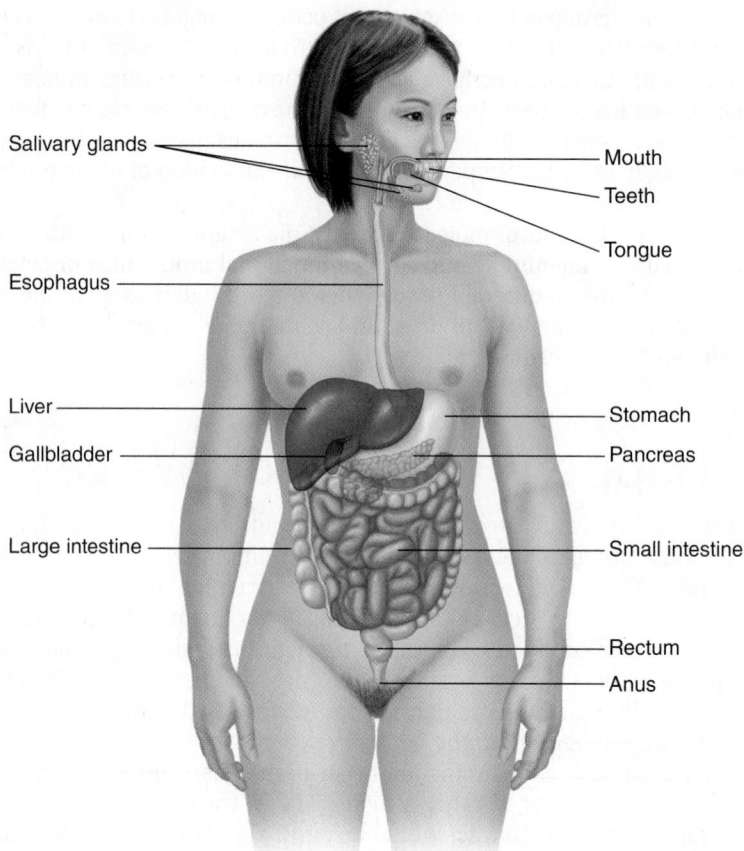

Salivary glands
Mouth
Teeth
Tongue
Esophagus
Liver
Gallbladder
Large intestine
Stomach
Pancreas
Small intestine
Rectum
Anus

saliva A mixture of water, mucus, enzymes, and other chemicals that moistens the mouth and food, binds food particles together, and begins the chemical digestion of carbohydrates.

salivary glands A group of glands found under and behind the tongue and beneath the jaw that release saliva continually as well as in response to the thought, sight, smell, or presence of food.

The presence of food in your mouth also begins chemical digestion. As your teeth cut and grind the different foods in your sandwich, more surface area is exposed to the digestive juices in your mouth. Foremost among these is **saliva**, which you secrete from your **salivary glands**. Saliva not only moistens your food but also begins the process of chemical breakdown. One component of saliva, called *amylase*, starts the process of carbohydrate digestion. Saliva also contains other components, such as

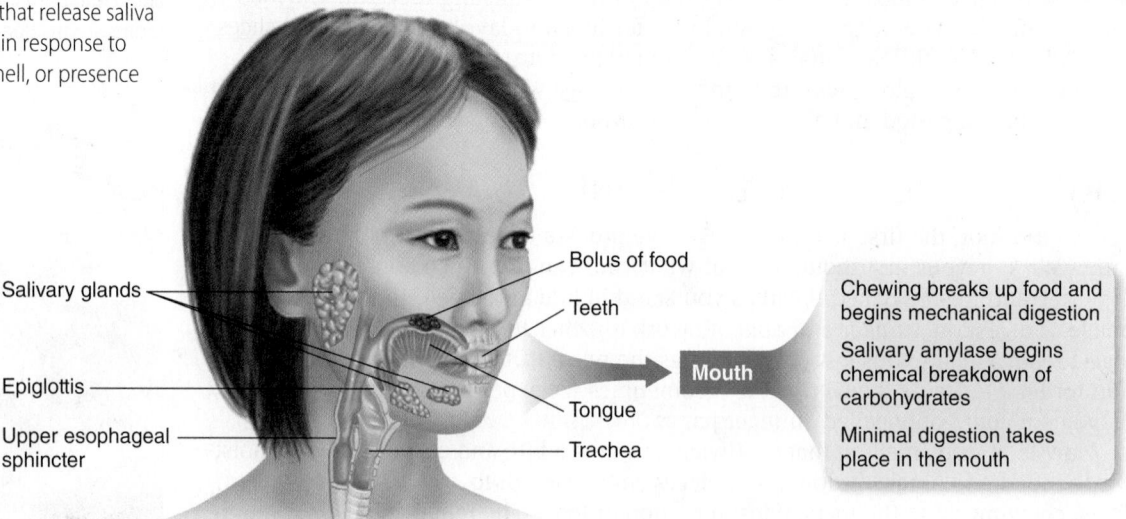

Salivary glands
Epiglottis
Upper esophageal sphincter
Bolus of food
Teeth
Tongue
Trachea

Mouth

Chewing breaks up food and begins mechanical digestion

Salivary amylase begins chemical breakdown of carbohydrates

Minimal digestion takes place in the mouth

◀ **Figure 3.6** Where your food is now: the mouth. Chewing moistens food and mechanically breaks it down into pieces small enough to swallow, while salivary amylase begins the chemical digestion of carbohydrates.

antibodies that protect the body from foreign bacteria entering the mouth and keep the oral cavity free from infection.

Salivary amylase is the first of many **enzymes** that assist the body in digesting and absorbing food. Since we will encounter enzymes throughout our journey through the GI tract, let's discuss them briefly here. Enzymes are small proteins that act on other chemicals to speed up body processes. Imagine them as facilitators: a chemical reaction that might take an hour to occur independently might happen in a few seconds with the help of one or more enzymes. Because they remain essentially unchanged by the chemical reactions they facilitate, enzymes can be reused repeatedly. The action of enzymes can result in the production of new substances or can assist in breaking substances apart. Our body makes hundreds of enzymes, and the process of digestion—as well as many other biochemical processes that go on in our body—could not happen without them. By the way, enzyme names typically end in –ase (as in *amylase*), so they are easy to recognize as we look at the digestive process.

In reality, very little digestion occurs in the mouth. This is because we do not hold food in the mouth for very long and because not all of the enzymes needed to break down food are present in saliva. Salivary amylase starts the digestion of carbohydrates in the mouth, and this digestion continues in the esophagus and the stomach. Once the salivary amylase mixes with the stomach acids, it is destroyed.

enzymes Small proteins that act on other chemicals to speed up body processes but are not apparently changed during those processes.

RECAP Digestion, absorption, and elimination take place in the gastrointestinal (GI) tract. In the cephalic phase of digestion, hunger and appetite work together to prepare the GI tract for digestion and absorption. Chewing initiates mechanical digestion by breaking the food mass apart and mixing it together. The release of saliva moistens food and starts the process of chemical digestion of carbohydrates through the action of the enzyme salivary amylase. This action continues during the transport of food through the esophagus and stops when food mixes with stomach acids.

The Esophagus Propels Food into the Stomach

The mass of food that has been chewed and moistened in the mouth is referred to as a bolus. This **bolus** is swallowed **(Figure 3.7)** and propelled to the stomach through the esophagus. Most of us take swallowing for granted. However, it is a very complex process involving voluntary and involuntary motion. A tiny flap of tissue called the *epiglottis* acts as a trap door covering the entrance to the trachea (windpipe). The epiglottis is normally open, allowing us to breathe freely even while chewing (Figure 3.7a). As a food bolus moves to the very back of the mouth, the brain is sent a signal to temporarily raise the soft palate and close the openings to the nasal passages, preventing the aspiration of food or liquid into the sinuses (Figure 3.7b). The brain also signals the epiglottis to close during swallowing, so that food and liquid cannot enter the trachea.

Sometimes this protective mechanism goes awry—for instance, when we try to eat and talk at the same time. When this happens, food or liquid enters the trachea. Typically, this causes us to cough involuntarily and repeatedly until the offending food or liquid is expelled.

As the trachea closes, the sphincter muscle at the top of the esophagus, called the *upper esophageal sphincter*, opens to allow the passage of food. The **esophagus** is a muscular tube that connects and transports food from the mouth to the stomach **(Figure 3.8)**. It does this by contracting two sets of muscles: inner sheets of circular muscle squeeze the food while outer sheets of longitudinal muscle push food along the length of the tube. Together, these rhythmic waves of squeezing and pushing are called **peristalsis**. We will see later in this chapter that peristalsis occurs throughout the GI tract.

Gravity also helps transport food down the esophagus, which explains why it is wise to sit or stand upright while eating. Together, peristalsis and gravity can transport a bite of food from our mouth to the opening of the stomach in five to eight seconds. At the bottom end of the esophagus is a sphincter muscle, the *gastroesophageal sphincter* (*gastro-* means "stomach"), which is normally tightly closed. When food reaches the end of the esophagus, this sphincter relaxes to allow the food to pass into the stomach. In some people, this sphincter is continually somewhat relaxed. Later in the chapter, we'll discuss this disorder and the unpleasant symptoms it causes.

bolus A mass of food that has been chewed and moistened in the mouth.

esophagus A muscular tube of the GI tract connecting the back of the mouth to the stomach.

peristalsis Waves of squeezing and pushing contractions that move food in one direction through the length of the GI tract.

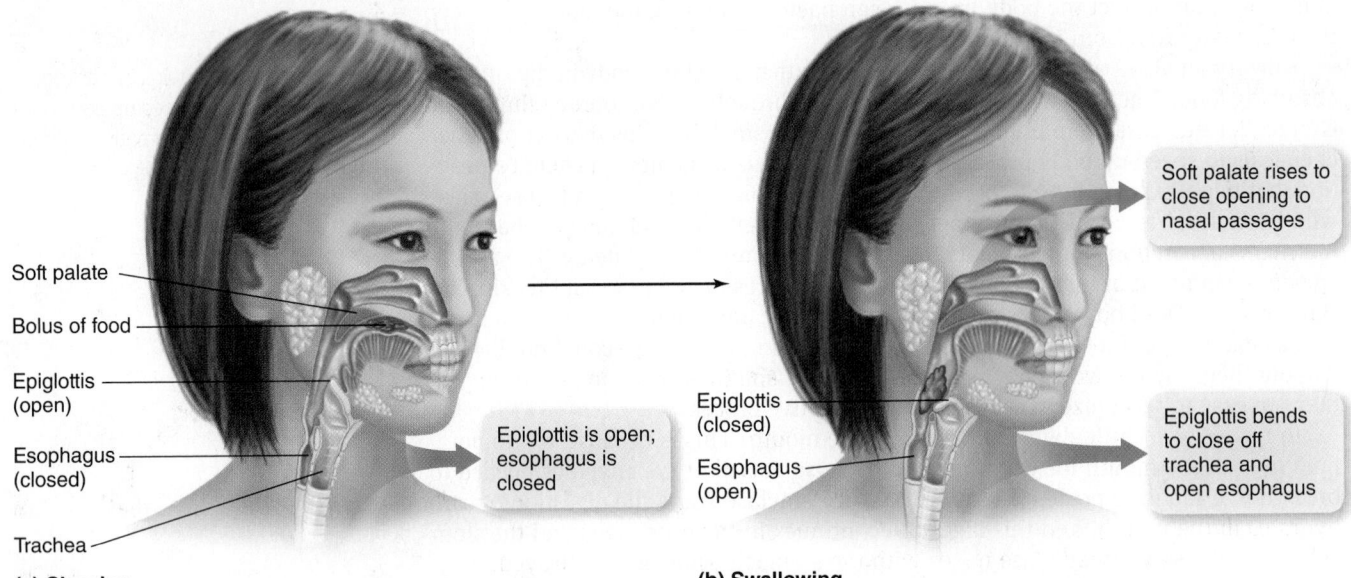

Soft palate

Bolus of food

Epiglottis (open)

Esophagus (closed)

Trachea

Epiglottis is open; esophagus is closed

(a) Chewing

Soft palate rises to close opening to nasal passages

Epiglottis (closed)

Esophagus (open)

Epiglottis bends to close off trachea and open esophagus

(b) Swallowing

🔺 **Figure 3.7** Chewing and swallowing are complex processes. **(a)** During the process of chewing, the epiglottis is open and the esophagus is closed, so that we can continue to breathe as we chew. **(b)** During swallowing, the epiglottis closes, so that food does not enter the trachea and obstruct our breathing. Also, the soft palate rises to seal off our nasal passages to prevent the aspiration of food or liquid into the sinuses.

The Stomach Mixes, Digests, and Stores Food

stomach A J-shaped organ where food is partially digested, churned, and stored until it is released into the small intestine.

gastric juice Acidic liquid secreted within the stomach; it contains hydrochloric acid, pepsin, water and other compounds.

The **stomach** is a J-shaped organ. Its size is fairly individual; in general, its volume is about 180 mL (6 fl. oz.) when it is empty. When the stomach is full, it can expand to hold about 1 litre (about 32 fl. oz.). Before any food reaches the stomach, the brain sends signals, telling it to be ready for the food to arrive. The hormone *gastrin* is secreted after you eat a meal; this hormone acts on gastric cells and stimulates them to secrete digestive juices. The stomach also prepares for your sandwich by secreting **gastric juice**, which contains several important compounds:

- *Hydrochloric acid (HCl)* keeps the stomach interior very acidic—the pH of gastric juice is about 2.0, the same as lemon juice. This acidic environment kills many of

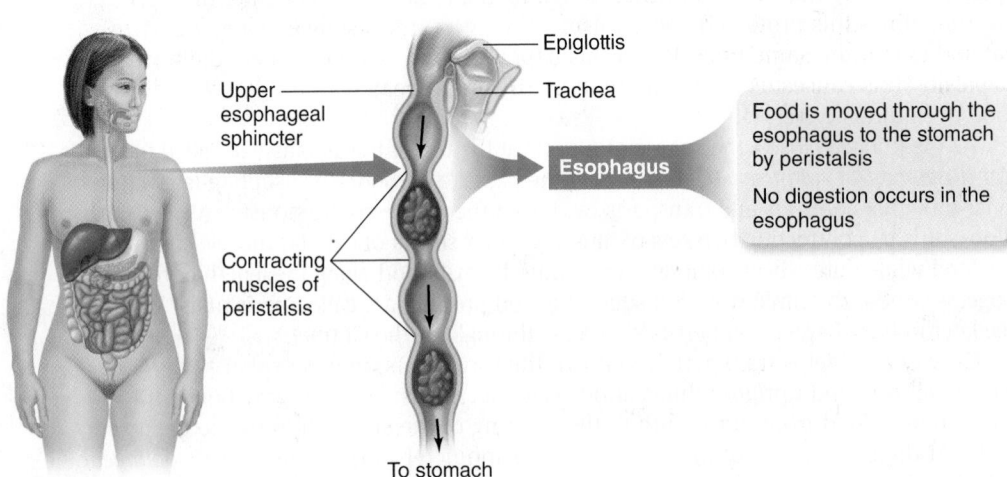

Upper esophageal sphincter

Epiglottis

Trachea

Esophagus

Contracting muscles of peristalsis

Food is moved through the esophagus to the stomach by peristalsis

No digestion occurs in the esophagus

To stomach

🔺 **Figure 3.8** Where your food is now: the esophagus. Peristalsis, the rhythmic contraction and relaxation of both circular and longitudinal muscles in the esophagus, propels food toward the stomach. Peristalsis occurs throughout the GI tract.

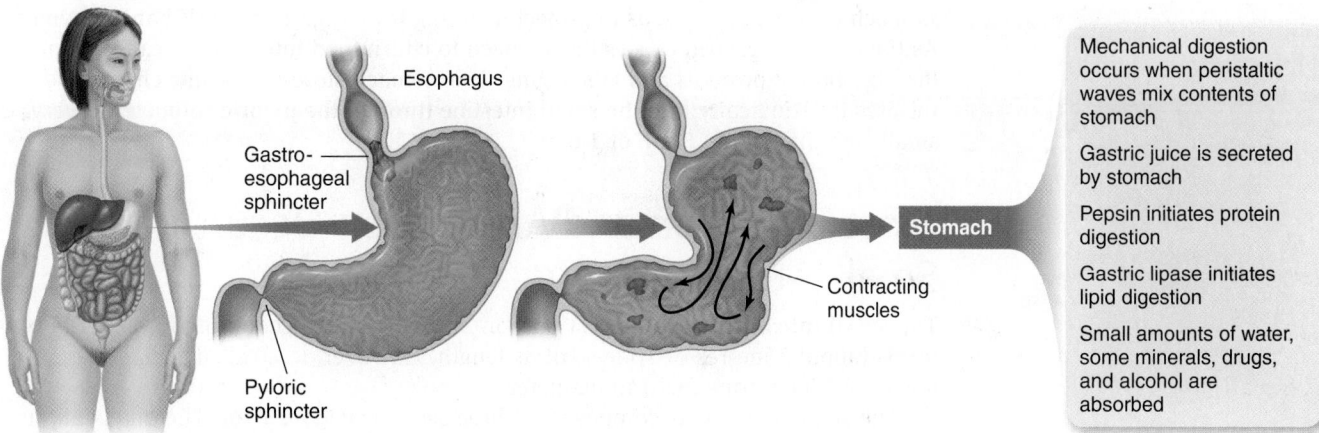

Esophagus

Gastro-esophageal sphincter

Pyloric sphincter

Contracting muscles

Stomach

Mechanical digestion occurs when peristaltic waves mix contents of stomach

Gastric juice is secreted by stomach

Pepsin initiates protein digestion

Gastric lipase initiates lipid digestion

Small amounts of water, some minerals, drugs, and alcohol are absorbed

Figure 3.9 Where your food is now: the stomach. In the stomach, the protein and fat in your sandwich begin to be digested. Your meal is churned into chyme and stored until released into the small intestine.

the bacteria that may have entered your body with your sandwich. HCl also starts to **denature** proteins, which means it uncoils the bonds that maintain their three-dimensional structure. This is an important preliminary step in protein digestion.

- HCl also converts *pepsinogen,* an inactive substance, into the active enzyme *pepsin,* which begins to digest proteins into smaller components. In addition, pepsin activates many other GI enzymes needed to digest your meal.
- *Gastric lipase* is an enzyme responsible for fat (lipid) digestion. It begins to break apart the fat in the turkey and the mayonnaise in your sandwich; however, only minimal digestion of fat occurs in the stomach because not much gastric lipase is produced in adults. (This enzyme is more important in babies.)
- Your stomach also secretes *mucus,* which protects its lining from being digested by the HCl and pepsin.

With these gastric juices already present, the chemical digestion of proteins and fats begins as soon as food enters your stomach **(Figure 3.9)**. In this *gastric phase* of digestion, the hormone gastrin is secreted. Gastrin increases the secretions of the gastric cells, making the gastric juices even more acidic. It also stimulates stomach contractions, which begin to mix and churn the food until it becomes a thick liquid called **chyme**. The stomach has three bands of muscles—longitudinal, circular, and diagonal—which give it the strongest muscles of any organ in the GI tract. This physical mixing and churning of food is another example of mechanical digestion. Enzymes can access the liquid chyme more readily than solid forms of food. This access facilitates chemical digestion.

Although most absorption occurs in the small intestine, the stomach lining does begin absorbing a few substances. These include water, some medium-chain fatty acids (components of certain types of fats), some minerals, and some drugs, including aspirin and alcohol (Davidson, 2003).

Another of your stomach's jobs is to store your sandwich (or what's left of it!) while the next part of the digestive tract, the small intestine, gets ready for the next wave of food. Remember that the stomach can hold about 1 litre (32 fl. oz.) of food. If this amount were to move suddenly into the small intestine all at once, it would overwhelm it. Instead, chyme stays in your stomach about two to four hours (a high-fat meal may remain for up to six hours) before being released periodically in small spurts (about 5 mL or 1 tsp) into the duodenum, which is the first part of the small intestine. Regulating this release is the *pyloric sphincter* (Figure 3.9).

RECAP The esophagus is a muscular tube that transports food from the mouth to the stomach via waves of peristalsis. The stomach prepares itself for digestion by secreting gastric juice. Gastric juice contains substances that assist in digestion, including hydrochloric acid and the enzymes pepsin and gastric lipase. The

denatuation The process by which proteins uncoil and lose their shape and function when they are exposed to heat, acids, bases, heavy metals, alcohol, and other damaging substances. Proteins must be denatured before they can be digested.

chyme A semi-fluid mass consisting of partially digested food, water, and gastric juices.

stomach also secretes mucus to protect its lining from digestion by HCl and enzymes. As the hormone gastrin causes the stomach to churn food into a liquid called chyme, the digestion of proteins and fats begins. The stomach stores the acidic chyme and releases it periodically into the small intestine through the pyloric sphincter in very small amounts (about 5 mL or 1 tsp).

Most Digestion and Absorption Occurs in the Small Intestine

The **small intestine** is the longest portion of the GI tract, accounting for about two-thirds (about 3 metres or 10 feet) of its length. However, it is called "small" because it is only 2.5 cm (one inch) in diameter.

The small intestine is composed of three sections (**Figure 3.10**). The *duodenum* is the section that is connected via the pyloric sphincter to the stomach. The *jejunum* is the middle portion, and the last portion is the *ileum*. It connects to the large intestine at another sphincter, called the *ileocecal valve*.

Most digestion and absorption takes place in the small intestine. Here, food is broken down into its smallest components, molecules that the body can then absorb into its internal environment. In the next section, we'll identify a variety of accessory organs, enzymes, and unique anatomical features of the small intestine that permit maximal absorption of most nutrients.

The Gallbladder and Pancreas Aid in Digestion

We left your sandwich as chyme, being released periodically into the small intestine. As the chyme enters the duodenum, a hormone-like substance called cholecystokinin (CCK) is released in response to the presence of protein and fat from the turkey and mayonnaise. This substance signals an accessory organ, the **gallbladder**, to contract. The gallbladder is located beneath the liver (see Figure 3.5), and it concentrates and stores a greenish fluid, **bile**, produced by the liver. Contraction of the gallbladder sends bile through the *common bile duct* into the duodenum. Bile then *emulsifies* the fat; that is, it reduces the fat into smaller globules and disperses them, so that they are more accessible to digestive enzymes. If you've ever noticed how a drop of liquid

small intestine The longest portion of the GI tract, where most digestion and absorption takes place.

gallbladder A tissue sac beneath the liver that concentrates and stores bile and secretes it into the small intestine.

bile Fluid produced by the liver and concentrated and stored in the gall-bladder; it emulsifies fats in the small intestine.

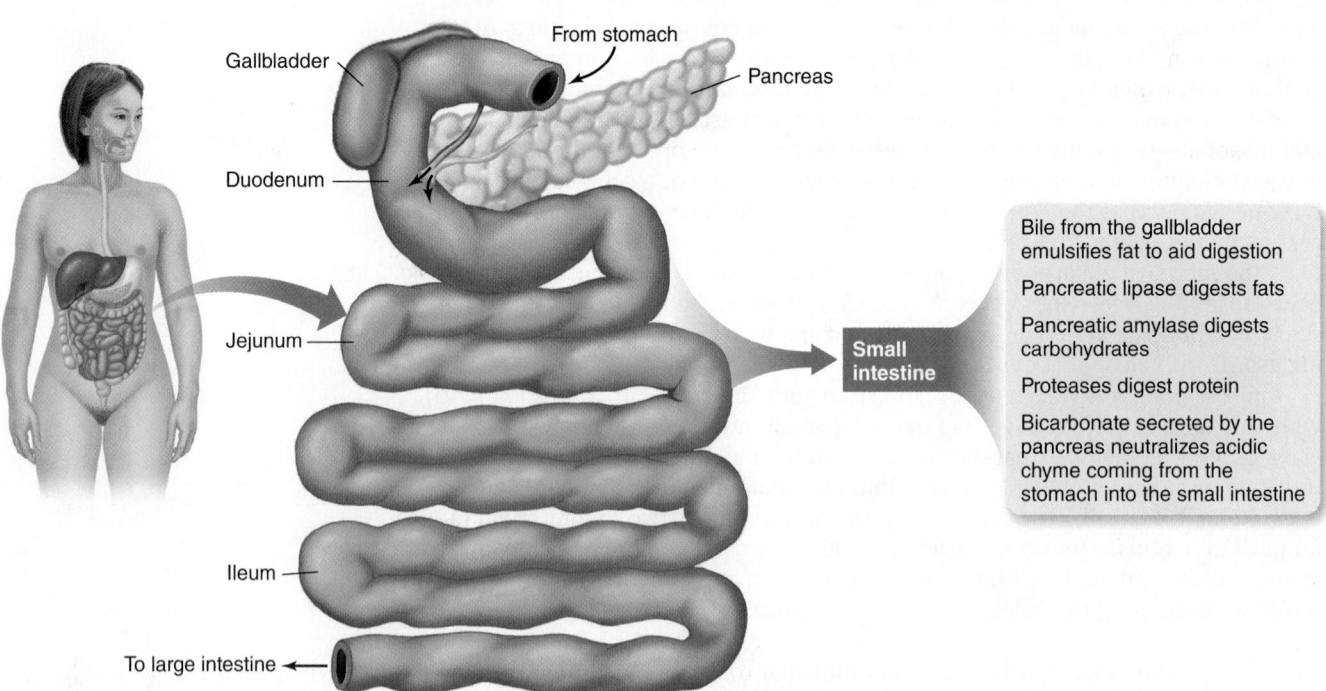

Bile from the gallbladder emulsifies fat to aid digestion

Pancreatic lipase digests fats

Pancreatic amylase digests carbohydrates

Proteases digest protein

Bicarbonate secreted by the pancreas neutralizes acidic chyme coming from the stomach into the small intestine

Figure 3.10 Where your food is now: the small intestine. Here, most of the digestion and absorption of the nutrients in your sandwich takes place.

detergent breaks up a film of fat floating at the top of a basin of greasy dishes, you understand the function of bile.

The **pancreas**, another accessory organ, manufactures, holds, and secretes different digestive enzymes. It is located behind the stomach (see Figure 3.5 and 3.10). Enzymes secreted by the pancreas include *pancreatic amylase,* which continues the digestion of carbohydrates, and *pancreatic lipase,* which continues the digestion of fats. *Proteases* such as trypsin are secreted in pancreatic juice to digest proteins. The pancreas is also responsible for manufacturing hormones that are important in metabolism. Earlier we mentioned insulin and glucagon, two pancreatic hormones that help regulate the amount of glucose in the blood.

Another essential role of the pancreas is to secrete bicarbonate into the duodenum. Bicarbonate is a base; like all bases, it is capable of neutralizing acids. Recall that chyme leaving the stomach is very acidic. The pancreatic bicarbonate neutralizes the acidic chyme. This action helps the pancreatic enzymes work more effectively. It also ensures that the lining of the duodenum is not eroded by the acidic chyme. The pH in the small intestine is approximately neutral (pH 7).

Now the protein, carbohydrate, and fat in your sandwich have been processed into a liquid that contains molecules of nutrients small enough for absorption. This molecular "soup" continues to move along the small intestine via peristalsis, encountering the absorptive cells of the intestinal lining all along the way.

A Specialized Lining Enables the Small Intestine to Absorb Food

The lining of the GI tract is especially well suited for absorption. If you were to look at the inside of the lining, which is also referred to as the mucosal membrane, you would notice that it is heavily folded **(Figure 3.11)**. This feature increases the surface area of the small intestine and allows it to absorb more nutrients than if it were smooth. Within these larger folds, you would notice even smaller, fingerlike projections called *villi,* whose constant movement helps them encounter and trap nutrient molecules. Inside each villus are *capillaries,* or tiny blood vessels, and a **lacteal**, which is a small lymph vessel. (The role of the lymphatic system is presented later in the chapter.) The capillaries absorb water-soluble nutrients directly into the bloodstream, whereas lacteals absorb fat-soluble nutrients into a watery fluid called *lymph.*

Covering the villi are specialized cells carpeted with hairlike structures called *microvilli.* Since this makes them look like tiny scrub brushes, these cells are sometimes referred to collectively as the **brush border**. The carpet of microvilli multiplies the surface area of the small intestine more than 500 times, tremendously increasing its absorptive capacity.

The deep crypt glands found between villi secrete intestinal juices into the small intestine. These intestinal juices contain enzymes that break down carbohydrate, fat, and protein into smaller components. The goblet cells found on the surface of the villi secrete mucus to protect the cells lining the small intestine from being harmed by digestive juices.

Intestinal Cells Readily Absorb Vitamins, Minerals, and Water

The turkey sandwich you ate contained several vitamins and minerals in addition to protein, carbohydrate, and fat. For example, the bread contained B vitamins and iron, and the tomato contained vitamin C. If you had a glass of milk with your sandwich, you also consumed the mineral calcium as well as vitamins A and D. The turkey contained some of the mineral zinc. Most of the sandwich also contained small amounts of sodium, potassium, and chloride.

Approximately three to four hours after you ate your turkey sandwich, the protein, fat, and carbohydrates it contained have been digested and the end products, as well as the vitamins and minerals, are ready to be removed from the lumen (interior) of the small intestine. They must pass through the cells of the intestinal wall to reach the bloodstream or lymphatic vessels that carry them through the body. This process of absorbing nutrients across the intestinal wall is typically one of simple diffusion or active transport **(Figure 3.12)**.

The vitamins and minerals are not really "digested" in the same way that macronutrients are. Vitamins do not have to be broken down because they are small

◀ A small amount of vinegar emulsifies the oil in this container.

pancreas A gland located behind the stomach that secretes digestive enzymes that break down proteins, carbohydrates, and fats.

lactea A small lymph vessel located inside the villi of the small intestine.

brush border The microvilli-covered lining cells of the small intestine's villi. These microvilli tremendously increase the small intestine's absorptive capacity.

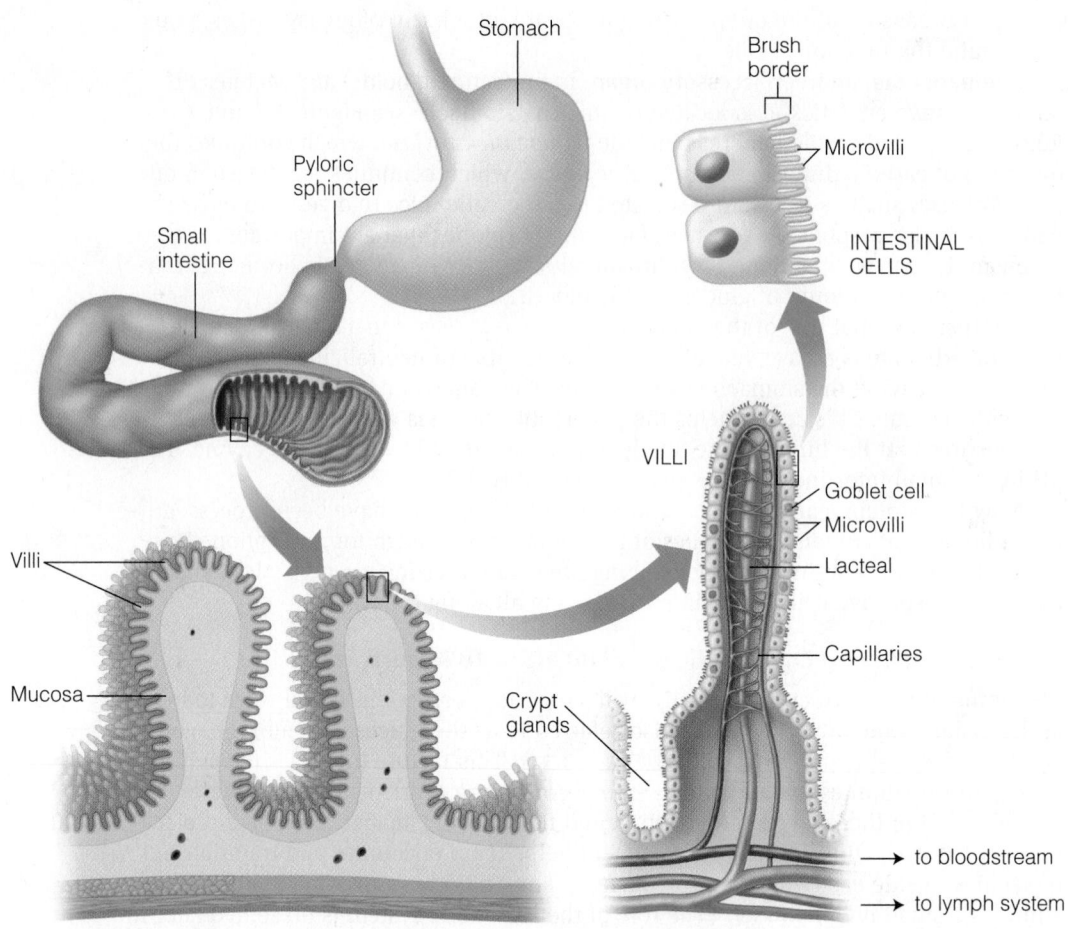

Stomach

Brush border

Pyloric sphincter

Microvilli

Small intestine

INTESTINAL CELLS

VILLI

Goblet cell

Microvilli

Lacteal

Villi

Capillaries

Mucosa

Crypt glands

to bloodstream

to lymph system

Figure 3.11 Absorption of nutrients occurs via the specialized lining of the small intestine. The lining of the small intestine is heavily folded and has thousands of fingerlike projections called villi. The cells covering the villi end in hairlike projections called microvilli, which together form the brush border. These features significantly increase the absorptive capacity of the small intestine.

enough to be readily absorbed by *simple diffusion*—sometimes called *passive diffusion*—across the intestinal wall. For example, fat-soluble vitamins, such as vitamins A, D, E, and K, are soluble in lipids and are absorbed into the intestinal cells along with the fats in our foods. Water-soluble vitamins, such as the B vitamins and vitamin C, typically use *facilitated diffusion*, which requires specific carriers to take them from one side of the cell wall to the other. This helps to ensure that the vitamins get absorbed from the small intestine. Such nutrients as glucose and amino acids need *active transport*, a process requiring energy, to be moved across the intestinal cell wall.

Minerals don't need to be digested because they are already the smallest possible units of matter. Thus, they are absorbed all along the small intestine, and in some cases in the large intestine as well, by a wide variety of mechanisms. For example, the absorption of sodium, potassium, and chloride is regulated by nerves and hormones working together to maintain water and salt balance (see Chapter 7). These minerals are absorbed in both the small and large intestines. Iron absorption increases or decreases according to the body's needs. One way the body regulates the amount of iron absorbed is by holding the iron in the mucosal cell until needed. The cells turn over every 24 to 72 hours, so any excess iron can be lost as the cell is sloughed off. There is also a specialized protein in the membrane of intestinal cells that can transport needed iron into the body (see Chapter 10). Zinc, copper, and manganese can each be absorbed with the help of a carrier protein, but they can also pass through the intestinal cells unassisted.

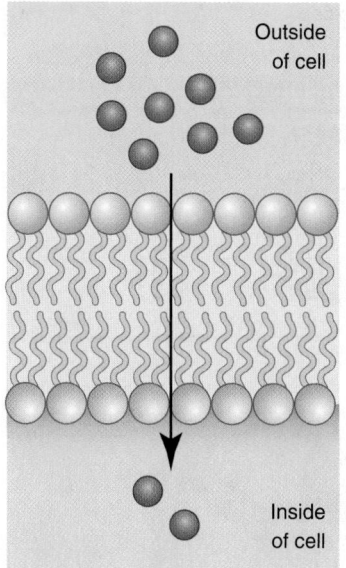

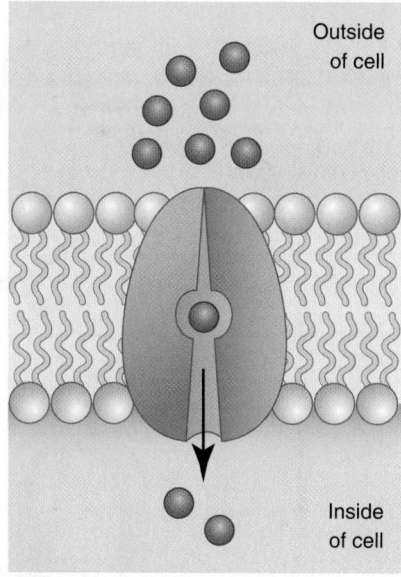

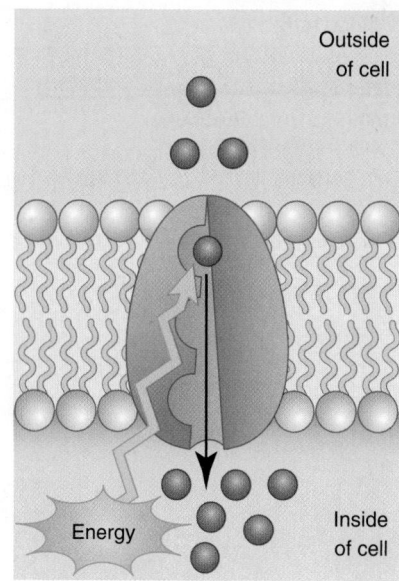

(a) Diffusion

(b) Facilitated diffusion

(c) Active transport

🔼 **Figure 3.12** Nutrient absorption by **(a)** simple diffusion, **(b)** facilitated diffusion, and **(c)** active transport.

Finally, a large component of food is water, and, of course, you also drink lots of water throughout the day. Water is readily absorbed along the entire length of the GI tract because it is a small molecule that can easily pass through the cell membrane. However, as we will see shortly, a significant percentage of water is absorbed in the large intestine.

Blood and Lymph Transport Nutrients and Fluids

We noted earlier that, within the intestinal villi, capillaries and lacteals absorb water-soluble and fat-soluble nutrients, respectively, into blood and lymph. These two fluids then transport the nutrients throughout the body. Blood travels through the cardiovascular system, and lymph travels through the lymphatic system **(Figure 3.13)**.

The oxygen we inhale into our lungs is absorbed by our red blood cells. This oxygen-rich blood then travels to the heart, where it is pumped out to the rest of the body. Blood travels to all of our tissues to deliver nutrients and other materials and pick up waste products. As blood travels through the GI tract, it picks up most of the nutrients, including water, that are absorbed through the mucosal membrane of the small intestine. This nutrient-rich blood is then transported to the liver. The role of the liver in packaging the arriving nutrients is described in the following section.

The lymphatic vessels pick up most fats, fat-soluble vitamins, and fluids that have escaped from the cardiovascular system and transport them in lymph. In its journey through the lymphatic vessels of the body, this lymph is filtered through *lymph nodes*, clusters of immune and other cells that trap particles and destroy harmful microbes. Eventually, lymph returns to the bloodstream in an area near the heart where the lymphatic and blood vessels join together.

Bear in mind that circulation also allows for the elimination of metabolic wastes. The waste products picked up by the blood as it circulates around the body are filtered and excreted by the kidneys in urine. In addition, much of the carbon dioxide remaining in the blood once it reaches the lungs is exhaled into the outside air, making room for oxygen to attach to the red blood cells and repeat this cycle of circulation.

The Liver Regulates Blood Nutrients

Once nutrients are absorbed from the small intestine, most enter the *portal vein*, which carries them to the **liver**. The liver is a triangular, wedge-shaped organ weighing about 1.4 kg (3 lb.) and resting almost entirely within the protection of the rib

🔼 Water is readily absorbed along the entire length of the GI tract.

liver The largest auxiliary organ of the GI tract and one of the most important organs of the body. Its functions include the production of bile and processing of nutrient-rich blood from the small intestine, and detoxifying harmful substances.

▶ **Figure 3.13** Blood travels through the cardiovascular system to transport nutrients and fluids and pick up waste products. Lymph travels through the lymphatic system and transports most fats and fat-soluble vitamins. (In the diagram red is oxygenated blood and blue is venous blood.)

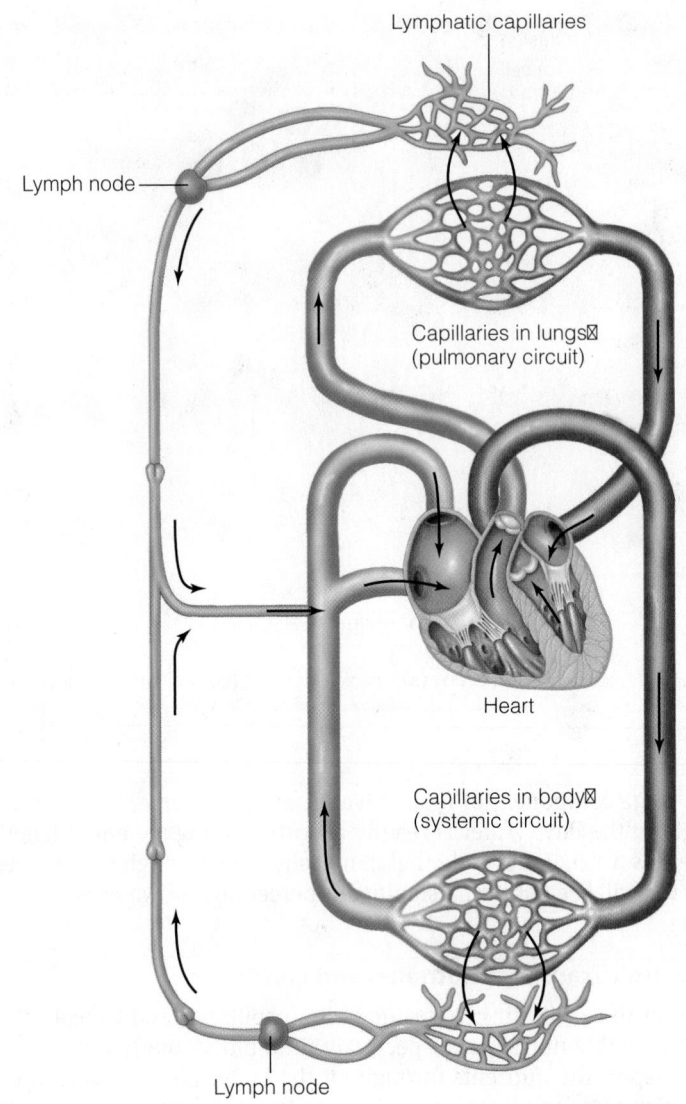

Lymphatic capillaries

Lymph node

Capillaries in lungs⊠ (pulmonary circuit)

Heart

Capillaries in body⊠ (systemic circuit)

Lymph node

cage on the right side of the body (see Figure 3.5). It is not only the largest digestive organ but also one of the most important organs in the body, performing more than 500 discrete functions.

One function of the liver is to receive the products of digestion and then release into the bloodstream those nutrients needed throughout the body. The liver also processes and stores simple sugars (monosaccharides), fats (triglycerides), and amino acids and plays a major role in regulating their levels in the bloodstream. For instance, after we eat a meal, the liver picks up excess glucose (a simple sugar) from the blood and stores it as glycogen, releasing it into the bloodstream when we need energy later in the day. It also stores certain vitamins. But the liver is more than a nutrient warehouse: it also manufactures blood proteins and can even make glucose when necessary to keep our blood glucose levels constant. Thus, the liver plays a major role in regulating the level and type of fuel or energy nutrients circulating in our blood.

Have you ever wondered why people who abuse alcohol are at risk for liver damage? It's because another of the liver's functions is to filter the blood, removing wastes and toxins such as alcohol, medications, and other drugs. When you drink, your liver works hard to break down the alcohol; but with heavy drinking over time, liver cells become damaged and scar tissue forms. The scar tissue blocks the free flow of blood through the liver, so that any further toxins accumulate in the blood, causing confusion, coma, and ultimately death.

Another important job of the liver is to synthesize many of the chemicals the body uses to carry out metabolic processes. For example, the liver synthesizes bile, which, as we just discussed, is then stored in the gallbladder until the body needs it to emulsify fats.

RECAP Most digestion and absorption occurs in the small intestine. Its three sections are the duodenum, the jejunum, and the ileum. The gallbladder concentrates and stores bile, which is produced by the liver. Bile emulsifies fats into pieces that are more easily digested. The pancreas synthesizes and secretes digestive enzymes that break down carbohydrates, fats, and proteins. The lining of the small intestine is heavily folded, with the surface area expanded by villi and microvilli. Nutrients are absorbed across the mucosal membrane by various processes and enter either the lymph or the bloodstream. The liver processes all the nutrients absorbed from the small intestine and stores and regulates energy nutrients (monosaccharides, fatty acids, and amino acids).

The Large Intestine Stores Food Waste Until It Is Excreted

The **large intestine** (also called the *colon or large bowel*) is a thick, tubelike structure that frames the small intestine on three-and-a-half sides **(Figure 3.14)**. It begins with a tissue sac called the *cecum*, which explains the name of the sphincter—the *ileocecal valve*—that connects it to the ileum of the small intestine. From the cecum, the large intestine continues up along the right side of the small intestine as the *ascending colon*. The *transverse colon* runs across the top of the small intestine, and then the *descending colon* comes down on the left right. The *sigmoid colon* is the last segment of the colon; it extends from the bottom left corner to the *rectum*. The last segment of the large intestine is the *anal canal*, which is about 4 cm (1.5 in.) long.

What has happened to your turkey sandwich? The undigested food components in the chyme finally reach the large intestine. By this time, the digestive mass entering the large intestine does not resemble the chyme that left the stomach several hours before. This is because most of the nutrients have been absorbed, leaving mainly non-digestible food material, such as fibre, as well as bacteria and water. As in the stomach, cells lining the large intestine secrete mucus, which helps protect it from the abrasive materials passing through it.

Bacteria colonizing the large intestine are normal and helpful residents, since they finish digesting some of the nutrients from your sandwich. The intestinal bacteria assist with the final fermentation of any remaining digestible food products; this

large intestine The final organ of the GI tract, consisting of the cecum, colon, rectum, and anal canal and in which most water is absorbed and feces are formed.

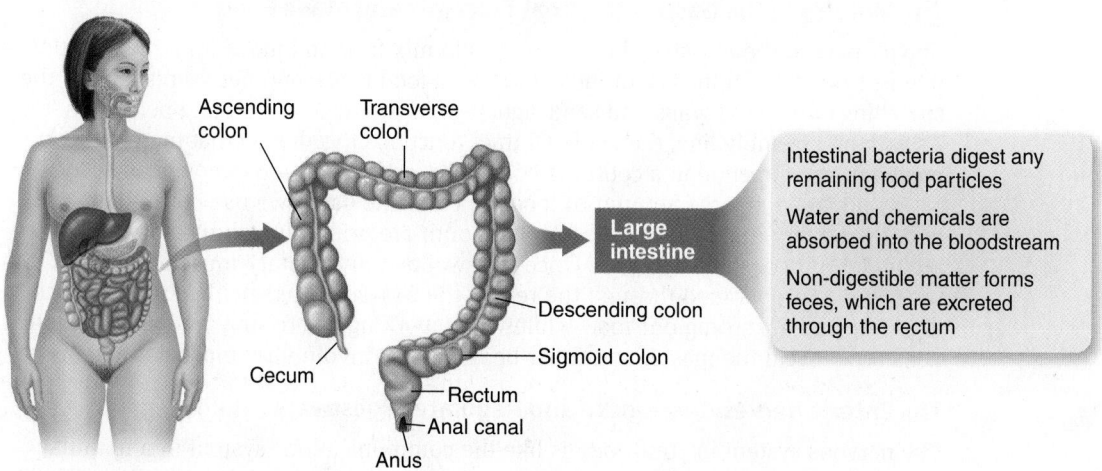

⬆ **Figure 3.14** Where your food is now: the large intestine. Most water absorption occurs here, as does the formation of food wastes into semi-solid feces. Peristalsis propels the feces to the body exterior.

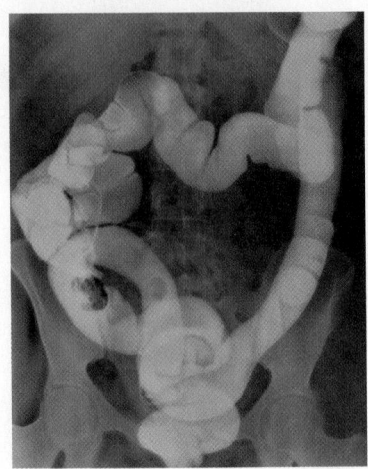

⬥ The large intestine is a thick, tube-like structure that stores the undigested mass exiting the small intestine, and also absorbs any remaining nutrients and water.

fermentation causes some gas production. The by-products of this digestion, such as short-chain fatty acids, are reabsorbed into the body, where they return to the liver and are either stored or used as needed. Intestinal bacteria, called *intestinal flora*, also help synthesize certain vitamins and are thought to promote intestinal motility. In fact, as we discussed in the Nutrition Debate in Chapter 2, the types of bacteria that thrive in our large intestine are so helpful that many people consume them deliberately in yogurt and probiotic supplements!

No other digestion occurs in the large intestine. Instead, its main functions are to store the digestive mass for 12 to 24 hours and, during that time, to absorb nutrients and water from it, leaving a semi-solid mass called *feces*. Peristalsis occurs weakly to move the feces through the colon, except for one or more stronger waves of peristalsis each day, which force the feces more powerfully toward the rectum for elimination.

Some people believe that so-called toxins in the colon are responsible for a wide variety of health problems. They say that colon cleansing—in which the person consumes a liquid "detox" diet, takes laxatives, uses a series of enemas, or undergoes a procedure called colonic irrigation—flushes away these toxins and restores health. What do the experts say? Check out the Nutrition Debate near the end of this chapter to find out!

RECAP The large intestine is composed of seven sections: the cecum, ascending colon, transverse colon, descending colon, sigmoid colon, rectum, and anal canal. Small amounts of undigested and indigestible food material, bacteria, and water enter the large intestine from the small intestine. The intestinal bacteria assist with the final fermentation of any remaining digestible food products; this fermentation causes some gas production. The main functions of the large intestine are to store the digestive mass and to absorb any remaining nutrients and water over a 12- to 24-hour period. A semi-solid mass, called feces or stool, is then eliminated from the body through the anus.

The Neuromuscular System Regulates the Activities of the GI Tract

Now that you can identify the organs involved in digestion, absorption, and elimination, and the job each performs, you might be wondering—who's the boss? In other words, what organ or system directs and coordinates all of these interrelated processes? The answer is the neuromuscular system. Both of its components, the nervous and muscular systems, are essential partners in regulating the activities of the GI tract.

The Muscles of the Gastrointestinal Tract Mix and Move Food

The purpose of the muscles of the GI tract is to mix food and move it in one direction—that is, from the mouth toward the anus. When food is present, nerves respond to the stretching of the tract walls and send signals to its muscles, stimulating peristalsis. As with an assembly line, the entire GI tract functions together so that materials are moved in one direction in a coordinated manner and wastes are removed as needed.

To process the large amount of food we consume daily, we use both voluntary and involuntary muscles. Muscles in the mouth are primarily voluntary; that is, they are under our conscious control. Once we swallow, involuntary muscles largely take over to propel food through the rest of the GI tract. This enables us to continue digesting and absorbing our food while we're working, exercising, and even sleeping. Let's now reveal the master controller behind these involuntary muscular actions.

The Enteric Nerves Coordinate and Regulate Digestive Activities

The nervous system in your body is like the communications system in a manufacturing plant. Within this communications system, the central nervous system (CNS), composed of the brain and spinal cord, is like the main control desk. For example, as discussed earlier in this chapter, the hypothalamus of the brain plays an important role in the control of hunger and satiation.

An intricate system of nerves branches out from the CNS; this system is called the peripheral nervous system. It includes the nerves of the GI tract, which are collectively known as the **enteric nervous system**.

Enteric nerves work both independently of and in collaboration with the CNS. For example, they can respond independently to signals produced within the GI tract without first relaying them to the CNS for interpretation or assistance. On the other hand, many jobs require the involvement of the CNS. For instance, as we discussed earlier, special nerves in the GI tract pick up mechanical signals indicating how far the tract wall is stretched—that is, how full it is. These receptors signal the brain that your digestive tract is full, and then your brain sends out messages that prompt you to stop eating. Another type of enteric nerve picks up chemical signals about how acidic the digestive environment is or if there is protein or fat present. The CNS receives and responds to these signals; for example, it may send out a message to the pancreas to secrete enzymes for fat and protein digestion.

All along the GI tract are a series of glands whose actions are also controlled by the nervous system. When food digestion products reach various locations within the GI tract, these glands are stimulated to release digestive enzymes, mucus, or water and electrolytes. For example, as chyme moves from the stomach into the small intestine, nerve signals are sent to stimulate the pancreas, gallbladder, and mucosal cells lining the intestinal tract. These signals cause these glands and cells to secrete digestive enzymes, bile, bicarbonate, and water—secretions necessary to continue digestion in the small intestine.

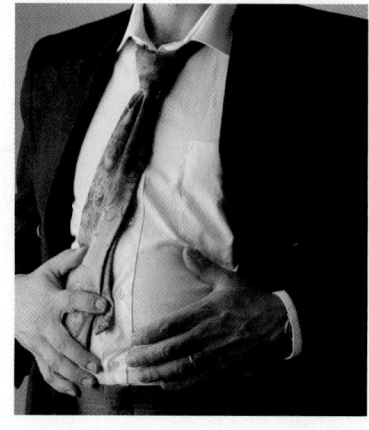

When we eat, both voluntary and involuntary muscles help us digest the food.

RECAP The coordination and regulation of digestion are directed by the neuromuscular system. The muscles of the GI tract mix food and move it from the mouth to the anus. Voluntary muscles, which are under our conscious control, assist us with chewing and swallowing. Once food is swallowed, the involuntary muscles along the entire length of the GI tract function together, so that materials are moved in one direction in a coordinated manner and wastes are removed as needed. The enteric nerves of the GI tract work with the CNS to achieve the digestion, absorption, and elimination of food.

What Disorders Are Related to Digestion, Absorption, and Elimination?

Considering the complexity of digestion, absorption, and elimination, it's no wonder that sometimes things go wrong. Disorders of the neuromuscular system, hormonal imbalances, infections, allergies, and a host of other disorders can disturb gastrointestinal functioning, as can merely consuming the wrong types or amounts of food for our unique needs. Whenever there is a problem with the GI tract, the absorption of nutrients can be affected and, over time, malnutrition can result. Let's look more closely at some GI tract disorders and what you might be able to do if they affect you.

Heartburn and Gastroesophageal Reflux Disease Are Caused by Reflux of Stomach Acid

When you eat food, your stomach secretes hydrochloric acid to start the digestive process. In many people, the amount of HCl secreted is occasionally excessive, or the gastroesophageal sphincter opens too soon. In either case, the result is that HCl seeps back up into the esophagus (**Figure 3.15**). Although the stomach is protected from HCl by a thick coat of mucus, the esophagus does not have this mucous coating. Thus, the HCl burns it. When this happens, a person experiences a painful sensation in the region of the chest behind the sternum (breastbone). This condition, clinically known as *gastroesophageal reflux* (*GER*), is commonly called **heartburn**. Many people take over-the-counter antacids to neutralize the HCl, thereby

enteric nervous system The nerves of the GI tract.

heartburn (gastroesophageal reflux [GER]) A painful sensation that occurs behind the sternum when hydrochloric acid backs up into the lower esophagus.

▶ **Figure 3.15** The mechanism of gastroesophageal reflux: acidic gastric juices seep backward through an open or relaxed sphincter into the lower portion of the esophagus, burning its lining. The pain is felt behind the sternum (breastbone), over the heart.

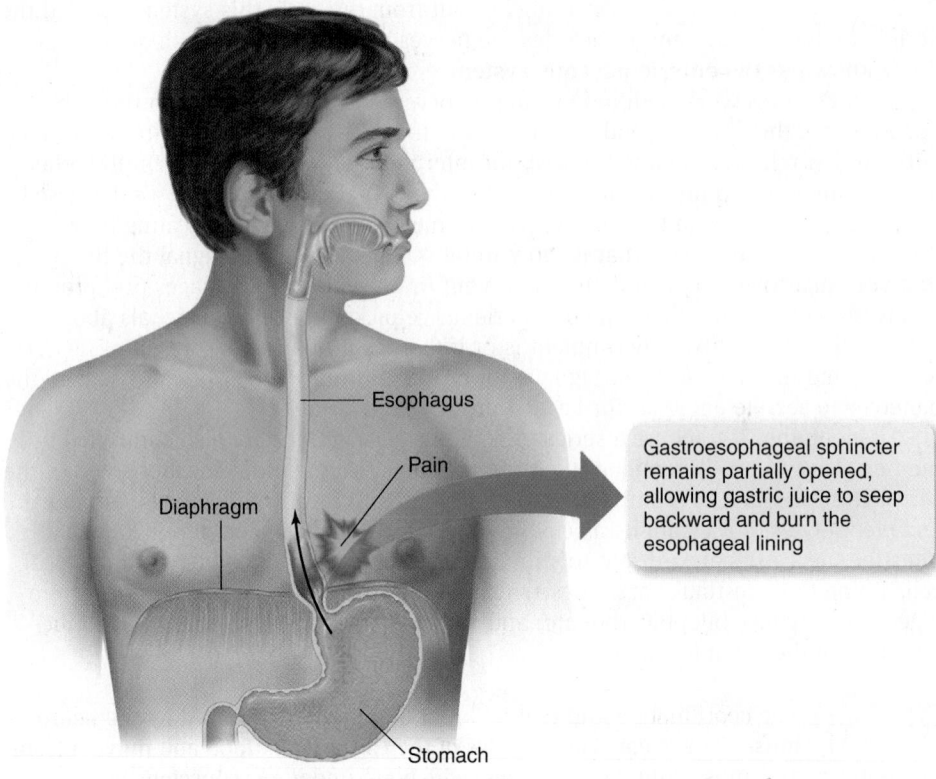

Esophagus

Pain

Diaphragm

Gastroesophageal sphincter remains partially opened, allowing gastric juice to seep backward and burn the esophageal lining

Stomach

gastroesophageal reflux disease (GERD) A more painful type of GER that occurs more than twice per week.

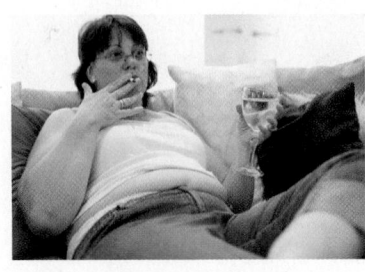

◀ Although the exact causes of gastroesophageal reflux disease (GERD) are unknown, smoking and being overweight may be contributing factors.

relieving the heartburn. A non-drug approach is to repeatedly swallow: this action causes any acid within the esophagus to be swept down into the stomach, eventually relieving the symptoms.

Gastroesophageal reflux disease (GERD) is a more painful type of GER that occurs more than twice per week. Like heartburn, it occurs when HCl flows backwards, from the stomach up into the esophagus. Although people who experience occasional GER usually have no structural abnormalities, many people with GERD have an overly relaxed or damaged lower esophageal sphincter or damage to the esophagus itself. Although the classic symptom of GERD is GER, with persistent heartburn and acid regurgitation, some people instead experience chest pain, trouble swallowing, burning in the mouth, the feeling that food is stuck in the throat, or hoarseness in the morning (NIDDK, 2007b).

The exact causes of GERD are unknown. However, a number of factors may contribute, including the following (NIDDK, 2007b):

- A *hiatal hernia*, which occurs when the upper part of the stomach lies above the diaphragm muscle. Normally, the horizontal diaphragm muscle separates the stomach from the chest cavity and helps keep acid from seeping into the esophagus. Stomach acid can more easily enter the esophagus in people with a hiatal hernia.
- Cigarette smoking
- Alcohol use
- Overweight
- Pregnancy
- Eating foods such as citrus fruits, chocolate, caffeinated drinks, fried foods, garlic and onions, spicy foods, and tomato-based foods, such as chili, pizza, and spaghetti sauce.
- Large, high-fat meals. These meals stay in the stomach longer and increase stomach pressure, making it more likely that acid will be pushed up into the esophagus.
- Lying down soon after a meal. In susceptible people, this is almost certain to bring on symptoms, since it positions the body so it is easier for the stomach acid to back up into the esophagus.

NUTRITION MYTH OR FACT?

Are Peptic Ulcers Caused by Stress, Alcohol, or Spicy Foods?

For decades, physicians believed that experiencing high levels of stress, drinking alcohol, and eating spicy foods were the primary factors responsible for peptic ulcers. But in 1982, Australian gastroenterologists Robin Warren and Barry Marshall detected the same species of bacteria in the majority of their ulcer patients' stomachs (Bauman, 2011). Treatment with an antibiotic effective against the bacterium, *Helicobacter pylori* (*H. pylori*), cured the ulcers. It is now known that *H. pylori* causes chronic inflammation and plays a key role in the development of most peptic ulcers as well as gastric (stomach) cancer (Wroblewski, Peek & Wilson, 2010). The hydrochloric acid (HCl) in gastric juice kills most bacteria, but *H. pylori* is unusual in that it thrives in acidic environments. Approximately 50% of people have strains of this bacterium in their stomachs, but most people do not develop ulcers or cancer (Wroblewski, Peek & Wilson, 2010). The reason for this is not known, but possible factors may include the level of HCl in gastric juices, immune responses, and the amount of sodium chloride (table salt) in people's diets

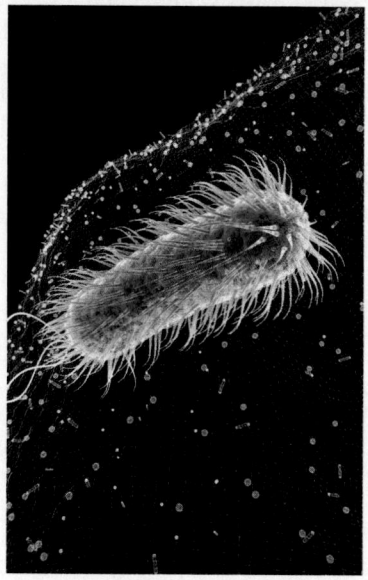

The *Helicobacter pylori* (*H. pylori*) bacterium plays a key role in the development of most peptic ulcers.

(Wroblewski, Peek & Wilson, 2010) Some studies suggest that high sodium diets encourage the expression or growth of *H. pylori* (Loh, Torres & Cover, 2007; Gancz, Jones & Merrell, 2008).

Because of the role of *H. pylori* in ulcer development, treatment usually involves antibiotics and acid-suppressing medications. Special diets and stress-reduction techniques are no longer typically recommended because they do not reduce acid secretion. However, people with ulcers should avoid specific foods they identify as causing them discomfort.

Although most peptic ulcers are caused by *H. pylori* infection, some are caused by prolonged use of non-steroidal anti-inflammatory drugs (NSAIDs); these drugs include pain relievers, such as aspirin, ibuprofen, and naproxen sodium. They appear to cause ulcers by suppressing the secretion of mucus and bicarbonate, which normally protect the stomach from its acidic gastric juice. Ulcers caused by NSAID use generally heal once a person stops taking the medication (NIDDK, 2004).

One way to reduce the symptoms of GERD is to identify the types of foods or situations that trigger episodes, and then avoid them. Eating smaller meals also helps. After a meal, wait at least three hours before lying down. Some people relieve their nighttime symptoms by elevating the head of their bed four to six inches—for instance, by placing a wedge between the mattress and the box spring. This keeps the chest area elevated and minimizes the amount of acid that can back up into the esophagus. People with GERD who smoke should stop, and, if they are overweight, they should lose weight. Taking an antacid before a meal can help prevent symptoms, and many other medications are now available to treat GERD.

It is important to treat GERD as it can cause serious health problems. GERD can lead to bleeding and ulcers in the esophagus. Scar tissue can develop in the esophagus, making swallowing very difficult. Some people can also develop a condition called Barrett's esophagus, which can lead to cancer. Asthma can also be aggravated or even caused by GERD.

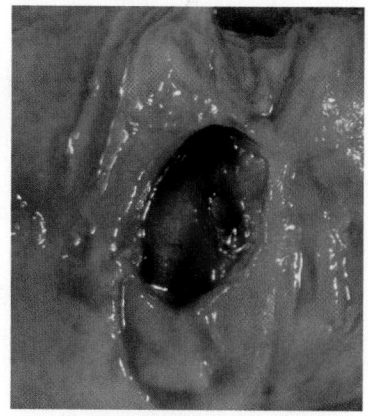

Figure 3.16 A peptic ulcer.

A Peptic Ulcer Is an Area of Erosion in the GI Tract

A **peptic ulcer** is an area of the GI tract that has been eroded away by a combination of hydrochloric acid and the enzyme pepsin **(Figure 3.16)**. In almost all cases, it is located in the stomach area (*gastric ulcer*) or the part of the duodenum closest to the stomach (*duodenal ulcer*). It causes a burning pain in the abdominal area, typically one to three hours after eating a meal. In serious cases, eroded blood vessels bleed

peptic ulcer An area of the GI tract that has been eroded away by the acidic gastric juice of the stomach.

⬆ When travelling, it is wise to avoid food from street vendors.

diarrhea A condition characterized by the frequent passage of loose, watery stools.

into the GI tract, causing vomiting of blood and/or blood in the stools, as well as anemia. If the ulcer entirely perforates the tract wall, stomach contents can leak into the abdominal cavity, causing a life-threatening infection.

You might have heard the advice that people with an ulcer should try to reduce their stress and avoid caffeine and spicy foods. But do these factors really cause or contribute to ulcers? Find the answer in the Nutrition Myth or Fact? box.

RECAP Heartburn is clinically known as gastroesophageal reflux (GER). It is caused by the seepage of gastric juices into the esophagus. Gastroesophageal reflux disease (GERD) is a more painful type of GER that occurs more than twice per week. Peptic ulcers are caused by erosion of the GI tract by hydrochloric acid and pepsin. Peptic ulcers are painful and can lead to serious health consequences such as internal bleeding, anemia, and potentially fatal infections. The two major causes of peptic ulcers are *Helicobacter pylori* infection and the use of non-steroidal anti-inflammatory drugs.

Some Disorders Affect Intestinal Function

GERD and ulcers involve the upper GI tract. In this section, we'll discuss disorders affecting intestinal function.

Diarrhea

Diarrhea is the frequent passage (more than three times in one day) of loose, watery stools. Other symptoms may include cramping, abdominal pain, bloating, nausea, fever, and blood in the stools. Diarrhea is usually caused by an infection of the gastrointestinal tract, a chronic disease, stress, or reactions to medications (NIDDK, 2007a). It can also occur as a reaction to a particular food or food ingredient. Disorders related to specific foods include food intolerances, allergies, and celiac disease. These are discussed **In Depth** following this chapter.

Whatever the cause, diarrhea can be harmful if it persists for a long period of time because the person can lose large quantities of water and minerals and become severely dehydrated. **Table 3.1** reviews the signs and symptoms of dehydration, which is particularly dangerous in infants and young children. In fact, a child can die from dehydration in just a few days. Adults, particularly the elderly, can also become dangerously ill if severely dehydrated. A doctor should be seen immediately if diarrhea persists for more than 24 hours in children or more than three days in adults or if diarrhea is bloody, fever is present, or there are signs of dehydration.

A condition referred to as *traveller's diarrhea* has become a common health concern due to the expansion in global travel. *Traveller's diarrhea* is experienced by people travelling to countries outside of their own and is usually caused by viral or bacterial infections. Diarrhea represents the body's way of ridding itself of an invasive agent. The large intestine and even some of the small intestine become irritated by the microbes and the body's defence against them. This irritation leads to increased secretion of fluid and increased motility of the large

TABLE 3.1 Signs and Symptoms of Dehydration in Adults and Children	
Symptoms in Adults	**Symptoms in Children**
Thirst	Dry mouth and tongue
Light-headedness	No tears when crying
Less frequent urination	No wet diapers for three hours or more
Dark coloured urine	High fever
Fatigue	Sunken abdomen, eyes, or cheeks
Dry skin	Irritable or listless Skin does not rebound when pinched and released

Data from National Digestive Diseases Information Clearinghouse (NDDIC). 2003. Diarrhea. NIH Publication No. 04–2749. http://digestive.niddk.nih.gov/ddiseases/pubs/diarrhea/index.htm.

intestine, causing watery and frequent bowel movements. In some cases, the person may also experience nausea, vomiting, and low-grade fever. Usually, people who are otherwise healthy recover completely within four to six days (DuPont, 2006).

People generally get traveller's diarrhea from consuming water or food that is contaminated with bacteria. Very risky foods include any raw or undercooked fish, meats, and raw fruits and vegetables. Tap water, ice made from tap water, and unpasteurized milk and dairy products are also common sources of infection.

QUICK TIPS

Avoiding Traveller's Diarrhea

- Do not drink tap water or use it to brush your teeth.
- Do not drink unpasteurized milk or dairy products.
- Do not use ice made from tap water. Freezing does not kill all microbes.
- Avoid raw or rare meats, and raw fruits and vegetables, including lettuce and fruit salads, unless they can be peeled and you peel them yourself.

- Do not eat meat or shellfish that is not hot when served.
- Do not eat food from street vendors.
- Do drink bottled water. Make sure you are the one to break the seal, and wipe the top of the bottle clean before doing so. You can also safely choose canned carbonated soft drinks and hot drinks made with boiling water, such as coffee or tea.
- Consult your doctor when planning your trip. Depending on where you are going and how long you will stay, your doctor may recommend that you take antibiotics before leaving to protect you from possible infection.

What can you do to prevent traveller's diarrhea? The Quick Tips from the National Institutes of Health should help (NIDDK, 2007a).

If you do suffer from traveller's diarrhea, it is important to replace the fluid and nutrients lost as a result of the illness. Specially formulated oral rehydration solutions are available in most countries. Antibiotics may also be taken to kill bacteria. Once treatment is initiated, the diarrhea should cease within two to three days. If the diarrhea persists for more than 10 days after the initiation of treatment, or if there is blood in your stools, you should see a physician immediately.

Constipation

At the opposite end of the spectrum from diarrhea is **constipation**, which is typically defined as a condition in which no stools are passed for two or more days; however, it is important to recognize that some people normally experience bowel movements only every second or third day. Thus, the definition of constipation varies from one person to another. In addition to being infrequent, the stools are usually hard, small, and somewhat difficult to pass.

The Bristol Stool Chart, shown in **Figure 3.17**, was developed at the University of Bristol and published in 1997 by the *Scandinavian Journal of Gastroenterology* (Lewis and Heaton, 1997). At the time, there was no simple way to assess "transit time"—whether intestinal contents were moving too quickly, normally, or too slowly—other than by asking people about the number of times a day or a week they had a "bowel movement" (i.e., the passed feces or stool). When the contents of the small and large intestine move too quickly (fast transit or short transit time), there is less time for nutrients to be fully digested and absorbed, for bacteria in the large intestine to ferment undigestible material and synthesize certain vitamins, and for nutrients and water to be reabsorbed (Lewis and Heaton, 1997), In contrast, when intestinal contents move too slowly (slow transit or long transit time) and the colon is holding fecal material, the growth of bacteria may be a problem and bile acid metabolism is impaired.

The Bristol Stool Chart is a way to assess and score the physical form of the feces, so that accurate diagnoses of diarrhea and constipation can be given, and changes in these conditions can be monitored during treatment. Types 1 and 2 indicate constipation, with types 3 and 4 considered to be "ideal stools", types 5 and 6 being "loose" stools, and type 7 indicating diarrhea. This way of categorizing the form and consistency of stool has been useful for people who have irritable bowel syndrome, which we will discuss in the next section.

Many people experience temporary constipation at some point in their lives, such as when they travel, when their schedule is disrupted, if they change their diet, or if they are on certain medications. Many healthcare providers suggest

constipation A condition characterized by the absence of bowel movements for a time that is significantly longer than normal for the individual. When a bowel movement does occur, stools are usually small, hard, and difficult to pass.

Consuming caffeinated drinks is one of several factors that have been linked with irritable bowel syndrome.

▶ **Figure 3.17** Bristol Stool Chart.
Source: Lewis S. J., Heaton K. W. (1997). "Stool form scale as a useful guide to intestinal transit time". *Scand. J. Gastroenterol.* 32(9): 920–4.

Bristol Stool Chart

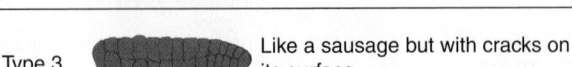

Type 1 — Separate hard lumps, like nuts (hard to pass)

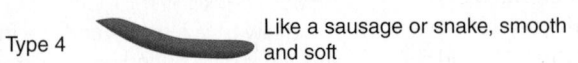

Type 2 — Sausage-shaped but lumpy

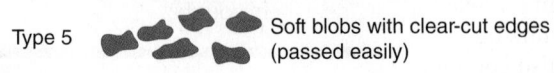

Type 3 — Like a sausage but with cracks on its surface

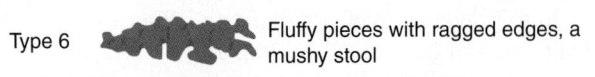

Type 4 — Like a sausage or snake, smooth and soft

Type 5 — Soft blobs with clear-cut edges (passed easily)

Type 6 — Fluffy pieces with ragged edges, a mushy stool

Type 7 — Watery, no solid pieces. **Entirely Liquid**

increasing fibre and fluid in the diet. Five to nine servings of fruits and vegetables each day and six or more servings of whole grains is recommended. If you eat breakfast cereal, make sure you buy a cereal containing at least 2 to 3 g of fibre per serving. The dietary recommendation for fibre and the role it plays in maintaining healthy elimination are discussed in detail in Chapter 4. Staying well hydrated is important when increasing your fibre intake. Regular exercise may also help reduce your risk for constipation.

Irritable Bowel Syndrome

irritable bowel syndrome (IBS)
A disorder of the large bowel or colon that interferes with normal functions of the colon.

Irritable bowel syndrome (IBS) is a disorder that interferes with the normal functions of the colon (commonly referred to as the "large bowel"). It is one of the most common medical diagnoses, and Canada is believed to have one of the highest rates of IBS in the world, with an estimated 5 million people affected (Canadian Digestive Health Foundation, 2011). More women than men appear to develop IBS. It may unexpectedly clear up for a long time and then reoccur. Symptoms include abdominal cramps, bloating, and either constipation or diarrhea. In some people with IBS, food moves too quickly through the colon and fluid cannot be absorbed fast enough, which causes diarrhea. In others, the movement of the colon is too slow and too much fluid is absorbed, leading to constipation.

IBS shows no sign of underlying disease that can be observed or measured. However, it appears that the colon is more sensitive to physiologic or emotional stress in people with IBS than in healthy people. Some researchers believe that the problem stems from conflicting messages between the central nervous system and the enteric nervous system. The immune system may also trigger symptoms of IBS. Approximately 30% of people with IBS developed it after some kind of infectious illness (Tobin et al., 2008). Recent research suggests that atopic disorders, which include asthma, food allergies, and eczema, are higher in people with IBS, and that there may be a specific subgroup of allergy and asthma sufferers who are susceptible to IBS (Tobin et al., 2008). Some of the foods thought to cause physiologic stress linked to IBS include caffeinated tea, coffee, and colas; chocolate; alcohol; dairy products; and wheat. Certain medications may also increase the risk.

If you think you have IBS, it is important to have a complete physical examination to rule out any other health problems, including celiac disease (see the **In Depth** essay at the end of this chapter). Treatment options include taking certain medications to treat diarrhea or constipation, managing stress, engaging in regular physical activity, eating smaller meals, avoiding foods that exacerbate symptoms, eating a higher-fibre diet, and drinking at least six to eight glasses of water each day (NIDDK, 2007c). Although IBS is uncomfortable, it does not appear to endanger long-term health. However, severe IBS can be disabling and can prevent people from leading normal lives; thus, accurate diagnosis and effective treatment are critical.

RECAP Diarrhea is the frequent passage of loose or watery stools. It should be treated quickly to avoid dehydration or even death. Constipation is failure to have a bowel movement within a time period that is normal for the individual. Irritable bowel syndrome (IBS) causes abdominal cramps, bloating, and constipation or diarrhea. The causes of IBS are unknown; however, physiologic and emotional stress are often involved.

Inflammatory Bowel Disease

Inflammatory bowel disease (IBD) describes two quite different diseases that cause inflammation (swelling and redness) in the intestines: Crohn's disease and ulcerative colitis. It's estimated that more than 250 000 men, women, and children in Canada suffer from IBD (Canadian Digestive Health Foundation, 2011). Recent research suggests that two specific bacteria (*Klebsiella pneumoniae* and *Proteus mirabilis*) may interact with the bacteria that naturally reside in the gut to trigger IBD among people with a genetic predisposition to the disease (Garrett et al., 2010).

In Crohn's disease, the last part of the small intestine, the end part of the ileum, is usually affected, but it can occur in patches in any part of the gastrointestinal tract. In 30% to 50% of cases, the colon or large bowel is also affected. The inflammation occurs in several layers of tissue through to the muscle, causing dilated blood vessels and extensive tissue damage. Sometimes the intestine becomes narrow and blocked, causing muscle spasms and requiring immediate medical attention. Because Crohn's disease affects the small intestine, the damage to the absorptive surface may interfere with nutrient absorption and lead to diarrhea, with unabsorbed fat (steatorrhea) and weight loss.

Ulcerative colitis usually involves only the colon and always begins at the anus or rectum and then continues up the colon for varying distances. The inflammation is generally limited to the inner mucosa of the colon, interfering with normal water reabsorption and frequently causing bloody diarrhea.

People with IBD need well-balanced diets, and may need vitamin and minerals supplements that include calcium, iron, and vitamin B_{12} (Canadian Digestive Health Foundation, 2011). The inflammation in both conditions can lead to muscle spasms, cramping, abdominal pain, and fever. When small amounts of blood are lost because of tears in the lining of the intestine and chronic bloody diarrhea, people can develop anemia over time. Inflammatory bowel disease may also be accompanied by other conditions, such as joint pain and arthritis, skin and mouth sores, liver disease, kidney stones, and eye inflammations. Surgery to remove badly damaged sections of the intestine or blockages is sometimes needed for people with inflammatory bowel disease.

inflammatory bowel disease (IBD) A term that includes two different autoimmune disorders with unknown causes that cause inflammation and swelling of the intestine: Crohn's disease and ulcerative colitis.

Nutrition DEBATE

Colon Cleansing: Does the Body Need Help Flushing Toxins Away?

Are you struggling with weight gain? Fatigue? Headaches? Sluggish bowel movements? Allergies? Joint pain? Recurring infections? Inability to concentrate? If so, have you ever thought that your symptoms might be due to a buildup of toxins in your colon, and that flushing out those toxins might cure you?

If you've read Chapter 1, you're probably thinking that this pitch sounds too good to be true. But isn't there something about it that seems sort of—logical? After all, the colon is the body's "solid waste disposal facility," so isn't it possible that toxins could build up in its tissues, and if so shouldn't regular cleansing be beneficial?

Before we consider the arguments for and against it, let's find out what colon cleansing really entails. In essence, the term refers to a single goal that can be achieved by any of several different activities. One form of colon cleansing is the use of standard enemas—often twice or even three times within a couple of hours—to force the expulsion of the contents of the colon. Another method is the consumption of laxative drugs or tablets, powders, or teas, some containing potent herbs. These either draw water into feces, making them easier to pass, or irritate the colon, promoting strong bowel contractions. Another method is the so-called detox liquid diet—such as the combination of water, lemon juice, maple syrup, and cayenne pepper that some pop stars have endorsed—which is supposed to be followed for a week to 10 days. A more sophisticated and expensive method, called *colonic irrigation*, is available only in clinics staffed by trained colonic therapists. In colonic irrigation, the person lies on a table while water (or a watery solution that may also contain herbs

or other substances) is pumped into the colon through a tube inserted in the rectum.

Supporters say that colon cleansing is beneficial because it removes toxins from the colon before they have a chance to enter the body. They claim that toxins enter the body in foods, water, and air—for instance, in pesticide residues and in chemicals that leach into foods from packaging materials. They say that such toxins build up on the walls of the colon and are readily absorbed into the bloodstream via the colon's lining cells. They conclude that these chemicals are responsible for a wide variety of health problems, including those listed earlier, as well as life-threatening illnesses, such as cancer.

So what does the research say about colon cleansing? Unfortunately, not much. There is very little evidence to either support or refute the claims for the benefits of this therapy (Mayo Clinic, 2009; WebMD, 2009).

Nonetheless, certain aspects of normal GI functioning suggest that colon cleansing is unnecessary. For instance, as you've learned in this chapter, helpful bacteria that are normal residents of the colon detoxify food wastes. In addition, both the liver and the kidneys remove blood-borne toxins, and lymph nodes cleanse harmful substances circulating in lymph. Moreover, the cells lining the colon are shed about every three days! Thus, physicians argue that your body doesn't need special procedures to protect against toxins.

So why do some people report improvements in health from colon cleansing? First, their positive response may be due in part to the placebo effect, which you learned about in Chapter 1. In addition, if they've been experiencing sluggish bowel movements, then simply emptying

the colon of its contents—toxins or no toxins—will relieve a wide range of symptoms. Also, liquid "detox" fasts may make adherents feel more spirited because they're consuming very little energy: voluntary calorie restriction can lead to heightened feelings of psychological well-being (Picco, 2008).

Finally, many physicians warn that colon cleansing regimes can be harmful. Their primary danger is dehydration, discussed in Chapter 7, which can seriously deplete the body of essential minerals. Other adverse effects include nausea, vomiting, cramps, an allergic reaction, and even bowel perforation (complete penetration of the intestinal wall). A safer alternative is a healthful intake of fibre from foods, such as fruits, vegetables, legumes, whole grains, and seeds, accompanied by an adequate fluid intake. These recommendations are discussed in more detail in Chapters 4 and 7.

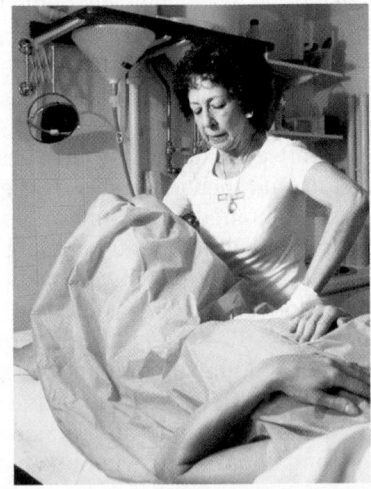

▲ The colonic irrigation, or "colon cleansing," procedure. There is currently little scientific evidence to either support or refute claims about its benefits.

Chapter Review

.Test Yourself ANSWERS

1. True. Sometimes we may have an appetite even though we are not hungry. These feelings are referred to as *cravings* and are associated with physical or emotional cues.

2. True. Although there are individual variations in how we respond to food, the entire process of

digestion and absorption of one meal usually takes about 24 hours.

3. True. Most ulcers result from an infection of the bacterium *Helicobacter pylori* (*H. pylori*). Contrary to popular belief, ulcers are not caused by stress or spicy food.

Find the Quack

When Petra left her home in the Czech Republic a year ago to enrol in an acting school in Los Angeles, she regarded her figure as *curvaceous*. Now when she looks in the mirror, she sees herself as *fat*. Convinced that she has been turned down at auditions because of her weight, she has been maintaining a strict high-protein, low-carbohydrate diet, plus diet pills and exercise, but the weight hasn't been coming off fast enough. What's more, she's constipated. At a step aerobics class, she sees a flyer recommending an all-natural weight-loss "tonic." The flyer states that the regular use of this "pleasant-tasting tonic" will take weight off and keep it off. It lists a website address where Petra can learn more. When Petra gets home, she goes online to the site. Here is what she reads:

- "Your colon can contain up to 25 pounds of undigested food and trapped fecal matter. Over time, these ferment and release toxins. Our patented tonic will flush this waste out of your body."

- "If you don't naturally have a bowel movement after every meal, then your intestines are very likely blocked. If you have difficulty losing weight, low energy, headaches, insomnia, bloating, or constipation, you almost certainly need our laxative tonic."

- "Our tonic was developed by a chemist and a nutritionist. It is a pleasant-tasting syrup containing a proprietary blend of organically grown herbs, roots, and other medicinals. Simply mix 2 tablespoons with a cup of pure water and drink each morning upon rising. Taken daily, it will help you maintain your new figure and trimmer waistline."

It will also increase your energy level, relieve headaches, help you sleep better, and prevent diseases of the digestive system."

- "Never before has it been so easy to eliminate up to 25 pounds of trapped wastes from your body! A 30-day supply is available for a limited time at the special price of just $29.99! That's less than a dollar a day to a slimmer, healthier you!"

1. Comment on the website's statements that the product was developed by a chemist and a nutritionist and that it is a "patented" formula containing a "proprietary" blend of ingredients.

2. In this chapter, you learned about the normal functions of digestion and elimination. Comment on the website's assertion "If you don't naturally have a bowel movement after every meal, then your intestines are very likely blocked."

3. Petra has been maintaining a diet high in meat, eggs, and other protein sources and low in carbohydrates, including fruits, vegetables, and grains. She has also been using diet pills, which typically act as diuretics, flushing fluids from the body. Could there be a link between these behaviours and her constipation? If so, identify the link.

4. If the tonic is actually just a very strong laxative, and Petra were to ingest the recommended dose daily, what do you think she might experience?

Answers can be found in the study area of MasteringNutrition.

Review Questions

1. Which of the following represents the levels of organization in the human body from smallest to largest?
   a. cells, molecules, atoms, tissues, organs, systems
   b. atoms, molecules, cells, organs, tissues, systems
   c. atoms, molecules, cells, tissues, organs, systems
   d. molecules, atoms, cells, tissues, organs, systems

2. Bile is a greenish fluid that
   a. is stored by the pancreas.
   b. is produced by the gallbladder.
   c. denatures proteins.
   d. emulsifies fats.

3. The region of brain tissue that is responsible for prompting us to seek food is the
   a. pituitary gland.
   b. cephalic phase.
   c. hypothalamus.
   d. peripheral nervous system.

4. Heartburn is caused by
   a. seepage of gastric acid into the esophagus.
   b. seepage of gastric acid into the cardiac muscle.
   c. seepage of bile into the stomach.
   d. seepage of salivary amylase into the stomach.

5. Most digestion of carbohydrates, fats, and proteins takes place in the
   a. mouth.
   b. stomach.
   c. small intestine.
   d. large intestine.

6. Early morning swim practices are hard on Mike, but they are important for the swim meet he has coming up next week. After completing the hour-long drill set, Mike's stomach is rumbling despite the breakfast he had before practice. Mike is hungry because of
   a. hunger, a psychological response.
   b. hunger, a physiologic response.
   c. appetite, a psychological response.
   d. appetite, a physiologic response.

7. Food is partially digested and churned in which organ?
   a. Large intestine
   b. Small intestine
   c. Stomach
   d. Mouth

8. Joyce is really excited to be on a weeklong cruise trip. Despite the lure of buffet-style meals every day, she's made a point of eating well during her vacation. At the breakfast buffet, Joyce surveys all the different types of entrees and sides she could choose from. The choices are endless! Everything looks so delicious! Since she knows that fruits and vegetables are rich in vitamins and minerals, Joyce approaches the fruit bar. She piles her plate with pineapple rings, honeydew chunks, grape clusters, kiwi slices, and a nice ripe banana. The bread section catches her eye and Joyce adds a whole-wheat bagel to her breakfast. Before returning to her seat to eat, she picks up a container of yogurt to accompany her fruit.
   a. At which point did Joyce undergo the cephalic phase of digestion?
   b. Her breakfast choice is high in vitamins and minerals. Where in the gastrointestinal system are these absorbed?
   c. Being on a trip, Joyce is at risk for traveller's diarrhea. What can she change in her breakfast to minimize her risk?

9. A person with celiac disease cannot tolerate foods containing or made from
   a. wheat, rye, and barley.
   b. seeds, nuts, and legumes.
   c. milk or milk products.
   d. phenylalanine.

10. Discuss some factors that can help prevent or relieve constipation.

11. Imagine the lining of your small intestine were smooth, like the inside of a rubber tube. Would this design be efficient in performing the main function of this organ? Why or why not? Why doesn't the acidic environment of the stomach cause it to digest itself?

12. After dinner, your roommate lies down to rest for a few minutes before studying. When he gets up, he complains of a sharp, burning pain in his chest. Offer a possible explanation for his pain.

Case Study

William is excited that his Grade 6 class is going on a trip to Ottawa to see the Parliament buildings and visit all the museums. At the last minute, however, William decides not to go because he is too embarrassed about his peanut allergy. Some girls in his class make fun of him for not being able to eat certain things, and he hates having to ask people not to eat peanut butter around him. Even worse, he is scared that the restaurants where they dine on the trip will not understand the severity of his condition and may accidentally contaminate his food with peanut products.

What strategy might William use to communicate his food allergy to servers at restaurants? What could he say to his classmates to give them a better understanding of why he cannot eat some foods? What other obstacles might William confront on a school trip because of his allergies?

Answers to Review Questions can be found at the back of this text.

Web Resources

www.ibsgroup.org/ibsassociation
Irritable Bowel Syndrome Self Help and Support Group

Visit this site for information on self-help measures and support for people diagnosed with IBS.

www.celiac.ca
Canadian Celiac Association

This website is a great resource for individuals who need to learn more about gluten-free diets.

www.cdhf.ca
Canadian Digestive Health Foundation

This website covers more than a dozen different digestive disorders, with information written by physicians.

www.badgut.org
Gastrointestinal Society, Canadian Society of Intestinal Research

This great website has lots of information for people suffering from digestive disorders.

www.ccfc.ca
Crohn's and Colitis Foundation of Canada

Another consumer-oriented website, this one is especially helpful for families with members suffering from Crohn's disease and ulcerative colitis.

www.hc-sc.gc.ca/hl-vs/iyh-vsv/index-eng.php
It's Your Health

Subscribe to this free bulletin from Health Canada that covers a wide range of health and safety topics, including diseases, lifestyle, and food.

digestive.niddk.nih.gov
National Digestive Diseases Information Clearinghouse (NDDIC)

Explore this site to learn more about diarrhea, celiac disease, irritable bowel syndrome (IBS), heartburn, and gastroesophageal reflux disease (GERD).

www.healthfinder.gov
Health Finder

Search this site to learn more about disorders related to digestion, absorption, and elimination.

www.nlm.nih.gov/medlineplus
MEDLINE Plus Health Information

Search "food allergies" to obtain additional resources as well as the latest news about food allergies.

www.foodinsight.org
International Food Information Council Foundation

Search for "food allergies" to come to a resource page for additional information of food allergies.

www.gfmall.com
Gluten-Free Mall

Find out where you can buy gluten-free products.

MasteringNutrition®

Assignments

Animations Basic Absorption Mechanisms • Overview of Digestion & Absorption • Control of Appetite: Hunger & Satiety
Activities NutriTools

Study Area

Video: Understanding Digestion & Absorption • Practice Tests • Diet Analysis • eText

Disorders Related to Specific Foods Related to Specific Foods

WANT TO FIND OUT...

- what the difference is between a food intolerance and a food allergy?

- which handful of foods are responsible for over 90% of all food allergies?

- why some people can't eat even a crumb of bread?

READ ON.

Trying to decide between two brands of energy bars, you compare their lists of ingredients. You notice that one of the bars has the statement "*May contain nuts", although no nuts are listed on the ingredient list. The other warns, "Contains wheat, milk, and soy." Why all the warnings? The reason is that, to some people, consuming these normally healthful foods can be dangerous, even life-threatening.

Disorders related to specific foods can be clustered into three main groupings: food intolerances, food allergies, and a genetic disorder called celiac disease. We discuss these disorders *In Depth* here.

Food Intolerances

A **food intolerance** is a cluster of GI symptoms (often gas, pain, and diarrhea) that occur following the consumption of a particular food. Commonly intolerance results when the body does not produce enough of the enzymes it needs to break down certain food components before they reach the colon. The immune system plays no role in intolerance, and, although episodes are unpleasant, they are usually transient, resolving after the offending food has been eliminated from the GI tract. People can have an intolerance to milk, wheat, soy, or other foods, but in all cases the symptoms can be prevented by avoiding the offending foods.

A common food intolerance is **lactose intolerance**, in which the cells lining the small intestine do not produce sufficient amounts of the enzyme lactase to digest foods containing the milk sugar *lactose*. Lactose intolerance should not be confused with a milk allergy. People who are allergic to milk experience an immune reaction to the proteins found in cow's milk. Symptoms of milk allergy include skin reactions, intestinal distress, and respiratory symptoms. In contrast, symptoms of lactose intolerance are limited to the GI tract and include intestinal gas, bloating, cramping, nausea, diarrhea, and discomfort. These symptoms resolve spontaneously within a few hours.

Although some infants are born with lactose intolerance, it is more common to see lactase enzyme activity decrease after two years of age. In fact, it is estimated that up to 70% of the world's adult population lose some ability to digest lactose as they age. Lactose intolerance is more common in Aboriginal, Asian, Hispanic, and African American adults than in Caucasians.

Not everyone experiences lactose intolerance to the same extent. Many people who report being lactose intolerant are able to tolerate multiple small servings of dairy products without symptoms (NIDDK, 2009). These people do not need to avoid all dairy products; they may simply need to eat smaller amounts and experiment to find foods that do not cause intestinal distress. Other people will experience symptoms after consuming minute amounts of lactose. These individuals should avoid not only all dairy products but also hidden sources of lactose in processed foods. If any of the following ingredients appears on a food label, the product contains lactose: milk, lactose, whey, curds, milk by-products, dry milk solids, or non-fat dry milk powder. Lactose is also used as a filler in some prescription and over-the-counter medications (NIDDK, 2009).

People with lactose intolerance need to find foods that can supply enough calcium for normal growth, development, and maintenance of bones. Many can tolerate specially formulated milk products that are low in lactose, whereas others take pills or use drops that contain the lactase enzyme when they eat dairy products. Calcium-fortified soy milk and orange juice are good substitutes for cow's milk. Many lactose-intolerant people can also digest aged cheese and yogurt with live and active cultures, as the moulds or bacteria used in these products break down the lactose during processing.

How can you tell if you are lactose intolerant? Many people discover that they have problems digesting dairy products by trial and error. But because intestinal gas, bloating, and diarrhea may indicate other health problems, you should consult a physician to determine the cause.

A common test for lactose intolerance in adults is a hydrogen breath test. First, the patient drinks a lactose-rich beverage. The breath is then analysed at regular intervals to measure the amount of hydrogen. Undigested lactose produces high levels of hydrogen, which suggests the diagnosis of lactose intolerance. In children, a stool sample is usually tested for levels of acids and other substances associated with undigested lactose (NIDDK, 2009). For those diagnosed with lactose intolerance, a consultation

For people who are lactose intolerant, milk products, such as ice cream, are difficult to digest.

with a registered dietitian may help in designing a diet that provides adequate nutrients.

Food Allergies

A **food allergy** is a hypersensitivity reaction of the immune system to a particular component (usually a protein) in a food. In some individuals, a new food protein will cause the body's immune system to respond by producing antibodies called immunoglobin E (IgE) (Health Canada, 2010). The next time the person is exposed to the same protein, the body releases IgE antibodies and powerful chemicals such as histamine, which can affect the gastrointestinal system, respiratory system, skin, or cardiovascular system (Health Canada, 2010). Allergic reactions can range from red and itchy skin, to swelling of the eyes, lips, tongue, and throat, to vomiting, to a drop in blood pressure and shock (CFIA, 2010). These reactions might

---

food intolerance Gastrointestinal discomfort caused by certain foods that is not a result of an immune system reaction.

lactose intolerance A disorder in which the body does not produce enough lactase enzyme to break down the sugar lactose, which is found in milk and milk products.

food allergy An inflammatory reaction to food generally caused by an immune system hypersensitivity.

▲ For some people, eating a meal of grilled shrimp with peanut sauce would cause a severe allergic reaction.

be immediate or in some cases they may take hours or days to appear. It is thought that up to 1.2 million Canadians may have food allergies, and the number of children experiencing food allergies appears to be growing worldwide (CFIA, 2010). In developed countries, an estimated 5%–6% of children and 3%–4% of adults have a food allergy. Although this makes them much less common than food intolerances, food allergies can be far more serious.

You may have heard stories of people being allergic to foods as common as peanuts. This is the case for Liz. She was out to dinner with her parents, celebrating her birthday, when the dessert cart came around. The caramel custard looked heavenly and was probably a safe choice, but she asked the waiter just to be sure that it contained no peanuts. He checked with the chef, then returned and assured her that, no, the custard was peanut-free—but within minutes of consuming it, Liz's skin became flushed, and she struggled to breathe. As her parents were dialing 911, she lost consciousness. Fortunately, the paramedics arrived within minutes and were able to resuscitate her. It was subsequently determined that, unknown to the chef, the spoon that his prep cook had used to scoop the baked custard into serving bowls had been resting on a cutting board where

he had chopped peanuts for a different dessert. Just this small exposure to peanuts was enough to cause a severe allergic reaction in Liz.

How can a food that most people consume regularly, such as peanuts, shellfish, eggs, or milk, cause another person's immune system to react so violently? In Liz's case, a trace amount of peanut stimulated immune cells throughout her body to release their inflammatory chemicals. In some people, the inflammation is localized, so the damage is limited.

For instance, some people's mouth and throat itch when they eat cantaloupe, whereas others develop a rash whenever they eat eggs. What made Liz's experience so terrifyingly different was that the inflammation was widespread, affecting essentially all of her body systems and sending her into a state called *anaphylactic shock*. Left untreated, anaphylactic shock is nearly always fatal, so many people with known food allergies carry with them a kit containing an injection of a powerful stimulant called epinephrine. This drug can reduce symptoms long enough to buy the victim time to get emergency medical care.

Physicians use a variety of tests to diagnose food allergies. Usually, the physician orders a skin test, commonly known as a "scratch test," in which a clinician swabs a small amount of fluid containing the suspected allergen onto the patient's skin, then lightly scratches or pricks the area so that the fluid seeps under the patient's skin. After 15–20 minutes, the clinician checks the area: redness and/or swelling indicates that the patient is allergic to the substance. However, people can have a positive response with allergy skin testing yet not have any problems with the specific substance in daily life (NIH, 2009). Thus, some physicians will perform a blood test, in which a sample of the patient's blood is tested for the presence of unique proteins, called *antibodies*, that the immune system produces in a person with an allergy. In Liz's case, the blood test detected antibodies specific to peanut allergen.

Beware of e-mail spam, Internet websites, and ads in popular magazines attempting to link a vast assortment of health problems to food allergies. Typically, these ads offer allergy-testing services for exorbitant fees, then make even more money by selling "nutritional counselling" and sometimes supplements and other products they say will help you cope with your allergies. If you suspect you might have a food allergy, consult a physician.

Health Canada, the Canadian Food Inspection Agency (CFIA), and medical experts have agreed upon 10 foods or substances that are the most common causes of food allergies (Health Canada, 2011). These "priority food allergens" are: peanuts, tree nuts (e.g., Brazil nut, hazelnut), sesame seeds, soy, milk, eggs, seafood (fish, crustaceans, and shellfish), wheat and other cereal grains that contain gluten, mustard, and sulphites. Information for consumers on these 10 allergens can be downloaded from www.inspection.gc.ca/english/fssa/labeti/allerg/allerge.shtml.

As we learned in Chapter 2, food labels on packaged products must include a list of ingredients in a product, in descending order by weight. The CFIA looks for "undeclared allergens"—that is, food allergens that are in a product but have not been listed on its labels—to protect consumers from life-threatening allergic reactions. When they discover undeclared allergens, they issue a recall of the food product and a warning to the public is posted on the CFIA website.

Health Canada has a Food Allergen Program that conducts research into new laboratory methods for detecting undeclared allergens in food products. To help affected consumers avoid products that pose a risk, new labelling requirements were announced by the federal government in February 2011, coming into effect on August 4, 2012. Some of the requirements for manufacturers follow (Health Canada, 2011):

- food allergens, gluten, and sulphites must be identified in the ingredient list or by a statement

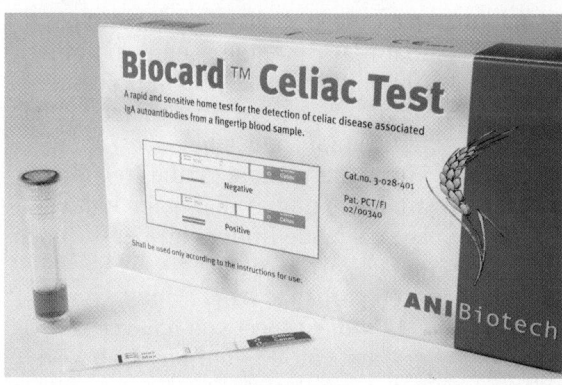

⬆ A simple blood test can identify celiac disease.

following the ingredient list that states "Contains: …" (e.g., "Contains; milk and peanuts")
- the food allergen or source of gluten must be listed using common words, such as "milk" or "wheat" or "hydrolyzed vegetable protein (soy)"

- sulphites in amounts above 10 parts per million must be declared
- if gluten or allergens are used in wax coatings on packaged fruits and vegetables, these must be declared on labels

The government hopes that these stricter labelling requirements will result in fewer food recalls and fewer serious reactions for consumers.

Celiac Disease

Celiac disease, also known as *celiac sprue*, is a disease that severely damages the lining of the small intestine and interferes with the absorption of nutrients. It is classified as an *autoimmune* disease; that is, the body's own immune system causes the destruction. Because there is a strong genetic predisposition to celiac disease, with the risk now linked to specific gene markers, it is also considered a genetic disorder. It is estimated that about 1 in 200 Canadians have celiac disease, but some researchers believe the prevalence is considerably higher (Canadian Society of Intestinal Research, 2012).

In celiac disease, the offending food component is *gliadin*, a fraction of a protein, called *gluten*, that

---

celiac disease An autoimmune disorder characterized by an inability to absorb a component of gluten called gliadin. This causes an inflammatory immune response that damages the lining of the small intestine.

⬆ Schoolchildren may have celiac disease and not know it. Undiagnosed celiac disease can lead to physical and mental disorders as children grow.

is found in wheat, rye, barley, and triticale. When people with celiac disease eat one of these grains, their immune system triggers an inflammatory response that erodes the villi of the small intestine. If the person is unaware of the disorder and continues to eat gluten, repeated immune reactions cause the villi to become greatly decreased, and there is less absorptive surface area. As a result, the person becomes unable to absorb certain nutrients properly—a condition known as *malabsorption*. Over time, malabsorption can lead to malnutrition (poor nutrient status). Deficiencies of iron, folic acid, calcium, and vitamins A, D, E, and K are common in those suffering from celiac disease (NIH, 2004).

Symptoms of celiac disease often mimic those of other intestinal disturbances, such as irritable bowel syndrome, so the condition is often misdiagnosed. Some of the symptoms of celiac disease are fatty stools (due to poor fat absorption); frequent stools, either watery or hard, with an odd odour; cramping; anemia; pallor; weight loss; fatigue; and irritability. However, some individuals have other symptoms that or which do not appear to involve the GI tract. These include an intensely itchy rash with blisters called *dermatitis herpetiformis,* osteoporosis (poor bone density), and infertility.

Diagnostic tests for celiac disease include a variety of blood tests that screen for the presence of antibodies to gluten, or for the genetic markers of the disease. Although the antibody test is considered generally reliable for diagnosing celiac disease, false negatives are not uncommon. Thus, the "gold standard" for diagnosis is a biopsy of the small intestine showing atrophy of the intestinal villi—the villi become flattened and there is less surface area for nutrients to be absorbed. Because one of the long-term complications of undiagnosed celiac disease is an increased risk for intestinal cancer, early diagnosis can be life-saving. Unfortunately, celiac disease is widely underdiagnosed. This is one

reason that some researchers and healthcare professionals favour screening school-age children for celiac disease, as is common in several European countries.

Currently, there is no cure for celiac disease. Treatment is with a special diet that excludes all forms of wheat, rye, barley, and triticale. Oats are allowed, but they are often contaminated with wheat flour from processing, and even a microscopic amount of gluten can cause an immune response. The diet is made

even more challenging by the fact that many binding agents and other unfamiliar ingredients in processed foods are derived from gluten. Thus, nutritional counselling is essential. Fortunately, more gluten-free foods are becoming available, including breads made from corn, rice, tapioca, potato, arrowroot, cassava, soy, and even garbanzo bean flours.

If you suspect you have celiac disease, consult your physician. Do not simply attempt to eliminate gluten from your diet, since if you then

For people with celiac disease, corn is a gluten-free source of carbohydrates.

decide to undergo antibody screening, being on a gluten-free diet will invalidate the results of the test. Moreover, a gluten-free diet is notoriously difficult to maintain without appropriate nutritional counselling and support.

Web Resources

www.nlm.nih.gov/medlineplus
MEDLINE Plus Health Information

Search for "food allergies" to obtain additional resources as well as the latest news about food allergies.

www.healthfinder.gov
Health Finder

Search this site to learn more about disorders related to digestion, absorption, and elimination.

www.celiac.ca
Canadian Celiac Association

This is a great resource for individuals who need to follow gluten-free diets.

www.cdhf.ca
Canadian Digestive Health Foundation

This website covers more than a dozen different digestive disorders, with information written by physicians.

www.badgut.org
Gastrointestinal Society, Canadian Society of Intestinal Research

This great website has lots of information for people suffering from digestive disorders.

www.gfmall.com
Gluten-Free Mall

Find out where you can buy gluten-free products.

4

Carbohydrates: Plant-Derived Energy Nutrients

CHAPTER OBJECTIVES

After reading this chapter you will be able to:

1. Describe the difference between simple and complex carbohydrates, pp. 113–117.

2. List four functions of carbohydrates in our body, pp. 117–119.

3. Discuss how carbohydrates are digested and absorbed by our body, pp. 120–122.

4. Define the Acceptable Macronutrient Distribution Range for carbohydrates, and the Adequate Intake for fibre, pp. 126, 129–130, 132.

5. Identify the potential health risks associated with diets high in refined sugars, pp. 127–129.

6. List five foods that are good sources of carbohydrates, pp. 130–131.

7. Identify three alternative sweeteners, pp. 134–135.

Test Yourself

1. (T) (F) Diets high in sugar cause hyperactivity in children.

2. (T) (F) Carbohydrates cause obesity.

3. (T) (F) Alternative sweeteners, such as aspartame, are safe for us to consume.

Test Yourself answers can be found at the end of the chapter.

W

hen Khalil lived at home, he snacked on whatever was around. That typically meant fresh fruit or his mom's homemade flatbread, and either plain water or skim milk. His parents never drank soft drinks, and the only time he ate sweets was on special occasions. Now Khalil is living on campus. When he gets hungry between classes, he visits the snack shack in the Student Union Building for one of their awesome chocolate-chunk cookies, a cinnamon roll, or a brownie and washes it down with a large cola. Studying at night, he munches on cheese curls or corn chips and drinks more cola to help him stay awake. Not surprisingly, Khalil has noticed lately that his clothes feel tight. When he steps on the scale, he's shocked to discover that, since starting college three months ago, he's gained 7 pounds!

Several popular diets—including the Zone Diet, Sugar Busters, and Dr. Atkins' New Diet Revolution—claim that carbohydrates are bad for your health. They recommend reducing carbohydrate consumption and eating more protein and fat (Atkins, 1992; Sears, 1995; Steward et al., 1995). Is this good advice? If you had a friend like Khalil who regularly consumed several soft drinks a day, plus chips, cookies, candy, and other high-carbohydrate snacks, would you say anything? Are carbohydrates a health menace, and is one type of carbohydrate as bad as another?

In this chapter, we'll explore the differences between simple and complex carbohydrates and learn why some carbohydrates really are better than others. We'll also learn how the human body breaks down carbohydrates and uses them to maintain our health and to fuel our activity and exercise. In the *In Depth* essay following this chapter, we'll discuss the relationship between carbohydrate intake and diabetes.

What Are Carbohydrates?

As we mentioned in Chapter 1, carbohydrates are one of the three macronutrients. As such, they are an important energy source for the entire body and are the preferred energy source for nerve cells, including those of the brain. We will say more about their functions later in this chapter.

The term carbohydrate literally means "hydrated carbon." Water (H_2O) is made of hydrogen and oxygen, and, when something is said to be *hydrated*, it contains water. Thus, the chemical abbreviation for carbohydrate (CHO) indicates the atoms it contains: **c**arbon, **h**ydrogen, and **o**xygen.

We obtain carbohydrates predominantly from plant foods, such as fruits, vegetables, and grains. Plants make the most abundant form of carbohydrate, called **glucose**, through a process called **photosynthesis**. During photosynthesis, the green pigment of plants, called *chlorophyll*, absorbs sunlight, which provides the energy needed to fuel the manufacture of glucose. As shown in **Figure 4.1**, water absorbed from the earth by the roots of plants combines with the carbon dioxide present in the leaves to produce the carbohydrate glucose. Plants continually store glucose and use it to support their own growth. Then, when we eat plant foods, our body digests, absorbs, and uses the stored glucose.

Carbohydrates can be classified as *simple* or *complex*. These terms are used to describe carbohydrates based on the number of molecules of sugar present (Topping & Clifton, 2001). Simple carbohydrates contain either one or two

glucose The most abundant sugar molecule, a monosaccharide generally found in combination with other sugars; it is the preferred source of energy for the brain and an important source of energy for all cells.

photosynthesis The process by which plants use sunlight to fuel a chemical reaction that combines carbon dioxide and water into glucose, which is then stored in their cells.

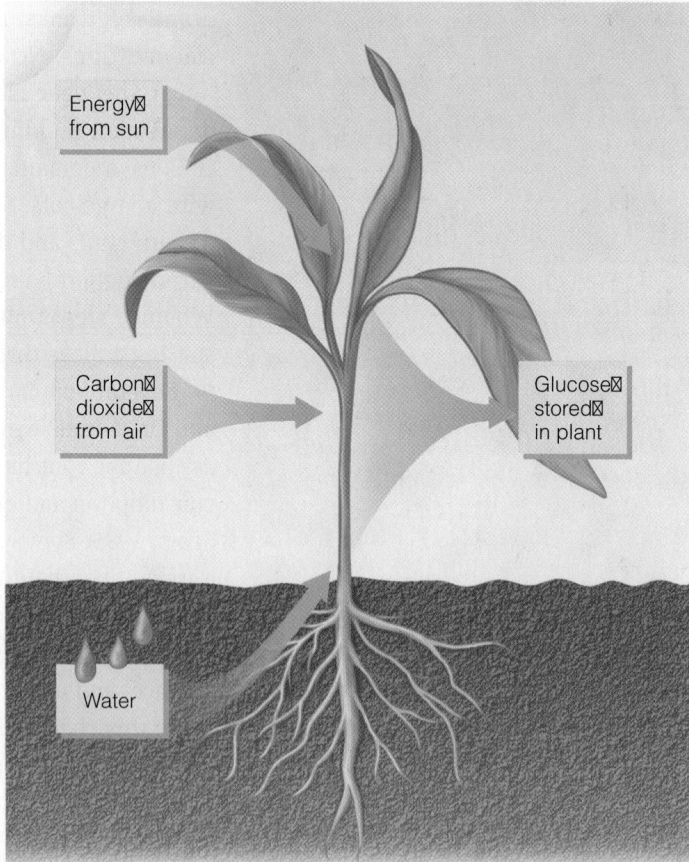

Figure 4.1 Plants make carbohydrates through the process of photosynthesis. Water, carbon dioxide, and energy from the sun are combined to produce glucose.

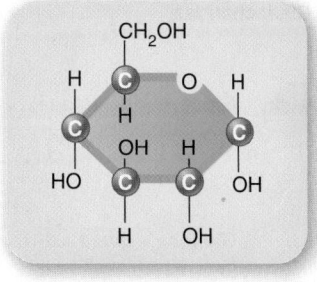 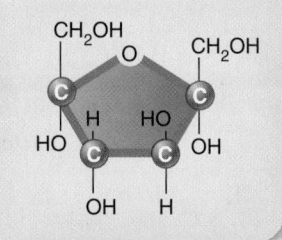 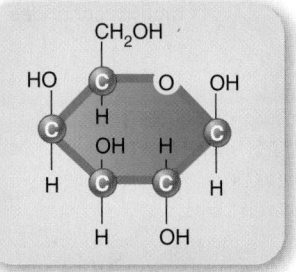

Glucose
Most abundant sugar molecule in our diet; good energy source

Fructose
Sweetest natural sugar; found in fruit, high-fructose corn syrup

Galactose
Does not occur alone in foods; binds with glucose to form lactose

◀ **Figure 4.2** The three most common monosaccharides. Notice that all three contain identical atoms: six carbon, twelve hydrogen, and six oxygen. It is only the arrangement of these atoms that differs among them.

molecules, whereas complex carbohydrates contain hundreds to thousands of molecules.

Simple Carbohydrates Include Monosaccharides and Disaccharides

Simple carbohydrates are commonly referred to as *sugars*. Four of these sugars are called **monosaccharides** because they consist of a single sugar molecule (*mono* means "one," and *saccharide* means "sugar"). The other three sugars are **disaccharides**, which consist of two molecules of sugar joined together (*di* means "two").

Glucose, Fructose, Galactose, and Ribose Are Monosaccharides

Glucose, fructose, and *galactose* are the three most common monosaccharides in our diet. Each of these monosaccharides contains six carbon atoms, twelve hydrogen atoms, and six oxygen atoms (**Figure 4.2**). Very slight differences in the arrangement of the atoms in these three monosaccharides cause major differences in their levels of sweetness.

Given what you have just learned about how plants manufacture glucose, it probably will not surprise you to discover that glucose is the most abundant sugar molecule in our diets and in our body. Glucose does not generally occur by itself in foods, but attaches to other sugars to form disaccharides and complex carbohydrates. In our body, glucose is the preferred source of energy for the brain, and it is a very important source of energy for all cells.

Fructose, the sweetest natural sugar, is found in fruits and vegetables. Fructose is also called *levulose*, or *fruit sugar*. In many processed foods, it comes in the form of *high-fructose corn syrup*. This syrup is manufactured from corn and is used to sweeten soft drinks, desserts, candies, and jellies.

Galactose does not occur alone in foods. It joins with glucose to create lactose, one of the three most common disaccharides.

Ribose is a five-carbon monosaccharide. Very little ribose is found in our diets; our body produces ribose from the foods we eat, and ribose is contained in the genetic material of our cells: deoxyribonucleic acid (DNA) and ribonucleic acid (RNA).

Lactose, Maltose, and Sucrose Are Disaccharides

The three most common disaccharides found in foods are *lactose, maltose,* and *sucrose* (**Figure 4.3**). **Lactose** (also called *milk sugar*) consists of one glucose molecule and one galactose molecule. Interestingly, human breast milk has more lactose than cow's milk does, making human breast milk taste sweeter.

▲ In our body, glucose is the preferred source of energy for the brain.

simple carbohydrate Commonly called sugar; can be either a monosaccharide (such as glucose) or a disaccharide.

monosaccharide The simplest of carbohydrates, consisting of one sugar molecule, the most common form of which is glucose.

disaccharide A carbohydrate compound consisting of two sugar molecules joined together.

fructose The sweetest natural sugar; a monosaccharide that occurs in fruits and vegetables; also called levulose, or fruit sugar.

galactose A monosaccharide that joins with glucose to create lactose, one of the three most common disaccharides.

ribose A five-carbon monosaccharide that is located in the genetic material of cells.

lactose A disaccharide consisting of one glucose molecule and one galactose molecule. It is found in milk, including human breast milk; also called milk sugar.

▶ **Figure 4.3** Galactose, glucose, and fructose join together to make the disaccharides lactose, maltose, and sucrose.

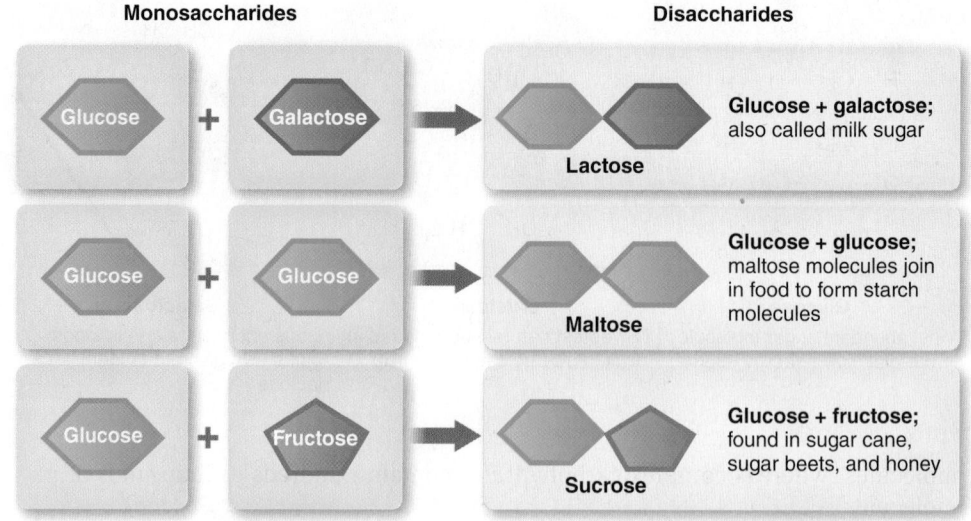

Monosaccharides

Disaccharides

Glucose + **Galactose** → **Glucose + galactose;** also called milk sugar
Lactose

Glucose + **Glucose** → **Glucose + glucose;** maltose molecules join in food to form starch molecules
Maltose

Glucose + **Fructose** → **Glucose + fructose;** found in sugar cane, sugar beets, and honey
Sucrose

maltose A disaccharide consisting of two molecules of glucose. It does not generally occur independently in foods but results as a by-product of digestion; maltose is also called malt sugar.

fermentation A process in which an agent causes an organic substance to break down into simpler substances and results in the production of ATP.

sucrose A disaccharide composed of one glucose molecule and one fructose molecule; sucrose is sweeter than lactose or maltose.

complex carbohydrate A nutrient compound consisting of long chains of glucose molecules, such as starch, glycogen, and fibre.

polysaccharide A complex carbohydrate consisting of long chains of glucose.

starch A polysaccharide stored in plants; the storage form of glucose in plants.

Maltose (also called *malt sugar*) consists of two molecules of glucose. It does not generally occur by itself in foods but, rather, is bound together with other molecules. As our body breaks these larger molecules down, maltose results as a by-product. Maltose is also the sugar that is fermented during the production of beer and liquor products. **Fermentation** is a process in which an agent, such as yeast, causes an organic substance to break down into simpler substances and results in the production of the energy molecule adenosine triphosphate (ATP). Maltose is formed during the breakdown of sugar in grains and other foods into alcohol. Contrary to popular belief, very little maltose remains in alcoholic beverages after the fermentation process is complete; thus, alcoholic beverages are not good sources of carbohydrate.

Sucrose is composed of one glucose molecule and one fructose molecule. Because sucrose contains fructose, it is sweeter than lactose or maltose. Sucrose provides much of the sweet taste found in honey, maple syrup, fruits, and vegetables. Table sugar, brown sugar, powdered sugar, and many other products are made by refining the sucrose found in sugarcane and sugar beets. Are honey and other naturally occurring forms of sucrose more healthful than manufactured forms? The Nutrition Myth or Fact? box investigates this question.

RECAP Carbohydrates contain carbon, hydrogen, and oxygen. Plants make one type of carbohydrate, glucose, through the process of photosynthesis. Simple carbohydrates include monosaccharides and disaccharides. Glucose, fructose, and galactose are monosaccharides; lactose, maltose, and sucrose are disaccharides.

Polysaccharides Are Complex Carbohydrates

Complex carbohydrates, the second major type of carbohydrate, generally consist of long chains of glucose molecules called **polysaccharides** (*poly* means "many"). They include starch, glycogen, and most fibres (**Figure 4.4**).

Starch Is a Polysaccharide Stored in Plants

Plants store glucose not as single molecules but as polysaccharides in the form of **starch**. Excellent food sources of starch include grains (wheat, rice, corn, oats, and barley), legumes (peas, beans, and lentils), and tubers (potatoes and yams). Our cells cannot use the complex starch molecules exactly as they exist in plants. Instead, our body must break them down into the monosaccharide glucose, from which we can then meet our energy needs.

Our body easily digests most starches; however, some starches in plants are not digestible and are called *resistant*. Technically, resistant starch is classified

NUTRITION MYTH OR FACT?

Is Honey More Nutritious Than Table Sugar?

Liz's friend Tiffany is dedicated to eating healthful foods. She advises Liz to avoid sucrose and to eat foods that contain honey, molasses, or raw sugar. Like many people, Tiffany believes these sweeteners are more natural and nutritious than refined table sugar. How can Liz sort sugar fact from fiction?

Remember that sucrose consists of one glucose molecule and one fructose molecule joined together. From a chemical perspective, honey is almost identical to sucrose, since honey also contains glucose and fructose molecules in almost equal amounts. However, enzymes in bees' "honey stomachs" separate some of the glucose and fructose molecules, resulting in honey looking and tasting slightly different than sucrose. Bees store honey in combs and fan it with their wings to reduce its moisture content. This also alters the appearance and texture of honey.

Honey does not contain any more nutrients than sucrose, so it is not a more healthful choice than sucrose. In fact, per tablespoon, honey has more energy than table sugar. This is because the crystals in table sugar take up more space on a spoon than the liquid form of honey, so a tablespoon contains less sugar. However, some people argue that honey is sweeter, so you use less.

It is important to note that honey commonly contains bacteria that can cause fatal food poisoning in infants. The more mature digestive system of older children and adults is immune to the effects of these bacteria, but babies younger than 12 months should never be given honey.

Are raw sugar and molasses more healthful than table sugar? Actually, the "raw sugar" available in Canada is not really raw. Truly raw sugar is made up of the first crystals obtained when sugar is processed. Sugar in this form contains dirt, parts of insects, and other by-products that make it illegal to sell in Canada. The raw sugar products in Canadian stores have actually gone through more than half of the same steps in the refining process used to make table sugar. Raw sugar has a coarser texture than white sugar and is unbleached; in most markets, it is also significantly more expensive.

Molasses is the syrup that remains when sucrose is made from sugar cane. It is reddish brown in colour

with a distinctive taste that is less sweet than table sugar. It does contain some iron, but this iron does not occur naturally. It is a contaminant from the machines that process the sugar cane! Incidentally, blackstrap molasses is the residue of a third boiling of the syrup. It contains less sugar than light or dark molasses but more minerals.

Table 4.1 compares the nutrient content of white table sugar, raw sugar, honey, and blackstrap molasses. As you can see, none of them contains many nutrients that are important for health. This is why highly sweetened products are referred to as "empty calories."

TABLE 4.1 Nutrient Comparison of Four Different Sugars

	Table Sugar	Honey	Molasses	Maple Syrup
Energy (kcal)	64.000	65.000	62.000	54.0000
Energy (kj)	267.000	273.000	257.000	226.0000
Carbohydrate (g)	16.800	17.700	15.860	13.4500
Fat (g)	0	0	0.020	0.0300
Protein (g)	0	0.060	0	0
Fibre (g)	0	0	0	0
Vitamin C (mg)	0	0.100	0	0
Vitamin A (RAE) μg	0	0	0	0
Thiamin (mg)	0.001	0	0.009	0.0035
Riboflavin (mg)	0.009	0.008	0	0.1465
Folate (μg)	1.000	0	0	0
Calcium (mg)	5.000	1.000	44.000	14.5000
Iron (mg)	0.150	0.090	1.000	0.2400
Sodium (mg)	14.000	1.000	8.000	2.5000
Potassium (mg)	13.000	11.000	311.000	43.0000

Data from U.S. Department of Agriculture, Agricultural Research Service. 2009. USDA National Nutrient Database for Standard Reference, Release 22. Nutrient Data Laboratory Home Page, www.ars.usda.gov/ba/bhnrc/ndl.
Table Sugar: Food Code 4330 (Sweets, syrups, table blends, corn, refiner's syrup and sugar)
Honey: Food Code 4294 (*Sweets, honey, strained or extracted*)
Molasses: Food Code 4299 (Sweets, molasses)
Maple Syrup, prepackaged Food Code 6175 (sweets, syrup, maple, prepackaged)
No data for Raw Sugar in the Canadian Nutrient Data File.

as a type of fibre. When our intestinal bacteria ferment resistant starch, a fatty acid called *butyrate* is produced. Consuming resistant starch may be beneficial: some research suggests that butyrate reduces the risk for cancer (Pan et al., 2000). Legumes contain more resistant starch than do grains, fruits, or vegetables. This quality, plus their high protein and fibre content, makes legumes a healthful food.

▶ **Figure 4.4** Polysaccharides include starch, glycogen, and fibre.

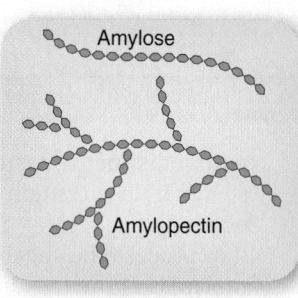

Amylose

Amylopectin

Starch

Storage form of glucose in plants; found in grains, legumes, and tubers

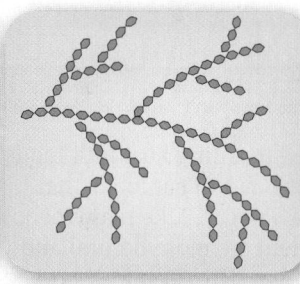

Glycogen

Storage form of glucose in animals; stored in liver and muscles

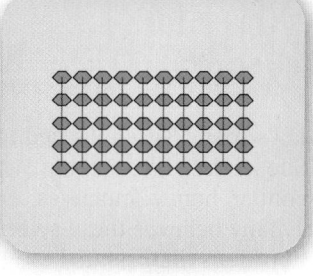

Fibre

Forms the support structures of leaves, stems, and plants

⬆ Tubers, such as these sweet potatoes, are excellent food sources of starch.

glycogen A polysaccharide; the storage form of glucose in animals. Glycogen is not found in plants.

dietary fibre The indigestible carbohydrate parts of plants that form the support structures of leaves, stems, and seeds.

functional fibre The indigestible forms of carbohydrates that are extracted from plants or manufactured in a laboratory and have known health benefits.

total fibre The sum of dietary fibre and functional fibre.

soluble fibres Natural pectins, mucilages, and gums that absorb water and form gels. In humans, these substances slow down the movement of materials through the small intestine.

Glycogen Is a Polysaccharide Stored by Animals

Glycogen is the storage form of glucose for animals, including humans. After an animal is slaughtered, most of the glycogen is broken down by enzymes found in animal tissues. Thus, very little glycogen exists in meat. As explained later in this chapter, we can break down glycogen into glucose when we need it for energy. We store glycogen in our liver and muscles; the storage and use of glycogen are discussed in more detail on pages 122–124.

Fibre Is a Polysaccharide That Gives Plants Their Structure

Like starch, fibre is composed of long polysaccharide chains; however, our body does not easily break down the bonds that connect fibre molecules. This means that most fibres pass through the digestive system without being digested and absorbed, so they contribute no energy to our diet. However, fibre offers many other health benefits, as we will see shortly (pages 117–120).

There are currently a number of definitions of fibre. Recently, the Food and Nutrition Board of the Institute of Medicine Institute of Medicine, 2002 proposed three distinctions: *dietary fibre*, *functional fibre*, and *total fibre*.

- **Dietary fibre** is the indigestible parts of plants that form the support structures of leaves, stems, and seeds (see Figure 4.4). In a sense, you can think of dietary fibre as a plant's "skeleton."
- **Functional fibre** consists of the indigestible forms of carbohydrates that are extracted from plants or manufactured in a laboratory and have known health benefits. Functional fibre is added to foods and is the form used in fibre supplements. Examples of functional fibre you might see on nutrition labels include cellulose, guar gum, pectin, and psyllium.
- **Total fibre** is the sum of dietary fibre and functional fibre.

Fibre can also be classified according to its chemical and physical properties as soluble or insoluble.

Soluble Fibres   **Soluble fibres** are types of dietary and functional fibres that absorb water and swell to form gels. These gels can trap nutrients, such as glucose, and slow down their absorption into the blood. Food stays in the small intestine longer, and this is useful for people with diabetes and for people with irritable bowel syndrome who suffer from diarrhea (discussed in Chapter 3). Soluble fibres are fermentable; that is, they are easily digested by bacteria in the colon. Soluble fibres are naturally found in citrus fruits, apples, berries, oat products, and legumes.

Research suggests that the regular consumption of soluble fibres reduces the risks for cardiovascular disease and type 2 diabetes by lowering blood cholesterol and blood glucose levels. The possible mechanisms by which fibre reduces the risk for various diseases are discussed in more detail on pages 119–120.

Soluble fibres include:

- *Pectins*, which contain chains of galacturonic acid and other monosaccharides. Pectins are found in the cell walls and intracellular tissues of many fruits and berries. They can be isolated and used to thicken foods, such as jams and yogurts.

- *Gums,* which contain galactose, glucuronic acid, and other monosaccharides. Gums are a diverse group of polysaccharides that are **viscous**. They are typically isolated from seeds and are used as thickening, gelling, and stabilizing agents. Guar gum and gum arabic are common gums used as food additives.
- *Mucilages,* which are similar to gums and contain galactose, mannose, and other monosaccharides. Two examples are psyllium and carrageenan. Psyllium is the husk of psyllium seeds, which are also known as plantago or flea seeds. Carrageenan comes from seaweed. Mucilages are used as food stabilizers.

Insoluble Fibres   **Insoluble fibres** are those that do not typically dissolve in water. These fibres are usually nonviscous (they do not form gels) and typically cannot be fermented by bacteria in the colon. They attract water, but they cling to it rather than absorbing it. Insoluble fibre and the water that it holds helps the contents of the large intestine move more quickly through the body and can help to prevent constipation. Insoluble fibres are generally found in whole grains, such as wheat, rye, and brown rice, and are found in many vegetables. These fibres are not associated with reducing cholesterol levels but are known for promoting regular bowel movements, and reducing the risk for diverticulosis (discussed later in this chapter). Examples of insoluble fibres include the following:

- *Lignins* are non-carbohydrate forms of fibre. Lignins are found in the woody parts of plant cell walls and in carrots and the seeds of fruits and berries. Lignins are also found in brans (the outer husk of grains such as wheat, oats, and rye) and other whole grains.
- *Cellulose* is the main structural component of plant cell walls. Cellulose is a chain of glucose units similar to amylose (shown in Figure 4.4) but, unlike amylose, cellulose contains bonds that are indigestible by humans. Cellulose is found in whole grains, fruits, vegetables, and legumes. It can also be extracted from wood pulp or cotton, and it is added to foods to prevent "caking" or clumping, to thicken, and to add texture to foods.
- *Hemicelluloses* contain glucose, mannose, galacturonic acid, and other monosaccharides. Hemicelluloses are found in plant cell walls and they surround cellulose. They are the primary component of cereal fibres and are found in whole grains and vegetables. Although many hemicelluloses are insoluble, some are also classified as soluble.

RECAP All complex carbohydrates are polysaccharides. The three types of polysaccharides are starch, glycogen, and fibre. Starch is the storage form of glucose in plants, whereas glycogen is the storage form of glucose in animals. Fibre forms the support structures of plants. Soluble fibres dissolve in water, are viscous, and slow down the movement of material through the intestinal tract. They can be fermented by bacteria in the colon. Insoluble fibres do not dissolve in water, are not viscous, and cannot be digested. They attract and hold onto water and speed up the movement of material through the large intestine.

Why Do We Need Carbohydrates?

We have seen that carbohydrates are an important energy source for our body. Let's learn more about this and discuss other functions of carbohydrates.

Carbohydrates Provide Energy

Carbohydrates, an excellent source of energy for all our cells, provide 17 kJ (4 kcal) of energy per gram. Some of our cells can also use fat and even protein for energy if necessary. However, our red blood cells can use only glucose, and our brain and other nervous tissues primarily rely on glucose. This is why we get tired, irritable, and shaky when we have not eaten any carbohydrate for a prolonged period of time.

⬆ Dissolvable laxatives are an example of one type of soluble fibre.

viscous Having a gel-like consistency; viscous fibres form a gel when dissolved in water.

insoluble fibres Components of plants that attract and cling to water, but do not dissolve in water. In humans, these substances speed up the movement of material through the large intestine.

⬆ Our red blood cells can use only glucose and other monosaccharides, and our brain and other nervous tissues rely primarily on glucose. This is why we get tired, irritable, and shaky when we have not eaten for a prolonged period of time.

Carbohydrate Use by Exercise Intensity

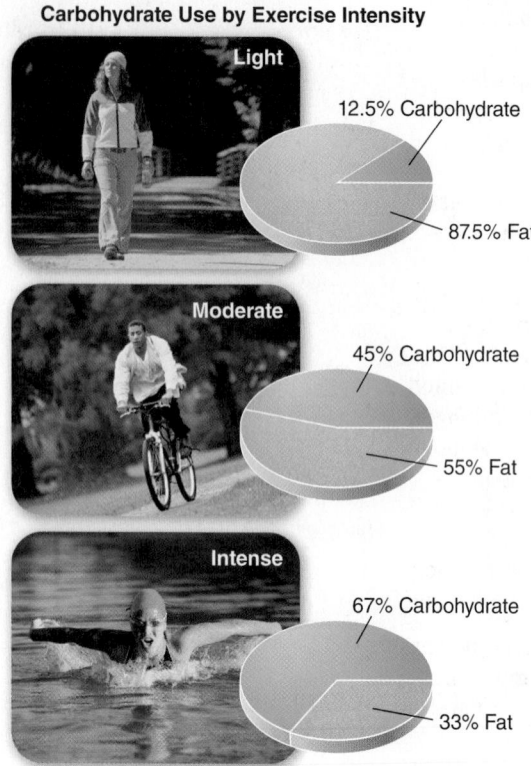

Light

12.5% Carbohydrate

87.5% Fat

Moderate

45% Carbohydrate

55% Fat

Intense

67% Carbohydrate

33% Fat

Figure 4.5 Amounts of carbohydrate and fat used during light, moderate, and intense exercise.
Source: Romijn, J. A., E. F. Coyle, L. S. Sidossis, A. Gastaldelli, J. F. Horowitz, E. Endert, and R. R. Wolfe. 1993. Regulation of endogenous fat and carbohydrate metabolism in relation to exercise intensity and duration. *Am. J. Physiol.* 265 [Endocrinol. Metab. 28]: E380–E391.

ketosis The process by which the breakdown of fat during fasting states results in the production of ketones.

ketones Substances produced during the breakdown of fat when carbohydrate intake is insufficient to meet energy needs. Ketones provide an alternative energy source for the brain when glucose levels are low.

ketoacidosis A condition in which excessive ketones are present in the blood, causing the blood to become very acidic, which alters basic body functions and damages tissues. Untreated ketoacidosis can be fatal. This condition is found in individuals with untreated diabetes mellitus.

gluconeogenesis The generation of glucose from the breakdown of proteins into amino acids.

Carbohydrates Fuel Daily Activity

Many popular diets—such as Dr. Atkins' New Revolution Diet and the Sugar Busters plan—are based on the idea that our body actually "prefers" to use fat and/or protein for energy. They claim that current carbohydrate recommendations are much higher than we really need.

In reality, the body relies mostly on both carbohydrates and fat for energy. In fact, as shown in **Figure 4.5**, our body always uses some combination of carbohydrates and fat to fuel daily activities. Fat is the predominant energy source used by our body at rest and during low-intensity activities, such as sitting, standing, and walking. Even during rest, however, our brain cells and red blood cells still rely on glucose.

Carbohydrates Fuel Exercise

When we exercise, whether running, briskly walking, bicycling, or performing any other activity that causes us to breathe harder and sweat, we begin to use more glucose than fat. Whereas fat breakdown is a slow process and requires oxygen, we can break down glucose very quickly either with or without oxygen. Even during very intense exercise, when less oxygen is available, we can still break down glucose very quickly for energy. That's why when you are exercising at maximal effort carbohydrates are providing almost 100% of the energy your body requires.

If you are physically active, it is important to eat enough carbohydrates to provide energy for your brain, red blood cells, and muscles. In Chapter 12, we discuss in more detail the carbohydrate recommendations for active people. In general, if you do not eat enough carbohydrate to support regular exercise, your body will have to rely on fat and protein as alternative energy sources. One advantage of becoming highly trained for endurance-type events, such as marathons and triathlons, is that our muscles are able to store more glycogen, which provides us with additional glucose we can use during exercise. (See Chapter 12 for more information on how exercise improves our use and storage of carbohydrates.)

Low Carbohydrate Intake Can Lead to Ketoacidosis

When we do not eat enough carbohydrate, our body seeks an alternative source of fuel for our brain and begins to break down stored fat. This process, called **ketosis**, produces an alternative fuel called **ketones**.

Ketosis is an important mechanism for providing energy to the brain during situations of fasting, low carbohydrate intake, or vigorous exercise (Pan et al., 2000). However, ketones also suppress appetite and cause dehydration and acetone breath (the breath smells like nail polish remover). If inadequate carbohydrate intake continues for an extended period of time, the body will produce excessive amounts of ketones. Because many ketones are acids, high ketone levels will cause the blood to become very acidic, leading to a condition called **ketoacidosis**. The high acidity of the blood interferes with basic body functions, causes the loss of lean body mass, and damages many body tissues. People with untreated diabetes are at high risk for ketoacidosis, which can lead to coma and even death. (We look at diabetes *In Depth* at the end of the chapter.)

Carbohydrates Spare Protein

If the diet does not provide enough carbohydrate, the body will make its own glucose from protein. This involves breaking down the proteins in blood and tissues into amino acids, then converting them to glucose. This process is called **gluconeogenesis** ("generating new glucose").

When our body uses amino acids for energy, they are not available to make new cells, repair tissue damage, support our immune system, or perform any of their other functions. During periods of starvation or when eating a diet that is very low in carbohydrate, our body will take amino acids from the blood first, and then from other tissues, such as muscles, heart, liver, and kidneys. Using amino acids in this manner over a prolonged period of time can cause serious, possibly irreversible, damage to these organs. (See Chapter 6 for more details on using protein for energy.)

Carbohydrates and Body Weight

Proponents of low-carbohydrate diets claim that eating carbohydrates makes you gain weight. However, anyone who consumes more energy than he or she expends will gain weight, whether the energy is in the form of simple or complex carbohydrates, protein, or fat. Moreover, fat is more energy dense than carbohydrate: it contains 37 kJ (9 kcal) per gram, whereas carbohydrate contains only 17 kJ (4 kcal) per gram. Thus, gram for gram, fat is twice as "fattening" as carbohydrate. In fact, eating carbohydrate sources that are high in fibre and other nutrients has been shown to reduce the overall risk for obesity, heart disease, and diabetes. Thus, all carbohydrates are not bad, and even a small amount of refined sugars can be included in a healthful diet.

Fibre Helps Us Stay Healthy

The terms *simple* and *complex* can cause confusion when discussing the health effects of carbohydrates. As we explained earlier, these terms are used to designate the number of sugar molecules present in the carbohydrate. However, when distinguishing carbohydrates in terms of their effect on our health, it is more appropriate to talk about them in terms of their nutrient density and their fibre content. Although we cannot digest fibre, it is a very important substance in our diet. Research indicates that it helps us stay healthy and may prevent many digestive and chronic diseases. The following are potential benefits of fibre consumption:

- May reduce the risk of colon cancer. Although there is some controversy surrounding this issue, many researchers believe that fibre binds cancer-causing substances and speeds their elimination from the colon. However, recent studies of colon cancer and fibre have shown that the relationship between them is not as strong as previously thought (Aune, Chan, and Lau, 2011; Park et al., 2005).
- Helps prevent hemorrhoids, constipation, and other intestinal problems by keeping our stools moist and soft. Fibre gives gut muscles "something to push on" and makes it easier to eliminate stools.
- Reduces the risk for *diverticulosis*, a condition that is caused in part by trying to eliminate small, hard stools. A great deal of pressure must be generated in the large intestine to pass hard stools. This increased pressure weakens intestinal walls, causing them to bulge outward and form pockets **(Figure 4.6)**. Feces and fibrous materials can get trapped in these pockets, which become infected and inflamed. This is a painful condition that must be treated with antibiotics or surgery.
- May reduce the risk of heart disease by delaying or blocking the absorption of dietary cholesterol into the bloodstream **(Figure 4.7)**. In addition, when soluble fibres are

When we exercise or perform any activity that causes us to breathe harder and sweat, we begin to use more glucose than fat.

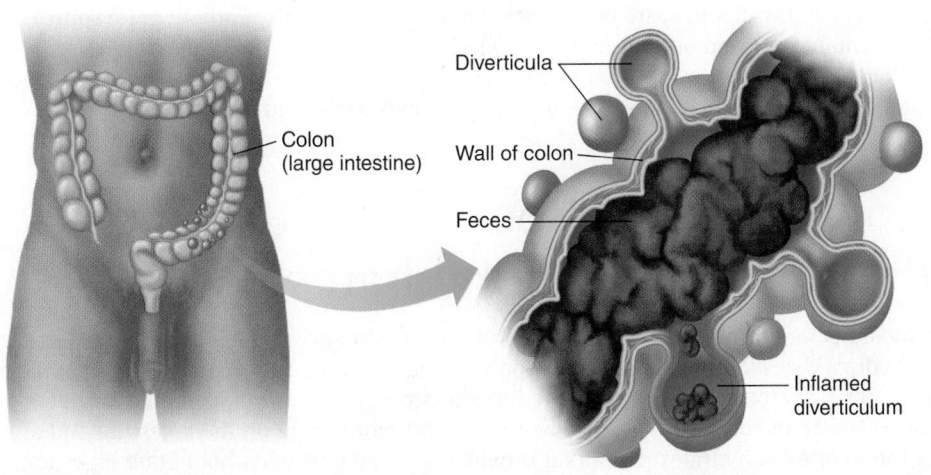

Colon (large intestine)

Diverticula

Wall of colon

Feces

Inflamed diverticulum

Figure 4.6 Diverticulosis occurs when bulging pockets form in the wall of the large intestine (colon). These pockets become infected and inflamed, requiring proper treatment.

▶ **Figure 4.7** How fibre might help decrease blood cholesterol levels. **(a)** When eating a high-fibre diet, fibre binds to the bile that is produced from cholesterol, resulting in relatively more cholesterol being excreted in the feces. **(b)** When a lower-fibre diet is consumed, less fibre (and thus less cholesterol) is bound to bile and excreted in the feces.

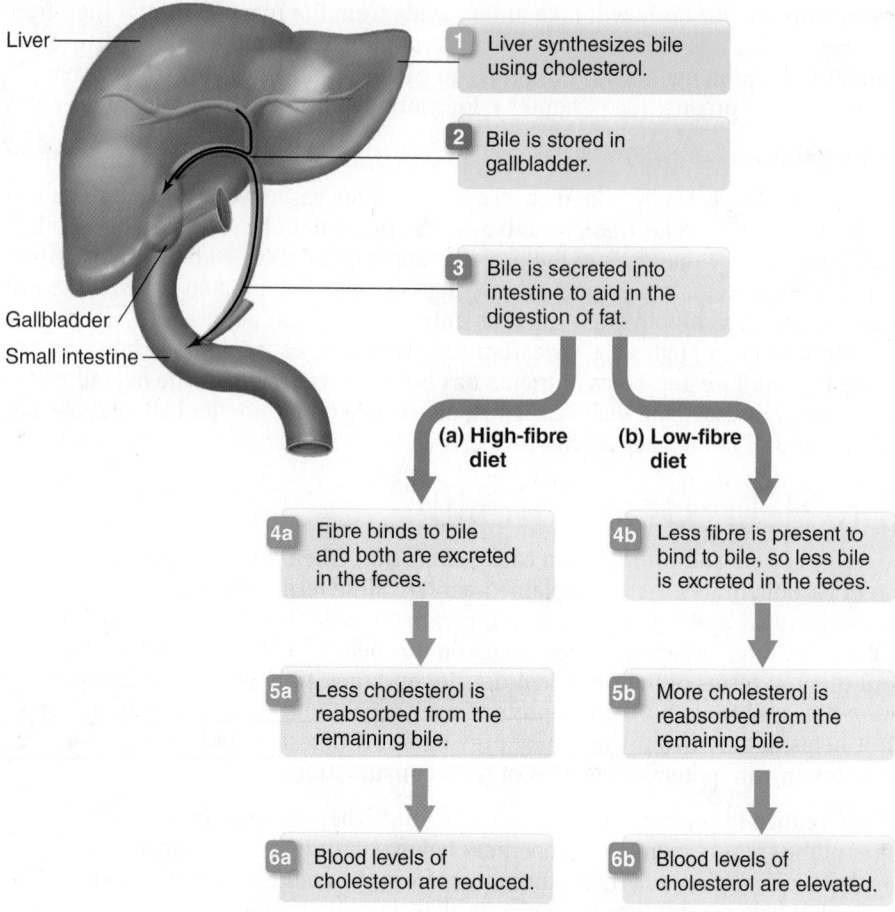

Liver

1 Liver synthesizes bile using cholesterol.

2 Bile is stored in gallbladder.

3 Bile is secreted into intestine to aid in the digestion of fat.

Gallbladder

Small intestine

(a) High-fibre diet

4a Fibre binds to bile and both are excreted in the feces.

5a Less cholesterol is reabsorbed from the remaining bile.

6a Blood levels of cholesterol are reduced.

(b) Low-fibre diet

4b Less fibre is present to bind to bile, so less bile is excreted in the feces.

5b More cholesterol is reabsorbed from the remaining bile.

6b Blood levels of cholesterol are elevated.

eaten, bacteria in the colon ferment them to produce short-chain fatty acids that may lower the production of low-density lipoprotein (LDL) to healthful levels in our body.
- May enhance weight loss, as eating a high-fibre diet causes a person to feel more full. Soluble fibre absorbs water, expands in the large intestine, and slows the movement of food through the upper part of the digestive tract. Also, people who eat a fibre-rich diet tend to eat fewer fatty and sugary foods.
- May lower the risk for type 2 diabetes. In slowing digestion and absorption, soluble fibre also slows the release of glucose into the blood. It thereby improves the body's regulation of insulin production and blood glucose levels.

⬅ Brown rice is a good food source of dietary fibre.

RECAP Carbohydrates are an important energy source at rest and during exercise, and they provide 17 kJ (4 kcal) of energy per gram. Carbohydrates are necessary in the diet to spare body protein and prevent ketosis. Carbohydrate sources that contain fibre and other nutrients can reduce the risk for obesity, heart disease, and diabetes. Fibre helps prevent hemorrhoids, constipation, and diverticulosis; may reduce the risk for colon cancer and heart disease; and may assist with weight loss.

How Does Our Body Break Down Carbohydrates?

Glucose is the form of sugar that our body uses for energy, and the primary goal of carbohydrate digestion is to break down polysaccharides and disaccharides into monosaccharides, which can then be converted to glucose. Chapter 3 provided an overview of digestion. Here, we focus specifically and in a bit more detail on the digestion and absorption of carbohydrates. **Figure 4.8** provides a visual tour of carbohydrate digestion.

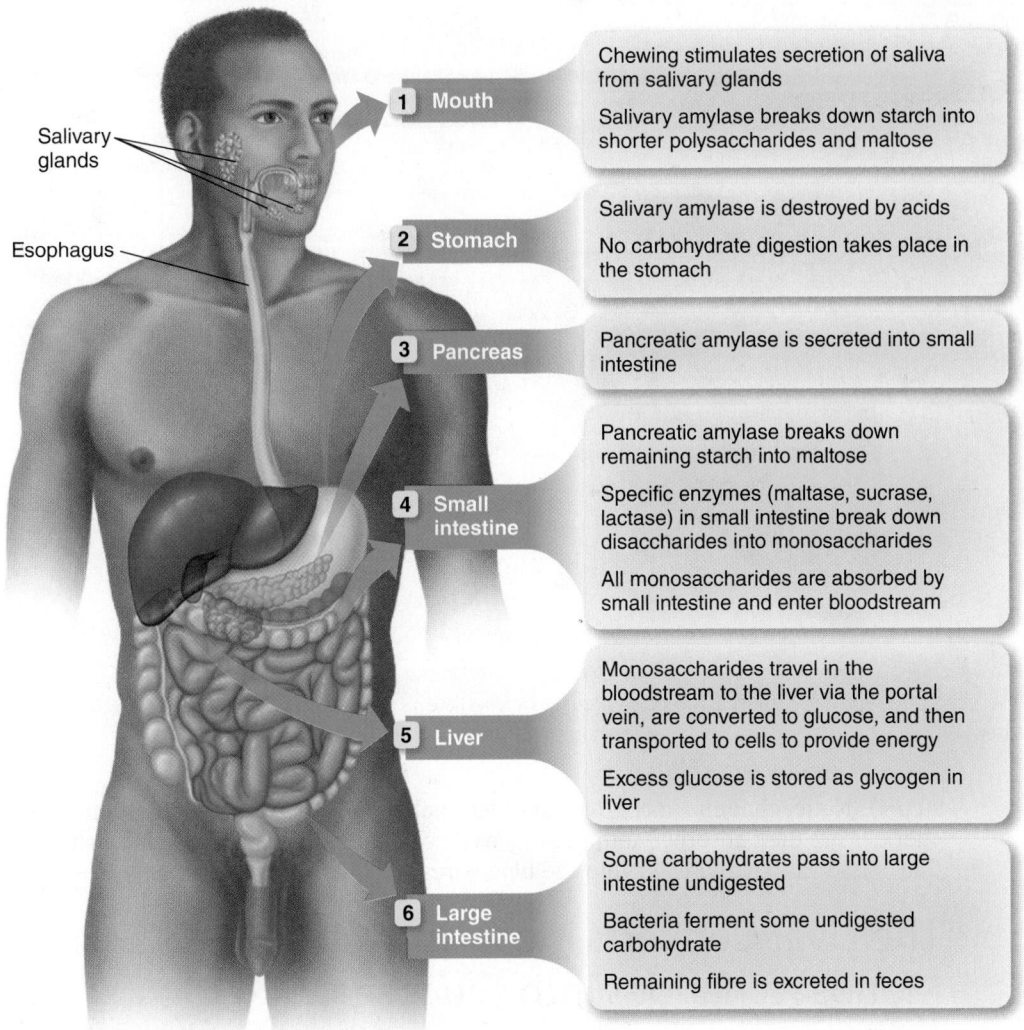

Salivary glands

Esophagus

1 Mouth
Chewing stimulates secretion of saliva from salivary glands

Salivary amylase breaks down starch into shorter polysaccharides and maltose

2 Stomach
Salivary amylase is destroyed by acids

No carbohydrate digestion takes place in the stomach

3 Pancreas
Pancreatic amylase is secreted into small intestine

4 Small intestine
Pancreatic amylase breaks down remaining starch into maltose

Specific enzymes (maltase, sucrase, lactase) in small intestine break down disaccharides into monosaccharides

All monosaccharides are absorbed by small intestine and enter bloodstream

5 Liver
Monosaccharides travel in the bloodstream to the liver via the portal vein, are converted to glucose, and then transported to cells to provide energy

Excess glucose is stored as glycogen in liver

6 Large intestine
Some carbohydrates pass into large intestine undigested

Bacteria ferment some undigested carbohydrate

Remaining fibre is excreted in feces

Figure 4.8 A review of carbohydrate digestion and absorption.

Digestion Breaks Down Most Carbohydrates into Monosaccharides

Carbohydrate digestion begins in the mouth (Figure 4.8, step 1). As you saw in Chapter 3, the starch in the foods you eat mixes with your saliva during chewing. Saliva contains an enzyme called **salivary amylase**, which breaks starch into smaller particles and eventually into the disaccharide maltose. The next time you eat a piece of bread, notice that you can actually taste it becoming sweeter; this indicates the breakdown of starch into maltose. Disaccharides are not digested in the mouth.

As the bolus (mouthful) of food leaves the mouth and enters the stomach, all digestion of carbohydrates ceases. This is because the acid in the stomach inactivates most of the salivary amylase enzyme (Figure 4.8, step 2).

The majority of carbohydrate digestion occurs in the small intestine. As the contents of the stomach enter the small intestine, the pancreas secretes an enzyme called **pancreatic amylase** into the small intestine (Figure 4.8, step 3). Pancreatic amylase continues to digest any remaining starch into maltose. Additional enzymes in the microvilli of the mucosal cells that line the intestinal tract work to break down disaccharides into monosaccharides. Maltose is broken down into glucose by the enzyme **maltase**. Sucrose is broken down into glucose and fructose by the enzyme **sucrase**. The enzyme **lactase** breaks down lactose into glucose and galactose (Figure 4.8,

salivary amylase An enzyme in saliva that breaks starch into smaller particles and eventually into the disaccharide maltose.

pancreatic amylase An enzyme secreted by the pancreas into the small intestine that digests any remaining starch into maltose.

maltase A digestive enzyme that breaks maltose into glucose.

sucrase A digestive enzyme that breaks sucrose into glucose and fructose.

lactase A digestive enzyme that breaks lactose into glucose and galactose.

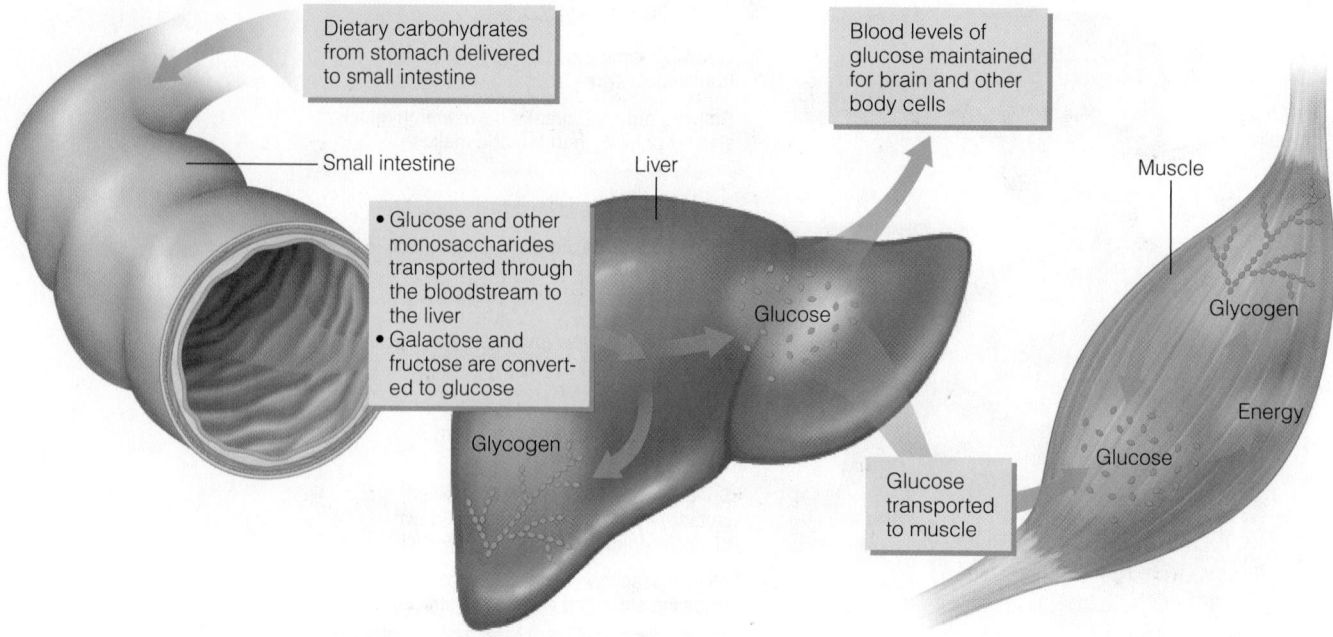

Dietary carbohydrates from stomach delivered to small intestine

Blood levels of glucose maintained for brain and other body cells

Small intestine

Liver

Muscle

- Glucose and other monosaccharides transported through the bloodstream to the liver
- Galactose and fructose are converted to glucose

Glucose

Glycogen

Glycogen

Energy

Glucose

Glucose transported to muscle

Glucose

Figure 4.9 Glucose is stored as glycogen in both liver and muscle. The glycogen stored in the liver maintains proper blood glucose levels between meals; muscle glycogen provides immediate energy to the muscle during exercise.

step 4). Notice that enzyme names are identifiable by the *–ase* suffix. All monosaccharides are then absorbed into the mucosal cells lining the small intestine, where they pass through and enter into the bloodstream.

The Liver Converts Most Non-Glucose Monosaccharides into Glucose

Once the monosaccharides enter the bloodstream, they travel to the liver, where fructose and galactose are converted to glucose (Figure 4.8, step 5). If needed immediately for energy, the glucose is released into the bloodstream, where it can travel to the cells to provide energy. If glucose is not needed immediately for energy, it is stored as glycogen in our liver and muscles. Enzymes in liver and muscle cells combine glucose molecules to form glycogen (an anabolic, or building, process) and break glycogen into glucose (a catabolic, or destructive, process), depending on the body's energy needs. On average, the liver can store 70 g (1170 kJ or 280 kcal) and the muscles can normally store about 120 g (2000 kJ or 480 kcal) of glycogen. Between meals, our body draws on liver glycogen reserves to maintain blood glucose levels and support the needs of our cells, including those of our brain, spinal cord, and red blood cells **(Figure 4.9)**.

The glycogen stored in our muscles continually provides energy to our muscle cells, particularly during intense exercise. Endurance athletes can increase their storage of muscle glycogen from two to four times the normal amount through a process called *carbohydrate loading* (see Chapter 12). Any excess glucose is stored as glycogen in the liver and muscles and saved for such future energy needs as exercise. Once the storage capacity of the liver and muscles is reached, any excess glucose can be stored as fat in adipose tissue.

Fibre Is Excreted from the Large Intestine

As previously mentioned, humans do not possess enzymes in the small intestine that can break down fibre. Thus, fibre passes through the small intestine undigested and enters the large intestine, or colon. There, bacteria ferment some previously undigested carbohydrates, causing the production of gases and a few short-chain fatty acids.

Is it Hunger—or Hypoglycemia?

After going for several hours without eating, have you ever felt confused, shaky, irritable, and weak? And did the symptoms subside once you'd eaten? If so, maybe you wondered if your symptoms were due to hypoglycemia.

In **hypoglycemia**, blood glucose falls to lower-than-normal levels. This commonly occurs in people with diabetes who are not getting proper treatment, but it can also happen in people who do not have diabetes if their pancreas secretes too much insulin after a high-carbohydrate meal. The characteristic symptoms usually appear about one to four hours after the meal and occur because the body clears glucose from the blood too quickly. People with this form of hypoglycemia must eat smaller meals more frequently to level out their blood insulin and glucose levels.

The trouble is, ordinary hunger can make you experience symptoms just like those of true hypoglycemia. So which is it—hunger or hypoglycemia? You can only find out for sure by getting a blood test, but unless you have diabetes it is probably not necessary. For most healthy people, eating regular meals and healthy snacks is the only "treatment" needed.

The cells of the large intestine use these short-chain fatty acids for energy. The fibre remaining in the colon adds bulk to our stools and is excreted (Figure 4.8, step 6) in feces. In this way, fibre assists in maintaining bowel regularity.

RECAP Carbohydrate digestion starts in the mouth and continues in the small intestine. Glucose and other monosaccharides are absorbed into the bloodstream and travel to the liver, where non-glucose sugars (galactose and fructose) are converted to glucose. Glucose either is used by the cells for energy or is converted to glycogen and stored in the liver and muscle for later use.

A Variety of Hormones Regulates Blood Glucose Levels

Our body regulates blood glucose levels within a fairly narrow range to provide adequate glucose to the brain and other cells. A number of hormones, including insulin, glucagon, epinephrine, norepinephrine, cortisol, and growth hormone assist the body with maintaining proper levels of blood glucose.

When we eat a meal, our blood glucose level rises. But glucose in our blood cannot help our nerves, muscles, and other organs function unless it can cross into their cells. Glucose molecules are too large to cross cell membranes independently. To get in, glucose needs assistance from the hormone **insulin**, which is secreted by the pancreas **(Figure 4.10a)**. Insulin is transported in the blood throughout the body, where it stimulates special molecules located in cell membranes to transport glucose into the cell. Insulin can be thought of as a key that opens the gates of the cell membrane, enabling the transport of glucose into the cell interior, where it can be used for energy. Insulin also stimulates the liver and muscles to take up glucose and store it as glycogen.

When you have not eaten for a period of time, your blood glucose level declines. This decrease in blood glucose stimulates the pancreas to secrete another hormone, **glucagon (Figure 4.10b)**. Glucagon acts in an opposite way to insulin: it causes the liver to convert its stored glycogen into glucose, which is then secreted into the bloodstream and transported to the cells for energy. Glucagon also assists in the breakdown of body proteins to amino acids, so that the liver can stimulate *gluconeogenesis*, the production of new glucose from amino acids.

Epinephrine, norepinephrine, cortisol, and growth hormone are additional hormones that work to increase blood glucose. Epinephrine and norepinephrine are secreted by the adrenal glands and nerve endings when blood glucose levels are low. They act to increase glycogen breakdown in the liver, resulting in a subsequent

hypoglycemia A condition marked by blood glucose levels that are below normal fasting levels.

insulin The hormone secreted by the beta cells of the pancreas in response to increased blood levels of glucose; it facilitates the uptake of glucose by body cells.

glucagon The hormone secreted by the alpha cells of the pancreas in response to decreased blood levels of glucose; it causes the breakdown of liver stores of glycogen into glucose.

▶ **Figure 4.10** Regulation of blood glucose by the hormones insulin and glucagon. **(a)** When blood glucose levels increase after a meal, the pancreas secretes insulin. Insulin opens "gates" in the cell membrane to allow the passage of glucose into the cell. **(b)** When blood glucose levels are low, the pancreas secretes glucagon. Glucagon enters liver cells, where it stimulates the breakdown of stored glycogen into glucose. This glucose is then released into the bloodstream.

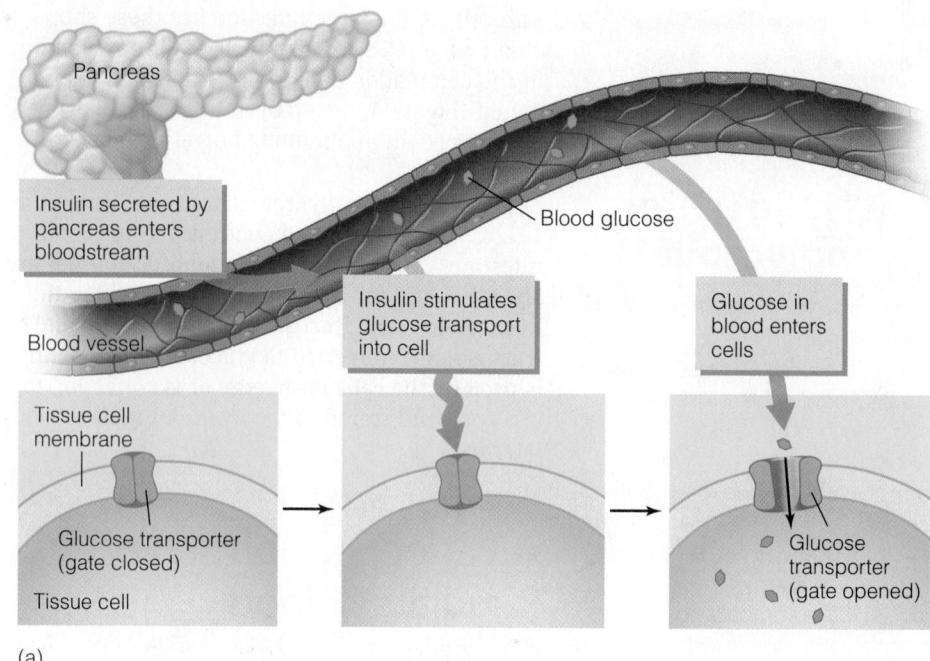

(a)

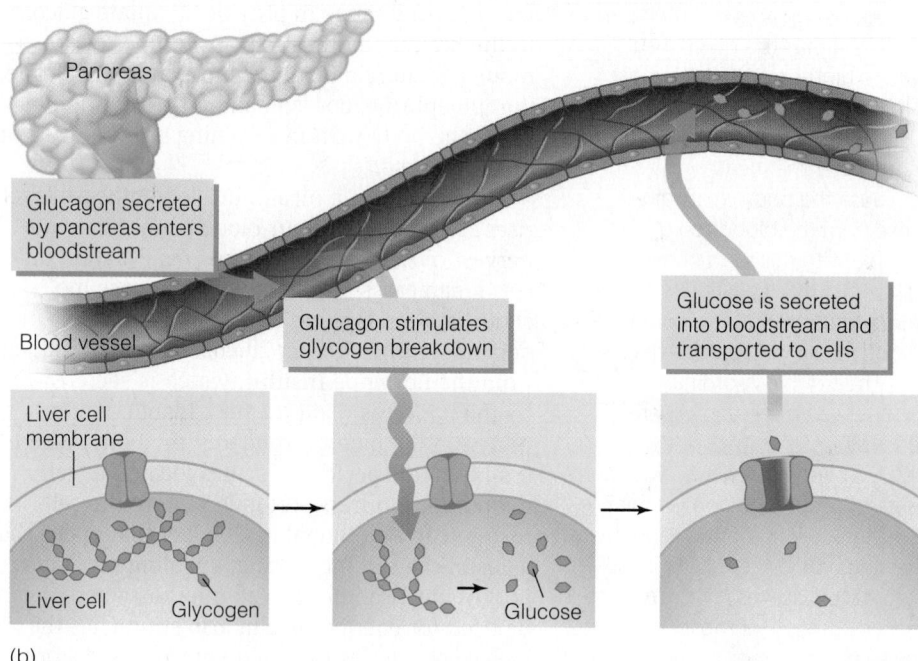

(b)

increase in the release of glucose into the bloodstream. They also increase gluconeogenesis. These two hormones are also responsible for our "fight-or-flight" reaction to danger; they are released when we need a burst of energy to respond quickly. Cortisol and growth hormone are secreted by the adrenal glands to act on liver, muscle, and adipose tissue. Cortisol increases gluconeogenesis and decreases the use of glucose by muscles and other body organs. Growth hormone decreases glucose uptake by our muscles, increases our mobilization and use of the fatty acids stored in our adipose tissue, and increases our liver's output of glucose.

Normally, the effects of these hormones balance each other to maintain blood glucose within a healthy range. An alteration in this balance can lead to health conditions such as diabetes (see the *In Depth* essay on pages 141–145) or hypoglycemia.

The Glycemic Index Shows How Foods Affect Our Blood Glucose Level

The **glycemic index** is a measure of the potential of foods to raise blood glucose levels. Foods with a high glycemic index cause a sudden surge in blood glucose. This in turn triggers a surge in insulin, which may then be followed by a dramatic drop in blood glucose. Foods with a low glycemic index cause low to moderate fluctuations in blood glucose. When foods are assigned a glycemic index value, they are often compared to the glycemic effect of pure glucose.

The glycemic index of a food is not always easy to predict. **Table 4.2** ranks certain foods according to their glycemic index. Do any of these rankings surprise you? Most people assume that foods containing simple sugars have a higher glycemic index than starches, but this is not always the case. For instance, compare the glycemic indexes for apples and instant potatoes. Although instant potatoes are a starchy food, they have a glycemic index value of 85, whereas the value for an apple is only 38!

The type of carbohydrate, the way the food is prepared, and its fat and fibre content can all affect how quickly the body absorbs it. It is important to note that we eat most of our foods combined into a meal. In this case, the glycemic index of the total meal becomes more important than the ranking of each food.

An apple has a lower glycemic index (38) than a serving of white rice (56).

TABLE 4.2 Selected High, Medium, and Low Glycemic Index (GI) Foods, Using Glucose as the Reference

Low GI (55 or less)* † Choose most often ✔✔✔	Medium GI (56–69)* † Choose more often ✔✔	High GI (70 or more)* † Choose less often ✔
Breads	**Breads**	**Breads**
100% stone ground whole wheat	Whole wheat	White bread
Heavy mixed grain	Rye	Kaiser roll
Pumpernickel	Pita	Bagel, white
Cereal	**Cereal**	**Cereal**
All Bran™	Grapenuts™	Bran flakes
Bran Buds with Psyllium™	Puffed wheat	Corn flakes
Oat Bran™	Oatmeal	Rice Krispies™
	Oats	
	Raisin Bran™ (Kellogg's)	
Grains	**Grains**	**Grains**
Barley	Basmati rice	Short-grain rice
Bulgar	Brown rice	
Pasta/noodles	Couscous	
Parboiled or converted rice		
Other	**Other**	**Other**
Sweet potato	Potato, new/white	Potato, baking (Russet)
Yam	Sweet corn	Potatoes, boiled and mashed
Legumes: lentils, chickpeas, kidney beans, split peas, soy beans, baked beans	Pineapple	French fries
	Raisins	Carrots, boiled
Fruit and juices: apples, apple juice, bananas, oranges, pears	Popcorn	Parsnip, Rutabaga
	Stoned Wheat Thins™	Watermelon
Plain yoghurt	Ryvita™ (rye crisps)	Pretzels
Skim milk	Black bean soup	Rice cakes
	Green pea or split pea soup	Soda crackers
		Doughnuts

*expressed as a percentage of the value for glucose.
†Canadian values where available.
Source: Adapted from *The Glycemic Index*, Canadian Diabetes Association, www.diabetes.ca/files/GlycemicIndex_08.pdf, accessed Nov. 2008; K. Foster-Powell, S. H. A. Holt, J. C. Brand-Miller. International table of glycemic index and glycemic load values. *Am J Clin Nutr.* 2002;76:5–76; and *The Glycemic Index*, The University of Sydney, Dec. 2005, www.glycemicindex.com, accessed Nov. 2008.

glycemic index The system that assigns ratings (or values) for the potential of foods to raise blood glucose and insulin levels.

glycemic load The amount of carbohydrate in a food multiplied by the glycemic index of the carbohydrate.

For determining the effect of a food on a person's glucose response, some nutrition experts believe that a food's **glycemic load** is more useful than the glycemic index. A food's glycemic load is the number of grams of carbohydrate it contains multiplied by the glycemic index of that carbohydrate. For instance, carrots are recognized as a vegetable having a relatively high glycemic index of about 68; however, the glycemic load of carrots is only 3 (Foster-Powell et al., 2002). This is because there is very little total carbohydrate in a serving of carrots. The low glycemic load of carrots means that carrot consumption is unlikely to cause a significant rise in glucose and insulin levels.

Why do we care about the glycemic index and glycemic load? Foods and meals with a lower glycemic load are better choices for someone with diabetes because they will not trigger dramatic fluctuations in blood glucose. They may also reduce the risk for heart disease and colon cancer because they generally contain more fibre, and fibre helps decrease fat levels in the blood. Recent studies have shown that people who eat lower GI diets have more healthful blood lipid levels and their blood glucose values are more likely to be normal (Buyken et al., 2001; Liu et al., 2001; Sloth et al., 2004). Diets with a low GI and low glycemic load are also associated with a reduced risk for prostate cancer (Augustin et al., 2004). Despite some encouraging research findings, the GI and glycemic load remain controversial. Many nutrition researchers feel that the evidence supporting their health benefits is weak. In addition, many believe the concepts of the glycemic index/load are too complex for people to apply to their daily lives. Other researchers insist that helping people choose foods with a lower glycemic index/load is critical in the prevention and treatment of many chronic diseases. Until this controversy is resolved, people are encouraged to eat a variety of fibre-rich and less processed carbohydrates, such as beans and lentils, fresh vegetables, and whole-wheat bread, because these forms of carbohydrates have a lower glycemic load and they contain a multitude of important nutrients.

RECAP Various hormones are involved in regulating blood glucose. Insulin lowers blood glucose levels by facilitating the entry of glucose into cells. Glucagon, epinephrine, norepinephrine, cortisol, and growth hormone raise blood glucose levels by a variety of mechanisms. The glycemic index is a value that indicates the potential of foods to raise blood glucose and insulin levels. The glycemic load is the amount of carbohydrate in a food multiplied by the GI of the carbohydrate in that food. Foods with a high glycemic index/load cause surges in blood glucose and insulin, whereas foods with a low glycemic index/load cause more moderate fluctuations in blood glucose.

How Much Carbohydrate Should We Eat?

Carbohydrates are an important part of a balanced, healthful diet. The Recommended Dietary Allowance (RDA) for carbohydrate is based on the amount of glucose the brain uses (Institute of Medicine, 2002). The current RDA for adults 19 years of age and older is 130 g of carbohydrate per day. It is important to emphasize that this RDA does not cover the amount of carbohydrate needed to support daily activities; it covers only the amount of carbohydrate needed to supply adequate glucose to the brain.

As introduced in Chapter 1, carbohydrates and the other macronutrients have been assigned an Acceptable Macronutrient Distribution Range (AMDR). This is the range of intake associated with a decreased risk of chronic diseases. The AMDR for carbohydrates is 45% to 65% of total energy intake, with added sugars providing 25% or less of total energy intake. Most health experts agree that the majority of the carbohydrates you eat each day should be complex—or whole-grain and unprocessed—carbohydrates. As recommended in *Eating Well with Canada's Food Guide*, ensuring that at least half of your grain products are whole grain or multigrain and choosing vegetables and fruit more often than juice will ensure that you get enough fibre and other complex carbohydrates in your diet. Keep in mind that fruits are

Eating the suggested daily amounts of vegetables and fruit, such as apricots, will ensure that you're getting enough fibre-rich carbohydrate in your diet.

predominantly comprised of simple sugar and contain little or no starch. They are healthful food choices, however, as they are good sources of vitamins, some minerals, and fibre, particularly if the skins are eaten.

RECAP The RDA for carbohydrate is 130 grams per day; this amount is only sufficient to supply adequate glucose to the brain. The AMDR for carbohydrate is 45% to 65% of total energy intake. Added sugars should provide 25% or less of total energy intake.

Most Canadians Eat Too Many Simple Carbohydrates

Data from the 2004 Canadian Community Health Survey (CCHS v.2) show that, on average, Canadian adults get half of their energy (50.1%) from carbohydrates and children get 55.4% of their energy from carbohydrates. Both values are well within the AMDR of 45%–65% of total energy (Garriguet, 2006; Health Canada, 2007). More adults than children and teens have carbohydrate intakes that fall below the AMDR. On average, 31.8% of men aged 19 and older, and 21.5% of women aged 19 and older had less than 45% of their total energy from carbohydrates.

Simple sugars account for approximately 21% of the carbohydrate calories (Statistics Canada, 2011). Where does all this sugar come from? Some sugar comes from healthful food sources, such as fruit and milk. However, much of our sugar intake comes from *added sugars*. **Added sugars** include white sugar, brown sugar, honey, maple syrup, and corn sweeteners (dextrose, glucose syrup, and high-fructose corn syrup) added to foods during processing or preparation (Canadian Sugar Institute, 2006).

One common source of added sugars is regular soft drinks; Canadians drink an average of 72 litres per person per year (Statistics Canada, 2009). Consider that one 355-mL (12 fl. oz.) can of regular cola contains 38.5 grams of sugar, or almost 50 mL (10 tsp). If you drink the average amount, you are consuming about 11 320 grams of sugar—almost 15 litres (60 cups)—each year! Other common sources of added sugars include cookies, cakes, pies, fruit drinks, fruit punches, and candy. In addition, a surprising number of processed foods you may not think of as "sweet" actually contain a significant amount of added sugar, including many brands of peanut butter, flavoured rice mixes, and even some canned soups!

Added sugars are not chemically different from naturally occurring sugars. However, foods and beverages with added sugars have lower levels of vitamins, minerals, and fibre than foods that naturally contain simple sugars. Given these nutrient limitations, it is best to choose and prepare foods and beverages with little added sugars. People who are very physically active are able to consume relatively more added sugars, whereas smaller or less active people should consume relatively less. The Nutrition Facts Panel includes a listing of total sugars, but a distinction is not generally made between added sugars and naturally occurring sugars. Thus, you may need to check the ingredients list. Refer to **Table 4.3** for a list of forms of sugar commonly used in foods. To maintain a diet low in added sugars, limit foods in which a form of added sugar is listed as one of the first few ingredients on the label (USDHHS and USDA, 2006).

Sugars Are Blamed for Many Health Problems

Why do sugars have such a bad reputation? First, they are known to cause tooth decay. Second, many people believe they cause hyperactivity in children. Third, eating a lot of sugar could increase the levels of unhealthful lipids, or fats, in our blood, increasing our risk for heart disease. High intakes of sugar have also been blamed for causing diabetes and obesity. Let's learn the truth about these accusations.

Sugar Causes Tooth Decay

Sugars do play a role in dental problems because the bacteria that cause tooth decay thrive on sugar. These bacteria produce acids, which eat away at tooth enamel and can eventually cause cavities and gum disease **(Figure 4.11)**. Eating sticky foods that adhere

Foods with added sugars, such as candy, have lower levels of vitamins and minerals than foods that naturally contain simple sugars.

added sugars Sugars and syrups that are added to food during processing or preparation.

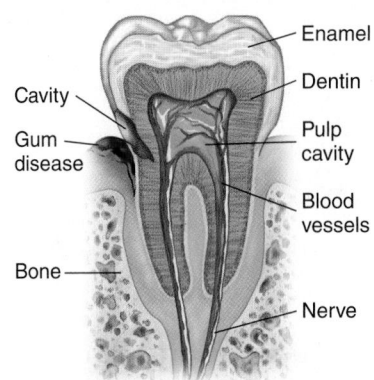

Figure 4.11 Eating simple carbohydrates can cause an increase in cavities and gum disease. This is because bacteria in the mouth consume simple carbohydrates present on the teeth and gums and produce acids, which eat away at these tissues.

TABLE 4.3 Forms of Sugar Commonly Used in Foods

Name of Sugar	Definition
Brown sugar	A highly refined sweetener made up of approximately 99% sucrose and produced by adding to white table sugar either molasses or burnt table sugar for colouring and flavour. The differences in colour between types of brown sugar (e.g., Brilliant Yellow; Demerara-style) depend upon the amount of molasses used.
Concentrated fruit juice sweetener	A form of sweetener made with concentrated fruit juice, commonly pear juice.
Confectioner's sugar	A highly refined, finely ground white sugar with approximately 3% added cornstarch to reduce clumping; also referred to as powdered sugar or icing sugar.
Corn sweetener	A general term for any sweetener made with cornstarch.
Corn syrup	A syrup produced by the partial hydrolysis of cornstarch.
Dextrose	An alternative term for glucose.
Fructose	A monosaccharide in fruits and vegetables, also called levulose or fruit sugar.
Glucose	The most abundant monosaccharide; it is the preferred source of energy for the brain and an important source of energy for all cells.
Granulated sugar	Another term for white sugar, or table sugar.
High-fructose corn syrup	A type of corn syrup in which part of the sucrose is converted to fructose, making it sweeter than sucrose or regular corn syrup; most high-fructose corn syrup contains 42% to 55% fructose.
Honey	A sweet, sticky liquid sweetener made by bees from the nectar of flowers; contains glucose and fructose.
Invert sugar	A sugar created by heating a sucrose syrup with a small amount of acid; inverting sucrose results in its breakdown into glucose and fructose, which reduces the size of the sugar crystals; its smooth texture makes it ideal for use in making candies, such as fondant, and some syrups.
Lactose	A disaccharide formed by one molecule of glucose and one molecule of galactose; occurs naturally in milk and other dairy products.
Levulose	Another term for fructose, or fruit sugar.
Maltose	A disaccharide consisting of two molecules of glucose; it does not generally occur independently in foods but is a by-product of digestion; also called malt sugar.
Mannitol	A type of sugar alcohol.
Maple sugar	A sugar made by boiling maple syrup.
Molasses	A thick, brown syrup that is separated from raw sugar during manufacturing; it is considered the least refined form of sucrose.
Raw sugar	The sugar that results from the processing of sugar beets or sugarcane; approximately 96% to 98% sucrose; true raw sugar contains impurities and is not stable in storage. It is not sold to Canadians because it does not meet Canadian Standards for health and hygiene (Canadian Sugar Institute n.d.).
Sorbitol	A type of sugar alcohol.
Turbinado-style sugar	A semi-refined specialty brown sugar that has been double-washed and coated with molasses.
White sugar	Another name for sucrose, or table sugar.
Xylitol	A type of sugar alcohol.

to teeth—such as caramels, crackers, sugary cereals, and licorice—and sipping sweetened beverages over a period of time are two behaviours that increase the risk for tooth decay. This means that people should not suck on hard candies or caramels, slowly sip pop or juice, or put babies to bed with a bottle unless it contains water. As we have seen, even breast milk contains sugar, which can slowly drip onto the baby's gums. As a result, infants should not routinely be allowed to fall asleep at the breast.

To reduce your risk for tooth decay, brush your teeth after each meal, especially after drinking sugary drinks and eating candy. Drinking fluoridated water and using a fluoride toothpaste will also help protect your teeth.

There Is No Link Between Sugar and Hyperactivity in Children

Although many people believe that eating sugar causes hyperactivity and other behavioural problems in children, there is little scientific evidence to support this claim. Some children actually become less active shortly after a high-sugar meal! However, it is important to emphasize that most studies of sugar and children's behaviour have only looked at the effects of sugar a few hours after ingestion. We know very little about the long-term effects of sugar intake on the behaviour of children. Behavioural and learning problems are complex issues, most likely caused by a multitude of factors. Because of this complexity, the Institute of Medicine (2002) has stated that, overall, there does not appear to be enough evidence to state that eating too much sugar causes hyperactivity or other behavioural problems in children. Thus, there is no Tolerable Upper Intake Level for sugar.

High Sugar Intake Can Lead to Unhealthful Levels of Blood Lipids

Research evidence suggests that consuming a diet high in sugars, particularly fructose, can lead to unhealthful changes in blood lipids. You will learn more about blood lipids (including cholesterol and lipoproteins) in Chapter 5. Briefly, higher intakes of sugars are associated with increases in our blood of both low-density lipoproteins (LDL, commonly referred to as "bad cholesterol") and triglycerides. At the same time, high sugar intake appears to *decrease* our high-density lipoproteins (HDL), which are protective and are often referred to as "good cholesterol"(Howard and Wylie-Rosett, 2002; Institute of Medicine, 2002). These changes are of concern, as increased levels of triglycerides and LDL and decreased levels of HDL are risk factors for heart disease. However, there is not enough scientific evidence at the present time to state with confidence that eating a diet high in sugar causes heart disease. Still, based on current knowledge, it is prudent for a person at risk for heart disease to eat a diet low in sugars. Because fructose, especially in the form of high-fructose corn syrup, is a component of many processed foods and beverages, careful label reading is advised.

High Sugar Intake Does Not Cause Diabetes but May Contribute to Obesity

There is no scientific evidence that eating a diet high in sugar causes diabetes. In fact, studies examining the relationship between sugar intake and type 2 diabetes report no association between sugar intake and diabetes, or an increased risk for diabetes associated with increased sugar intake and weight gain, or a decreased risk for diabetes with increased sugar intake (Colditz et al., 1992; Meyer et al., 2000; Schultze et al., 2004). However, people who have diabetes need to moderate their intake of sugar and closely monitor their blood glucose levels.

There is somewhat more evidence linking sugar intake with obesity. For example, a study found that overweight children consumed more sugared soft drinks than did children of normal weight (Colditz et al., 1992). Another study found that for every extra sugared soft drink a child consumes per day, the risk for obesity increases by 60% (IFICF, 2009). We also know that if you consume more energy than you expend, you will gain weight. It makes intuitive sense that people who consume extra energy from high-sugar foods are at risk for obesity, just as people who consume extra energy from fat or protein gain weight. In addition to the increased potential for obesity, another major concern about high-sugar diets is that they tend to be low in nutrient density because the intake of high-sugar foods tends to replace that of more nutritious foods. The relationship between regular soft drinks and obesity is highly controversial and is discussed in more detail in the Nutrition Debate on page 137.

RECAP The RDA for carbohydrate is 130 g per day; this amount is only sufficient to supply adequate glucose to the brain. The AMDR for carbohydrate is 45% to 65% of total energy intake. Added sugars are sugars and syrups added to foods during processing or preparation. Sugar causes tooth decay but does not appear to cause hyperactivity in children. High intakes of sugars are associated with increases in unhealthful blood lipids. Diets high in sugar are not confirmed to cause diabetes but may contribute to obesity.

▲ Whole-grain foods provide more nutrients and fibre than foods made with enriched flour.

Most North Americans Eat Too Few Complex Carbohydrates

Do you get enough complex carbohydrates each day? Do you eat whole grains and legumes every day? Many people eat plenty of breads, pastas, and cereals, but most do not consistently choose whole-grain products. As we explained

TABLE 4.4 Terms Used to Describe Grains and Cereals on Nutrition Labels

Term	Definition
Brown bread	Bread coloured by the use of whole-wheat flour, graham flour, bran, molasses or caramel
Enriched white bread	Bread made using only enriched wheat flour; contains thiamin, riboflavin, niacin, folic acid, iron; may contain vitamin B_6, pantothenic acid, magnesium, calcium
Whole-wheat bread	Bread containing not less than 60% whole-wheat flour in relation to the total amount of flour used
Whole-wheat flour or entire wheat flour	Bread containing not less than 95% of the natural constituents of the wheat berry
Graham flour	Flour with additional bran and other constituents of the wheat berry
Cracked wheat flour	Flour containing the natural constituents in the proportions found in the wheat used.

Source: Canadian Food Inspection Agency. Reproduced or adapted with the permission of the Minister of Public Works and Government Services Canada, 2012.

enriched foods Foods in which nutrients that were lost during processing have been added back, so that the food meets a specified standard.

fortified foods Foods in which nutrients are added that did not originally exist in the food, or which existed in insignificant amounts.

earlier, whole-grain foods have a lower glycemic index than simple carbohydrates; thus, they prompt a more gradual release of insulin and result in less severe fluctuations in blood levels of insulin and glucose. Whole-grain foods also provide more nutrients and fibre than foods made with enriched flour.

Table 4.4 defines terms commonly used on nutrition labels for breads and cereals. Read the label for the breads you eat—does it list *whole-wheat flour* or just enriched *wheat flour*? Although most labels for breads and cereals list enriched wheat flour as the first ingredient, this term actually refers to enriched white flour, which is made when wheat flour is processed. Don't be fooled—becoming an educated consumer will help you select whole grains instead of processed foods.

In addition to stripping a grain of its fibre, the refining process reduces many of the grain's original nutrients. To make up for some of the lost nutrients, manufacturers sometimes enrich the product. **Enriched foods** are foods in which nutrients that were lost during processing have been added back, so that the food meets a specified standard. Notice that the terms *enriched* and *fortified* are not synonymous: **fortified foods** have nutrients added that did not originally exist in the food (or existed in insignificant amounts). For example, some breakfast cereals have been fortified with iron, a mineral that is not present in cereals naturally.

Eating Right All Day

Breakfast
Oatmeal instead of sugary cereal!

Lunch
Bean soup instead of pizza!

Dinner
Sweet potato instead of french fries!

Snack
Fresh fruit instead of a candy bar!

We Need at Least 25 Grams of Fibre Daily

How much fibre do we need? The Adequate Intake for fibre is 25 g per day for women and 38 g per day for men, or 14 g of fibre for every 4200 kJ (1000 kcal) per day that a person eats (Institute of Medicine, 2002). Average daily intakes of men and women aged 19 and over are 19.1 grams and 15.6 grams of fibre, respectively (Health Canada, 2007). Although fibre supplements are available, it is best to get fibre from food because foods contain additional nutrients, such as vitamins and minerals.

It is also important to drink plenty of fluid as you increase your fibre intake, as fibre binds with water to soften stools. Inadequate fluid intake with a high-fibre diet can actually result in hard, dry stools that are difficult to pass through the colon. At least eight 250 mL glasses of fluid each day are commonly recommended.

Can you eat too much fibre? Excessive fibre consumption can lead to problems such as intestinal gas, bloating, and constipation. Because fibre binds with water, it causes the body to eliminate more water in the feces, so a very-high-fibre diet could result in dehydration. Fibre also binds many vitamins and minerals, so a high-fibre diet can reduce our absorption of important nutrients, such as iron, zinc, and calcium. In children, some elderly, the chronically ill, and other at-risk populations, extreme fibre intake can even lead to malnutrition—they feel full before they have eaten enough to provide adequate energy and nutrients. So, although some societies are accustomed to a very-high-fibre diet, most people in Canada find it difficult to tolerate more than 25 g of fibre per day.

QUICK TIPS

Hunting for Fibre

▶ Select breads made with whole grains, such as wheat, oats, barley, and rye. Two slices of whole-grain bread provide 4–6 grams of fibre.

▶ Switch from a low-fibre breakfast cereal to one that has at least 4 grams of fibre per serving.

▶ For a mid-morning snack, stir 1–2 tablespoons of whole ground flaxseed meal (4 grams of fibre) into a cup of low-fat or non-fat yogurt. Or choose an apple or a pear, with the skin left on (approximately 5 grams of fibre).

▶ Instead of potato chips with your lunch-time sandwich, have a side of carrot sticks or celery sticks (approximately 2 grams of fibre per serving).

▶ Eat legumes every day, if possible (approximately 6 grams of fibre per serving). Have them as your main dish, as a side, or in soups, chili, and other dishes.

▶ Don't forget the vegetables! A cup of cooked leafy greens provides about 4 grams of fibre, and a salad is rich in fibre.

▶ For dessert, try fresh, frozen, or dried fruit or a high-fibre granola cereal with sweetened soy milk.

▶ When shopping, choose fresh fruits and vegetables whenever possible. Buy frozen vegetables and fruits when fresh produce is not available. Check frozen selections to make sure there is no sugar or salt added.

▶ Be careful when buying canned fruits, vegetables, and legumes, as they may be high in added sugar or sodium. Select versions without added sugar or salt, or rinse before serving.

Food Sources of Fibre

Eating the amounts of whole grains, vegetables, fruits, nuts, and legumes recommended in *Eating Well with Canada's Food Guide* will ensure that you eat enough fibre. **Table 4.5** shows some common foods and their fibre content. You can use this information to design a diet that includes adequate fibre.

To help you eat right all day, see the menu choices in Eating Right All Day on page 130 that are high in fibre. Each of these choices is also packed with vitamins, minerals, and phytochemicals. For instance, a sweet potato is loaded with beta-carotene, a phytochemical the body converts to vitamin A.

See the Quick Tips box above for suggestions on selecting carbohydrate sources rich in fibre.

Try the Nutrition Label Activity to learn how to recognize various carbohydrates on food labels. Armed with this knowledge, you are now ready to make more healthful food choices.

RECAP The Adequate Intake for fibre is 25 g per day for women and 38 g per day for men. Most North Americans eat only half of the fibre they need each day. Foods high in fibre and nutrient density include whole grains and cereals, fruits, and vegetables. The more processed the food, the fewer fibre-rich carbohydrates it contains.

Contrary to reports claiming severe health consequences related to the consumption of alternative sweeteners, major health agencies have determined that they are safe to consume.

TABLE 4.5 Fibre Content of Common Foods

Food	Fibre Content (grams)
Breads and Cereals:	
Bagel, 1 each plain, 9 cm (3 1/2 in.) diameter	2
French bread, 1 small slice	2
White bread, 1 slice	1
Pumpernickel bread, 1 small slice	2
Whole-wheat bread, 1 slice	2
Oatmeal, quick, 250 mL (1 cup)	4
Cheerios, 250 mL (1 cup)	1
Corn Flakes, 300 mL (1 1/4 cup)	1
Lucky Charms, 250 mL (1 cup)	1
Fruits and Juices:	
Apple, 1 small, with peel	3
Apple juice, 250 mL (8 fl. oz.)	1
Blackberries, 250 mL (1 cup)	6
Banana, 1 medium	2
Orange, 1 small, peeled	3
Orange juice, 250 mL (8 fl. oz.), from concentrate	1
Pear, 1 medium, with skin	5
Vegetables:	
Asparagus, cooked, 6 spears	2
Broccoli, raw, chopped, 250 mL (1 cup)	3
Broccoli, cooked, chopped, 250 mL (1 cup)	5
Cabbage, raw, chopped, 250 mL (1 cup)	1
Collard greens, cooked, 125 mL (1/2 cup)	2
Corn, canned, whole kernel, 125 mL (1/2 cup)	6
Kale, cooked, 125 mL (1/2 cup)	1
Lettuce, iceberg, shredded, 250 mL (1 cup)	1
Legumes:	
Black beans, cooked, 125 mL (1/2 cup)	7
Lima beans, cooked, 125 mL (1/2 cup)	7
Navy beans, cooked, 125 mL (1/2 cup)	8
Kidney beans, cooked, 125 mL (1/2 cup)	8
Lentils, cooked, 125 mL (1/2 cup)	5

Source: U.S. Department of Agriculture, Agricultural Research Service, USDA National Nutrient Database for Standard Reference, Release 16, 2004, Nutrient Data Laboratory homepage, www.nal.usda.gov/fnic/foodcomp. Values obtained from the USDA Nutrient Database for Standard Reference, Release 16.
Note: The Adequate Intake for fibre is 25 grams per day for women and 38 grams per day for men

What's the Story on Alternative Sweeteners?

Most of us love sweets but want to avoid the extra energy and tooth decay that go along with eating refined sugars. That's why we turn to alternative sweeteners.

Nutritive Sweeteners Include Sugars and Sugar Alcohols

nutritive sweeteners Sweeteners, such as sucrose, fructose, honey, and brown sugar, that contribute energy.

Remember that all carbohydrates, including simple and complex, contain 17 kJ (4 kcal) of energy per gram. Because sweeteners such as sucrose, fructose, honey, and brown sugar contribute Calories (or energy), they are called **nutritive sweeteners**.

NUTRITION LABEL ACTIVITY
Recognizing Carbohydrates on the Label

Figure 4.12 shows portions of labels for two breakfast cereals. The cereal on the left (a) is processed and sweetened, whereas the one on the right (b) is a whole-grain product with no added sugar.

- Check each label to locate the amount of total carbohydrate. For Cereal A, the total carbohydrate is 30 grams, and for Cereal B it is 22 grams for the same serving size.

- Look at the information listed as subgroups under Carbohydrate. The label for Cereal A shows that the cereal contains 1 gram of dietary fibre, 8 grams of sugars, and 21 grams of starch per serving.

- The label for Cereal B lists only the fibre (6 grams) and sugars (1 gram) per serving. In this case, the amount of starch is the difference between the total carbohydrate and the sum of dietary fibre and sugars, or 22 grams −7 grams = 15 grams of starch.

Nutrition Facts (A) Serving 1 cup (30 g)		
Amount	Cereal Only	With 1/2 cup 2% milk
Calories	130	190
		% Daily Value
Fat 0 g*	0%	4%
Saturated 0 g + Trans 0 g	0%	8%
Cholesterol 0 g	0%	3%
Sodium 160 mg	7%	10%
Carbohydrate 30 g	10%	12%
Fibre 1 g	4%	4%
Sugars 8 g		
Starch 21 g		
Protein 3 g		
Vitamin A	0%	8%
Vitamin C	0%	0%
Calcium	10%	20%
Iron	30%	30%
Vitamin D	0%	25%
Thiamin	45%	50%
Riboflavin	35%	50%
Niacin	8%	15%
Vitamin B$_6$	10%	15%
Folate	10%	10%
Vitamin B$_{12}$	0%	25%
Pantothenate	6%	15%
Phosphorus	10%	20%
Magnesium	10%	15%
Zinc	6%	10%
*Amount in cereal		

(a) sweetened cereal

Nutrition Facts (B) Serving 1 cup (30 g)		
Amount	Cereal Only	With 1/2 cup 2% milk
Calories	110	170
		% Daily Value
Fat 2 g*	3%	7%
Saturated 0.4 g + Trans 0 g	2%	10%
Cholesterol 0 g	0%	3%
Sodium 280 mg	12%	14%
Carbohydrate 22 g	16%	18%
Fibre 6 g	24%	24%
Sugars 1 g		
Starch		
Protein 4 g		
Vitamin A	0%	7%
Vitamin C	0%	0%
Calcium	9%	23%
Iron	30%	30%
Vitamin D	0%	25%
Thiamin	40%	44%
Riboflavin	2%	15%
Niacin	3%	8%
Vitamin B$_6$	13%	16%
Folate	8%	10%
Vitamin B$_{12}$	0%	23%
Pantothenate	12%	18%
Phosphorus	10%	20%
Magnesium	9%	16%
Zinc	8%	15%
*Amount in cereal		

(b) whole-grain cereal

Figure 4.12 Labels for two breakfast cereals: **(a)** sweetened cereal; **(b)** whole-grain cereal.

(continued)

NUTRITION LABEL ACTIVITY *(continued)*

- Now look at the percentage values listed to the right of the Carbohydrate section (for cereal only, without milk). For the processed and sweetened Cereal A, the percentage contribution to the daily value for carbohydrate is 10%. For the whole-grain Cereal B, the percentage contribution to daily value for carbohydrate is 7%. This does not mean that 10% and 7%, respectively, of the Calories in Cereals A and B come from carbohydrates. Instead, this percentage refers to the daily values. For a person consuming a 8400 kJ (2000 kcal) diet, the recommended amount of carbohydrate each day is 300 grams. One serving of Cereal A contains 30 grams ÷ 300 grams, or 10% of the recommended amount, and 1 serving of Cereal B contains 22 grams ÷ 300 grams, or about 7% of the recommended amount of carbohydrates.

To calculate the percentage of Calories that comes from carbohydrate, do the following:

a. Calculate the Calories in the cereal that come from carbohydrate. Multiply the total grams of carbohydrate per serving by the energy value of carbohydrate:

    Cereal A: 30 grams of carbohydrate × 17 kJ (4 kcal) per gram = 510 kJ (120 kcal) from carbohydrate

    Cereal B: 22 grams of carbohydrate × 17 kJ (4 kcal) per gram = 370 kJ (88 kcal)

b. Calculate the percent of Calories in the cereal that come from carbohydrate. Divide the Calories from carbohydrate by the total Calories for 1 serving:

    Cereal A: 120 kcal ÷ 130 kcal = 92% of kcal from carbohydrate

    Cereal B: 88 kcal ÷ 110 kcal = 80% of kcal from carbohydrate

Which cereal should you choose? Both cereals are good choices, with 30% of the daily value for iron, no trans fatty acids, little or no fat, and many B vitamins. Although the sweetened, more refined product (Cereal A) is enriched with more B vitamins, most people get adequate amounts of B vitamins from other food sources but need more dietary fibre in their diets. Therefore for most people, Cereal B is a better choice.

Other nutritive sweeteners are the *sugar alcohols,* such as mannitol, sorbitol, isomalt, and xylitol. Popular in sugar-free gums and mints, sugar alcohols are less sweet than sucrose. Foods with sugar alcohols have health benefits that foods made with sugars do not have, such as a reduced glycemic response and a decreased risk for dental caries. Also, because sugar alcohols are absorbed slowly and incompletely from the small intestine, they provide less energy than sugar, usually 8 to 17 kJ (2 to 4 kcal) of energy per gram. However, because they are not completely absorbed from the small intestine, they can attract water into the large intestine and cause diarrhea.

Alternative Sweeteners Are Non-Nutritive

A number of other products have been developed to sweeten foods without promoting tooth decay and weight gain. Because these products provide little or no energy, they are called **non-nutritive,** or *alternative,* **sweeteners.**

Limited Use of Alternative Sweeteners Is Not Harmful

non-nutritive sweeteners Manufactured sweeteners that provide little or no energy; also called alternative sweeteners.

Acceptable Daily Intake (ADI) An estimate made by Health Canada of the amount of a food additive that someone can consume each day over a lifetime without adverse effects.

Contrary to popular belief, alternative sweeteners have been determined to be safe to consume for adults, children, and individuals with diabetes. It appears safe for pregnant women to consume some alternative sweeteners in amounts within the Health Canada guidelines (Dietitians of Canada, 2010).

    The **Acceptable Daily Intake (ADI)** is an estimate made by Health Canada of the amount of a food additive (e.g., chemical compounds such as flavourings, sweeteners, colourings, etc.) that someone can consume each day over a lifetime without adverse effects. The estimates are based on studies conducted on laboratory animals, and they include a 100-fold safety factor. It is important to emphasize that actual intake by humans is typically well below the ADI.

The major alternative sweeteners currently available on the Canadian market are saccharin, cyclamates, acesulfame-potassium (acesulfame-K), aspartame, and sucralose.

Saccharin

Discovered in the late 1800s, *saccharin* is about 300 times sweeter than sucrose. Evidence to suggest that saccharin may cause bladder tumours in rats surfaced in the 1970s; however, more than 20 years of scientific research has shown that saccharin is not related to bladder cancer in humans. Health Canada has recently reviewed the scientific information available and is considering allowing saccharin to be used again as a sweetener in certain foods (Health Canada, 2010b). Saccharin is sold as Sweet 'N Low.

Acesulfame-K

Acesulfame-K (acesulfame potassium) is marketed under the names Sunette and Sweet One. It is a Calorie-free sweetener that is 200 times sweeter than sugar. It is used to sweeten gums, candies, beverages, instant tea, coffee, gelatines, and puddings. The taste of acesulfame-K does not change when it is heated, so it can be used in cooking. The body does not metabolize acesulfame-K, so it is excreted unchanged by the kidneys.

Aspartame

Aspartame, also called Equal ("the blue packet") and NutraSweet, is one of the most popular alternative sweeteners in foods and beverages. Aspartame is composed of two amino acids, phenylalanine and aspartic acid. When these amino acids are separate, one is bitter and the other has no flavour—but joined together they make a substance that is 180 times sweeter than sucrose. Although aspartame contains 17 kJ (4 kcal) of energy per gram, it is so sweet that only small amounts are necessary; thus, it ends up contributing little or no energy. Because aspartame is made from amino acids, its taste is destroyed with heat (see Chapter 6), so it cannot be used in cooking.

A significant amount of research has been done to test the safety of aspartame. Although a number of false claims have been published, especially on the Internet, there is no scientific evidence to support the claim that aspartame causes brain tumours, Alzheimer's disease, or nerve disorders.

The ADI for aspartame is 40 mg per kg body weight per day. Although eating less than the ADI is considered safe, note that children who consume many powdered drinks, diet sodas, and other aspartame-sweetened products could potentially exceed this amount. Drinks sweetened with aspartame are extremely popular among children and teenagers, but they are very low in nutritional value and should not replace healthful beverages, such as milk, water, and 100% fruit juice.

Some people should not consume any aspartame: those with the disease *phenylketonuria (PKU)*. This is a genetic disorder that prevents the breakdown of the amino acid phenylalanine. Because a person with PKU cannot metabolize phenylalanine, it builds up in the tissues of the body and causes irreversible brain damage. In North America, all newborn babies are tested for PKU; those who have it are placed on a phenylalanine-limited diet. Some foods that are common sources of protein and other nutrients for growing children, such as meats and milk, contain phenylalanine. Thus, it is critical that children with PKU not waste what little phenylalanine they can consume on nutrient-poor products sweetened with aspartame.

Sucralose

Sucralose is marketed under the brand name Splenda and is known as "the yellow packet." It is made from sucrose, but chlorine atoms are substituted for the hydrogen and oxygen normally found in sucrose, and it passes through the digestive tract unchanged, without contributing any energy. It is 600 times sweeter than sucrose and is stable when heated, so it can be used in cooking. It has been approved for use in many foods, including chewing gum, salad dressings, beverages, gelatine and pudding products, canned fruits, frozen dairy desserts, and baked goods. Safety studies have not shown sucralose to cause cancer or to have other adverse health effects.

Stevia

Stevia is a plant-based sweetener. The leaves and compounds isolated from the leaves can be used to sweeten foods. In Canada, the leaves may be purchased for culinary use but foods containing stevia leaves as an ingredient cannot be sold. Health Canada recently consulted with scientists about its proposal to approve stevia as a table-top sweetner and food additive (Health Canada 2012). Stevia and stevia extracts have been approved for use in Natural Health Products as both a medicinal and non-medicinal ingredient (Health Canada 2010a).

RECAP Alternative sweeteners can be used in place of sugar to sweeten foods. Most of these products do not promote tooth decay and contribute little or no energy. The alternative sweeteners approved for use in Canada are considered safe when eaten in amounts less than the acceptable daily intake.

Nutrition DEBATE

Is High-Fructose Corn Syrup the Cause of the Obesity Epidemic?

Over the past 30 years, obesity rates have increased dramatically for adults and children. Obesity has become public health enemy number one, as many chronic diseases, such as type 2 diabetes, heart disease, high blood pressure, and arthritis, go hand in hand with obesity.

Factors contributing to obesity include genetic influences, lack of adequate physical activity, and excessive consumption of energy. Genetics cannot be held solely responsible for the rapid rise in obesity that has occurred over the past 30 years. Our genetic makeup takes thousands of years to change; humans who lived 100 years ago had essentially the same genetic makeup as we do. We need to look at the effect of our lifestyle changes over the same period.

One lifestyle factor that has come to the forefront of nutrition research is the contribution of high-fructose corn syrup (HFCS) to overweight and obesity. HFCS is made by converting the starch in corn to glucose and then converting some of the glucose to fructose, which is sweeter. Unfortunately, fructose is metabolized differently than glucose, because it is absorbed farther down in the small intestine and, unlike glucose, it does not stimulate insulin release from the pancreas. Since insulin inhibits food intake in humans, this failure to stimulate insulin release could increase energy intake. In addition, fructose enters body cells via a transport protein not present in brain cells; thus, unlike glucose, fructose cannot enter brain cells and stimulate satiety signals. If we do not feel full, we are likely to continue eating or drinking.

However, the culprit in our increasing obesity rates may not be HFCS itself but, rather, the sweetened soft drinks and other products in which it is found. Statistics Canada does not re-

port on the consumption of HFCS. We do know that 40% of beverages consumed by 14-18 year olds are sweetened beverages (Statistics Canada, 2008), and the per-person consumption of soft drinks has risen from 57 litres per year in 1981 to 72 litres per person, per year in 2009 (Statistics Canada, 2009).

This alarming information has led to dramatic changes in soft drink availability in schools and school nutrition policies in several provinces in Canada restrict the sales of soft drinks.

Although the evidence pinpointing HFCS as a major contributor to the obesity epidemic may appear strong, other nutrition professionals disagree. It has been proposed that soft drinks would have contributed to the obesity epidemic whether the sweetener was sucrose or fructose, and that their contribution to obesity is due to

increased consumption as a result of advertising, increases in serving sizes, and virtually unlimited access to soft drinks (Jacobson, 2004). Also, a recent study found that increased fructose consumption does not cause weight gain in humans (Lê et al., 2006). It is possible that the obesity epidemic has resulted from increased consumption of energy (from sweetened soft drinks and other high-energy foods) *and* a reduction in physical activity levels, and HFCS itself is not to blame. Evidence to support this stems from the fact that obesity rates are rising around the world, and many countries experiencing this epidemic do not use HFCS as a sweetener.

This issue is extremely complex, and more research needs to be done in humans before we can fully understand how HFCS contributes to our diet and our health (Elliott et al., 2002).

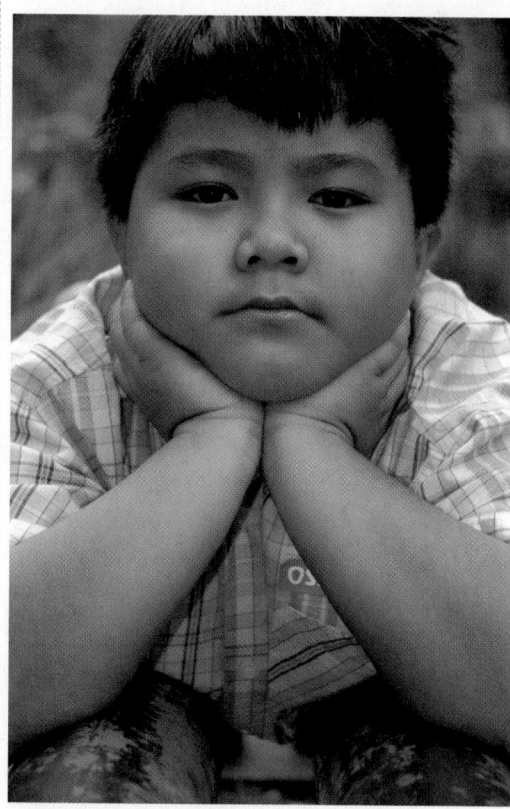

◀ It is estimated that the rate of overweight in children has increased 100% since the mid-1970s.

Chapter Review

1. False. There is no evidence that diets high in sugar cause hyperactivity or diabetes in children.

2. False. At 17 kJ/g (4 kcal/g), carbohydrates have less than half the energy of a gram of fat. Eating a high-carbohydrate diet will not cause people to gain body fat unless their total diet contains more energy (kcal) than they expend. In fact,

eating a diet high in complex, fibre-rich carbohydrates is associated with a lower risk for obesity.

3. True. Contrary to recent reports claiming harmful consequences related to the consumption of alternative sweeteners, major health agencies have determined that these products are safe for most of us to consume in limited quantities.

Find the Quack

Christina is surfing the Internet looking for information for a report on carbohydrates for her nutrition class, when she spots something that intrigues her: Cure Diseases with Sugar! She wonders what it's all about and clicks to bring up the site. Glyconutrients! the homepage proclaims, stating that these special nutrients will reverse aging, increase sports performance, and help you achieve optimal health. Beside a photo of a slender, tanned couple walking along a beach are statements claiming that:

- "Processed foods are devoid of nourishment and have no nutritional value. They are also toxic. We both starve and poison ourselves by consuming these foods. This is why every degenerative disease condition is on the rise."
- "Pharmaceuticals (prescription and over-the-counter medications) do not work."
- "Glyconutrients are plant monosaccharides, essential plant sugars that have recently been shown to be essential to human life. We must consume glyconutrient supplements to protect our health. Without them, our cells will lose the ability to communicate with one another and perform the functions they were designed to do. We will then develop chronic diseases, such as cancer and diabetes."

- "A total of 96 patents have been filed on a range of glyconutrient products."
- "Just about every respected scientific journal has now published documents and articles on glycobiology and glyconutrients."
- "Your doctor will not know about glyconutrients because the topic is only just beginning to be taught in medical schools."

1. In Chapter 1, you learned how to spot false nutrition claims (pages 19–21). Discuss the validity of the website's statement about processed foods.

2. Comment on the website's definition of glyconutrients as plant monosaccharides that are essential for human life.

3. Are you impressed with the statement that "96 patents have been filed on a range of glyconutrient products"? Why or why not?

4. What motive do you think might lurk behind the assertion that your doctor will not know about glyconutrients because the topic "is only just beginning to be taught in medical schools"?

Answers can be found in the study area of MasteringNutrition.

**NutriTools**

Visit MasteringNutrition to access interactive animations, including:

- Food Label: Find the Carbohydrates
- Know Your Carbohydrate Sources
- Digestion and Absorption: Carbohydrates

Review Questions

1. The glycemic index rates the
   a. acceptable amount of alternative sweeteners to consume in one day.
   b. potential of foods to raise blood glucose and insulin levels.
   c. risk of a given food for causing diabetes.
   d. ratio of soluble to insoluble fibre in a complex carbohydrate.

2. Carbohydrates contain
   a. carbon, nitrogen, and water.
   b. carbonic acid and a sugar alcohol.
   c. hydrated sugar.
   d. carbon, hydrogen, and oxygen.

3. The most common source of added sugar in the North American diet is
   a. table sugar.
   b. white flour.
   c. alcohol.
   d. sweetened soft drinks.

4. Glucose, fructose, and galactose are
   a. monosaccharides.
   b. disaccharides.
   c. polysaccharides.
   d. complex carbohydrates.

5. Aspartame should not be consumed by people who have
   a. phenylketonuria.
   b. type 1 diabetes.
   c. lactose intolerance.
   d. diverticulosis.

6. A drop in blood glucose levels stimulates the release of
   a. insulin.
   b. ketones.
   c. glucagon.
   d. gastric acid.

7. Which two monosaccharides join to form the disaccharide lactose?
   a. glucose + glucose
   b. glucose + galactose
   c. galactose + fructose
   d. fructose + glucose

8. Which of the following is a characteristic of insoluble fibre?
   a. Able to absorb water.
   b. Slows nutrient absorption in the blood.
   c. Forms a gel.
   d. Speeds up movement of contents in the large intestine.

9. Which one of the following statements is NOT correct?
   a. Sugar causes tooth decay.
   b. Eating sugar does not lead to hyperactivity in children.
   c. Sugar causes diabetes.
   d. High sugar may increase triglyceride levels.

10. The process of breaking down proteins into amino acids and converting them to glucose is called
    a. gluconeogenesis.
    b. ketoacidosis.
    c. photosynthesis.
    d. glycolysis.

11. Compare and contrast the actions of soluble fibre and insoluble fibre in the small intestine.

12. Identify at least four ways in which fibre helps us maintain a healthy digestive system.

13. Explain why complex carbohydrates are a superior food choice to simple carbohydrates.

14. Defend the statement that obesity can trigger type 2 diabetes.

15. While eating lunch with your friends at the cafeteria, you notice that your friend Sonomi has ordered plain spaghetti, a piece of bread, a glass of apple juice, and some pudding for dessert. Another friend, Matthieu, informs Sonomi that her lunch is very unhealthy because it's basically a tray full of sugar. Sonomi disagrees and says that pasta is nothing like sugar, and she and Matthieu continue to argue for the rest of lunch.

    Is Matthieu or Sonomi correct? After learning about carbohydrate digestion, how would you explain what happens to Sonomi's meal once it enters her body? Is Sonomi's meal balanced? If not, what is she missing and what would you suggest that she add to her lunch tray?

Answers to Review Questions can be found at the back of this text.

Web Resources

www.ific.org
International Food Information Council Foundation (IFIC)

Search this site to find out more about sugars and low-calorie sweeteners.

www.ada.org
American Dental Association

Go to this site to learn more about tooth decay as well as other oral health topics.

www.nidcr.nih.gov
National Institute of Dental and Craniofacial Research (NIDCR)

Find out more about recent oral and dental health discoveries and obtain statistics and data on the status of dental health in the United States.

MasteringNutrition®

Assignments

Animations Carbohydrate Absorption • Carbohydrate Digestion • Diverticulosis & Fibre • Blood Glucose

Study Area

Video: Understanding Carbohydrates • Practice Tests • Diet Analysis • eText

Diabetes

WANT TO FIND OUT...

- **if eating carbohydrates leads to diabetes?**

- **what the link is between diabetes and obesity?**

- **if you're at risk for diabetes?**

READ ON.

It was a typical day at a large medical centre in Toronto: two patients were having toes amputated, another had nerve damage, one was being treated for kidney failure, another for infection, and another was blind. Despite their variety, these problems were due to just one disease: diabetes. On an average day, nearly half of the inpatients at the medical centre have diabetes. And the problem is not limited to Toronto. In Canada, diabetes is the leading cause of blindness, and the cause of 70% of non-traumatic limb amputations. In 2004, 42% of new kidney dialysis patients had diabetes (Canadian Diabetes Association, 2012). A little over a decade ago, these complications, which typically develop about 10 to 15 years after the onset of the disease, were rarely seen in people younger than age 60. But now, as more and more children and adolescents are being diagnosed with diabetes, experts are predicting that the typical patient will be more like Iris, one of the patients with diabetes at the medical centre this day. Iris is 26 years old (Kleinfield, 2006).

What is diabetes? Does eating carbohydrates lead to diabetes? Is obesity linked to diabetes? Here we'll explore *In Depth* the differences between type 1 and type 2 diabetes and the relationship between carbohydrates and a person's risk for diabetes. We'll also explore the link between diabetes, obesity, and other chronic diseases.

What Is Diabetes?

Diabetes is a chronic disease in which the body can no longer regulate glucose within normal limits, and blood glucose levels become dangerously high. It is imperative to detect and treat the disease as soon as possible because excessive fluctuations in glucose injure tissues throughout the body. As noted in the introduction, if not controlled, diabetes can lead to blindness, seizures, stroke, kidney failure, nerve disease, and cardiovascular disease. Damage to the body's nerves and blood vessels is especially problematic in the lower limbs. Along with an increased risk for infection, this increases the incidence of tissue death (necrosis), leading to a greatly increased number of toe, foot, and lower leg amputations in people with diabetes. Uncontrolled diabetes can also lead to ketoacidosis, which may result in coma and death. The direct and indirect costs of diabetes in Canada are estimated to be $13.2 billion each year and are projected to increase to 16.9 billion per year by 2020 (Canadian Diabetes Association, 2012).

TABLE 1 Symptoms of Type 1 and Type 2 Diabetes	
Type 1 Diabetes	**Type 2 Diabetes***
Frequent urination	Any of the type 1 symptoms
Unusual thirst	Frequent infections
Extreme hunger	Blurred vision
Unusual weight loss	Cuts/bruises that are slow to heal
Extreme fatigue	Tingling/numbness in the hands or feet
Irritability	Recurring skin, gum, or bladder infections

Copyright 2012 American Diabetes Association. From http://www.diabetes.org. Reprinted with permission from The American Diabetes Association.
*Some people with type 2 diabetes experience no symptoms.

It is estimated that 9 million Canadians have pre-diabetes or diabetes (Canadian Diabetes Association, 2012). According to the Canadian Diabetes Association (2012), diabetes is related to the deaths of approximately 41 500 people annually, and about 80% of people with diabetes will die from heart disease or stroke. It is estimated that people from the First Nations have three to five times the risk of type 2 diabetes as the general population of Canada (Canadian Diabetes Association, 2012). Because these rates are so much higher and are increasing more quickly than the rates in the rest of the population, diabetes is considered an epidemic among First Nations peoples. It is interesting to note that 50 years ago diabetes was virtually non-existent among First Nations or Aboriginal populations.

The two main forms of diabetes are type 1 and type 2. Some women develop a third form, *gestational diabetes,* during pregnancy; we will discuss this in more detail in Chapter 14.

In Type 1 Diabetes, the Body Does Not Produce Enough Insulin

Approximately 10% of people with diabetes have **type 1 diabetes**, in which the body cannot produce enough insulin.

When people with type 1 diabetes eat a meal and their blood glucose rises, the pancreas is unable to secrete insulin in response. Glucose levels soar, and the body tries to expel the excess glucose by excreting it in the urine. In fact, the medical term for the disease is *diabetes mellitus* (from the Greek *diabainein,* "to pass through," and Latin *mellitus,* "sweetened with honey"), and frequent urination is one of its warning signs (see **Table 1** for other symptoms). If blood glucose levels are not controlled, a person with type 1 diabetes will become confused and lethargic and have trouble breathing. This is because the brain is not getting enough glucose to function properly. As discussed earlier in this chapter,

diabetes A chronic disease in which the body can no longer regulate glucose normally.

type 1 diabetes A disorder in which the body cannot produce enough insulin.

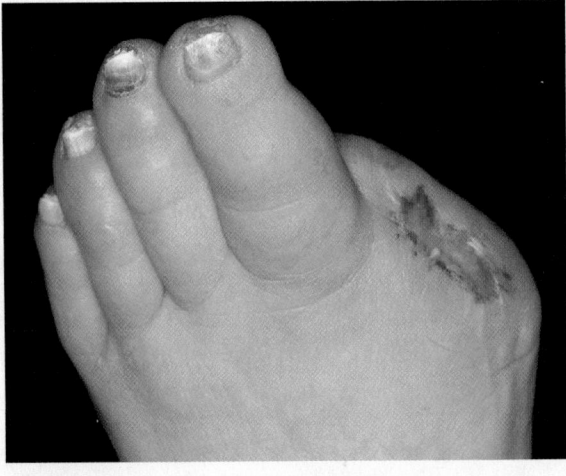
◀ Amputations are a common complication of uncontrolled diabetes.

Diabetes Goes High-Tech

Vincent was diagnosed with type 1 diabetes when he was 10 years old. Now he's a university student and has been living with the disease for nine years. In that time, advances in diabetes monitoring and treatment have made Vincent's life just a little easier.

For instance, all people with diabetes have to test their blood glucose level many times each day. Until recently, Vincent had to prick his fingers to do this, and they would get tender and develop calluses. Health Canada has now approved several devices that measure blood glucose without pricking the finger. Some of them can read glucose levels through the skin, and others take readings from a small needle implanted in the body. Also, during his first few years with diabetes, Vincent had to give himself two to four shots of insulin each day. Now he uses an insulin infusion pump, which looks like a small pager, and which gradually, throughout the day, delivers insulin into his body through a thin tube.

Insulin pumps are expensive, and until Vincent was accepted into the Assistive Devices Program from the Ontario Government he could not afford to buy a pump or the supplies he needs to use it. Ontario now has funding for type 1 diabetics for the price of the insulin pump and up to $2,400 per year towards supplies. The funding means that Vincent can afford to use an insulin pump!

Sure, Vincent still has to watch his diet carefully, eating three nutritious meals a day and limiting snacks. But with an insulin pump, it's easier to control his blood glucose, and he can play sports, travel, and do most of the things he wants to do, just like his friends.

Insulin pumps can help those with diabetes eat a wider range of foods.

uncontrolled diabetes can lead to ketoacidosis; left untreated, the ultimate result is coma and death.

The cause of type 1 diabetes is unknown, but it may be an *autoimmune disease*. This means that the body's immune system attacks and destroys its own tissues—in this case, the insulin-producing cells of the pancreas. Some recent research suggests that there may also be a link to viral infections or other environmental toxins. Of particular interest are infections caused by a group of non-polio enteroviruses called Coxsackie viruses (CDC, 2000). Being exposed to these viruses early in life may trigger the abnormal antibody responses that damage the beta cells that manufacture insulin. Some researchers are looking at methods of measuring these antibodies and other substances that are indicators of autoimmune reactions.

Most cases of type 1 diabetes are diagnosed in adolescents around 10 to 14 years of age, although the disease can appear in infants, young children, and adults. It has a genetic link, so siblings and children of those with type 1 diabetes are at greater risk (American Diabetes Association, 2010).

The only treatment for type 1 diabetes is the administration of insulin by injection or pump several times daily. Insulin is a hormone composed of protein, so it would be digested in the small intestine if taken as a pill.

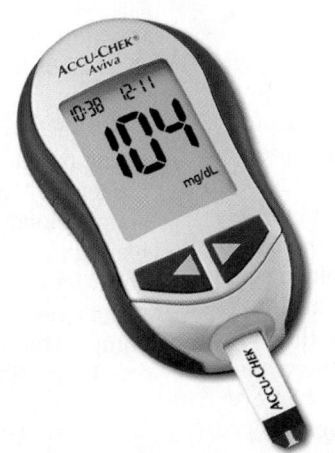

Figure 1 Monitoring blood glucose requires pricking the fingers and measuring the blood using a glucometer each day.

Individuals with type 1 diabetes must monitor their blood glucose levels closely using a *glucometer* to ensure that they remain within a healthful range (Figure 1).

In Type 2 Diabetes, Cells Become Less Responsive to Insulin

In **type 2 diabetes**, body cells become resistant (less responsive) to insulin. This type of diabetes develops progressively, meaning that the biological changes resulting in the disease occur over a long period of time.

Obesity is the most common trigger for a cascade of changes that eventually results in this disorder. It is estimated that 80% to 90% of the people with type 2 diabetes are overweight or obese. Specifically, the cells of many obese people are less responsive to insulin, exhibiting a condition called *insulin insensitivity* (sometimes called insulin resistance). The pancreas attempts to compensate for this insensitivity by secreting more insulin. At first, the increased secretion of insulin is sufficient to maintain normal blood glucose levels. However, over time the blood of a person who is insulin insensitive will have to circulate very high levels of insulin to use glucose for energy. Eventually, this excessive production becomes insufficient for preventing a rise in fasting blood glucose. The resulting condition is referred to as **impaired fasting glucose**, meaning glucose levels are higher than normal but not high enough to indicate a diagnosis of type 2 diabetes. Some health professionals refer to this condition as *pre-diabetes*, as people with impaired

type 2 diabetes A progressive disorder in which body cells become less responsive to insulin.

impaired fasting glucose Fasting blood glucose levels that are higher than normal but not high enough to lead to a diagnosis of type 2 diabetes; also called pre-diabetes.

fasting glucose are more likely to get type 2 diabetes than people with normal fasting blood glucose levels. Ultimately, the pancreas becomes incapable of secreting these excessive amounts of insulin and stops producing the hormone altogether. Thus, blood glucose levels may be elevated because (1) of insulin insensitivity, (2) the pancreas can no longer secrete enough insulin, or (3) the pancreas has entirely stopped insulin production.

Who Is at Risk for Type 2 Diabetes?

As noted, obesity is the most common trigger for type 2 diabetes. But many other factors also play a role. For instance, relatives of people with type 2 diabetes are at increased risk, as are people with a sedentary lifestyle. A cluster of risk factors referred to as the *metabolic syndrome* is also known to increase the risk

for type 2 diabetes. The criteria for metabolic syndrome are having a waist circumference > 88 cm (35 in.) (Grundy et al., 2005) for women and > 102 cm (40 in.) for men, elevated blood pressure, and unhealthful levels of certain blood lipids and blood glucose.

Increased age is another risk factor for type 2 diabetes (Canadian Diabetes Association, 2012). Once commonly known as *adult-onset diabetes,* type 2 diabetes in children was virtually unheard of until recently.

HIGHLIGHT

Diabetes Complications: The Long-Term Picture

Both type 1 and type 2 diabetes are associated with a number of serious complications over the longer term. Heart disease, for example, is common in many people with diabetes; genetics may have a role, and poorly controlled blood glucose levels do as well.

Arteries

Diabetes can cause blood vessel problems such as atherosclerosis (the buildup of plaque deposits in the blood vessels). This buildup can be particularly serious when it affects the coronary arteries, which supply your heart with blood. Also known as *macrovascular disease,* or large blood vessel disease, partial or total blockage of the coronary arteries can lead to a number of very serious complications, such as angina (chest pains) and heart attack. We do not know yet why people with diabetes are more likely to develop cardiovascular disease. But research has found that high blood sugar levels do cause damage to the arteries.

Eyes

Did you know that diabetes is the most common cause of adult blindness in the Western world? *Microvascular disease,* or small blood vessel disease, begins the process that can lead to partial and—if left untreated—total loss of vision. Retinopathy occurs when the small blood vessels in the retina, the light-sensitive inner lining at the back of the eye, become damaged as a result of high blood sugar levels. Damage to the eye may include hemorrhaging, the development of scar tissue, and detachment of the retina. Because symptoms do not arise until the advanced stages of the disease, only regular eye examinations by an eye specialist will detect the early stages of the disease. Fortunately, with early detection, laser treatment may prevent further damage.

Nerves

Chronic high blood sugar can damage the nerves—a condition called neuropathy. Neuropathy can be "sensory"—nerve damage that affects the legs, arms, hands, chest, or abdomen, resulting in a loss of sensation, pins and needles, tingling, or pain (and, in some cases, amputation). It can also be "autonomic" damage to the nerves that control the actions of a number of organs, including the bladder, stomach, intestine, and penis (for example, nerve damage can cause impotence).

Kidneys

The kidneys filter out waste products from the blood into the urine. Chronic high blood sugar levels over time damage the filtering units in kidneys. The problem is that once the kidneys are damaged in this way, they cannot be repaired. Early treatment can slow the progress of kidney (renal) disease and slow the onset of end-stage renal disease. End-stage renal disease occurs when the kidneys function at only 10% or less of their capacity and requires dialysis or kidney transplants.

Ensuring Good Blood Sugar Control

Home monitoring of blood glucose with a glucometer gives the level of sugar in the blood at that exact moment. A simple blood test done by a doctor, called the glycosylated hemoglobin (HbA1c or A1C) test, shows the average blood sugar level over the past three months. It is a good indicator of overall diabetes control and a predictor of long-term complications. People with diabetes should ask their doctors for an HbA1c or A1C test every three to six months.

Source: Adapted from the Canadian Diabetes Association, "Complications: The Long Term Picture," www.diabetes.ca/diabetes-and-you/living/complications (accessed July 2012).

Unfortunately, the disease is increasing dramatically among children and adolescents (Canadian Diabetes Association, 2012), and because approximately one-half of children with type 2 diabetes have no symptoms, they are diagnosed only when they are being screened for health problems related to overweight or obesity (Canadian Diabetes Association, 2012).

Lifestyle Choices Can Help Prevent or Control Diabetes

Type 2 diabetes is increasing in North America because of a combination of poor eating habits, sedentary lifestyles, increased incidence of obesity, and an aging population. We cannot control our age, but we can and do control how much and what types of foods we eat and how much physical activity we engage in—and that, in turn, influences our risk for obesity. Currently, 23% of 18- and 19-year-old Canadians are either overweight or obese (Statistics Canada, 2011). Although adopting a healthful diet is important, moderate daily exercise may prevent the onset of type 2 diabetes more effectively than dietary changes alone (Pan et al., 1997). (See Chapter 14 for examples of moderate exercise programs.) Exercise will also assist in weight loss, and studies show that losing only 10 to 30 pounds can reduce or eliminate the symptoms of type 2 diabetes (American College

Jerry Garcia, a member of the Grateful Dead, had type 2 diabetes.

of Sports Medicine, 2000). In summary, by eating a healthy diet, staying active, and maintaining a healthful body weight, you should be able to keep your risk for type 2 diabetes low.

But what if you have already been diagnosed with type 2 diabetes? In general, you should follow many of the same dietary guidelines recommended for people without diabetes (see Chapter 2). Carbohydrates are still an important part of the diet. Choose low glycemic index foods that are rich in nutrients and fibre. Precise nutritional recommendations vary according to each individual's responses to foods, so consulting with a registered dietitian is essential.

In addition, people with diabetes should avoid alcoholic beverages, which can cause hypoglycemia. The symptoms of alcohol intoxication and hypoglycemia are very similar. People with diabetes, their companions, and even healthcare providers may confuse these conditions; this can result in a potentially life-threatening situation.

When blood glucose levels cannot be adequately controlled with lifestyle changes, oral medications may be required. These drugs work in either of two ways: they improve body cells' sensitivity to insulin or reduce the amount of glucose the liver produces. Finally, if the pancreas can no longer secrete enough insulin, then people with type 2 diabetes must have daily insulin injections, just like people with type 1 diabetes.

Web Resources

www.diabetes.ca
Canadian Diabetes Association

An excellent website with all kinds of information about risk factors for diabetes, diabetes management, the glycemic index, and research that is being funded in Canada.

www.diabetes.org
American Diabetes Organization

Find out more about the nutritional needs of people living with diabetes.

www.niddk.nih.gov
National Institute of Diabetes and Digestive and Kidney Diseases (NIDDK).

Learn more about diabetes including treatment, complications, U.S. statistics, clinical trials, and recent research.

Fats: Essential Energy-Supplying Nutrients

5

CHAPTER OBJECTIVES

After reading this chapter you will be able to:

1. List and describe the three types of lipids found in foods, pp. 148–155.

2. Discuss how the level of saturation affects the shape and form of fatty acids, pp. 150–151.

3. Identify the primary difference between a *cis* fatty acid and a *trans* fatty acid, pp. 150–152.

4. List three functions of fat in our bodies, pp. 160–164.

5. Describe the steps involved in fat digestion, pp. 155–160.

6. Define the recommended dietary intakes for total fat, saturated fat, and the two essential fatty acids, pp. 164–165.

7. Identify and describe the functions of four blood lipoproteins p. 180–183.

8. Describe the role of dietary fat in the development of cardiovascular disease, pp. 180–182.

Test Yourself

1. **T F** Some fats are essential for good health.

2. **T F** Fat is an important source of energy during rest and exercise.

3. **T F** Fried foods are relatively nutritious as long as vegetable oils are used to fry the foods.

4. **T F** Reduced-fat and fat-free foods usually contain less than half the calories of full-fat versions of the same foods.

Test Yourself answers can be found at the end of the chapter.

How would you feel if you purchased a bag of potato chips and were charged an extra 5% "fat tax"? What if you ordered fish and chips in your favourite restaurant, only to be told that, in an effort to avoid lawsuits, fried foods were no longer being served? Sound surreal? These and similar scenarios are being proposed and defended around the globe as local and national governments and health care policy advisors are scrambling to find effective methods for combating cardiovascular disease. For reasons we explore in this chapter, many of the proposals focus on limiting consumption of foods high in saturated and trans fats—for instance, threatening extra taxes for such foods; asking manufacturers to voluntarily reduce the trans fat content of packaged foods; removing them from vending machines; banning advertisements of these foods to children; and using health and nutrient claims on food labels to encourage consumers to choose foods lower in saturated and trans fats. At the same time, "food litigation" lawsuits have been increasing, including allegations against restaurant chains and food companies for failing to warn consumers of the health dangers of eating their energy-dense, high-saturated-fat foods.

Is fat really such a menace? If so, why? Does healthy fat sound like an oxymoron to you? Did you know that there are important sources of fat in your diet that are good for you? After all these years of hearing that lower-fat diets are the best way to go, are you hesitant to add any kind of fat to your diet? In this chapter, we'll answer these questions, plus identify some small changes you can make to shift your diet toward more healthful fats. We'll discuss the function of fat in the human body and help you distinguish between the types of dietary fat. The role of dietary fats in cardiovascular disease is discussed *In Depth* following this chapter.

What Are Fats?

Fats are just one form of a much larger and more diverse group of organic substances called **lipids**, which are distinguished by the fact that they are insoluble in water. Think of a salad dressing made with vinegar, which is mostly water, and olive oil, which is a lipid. Shaking the bottle *disperses* the oil but does not *dissolve* it: that is why it separates back out again so quickly. Lipids are found in all sorts of living things, from bacteria to plants to human beings. In fact, their presence on your skin explains why you cannot clean your face with water alone: you need some type of soap to break down the insoluble lipids before you can wash them away. In this chapter, we focus on the small group of lipids that are found in foods.

Fats and oils are two different types of lipids found in foods. Fats, such as butter, are solid at room temperature, whereas oils, such as olive oil, are liquid at room temperature. Because most people are more comfortable with the term *fats* instead of *lipids*, we will use that term generically throughout this book, including when we are referring to oils. Three types of fats are commonly found in foods; triglycerides, phospholipids, and sterols. Let's take a look at each.

Triglycerides Are the Most Common Food-Based Fat

Most of the fat we eat (95%) is in the form of triglycerides (also called *triacylglycerols*), which is the same form in which most of the fat in our body is stored. As reflected in the prefix *tri-*, a **triglyceride** is a molecule consisting of *three* fatty acids attached to a *three*-carbon glycerol backbone. **Fatty acids** are long chains of carbon atoms bound to each other as well as to hydrogen atoms. They are acids because they contain an acid group (carboxyl group) at one end of their chain. **Glycerol**, the backbone of a triglyceride molecule, is an alcohol composed of three carbon atoms. The carboxyl (COOH) end of a fatty acid attaches to the OH group of the glycerol, releasing one molecule of water (H_2O) **(Figure 5.1a)**.

Triglycerides Are Classified by Their Length, Saturation, and Shape

To understand why we want more of some fats than others, we need to know more about their properties and how they work in our body. In general, triglycerides can be classified by their chain length (number of carbons in each fatty acid), their level of saturation (how much hydrogen, H, is attached to each carbon atom in the fatty acid chain), and their shape, which is determined in some cases by how they are commercially processed. All of these factors influence how we use the triglycerides within our bodies.

Chain Length   The fatty acids attached to the glycerol backbone can vary in the number of carbons they contain, referred to as their *chain length*.

- Short-chain fatty acids are usually fewer than six carbon atoms in length.
- Medium-chain fatty acids are six to 12 carbons in length.
- Long-chain fatty acids are 14 or more carbons in length.

The carbons of a fatty acid can be numbered beginning with the carbon of the carboxyl end (COOH), which is designated the α-carbon (that is, the alpha or first carbon), or from the carbon of the last methyl group (CH_3), called the ω-carbon (the omega or last carbon, see **Figure 5.1c**). Fatty acid chain length is important because it determines the method of fat digestion and absorption and affects how fats function within the body. For example, short- and medium-chain fatty acids are digested and transported more quickly than long-chain fatty acids. In general, long-chain fatty acids are more abundant in nature, and thus more abundant in our diet, than short- or medium-chain fatty acids. We will discuss the digestion and absorption of fats in more detail shortly. In addition, chain length can determine saturation, as discussed in the next section.

⬆ Some fats, such as olive oil, are liquid at room temperature.

lipids A diverse group of organic substances that are insoluble in water; lipids include triglycerides, phospholipids, and sterols.

triglyceride A molecule consisting of three fatty acids attached to a three-carbon glycerol backbone.

fatty acids Long chains of carbon atoms bound to each other as well as to hydrogen atoms.

glycerol An alcohol composed of three carbon atoms; it is the backbone of a triglyceride molecule.

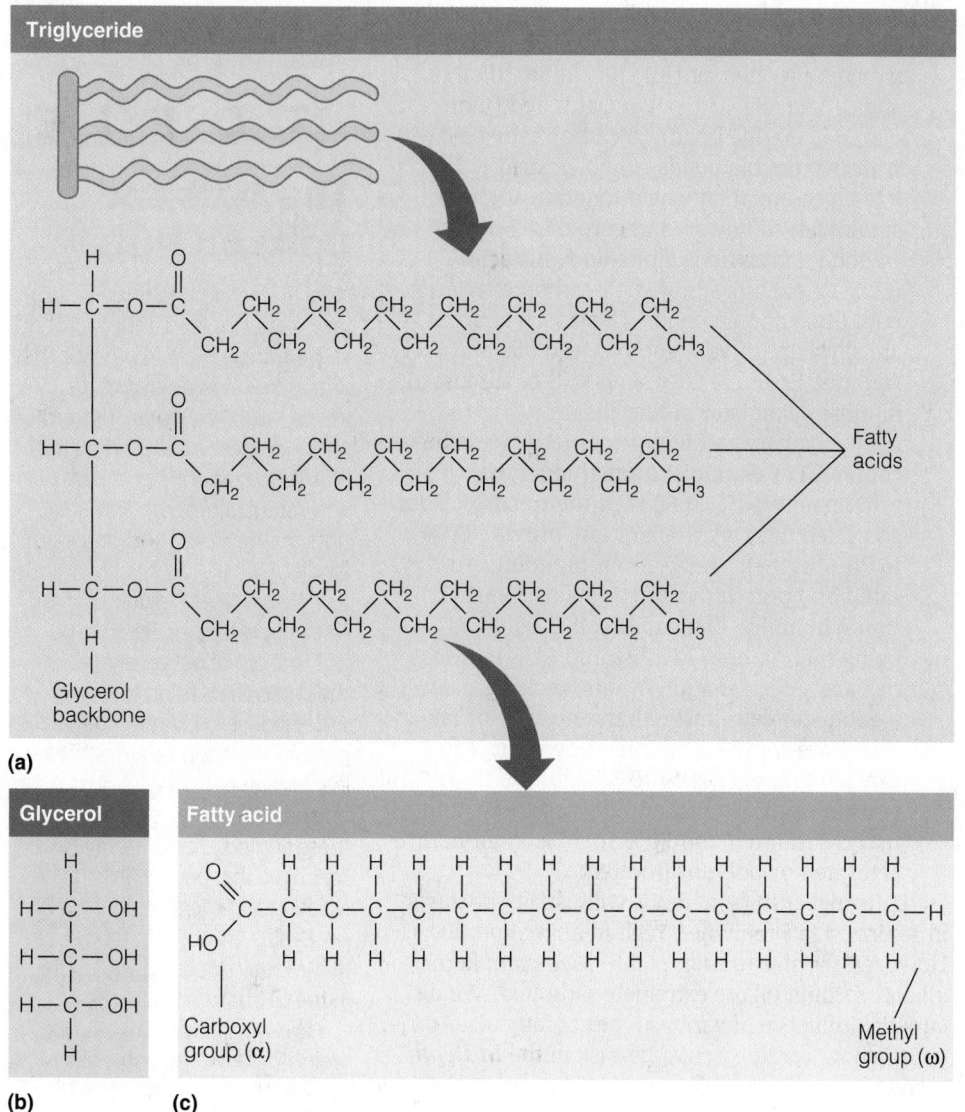

(a)

(b)   **(c)**

Figure 5.1 **(a)** A triglyceride consists of three fatty acids attached to a three-carbon glycerol backbone. **(b)** Structure of glycerol. **(c)** Structure of a fatty acid showing the carboxyl carbon (α) and the methyl carbon (ω) ends.
Source: (Thompson, Janice; Manore, Melinda; Vaughan, Linda, The Science of Nutrition, 2nd Ed., ©2011. Reprinted and Electronically reproduced by permission of Pearson Education, Inc., Upper Saddle River, New Jersey.)

Level of Saturation   Triglycerides can also vary by the types of bonds found in the fatty acids. If a fatty acid has no carbons bonded together with a double bond, it is referred to as a **saturated fatty acid (SFA)** (**Figures 5.2a** and **5.3a**). This is because every carbon atom in the chain is *saturated* with hydrogen: each has the maximum amount of hydrogen bound to it. Most, but not all, saturated fatty acids are solid at room temperature. Some foods that are high in saturated fatty acids are coconut oil, palm kernel oil, butter, lard, and beef fat.

If two carbons are bound to each other with a double bond, for each carbon atom of the double bond. This lack of hydrogen at *one* part of the molecule results in a fat that is referred to as *monounsaturated* (recall from Chapter 4 that the prefix *mono-* means "one"). A monounsaturated molecule is shown in Figures 5.2b and 5.3a. **Monounsaturated fatty acids (MUFAs)** are usually liquid at room temperature. Foods that are high in monounsaturated fatty acids are olive oil, canola oil, and cashew nuts.

If the fat molecules have *more than one* double bond, they contain even less hydrogen and are referred to as **polyunsaturated fatty acids (PUFAs)** (see Figure 5.3a.) Polyunsaturated fatty acids are also liquid at room temperature and include soybean, sunflower, corn, and safflower oils.

Scientists use an abbreviated system to describe fatty acids—a ratio of the number of carbons to the number of double bonds. For example, the saturated (no double bonds) 18-carbon fatty acid would be written as 18:0; this is stearic acid, and it is found in most

saturated fatty acids (SFAs) Fatty acids that have no carbons joined together with a double bond; these types of fatty acids are generally solid at room temperature.

monounsaturated fatty acids (MUFAs) Fatty acids that have two carbons in the chain bound to each other with one double bond; these types of fatty acids are generally liquid at room temperature.

polyunsaturated fatty acids (PUFAs) Fatty acids that have more than one double bond in the chain; these types of fatty acids are generally liquid at room temperature.

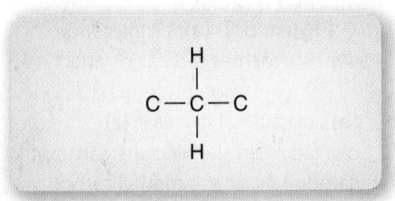

(a) Saturated fatty acid

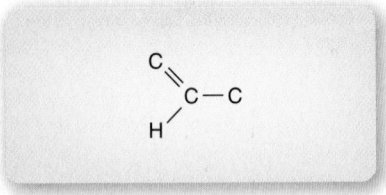

(b) Unsaturated fatty acid

Figure 5.2 An atom of carbon has four attachment sites. In fatty acid chains, two of these sites are filled by adjacent carbon atoms. **(a)** In saturated fatty acids, the other two sites are always filled by two hydrogen atoms. **(b)** In unsaturated fatty acids, at one or more points along the chain, a double bond to an adjacent carbon atom takes up one of the attachment sites that would otherwise be filled by hydrogen.

animal fats. The monounsaturated (one double bond) 18-carbon fatty acid called oleic acid would be written as 18:1; it is found in olive and canola oils. The polyunsaturated (more than one double bond) 18-carbon fatty acid with two double bonds is linoleic acid (18:2). It is an essential fatty acid found in soybean, sunflower, safflower, and corn oils. Another essential fatty acid is alpha-linolenic acid (18:3), a polyunsaturated 18-carbon fatty acid with three double bonds. Good food sources are soybean, canola, and flaxseed oils and walnuts. Essential fatty acids will be discussed in more detail later in this chapter.

Foods vary in the types of fatty acids they contain. For example, animal fats provide approximately 40% to 60% of their energy from saturated fats, while plant fats provide 80% to 90% of their energy from monounsaturated and polyunsaturated fats **(Figure 5.4)**. You will notice that canola oil is listed as being high in both MUFAs and PUFAs. Most oils are a combination of fats, making them a good source of more than one type of fat. There are some exceptions, however. You can see that only 20% to 30% of the fat in cooked skinless chicken breast, turkey, and fish is saturated and 70% to 80% is monounsaturated or polyunsaturated.

Diets higher in plant foods will usually be lower in saturated fats than diets high in animal products. However, the short-chain, plant-based palm kernel oil and coconut oil are extremely saturated. We discuss the influence of various types of fatty acids on your risk for cardiovascular disease in the ***In Depth*** section immediately following this chapter.

Shape Have you ever noticed how many toothpicks are packed into a small box? A hundred or more! But if you were to break a bunch of toothpicks into V shapes anywhere along their length, how many could you then fit into the same box? It would be very few because the bent toothpicks would jumble together, taking up much more space. Molecules of saturated fat are like straight toothpicks: they have no double carbon bonds and always form straight, rigid chains. As they have no kinks, these chains can pack together tightly (see **Figure 5.3b**). That is why saturated fats, such as the fat in meats, are solid at room temperature.

In contrast, each double carbon bond of unsaturated fats gives them a kink along their length (see **Figure 5.3c**). This means that they are unable to pack together tightly—for example, to form a stick of butter—and instead are liquid at room temperature. In addition, unsaturated fatty acids can occur on either a *cis* or a *trans* shape. The prefix *cis* means things are located on the same side or near each other, whereas *trans* is a prefix that denotes across or opposite. These

HOT TOPIC

The Nuts and Bolts on Nuts

Nuts are rich in healthful unsaturated fats, not to mention protein, some minerals, and fibre. But they are also high in energy: 670–750 kJ (160–180 kcal) for a 30 gram (1 ounce) serving (about 60 mL or 4 Tbsp, depending on the nut) and salt (sodium). So why are nuts the new "in" food on popular diet plans?

Well, in several studies, when researchers fed people 30 to 60 g (1 to 2 oz.) of nuts every day, the participants failed to gain the expected weight. And, in general, people who eat nuts are typically leaner than people who do not. No one has a definitive explanation for these findings. Some researchers speculate that people find nuts satiating and therefore eat less later on. Others propose that the energy in nuts may not be fully absorbed in the GI (gastrointestinal) tract.

Will nuts help you control your weight? Maybe—if you can limit yourself to approximately 30 to 60 g (an ounce or two) a day and choose unsalted varieties. Trouble is, they taste so good, it is easy to overdo it.

Walnuts and cashews are high in monounsaturated fatty acids. Choose unsalted varieties to avoid extra sodium in your diet.

Fatty acids

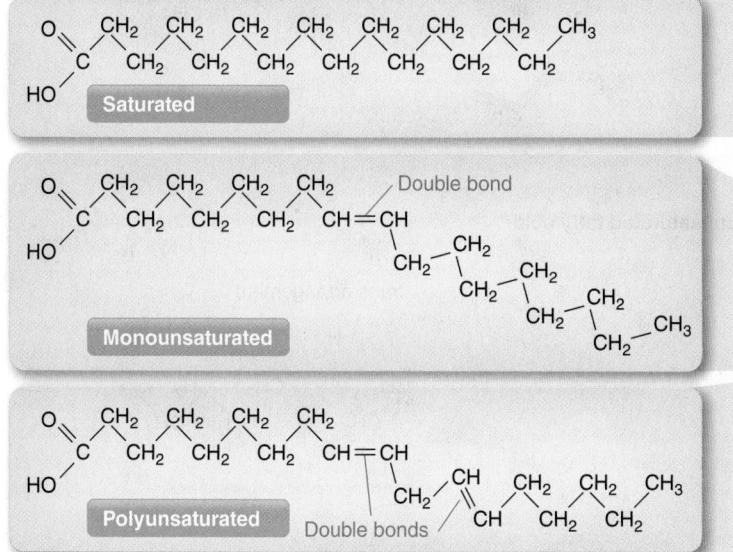

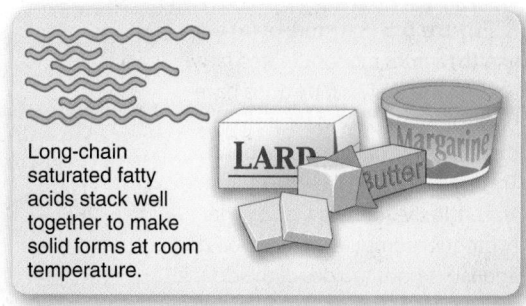

Long-chain saturated fatty acids stack well together to make solid forms at room temperature.

(b)

Monounsaturated and polyunsaturated fatty acids do not stack well together because they are bent. These fatty acids are liquid at room temperature.

(a)

(c)

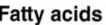 **Figure 5.3** Examples of levels of saturation among fatty acids and how these levels of saturation affect the shape of fatty acids. **(a)** Saturated fatty acids are saturated with hydrogen, meaning they have no carbons bonded together with a double bond. Monounsaturated fatty acids contain two carbons bound by one double bond. Polyunsaturated fatty acids have more than one double bond linking carbon atoms. **(b)** Saturated fats have straight fatty acids packed tightly together and are solid at room temperature. **(c)** Unsaturated fats have "kinked" fatty acids at the area of the double bond, preventing them from packing tightly together; they are liquid at room temperature.

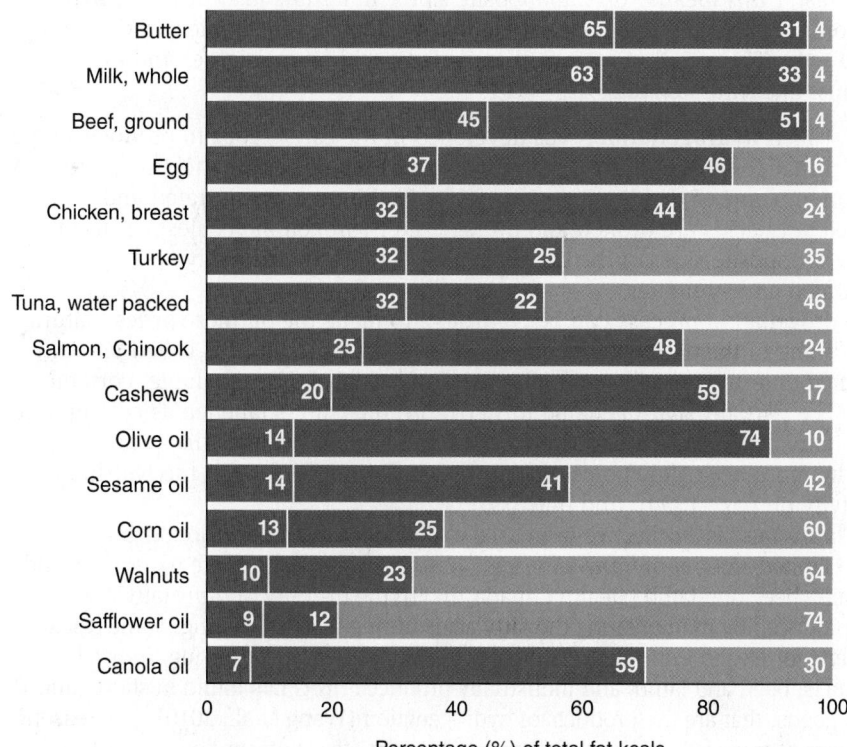

Percentage (%) of total fat kcals

Key:
- Saturated fatty acids
- Monosaturated fatty acids
- Polyunsaturated fatty acids

Figure 5.4 Major sources of dietary fat.

▶ **Figure 5.5** Structure of **(a)** a *cis* and **(b)** a *trans* monosaturated fatty acid. Notice that *cis* fatty acids have both hydrogen atoms located on the same side of the double bond. This positioning makes the molecule kinked. In the *trans* fatty acids, the hydrogen atoms are attached on diagonally opposite sides of the double carbon bond. This positioning makes them straighter and more rigid.

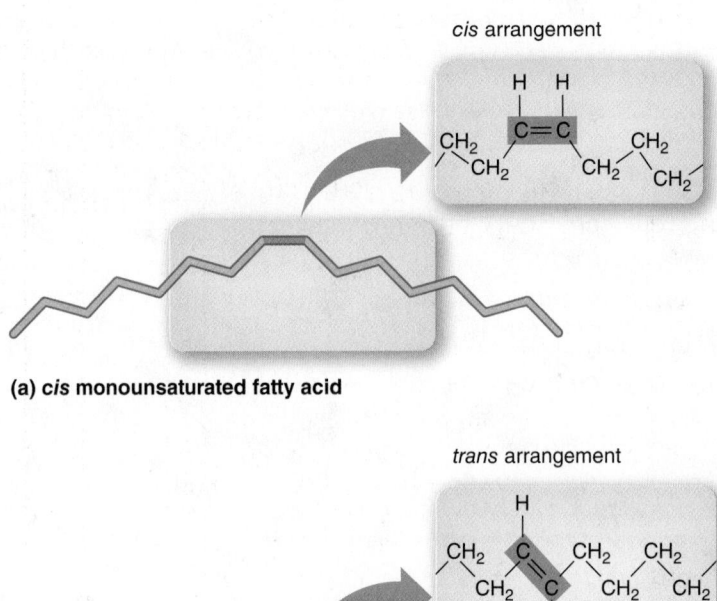

cis arrangement

(a) *cis* **monounsaturated fatty acid**

trans arrangement

(b) *trans* **monounsaturated fatty acid**

terms describe the positioning of the hydrogen atoms around the double carbon bond as follows:

- The prefix *cis* means "on the same side." A *cis fatty acid* has both hydrogen atoms located on the same side of the double bond **(Figure 5.5a)**. This positioning gives the *cis* molecule a pronounced kink at the double carbon bond. We typically find the *cis* fatty acids in nature, and thus in foods such as olive oil.
- In contrast, *trans* means "on the opposite side." In a *trans fatty acid*, the hydrogen atoms are attached on diagonally opposite sides of the double carbon bond **(Figure 5.5b)**. This positioning makes *trans* fatty acid fats straighter and more rigid, just like saturated fats.

A process, called **hydrogenation**, was developed in the early 1900s to produce a type of cheap fat that could be stored in a solid form and would resist rancidity. During hydrogenation, some of the double bonds found in the monounsaturated and polyunsaturated fatty acids are broken and pressurized hydrogen molecules are inserted at diagonally opposite sides of the double bonds. As a result, the fatty acid becomes more saturated and straighter.

The hydrogenation process can be controlled to make the oil more or less saturated: if only some of the double bonds are broken, the fat produced is called *partially hydrogenated*, a term you will see frequently on food labels. For example, corn oil margarine is a partially hydrogenated form of corn oil. Unless labelled as containing zero *trans* fatty acids, most margarines have more *trans* fatty acids than butter. So which is the more healthful choice—butter or margarine? Check out the Nutrition Label Activity on page 153 to find out!

Thus, "trans fats" is a collective term used to define fats with *trans* double bonds. Although a limited amount of *trans* fatty acids (2% to 5% of total fat) are naturally found in cow's milk, beef, and lamb (Health Canada, 2009), the majority of *trans* fatty acids in foods are produced by manipulating the fatty acids during food processing. Some researchers are calling for Health Canada to distinguish between naturally occurring *trans* fats in dairy products, beef, and lamb, and industrially-produced *trans* fats found in shortening and baked goods, that are the products of hydrogenation (Wang et al., 2010). The reason? The two types of *trans* fats appear to have very different effects on cardiovascular health.

hydrogenation The process of adding hydrogen to unsaturated fatty acids, making them more saturated and thereby more solid at room temperature.

⬥ In 2003 Health Canada ruled that trans fatty acids, or trans fat, must be listed on Nutrition Facts labels for conventional foods and some dietary supplements.

Research has shown that the saturated and industrial *trans* fats we eat contribute to high blood cholesterol levels and an increased risk of heart disease: both industrial *trans* fatty acids and saturated fatty acids raise blood cholesterol levels and appear to change cell membrane function. Because of the concerns related to *trans* fatty acid consumption and heart disease, manufacturers are required to list the amount of *trans* fatty acids per serving on the food label.

However, new research shows that not all *trans* fats are bad for you! A University of Alberta research team led by Dr. Spencer Proctor has shown that the naturally occurring *trans* fatty acids that are synthesized by bacteria in the gut of ruminant animals may actually be good for your heart. The most common naturally occurring *trans* fat, vaccenic acid (trans-11 C18:1), has a different composition than the main *trans* fats produced during hydrogenation (trans-9 C18:1 and trans-10 C18:1) (Wang et al., 2010). The researchers believe that these different compositions lead to different health effects in the body, and naturally occurring *trans* fats may behave more like polyunsaturated fats than saturated fats. Their studies with rats have shown that supplements of vaccenic acid for four months made substantial improvements in the blood cholesterol levels of these animals and even improved fatty liver disease (liver steatosis). Clinical trials with humans are needed to see if similar results will be found.

NUTRITION LABEL ACTIVITY

How to Choose a Healthy Margarine

There are so many different types of margarines on the market, how do you choose one that is good for you? The Nutrition Facts Table and ingredient list below are from a regular margarine (versus ones on the market that are labelled "light," "salt-free," or "added olive oil").

Nutrition Facts per 10 g (2 tsp) serving

Energy	70 Calories	%DV*
Total Fat	8 g	12%
Saturated	1 g	1%
+ *Trans*	0 g	
Polyunsaturated	2.5 g	
Omega-6	2.0 g	
Omega-3	0.4 g	
Monounsaturated	3.5 g	
Cholesterol	0 mg	0%
Sodium	70 mg	3%
Total Carbohydrate	0 g	0%
Dietary fibre	0 g	0%
Sugars	0 g	
Protein	0 g	
Vitamin A		10%
Vitamin B		0%
Calcium		0%
Iron		0%
Vitamin D		30%
Vitamin E		15%

*Based on a 2000-Calorie diet.
Ingredients: Canola and sunflower oils 74%, water, modified palm and palm kernel oils 6%, salt 1.8%, whey protein concentrate 1.4%, soy lecithin 0.2%, vegetable monoglycerides, potassium sorbate, vegetable colour, artificial flavour, citric acid, vitamin A palmitate, vitamin D3, alpha-tocopherol acetate.

First, notice that the serving size is 10 mL (2 tsp) or 10 g. Of the 8 grams of fat in this serving, only 1 gram is saturated, and there are no *trans* fatty acids in the product. Look at the ingredient list and you will see that 6% of the margarine (by weight) is from modified palm and palm kernel oils, whereas approximately three-quarters of the margarine is canola and sunflower oils. Modified palm and palm kernel oils are contributing to the saturated fat content. Canola oil is high in both monounsaturated and polyunsaturated fatty acids, and sunflower oil is high in polyunsaturated fatty acids. Since these are the main ingredients in the margarine, they account for the high amounts of monounsaturated (3.5 grams of the total 8 grams) and polyunsaturated (2.5 grams of the total 8 grams) fatty acids. No hydrogenated or partially hydrogenated vegetable oils or shortenings are found on the ingredient list; therefore, the canola and sunflower oils used in making this margarine were not hydrogenated (i.e., had hydrogen atoms added to the double bonds) and this product does not contain *trans* fats.

Remember that margarines are made from plant oils, which do not contain cholesterol or dietary fibre. Although some whey (milk) protein concentrate is added to mimic the consistency and flavour of butter, the amount is so small that it does not contribute to the % daily value for protein. The fat-soluble vitamins A, D, and E are also added.

Is this margarine a good choice? Yes. It is non-hydrogenated, low in saturated fat, and contains no *trans* fats. "Light" margarines will generally have water listed as the first ingredient, may contain gelatine to help stabilize the product, and often have half the energy of regular margarine. Because they contain so much water (e.g., 58%) they do not melt smoothly, and are not generally recommended for baking and frying, but can be good choices for table spreads.

Unfortunately, our current food labels do not differentiate between naturally occurring and industrially-produced *trans* fats. If you pick up a tub of full-fat yogurt, for example, almost all of the *trans* fat listed on the label will be natural *trans* fat. In Europe, only industrial *trans* fats are listed on food labels.

Incidentally, even when a product *is* labelled as having "zero" *trans* fats, there can still be *trans* fatty acids in the product! That is because Health Canada allows products that have up to 0.2 grams of *trans* fat per serving to claim that they are *trans* fat free; these products must also have less than 2 grams of saturated fat. If the ingredient list states that the product contains partially hydrogenated oils, it contains *trans* fats.

Phospholipids Combine Lipids with Phosphate

Along with the triglycerides just discussed, we also find phospholipids and sterols in the foods we eat. **Phospholipids** consist of two fatty acids and a glycerol backbone with another compound that contains phosphate **(Figure 5.6)**. This addition of a phosphate compound makes phospholipids soluble in water, a property that enables phospholipids to emulsify and assist in transporting fats in our bloodstream. We discuss this concept in more detail later in this chapter. Also, as you may recall from Chapter 3, phospholipids in our cell membranes regulate the transport of substances into and out of the cell. Phospholipids also help with the digestion of dietary fats: the liver uses phospholipids called *lecithins* to make bile. Note that our bodies manufacture phospholipids, so they are not essential for us to include in our diets. What *is* essential is phosphorus, a mineral that is combined with oxygen to make phosphate. See Chapter 9 to learn more about your requirements for phosphorus.

phospholipids A type of lipid with a glycerol backbone to which two fatty acids and another compound that contains phosphate are attached; unlike other lipids, phospholipids are soluble in water.

sterols A type of lipid found in foods and the body that has a ring structure; cholesterol is the most common sterol that occurs in our diets. Plant sterols block the absorption of cholesterol.

Sterols Have a Ring Structure

Sterols are also a type of lipid found in foods and in the body, but their multiple-ring structure is quite different from that of triglycerides **(Figure 5.7a)**. Sterols are found in both plant and animal foods and are produced in the body. Plant sterols are naturally found in small amounts in the cell membranes of fruits, vegetables, nuts, seeds, grains, and legumes; soybean oil is a particularly rich source. Plant sterols appear to block the absorption of dietary cholesterol in the small intestine, and their potential health benefits have been studied for over 50 years (Klingberg et al., 2008). It was believed that people do not typically consume enough plant sterols each day to significantly lower their blood cholesterol levels, so sterols in the form of esters have been added to high-fat food products such as margarine and mayonnaise. Research suggests that these added sterol esters reduce blood levels of total cholesterol 5% to 13%, and blood levels of LDL cholesterol 5% to 24% (Lau, Journoud, and Jones, 2005), without adverse effects on HDL cholesterol. More recent research suggests

▶ **Figure 5.6** Structure of a phospholipid. Phospholipids consist of a glycerol backbone with two fatty acids and a compound that contains phosphate.

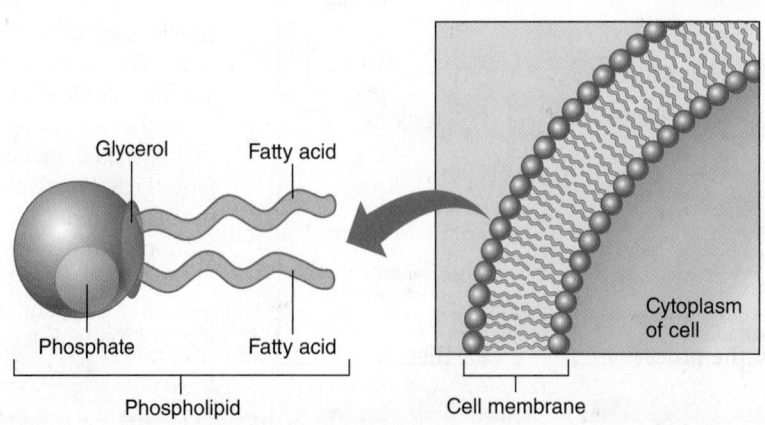

Glycerol   Fatty acid

Phosphate   Fatty acid

Phospholipid

Cytoplasm of cell

Cell membrane

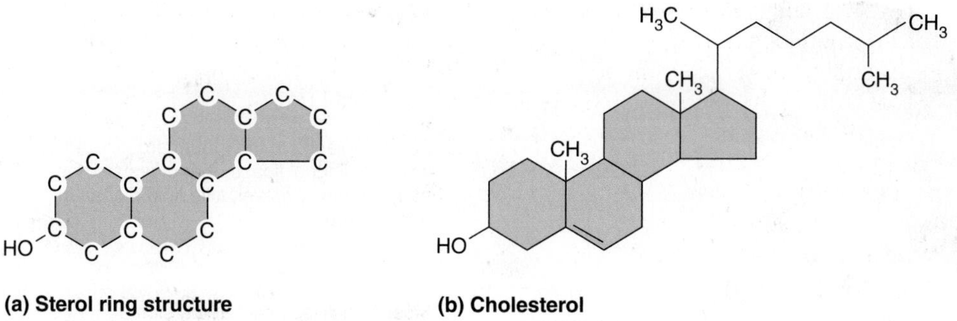

Figure 5.7 Sterol structure.
(a) Sterols are lipids that contain multiple-ring structures. **(b)** Cholesterol is the most commonly occurring sterol in the diet.

(a) Sterol ring structure

(b) Cholesterol

that plant sterols consumed naturally as plant foods in a typical diet may be sufficient to reduce blood levels of cholesterol in people with high levels (Klingberg et al., 2008). As discussed in Chapter 2, Canada now permits a health claim for plant sterols (also called plant stanols).

Cholesterol is found only in the fatty part of animal products such as butter, egg yolks, whole milk, meats, and poultry. Low- or reduced-fat animal products, such as lean meats and skim milk, have less cholesterol. Products like vegetable oils and peanut butter that are derived from plants are sometimes labelled "cholesterol free"—a misleading claim, since plants do not contain cholesterol.

We do not need to consume cholesterol in our diet because our body continually synthesizes it, mostly in the liver and intestines. This continuous production is essential because cholesterol is part of every cell membrane, where it works in conjunction with fatty acids to help maintain cell membrane integrity. It is particularly plentiful in the neural cells that make up our brain, spinal cord, and nerves. The body also uses cholesterol to synthesize several important compounds, including sex hormones (estrogen, androgen, and progesterone), bile acids, adrenal hormones, and vitamin D. Thus, despite cholesterol's bad reputation, it is absolutely essential to human health.

RECAP Fat is essential for health. Three types of fat are found in foods: triglycerides, phospholipids, and sterols. Triglycerides are the most common. A triglyceride is made up of glycerol and three fatty acids. These fatty acids can be classified based on chain length, level of saturation, and shape. Industrial *trans* fatty acids appear to increase our risk for cardiovascular disease, whereas naturally occurring *trans* fats may be protective. Phospholipids combine two fatty acids and a glycerol backbone with a phosphate-containing compound, making them soluble in water. Sterols have a multiple-ring structure; cholesterol is the most commonly occurring sterol in our diet. It is not essential in our diet, however, because our livers and intestines manufacture cholesterol.

How Does Our Body Break Down Fats?

Because fats are not soluble in water, they cannot enter our bloodstream easily from the digestive tract. Thus, dietary fats must be digested, absorbed, and transported within the body differently than carbohydrates and proteins, which are water-soluble substances.

The digestion and absorption of dietary fat were discussed in Chapter 3, but we briefly review the process in **(Figure 5.8)**. Dietary fats usually come mixed with other foods, which we chew and then swallow. Salivary enzymes released during chewing have a limited role in the breakdown of fats, so most fat reaches the stomach intact

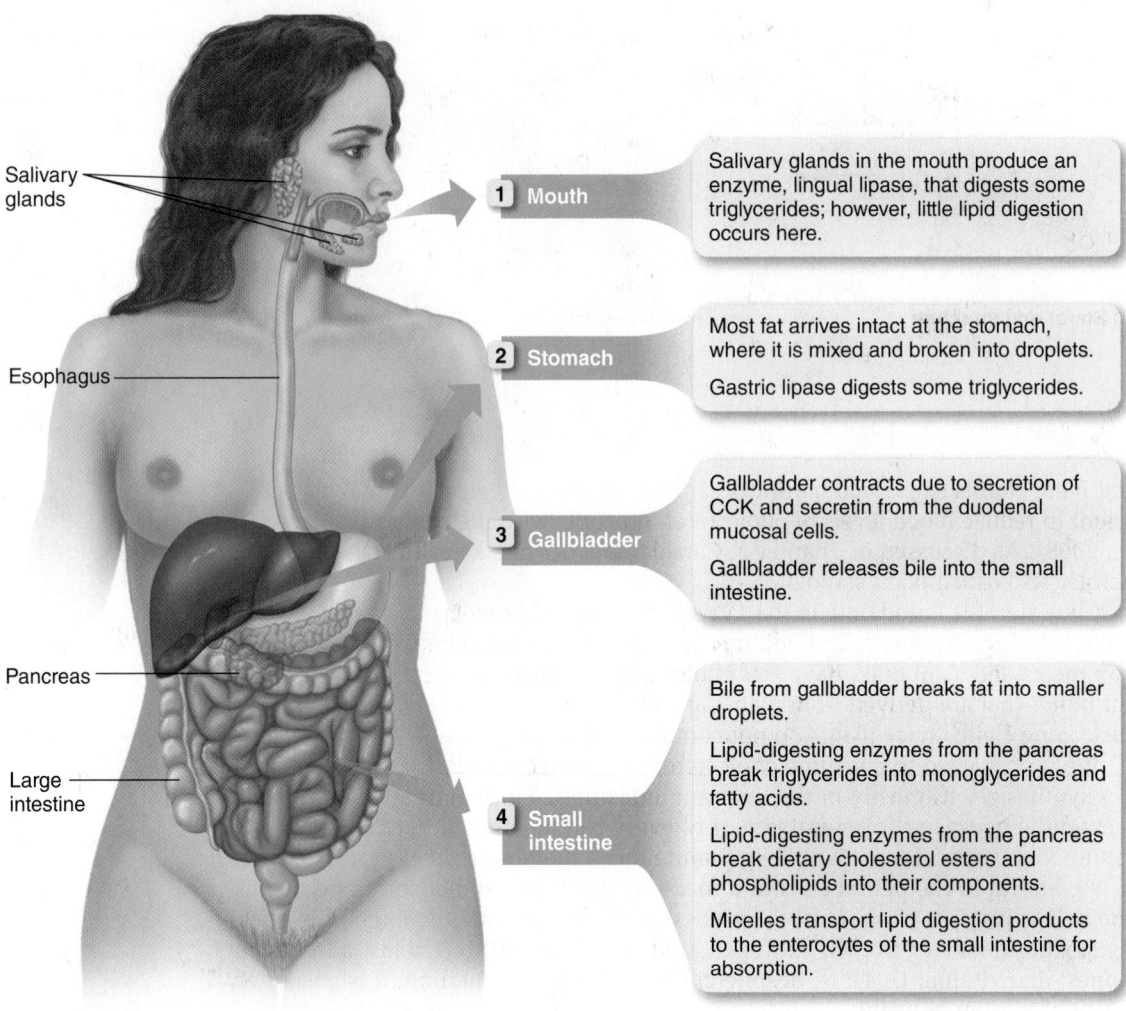

Salivary glands

Esophagus

Pancreas

Large intestine

1 Mouth
Salivary glands in the mouth produce an enzyme, lingual lipase, that digests some triglycerides; however, little lipid digestion occurs here.

2 Stomach
Most fat arrives intact at the stomach, where it is mixed and broken into droplets.

Gastric lipase digests some triglycerides.

3 Gallbladder
Gallbladder contracts due to secretion of CCK and secretin from the duodenal mucosal cells.

Gallbladder releases bile into the small intestine.

4 Small intestine
Bile from gallbladder breaks fat into smaller droplets.

Lipid-digesting enzymes from the pancreas break triglycerides into monoglycerides and fatty acids.

Lipid-digesting enzymes from the pancreas break dietary cholesterol esters and phospholipids into their components.

Micelles transport lipid digestion products to the enterocytes of the small intestine for absorption.

Figure 5.8 The process of fat digestion.

Source: (Thompson, Janice; Manore, Melinda; Vaughan, Linda, The Science of Nutrition, 2nd Ed., ©2011. Reprinted and Electronically reproduced by permission of Pearson Education, Inc., Upper Saddle River, New Jersey.)

(Figure 5.8, step 1). The primary role of the stomach in fat digestion is to mix and break up the fat into small droplets. Some digestion takes place in the stomach when gastric lipase is released. Because they are not soluble in water, these fat droplets typically float on top of the watery digestive juices in the stomach until they are passed into the small intestine (Figure 5.8, step 2).

The Gallbladder, Liver, and Pancreas Assist in Lipids Digestion

Because lipids are not soluble in water, their digestion requires the help of digestive enzymes from the pancreas and bile (also called bile acids) from the gallbladder. Recall from Chapter 3 that the gallbladder is a sac attached to the underside of the liver and the pancreas is an oblong-shaped organ sitting below the stomach. Both have a duct connecting them to the small intestine. As fat enters the small intestine from the stomach, the cells of the intestinal wall respond by secreting the hormone cholecystokinin (CCK). This hormone acts on the gallbladder, causing it to contract and release bile (Figure 5.8, step 3) into the common bile duct, which leads to the duodenum (the first part of the small intestine). Cholecystokinin also slows down the motility (movement) in the gastrointestinal tract. Secretin, another hormone released from the cells of the intestinal wall, also plays a role in gallbladder contraction.

Bile is produced in the liver from cholesterol and is concentrated and stored in the gallbladder until needed. Bile is composed mainly of bile salts made from cholesterol, lecithins and other phospholipids, and electrolytes (for example, sodium, potassium, chloride, and calcium). You can think of bile acting much as soap does, breaking up the fat into smaller and smaller droplets. At the same time, fat-digesting enzymes produced in the pancreas travel through the pancreatic duct into the small intestine. Once bile has broken the fat into small droplets, these pancreatic enzymes (called pancreatic lipases) take over, breaking the fatty acids away from their glycerol backbones. Each triglyceride molecule is broken down into two free fatty acids and one *monoglyceride,* a glycerol molecule with one fatty acid still attached **(Figure 5.9a)**.

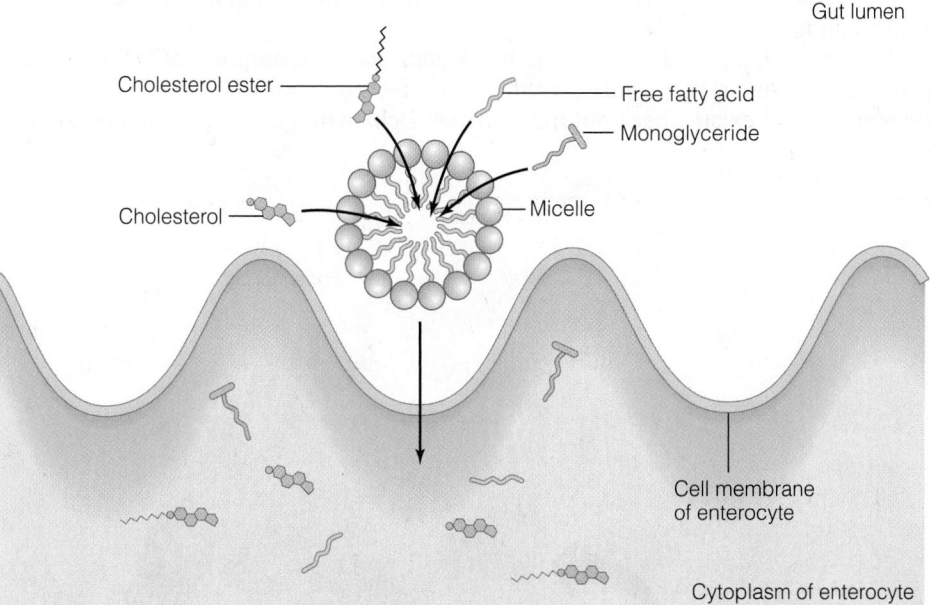

(a) Triglyceride digestion

(b) Micelle transport into enterocyte

Figure 5.9 Lipid digestion and absorption. **(a)** in the presence of enzymes, triglycerides are broken down into fatty acids and monoglycerides. **(b)** These products, along with free cholesterol and other products, are trapped in the micelle, a spherical compound made up of bile salts and phospholipids. The micelle then transports these lipid digestion products to the intestinal mucosal cell, and these products are then absorbed into the cell.

Absorption of Fats Occurs Primarily in the Small Intestine

The majority of fat absorption occurs in the mucosal lining of the small intestine with the help of a micelle (Figure 5.8, step 4). A *micelle* is a spherical compound made up of bile and phospholipids that can trap the free fatty acids and the monoglycerides. Because the micelles are water soluble, they can transport the free fatty acids, monoglycerides, and other products to the mucosal cells for absorption **(Figure 5.9b)**.

How does the absorbed fat get into the bloodstream? Because fats do not mix with water, most fats cannot be transported freely in the bloodstream. To solve this problem, the longer-chain fatty acids and monoglycerides are reformulated back into triglycerides in the mucosal cells of the intestinal wall. They are then packaged with proteins and phospholipids into transport vessels called lipoproteins before being released into the bloodstream. A **lipoprotein** is a spherical compound in which the triglycerides accumulate in the centre and phospholipids and proteins form the outside of the sphere **(Figure 5.10)**.

The specific lipoprotein produced in the mucosal cell to transport fat from a meal is called a **chylomicron**. This unique compound is now soluble in water because phospholipids and proteins are water soluble. Like micelles, the chylomicrons are vehicles that can keep fat soluble so that it can be transported outside the gastrointestinal tract. The chylomicrons are then released into the lymphatic system and travel through the lymph until they reach the thoracic duct near the heart, where they enter the bloodstream **(Figure 5.11)**. Thus, the chylomicrons bypass the liver at first and carry the triglycerides through the bloodstream, directly to the body's cells to be used for energy or stored as fat. In this way, dietary fat finally arrives in your blood.

As mentioned earlier, short- and medium-chain fatty acids (those fewer than 14 carbons in length) can be transported in the body more readily than the long-chain fatty acids. When short- and medium-chain fatty acids are digested and transported to the mucosal cells of the small intestine, they do not have to be re-formed into triglycerides and incorporated into chylomicrons. Instead, they can travel in the bloodstream bound to either a transport protein, such as albumin, or a phospholipid. For this reason, shorter-chain fatty acids can get into the system more quickly than long-chain fatty acids.

Imagine a "magic pill" that would block your body's absorption of fat, allowing you to eat all the fat you wanted without any effects on your weight or your heart. Does such a pill exist? Check out the Nutrition Debate on page 172 to find out.

lipoprotein A spherical compound in which triglycerides stay in the centre and phospholipids and proteins form the outside of the sphere.

chylomicron A lipoprotein produced in the mucosal cell of the intestine; transports dietary fat out of the intestinal tract into the lymphatic system.

▶ **Figure 5.10** Structure of a lipoprotein. Notice that the triglycerides stay in the centre of the molecule. The phospholipids and proteins form the outside of the sphere. The fat-soluble phospholipid tails are oriented towards the centre of the molecule and the phospholipid heads, which are water soluble, form the outside of the sphere. This enables lipoproteins to transport fats in the bloodstream.

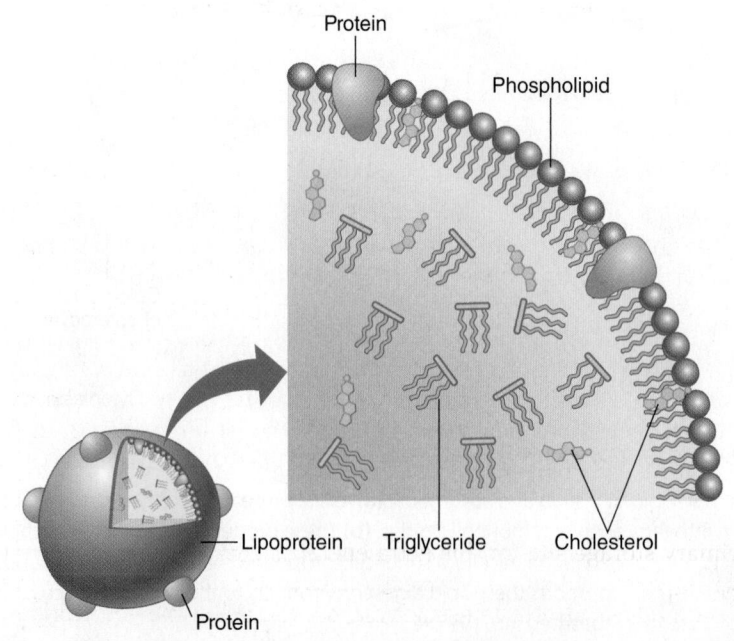

Protein

Phospholipid

Lipoprotein   Triglyceride   Cholesterol

Protein

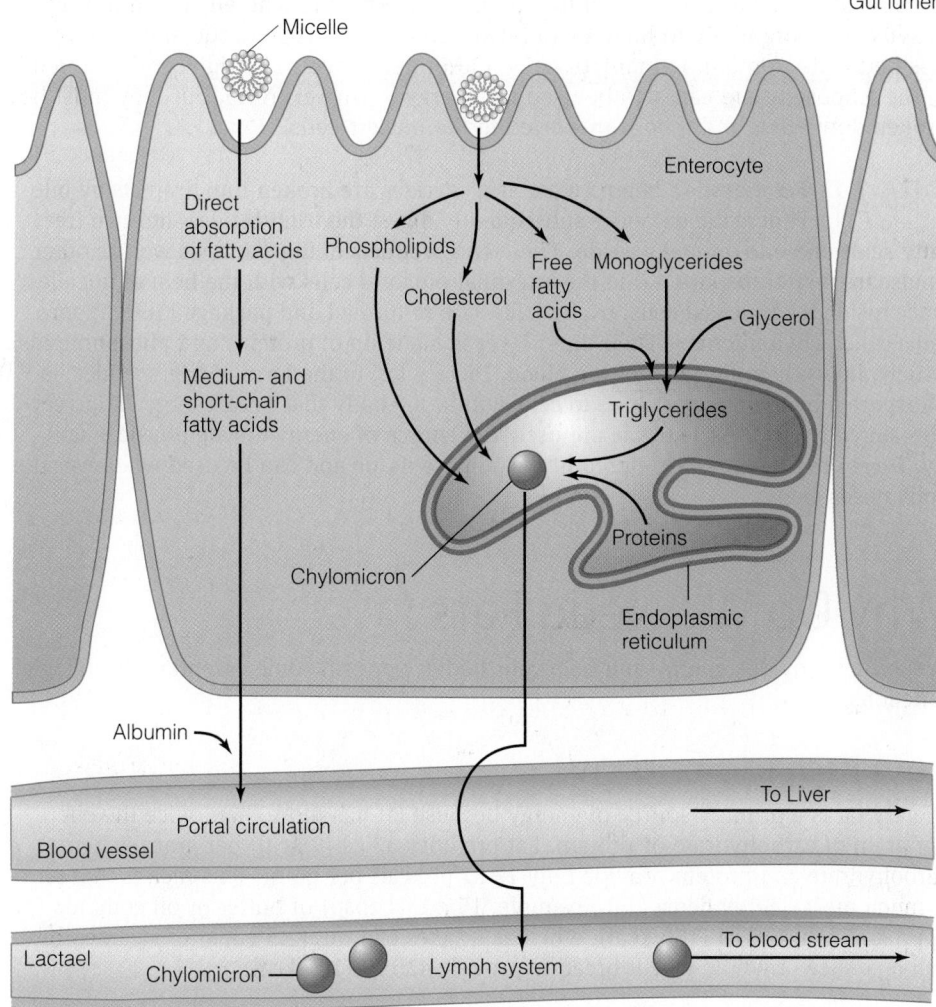

Gut lumen

◀ Figure 5.11 The reassembly of the lipid components (for example, triglycerides) into a chylomicron, which is released into the lymph stream and then into the bloodstream at the thoracic duct (at the heart). Short- and medium-chain fatty acids pass directly into the blood stream and go to the liver.

Triglycerides Are Stored in Adipose Tissues for Later Use

The chylomicrons, which are filled with the dietary triglycerides you just ate, now begin to circulate through the blood, looking for a place to deliver their load. There are three primary fates of these dietary triglycerides:

1. They can immediately be taken up and used as a source of energy for the cells.
2. They can be used to make lipid-containing compounds in the body.
3. They can be stored in the muscle or adipose tissue for later use.

How do the triglycerides get out of the chylomicrons and into the cell? This process occurs with the help of an enzyme called **lipoprotein lipase**, or LPL, which sits on the outside surface of our adipose cells. LPL comes in contact with the chylomicrons when they touch the surface of the adipose cell. As a result of this contact, LPL breaks apart the triglycerides in the core of the chylomicrons. This process results in the movement of individual fatty acids from within the core of the chylomicrons and out into the adipose cell. If the adipose cell needs the fat for energy, these fatty acids are quickly transported into the mitochondria and used as fuel. If the body does not need the fatty acids for immediate energy, the cell can re-create the triglycerides and store them for later use.

The primary storage site for this extra energy is the adipose cell, shown in **Figure 5.12**. However, if you are physically active, your body will preferentially store this extra fat in the muscle tissue first, so, the next time you work out, the

lipoprotein lipase An enzyme that sits on the outside surface of cells and breaks apart triglycerides so that their fatty acids can be removed and taken up by the cell.

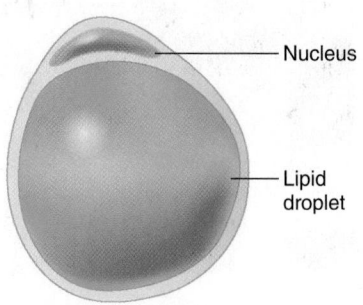

◆ Figure 5.12 Diagram of an adipose cell.

fat is readily available to the cell for energy. Thus, people who engage in physical activity are more likely to have extra fat stored in the muscle tissue and to have less body fat—something many of us would prefer. Of course, triglycerides stored in the adipose tissue can also be used for energy during exercise, but they must be broken down first and then transported to the muscle cells.

RECAP Fat digestion begins when triglycerides are broken into droplets by bile. Pancreatic enzymes subsequently digest the triglycerides into two free fatty acids and one monoglyceride. These end products of digestion, as well as other lipids, are then transported into the intestinal mucosal cells with the help of micelles. Once inside the mucosal cells, triglycerides are re-formed and packaged into lipoproteins called chylomicrons. Their outer layer is made up of proteins and phospholipids, which allows them to travel in the blood. Dietary fat, in the form of triglycerides, is transported by the chylomicrons to cells within the body that need energy. Triglycerides stored in the muscle tissue are used as a source of energy during physical activity. Excess triglycerides are stored in the adipose tissue and can be used whenever the body needs energy.

Why Do We Need Fats?

Dietary fat provides energy and helps our bodies perform some essential physiologic functions.

Fats Provide Energy

Dietary fat is a primary source of energy because fat has more than twice the energy per gram of carbohydrate or protein. Fat provides 37 kJ (9 kcal) per gram, whereas carbohydrate and protein provide only 17 kJ (4 kcal) per gram. This means that fat is much more energy dense. For example, 15 mL (1 tbsp) of butter or oil contains approximately 420 kJ (100 kcal), whereas it takes 625 mL (2.5 cups) of steamed broccoli or 1 slice of whole-wheat bread to provide 420 kJ (100 kcal).

Fats Are a Major Fuel Source When We Are at Rest

At rest, we are able to deliver plenty of oxygen to our cells, so that metabolic functions can occur. Just as a candle needs oxygen for the flame to burn the tallow, our cells need oxygen to burn fat for energy. Thus, approximately 30%–70% of the energy used at rest by the muscles and organs comes from fat (Jebb et al., 1996). The exact percentage varies, according to how much fat you are eating in your diet, how physically active you are, and whether you are gaining or losing weight. If you are dieting, more fat will be used for energy than if you are gaining weight. During times of weight gain, more of the fat consumed in the diet is stored in the adipose tissue, and the body uses more dietary protein and carbohydrate as fuel sources at rest.

Fats Fuel Physical Activity

Fat is a major energy source during physical activity, and it can be mobilized from any of the following sources: muscle tissue, adipose tissue, blood lipoproteins, and/or any dietary fat consumed during exercise. A number of hormonal changes signal the body to break down stored energy to fuel the working muscles. The hormonal responses, and the amount and source of the fat used, depend on your level of fitness; the type, intensity, and duration of the exercise; and how well fed you are before you exercise.

For example, adrenaline strongly stimulates the breakdown of stored fat. Blood levels of adrenaline rise dramatically within seconds of beginning exercise, and this action activates additional hormones within the fat cell to begin breaking down fat. Adrenaline also signals the pancreas to *decrease* insulin production. This is important, because insulin inhibits fat breakdown. Thus, when the need for fat as an energy source is high, blood insulin levels are typically low. As you might guess, blood

Dietary fat provides energy.

The longer you exercise, the more fat you use for energy. Cyclists in long-distance races use fat stores for energy.

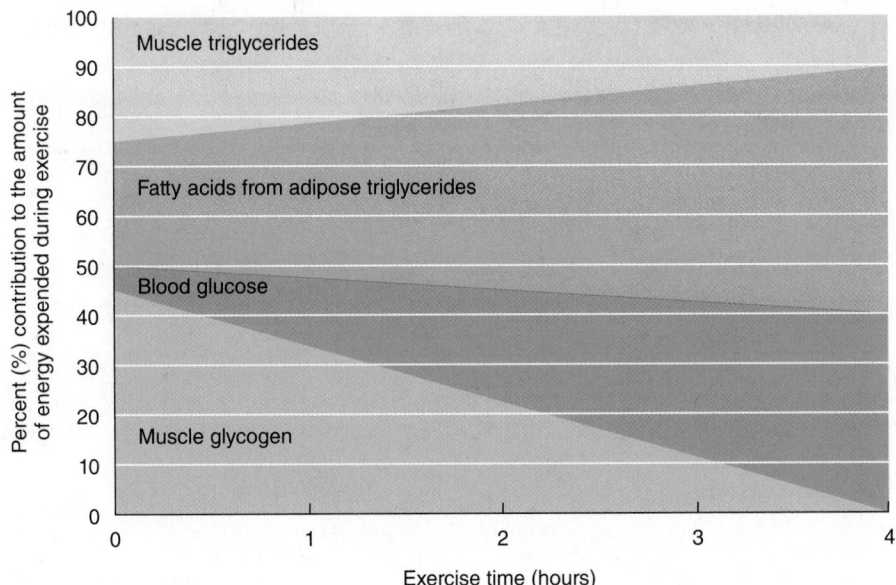

Figure 5.13 Various sources of energy used during exercise. As a person exercises for a prolonged period of time, fatty acids from adipose cells contribute relatively more energy than do carbohydrates stored in the muscle or circulating in our blood. Data from Coyle, E. F. 1995. Substrate utilization during exercise in active people. Am. J. Clin. Nutr. 6[Suppl]: 958S–979S.

insulin levels are high after eating, when our need for getting energy from stored fat is low and the need for fat storage is high.

Once fatty acids are released from the adipose cell, they travel in the blood attached to a protein, *albumin,* to the muscles, where they enter the mitochondria and use oxygen to produce ATP, which is the cell's energy source. Becoming more physically fit means you can deliver more oxygen to the muscle to use the fat that is delivered there. In addition, you can exercise longer when you are fit. Since the body has only a limited supply of stored carbohydrate as glycogen in muscle tissue, the longer you exercise, the more fat you use for energy. This point is illustrated in **Figure 5.13**. In this example, an individual is running for four hours at a moderate intensity. The longer the individual runs, the more depleted the muscle glycogen levels become and the more fat from adipose tissue is used as a fuel source for exercise.

Body Fat Stores Energy for Later Use

Our body stores extra energy in the form of body fat, which then can be used for energy at rest, during exercise, or during periods of low energy intake. Having a readily available energy source in the form of fat allows the body to always have access to energy, even when we choose not to eat (or are unable to eat), when we are exercising, and while we are sleeping. Our bodies have little stored carbohydrate—only enough to last about one to two days—and there is no place where our body can store extra protein. We cannot consider our muscles and organs as a place where "extra" protein is stored! For these reasons, the fat stored in our adipose and muscle tissues is necessary to keep the body going. Although we do not want too much stored adipose tissue, some fat storage is essential to good health.

Fats Contain Essential Fatty Acids

There has been a lot of press lately about "omega" fatty acids, so you might be wondering what they are and why they are so important. First, let's explain the Greek name. As illustrated in **Figure 5.14**, one end of a fatty acid chain is designated the α (alpha) end (α is the first letter in the Greek alphabet). The other end of a fatty acid chain is called the ω (omega) end (ω is the last letter in the Greek alphabet). Two fatty acids with a unique structure are known to be essential to human growth and health: one of these has a double bond six carbons from the omega end (at ω-6), and the other has a double bond three carbons from the omega end (at ω-3). When synthesizing fatty acids, the body cannot insert double bonds before the ninth carbon from the omega end (Champe et al., 2008). This means that we have to obtain ω-6 and ω-3 fatty acids, more commonly called n-6 and n-3, from

Adipose tissue pads our body and protects our organs when we fall or are bruised.

▶ **Figure 5.14** The two essential fatty acids: linoleic acid, an omega-6 fatty acid with 18 carbons and two double bonds, C18:2n-6, and alpha-linolenic acid, an omega-3 fatty acid with 18 carbons and three double bonds, C18:3n-3.

Essential fatty acids

Linoleic acid

Alpha-linolenic acid

essential fatty acids (EFAs) Fatty acids that must be consumed in the diet because they cannot be made by our bodies. The two essential fatty acids are linoleic acid (an ω-6 or n-6 fatty acid) and alpha-linolenic acid (an ω-3 or n-3 fatty acid).

◀ Salmon is high in omega-3 fatty acid content.

linoleic acid An essential omega-6 fatty acid found in vegetable and nut oils; C18:2n-6.

alpha-linolenic acid An essential fatty acid found in leafy green vegetables, flaxseed oil, soy oil, fish oil, and fish products; C18:3n-3.

food. They are considered **essential fatty acids (EFAs)** because the body cannot make them, yet it requires them for healthy functioning.

EFAs are essential to growth and health because they are precursors to important biological compounds called *eicosanoids*, which are produced in nearly every cell in the body (Smith et al., 2005). Eicosanoids get their name from the Greek word *eicosa*, which means "twenty," as they are synthesized from fatty acids with twenty carbon atoms. In the body, eicosanoids are potent regulators of cellular function. For example, they help regulate gastrointestinal tract motility, blood clotting, blood pressure, the permeability of our blood vessels to fluid and large molecules, and the process of inflammation.

The body's synthesis of various eicosanoids depends in part on the abundance of the EFAs available as precursors. Since they play an important role in "regulating" biological processes, we need a balance of the various eicosanoids and thus a balance of EFAs.

Linoleic Acid

Linoleic acid, an *omega-6 (n-6) fatty acid*, is found in vegetable and nut oils, such as sunflower, safflower, corn, soy, and peanut oil. If you eat lots of vegetables or use vegetable-oil-based margarines or vegetable oils, you are probably getting adequate amounts of this essential fatty acid in your diet. Linoleic acid has 18 carbons and two double bonds, denoted as C18:2n-6, and is metabolized in the body to arachidonic acid (C20:4n-6), which is a precursor to a number of eicosanoids that regulate body functions, such as blood clotting and blood pressure. Linoleic acid is also needed for cell membrane structure and is required for the lipoproteins that transport fats in our blood. The omega-6 class of fatty acids has the first double bond at the sixth carbon from the methyl (CH_3) end (see Figure 5.14).

Alpha-Linolenic Acid

Alpha-linolenic acid, an *omega-3 (n-3) fatty acid*, was only recognized to be essential in the mid-1980s. The omega-3 class of fatty acids has the first double bond at the third carbon from the methyl (CH_3) end (see Figure 5.14). Alpha-linolenic acid has 18 carbons and three double bonds, denoted as C18:3n-3. It is found primarily in dark green, leafy vegetables, flaxseeds and flaxseed oil, soybeans and soybean oil, walnuts and walnut oil, canola oil, and seafood and fish oils.

You may also have read news reports of the health benefits of two very long-chain omega-3 fatty acids found in fish, shellfish, and fish oils: **eicosapentaenoic acid or EPA** (C20:5n-3) and **docosahexaenoic acid or DHA** (C22:6n-3). Fish that naturally contain more oil, such as salmon and tuna, are higher in EPA and DHA than lean fish, such as cod or flounder, although all seafood contains these fatty acids. Research indicates that diets high in EPA and DHA stimulate the production of regulatory compounds that reduce an individual's risk for heart disease (Wijendran and Hayes, 2004; Din et al., 2004).

Fats Enable the Transport of Fat-Soluble Vitamins

Dietary fat enables the transport of the fat-soluble vitamins (A, D, E, and K) our body needs for many essential metabolic functions. For example, vitamin A is especially important for normal vision and gives us the ability to see at night. Vitamin D is important for regulating blood calcium and phosphorus concentrations within normal ranges, which indirectly helps maintain bone health. If vitamin D is low, blood calcium levels will drop below normal, and the body will draw calcium from the bones to maintain blood levels. Vitamin E functions primarily as an antioxidant in our body and keeps cell membranes healthy by preventing the oxidation of body fats. Finally, vitamin K is important for proteins involved in blood clotting and bone health. We discuss these vitamins in detail in Chapters 8 and 9.

eicosapentaenoic acid (EPA) A metabolic derivative of alpha-linolenic acid; C20:5n-3.

docosahexaenoic acid (DHA) Another metabolic derivative of alpha-linolenic acid; C22:6n-3.

Fats Help Maintain Cell Function

Fats, especially PUFAs and phospholipids, are a critical part of every cell membrane, where they help to maintain membrane integrity, determine what substances are transported into and out of the cell, and regulate what substances can bind to the cell; thus, fats strongly influence the function of cells. In addition, fats help maintain cell fluidity and other physical properties of the cell membrane. For example, wild salmon live in very cold water and have high levels of omega-3 fatty acids in their cell membranes. These fats stay fluid and flexible even in very cold environments, which allow the fish to swim in extremely cold water. In the same way, fats help our membranes stay fluid and flexible. For example, they enable our red blood cells to bend and move through the smallest capillaries in our body, delivering oxygen to all our cells.

Fats, especially PUFAs, are also primary components of the tissues of the brain and spinal cord, where they facilitate the transmission of information from one cell to another. We need fats for the development, growth, and maintenance of these tissues.

Fat adds texture and flavour to foods.

Stored Fat Provides Protection to the Body

Stored body fat also plays an important role in our body. Besides being the primary site of stored energy, adipose tissue pads our body and protects our organs, such as the kidneys and liver, when we fall or are bruised. The fat under our skin acts as insulation to help us retain body heat. Although we often think of body fat as "bad," it plays important roles in keeping our body healthy and functioning properly.

Fats Contribute to the Flavour and Texture of Foods

Dietary fat helps food taste good because it contributes to texture and flavour. Fat makes salad dressings smooth and ice cream "creamy," and it gives cakes and cookies their moist, tender texture. Frying foods in melted butter, lard, or oils gives them a crisp, flavourful coating.

Fats and oils do not dissolve readily in water.

Fats Help Us Feel Satiated

Fats in foods help us feel satiated after a meal. Two factors probably contribute to this effect: first, fat has a much higher energy density than carbohydrate or protein. For example, a pat of butter weighing 5 g contains 145 kJ (35 kcal); 5 g of an apple contain only 13 kJ (3 kcal). For every gram of fat you consume, you get 2.25 times the amount of energy that you get with the same number of grams consumed in protein or carbohydrate.

Second, fat takes longer to digest than protein or carbohydrate because more steps are involved in the digestion process, which may make you feel fuller for a longer period of time because energy is slowly being released into your body.

On the other hand, you can eat more fat in a meal without feeling overfull because fat is generally compact in its size. Going back to our apple and butter example, one medium apple weighs 117 g (approximately 4 oz) and has 290 kJ (70 kcal), but the same amount of energy as butter—two pats—would hardly make you feel full! Looked at another way, an amount of butter weighing the same number of grams as a medium apple would contain 3510 kJ (840 kcal)!

RECAP Dietary fats provide more than twice the energy of protein and carbohydrate, at 37 kJ (9 kcal) per gram, and provide the majority of the energy required at rest. Fats are also a major fuel source during exercise, especially endurance exercise. Dietary fats help transport the fat-soluble vitamins into the body and help regulate cell function and maintain membrane integrity. Stored body fat in the adipose tissue helps protect vital organs and pad the body. Fats contribute to the flavour and texture of foods and the satiety we feel after a meal.

How Much Dietary Fat Should We Eat?

Without a doubt, most people think dietary fat is bad! How many people have you heard say they are trying to dramatically reduce the level of fat in their diet? Yet, because fat plays such an important role in keeping our bodies healthy, we do need to include a moderate amount in our diet. But what, exactly, is a moderate amount? And what foods contain the most healthful fats? We'll explore these questions here.

Dietary Reference Intake for Total Fat

The Acceptable Macronutrient Distribution Range (AMDR) for fat is 20%–35% of total energy (Institute of Medicine, 2002). This recommendation is based on evidence indicating that higher intakes of fat increase the risk for obesity and its complications, especially heart disease, but that diets too low in fat and too high in carbohydrate can also increase the risk for heart disease if they cause blood triglycerides to increase (Institute of Medicine, 2002). We are also advised to keep our intake of saturated and trans fats low to reduce our risk of heart disease.

So how are Canadians doing? Data from the 2004 Canadian Community Health Survey (Health Canada, 2007a) suggest that 30% to 31% of calories are from fat, which is within the recommended range. The recommendation is to keep intakes of saturated fat as low as possible (Institute of Medicine, 2002); unfortunately, our estimated average intake of saturated fats is 10% of energy (Health Canada, 2007a). The Institute of Medicine (2002) also recommends that we keep our intake of trans fatty acids to an absolute minimum. Determining the actual amount of trans fatty acids consumed in Canada has been hindered by the lack of an accurate and comprehensive database of foods containing trans fatty acids. This is partly because many food manufacturers and fast-food companies are in the midst of reformulating their food items to reduce or eliminate industrial trans fats.

If you are an athlete, you have probably been advised to consume less fat and more carbohydrate to replenish your glycogen stores, especially if you participate in endurance activities. Specifically, you should consume 20%–25% of your total energy from fat, 55%–60% of energy from carbohydrate, and 12%–15% of energy from protein (Cialdella-Kam and Manore, 2009; Rodriguez et al., 2009). This percentage of fat intake is still within the AMDR and represents approximately 45 to 55 g of fat per day for an athlete consuming 8400 kJ (2000 kcal) per day, and 78 to 97 g of fat per day for an athlete consuming 14 700 kJ (3500 kcal) per day.

Although many people trying to lose weight consume less than 20% of their energy from fat, this practice may do more harm than good, especially if they are also limiting energy intake by eating fewer than 6290 kJ (1500 kcal) per day. Research suggests that very-low-fat diets, those with less than 15% of energy from fat, do not provide additional health or performance benefits over moderate-fat diets and are usually very difficult to follow (Lichtenstein and Van Horn, 1998). In fact, most people find they feel better, are more successful in weight maintenance, and are less preoccupied with food if they keep their fat intake at 20%–25% of energy intake. Additionally, people attempting to reduce their dietary fat frequently eliminate foods such as meats, dairy, eggs, and nuts, which are sources of protein and many essential vitamins and minerals. Diets extremely low in fat may also be deficient in essential fatty acids and fat-soluble vitamins.

Dietary Reference Intakes for Essential Fatty Acids

Dietary Reference Intakes (DRIs) for the two essential fatty acids were set for the first time in 2002 (Institute of Medicine, 2002).

Many people eat too many saturated and trans fats.

- *Linoleic acid.* The Adequate Intake (AI) for linoleic acid (an omega-6 FA) is 14 to 17 g per day for adult men and 11 to 12 g per day for women 19 years and older. Using the typical energy intakes for adult men and women, this translates into an AMDR of 5%–10% of total energy intake.
- *Alpha-linolenic acid.* The AI for alpha-linolenic acid (an omega-3 FA) is 1.6 g per day for adult men and 1.1 g per day for adult women. This translates into an AMDR of 0.6%–1.2% of total energy. These recommendations are for omega-3 fatty acids as a group. Up to 10% of the AMDR can be consumed as EPA and/or DHA. So how do you know if you are getting enough in your diet? Look through **Table 5.2** on page 170 to see if you are consuming any good food sources of these essential acids.

Following these recommendations, an individual consuming 8400 kJ (2000 kcal) per day should consume about 11 to 22 g per day of linoleic acid and about 1.3 to 2.6 g per day of alpha-linolenic acid. Notice that the recommended intake of linoleic acid is close to ten times higher than the recommended intake of alpha-linolenic acid. This is in keeping with the 5:1 to 10:1 ratio of linoleic:alpha-linolenic acid recommended by the World Health Organization and supported by the Institute of Medicine (2002). Because these EFAs compete for the same enzymes to produce various eicosanoids, this ratio helps keep eicosanoid production in balance; that is, one is not overproduced at the expense of the other.

Baked goods are often high in hidden fats and may contain industrial trans fats.

RECAP The Acceptable Macronutrient Distribution Range (AMDR) for total fat is 20%–35% of total energy. The Adequate Intake (AI) for linoleic acid is 14 to 17 g per day for adult men and 11 to 12 g per day for adult women. The AI for alpha-linolenic acid is 1.6 g per day for adult men and 1.1 g per day for adult women.

Don't Let the Fats Fool You!

Like many things, a little can be good, but too much can be harmful. We know that unsaturated fats are necessary for good health, but too much fat, regardless of type, can be unhealthful. However, before you can make healthful reductions in your fat intake, you need to know where the fat in your diet is coming from.

Recognize the Fat in Foods

It is easy to eat a high-fat diet. First, we add fats, such as oils, butter, cream, margarine, mayonnaise, and salad dressings to foods because they make food taste

⬆ This skinless roasted chicken breast provides 1 g saturated fat and 550 kJ (131 kcal; with the skin, it would provide 3 g saturated fat and 990 kJ (235 kcal).

good. This type of fat is called **visible fat** because we can easily see that we are adding it to our food. When we add fat to foods ourselves, we generally know how much we are adding. Still, we may not be aware of the type of fat we are using, the amount we are using, and the number of kcal it adds to our meal. For instance, it is easy to make a salad into a high-fat meal by adding 30 or 45 mL (2 or 3 Tbsp) of full-fat salad dressing. Doing so also transforms the salad into a high-energy meal: concentrated fats, such as butter, oil, and salad dressings, can have 420 kJ (100 kcal) per 15 mL (1 Tbsp).

Limiting your intake of visible fats is important, but it is only the first step. You must also be on the lookout for **hidden fats**—that is, fats added to processed and prepared foods to improve taste and texture. Over the past decade, our intake of visible fats has decreased, while our intake of hidden fats has increased. That is partly because, when fat exists naturally within a food or is added during food preparation, we are less aware of how much or what type of fat is actually there. Do you read the information about fat on the Nutrition Facts table of the foods you buy? When eating out, do you look for or ask about the fat and energy content of the menu items you are considering?

What is more, when fats are hidden, it is easy to choose higher-fat foods over more healthful versions. For example, a slice of yellow cake is much higher in fat (40% of total energy) than a slice of angel food cake (1% of total energy), yet many consumers just assume the fat content of these foods is the same, since they are both cake. In addition to baked goods, foods that can be high in hidden fats include dairy products, frozen entrées, processed meats or meats that are not trimmed, and most convenience and fast foods, such as hamburgers, hot dogs, chips, ice cream, french fries, and other fried foods. When purchasing packaged foods, read the Nutrition Facts table and find out whether or not the product is high in hidden fats!

Food manufacturers have been more than happy to provide consumers with lower-fat alternatives to their favourite foods. However, these lower-fat foods may not always have less energy. Read the Highlight box on p. 167 and **Table 5.1** to learn how to be a better consumer of reduced-fat foods.

RECAP Visible fats are those foods that can be easily recognized as containing fat. Hidden fats are those fats added to our food during the manufacturing or cooking process, so we are not aware of how much fat has been added. By making simple substitutions when shopping and eating out, you can reduce the quantity of saturated and industrial *trans* fatty acids in your diet and increase your intake of healthful fats.

Current Advice: Limit Saturated and Trans Fats

Research over the last two decades suggested that diets high in SFAs negatively influenced blood lipid levels, increasing our risk for heart disease. We also learned that *trans* fatty acids appear to function much like SFAs in our diet: both *trans* and saturated fatty acids raise blood levels of low-density lipoproteins (LDL cholesterol, sometimes referred to as the "bad" cholesterol), change cell membrane function, and alter the way cholesterol is removed from the blood. Further, *trans* fatty acids lower blood levels of high-density lipoproteins (HDL cholesterol, sometimes referred to as the "good" cholesterol). For these reasons, researchers have believed that diets high in saturated and *trans* fatty acids can increase the risk for cardiovascular disease.

However, as we mentioned earlier, new research suggests that industrial *trans* fats and naturally occurring *trans* fats do not behave the same way, and in fact, natural *trans* fats may actually protect against cardiovascular disease. Similarly, new research on the role of saturated fats in cardiovascular disease shows that not all SFAs behave the same way. Further, there is some strong evidence that saturated fats may have no significant relationship with cardiovascular disease (Micha et al., 2010). These new studies clearly challenge the existing advice for people to limit their consumption of red meat, full-fat dairy products, and other foods high in saturated

visible fats Fat we can see in our foods or see added to foods, such as butter, margarine, cream, salad dressings, chicken skin, and untrimmed fat on meat.

hidden fats Fats that are hidden in foods, such as the fats found in baked goods, regular-fat dairy products, marbling in meat, and fried foods.

HIGHLIGHT

Low-Fat, Reduced-Fat, Non-Fat … What's the Difference?

Although most of us love high-fat foods, we also know that eating too much fat is not good for our health or our waistlines. Because of this concern, food manufacturers have produced a host of modified-fat foods—so you can have your cake and eat it too!

In **Table 5.1**, we list a number of full-fat foods with their lower-fat alternatives. These products, if incorporated in the diet on a regular basis, can significantly reduce the amount of fat consumed but may or may not reduce the amount of energy consumed. For example, drinking skim milk (360 kJ or 86 kcal and <0.5 g fat per serving) instead of whole milk (640 kJ or 150 kcal and 8.2 g fat per serving) will dramatically reduce both fat and energy intake. However, eating Oreo's 25% less fat cookies (three cookies have 540 kJ or 130 kcal and 5 grams of fat) instead of regular Oreos (three cookies have 670 kJ or 160 kcal and 7 grams of fat) will have little impact on your energy and fat intakes.

Thus, if you think that eating fat-free foods means you are not getting any energy and can eat all you want without gaining weight, you are mistaken. The reduced

fat is often replaced with added carbohydrate, as with the Oreos example, resulting in a very similar total energy intake. Thus, if you want to reduce both the amount of fat and energy you consume, you must read the labels of modified-fat foods carefully before you buy.

TABLE 5.1 Comparison of Full-Fat, Reduced-Fat, and Low-Fat Foods

Product	Serving Size	Energy (kcal)	Protein (g)	Carbohydrate (g)	Fat (g)
Milk, whole (3.3% fat)	250 mL (8 fl. oz.)	150	8.0	11.4	8.2
Milk, 2% fat	250 mL (8 fl. oz.)	121	8.1	11.7	4.7
Milk, 1% fat	250 mL (8 fl. oz.)	102	8.0	11.7	2.6
Milk, skim (non-fat)	250 mL (8 fl. oz.)	86	8.4	11.9	0.5
Cheese, cheddar regular	30 g (1 oz.)	111	7.1	0.5	9.1
Cheese, cheddar low-fat	30 g (1 oz.)	81	9.1	0.0	5.1
Mayonnaise, regular	15 mL (1 Tbsp)	100	0.0	0.0	11.0
Mayonnaise, light	15 mL (1 Tbsp)	50	0.0	1.0	5.0
Mayonnaise, fat-free	15 mL (1 Tbsp)	10	0.0	2.0	0.0
Margarine, regular corn oil	15 mL (1 Tbsp)	100	0.0	0.0	11.0
Margarine, reduced-fat	15 mL (1 Tbsp)	60	0.0	0.0	7.0
Peanut butter, regular	15 mL (1 Tbsp)	95	4.1	3.1	8.2
Peanut butter, reduced-fat	15 mL (1 Tbsp)	81	4.4	5.2	5.4
Cream cheese, soft regular	15 mL (1 Tbsp)	50	1.0	0.5	5.0
Cream cheese, soft light	15 mL (1 Tbsp)	35	1.5	1.0	2.5
Crackers, Wheat Thins Original	18 crackers	158	2.3	21.4	6.8
Crackers, Wheat Thins 33% less fat	18 crackers	120	2.0	21.0	4.0
Cookies, Oreos regular	3 cookies	160	2.0	23.0	7.0
Cookies, Oreos 25% less fat	3 cookies	130	2.0	25.0	5.0
Cookies, Fig Newtons regular	3 cookies	210	3.0	30.0	4.5
Breakfast bars, regular	1 bar	140	2.0	27.0	2.8

Source: Data from Food Processor SQL, Version 10.3, ESHA Research, Salem, OR.

fats. We briefly discuss this controversy about the influence of SFAs on your risk for cardiovascular disease in the following section.

What is the Role of Saturated Fat in Cardiovascular Disease?

For many years, health professionals have advised us to limit the amount of saturated fat in our diets by avoiding fatty meats, removing the skin from poultry, and limiting high-fat dairy products such as butter, cheese, and whole milk. All SFAs were thought to behave the same way, and there was little attention given to specific SFAs. Many of the larger studies used measures of total and LDL cholesterol to assess changes in cardiovascular disease risk, but did not look at other conditions such as stroke or high blood pressure. Population-wide studies showed that as people were eating less SFAs, they were replacing the SFA with carbohydrates rather than MUFAs and PUFAs.

Some recent reviews of the evidence and meta-analyses of large studies, now suggest that (1) not all SFAs behave the same way in the body, (2) the effect of lowering SFA intakes may depend upon what replaces the saturated fat, and (3) the relationship between SFAs and cardiovascular disease varies depending upon how cardiovascular disease is measured—the endpoint used in the study (e.g., blood pressure, LDL cholesterol, insulin resistance, stroke) (Micha & Mozaffarian, 2010).

What do these new findings mean? Advice to eat less SFA to lower the risk of cardiovascular disease may be too simplistic; more research is needed to understand what happens when SFAs are replaced with MUFAs, PUFAs, and carbohydrates, and the effects not only on blood lipids but also stroke, diabetes, and high blood pressure (Micha & Mozaffarian, 2010).

Avoid Industrial Trans Fatty Acids

Although it is likely that industrial *trans* fatty acids make up only a small fraction of the average Canadian diet, their negative effect on our health appears to be dramatic. Many health professionals feel that diets high in *trans* fatty acids increase the risk for heart disease even more than diets high in saturated fats (Teegala et al., 2009). A research review that involved over 140 000 individuals showed that, for every 2% increase in energy intake from *trans* fatty acids, there was a 23% increase in incidence of heart disease (Teegala et al., 2009). Other researchers have concluded that the scientific evidence showing that *trans* fatty acids negatively affect health is so strong that it is unethical to do any additional long-term human research trials comparing the health effects of *trans* fatty acids to other types of fatty acids.

Because of the evidence linking *trans* fatty acid consumption to heart disease, Health Canada requires manufacturers to list the amount of *trans* fatty acids per serving on the Nutrition Facts table. As we mentioned earlier, there is no distinction between naturally occurring *trans* fats from ruminant animals and industrial *trans* fats produced through hydrogenation on the Nutrition Facts table. Unfortunately, foods intended for children under the age of two years are not required to declare their *trans* fat content.

As well, in June 2007 Health Canada endorsed the recommendations of the Trans Fat Task Force, which included the Heart and Stroke Foundation of Canada and other stakeholders, and called upon the food and restaurant industries to "limit the *trans* fat content:

- of vegetable oils and soft margarines to 2% of the total fat content; and
- for all other foods to 5% of the total fat content." (Health Canada, 2007c)

It established a Trans Fat Monitoring Program in 2007 to track the progress of the food and restaurant industries. In 2009 the fourth and final set of reports was published online. Some fast-food restaurants and retailers had made good progress towards meeting these recommendations by lowering *trans* fats and not replacing them with equally harmful saturated fats, whereas other fast-food restaurants had made little progress. This resulted in calls for using legislation to enforce the reduction of *trans* fats.

In addition, some jurisdictions have total bans on *trans* fatty acids in restaurants. For example, in 2009, British Columbia was the first province to bring in legislation to restrict the use of *trans* fats in food service establishments.

HIGHLIGHT
Is There an Alternative to *Trans* Fatty Acids?

Since Health Canada's release of new labelling regulations in 2003, food manufacturers have taken on the challenge of creating products that can be labelled as "*trans* fat free." One possible strategy is to replace all *trans* fat found in processed food products (chips, cookies, etc) with a healthier alternative that mimics the functional properties of a *trans* fatty acid.

Dr. Alejandro Marangoni, of the Department of Food Science at the University of Guelph, and his international research team have developed a solid fat product with similar functional properties to *trans* fatty acids, but none of the detrimental effects related to cardiovascular risk.

Marangoni explains, "There will always be people who consume junk food; the aim is to create healthier alternatives with the same eating qualities, taste, and value. For example, an individual can consume over 25% of their daily fat requirements in one store-bought muffin alone, most of it being unhealthy saturated and *trans* fats. By eliminating *trans* fats and reducing saturates in the muffin but maintaining similar qualities such as taste, an individual can still enjoy the food without the potentially harmful side effects."

What is the secret to this "healthier" fat? It is a simple oil, water, monoglyceride, and fatty acid mixture that functions as a solid fat at room temperature, is spreadable, and can withstand high baking and heating temperatures. The mixture is run through a machine called a Roto-Stator, which uses shear force to mix the two phases (oil and water) and produce monoglyceride vesicles filled with oil (or microencapsulated) and surrounded by water. The result is "a solid crystalline structure, which gives a lot of resistance. Eventually the crystals will pack together enough to squeeze the water out, forming a β gel (or Coagel) which is solid at room temperature."

Not only can this *trans* fat-free gel replace the fats found in spreads and other processed foods, Marangoni has also shown that the gel can lower triglyceride and free fatty acid levels in the blood after eating, which in turn results in lower insulin levels (Marangoni et al., 2007). "We gave a sample of individuals 60 g of the monoglyceride gel to eat and saw a decrease in serum

⬆ Dr. Alejandro Marangoni, University of Guelph.

triglycerides and free fatty acids after consumption" explains Marangoni. "Glucose levels remained the same but we saw a decrease in insulin resistance." This controlled release of lipids in the body combined with the regulation of insulin may potentially lower the risks of type 2 diabetes.

Marangoni and his team have been approached by *Tasty Collections*, a company that distributes products to brand-name chains such as Metro and Walmart, to produce a cookie made with their *trans* fat alternative. Marangoni goes on to say that "with the addition of our *trans* fat–free gel, the following claims are permitted on the cookie's packaging: (1) *trans* fat free; (2) low in saturated fats; (3) A source of omega-3 fatty acids; and (4) the health claim 'A healthy diet low in saturated and *trans* fats can reduce the risk of heart disease.'" Other Canadian and European manufacturers are interested in incorporating this *trans* fat alternative in candy bars and processed breakfast foods geared towards children aged 6 to 12.

Marangoni cautions that there are technical issues that need to be addressed, such as the ability to produce vast amounts of the gel in large-scale production. "However, we are almost there!" he says.

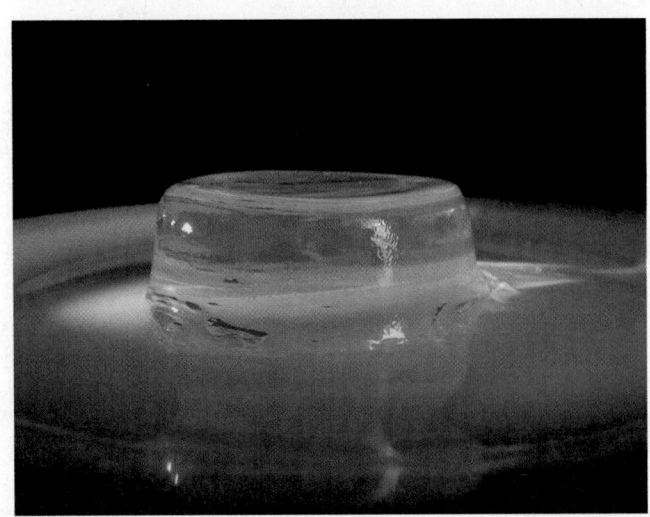

TABLE 5.2 Omega-3 Fatty Acid Content of Selected Foods

Food Item	Total Omega-3	DHA	EPA*
	g/serving		
Flaxseed oil, 15 mL (1 Tbsp)	7.25	0.00	0.00
Salmon oil (fish oil), 15 mL (1 Tbsp)	4.39	2.48	1.77
Sardine oil, 15 mL (1 Tbsp)	3.01	1.45	1.38
Flaxseed, whole, 15 mL (1 Tbsp)	2.50	0.00	0.00
Herring, Atlantic, broiled, 90 g (3 oz.)	1.83	0.94	0.77
Anchovies w/oil, each	1.76	0.65	1.10
Herring oil, 15 mL (1 Tbsp)	1.53	0.57	0.85
Salmon, Coho, steamed, 90 g (3 oz.)	1.34	0.71	0.46
Canola oil, 15 mL (1 Tbsp)	1.28	0.00	0.00
Sardines, Atlantic, w/ bones and oil, 90 g (3 oz.)	1.26	0.43	0.40
Trout, rainbow fillet, baked, 90 g (3 oz.)	1.05	0.70	0.28
Walnuts, English, 15 mL (1 Tbsp)	0.66	0.00	0.00
Halibut, fillet, baked, 90 g (3 oz.)	0.53	0.31	0.21
Shrimp, canned, 90 g (3 oz.)	0.47	0.21	0.25
Tuna, white, in oil, 90 g (3 oz.)	0.38	0.19	0.04
Crab, Alaska King, steamed, 90 g (3 oz.)	0.36	0.10	0.25
Scallops, broiled, 90 g (3 oz.)	0.31	0.14	0.17
Tuna, light, in water, 90 g (3 oz.)	0.23	0.19	0.04
Avocado, Calif., fresh, whole	0.22	0.00	0.00
Spinach, cooked, 250 mL (1 cup)	0.17	0.00	0.00

Note: *EPA = eicosapentaenoic acid; DHA = docosahexaenoic acid.
Data from Food Processor SQL, Version 10.3, ESHA Research, Salem, OR.

As we noted at the beginning of this chapter, legislators and food policy experts around the world are lobbying for the labelling of *trans* fatty acids on menus and/or the elimination of industrial *trans* fatty acids from restaurant foods and other ready-to-eat foods. Although this is a step in the right direction, if we are to achieve our goals for public health, we need to make sure that, in eliminating *trans* fatty acids from foods, we do not simply substitute saturated fats. Food establishments and food manufacturers need to switch to unsaturated fats or find other alternatives to *trans* fats if we are to reduce our risk for heart disease. See the Highlight box on page 169 to learn about one scientist's efforts to create an alternative to trans fats.

QUICK TIPS

Shopping for Foods Low in Saturated and Industrial *Trans* Fats

▶ Read food labels. Look for foods with no hydrogenated oils and low amounts of saturated fats per serving.

▶ Select tub margarine over hard stick forms. Fats that are solid at room temperature are usually high in hydrogenated *trans* or saturated fatty acids. Also, select margarines made from healthful fats, such as canola oil.

▶ Buy naturally occurring oils, such as olive and canola oil. These types of oils have not been hydrogenated and contain healthful unsaturated fatty acids and no *trans* fatty acids.

▶ Select baked products, such as crackers, chips, cookies, and muffins, that are labelled as being "*trans* fat free," if possible.

▶ Cut back on packaged pastries, such as Danishes, croissants, donuts, cakes, tarts, pies, and brownies. These baked goods are typically high in saturated and industrial *trans* fatty acids.

▶ Select reduced-fat salad dressing and mayonnaise or select those made with healthful fats, such as olive oil and canola oil. If you select the full-fat versions, remember that 15 mL (1 Tbsp) of oil or full-fat mayonnaise contains 420 kJ (100 kcal).

▶ Add fish, especially those high in omega-3 fatty acids (**Table 5.2**), to your shopping list. The recommendation in *Eating Well with Canada's Food Guide* (Health Canada, 2007b) is to eat at least 2 *Food Guide* servings (75 grams each, for a total of 150 grams) of fish each week

Select Beneficial Fats

As mentioned earlier, it is best to switch to healthful fats without increasing your total fat intake. Canadians appear to get adequate amounts of omega-6 fatty acids, probably because of the large amount of salad dressings, vegetable oils, margarine, and mayonnaise we eat; however, our consumption of omega-3 fatty acids is more variable and can be low in the diets of people who do not eat leafy green vegetables, fish, or walnuts; drink soy milk; or use soybean, canola, or flaxseed oil.

How can you specifically increase your intake of omega-3 fatty acids? In Table 5.2 e identify the omega-3 fatty acid content of various foods and supplements. Use this table to determine how you can increase your intake of omega-3 fatty acids. For example, consider including fish in your diet at least twice a week, use canola oil when baking, and add ground flaxseeds to your cereal or walnuts to your salad. You might also consider taking a daily fish oil supplement, using flaxseed oil, or buying products with omega-3 fatty acids added. As a consumer, you need to read the labels of these products carefully to determine if the omega-3 fatty acid content of the product is worth the extra cost.

It is important to recognize that there can be some risk associated with eating certain fish on a regular basis. Predatory fish tend to accumulate higher levels of mercury and therefore should be eaten less often by young children and women who are or may become pregnant or are breastfeeding. These fish species include fresh, frozen, or canned Albacore (white) tuna, shark, swordfish, marlin, orange roughy, and escolar (sometimes called snake mackerel or oilfish). For more information on seafood contamination, see Chapter 13.

Of course, healthful fats include not only the essential fatty acids but also polyunsaturated and monounsaturated fats in general. Plant oils are excellent sources of unsaturated fats, as are avocados, olives, nuts and nut butters, and seeds. Substituting beneficial fats for saturated or industrial *trans* fats is not difficult. See the Eating Right All Day feature below for some simple menu choices to help you eat right all day.

◆ Consumers can buy many products with added omega-3 fatty acids.

Watch Out When You're Eating Out!

Many college and university students eat most of their meals in dining halls, fast-food restaurants, and other food establishments. If that describes you, watch out! The menu items you choose each day may be increasing the amount of fat in your diet, including your intake of saturated and industrial *trans* fats. A high fat intake is especially difficult to avoid if you regularly eat fast food. In Chapter 2, we provided a list of general Quick Tips for Eating Right When You're Eating Out.

RECAP The types of fats we eat can significantly affect our health and risk for disease. Diets high in industrial *trans* fatty acids increase our risk for heart disease; the role of saturated fatty acids is controversial, and it may depend upon factors such as the length of the carbon chains and the nutrients that are replacing saturated fats (e.g., replacing SFA with PUFA may reduce our risk for heart disease).

Eating Right All Day

Breakfast
Non-fat yogurt with walnuts instead of bacon and eggs!

Lunch
Veggie pita instead of a ham and cheese sandwich!

Dinner
Grilled salmon instead of steak!

Snack
Whole-grain crackers with peanut butter instead of potato chips!

Nutrition DEBATE
Fat Blockers—Help or Hype?

In the last 30 years, the rate of obesity has steadily increased among North Americans. And growing right alongside our waistlines is the market for weight-loss supplements. It's a multibillion-dollar industry, with new products continually tempting us with promises of quick, effortless, and dramatic results.

One popular group of weight-loss supplements are the so-called fat blockers. Do these products really "block" fat? Can they really help you lose weight?

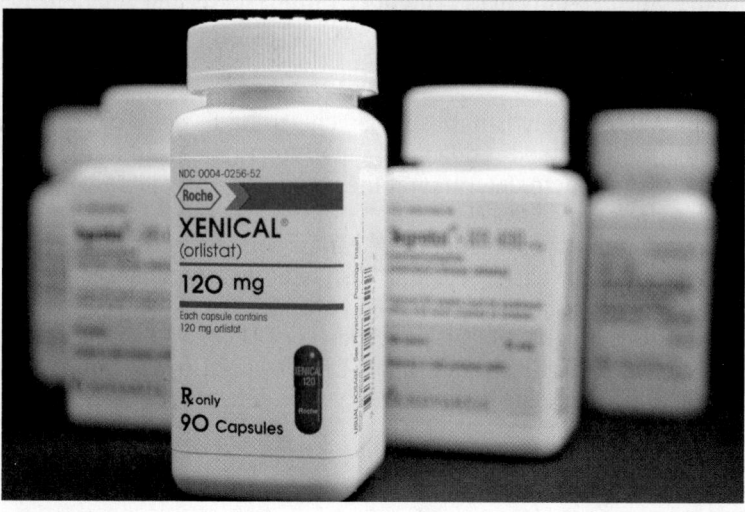

What Are the Claims?

One way to reduce energy intake and body weight would be to block the absorption of energy-containing macronutrients—such as fat, which contains 37 kJ (9 kcal) per gram. If we could block fat absorption, then we could eat large portions of our favourite high-fat foods, including fast foods, snacks, and desserts, without worrying about gaining weight. Fat blockers are said to decrease the amount of fat absorbed in the small intestine, leaving more to be excreted from the body.

Orlistat (brand name Xenical) is an example of a fat blocker. It inhibits the production of gastric and pancreatic lipases. Recall that these enzymes are responsible to breaking down triglycerides into free fatty acids and monoglycerides. Without these enzymes available, the triglycerides in foods are not broken down in the gut and therefore not absorbed. They pass through the intestine and are excreted, without having been digested.

It all sounds good, but is there any evidence that fat blockers work? Let's review the research.

What Does the Research Say?

Recent research shows that orlistat results in significant weight loss in obese adolescents, and adults experience significant weight loss and improved blood lipid profiles when orlistat is combined with an energy-restricted diet (Chanoine et al., 2005; Hutton and Fergusson, 2004).

A systematic review was done to assess the effectiveness and safety of orlistat as a weight-loss aid (Hutton and Fergusson, 2004). Twenty-eight randomized trials were included in the review. Seventeen studies found that over a one year period, patients given orlistat were more likely to lose weight than patients given a placebo, in addition to a low calorie diet. The results showed that the group receiving orlistat was 1.74 times more likely to lose 5% of their body weight compared to the placebo group, and 1.96 times more likely to achieve a weight loss of 10% compared to the placebo group. Blood lipid profiles improved more for the group taking orlistat versus those who received a placebo. However, patients receiving orlistat were more likely to experience gastrointestinal discomfort compared to the patients receiving the placebo.

In a large trial, 539 adolescents were either given a 120 mg dose of orlistat or a placebo three times daily, in addition to exercise, behavioural therapy, and a 'mildly hypocaloric diet (30% fat calories)' for 54 weeks. The group that received orlistat had an average decrease in their BMI of 0.55, compared to an increase in BMI of 0.31 observed in the placebo group. The group receiving orlistat also experienced more mild to moderate gastrointestinal distress.

Are There Any Side Effects?

The side effects of orlistat include abdominal pain, fatty and loose stools, leaky stools, flatulence (intestinal gas), and reduced absorption of fat-soluble nutrients, such as vitamins D and E. Both the systematic review, and the randomized trial discussed above reported more gastrointestinal events for the patients who received orlistat.

There is controversy over the use of orlistat, however, since there have been 13 cases of severe liver injury reported, including two deaths and three patients who needed liver transplants (US FDA, 2010).

You Be the Judge

Orlistat is available in Canada by prescription. What would you think if your doctor suggested orlistat for weight loss? Would you want to try it? Would you want to experience the side effects?

Chapter Review

1. True. Although eating too much fat, or too much of unhealthful fats (such as saturated and *trans* fatty acids), can increase our risk for diseases such as cardiovascular disease and obesity, some fats are essential to good health. We need to consume a certain minimum amount to provide adequate levels of essential fatty acids and fat-soluble vitamins.

2. True. Fat is our primary source of energy, both at rest and during low- and moderate-intensity exercise. Fat is also an important fuel source during prolonged exercise. During periods of high-intensity exercise, carbohydrate becomes the dominant fuel source.

3. False. While vegetable oils are better than vegetable shortening, which contains *trans* fats, fried foods are high in fat and energy and can contribute to overweight and obesity.

4. False. You need to check the Nutrition Facts table! In some foods, the missing fat has been replaced by carbohydrates, and there may not be much difference in the calories.

Find the Quack

Like everyone else in his family, Luiz is overweight. In addition, both of Luiz's parents take prescription medications to manage their high blood pressure, and his paternal grandfather died at age 42 from a heart attack. Understandably, Luiz is concerned about his own risk for cardiovascular disease. On this morning's news broadcast, the health segment discusses the Dr. Dean Ornish Diet. It is supposed to be designed specifically for people at risk for cardiovascular disease. Luiz learns that the diet consists of the following:

- "Abundant consumption of legumes, fruits, vegetables, and whole grains"
- "Moderate consumption of non-fat dairy products and non-fat or very-low-fat processed foods (such as non-fat yogurt bars, very-low-fat frozen dinners, and so on)"
- "Avoidance of all of the following: meats, oils, oil-containing products (such as margarines and salad dressings), avocados, nuts, seeds, alcohol, and sugars (including honey, molasses, and high-fructose corn syrup)"
- "Adding 30 minutes a day of moderate physical activity or three 1-hour sessions per week"

The TV health segment states that the Dr. Dean Ornish Diet has been proven in clinical studies to reduce the risk factors for cardiovascular disease.

1. Compare the Dr. Dean Ornish Diet to *Eating Well with Canada's Food Guide*, illustrated in Chapter 2. What are the main similarities? What are the main differences you see?

2. Comment on the level of essential fatty acids the Dr. Dean Ornish Diet provides.

3. Based on the diet's recommendations, how much total fat do you think this diet provides?

4. Do you think the Dr. Dean Ornish Diet is a quack diet or a legitimate diet? If legitimate, do you think it is advisable for someone with a family history of cardiovascular disease, such as Luiz? Why or why not?

Answers can be found in the study area of MasteringNutrition.

Review Questions

1. Omega-3 fatty acids are
   a. a form of *trans* fatty acid.
   b. metabolized in the body to arachidonic acid.
   c. synthesized in the liver and small intestine.
   d. found in leafy green vegetables, flaxseeds, soy milk, and fish.

2. One of the most sensible ways to reduce body fat is to
   a. limit intake of fat to less than 15% of total energy consumed.
   b. exercise regularly and watch portion sizes.
   c. avoid all consumption of *trans* fatty acids.
   d. restrict total energy to 5020 kJ (1200 kcal) per day.

3. Fats in chylomicrons are taken up by cells with the help of
   a. lipoprotein lipase.
   b. micelles.
   c. sterols.
   d. pancreatic enzymes.

4. The risk for heart disease is increased in people who
   a. consume a diet high in polyunsaturated fats.
   b. consume a diet high in industrial *trans* fats.
   c. consume a diet high in plant sterols.
   d. All of the above.

5. Triglycerides with a double bond at one part of the molecule are referred to as
   a. monounsaturated fats.
   b. hydrogenated fats.
   c. saturated fats.
   d. sterols.

6. Choose the incorrect statement:
   a. Most of the fat in our body is stored in the form of triglycerides.
   b. Phospholipids aid in transporting fats in our bloodstream.
   c. Sterols are lipids containing a single ring structure.
   d. In the small intestine, plant sterols appear to block dietary cholesterol absorption.

7. Select the correct statement regarding fat digestion:
   a. Bile is stored in the liver.
   b. Digestion primarily occurs in the stomach.
   c. Bile breaks fat into small droplets.
   d. The triglyceride molecule is broken down into one free fatty acid and two diglycerides.

8. Which one of the following is strongly associated with an increase in blood cholesterol?
   a. High-density lipoproteins
   b. Low-density lipoproteins
   c. Dietary cholesterol
   d. Free fatty acids

9. Explain how the straight, rigid shape of the saturated and *trans* fatty acids we eat affects our health.

10. You have volunteered to participate in a walk-a-thon to raise money for a local charity. You have been training for several weeks, and the event is now two days away. An athlete friend of your advises you to "load up on carbohydrates" today and tomorrow and says you should avoid eating any foods that contain fat during the day of the walk-a-thon. Do you take this advice? Why or why not?

11. Your father is feeling down after an appointment with his doctor. He tells you that his "blood test didn't turn out so good." He then adds, "My doctor told me I can't eat any of my favourite foods anymore. He says red meat and butter have too much fat. I guess I'll have to switch to cottage cheese and margarine!" What type of blood test do you think your father had? How would you respond to his intention to switch to cottage cheese and margarine? Finally, suggest a non-dietary lifestyle choice that might improve his health.

12. Your friend Maria has determined that she needs to consume about 8400 kJ (2000 kcal) per day to maintain her healthy weight. Create a chart for Maria showing the recommended maximum number of Calories she should consume in each of the following forms: total fat, saturated fat, linolenic acid, alpha-linolenic acid, and *trans* fatty acids.

Case Study

Let's meet Kyle, a 20-year-old university student and varsity soccer player. Currently, Kyle's BMI (see Chapter 11 for a detailed discussion of Body Mass Index) places him within the "overweight" category leading to increased health risks. Kyle and one of his housemates have decided to make an effort to lose weight. Kyle has decided his primary weight-loss goal is to dramatically decrease the amount of fat in his diet. However, what he may not realize is that fat plays an important role in good health, and a very low-fat diet can be unhealthy. It is important for Kyle to realize the differences between "good" fats and "bad" fats.

Kyle's Typical Daily Intake

Breakfast: 250 mL (8 fl. oz.) orange juice, 3 eggs, 3 slices of bacon

Mid-morning snack: 1 energy bar

Lunch: 1 foot-long steak and cheese sub with mayonnaise and butter, 500 mL (16 fl. oz.) orange juice

Mid-afternoon snack: 2 chocolate chip cookies, 1 medium banana, 1 medium coffee (180 mL) with cream and sugar

Dinner: Stir fir: broccoli, carrots, red pepper, and cashews fried in shortening, 2 pieces of beer-battered cod, 2 large baked potatoes, 250 mL (8 fl. oz.) 2% milk

Evening snack: 500 mL (2 cups) macaroni and cheese

a. There are three levels of saturation for fatty acids: saturated, monounsaturated, and polyunsaturated. Discuss the health implications of saturated fats and identify two sources in Kyle's diet. How could Kyle reduce his consumption of saturated fats?

b. Kyle has decided one diet change he would like to make is to substitute margarine for butter. However, some margarines undergo hydrogenation, which results in *trans* fatty acids. Explain what Kyle should look for on margarine labels to make a healthy choice.

c. Although decreasing fat intake plays a role in helping Kyle to lose weight, can you think of additional dietary changes he could make to improve his diet?

d. Distinguish between the two essential fatty acids: linoleic acid and alpha-linoleic acid. How can Kyle incorporate them into his diet?

e. List several drawback of very-low-fat diets (<15% energy from fat) compared with moderate-fat diets (20%–35% energy from fat).

f. List three functions of fat that might motivate Kyle to maintain a moderate-fat diet rather than a very-low-fat diet.

Answers to Review Questions can be found at the back of this text.

Web Resources

www.fcpc.ca/issues-policy/supporting-canadians-health-wellness/eliminating-trans-fat
Food and Consumer Products of Canada

Look at the *trans* fat issues from the perspective of food manufacturers.

www.heartandstroke.com
Heart and Stroke Foundation of Canada

Visit this website and find out more about your personal risk factors for cardiovascular disease and stroke.

www.hc-sc.gc.ca/fn-an/nutrition/gras-trans-fats/index-eng.php
Health Canada's Trans Fat Monitoring Program

Visit this site to see the latest findings from Health Canada's Trans Fat Monitoring Program

www.nlm.nih.gov/medlineplus
MEDLINE Plus Health Information

Search for "fats" or "lipids" to obtain additional resources and the latest news on dietary lipids, heart diseases, and cholesterol.

www.hsph.harvard.edu/nutritionsource
The Nutrition Source: Knowledge for Healthy Eating, Harvard School of Public Health

Go to this site, and click on "Nutrition A to Z" and then "Fats & Cholesterol" to find out how selective fat intake can be part of a healthful diet.

www.foodinsight.org
International Food Information Council Foundation

Access this site to find out more about fats and dietary fat replacers.

MasteringNutrition®

Assignments
Animations Fats in Food • Fat Digestion • Lipid Absorption • Lipoproteins: VLDL, LDL, and HDL

Study Area
Video: Understanding Lipids • Practice Tests • Diet Analysis • eText

Cardiovascular Disease

WANT TO FIND OUT...

- **if high blood pressure and heart disease are the same thing?**

- **what makes "good cholesterol" good and "bad cholesterol" bad?**

- **whether you're at risk for cardiovascular disease?**

READ ON.

Only couch potatoes develop heart disease . . . or so we like to think. That's why the world was stunned in the summer of 2002 when Darryl Kile, a 33-year-old Major League Baseball pitcher for the St. Louis Cardinals, died of a heart attack in his Chicago hotel room the night before a scheduled game. An autopsy revealed a 90% blockage in two of Kile's coronary arteries—the vessels that supply blood to the heart. Although cardiovascular disease in an athlete is rare, Kile's family history revealed one very important risk factor: his father died of a heart attack at age 44.

What causes a heart attack? Are genetics always to blame? If you have a family history of cardiovascular disease, is there anything you can do to reduce your risk? We explore these questions *In Depth* here.

What Is Cardiovascular Disease?

Cardiovascular disease is a general term used to refer to any abnormal condition involving dysfunction of the heart (*cardio-* means "heart") and blood vessels (*vasculature*). There are many forms of this disease, but the three most common are the following:

- *Coronary heart disease* occurs when blood vessels supplying the heart (the *coronary arteries*) become blocked or constricted; such blockage reduces the flow of blood—and the oxygen and nutrients it carries—to the heart. This can result in chest pain, called *angina pectoris*, and lead to a heart attack.
- *Stroke* is caused by a blockage of one of the blood vessels supplying the brain (the *cerebral arteries*). When this occurs, the region of the brain that depends on that artery for oxygen and nutrients cannot function. As a result, the

movement, speech, or other body functions controlled by that part of the brain suddenly stop.
- *Hypertension*, also called *high blood pressure*, is a condition that may not cause any symptoms, but it increases your risk for a heart attack or stroke. If your blood pressure is high, it means that the force of the blood flowing through your arteries is above normal.

To understand cardiovascular disease, we need to look at a condition called *atherosclerosis*, which is responsible for the blockage of arteries that leads to heart attacks and strokes. What is more, hypertension is often a sign of underlying atherosclerosis. So let's take a closer look.

Atherosclerosis Is Narrowing of Arteries

Atherosclerosis is a disease in which arterial walls accumulate deposits of lipids and scar tissue that build up to such a degree that they impair blood flow. It is a complex process that begins with injury to the cells that line the insides of all arteries. Factors that commonly promote such injury are the forceful pounding of blood under high pressure and blood-vessel damage from irritants, such as the nicotine in tobacco or the excessive blood glucose in people with poorly controlled diabetes. Whatever the cause, the injury leads to vessel inflammation, which is increasingly being

recognized as an important marker of cardiovascular disease (Wilson, 2004). Inflamed vessels become weakened, allowing lipids, mainly cholesterol, to seep through the layers of the vessel wall and eventually become trapped in thick, grainy deposits called *plaque*. The term *atherosclerosis* reflects the presence of these deposits: *athere* is a Greek word meaning "a thick porridge."

As plaques form, they narrow the interior of the blood vessel **(Figure 1)**. This slowly diminishes the blood supply to any tissues "downstream." As a result, these tissues—including heart muscle—wither, and gradually lose their ability to function. Alternatively, the blockage may occur suddenly, because a plaque ruptures and *platelets*, substances in blood that promote clotting, stick to the damaged area. This quickly obstructs the artery, causing the death of the tissue it supplies. As a result, the person experiences a heart attack or stroke.

Arteries damaged by atherosclerosis become stiff; that is, they lose their

cardiovascular disease A general term that refers to abnormal conditions involving dysfunction of the heart and blood vessels; cardiovascular disease can result in heart attack or stroke.

atherosclerosis A condition characterized by accumulation of deposits of lipids and scar tissue on artery walls. These deposits build up to such a degree that they impair blood flow.

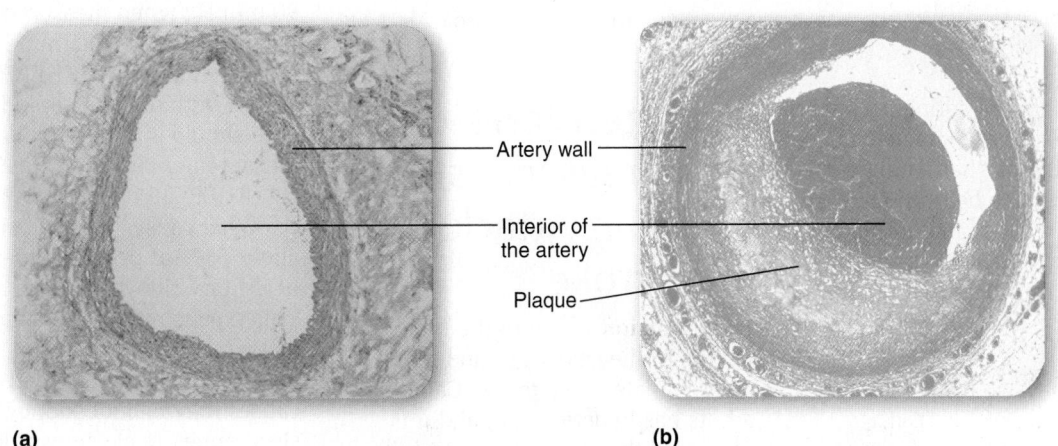

(a) **(b)**

Figure 1 These light micrographs show a cross section of **(a)** a normal artery containing little plaque and allowing adequate blood flow through the heart and **(b)** an artery that is partially blocked with cholesterol-rich plaque, which can lead to a heart attack.

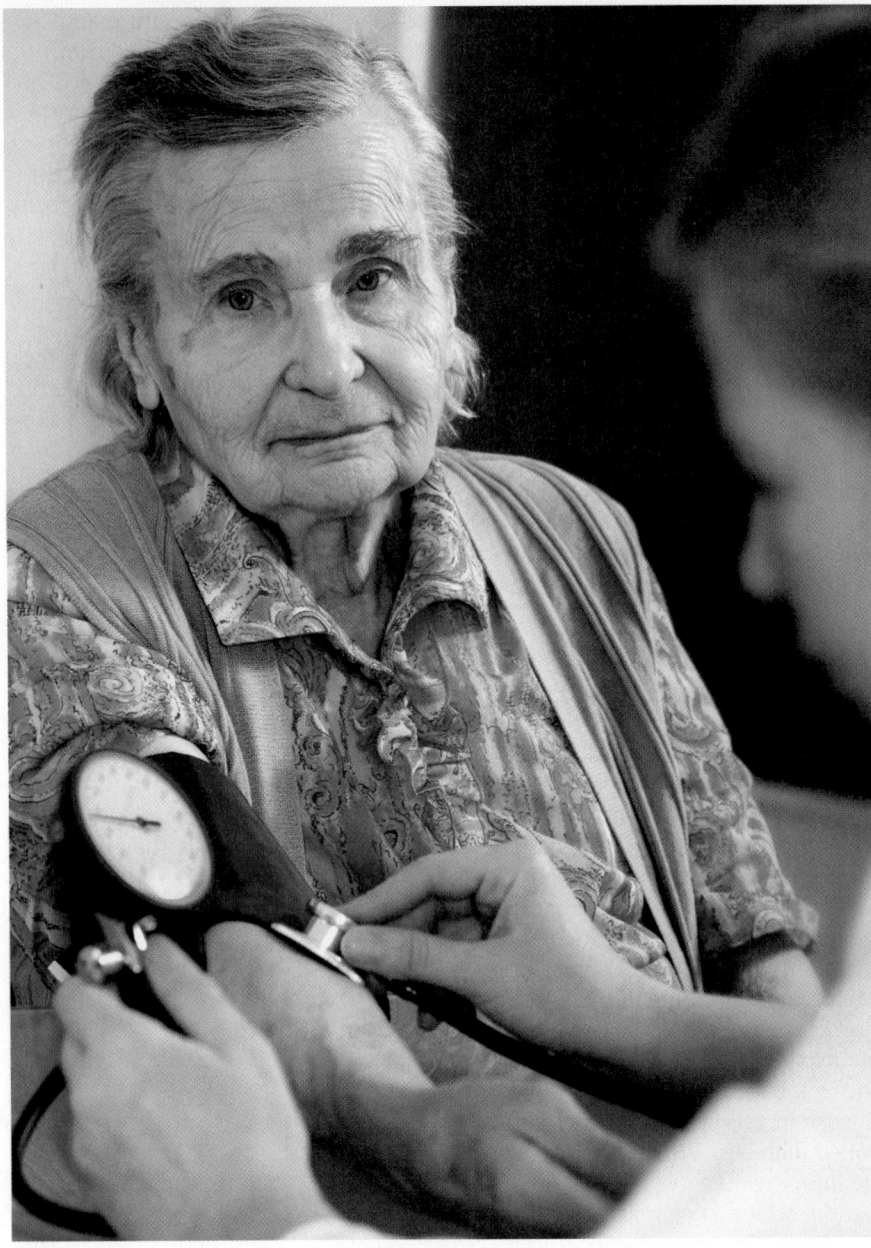

▲ More than one in five adult Canadians has hypertension (Hypertension Canada, 2011).

is often without symptoms, it is a warning sign that a person's risk for heart disease and stroke is increased. In fact, the most important risk factor for stroke is high blood pressure, and Canadians suffer 40 000 to 50 000 strokes each year (Health Canada, 2006). Approximately 15 000 people die from strokes each year; 59% of stroke deaths are women. Hypertension can also damage the kidneys, reduce brain function, and impair physical mobility.

When we define hypertension as blood pressure above the normal range, what exactly do we mean? Well, we measure blood pressure in two phases, systolic and diastolic. *Systolic blood pressure* represents the pressure exerted in our arteries at the moment that the heart contracts, sending blood into our blood vessels. *Diastolic blood pressure* represents the pressure in our arteries between contractions, when our heart is relaxed.

Blood pressure measurements are recorded in millimetres of mercury (mm Hg). Optimal systolic blood pressure is *less than* 120 mm Hg, while optimal diastolic blood pressure is *less than* 80 mm Hg. *Prehypertension* is defined as a systolic blood pressure between 120 and 139 mm Hg, or a diastolic blood pressure between 80 and 89 mm Hg. An estimated 20% of adults in Canada are prehypertensive. You would be diagnosed with true hypertension if your systolic blood pressure were greater than or equal to 140 mm Hg or your diastolic blood pressure were greater than or equal to 90 mm Hg when measured in a doctor's office or 135/85 mm Hg when measured at home (CHEP, 2011). People with diabetes or kidney disease should aim for a blood pressure measurement lower than 130/80 mm Hg (CHEP, 2011).

What causes hypertension? For about 55% of people, hypertension is hereditary (Lloyd-Jones et al., 2010). This type is referred to as *primary* or *essential hypertension*. For the other 45% of people with hypertension, causes may include kidney disease, sleep apnea (a sleep disorder that affects breathing), certain medications, psychosocial stressors, tobacco use, obesity, low physical activity,

ability to stretch and spring back with each heartbeat. This characteristic, often referred to as "hardening of the arteries," forces the heart to increase the pressure of each burst of blood it ejects into the stiffened vessels. Physicians refer to this increased pressure as *systolic hypertension*, as we explain next.

---

hypertension A chronic condition characterized by above-average blood pressure readings—specifically, systolic blood pressure over 140 mm Hg or diastolic blood pressure over 90 mm Hg.

Hypertension Signals an Increased Risk for Heart Attack and Stroke

Hypertension is one of the major risk factors for heart disease and stroke. Approximately one in five Canadian adults has hypertension, and it is estimated that 42% of those adults are not aware that they have it (Heart and Stroke Foundation of Canada, 2008). Although hypertension itself

excessive alcohol intake, and dietary factors, including sensitivity to salt and low potassium intake (Lloyd-Jones et al., 2010).

Who Is at Risk for Cardiovascular Disease?

According to a 2003 report by Health Canada's Centre for Chronic Disease Prevention and Control, the Canadian Cardiovascular Society, and the Heart and Stroke Foundation of Canada, cardiovascular diseases are the underlying cause of death for one-third of Canadians.

Many Risk Factors Are Within Your Control

Over the last two decades, researchers have identified a number of factors that contribute to an increased risk for cardiovascular disease. Some of these risk factors are non-modifiable, meaning they are beyond your control. These include age—the older you are, the higher your risk—male gender, and family history. Like pitcher Darryl Kile, you have an increased risk for cardiovascular disease if a parent suffered a heart attack, especially at a young age.

Other risk factors are modifiable—meaning they are at least partly within your control. Following is a brief description of each of these modifiable risk factors. Notice that many of them have a dietary component.

- *Overweight.* Being overweight is associated with cardiovascular disease and higher rates of death from cardiovascular disease. The risk is due primarily to a greater occurrence of high blood pressure, inflammation, abnormal blood lipids (discussed in more detail shortly), and higher rates of type 2 diabetes in people who are overweight. In general, an overweight condition develops from an energy imbalance from eating too much and exercising too little (see Chapter 11).

- *Physical inactivity.* Numerous research studies have shown that physical activity can reduce your risk for cardiovascular disease by improving several risk factors associated with the disease, including improved blood lipid levels, lower resting blood pressure, lower body fat and weight, and improved blood glucose levels both at rest and after eating. Physical activity can also significantly reduce the risk for type 2 diabetes, a major cardiovascular disease risk factor (Marwick et al., 2009).

- *Smoking.* There is strong evidence that smoking increases your risk for blood-vessel injury and cardiovascular disease. Research indicates that smokers have a two- to threefold greater chance of developing cardiovascular disease than non-smokers (Hahn and Heath 1998). If you smoke, quitting is one of the best ways to reduce your risk for cardiovascular disease. People who stop smoking live longer than those who continue to smoke, and a 15-year cessation period will reduce your risk factors for cardiovascular

▲ Being overweight is associated with higher rates of death from cardiovascular disease.

disease to those of a non-smoker (DHHS, 2010).

- *Type 2 diabetes mellitus.* As discussed **In Depth** in Chapter 4, in many individuals with type 2 diabetes, the condition is directly related to being overweight or obese, which is also associated with abnormal blood lipids and high blood pressure. The risk for cardiovascular disease is three times higher in women with diabetes and two times higher in men with diabetes compared to individuals without diabetes.

- *Inflammation.* We noted earlier that inflammation is considered a major contributor to cardiovascular disease. When injury occurs to the arteries, the resulting inflammatory response eventually leads to the deposition of plaque in the arterial walls. Plaque buildup increases the risk for a heart attack or stroke. C-reactive protein (CRP) is a nonspecific marker of inflammation that is associated with cardiovascular disease. Risk for cardiovascular disease appears to be higher in individuals who have high CRP levels in addition to other risk factors, such as high blood lipids (Libby et al., 2002). Thus, reducing the factors that promote inflammation, such as obesity and a diet low in omega-3 fatty acids and high in saturated fats, can lower your risk for cardiovascular disease.

⬆ Because foods fried in hydrogenated vegetable oils, such as french fries, are high in *trans* fatty acids, these types of foods should be limited in our diet.

- *Abnormal blood lipids.* As we explain next, high LDL-cholesterol and triglycerides and low HDL-cholesterol are associated with an increased risk for cardiovascular disease. Making lifestyle changes, such as lowering your intake of saturated and *trans* fat, increasing your physical activity and soluble fibre intake, and achieving a healthful body weight, can help improve your blood lipid profile.

The Role of Dietary Fats in Cardiovascular Disease

Recall that lipids are transported in the blood by lipoproteins made up of a lipid centre and a protein outer coat. The names of lipoproteins reflect their proportion of lipid, which is less dense, to protein, which is very dense. For example, very-low-density lipoproteins (VLDLs) have a high ratio of lipid to protein. Because lipoproteins are soluble in blood, they are commonly called *blood lipids*.

Our intake of certain types of dietary fats influences our risk for heart disease by increasing or decreasing certain blood lipids. Research indicates that high intakes of saturated and *trans* fatty acids increase the blood's level of those lipids associated with heart disease—namely, total blood cholesterol and the cholesterol found in very-low-density lipoproteins (VLDLs) and low-density lipoproteins (LDLs). Conversely, omega-3 fatty acids decrease our risk for heart disease in a number of ways, such as by reducing inflammation and blood triglycerides (Kris-Etherton et al., 2002) and increasing high-density lipoproteins (HDLs) (Harris, 1997) Let's look at each of these blood lipids in more detail to determine how they are linked to your risk for heart disease (**Figure 2**).

Chylomicrons

Only after a meal does the blood contain chylomicrons, which we learned earlier are produced in the small intestine to transport dietary fat into the

lymphatic vessels and from there into the bloodstream. At 85% triglyceride, chylomicrons have the lowest density.

Very-Low-Density Lipoproteins

More than half of the substance of **very-low-density lipoproteins (VLDLs)** is triglyceride. The liver is the primary source of VLDLs, but they are also produced in the intestines. VLDLs are primarily transport vehicles ferrying triglycerides from their source to the body's cells, including to adipose tissues for storage. The enzyme lipoprotein lipase frees most of the triglyceride from the VLDL molecules, resulting in its uptake by the body's cells.

Diets high in fat, simple sugars, and extra calories can increase the production of endogenous VLDLs, whereas diets high in omega-3 fatty acids can help reduce their production. In addition, exercise can reduce VLDLs because the fat produced in the body is quickly used for energy instead of remaining to circulate in the blood.

Low-Density Lipoproteins

The molecules resulting when VLDLs release their triglyceride load are much higher in cholesterol, phospholipids, and protein and therefore somewhat more dense. These **low-density lipoproteins (LDLs)** circulate in the blood, delivering their cholesterol to cells. Diets high in saturated fat *decrease* the removal of LDLs by body cells.

What happens to LDLs not taken up by body cells? As LDLs degrade over time, they release their cholesterol; thus, failure to remove LDLs from the bloodstream results in an increased load of cholesterol in the blood. The more cholesterol circulating in the blood, the greater the risk that some of

---

very-low-density lipoprotein (VLDL) A lipoprotein made in the liver and intestine that functions to transport endogenous lipids, especially triglycerides, to the tissues of the body.

low-density lipoprotein (LDL) A lipoprotein formed in the blood from VLDLs that transports cholesterol to the cells of the body. Often called the "bad cholesterol."

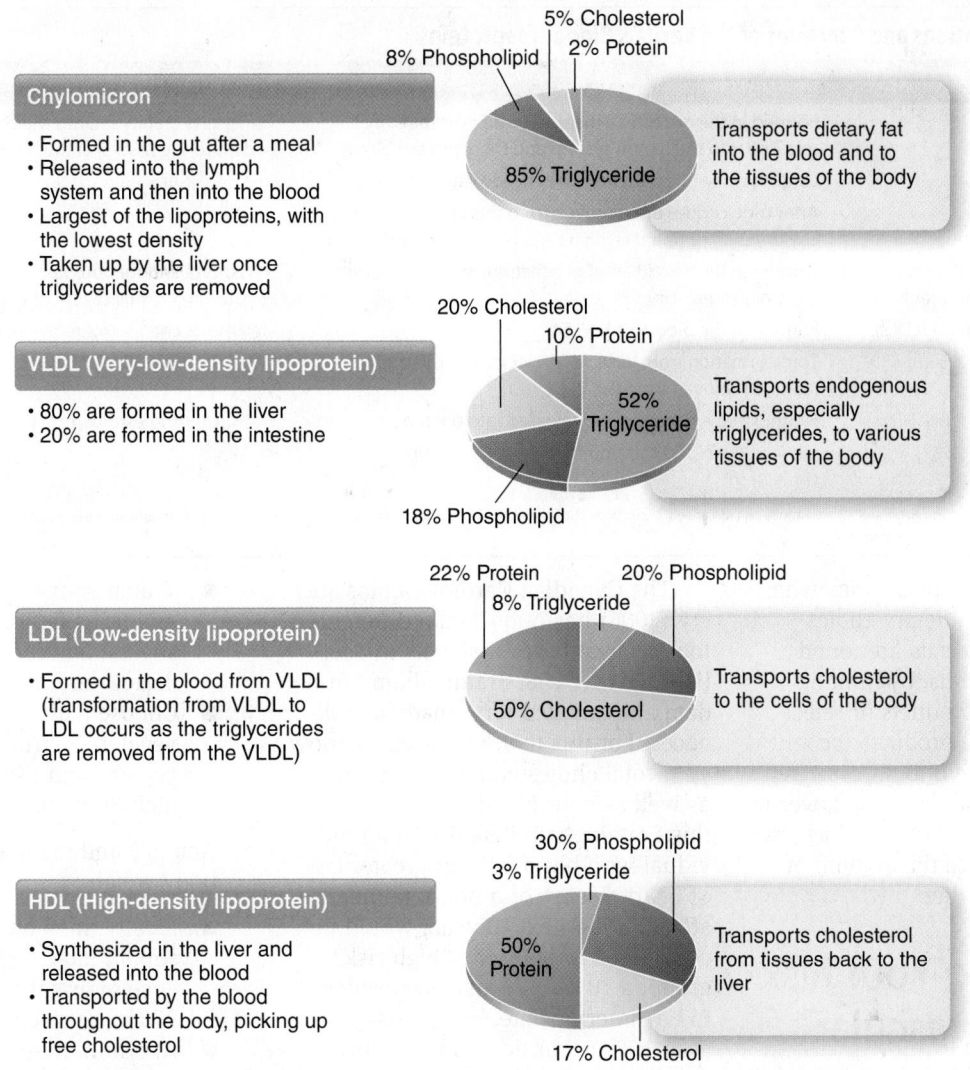

Figure 2 The chemical components of various lipoproteins. Notice that chylomicrons contain the highest proportion of triglycerides, making them the least dense, whereas high-density lipoproteins (HDLs) have the highest proportion of protein, making them the most dense.

it will adhere to the walls of the blood vessels, contributing to the development of atherosclerosis. Because high blood levels of LDL cholesterol increase the risk for heart disease, it is often labelled the "bad cholesterol."

High-Density Lipoproteins

As their name indicates, **high-density lipoproteins (HDLs)** are small, dense lipoproteins with a very low cholesterol content and a high protein content. They are released from the liver and intestines to circulate in the blood, picking up cholesterol from dying cells and arterial plaques and transferring it to other lipoproteins, which return it to the liver. The liver takes up the cholesterol and uses it

to synthesize bile, thereby removing it from the circulatory system. High blood levels of HDL cholesterol are therefore associated with a low risk for coronary artery disease. That is why HDL cholesterol is often referred to as the "good cholesterol." There is some evidence that diets high in omega-3 fatty acids and participation in regular physical exercise can modestly increase HDL cholesterol levels (Zoeller, 2007).

A summary of the functions of these blood lipoproteins is provided in **Table 1**.

Total Blood Cholesterol

Normally, as the dietary level of cholesterol increases, the body decreases

the amount of cholesterol it makes, which keeps the body's level of cholesterol constant. Unfortunately, this feedback mechanism does not work well in everyone. For some individuals, eating dietary cholesterol does not decrease the amount of cholesterol produced in the body, and their total body cholesterol level rises. This also increases the level of cholesterol in the blood. These individuals benefit from reducing their intake of dietary cholesterol.

---

high-density lipoprotein (HDL) A lipoprotein made in the liver and released into the blood. HDLs function to transport cholesterol from the tissues back to the liver. Often called the "good cholesterol."

TABLE 1 Descriptions and Functions of the Various Blood Lipoproteins

Lipoprotein	Description	Primary Function
Chylomicrons	Formed in the gut after a meal, these lipoproteins are released into the lymph system and then into the blood Largest of the lipoproteins, with the lowest density After triglycerides are removed from this lipoprotein, a chylomicron remnant remains and is taken up by the liver	Transports dietary fat into the blood and transports it to the tissues of the body
Very low-density lipoproteins (VLDLs)	Formed in the liver (80% of production) and the intestine (20% of production)	Transports endogenous lipids, especially triglycerides, to the various tissues of the body
Low-density lipoproteins (LDLs)	Formed in the blood from VLDL Transformation from VLDL to LDL occurs as the triglycerides are removed from the VLDL	Transports cholesterol to the cells of the body
High-density lipoproteins (HDLs)	Synthesized in the liver and released into the blood Move in the blood through the body, picking up free cholesterol	Transports cholesterol from tissues back to the liver

Source: Based on information from Heart and Stroke Foundation of Canada, Living with Cholesterol: Cholesterol and Healthy Living; p. 183: Based on Heart and Stroke Foundation of Canada, Cholesterol Article Updates, Nov. 7, 2005. www. heartandstroke.ca.

Although this appears somewhat complicated, both dietary cholesterol and saturated fats are found in animal foods; thus, by limiting intake of animal products or selecting low-fat animal products, people reduce their intake of both saturated fat and cholesterol. Selecting lower-fat meat, poultry, and dairy products can dramatically reduce the amount of cholesterol in the diet.

Calculating Your Risk for Cardiovascular Disease

The Heart and Stroke Foundation of Canada has an online tool called "My Heart&Stroke Risk Assessment™" that you can use to estimate your personal risk for heart disease and stroke. Try it out at www.heartandstroke.com/site/c.ikIQLcMWJtE/b.5374487/k.62BF/HeartStroke_Action_Plans.htm Once you have calculated your risk, you can choose from two different action plans. "My Blood Pressure Action Plan™" helps you to set goals, track your blood pressure, and you can even request electronic messages reminding you to take blood pressure medication! "My Healthy Weight Action Plan™" is a 12-week online program to help you reach and keep a healthy weight. For people who know that they benefit from extra support, there is also "My Health eSupport™," designed to provide reminders and encouragement through electronic messages.

The Canadian Cardiovascular Society (2006) has published a different tool for health professionals to use, based on the U.S. Framingham Study data and adapted for Canadian audiences. For this tool, you need to know your total cholesterol and HDL levels, as well as your blood pressure. Using this Framingham Risk Score, an individual who has a 20% or greater risk of heart disease or a non-fatal heart attack in the next 10 years would be considered to be in the "high risk" group, a 10%–19% risk is considered to be "intermediate," and a risk less than 10% is considered to be "low risk."

Lifestyle Choices Can Help Prevent or Control Cardiovascular Disease

If you are in a low or intermediate/moderate risk group for cardiovascular disease, continuing to make healthy lifestyle choices is the best way to prevent heart disease and stroke in the future. The Canadian Cardiovascular Society has the following recommendations (2006):

- Don't smoke.
- Have a healthy diet:

  - Watch your intake of saturated and trans fatty acids, simple sugars, and refined carbohydrates; and
  - Choose a diet with lots of vegetables, fruits, whole-grain cereals, and PUFA and MUFA, including omega-3 fatty acids.

- Achieve and maintain a healthy body weight:

  - Ideally, men and women should have a waist circumference of less than 94 cm and 80 cm, respectively; and
  - At a minimum, have a BMI less that 27 kg/m^2; ideally, a BMI of less than 25 kg/m^2.

- Participate in regular physical activity:

  - 60 min. of light, 30 to 60 min. of moderate, or 20 to 30 min. of vigorous activity four to seven days a week.

Prescription Medications Can Improve Blood Lipids and Blood Pressure

For some individuals, lifestyle changes are not completely effective in normalizing blood lipids and blood pressure. When this is the case, a variety of medications can be prescribed. Some, called statins, inhibit

What About You?

Blood Lipid Levels: Know Your Numbers!

One of the most important steps you can take to reduce your risk of heart disease is to know your "numbers"—that is, your blood lipid values. However, cholesterol testing is not necessary for everyone of all ages. Canadian Dyslipidemia guidelines released in 2009 recommend that you have your blood cholesterol tested if you:

1. are male and 40 years of age or older
2. are female and 50 years of age or older
3. are female and post-menopause,
4. are obese
5. have diabetes,
6. have high blood pressure,
7. have chronic kidney disease, inflammatory diseases (systemic lupus erythematosis, rheumatoid arthritis, psoriasis), or evidence of atherosclerosis,
8. smoke, or
9. have a strong family history of premature (before the age of 60) heart disease" 2009 Canadian Cardiovascular Society Clinical Practice Guidelines

If you fall into one of the above categories, your doctor might begin by testing your total LDL- ("bad") and HDL- ("good") cholesterol levels. Record these values. In this way you can know your own blood levels and keep track of your risk for heart disease.

How are your blood lipids actually measured? Generally, you want blood lipid levels similar to those described in **Table 2** below. However, the more risk factors you have for heart disease or stroke, the lower your target levels should be. "When deciding the 'right' target levels for you, your doctor will take into account factors that increase your risk of heart disease and stroke, such as your age, sex, blood pressure, and whether you have diabetes or stroke. If any of your cholesterol levels are outside the 'right' target level for you, your doctor will discuss lifestyle changes and may prescribe medication to keep your levels in balance" (Heart and Stroke Foundation of Canada, 2005).

In Canada, the results of the cholesterol tests are given in millimoles per litre (mmol/L), but in the United States, the results are expressed in milligrams per decilitre (mg/dL); these values are shown in brackets in Table 2 below.

TABLE 2 Blood Lipid Values for those at Moderate Risk of Developing Heart Disease or Stroke

Blood Lipid	Suggested Target Levels
Total cholesterol	Less than 5.2 mmol/L [200 mg/dL]
LDL cholesterol	Less than 3.5 mmol/L [about 130 mg/dL]
HDL cholesterol	Greater than 1.0 mmol/L for men and 1.2 mmol/L for women [about 40 mg/dL]
Total cholesterol: HDL cholesterol ratio	Less than 5.0

Source: Heart and Stroke Foundation of Canada, Cholesterol Article Updates, Nov. 7, 2005. © Reproduced with the permission of the Heart and Stroke Foundation of Canada, 2006. www.heartandstroke.ca.

the body's production of cholesterol. Common statins are atorvastatin (Lipitor), fluvastatin (Lescol) and lovastatin (Mevacor). Others prevent cholesterol and bile acids from being reabsorbed in the GI tract—ezetimibe (brand name Ezetrol) and cholestyramine are used in Canada. Since bile is made from cholesterol, blocking its reabsorption means the liver must draw on cholesterol stores to make more. Diuretics may be prescribed to flush excess water and sodium from the body, reducing blood pressure. Other hypertension medications work to relax the blood vessel walls, giving more room for blood flow. Individuals taking such medications should also continue to practice the lifestyle changes listed earlier in this section, as these changes will continue to benefit their long-term health.

Web Resources

www.heartandstroke.ca
Heart and Stroke Foundation of Canada

Visit this website and find out more about your personal risk factors for cardiovascular disease and stroke.

www.hc-sc.gc.ca/hc-ps/tobac-tabac/quit-cesser/now-maintenant/index-eng.php
Health Canada—Quit Smoking Now

Visit this website for programs and resources designed to help you quit smoking for life.

www.hc-sc.gc.ca/fn-an/nutrition/gras-trans-fats/index-eng.php
Health Canada—Trans Fats

Health Canada's Trans Fat Monitoring Program and progress reports are available here.

www.nhlbi.nih.gov
National Heart, Lung, and Blood Institute

Use this online risk assessment tool to estimate your 10-year risk of having a heart attack.

www.nlm.nih.gov/medlineplus
MEDLINE Plus Health Information

Find the latest news on dietary lipids and cardiovascular disease.

Proteins: Crucial Components of All Body Tissues

6

CHAPTER OBJECTIVES

After reading this chapter you will be able to:

1. Describe how proteins differ from carbohydrates and fats, p. 186.

2. Identify non-meat food combinations that are complete protein sources, pp. 192–193.

3. Describe four functions of proteins in our bodies, pp. 194–197.

4. Discuss how proteins are digested, absorbed, and synthesized by our bodies, pp. 197–199.

5. Calculate your recommended daily allowance for protein, p. 202.

6. List five foods that are good sources of protein, pp. 203–206.

7. Identify the potential health risks associated with high-protein diets, p. 209.

8. Describe two disorders related to inadequate protein intake, pp. 209–211.

Test Yourself

1. (T) (F) Protein is a primary source of energy for our bodies.

2. (T) (F) Vegetarian diets are inadequate in protein.

3. (T) (F) Most people in Canada consume enough protein to meet their needs.

Test Yourself answers can be found at the end of the chapter.

Y

ou may have heard of vegetarians, or lacto-ovo vegetarians (where dairy and eggs are allowed), even vegans, but have you heard of pescetarians? Pescetarians eat a relatively vegetarian-based diet, but also allow themselves to consume fish and seafood. How about flexitarians? Flexitarian diets are quickly becoming one of the most popular dietary lifestyles, because as their name might suggest, they are quite flexible in the foods that are allowed. People with a flexitarian lifestyle choose to consume a mostly vegetarian-based diet, but also enjoy meat, poultry, fish, seafood, dairy, and eggs as they please. Flexitarian diets are increasing in popularity for a number of reasons; they can be less expensive than eating meat all the time, and they generally include a wider variety of foods.

Meatless Mondays is a weekly tradition often enjoyed by flexitarians and their families across North America, where dinner features a plant protein source, usually beans, lentils, or whole grains like quinoa. Do you think it is possible to get enough protein on a flexitarian, vegetarian, or vegan diet? Are there advantages to eating meat, or is plant protein just as good? What exactly is a protein, and what makes it so different from carbohydrates and fats? How much protein do you really need, and do you get enough in your daily diet? In this chapter, we address these and other questions to clarify the importance of protein in the diet and dispel common myths about this critical nutrient.

Proteins are an integral part of our body tissues, including our muscle tissue.

What Are Proteins?

Proteins are large, complex molecules found in the cells of all living things. Although proteins are best known as a part of our muscle mass, they are, in fact, critical components of all the tissues of the human body, including bones, blood, and skin. Proteins also function in metabolism, immunity, fluid balance, and nutrient transport, and they can provide energy in certain circumstances. The functions of proteins will be discussed in detail later in this chapter.

How Do Proteins Differ from Carbohydrates and Lipids?

As we saw in Chapter 1, proteins are one of the three macronutrients. Like carbohydrates and lipids, proteins are found in a wide variety of foods; plus, the human body is able to synthesize them. But unlike carbohydrates and lipids, proteins are made according to instructions provided by our genetic material, or DNA. We'll explore how DNA dictates the structure of proteins shortly.

Another key difference between proteins and the other macronutrients lies in their chemical makeup. In addition to the carbon, hydrogen, and oxygen also found in carbohydrates and lipids, proteins contain a special form of nitrogen that our bodies can readily use. This nitrogen is found in amino acids, which are the building blocks of proteins. Our bodies are able to break down the proteins in plant and animal foods and use the nitrogen for many important body processes. Carbohydrates and lipids do not provide nitrogen.

The Building Blocks of Proteins Are Amino Acids

The proteins in our bodies are made from a combination of building blocks called **amino acids**, molecules composed of a central carbon atom connected to four other groups: an amine group, an acid group, a hydrogen atom, and a side chain **(Figure 6.1a)**. The word *amine* means "nitrogen containing," and nitrogen is indeed the essential component of the amine portion of the molecule.

As shown in Figure 6.1b, the portion of the amino acid that makes each unique is its side chain. The amine group, acid group, and carbon and hydrogen atoms do not vary. Variations in the structure of the side chain give each amino acid its distinct properties.

The singular term *protein* is misleading, as there are potentially an infinite number of unique types of proteins in living organisms. Most of the proteins in our

amino acids Nitrogen-containing molecules that combine to form proteins.

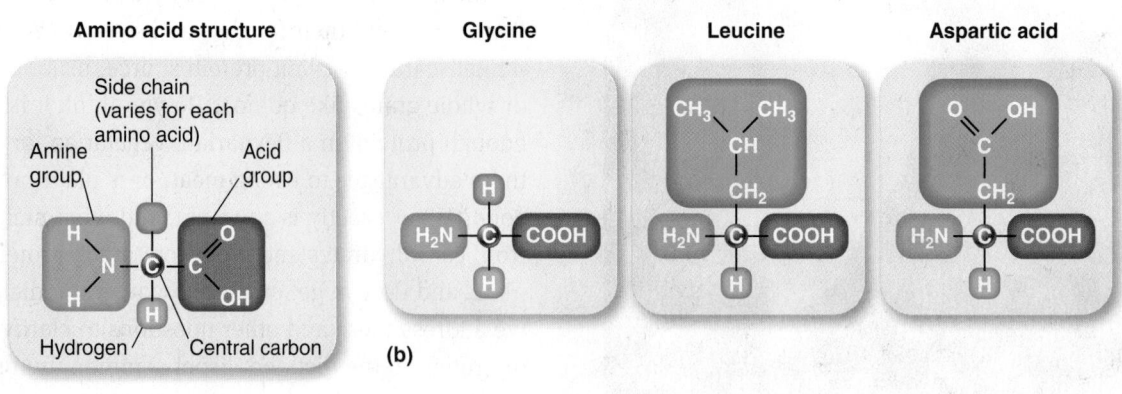

(a)

(b)

Figure 6.1 Structure of an amino acid. **(a)** All amino acids contain five parts: a central carbon atom, an amine group around the atom that contains nitrogen, an acid group, a hydrogen atom, and a side chain. **(b)** Only the side chain differs for each of the 20 amino acids, giving each its unique properties.

TABLE 6.1 Amino Acids of the Human Body

Essential Amino Acids	Non-essential Amino Acids
These amino acids must be consumed in the diet.	These amino acids can be manufactured by the body.
Histidine	Alanine
Isoleucine	Arginine
Leucine	Asparagine
Lysine	Aspartic acid
Methionine	Cysteine
Phenylalanine	Glutamic acid
Threonine	Glutamine
Tryptophan	Glycine
Valine	Proline
	Serine
	Tyrosine

bodies are made from combinations of just 20 amino acids, identified in **Table 6.1**. By combining a few dozen to more than 300 copies of these 20 amino acids in various sequences, our bodies form an estimated 10 000 to 50 000 unique proteins. Two of the 20 amino acids listed in Table 6.1, cysteine and methionine, are unique in that, in addition to the components present in the other amino acids, they contain sulphur.

We Must Obtain Essential Amino Acids from Food

Of the 20 amino acids in our bodies, 9 are classified as essential. This does not mean that they are more important than the 11 non-essential amino acids. Instead, an **essential amino acid** is one that our bodies cannot produce at all or cannot produce in sufficient quantities to meet our physiologic needs. Thus, we must obtain essential amino acids from our food. Without the proper amount of essential amino acids in our bodies, we lose our ability to make the proteins and other nitrogen-containing compounds we need.

Our Body Can Make Non-essential Amino Acids

Non-essential amino acids are just as important to our bodies as essential amino acids, but our bodies can make them in sufficient quantities, so we do not need to consume them in our diet. We make non-essential amino acids by transferring the amine group from an essential amino acid to a different acid group and side chain. This process is called **transamination**, and it is shown in **Figure 6.2**. The acid groups and side chains can be donated by amino acids, or they can be made from the breakdown products of carbohydrates and fats. Thus, by combining parts of different amino acids, the non-essential amino acids can be made.

essential amino acids Amino acids not produced by the body that must be obtained from food.

non-essential amino acids Amino acids that can be manufactured by the body in sufficient quantities and therefore do not need to be consumed regularly in our diet.

transamination The process of transferring the amine group from one amino acid to another to manufacture a new amino acid.

Transamination

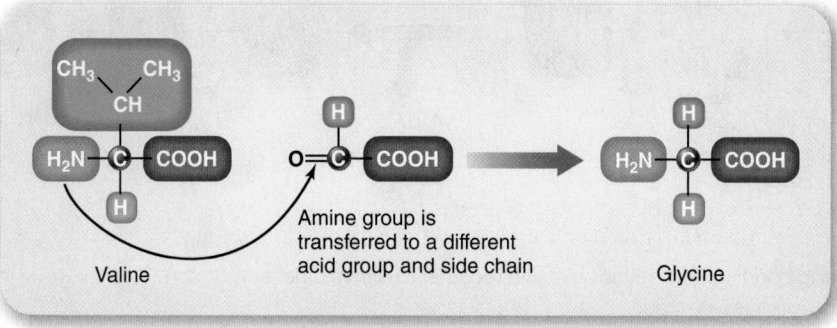

◀ **Figure 6.2** Transamination. Our bodies can make non-essential amino acids by transferring the amine group from an essential amino acid to a different acid group and side chain.

Under some conditions, a non-essential amino acid can become an essential amino acid. In this case, the amino acid is called a *conditionally essential amino acid.* Consider what occurs in the disease known as phenylketonuria (PKU). As discussed in Chapter 4, someone with PKU cannot metabolize phenylalanine (an essential amino acid). Normally, the body uses phenylalanine to produce the non-essential amino acid tyrosine, so the inability to metabolize phenylalanine results in failure to make tyrosine. If PKU is not diagnosed immediately after birth, it results in irreversible brain damage. In this situation, tyrosine becomes a conditionally essential amino acid that must be provided by the diet. Other conditionally essential amino acids are arginine, cysteine, glycine, proline, serine and glutamine.

RECAP Proteins are critical components of all the tissues of the human body. Like carbohydrates and lipids, they contain carbon, hydrogen, and oxygen. Unlike the other macronutrients, they also contain nitrogen and some contain sulphur, and their structure is dictated by DNA. The building blocks of proteins are amino acids. The amine group of the amino acid contains nitrogen. The portion of the amino acid that changes, giving each amino acid its distinct identity, is the side chain. The body cannot make essential amino acids, so we must obtain them from our diet. Our bodies can make non-essential amino acids from parts of other amino acids, carbohydrates, and fats.

How Are Proteins Made?

As we have stated, our bodies can synthesize proteins by selecting the needed amino acids from the pool of all amino acids available at any given time. Let's look more closely at how this occurs.

Amino Acids Bond to Form a Variety of Peptides

Figure 6.3 shows that, when two amino acids join together, the amine group of one binds to the acid group of another in a unique type of chemical bond called a **peptide bond**. In the process, a molecule of water is released as a by-product.

Two amino acids joined together form a *dipeptide,* and three amino acids joined together are called a *tripeptide.* The term *oligopeptide* is used to identify a string of four to nine amino acids, while a *polypeptide* is ten or more amino acids bonded together. As a polypeptide chain grows longer, it begins to fold into any of a variety of complex shapes that give proteins their sophisticated structure.

Genes Regulate Amino Acid Sequences

Each of us is unique because we inherited a specific genetic "code" that integrates the code from each of our parents. Each person's genetic code dictates minor differences in amino acid sequences, which in turn lead to differences in our bodies'

peptide bonds Unique types of chemical bonds in which the amine group of one amino acid binds to the acid group of another to manufacture dipeptides and all larger peptide molecules.

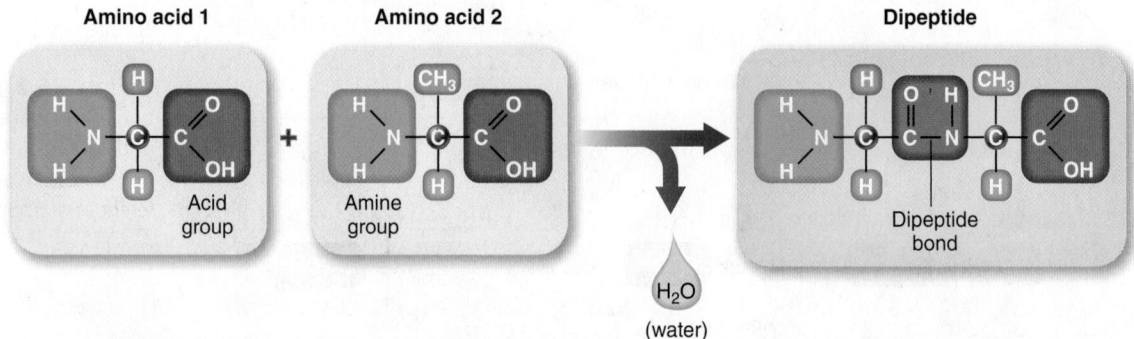

Figure 6.3 Amino acid bonding. Two amino acids join together to form a dipeptide. By combining multiple amino acids, proteins are made.

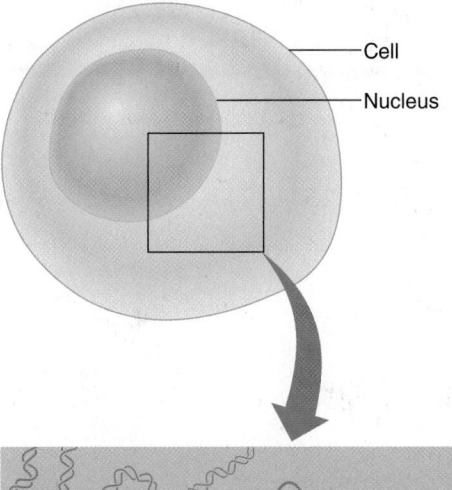

Cell

Nucleus

◀ **Figure 6.4** Gene expression. Messenger RNA (mRNA) transcribes the genetic information from DNA in the nucleus and carries it to the ribosomes in the cytoplasm. At the ribosome, this genetic information is translated into a chain of amino acids that eventually make a protein.

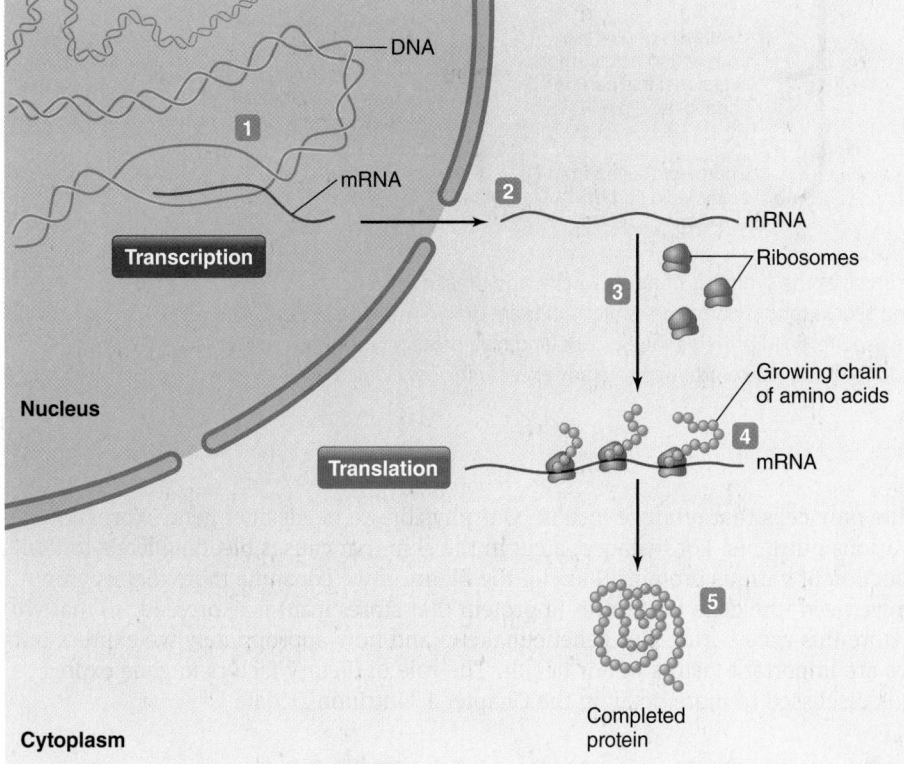

DNA

1

mRNA

2

mRNA

Transcription

Ribosomes

3

Growing chain of amino acids

4

mRNA

Translation

5

Nucleus

Completed protein

Cytoplasm

1 Part of the DNA unwinds, and a section of its genetic code is transcribed to the mRNA inside the nucleus.

2 The mRNA leaves the nucleus via a nuclear pore and travels to the cytoplasm.

3 Once the mRNA reaches the cytoplasm, it binds to a ribosome. The code on the mRNA is translated into the instructions for a specific order of amino acids.

4 Amino acids are added to the growing amino acid chain, and eventually a complete protein is produced.

5 Once the synthesis of the new protein is complete, the protein is released from the ribosome. The protein may go through further modifications in the cell, or can be functional in its current state.

individual proteins. These differences in proteins result in the unique physical and physiologic characteristics each one of us possesses.

As mentioned earlier, DNA dictates the structure of each protein our bodies synthesize. **Figure 6.4** shows how this process occurs. Cells use segments of DNA called *genes* as templates for assembling—or *expressing*—particular proteins. Thus, this process is referred to as **gene expression**. Since proteins are manufactured at the site of ribosomes in the cytoplasm, and DNA never leaves the nucleus, a special molecule is needed to copy, or transcribe, the information from DNA and carry it to the ribosome. This is the job of *messenger RNA* (*messenger ribonucleic acid*, or *mRNA*); during **transcription**, mRNA copies the genetic information from DNA in the nucleus and carries it to the ribosomes in the cytoplasm. Once this genetic information is at the ribosome, **translation** occurs: genetic information from the mRNA is translated into a growing chain of amino acids that are bonded together to make a specific protein.

Although the DNA for making every protein in our bodies is contained within each cell nucleus, not all genes are expressed and each cell does not make every type of protein. For example, each cell contains the DNA to manufacture the hormone insulin. However, only the cells of the pancreas express the insulin gene; that is, they

gene expression The process of using a gene to make a protein.

transcription The process through which messenger RNA copies genetic information from DNA in the nucleus.

translation The process that occurs when the genetic information carried by messenger RNA is translated into a chain of amino acids at the ribosome.

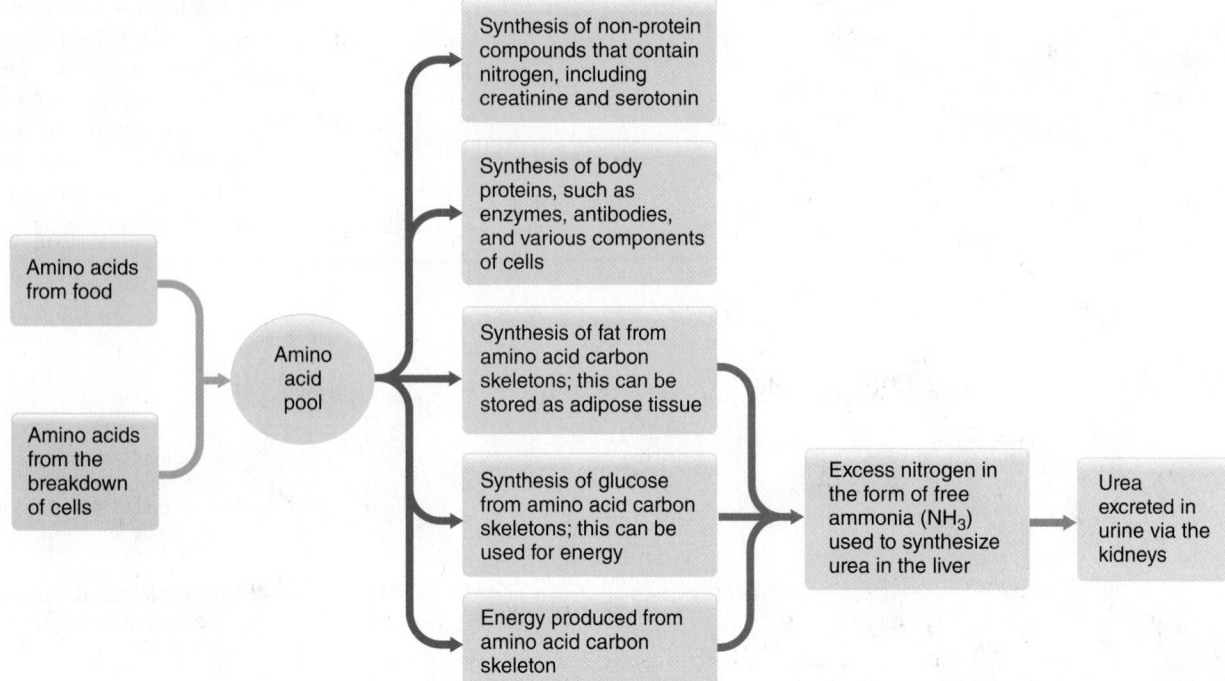

◆ Figure 6.5 Protein turnover involves the synthesis of new proteins and breakdown of existing proteins to provide building blocks for new proteins. Amino acids are drawn from the body's amino acid pool and can be used to build proteins, fat, glucose, and non-protein nitrogen-containing compounds. Urea is produced as a waste product from any excess nitrogen, which is then excreted by the kidneys.

are the only cells that produce insulin. Our physiologic needs alter gene expression, as do various nutrients. For instance, a cut in the skin that causes bleeding leads to the production of various proteins that clot the blood. If we consume more dietary iron than we need, the gene for ferritin (a protein that stores iron) is expressed, so that we can store this excess iron. Our genetic makeup and how appropriately we express our genes are important factors in our health. The role of dietary factors in gene expression is discussed in more detail in the Chapter 1 Nutrition Debate.

Protein Turnover Involves Synthesis and Degradation

Our bodies constantly require new proteins to function properly. *Protein turnover* involves both the synthesis of new proteins and the degradation of existing proteins to provide the building blocks for those new proteins **(Figure 6.5)**. This process allows the cells to respond to the constantly changing demands of physiologic functions. For instance, skin cells live for only about 30 days and must continually be replaced. The amino acids needed to produce these new skin cells can be obtained from the body's *amino acid pool,* which includes those amino acids we consume in our diet as well as those that are released from the breakdown of other cells in our bodies. The body's pool of amino acids is used to produce not only new amino acids but also other products, including glucose and fat.

Protein Organization Determines Function

Four levels of protein structure have been identified **(Figure 6.6)**. The sequential order of the amino acids in a protein is called the *primary structure* of the protein. The different amino acids in a polypeptide chain possess unique chemical characteristics that cause the chain to twist and turn into a characteristic spiral shape, referred to as

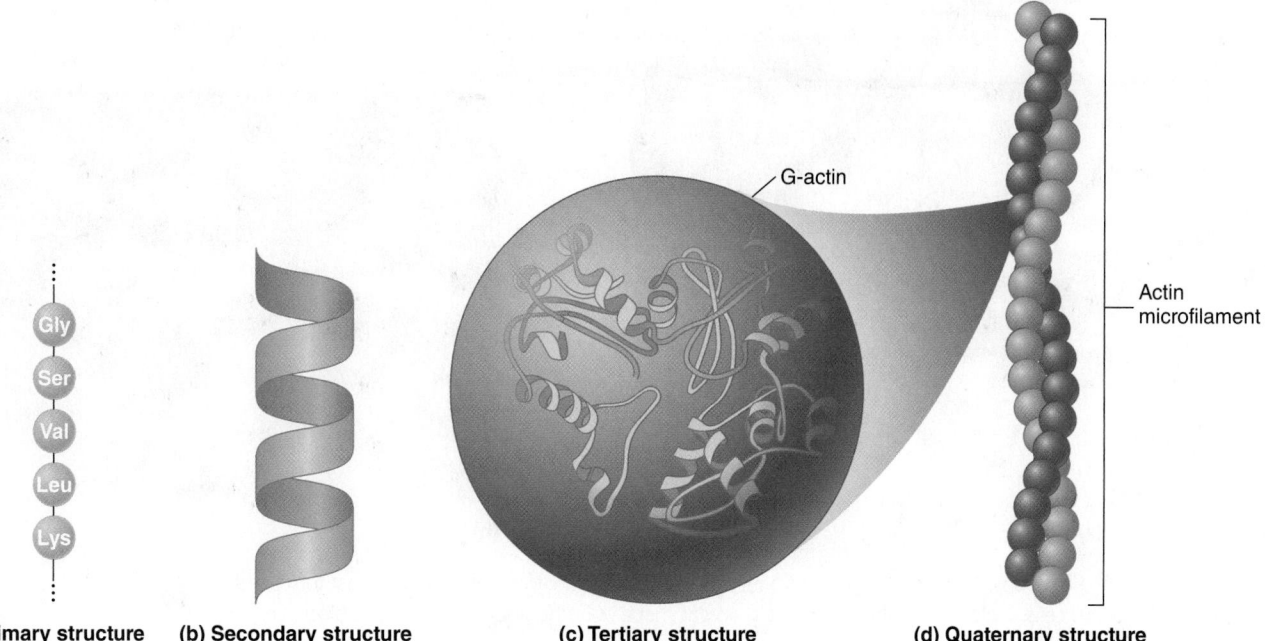

(a) Primary structure   **(b) Secondary structure**   **(c) Tertiary structure**   **(d) Quaternary structure**

Figure 6.6 Levels of protein structure. **(a)** The primary structure of a protein is the sequential order of amino acids. **(b)** The secondary structure of a protein is the folding of the amino acid chain. **(c)** The tertiary structure is a further folding that results in the three-dimensional shape of the protein. **(d)** The quaternary structure of a protein refers to molecules containing two or more polypeptides that bond to form a larger protein, such as the actin molecule illustrated here. In this figure, strands of actin molecules intertwine to form contractile elements involved in generating muscle contractions.

the protein's *secondary structure.* The stability of the secondary structure is achieved through the bonding of hydrogen atoms or sulphur atoms; these bonds create a bridge between two protein strands or two parts of the same strand of protein. The spiral of the secondary structure further folds into a unique three-dimensional shape, referred to as the protein's *tertiary structure;* this structure is critically important because it determines each protein's function in the body. Often, two or more separate polypeptides bond to form an even larger protein with a *quaternary structure,* which may be *globular* or *fibrous.*

The importance of the shape of a protein to its function cannot be overemphasized. For example, the protein strands in muscle fibres are much longer than they are wide (see Figure 6.6d). This structure plays an essential role in enabling muscle contraction and relaxation. In contrast, the proteins that form red blood cells are globular in shape, and they result in the red blood cells being shaped like flattened discs with depressed centers, similar to a miniature doughnut **(Figure 6.7)**. This structure and the flexibility of the proteins in the red blood cells permit them to change shape and flow freely through even the tiniest capillaries to deliver oxygen and still return to their original shape.

Proteins can uncoil and lose their shape when they are exposed to heat, acids, bases, heavy metals, alcohol, and other damaging substances. The term used to describe this change in the shape of proteins is denaturation. Everyday examples of protein denaturation that we can see are the stiffening of egg whites when they are whipped, the curdling of milk when lemon juice or another acid is added, and the solidifying of eggs as they cook.

Denaturation does not affect the primary structure of proteins. However, when a protein is denatured, its function is lost. For instance, denaturation of a critical enzyme on exposure to heat or acidity is harmful, because it prevents the enzyme from doing its job. This type of denaturation can occur during times of high fever or when the level of acid in the blood is out of the normal range. In some cases, denaturation

Stiffening egg whites denatures some of the proteins within them.

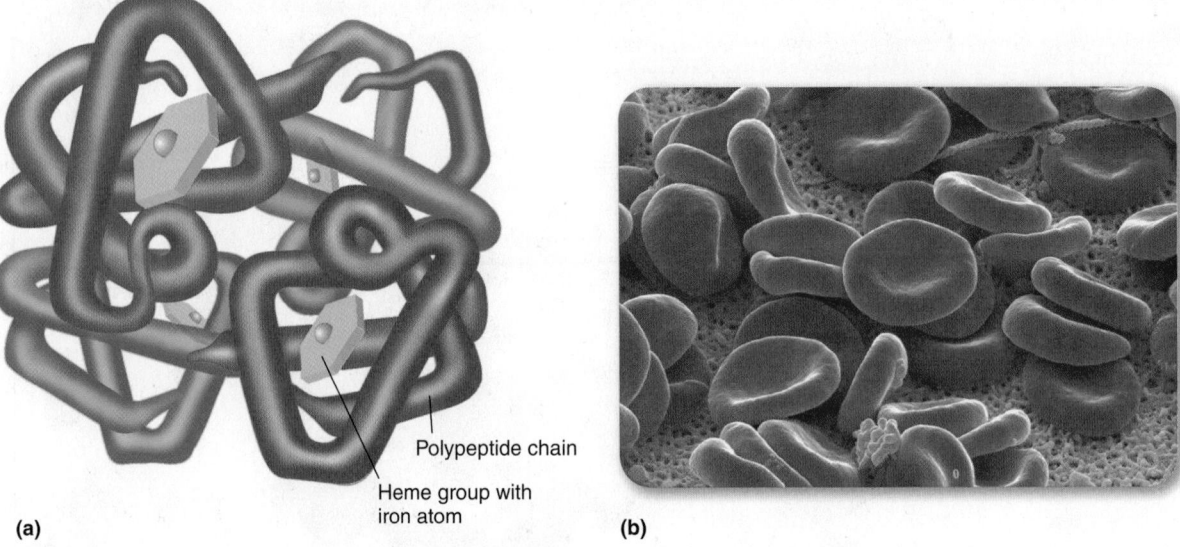

Polypeptide chain

Heme group with iron atom

(a)　　　　　　　　　　　　　　　　　　　　　　　**(b)**

Figure 6.7 Protein shape determines function. **(a)** Hemoglobin, the protein that forms red blood cells, is globular in shape. **(b)** The globular shape of hemoglobin results in red blood cells being shaped like flattened discs.

is helpful. For instance, denaturation of proteins during the digestive process allows for their breakdown into amino acids and the absorption of these amino acids from the digestive tract into the bloodstream.

RECAP Amino acids bind together to form proteins. Genes regulate the amino acid sequence, and thus the structure, of all proteins. The shape of a protein determines its function. When a protein is denatured by damaging substances, such as heat and acids, it loses its shape and its function.

Protein Synthesis Can Be Limited by Missing Amino Acids

For protein synthesis to occur, all essential amino acids must be available to the cell. If this is not the case, the amino acid that is missing or in the smallest supply is called the **limiting amino acid**. Without the proper combination and quantity of essential amino acids, protein synthesis slows to the point at which proteins cannot be generated. For instance, the protein hemoglobin contains the essential amino acid histidine. If we do not consume enough histidine, it becomes the limiting amino acid in hemoglobin production. As no other amino acid can be substituted, our bodies become unable to make adequate hemoglobin, and we lose the ability to transport oxygen to our cells.

Inadequate energy consumption also limits protein synthesis. If there is not enough energy available from our diets, our bodies will use any accessible proteins for energy, thus preventing them from being used to build new proteins.

A protein that does not contain all of the essential amino acids in sufficient quantities to support growth and health is called an **incomplete** *(low-quality)* **protein**. Proteins that have all nine of the essential amino acids in sufficient amounts to meet needs are considered **complete** *(high-quality)* **proteins**. The most complete protein sources are foods derived from animals and include egg whites, meat, poultry, fish, and milk. Soybeans are the most complete source of plant protein, with the same protein quality rating as egg white protein. (See the section on protein digestibility on p. 199 for more on protein quality.) Quinoa, a grain-like product used by the ancient Incas, contains all nine essential amino acids, but there is some

limiting amino acid The essential amino acid that is missing or in the smallest supply in the amino acid pool and is thus responsible for slowing or halting protein synthesis.

incomplete proteins Proteins that do not contain all of the essential amino acids in sufficient amounts to support growth and health.

complete proteins Proteins that contain all nine essential amino acids in sufficient quantities for protein synthesis. Proteins from animal sources are complete proteins. Soybeans are considered to be the only complete plant proteins.

controversy about whether the amino acids are present in sufficient amounts to produce proteins for biological functions in the human body. In general, the typical Canadian diet is very high in complete proteins, as we eat proteins from a variety of food sources.

Protein Synthesis Can Be Enhanced by Mutual Supplementation

Many people believe that we must consume meat or dairy products to obtain complete proteins. Not true! Consider a meal of beans and rice. Beans are low in the amino acids methionine and cysteine but have adequate amounts of isoleucine and lysine. Rice is low in isoleucine and lysine but contains sufficient methionine and cysteine. By combining beans and rice, we create a complete protein.

Mutual supplementation is the process of combining two or more incomplete protein sources to make a complete protein. The two foods involved are called complementary foods; these foods provide **complementary proteins (Figure 6.8)**, which, when combined, provide all nine essential amino acids.

It is not necessary to eat complementary proteins at the same meal. Recall that we maintain a free pool of amino acids in the blood; these amino acids come from food and sloughed-off cells. When we eat one complementary protein, its amino acids join those in the free amino acid pool. These free amino acids can then combine to synthesize complete proteins. However, it is wise to eat complementary protein foods during the same day, as partially completed proteins cannot be stored and saved for a later time. Mutual supplementation is important for people eating a vegetarian diet, particularly if they consume no animal products whatsoever.

mutual supplementation The process of combining two or more incomplete protein sources to make a complete protein.

complementary proteins Two or more foods that together contain all nine essential amino acids necessary for a complete protein. It is not necessary to eat complementary proteins at the same meal.

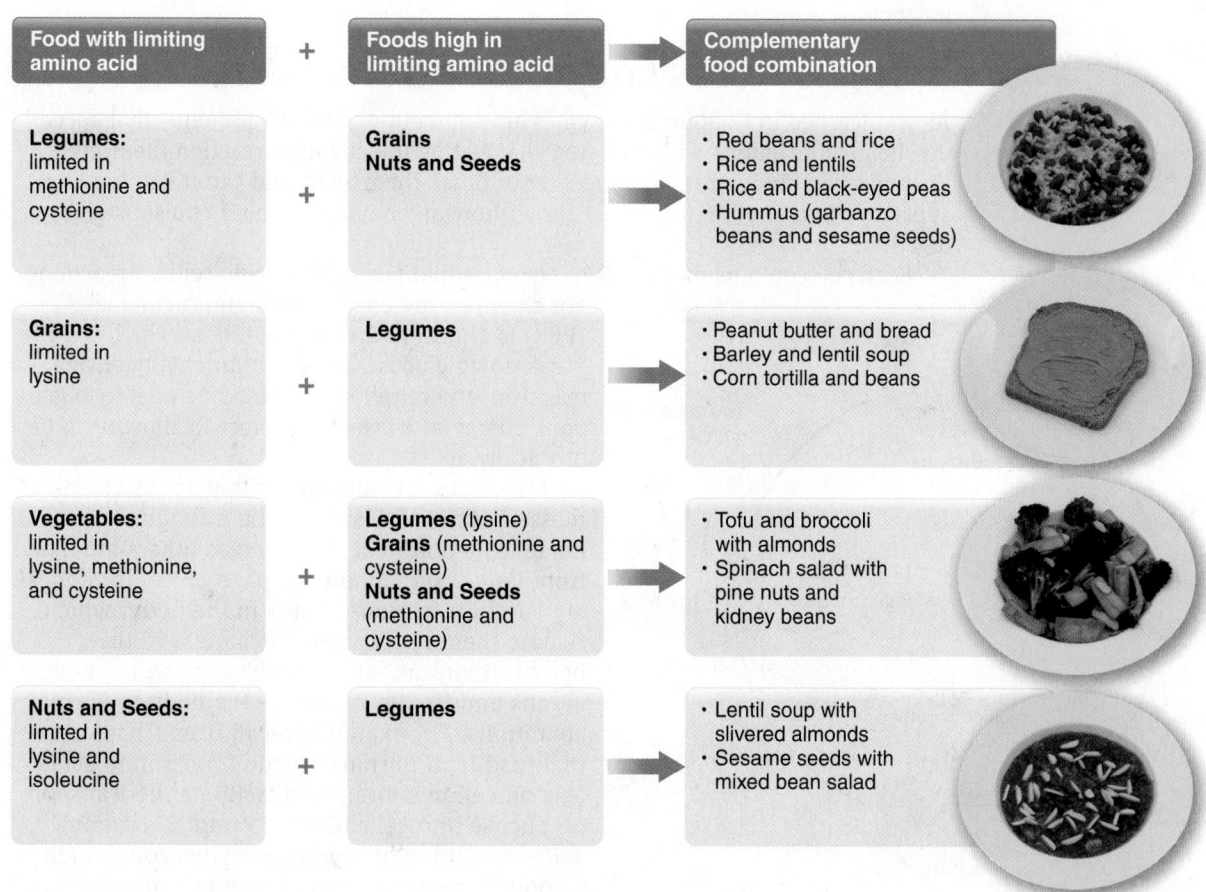

Food with limiting amino acid	+	Foods high in limiting amino acid	→	Complementary food combination
Legumes: limited in methionine and cysteine	+	**Grains** **Nuts and Seeds**	→	· Red beans and rice · Rice and lentils · Rice and black-eyed peas · Hummus (garbanzo beans and sesame seeds)
Grains: limited in lysine	+	**Legumes**	→	· Peanut butter and bread · Barley and lentil soup · Corn tortilla and beans
Vegetables: limited in lysine, methionine, and cysteine	+	**Legumes** (lysine) **Grains** (methionine and cysteine) **Nuts and Seeds** (methionine and cysteine)	→	· Tofu and broccoli with almonds · Spinach salad with pine nuts and kidney beans
Nuts and Seeds: limited in lysine and isoleucine	+	**Legumes**	→	· Lentil soup with slivered almonds · Sesame seeds with mixed bean salad

Figure 6.8 Complementary food combinations.

RECAP When a particular amino acid is limiting, protein synthesis cannot occur. A complete protein provides all nine essential amino acids. Mutual supplementation combines two complementary protein sources to make a complete protein.

Why Do We Need Proteins?

The functions of proteins in the body are so numerous that only a few can be described in detail in this chapter. Note that proteins function most effectively when we also consume adequate amounts of energy as carbohydrates and fat. When there is not enough energy available, the body uses proteins as an energy source, limiting their availability for the functions described in this section.

Proteins Contribute to Cell Growth, Repair, and Maintenance

The proteins in our bodies are dynamic, meaning that they are constantly being broken down, repaired, and replaced. When proteins are broken down, many amino acids are recycled into new proteins. Think about all of the new proteins that are needed to allow an infant to develop and grow into a mature adult.

Even in adulthood, our cells are constantly turning over, as damaged or worn-out cells are broken down and their components are used to create new cells. Our red blood cells live for only three to four months and then are replaced by new cells that are produced in bone marrow. The cells lining our intestinal tract are replaced every three to six days. The "old" intestinal cells are treated just like the proteins in food; they are digested and the amino acids absorbed back into the body. The constant turnover of proteins from our diet is essential for such cell growth, repair, and maintenance.

Proteins Act as Enzymes and Hormones

As you learned in Chapter 3, enzymes are compounds, usually proteins, that speed up chemical reactions without being changed by the chemical reaction themselves. Enzymes can bind substances together or break them apart and can transform one substance into another. **Figure 6.9** shows how an enzyme can bind two substances together.

Each cell contains thousands of enzymes that facilitate specific cellular reactions. For example, the enzyme phosphofructokinase (PFK) is critical to driving the rate at which we break down glucose and use it for energy during exercise. Without PFK, we would be unable to generate energy at a fast enough rate to allow us to be physically active.

Hormones are substances that act as chemical messengers in the body. Some hormones are made from amino acids, whereas others are made from lipids (see Chapter 5, page 155). Hormones are stored in various glands in the body, which release them in response to changes in the body's environment. They then act on the body's organs and tissues to restore the body to normal conditions. For example, recall from Chapter 4 that insulin, a hormone made from amino acids, acts on cell membranes to facilitate the transport of glucose into cells. Other examples of amino acid–containing hormones are glucagon, which responds to conditions of low blood glucose, and thyroid hormone, which helps control our resting metabolic rate.

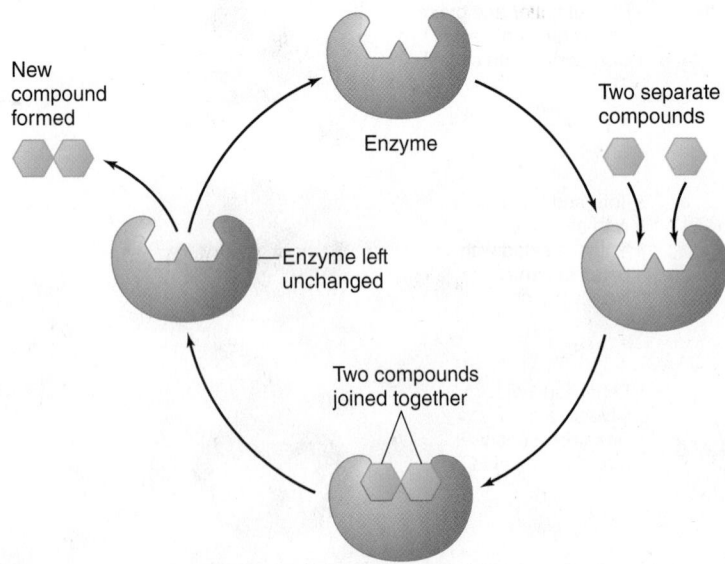

New compound formed

Enzyme

Two separate compounds

Enzyme left unchanged

Two compounds joined together

Figure 6.9 Proteins act as enzymes. Enzymes facilitate chemical reactions, such as joining two compounds together.

Proteins Help Maintain Fluid and Electrolyte Balance

Electrolytes are electrically charged particles that assist in maintaining fluid balance. For our bodies to function properly, fluids and electrolytes must be maintained at healthy levels inside and outside cells and within blood vessels. Proteins attract fluids, and the proteins that are in the bloodstream, in the cells, and in the spaces surrounding the cells work together to keep fluids moving across these spaces in the proper quantities to maintain fluid balance and blood pressure. When protein intake is deficient, the concentration of proteins in the bloodstream is insufficient to draw fluid from the tissues and across the blood vessel walls. Fluid then collects in the tissues, causing **edema** (Figure 6.10). In addition to being uncomfortable, edema can lead to serious medical problems.

Sodium (Na$^+$) and potassium (K$^+$) are examples of common electrolytes. Under normal conditions, Na$^+$ is more concentrated outside the cell, and K$^+$ is more concentrated inside the cell. This proper balance of Na$^+$ and K$^+$ is accomplished by the action of **transport proteins** located within the cell membrane. Figure 6.11 shows how these transport proteins work to pump Na$^+$ outside and K$^+$ inside of the cell. The conduction of nerve signals and contraction of muscles depend on a proper

edema A disorder in which fluids build up in the tissue spaces of the body, causing fluid imbalances and a swollen appearance.

transport proteins Protein molecules that help transport substances throughout the body and across cell membranes.

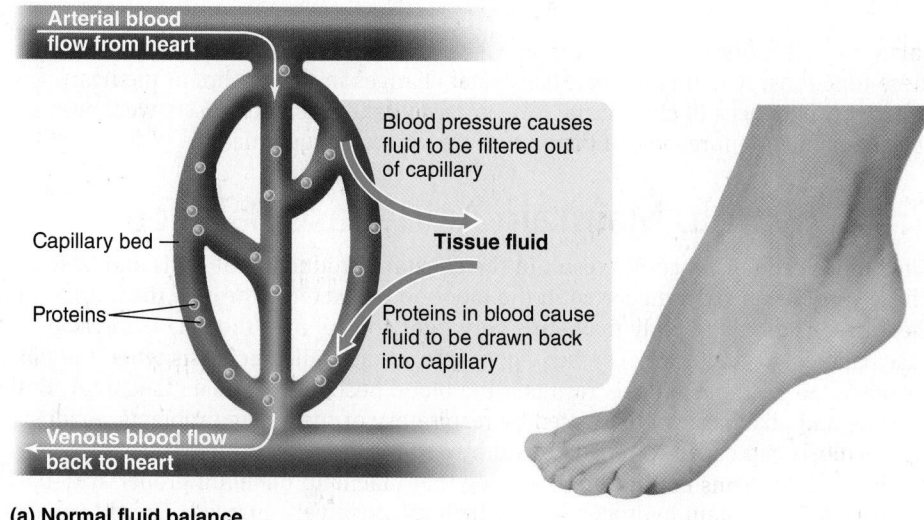

(a) Normal fluid balance

◀ **Figure 6.10** The role of proteins in maintaining fluid balance. The heartbeat exerts pressure that continually pushes fluids in the bloodstream through the arterial walls and out into the tissue spaces. By the time blood reaches the veins, the pressure of the heartbeat has greatly decreased. In this environment, proteins in the blood are able to draw fluids out of the tissues and back into the bloodstream. **(a)** This healthy (non-swollen) tissue suggests that body fluids in the bloodstream and in the tissue spaces are in balance. **(b)** When the level of proteins in the blood is insufficient to draw fluids out of the tissues, edema can result. This foot with edema is swollen due to fluid imbalance.

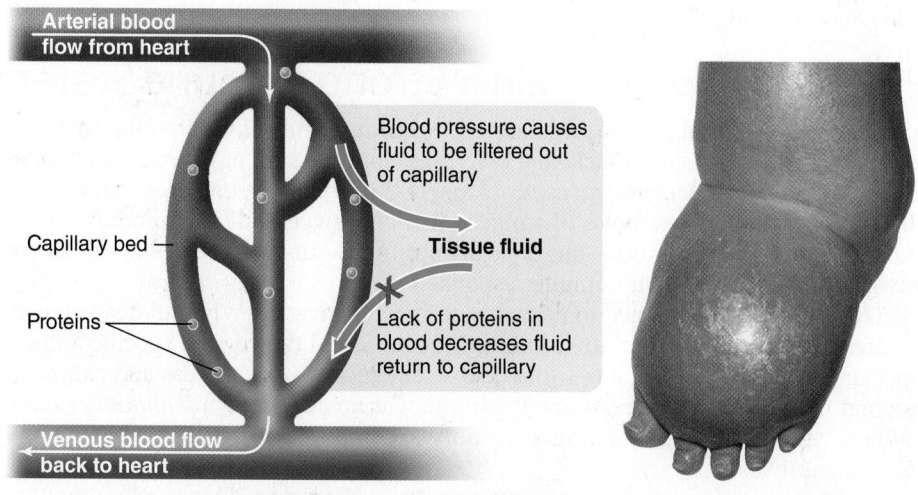

(b) Edema caused by insufficient protein in bloodstream

▶ **Figure 6.11** Transport proteins help maintain electrolyte balance. Transport proteins in the cell membrane pick up potassium and sodium and transport them across the cell membrane.

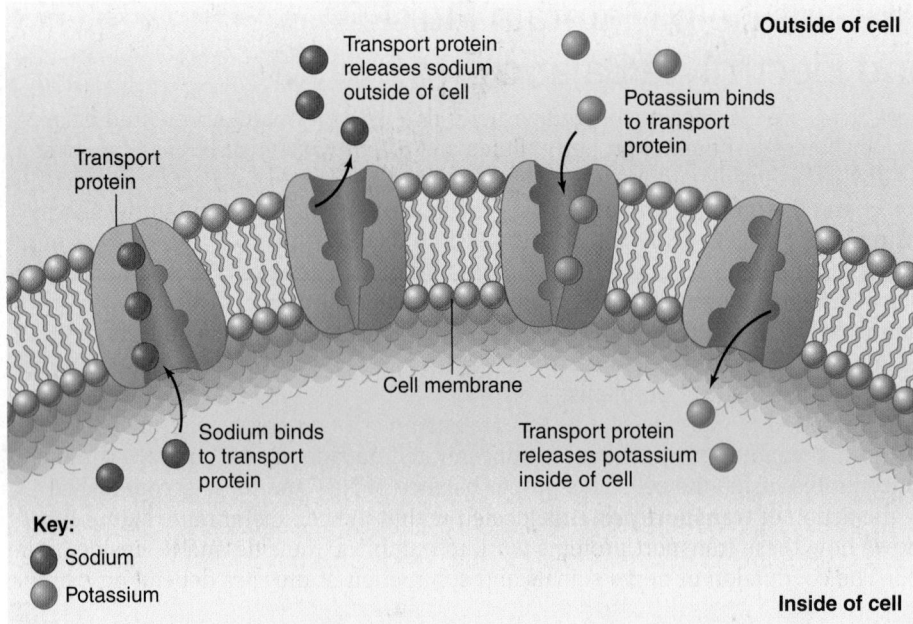

balance of electrolytes. If protein intake is deficient, we lose our ability to maintain these functions, resulting in potentially fatal changes in the rhythm of the heart. Other consequences of chronically low protein intakes include muscle weakness and spasms, kidney failure, and, if conditions are severe enough, death.

Proteins Help Maintain Acid–Base Balance

The body's cellular processes result in the constant production of acids and bases. These substances are transported in the blood to be excreted through the kidneys and the lungs. The human body maintains very tight control over the **pH**, or the acid–base balance, of the blood. The body goes into a state called **acidosis** when the blood becomes too acidic. **Alkalosis** results if the blood becomes too basic (alkaline). Both acidosis and alkalosis can be caused by respiratory or metabolic problems. Acidosis and alkalosis can cause coma and death by denaturing body proteins.

Proteins are excellent **buffers**, meaning that they help maintain proper acid–base balance. Acids contain hydrogen ions, which are positively charged. The side chains of proteins have negative charges that attract the hydrogen ions and neutralize their detrimental effects on the body. Proteins can release the hydrogen ions when the blood becomes too basic. By buffering acids and bases, proteins maintain acid–base balance and blood pH.

Proteins Help Maintain a Strong Immune System

Antibodies are special proteins that are critical components of the immune system. When a foreign substance attacks the body, the immune system produces antibodies to defend against it. Bacteria, viruses, toxins, and allergens (substances that cause allergic reactions) are examples of antigens that can trigger antibody production. (An *antigen* is any substance—but typically a protein—that our bodies recognise as foreign and that triggers an immune response.)

Each antibody is designed to destroy one specific invader. When that substance invades the body, antibodies are produced to attack and destroy the specific antigen. Once antibodies have been made, the body "remembers" this process and can respond more quickly the next time that particular invader appears. *Immunity* refers to the development of the molecular memory to produce antibodies quickly upon subsequent invasions.

Adequate protein is necessary to support the increased production of antibodies that occurs in response to a cold, the flu, or an allergic reaction. If we do not

pH Stands for percentage of hydrogen. It is a measure of the acidity—or level of hydrogen—of any solution, including human blood.

acidosis A disorder in which the blood becomes acidic; that is, the level of hydrogen in the blood is excessive. It can be caused by respiratory or metabolic problems.

alkalosis A disorder in which the blood becomes basic; that is, the level of hydrogen in the blood is deficient. It can be caused by respiratory or metabolic problems.

buffers Proteins that help maintain proper acid–base balance by attaching to, or releasing, hydrogen ions as conditions change in the body.

antibodies Defensive proteins of the immune system. Their production is prompted by the presence of bacteria, viruses, toxins, allergens, and so on.

consume enough protein, our resistance to illnesses and disease is weakened. On the other hand, eating more protein than we need does not improve immune function.

Proteins Serve as an Energy Source

The body's primary energy sources are carbohydrate and fat. Remember that both carbohydrate and fat have specialized storage forms that can be used for energy—glycogen for carbohydrate and triglycerides for fat. Proteins do not have a specialized storage form for energy. This means that, when proteins need to be used for energy, they are taken from the blood and body tissues, such as the liver and skeletal muscle. In healthy people, proteins contribute very little to energy needs. Because we are efficient at recycling amino acids, protein needs are relatively low as compared to needs for carbohydrate and fat.

To use proteins for energy, the liver removes the amine group from the amino acids in a process called **deamination**. The nitrogen bonds with hydrogen, creating ammonia, which is quickly converted to *urea*. The urea is then transported to the kidneys, where it is excreted in the urine. The remaining fragments of the amino acid contain carbon, hydrogen, and oxygen. The body can use these fragments to generate energy or to build carbohydrates. Certain amino acids can be converted into glucose via gluconeogenesis. This is a critical process during times of low carbohydrate intake or starvation. Fat cannot be converted into glucose, but body proteins can be broken down and converted into glucose to provide needed energy to the brain.

To protect the proteins in our body tissues, it is important that we regularly eat an adequate amount of carbohydrate and fat to provide energy. We also need to consume enough dietary protein to perform the required work without using up the proteins that already are playing an active role in our bodies. Unfortunately, our bodies cannot store excess dietary protein. As a consequence, eating too much protein results in the removal and excretion of the nitrogen in the urine and the use of the remaining components for energy. Any remaining components not used for energy can be converted and stored as body fat.

deamination The process by which an amine group is removed from an amino acid. The nitrogen is then transported to the kidneys for excretion in the urine, while the carbon and other components are metabolized for energy or used to make other compounds.

RECAP Proteins serve many important functions, including (1) enabling the growth, repair, and maintenance of body tissues; (2) acting as enzymes and hormones; (3) maintaining fluid and electrolyte balance; (4) maintaining acid–base balance; (5) making antibodies, which strengthen our immune system; and (6) providing energy when carbohydrate and fat intake are inadequate. Proteins function best when we also consume adequate amounts of carbohydrate and fat.

How Do Our Bodies Break Down Proteins?

Our bodies do not directly use proteins from the diet to make the proteins we need. Dietary proteins are first digested and broken into smaller particles, such as amino acids, dipeptides, and tripeptides, so that they can be absorbed and transported to the cells. In this section, we will review how proteins are digested and absorbed. As you read about each step in this process, refer to **Figure 6.12** for a visual tour through the digestive system.

Stomach Acids and Enzymes Break Proteins into Short Polypeptides

Virtually no enzymatic digestion of proteins occurs in the mouth. As shown in step 1 in Figure 6.12, proteins in food are chewed, crushed, and moistened with saliva to ease swallowing and to increase the surface area of the protein for more efficient digestion. There is no further digestive action on proteins in the mouth.

When proteins reach the stomach, *hydrochloric acid* denatures (uncoils or untwists) the protein strands so that the enzymes can begin to break down the

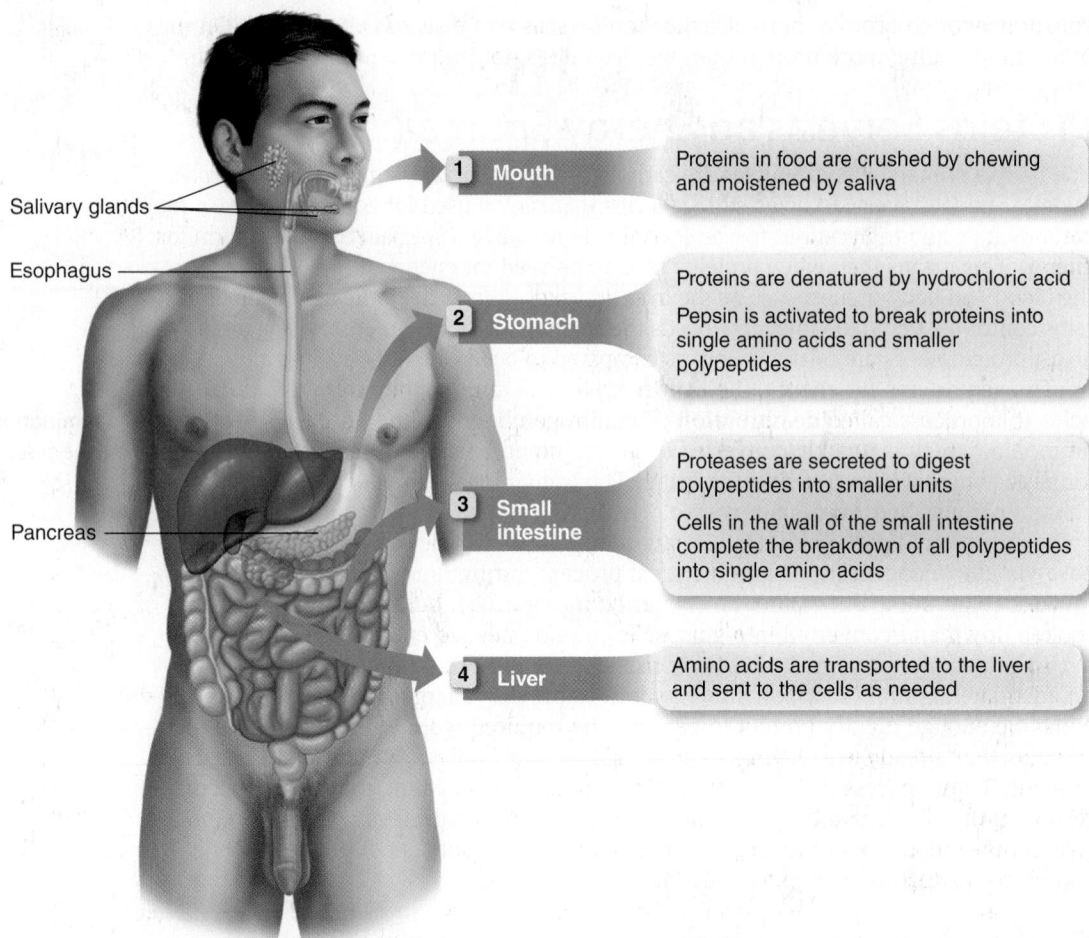

Salivary glands

Esophagus

Pancreas

1 **Mouth** — Proteins in food are crushed by chewing and moistened by saliva

2 **Stomach** — Proteins are denatured by hydrochloric acid

Pepsin is activated to break proteins into single amino acids and smaller polypeptides

3 **Small intestine** — Proteases are secreted to digest polypeptides into smaller units

Cells in the wall of the small intestine complete the breakdown of all polypeptides into single amino acids

4 **Liver** — Amino acids are transported to the liver and sent to the cells as needed

Figure 6.12 The process of protein digestion.

polypeptides (Figure 6.12, step 2). It also converts the inactive enzyme *pepsinogen* into its active form, **pepsin**. Although pepsin is itself a protein, it is not denatured by the acid in the stomach because it has evolved to work optimally in an acidic environment. The hormone *gastrin* controls both the production of hydrochloric acid and the release of pepsin; thinking about food or actually chewing food stimulates the gastrin-producing cells located in the stomach. Pepsin begins breaking proteins into single amino acids and shorter polypeptides; these amino acids and polypeptides then travel to the small intestine for further digestion and absorption.

Enzymes in the Small Intestine Break Polypeptides into Single Amino Acids

As the polypeptides reach the small intestine, the pancreas and the small intestine secrete enzymes that digest them into oligopeptides, tripeptides, dipeptides, and single amino acids (Figure 6.12, step 3). The enzymes that digest proteins in the small intestine are called **proteases**.

The cells in the wall of the small intestine then absorb the single amino acids, dipeptides, and tripeptides. Enzymes in the intestinal cells break the dipeptides and tripeptides into single amino acids. The amino acids are then transported via the portal vein into the liver. Once in the liver, amino acids may be converted to glucose or fat, combined to build new proteins, used for energy, or released into the bloodstream and transported to other cells as needed (Figure 6.12, step 4).

The cells of the small intestine have different sites that specialize in transporting certain types of amino acids, dipeptides, and tripeptides. This fact has implications

pepsin An enzyme in the stomach that begins the breakdown of proteins into shorter polypeptide chains and single amino acids.

proteases Enzymes that continue the breakdown of polypeptides in the small intestine.

for users of amino acid supplements. When very large doses of single amino acids are taken on an empty stomach, they typically compete for the same absorption sites. This competition can block the absorption of other amino acids, causing an imbalance of amino acids and leading to various amino acid deficiencies. Some people believe that this is why it is not beneficial to consume individual amino acid supplements. In reality, people rarely take very large doses of single amino acids on an empty stomach. The primary reason people should not take single amino acids is that the amount taken is usually so small that they do not have any beneficial effect. For more information on amino acid supplements, see Chapter 12.

Meats are highly digestible sources of dietary protein.

Protein Digestibility Affects Protein Quality

Earlier in this chapter, we discussed how various protein sources differ in quality of protein. The quantity of essential amino acids in a protein determines its quality: higher-protein-quality foods are those that contain more of the essential amino acids in sufficient quantities needed to build proteins, and lower-quality-protein foods contain fewer essential amino acids. Another factor in protein quality is *digestibility,* or how well our bodies can digest a protein. Animal protein sources, such as meat and dairy products, are highly digestible, as are many soy products; we can absorb more than 90% of the amino acids in these protein sources. Legumes are also highly digestible (about 70% to 80%). Grains and many vegetable proteins are less digestible, ranging from 60% to 90%.

The **protein digestibility–corrected amino acid score (PDCAAS)** is a measurement of protein quality that considers the balance of essential amino acids as well as the digestibility of the protein in the food. To calculate the PDCAAS, the amount of each essential amino acid is first calculated in milligrams per gram of the protein. These amounts are then compared to the amounts in a reference protein, which has been calculated from the amino acid requirements of a preschool-aged child. The most limiting essential amino acid determines the protein's *amino acid score.* The amino acid score is then multiplied by a digestibility factor based on fecal digestibility measured in studies of rats. The maximum PDCAAS value allowed is 100%, so the calculated values for the milk protein casein (121) and egg white protein (118), the highest-quality proteins, have been reduced to 100. The PDCAAS for beef, soy, and wheat are 92, 91, and 42 respectively (Schaafsma, 2000).

Some scientists have recently questioned the use of a reference protein based on data obtained many years ago from amino acid balance studies using two-year-old children, as well as the measurement of digestibility using fecal values that do not account for losses of amino acids in the small intestine. Schaafsma (2005) has also noted that the bioavailability can be lowered by the effects of processing, such as the effect of heat on the amino acid lysine and the effect of treatment on soy protein isolate, which drops the PDCAAS score from 100 to 49. He has also argued against truncating PDCAAS to 100% (Schaafsma, 2005). However, the PDCAAS is widely used and is still the method that the Food and Agriculture Organization (FAO) of the United Nations and the World Health Organization (WHO) jointly recommend for assessing protein quality in human diets.

Other measures of protein quality include the protein efficiency ratio and net protein utilization. The *protein efficiency ratio* assesses protein quality by comparing the weight gained by a laboratory animal consuming a test protein with the weight gained by a laboratory animal consuming an equivalent amount of a reference, or standardized, protein. *Net protein utilization* is a process that compares the amount of nitrogen retained in our bodies with the amount of nitrogen we consume in our diets. The more nitrogen we retain, the higher the quality of the protein we have consumed.

These measures of protein quality are useful when determining the quality of protein available to populations of people. However, these measures are not practical or useful for individual diet planning.

protein digestibility–corrected amino acid score (PDCAAS) A measurement of protein quality that considers the balance of essential amino acids as well as the digestibility of the protein in the food.

RECAP In the stomach, hydrochloric acid denatures (uncoils or untwists) protein molecules and converts pepsinogen to pepsin; pepsin breaks proteins into smaller polypeptides and individual amino acids. In the small intestine, proteases break polypeptides into smaller fragments and single amino acids. The cells in the wall of the small intestine break the smaller peptide fragments into single amino acids, which are then transported to the liver for distribution to our cells. Protein digestibility, as well as the availability of adequate amounts of essential amino acids, influences protein quality.

How Much Protein Should We Eat?

Consuming adequate protein is a major concern of many people. In fact, one of the most common concerns among active people and athletes is that their diets are deficient in protein (see the Nutrition Myth or Fact? box below for a discussion of this topic). This concern about dietary protein is generally unnecessary, as we can easily consume the protein our bodies need by eating an adequate and varied diet.

Nitrogen Balance Is a Method Used to Determine Protein Needs

A highly specialized *nitrogen balance* procedure is used to determine a person's protein needs. Nitrogen is excreted through the body's processes of recycling or using proteins; thus, the balance can be used to estimate whether protein intake is adequate to meet protein needs.

Typically performed only in experimental laboratories, the nitrogen balance procedure involves measuring both nitrogen intake and nitrogen excretion over a two-week period. A standardized diet, the nitrogen content of which has been measured and recorded, is fed to the study participant. The person is required to consume all of the foods provided. Because the majority of nitrogen is excreted in the urine and feces, laboratory technicians directly measure the nitrogen content of the subject's urine and fecal samples. Small amounts of nitrogen are excreted in the skin, hair, and body fluids such

NUTRITION MYTH OR FACT?
Do Athletes Need More Protein than Inactive People?

At one time, it was believed that the Recommended Dietary Allowance (RDA) for protein, which is 0.8 g per kg body weight, was sufficient for both inactive people and athletes. Recent studies, however, show that athletes' protein needs are higher.

Why do athletes need more protein? Regular exercise increases the transport of oxygen to body tissues, requiring changes in the oxygen-carrying capacity of the blood. To carry more oxygen, we need to produce more of the protein that carries oxygen in the blood (i.e., hemoglobin). During intense exercise, we use a small amount of protein directly for energy. We also use protein to make glucose to maintain adequate blood glucose levels and to prevent hypoglycemia (low blood sugar) during exercise. Regular exercise stimulates tissue growth and causes tissue damage, which must be repaired by additional proteins. Strength athletes (such as bodybuilders and weightlifters) need 1.8 to 2 times more protein than the current RDA, and

⬆ Some athletes who persistently diet are at risk for low protein intake.

endurance athletes (such as distance runners and triathletes) need 1.5 to 1.75 times more protein than the current RDA. Later in this chapter, we will calculate the protein needs for inactive and active people.

If you are active, does this mean you should add more protein to your diet? Not necessarily. For healthy individuals, evidence does not support eating more than two times the RDA for protein to increase strength, build muscle, or improve athletic performance. In fact, eating more protein as food or supplements or taking individual amino acid supplements does not cause muscles to become bigger or stronger. Only regular strength training can achieve these goals. By eating a balanced diet and consuming a variety of foods, both inactive and active people can easily meet their protein requirements.

as mucus and semen, but, because of the complexity of collecting nitrogen excreted via these routes, the measurements are estimated. Technicians add the estimated nitrogen losses to the nitrogen measured in the subject's urine and feces. Nitrogen balance is then calculated as the difference between nitrogen intake and nitrogen excretion.

People who consume more nitrogen than is excreted are considered to be in positive nitrogen balance **(Figure 6.13)**. This state indicates that the body is retaining or adding protein, and it occurs during periods of growth, pregnancy, or recovery from illness or a protein deficiency.

People who excrete more nitrogen than they consume are in negative nitrogen balance. This situation indicates that the body is losing protein, and it occurs during starvation or when people are consuming very-low-energy diets. This is because, when

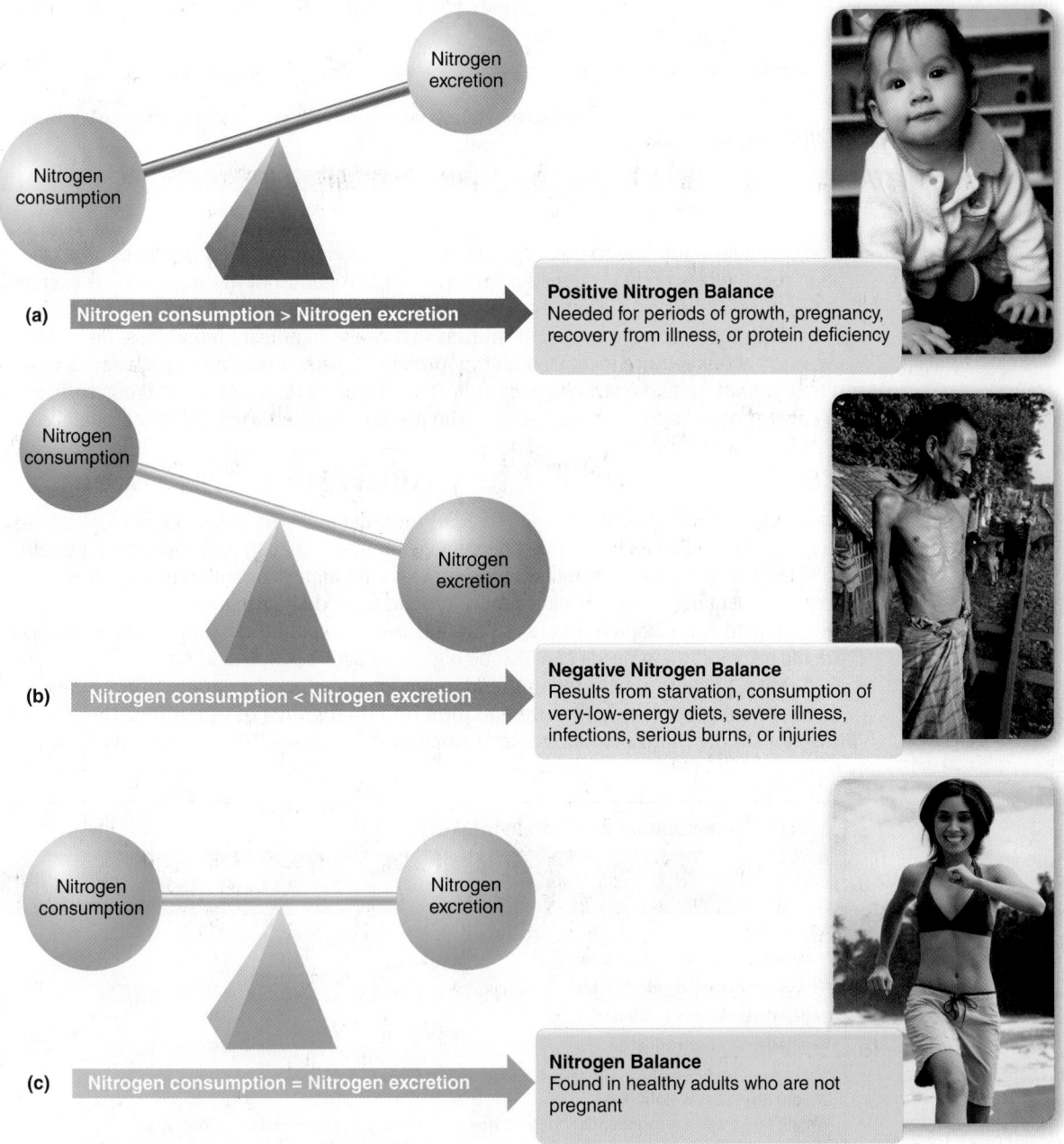

(a) Nitrogen consumption > Nitrogen excretion

Positive Nitrogen Balance
Needed for periods of growth, pregnancy, recovery from illness, or protein deficiency

(b) Nitrogen consumption < Nitrogen excretion

Negative Nitrogen Balance
Results from starvation, consumption of very-low-energy diets, severe illness, infections, serious burns, or injuries

(c) Nitrogen consumption = Nitrogen excretion

Nitrogen Balance
Found in healthy adults who are not pregnant

Figure 6.13 Nitrogen balance describes the relationship between how much nitrogen (or protein) we consume and excrete each day. **(a)** Positive nitrogen balance occurs when nitrogen consumption is greater than excretion. **(b)** Negative nitrogen balance occurs when nitrogen consumption is less than excretion. **(c)** Nitrogen balance is maintained when nitrogen consumption equals excretion.

YOU DO THE MATH
Calculating Your Protein Needs

Matthew wants to know how much protein he needs each day. During the off-season, he works out three times a week at a gym and practices basketball with friends every Friday night. He is not a vegetarian. Although Matthew exercises regularly, he does not qualify as an endurance athlete or as a strength athlete. At this level of physical activity, Matthew's RDA for protein probably ranges from the RDA of 0.8 up to 1.0 g per kg body weight per day. To calculate the total number of grams of protein he should eat each day:

1. Convert Matthew's weight from pounds to kilograms. He presently weighs 200 pounds. To convert this value to kilograms, divide by 2.2:

$$200 \text{ pounds} \div 2.2 \text{ pounds/kg} = 91 \text{ kg}$$

2. Multiply Matthew's weight in kilograms by his RDA for protein:

$$91 \text{ kg} \times 0.8 \text{ g/kg} = 72.8 \text{ grams of protein per day}$$
$$91 \text{ kg} \times 1.0 \text{ g/kg} = 91 \text{ grams of protein per day}$$

What happens during basketball season, when Matthew practices or has games five or six days a week? This will probably raise his protein needs to approximately 1.0 to 1.2 g per kg body weight per day. How much more protein should he eat?

$$91 \text{ kg} \times 1.2 \text{ g/kg} = 109.2 \text{ grams of protein per day}$$

Now calculate your recommended protein intake based on your activity level.

---

energy intake is too low to meet energy demands over a prolonged period of time, the body metabolizes body proteins for energy. The nitrogen from these proteins is excreted in the urine and feces. Negative nitrogen balance also occurs during severe illness, infections, high fever, serious burns, or injuries that cause significant blood loss. People in these situations require increased dietary protein. A person is in nitrogen balance when nitrogen intake equals nitrogen excretion. This indicates that protein intake is sufficient to cover protein needs. Healthy adults who are not pregnant are in nitrogen balance.

Recommended Dietary Allowance for Protein

How much protein should we eat? The RDA for sedentary people is 0.8 g per kg body weight per day. The recommended percentage of energy that should come from protein is 10% to 35% of total energy intake. Protein needs are higher for children, adolescents, and pregnant/lactating women because more protein is needed during times of growth and development (see Chapters 14 and 15 for details on protein needs during these portions of the life cycle). Protein needs can also be higher for active people and for vegetarians.

Table 6.2 lists the daily recommendations for protein for a variety of lifestyles. How can we convert this recommendation into total grams of protein for the day? In the You Do the Math box above, let's calculate Matthew's RDA for protein.

TABLE 6.2 **Recommended Protein Intakes**	
Group	Protein Intake (grams per kilogram* body weight per day)
Most adults[†]	0.8
Non-vegetarian endurance athletes[‡]	1.2 to 1.4
Non-vegetarian strength athletes[‡]	1.2 to 1.7
Vegetarian endurance athletes[‡]	1.3 to 1.5
Vegetarian strength athletes[‡]	1.3 to 1.8

*To convert body weight to kilograms, divide weight in pounds by 2.2.
Weight (lb)/2.2 = Weight (kg)
Weight (kg) protein recommendation (g/kg body weight/day) = protein intake (g/day)
[†]Data from Food and Nutrition Board, Institute of Medicine. 2002. Dietary Reference Intakes for Energy, Carbohydrate, Fibre, Fat, Fatty Acids, Cholesterol, Protein, and Amino Acids (Macronutrients), pp. 465–608. Washington, DC: National Academies Press.
[‡]Data from American College of Sports Medicine, American Dietetic Association, and Dietitians of Canada. 2009. Joint Position Statement. Nutrition and athletic performance. Med. Sci. Sports Exerc. 41(3):709–731.

Amino Acid Supplements: Necessity or Waste?

"Amino acid supplements—you can't gain without them!" This is just one of the headlines found in bodybuilding magazines and internet sites touting amino acid supplements as the key to achieving power, strength, and performance "perfection." Many athletes who read these claims believe that taking amino acid supplements will boost their energy during performance, replace proteins metabolized for energy during exercise, enhance muscle growth and strength, and hasten recovery from intense training or injury. Should you believe the hype?

As noted earlier in this chapter, we use very little protein for energy during exercise. Consuming adequate energy and up to two times the RDA for protein in the diet is more than enough to support either strength or endurance exercise training and performance. What about the claims related to muscle-building? Although some research has shown that intravenous infusions of various amino acids in the laboratory can stimulate certain hormones that enhance the building of muscle, there is little evidence that taking individual amino acids or protein supplements orally can build muscle or improve strength (Manore et al., 2009). Since these supplements are relatively expensive, getting enough protein via your diet alone will put a lot less strain on your wallet!

Most Canadians Meet the AMDR for Protein

The 2004 Canadian Community Health Survey (Health Canada, 2007) results show that the average protein intake among adults is 16.8%, well within the AMDR of 10%–35%. Very few people fell below or above this range of protein intakes, suggesting that almost all Canadians have average protein intakes that meet current dietary recommendations.

What are the typical protein intakes of active people? Research indicates that the self-reported intake of athletes participating in a variety of sports can well exceed current RDA recommendations (Manore et al., 2009). For instance, the protein intake for some female distance runners is 1.2 g per kg of body weight per day, accounting for 15% of their total daily energy intake. In addition, some male bodybuilders consume 3 g per kg of body weight per day, accounting for almost 38% of their total daily energy intake! However, there are certain groups of athletes who are at risk for low protein intakes. Athletes who consume inadequate energy and limit food choices, such as some distance runners, figure skaters, female gymnasts, and wrestlers who are dieting, are all at risk for low protein intakes. Unlike people who consume adequate energy, individuals who are restricting their total energy intake (kilocalories) need to pay close attention to their protein intake.

Protein: Much More Than Meat!

Table 6.3 compares the protein content of a variety of foods. Although some people think that the only good sources of protein are flesh foods (beef, pork, poultry, seafood), many other foods are rich in proteins. These include dairy products (milk, cheese, yogurt, etc.), eggs, legumes (including soy products), whole grains, and nuts. Fruits and many vegetables are not particularly high in protein; however, these foods provide fibre and many vitamins and minerals and are excellent sources of carbohydrates. Thus, eating them can help provide the carbohydrates and energy you need, so that your body can use proteins for building and maintaining tissues.

After reviewing Table 6.3, you might be wondering how much protein you typically eat. See the What About You? feature box on page 205 to find out.

Legumes

Legumes include soybeans, kidney beans, pinto beans, black beans, garbanzo beans (chickpeas), lentils, green peas, black-eyed peas, and lima beans. In addition to being

TABLE 6.3 Protein Content of Commonly Consumed Foods

Food	Serving Size	Protein (g)
Beef, ground, lean, crumbled, pan-fried	75 g	22
Beef, prime rib (standing rib roast, lean + fat), roasted	75 g	23
Beef, top sirloin steak, lean + fat, roasted	75 g	21
Beans, refried	175 mL	10
Beans, kidney, red, canned, not drained	175 mL	10
Beans, black, canned, not drained	175 mL	11
Chicken breast, bone and skin removed, roasted	75 g	25
Chicken thigh, bone and skin removed, roasted	75 g	19
Turkey, light meat, bone and skin removed, roasted	75 g	21
Peanuts, shelled, dry roasted	60 mL	9
Peanut butter, creamy	30 mL	8
Almonds, dried	60 mL	8
Cod, Atlantic, baked or broiled	75 g	17
Salmon, coho, baked or broiled	75 g	18
Shrimp, boiled or steamed	6 medium	6
Tuna, in water, drained	75 g	19
Oatmeal, quick instant	175 mL	4
Cheerios	250 mL	3
Grape-Nuts	125 mL	6
Raisin Bran	250 mL	5
Brown rice, long-grain, cooked	125 mL	3
Whole-wheat bread	1 slice	3
Bagel, plain, 10 cm diameter	1	7
Pork loin chop, lean + fat, roasted	75 g	22
Ham, lean, roasted	75 g	19
Milk, whole, 3.3% fat	250 mL	8
Milk, partly skimmed, 1% M.F.	250 mL	9
Milk, skim	250 mL	9
Yogurt, plain, 1%-2% M.F.	175 mL	10
Cheddar	50 g	12
Cottage cheese (1% M.F.)	125 mL	15
Carrots, baby, raw	8	1
Broccoli, raw, chopped	125 mL	1
Kale, chopped, boiled	125 mL	1
Spinach, raw	250 mL	1
Tofu, regular, firm	150 g	21
Wiener, meatless	1	9
Soy beverage, original, enriched	250 mL	7

Source: Nutrient Value of Some Common Foods. Health Canada, 2008. Reproduced with the permission from the Minister of Health, 2012.

◀ The quality of the protein in some legumes is almost equal to that of meat.

excellent sources of protein, legumes are high in fibre, iron, calcium, and many of the B vitamins. They are also low in saturated fat and cholesterol. Eating legumes regularly, including foods made from soybeans, may help reduce the risk for heart disease by lowering blood cholesterol levels. Diets high in legumes and soy products are also associated with lower rates of some cancers. Legumes are not nutritionally complete, however, as they do not contain vitamins B_{12}, C, or A. They are also deficient in methionine, an essential amino acid; however, combining them with grains, nuts, or seeds gives you a complete protein.

Considering their nutrient profile, satiety value, and good taste, it is no wonder that many experts consider legumes an almost perfect food.

What About You?

How Much Protein Do You Eat?

One way to find out if your diet contains enough protein is to keep a food diary. Record everything you eat and drink for at least three days, and the grams of protein each item provides. To determine the grams of protein, for packaged foods, use the Nutrition Facts Panel, and make sure to adjust for the serving size you actually consume. For products without labels, check Table 6.3 on page 204, or use the diet analysis tools that accompany this text. There is also a Health Canada online catalogue called the *Nutrient Values of Some Common Foods* that lists the energy and nutrient content of thousands of foods (www.hc-sc.gc.ca/fn-an/nutrition/fiche-nutri-data/nutrient_value-valeurs_nutritives-eng.php).

Below is an example, using Matthew's food choices for one day. Do you think he's meeting his protein needs?

As calculated in the You Do the Math box on page 202, Matthew's RDA is 72.8 to 91 g of protein. He is consuming 2 1/2 to 3 times that amount! You can see that he does not need to use amino acid or protein supplements, since he has more than adequate amounts of protein to build lean tissue. Now calculate your own protein intake. Are you getting enough protein each day?

(Health Canada. 2007. Canadian Community Health Survey, Cycle 2.2, Nutrition (2004). Nutrient Intakes from Food. Provincial, Regional and National Summary Data Tables, Volume 1. Cat.: H164-45/1-2007E-PDF. www.hc-sc.gc.ca/fn-an/pubs/cchs-nutri-escc/index_e.html.)

Foods Consumed	Protein Content (g)
Breakfast:	
Brewed coffee (500 mL or 2 cups) with 30 mL (2 Tbsp) cream	1
1 large bagel (5 in. or 12.5 cm diameter)	10
Low-fat cream cheese (45 g or 1.5 oz.)	4.5
Mid-morning snack:	
Cola beverage (1 L or 32 fl. oz.)	0
Low-fat strawberry yogurt (250 mL or 1 cup)	10
Snackwells Apple Cinnamon Bars (2)	2
Lunch:	
Ham and cheese sandwich:	
Whole-wheat bread (2 slices)	4
Mayonnaise (25 mL or 1.5 Tbsp)	1
Lean ham (120 g or 4 oz.)	24
Swiss cheese (50 g or 2 oz.)	16
Iceberg lettuce (2 leaves)	0.5
Sliced tomato (3 slices)	0.5
Banana (1 large)	1
Triscuit crackers (20 crackers)	7
Bottled water (625 mL or 20 fl. oz.)	0

Foods Consumed	Protein Content (g)
Afternoon snack:	
Dry roasted peanuts (30 g or 1 oz.)	7
2% low-fat milk (250 mL or 1 cup)	8
Dinner:	
Cheeseburger:	
Broiled ground beef (250 g or 1/2 lb.)	64
Slice of processed cheese (30 g or 1 oz.)	6
Seeded bun (1 large)	6
Ketchup (30 mL or 2 Tbsp)	1
Mustard (15 mL or 1 Tbsp)	1
Shredded lettuce (125 mL or 1/2 cup)	0.5
Sliced tomato (3 slices)	0.5
French fries (30 fries)	6
Baked beans (500 mL or 2 cups)	28
2% low-fat milk (250 mL or 1 cup)	8
Evening snack:	
Chocolate chip cookies (7.5 cm or 4 3 in. diameter cookies)	3
2% low-fat milk (250 mL or 1 cup)	8
Total Protein Intake for the Day:	**228.5 g**

"New" Foods

A new source of non-meat protein that is available on the market is *quorn*, a protein product derived from fermented fungus ("mycoprotein"). It is mixed with a variety of other foods to produce various types of meat substitutes such as chicken-like patties, nuggets, or cutlets. However, according to the Centre for Science in the Public Interest (CSPI), some people who consume quorn experience allergic reactions including nausea, vomiting, and diarrhea, as well as more serious, life-threatening anaphylactic reactions, difficulty breathing, and hives. The CSPI has asked the Food and Drug Administration in the United States to take quorn off the market, or at a minimum, require warning labels indicating that the product causes allergic reactions in some people (CSPI, 2011).

Other "new" foods high in protein include some very ancient grains! For instance, you may have heard of pastas and other products made with quinoa (pronounced keen-wah), a plant so essential to the diet of the ancient Incas that they considered it sacred. No wonder: quinoa, cooked much like rice, provides 8 g of protein in a 1 cup (250 mL) serving. It is highly digestible and, unlike many more familiar grains, provides all nine essential amino acids with a PDCAAS of 79 (Owusu-Apenten, 2002). A similar grain, called amaranth, also provides complete protein. Teff, millet, and sorghum are grains long cultivated in Africa as rich sources of protein. Although these three grains are low in the essential amino acid lysine, combining them with legumes produces a complete-protein meal.

With such a wide variety of protein sources to choose from, it is easy to eat right all day! See the Eating Right All Day feature for some simple high-protein menu choices that are low in saturated fat and high in nutrients and phytochemicals.

RECAP The RDA for protein for most non-pregnant, non-lactating, non-vegetarian adults is 0.8 g per kg body weight. Children, pregnant women, and nursing mothers need slightly more. Vegetarians and active people may also need more, depending upon the quality of the protein they consume and their level of physical activity. Most people who eat enough kilocalories and carbohydrates have no problem meeting their RDA for protein. Good sources of protein include meats, poultry, fish, eggs, dairy products, legumes, whole grains, and nuts.

Can a Vegetarian Diet Provide Adequate Protein?

vegetarian diet A diet that does not include meat (including poultry) or seafood, or products containing those foods.

The Dietitians of Canada and the American Dietetic Association (2003) have defined a **vegetarian diet** as "one that does not include meat (including fowl) or seafood, or products containing those foods." Results from a 2002 survey suggest that approximately 4% of Canadian adults (900 000 people) follow vegetarian diets. Many vegetarians are college students; moving away from home and taking responsibility for one's eating habits appears to influence some young adults to try vegetarianism as a lifestyle choice.

Types of Vegetarian Diets

There are almost as many types of vegetarian diets as there are vegetarians. Some people who consider themselves vegetarians regularly eat poultry and fish. Others avoid the flesh of animals but consume eggs, milk, and cheese liberally. Still others strictly avoid all products of animal origin, including milk and eggs, and even by-products such as candies and puddings made with gelatine. A type of "vegetarian" diet receiving significant media attention recently is the *flexitarian* diet: flexitarians are considered semi-vegetarians who eat mostly plant foods, eggs, and dairy but occasionally eat red meat, poultry, and/or fish.

Table 6.4 identifies the various types of vegetarian diets, ranging from the most inclusive to the most restrictive. Notice that, the more restrictive the diet, the more challenging it becomes to achieve an adequate protein intake.

Why Do People Become Vegetarians?

When discussing vegetarianism, one of the most often asked questions is why people would make this food choice. The most common responses are included here.

Religious, Ethical, and Food-Safety Reasons

Some make the choice for religious or spiritual reasons. Several religions prohibit or restrict the consumption of animal flesh; however, generalizations can be misleading. For example, while certain sects within Hinduism forbid the consumption of meat, perusing the menu at any Indian restaurant will reveal that many other Hindus regularly consume small quantities of meat, poultry, and fish. Many Buddhists are vegetarians, as are some Christians, including Seventh-Day Adventists.

Soy products are a good source of dietary protein.

TABLE 6.4 Terms and Definitions of a Vegetarian Diet

Type of Diet	Foods Consumed	Comments
Semi-vegetarian (also called partial vegetarian or flexitarian)	Vegetables, grains, nuts, fruits, legumes; sometimes seafood, poultry, eggs, and dairy products	Typically excludes or limits red meat; may also avoid other meats
Pesco-vegetarian	Similar to semi-vegetarian but excludes poultry	Pesco means "fish," the only animal source of protein in this diet
Lacto-ovo-vegetarian	Vegetables, grains, nuts, fruits, legumes, dairy products (lacto) and eggs (ovo)	Excludes animal flesh and seafood
Lacto-vegetarian	Similar to lacto-ovo-vegetarian but excludes eggs	Relies on milk and milk products such as yogurt and cheese for animal sources of protein
Ovo-vegetarian	Vegetables, grains, nuts, fruits, legumes, and eggs	Excludes dairy, flesh, and seafood products
Vegan (also called strict vegetarian)	Only plant-based foods (vegetables, grains, nuts, seeds, fruits, legumes)	May not provide adequate vitamin B_{12}, zinc, iron, or calcium
Macrobiotic diet	Vegan-type of diet; becomes progressively more strict until almost all foods are eliminated; at the extreme, only brown rice and small amounts of water or herbal tea are consumed	Taken to the extreme, can cause malnutrition and death
Fruitarian	Only raw or dried fruit, seeds, nuts, honey, and vegetable oil	Very restrictive diet; deficient in protein, calcium, zinc, iron, vitamin B_{12}, riboflavin, and other nutrients

Many vegetarians are guided by their personal philosophy to choose vegetarianism. These people feel that it is morally and ethically wrong to consume animals and any products from animals (such as dairy or egg products) because they view the practices in the modern animal industries as inhumane. They may consume milk and eggs but choose to purchase them only from family farms where animals are treated humanely.

Some people have concerns about contaminated meat, which has found its way into our food supply. However, food-borne illness outbreaks are far more common in produce than in meat, and vegetarians have had to face scares about *Listeria monocytogenes* in cantaloupes and *E. coli* 0104:H in alfalfa and other sprouts. See Chapter 13 for a review of food-borne illness.

Ecological Benefits

Many people choose vegetarianism because of their concerns about the effect of meat industries on the global environment. Due to the high demand for meat in developed nations, meat production has evolved from small family farming operations to the larger system of agribusiness. Critics point to the environmental costs of agribusiness, including massive uses of water and grain to feed animals, methane gases and other wastes produced by animals themselves, and increased land use to support livestock.

Health Benefits

Still others practice vegetarianism because of its health benefits. Research over several years has consistently shown that a varied and balanced vegetarian diet can reduce the risk for many chronic diseases. Its health benefits include the following (Dietitians of Canada, 2003):

- Reduced intake of fat and total energy, which reduces the risk for obesity. This may in turn lower a person's risk for type 2 diabetes.
- Lower blood pressure, which may be due to a higher intake of fruits and vegetables. People who eat vegetarian diets tend to be non-smokers, drink little or

People who follow certain sects of Hinduism refrain from eating meat.

no alcohol, and exercise more regularly, which are also factors known to reduce blood pressure and help maintain a healthy body weight.

- Reduced risk for heart disease, which may be due to lower saturated fat intake and a higher consumption of *antioxidants* that are found in plant-based foods. Antioxidants, discussed in detail in Chapter 8, are substances that can protect our cells from damage. They are abundant in fruits and vegetables.
- Fewer digestive problems such as constipation and diverticular disease, perhaps due to the higher fibre content of vegetarian diets. Diverticular disease, discussed in Chapter 4, occurs when the wall of the bowel (large intestine) develops pouches and becomes inflamed.
- Reduced risk for some cancers. Research shows that vegetarians may have lower rates of cancer, particularly colon cancer (Dietitians of Canada, 2003). Many components of a vegetarian diet might contribute to reducing cancer risks, including higher fibre and antioxidant intakes, lower dietary fat intake, lower consumption of carcinogens (cancer-causing agents) that are formed when cooking meat, and higher consumption of soy protein, which may have anticancer properties (Dietitians of Canada, 2003).
- Reduced risk for kidney disease, kidney stones, and gallstones. The lower protein contents of vegetarian diets, plus the higher intake of legumes and vegetable proteins (such as soy), may be protective against these conditions.

What Are the Challenges of a Vegetarian Diet?

Although a vegetarian diet can be healthful, it also presents many challenges. Limiting the consumption of flesh and dairy products introduces the potential for inadequate intakes of certain nutrients, especially for people consuming a vegan, macrobiotic, or fruitarian diet. **Table 6.5** lists the nutrients that can be deficient in a vegan-type diet plan and describes good non-animal sources that can provide these nutrients. Vegetarians who consume dairy and/or egg products obtain these nutrients more easily.

Research indicates that a sign of disordered eating in some college females is the switch to a vegetarian diet (Klopp et al., 2003). Instead of eating a healthy variety of non-animal foods, people struggling with this problem may use vegetarianism as an excuse to restrict many foods from their diets.

Can a vegetarian diet provide enough protein? Because high-quality non-meat protein sources are quite easy to obtain in developed countries, a well-balanced vegetarian diet can provide adequate protein. In fact, the American Dietetic Association and Dietitians of Canada (2003) endorse an appropriately planned vegetarian

Beans, nuts, seeds, eggs, or meat substitutes are good sources of protein for vegetarians.

TABLE 6.5 Nutrients of Concern in a Vegan Diet		
Nutrient	**Functions**	**Non-Meat/Non-Dairy Food Sources**
Vitamin B_{12}	Assists with DNA synthesis; protection and growth of nerve fibres	Vitamin B_{12}–fortified cereals, yeast, soy products, and other meat analogs; vitamin B_{12} supplements
Vitamin D	Promotes bone growth	Vitamin D–fortified cereals, margarines, and soy products; adequate exposure to sunlight; supplementation may be necessary for those who do not get adequate exposure to sunlight
Riboflavin (vitamin B_2)	Promotes release of energy; supports normal vision and skin health	Whole and enriched grains, green leafy vegetables, mushrooms, beans, nuts, and seeds
Iron	Assists with oxygen transport; involved in making amino acids and hormones	Whole-grain products, prune juice, dried fruits, beans, nuts, seeds, and leafy vegetables (such as spinach)
Calcium	Maintains bone health; assists with muscle contraction, blood pressure, and nerve transmission	Fortified soy milk and tofu, almonds, dry beans, leafy vegetables, and calcium-fortified juices
Zinc	Assists with DNA and RNA synthesis, immune function, and growth	Whole-grain products, wheat germ, beans, nuts, and seeds

diet as healthful, nutritionally adequate, and beneficial in reducing and preventing various diseases. As you can see, the emphasis is on a *balanced* and *adequate* vegetarian diet; thus, it is important for vegetarians to consume soy products, eat complementary proteins, and obtain enough energy from other macronutrients to spare protein from being used as an energy source. Although the digestibility of a vegetarian diet is potentially lower than that of an animal-based diet, there is no separate protein recommendation for vegetarians who consume complementary plant proteins (IOM, 2002).

RECAP A balanced vegetarian diet may reduce the risk for obesity, type 2 diabetes, heart disease, digestive problems, some cancers, kidney disease, kidney stones, and gallstones. Whereas varied vegetarian diets can provide enough protein, vegetarians who consume no animal products need to make sure they consume adequate plant sources of protein and supplement their diet with good sources of vitamin B_{12}, vitamin D, riboflavin, iron, calcium, and zinc.

A well-balanced vegetarian diet can provide adequate protein and other nutrients.

What Health Problems Are Related to Protein Intake?

Consuming inadequate protein can result in severe illness and death. Typically, this occurs when people do not consume enough energy, but a diet deficient specifically in protein can have similar effects. Is it possible to consume too much protein? If you recall, the AMDR for protein is 10%–35%, suggesting that a diet where one-third of the energy comes from protein can be acceptable. There is no well-established risk for protein intakes above the upper level in the AMDR, but longer term studies have not been conducted. Very high protein intakes could potentially be harmful for individuals who have heart disease or kidney disease.

As you learned in Chapter 5, animal sources of protein are typically high in saturated fat and cholesterol. Thus, very-high-protein diets composed of predominantly animal sources are associated with unhealthful blood lipid profiles, and this could be potentially be harmful for people who have heart disease.

A second risk associated with very high protein intakes is kidney disease. People with kidney problems are advised to eat a low-protein diet because a high-protein diet can increase the risk of acquiring kidney disease in people who are susceptible. People with diabetes have higher rates of kidney disease, and may lose some protein in their urine. Recent Canadian guidelines for people with diabetes and chronic kidney disease suggest following the RDA of 0.8 g/kg/day of protein, with at least 50% of protein coming from high biological-value protein sources (Canadian Diabetes Association, 2009).

It is important for people who consume a lot of protein to drink more water. This is because eating more protein increases protein metabolism and urea production. As mentioned earlier, urea is a waste product that forms when nitrogen is removed during amino acid metabolism. Adequate fluid is needed to flush excess urea from the kidneys. This is particularly important for athletes, who need more fluid to counterbalance higher sweat losses.

Protein-Energy Malnutrition Can Lead to Debility and Death

When a person consumes too little protein and energy, the result is **protein–energy malnutrition** (also called *protein–calorie malnutrition*). Two diseases that can follow are marasmus and kwashiorkor **(Figure 6.14)**.

Marasmus Results from Grossly Inadequate Energy Intakes

Marasmus is a disease that results from grossly inadequate intakes of protein, energy, and other nutrients. Essentially, people with marasmus slowly starve to death.

protein–energy malnutrition A disorder caused by inadequate consumption of protein and energy. It is characterized by severe wasting.

marasmus A form of protein–energy malnutrition that results from grossly inadequate intakes of protein, energy, and other nutrients.

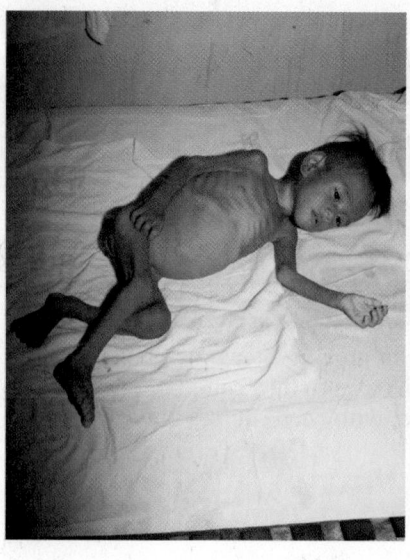
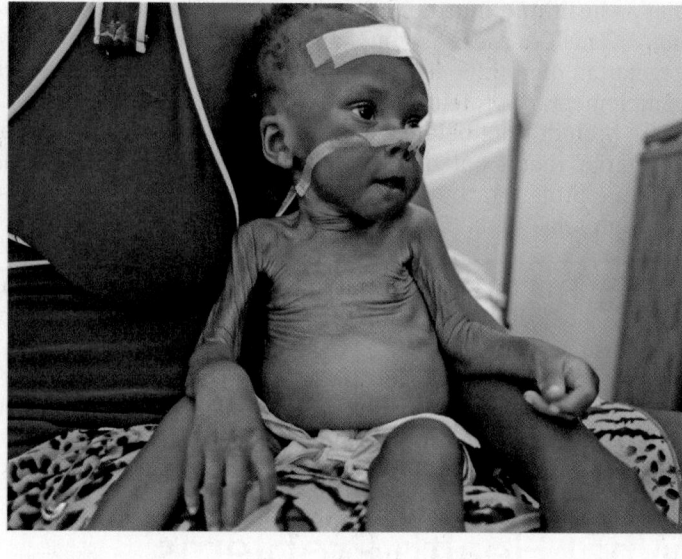

(a)   **(b)**

◆ **Figure 6.14** Two forms of protein–energy malnutrition are **(a)** marasmus and **(b)** kwashiorkor.

It is most common in young children (6 to 18 months of age) living in impoverished conditions who are severely undernourished. For example, the children may be fed diluted cereal drinks that are inadequate in energy, protein, and most nutrients. People suffering from marasmus have the look of "skin and bones" as their body fat and tissues are wasting. The consequences of marasmus include the following:

- Wasting and weakening of muscles, including the heart muscle
- Stunted brain development and learning impairment
- Depressed metabolism and little insulation from body fat, causing a dangerously low body temperature
- Stunted physical growth and development
- Deterioration of the intestinal lining, which further inhibits the absorption of nutrients
- Anemia (abnormally low levels of hemoglobin in the blood)
- Severely weakened immune system
- Fluid and electrolyte imbalances

If marasmus is left untreated, death from dehydration, heart failure, or infection will result. Treating marasmus involves carefully correcting fluid and electrolyte imbalances. Protein and carbohydrates are provided once the body's condition has stabilized. Fat is introduced much later, as the protein levels in the blood must improve to the point at which the body can use them to carry fat, so that it can be safely metabolized by the body.

Kwashiorkor Results from a Low-Protein Diet

kwashiorkor A form of protein–energy malnutrition that is typically seen in developing countries in infants and toddlers who are weaned early because of the birth of a subsequent child. Denied breast milk, they are fed a cereal diet that provides adequate energy but inadequate protein.

Kwashiorkor often occurs in developing countries where infants are weaned early due to the arrival of a subsequent baby. This deficiency disease is typically seen in young children (one to three years of age) who no longer drink breast milk. Instead, they often are fed a low-protein, starchy cereal. Unlike marasmus, kwashiorkor often develops quickly and causes the person to look swollen, particularly in the belly. This is because the low protein content of the blood is inadequate to keep fluids from seeping into the tissue spaces. These are other symptoms of kwashiorkor:

- Some weight loss and muscle wasting, with some retention of body fat
- Retarded growth and development; less severe than that seen with marasmus
- Edema, which results in extreme distension of the belly and is caused by fluid and electrolyte imbalances
- Fatty degeneration of the liver

- Loss of appetite, sadness, irritability, apathy
- Development of sores and other skin problems; skin pigmentation changes
- Dry, brittle hair that changes colour, straightens, and falls out easily

Kwashiorkor can be reversed if adequate protein and energy are given in time. Because of their severely weakened immune systems, many individuals with kwashiorkor die from diseases they contract in their weakened state. Of those who are treated, many return home to the same impoverished conditions, only to develop this deficiency once again.

Many people think that only children in developing countries suffer from these diseases. However, protein–energy malnutrition occurs in all countries and affects both children and adults. In the United States and Canada, poor people living in inner cities and isolated rural areas may be affected. Others at risk include the elderly, the homeless, individuals with eating disorders, those addicted to alcohol and other drugs, and individuals with wasting diseases, such as AIDS or cancer. The **In Depth** on Global Nutrition following Chapter 13 provides more information on malnutrition and hunger.

RECAP Protein–energy malnutrition can lead to marasmus and kwashiorkor. These diseases primarily affect impoverished children in developing nations. However, residents of developed countries are also at risk, especially the elderly, the homeless, people struggling with substance abuse, and people with AIDS, cancer, and other wasting diseases.

Nutrition DEBATE

Do Meat-Based Diets Contribute to Global Warming?

Which causes more greenhouse gas emissions: livestock production or traffic? The answer may surprise you: according to the United Nations Food and Agriculture Organization (FAO), livestock production generates more of the gases responsible for global warming—18%—than transportation (FAO, 2006). The FAO estimates that livestock production accounts for

- 9% of all carbon dioxide (CO_2) production from human activity;
- 37% of all human-induced methane;
- 64% of ammonia;
- 65% of human-related production of nitrous oxide.

How does this compare to emissions generated from the production of plant foods? Researchers at the University of Chicago concluded that an adult consuming an average amount of energy from a typical mixed North American diet causes the emission of 1485 kg of greenhouse gases *above* the emission associated with consuming the same number of kilocalories from plant sources (Eshel and Martin, 2006).

Livestock production is also a major source of land degradation, using 30% of the earth's land surface for pasture or feed production. In the Amazon, about 60%–70% of the deforestation has been to clear land for grazing (FAO, 2006). In addition, the production of feed crops for livestock uses 33% of global arable land. Livestock's presence in vast tracts of land and its demand for feed crops also have contributed significantly to a reduction in biodiversity and decline in ecosystems (FAO, 2006).

It is also estimated that in the United States it takes approximately 1650 litres (430 gallons) of water to produce 0.5 kg (1 lb.) of pork. This is in contrast to the 580 litres (151 gallons) of water it takes to produce 0.5 kg (1 lb.) of wheat. Animal waste, antibiotics, hormones, and fertilizers and pesticides used on feed crops can run off into neighbouring streams, rivers, and lakes and into nearby irrigation fields used to produce crops for human consumption.

Considering the damage that livestock production wreaks on the environment, should you adopt a vegetarian—or semi-vegetarian (flexitarian)—diet? The world's leading authority on global warming thinks you should. In 2008, Dr. Rajendra Pachauri, chair of the United Nations Intergovernmental Panel on Climate Change, which earned a joint share of the Nobel Peace Prize in 2007, released a statement calling upon individuals to have one meat-free day a week and to progressively reduce their meat consumption even further (Jowit, 2008). Pachauri noted that reducing meat consumption is an action that anyone can take immediately, and one that can have a significant impact on global warming in a short period of time.

But not everyone agrees. In response to many of the claims of environmental degradation from livestock production, meat industry organizations have published information in defense of their practices. A 2003 fact sheet from the U.S. National Cattlemen's Beef Association states (National Cattlemen's Beef Association, 2010):

- Waste produced by cattle is minor, with about 2.5% of the total methane production in the United States coming from domestic livestock.
- Less than 1% of the total 2001 beef supply in the United States was imported from rain forest countries, and the largest fast-food chains have policies prohibiting the purchase of beef from these countries.
- Livestock production accounts for only 11% of the total amount of water used in the United States each year.

If people were to significantly reduce their consumption of meat, it might be possible to return to small family farming, which is more environmentally friendly. When animals are raised on smaller farms and/or allowed to range freely, they consume grass, crop wastes, and scraps recycled from the kitchen, which efficiently utilizes unused food sources.

(a)

(b)

⬆ Livestock production (a) and aggressive deforestation (b) both contribute to greenhouse emissions.

Chapter Review

1. False. Although protein can be used for energy in certain circumstances, fats and carbohydrates are the primary sources of energy for our bodies.

2. False. Vegetarian diets can meet and even exceed an individual's protein needs, assuming that adequate energy-yielding macronutrients, a variety of protein sources, and complementary protein sources are consumed.

3. True. Most people in Canada meet or exceed their requirements for protein.

Find the Quack

Colby works out at a gym three times a week, trying to gain muscle mass. One afternoon, as he is leaving the workout room to head for the showers, he is approached by a friendly looking young man he has never seen at the gym before. Introducing himself as Russ, a new member of the gym, the man compliments Colby on his workout. Colby can't help noticing Russ's extremely muscular physique, and so when he offers to tell Colby all about how he, too, can build muscle fast, Colby agrees to talk with him. Here is what Russ tells him:

- Protein shakes are the secret to gaining muscle.
- Bodybuilding causes microscopic tears in the muscle tissue, which have to be repaired with protein. This process of tearing down and rebuilding is increasing Colby's protein requirement so much that he cannot get the amount of protein he needs from foods alone.
- Russ tells Colby that bodybuilders need to eat at least a gram of protein per pound of body weight per day. He says this means that Colby needs to eat a minimum of 150 g of protein every day and asks him how much protein he is currently consuming. Colby answers that he eats a sandwich with meat or poultry for lunch most days and usually has meat at dinner. Russ raises his eyebrows. "That's all?" he asks. "You're only getting maybe 50 g of protein a day! How do you expect to build muscle on that?"
- Russ then tells Colby that he must start drinking protein shakes three times a day, in the morning and as a mid-afternoon and evening snack. He also insists that, in addition to three shakes, Colby drink a protein shake after every workout. He says that, after a workout, the muscles get totally depleted of their protein stores and need to have them replenished. Then he assures Colby that every scoop of the protein powder used for one shake will provide 25 g of pure protein with no fat and no carbohydrates.

When Colby asks how much the protein powder costs, Russ hands him a brochure. "Visit my website and register as a first-time buyer and you can order all you want for half-price! It's a lot less expensive than eating five or six steaks a day, and a lot more convenient, too!"

1. Russ claims that bodybuilders need to consume at least a gram of protein per pound of body weight per day. Does this assertion sound correct to you?

2. Colby weighs 68.2 kg (150 lbs.) and works out intensely with weights three times a week. Refer to the information on page 202 of this chapter. How much protein does Colby actually need to consume each day? Do you think that he is only consuming about 50 g of protein a day, as Russ claims? (If you need a hint, return to the What About You? feature on page 205.)

3. Do our muscles get "totally depleted of their protein stores" after an intensive workout, as Russ claims? Explain your answer.

4. Colby consumes about 2500 kcal a day. Is he at risk for any health problems if he begins to consume 150 g of protein every day, as Russ suggests?

Answers can be found in the study area of MasteringNutrition

Review Questions

1. The process of combining peanut butter and whole-wheat bread to make a complete protein is called
   a. deamination.
   b. vegetarianism.
   c. transamination.
   d. mutual supplementation.

2. Which of the following meals is typical of a vegan diet?
   a. Rice, pinto beans, acorn squash, soy butter, and almond milk
   b. Veggie dog, bun, and a banana blended with yogurt
   c. Brown rice and green tea
   d. Egg salad on whole-wheat toast, broccoli, carrot sticks, and soy milk

3. The substance that breaks down polypeptides in the small intestine is called
   a. hydrochloric acid.
   b. pepsin.
   c. protease.
   d. ketones.

4. The portion of an amino acid that contains nitrogen is called the
   a. side chain.
   b. amine group.
   c. acid group.
   d. nitrate cluster.

5. Proteins contain
   a. carbon, oxygen, and nitrogen.
   b. oxygen and hydrogen.
   c. carbon, oxygen, hydrogen, and nitrogen.
   d. carbon, oxygen, and hydrogen.

6. Which of the following is not characteristic of marasmus?
   a. Wasted and weakened muscles
   b. Stunted physical growth
   c. Edema
   d. Low body temperature

7. Which one of the following statements about proteins is not correct?
   a. When denatured, function is lost
   b. Amino acids are the building blocks of proteins
   c. Most enzymatic digestion occurs in the mouth
   d. Proteins act as enzymes and hormones

8. Choose the correct statement about amino acids.
   a. There are 11 essential and 9 non-essential amino acids
   b. A non-essential amino acid can never become an essential amino acid
   c. An oligopeptide refers to a string of ten or more amino acids
   d. Amino acid bonding and attraction determine protein shape

9. Derek, a moderately active male weighing 70 kg, consumes about 61 grams of protein per day. How many grams of protein per kilogram of body weight is Derek consuming?
   a. 1.37
   b. 1.15
   c. 0.87
   d. 0.80

10. Explain the relationship between inadequate protein intake and the swollen bellies of children with kwashiorkor.

11. Explain the relationship between excessive protein intake and an increased risk for kidney disease.

12. List and describe four functions of protein in our bodies.

13. Create a healthful one-day diet plan for an active 20-year-old lacto-ovo-vegetarian.

14. Draw a sketch showing how amino acids bond to form proteins.

15. You're over at your friend Stuart's house for dinner. You notice that his mother is looking better than ever—she seems so lean and fit! You ask him what she's been doing lately, and he tells you that she has been on a high-protein diet for the past two months. When you sit down at the dinner table, there are no breads or potatoes to go with the steak. Instead of vegetables there are scrambled eggs, dripping with butter. For dessert, there's ice cream piled with nuts. Stuart's mother comments on how she never feels hungry anymore. You think about all the pasta and bread you eat, and realize that you're often hungry between meals. Could it be that carbohydrates really are the enemy? For many years, using high-protein diets for weight loss has been a major controversy. Popular diets such as the Atkins Diet, the Zone Diet, and the Sugar Busters plan support the use of high-protein—or low carbohydrate—meals to lose weight. What concerns would you have about the safety of this diet? Would they change if you knew that Stuart's mother had high LDL cholesterol and a family history of heart disease? What advice might you give her about adapting her diet?

16. Haley is the star of your school's basketball team. She is muscular and fit and always seems to have endless energy. You learn that she is a passionate vegan and never consumes any meat or dairy products. Your friend Rabyah, another avid athlete, refuses to believe that Haley doesn't eat meat. Rabyah says she always craves meat after a hard workout and argues that animal protein is what fuels muscle. Is meat truly essential in an athlete's diet? Are the claims Rabyah makes about the role of meat really valid? Given what you know about the nature of plant and animal proteins, how would you explain to Rabyah that a vegetarian or vegan diet can be healthy?

Case Study

Stephanie, a 20-year-old college student studying nutrition, has recently become very interested in vegetarianism. Learning the various health benefits has sparked her interest. However, Stephanie is concerned she will not be able to consume adequate amounts of certain nutrients. Stephanie is an endurance female athlete weighing 59 kg (130 lb.). Completing the following questions will let you help Stephanie to see that when a vegetarian diet is planned appropriately, it can be healthful and nutritionally adequate.

a. Over the years, research has consistently shown benefits to adopting a vegetarian diet. List three benefits you feel would be important for Stephanie to know.

b. A primary concern of the vegetarian diet is inadequate protein intake, since the most complete protein sources are from animal sources. Explain mutual supplementation and its importance to Stephanie regarding initiation of a vegetarian diet. Include discussion of incomplete and complete proteins in your answer. What is the only complete source of vegetable protein? What other foods are good sources of protein?

c. Stephanie is unsure of how much protein she actually requires in her diet. Refer to the Recommended Dietary Allowance (RDA) for protein to calculate how much protein Stephanie should be consuming if she begins a vegetarian diet. Why do active individuals generally require a diet higher in protein than sedentary individuals?

Answers to Review Questions can be found at the back of this text.

Web Resources

www.dietitians.ca
Dietitians of Canada

On the home page of Dietitians of Canada's website, click on *Your Health* and then search in *Nutrition-A-Z* for helpful resources on vegetarian diets including *Eating Guidelines for Vegans*.

www.nal.usda.gov/fnic/pubs/bibs/gen/vegetarian.pdf
Food and Nutrition Information Centre: Vegetarian Nutrition Resource List

A list of reliable websites, magazines, newsletters, and books that the vegetarian consumer will find useful and interesting. Topics include vegetarianism through the life cycle and vegetarianism for athletes.

www.vrg.org
The Vegetarian Resource Group

Obtain vegetarian and vegan news, recipes, information, and additional links.

www.eatright.org
Academy of Nutrition and Dietetics

Search for vegetarian diets to learn how to plan healthful meat-free meals.

www.who.int/nut/en
World Health Organization Nutrition Site

Visit this site to find out more about the worldwide magnitude of protein–energy malnutrition and the diseases that can result from inadequate intakes of protein, energy-yielding carbohydrates and fats, and various additional nutrients.

www.worldbank.org/nutrition
World Bank

Visit this site to learn about programs developed by the World Bank to alleviate hunger and low birth weights in the developing world. Check out the Nutrition Toolkit they use for these programs.

www.cattle.ca
Canadian Cattlemen's Association

Visit this site to learn more about the industry's involvement in the Green House Gas Mitigation Program and other issues.

MasteringNutrition®

Assignments

Animations Deamination & Transamination • Nitrogen Balance • Enzymes • Protein Digestion • Protein Synthesis • Protein Absorption • The Building Blocks of Proteins

Study Area

Video: Understanding Proteins • Practice Tests • Diet Analysis • eText

Vitamins and Minerals: Micronutrients with Macro Powers

WANT TO FIND OUT...

- how a few fortunate accidents led to the discovery of micronutrients?

- why large doses of certain micronutrients could kill you—and which ones?

- whether micronutrient supplements have the same health benefits as nutrients found in whole foods?

R EAD ON.

Have you heard the one about the college student on the junk-food diet who developed scurvy, a disease caused by inadequate intake of vitamin C? This "urban legend" seems to circulate on most college campuses every year, but that might be because there's some truth behind it. Away from their families, many college students do adopt diets that are deficient in one or more micronutrients. For instance, some students adopt a vegan diet with insufficient iron, whereas others stop choosing foods rich in calcium and vitamin D. Why is it important to consume adequate levels of the micronutrients, and exactly what constitutes a micronutrient, anyway? This *In Depth* explores the discovery of micronutrients, their classification and naming, and their impact on our health.

Discovering the "Hidden" Nutrients

As you recall from Chapter 1, there are three general classes of nutrients. Fluids provide water, which is essential for our survival and helps regulate many body functions. Macronutrients, which include carbohydrates, fats, and proteins, provide energy; thus, we need to consume them in relatively large amounts. Micronutrients, which include vitamins and minerals, are needed in much smaller amounts. They assist body functions such as energy metabolism and the formation and maintenance of healthy cells and tissues.

Much of our knowledge of vitamins and minerals comes from accidental observations of animals and humans. For instance, in the 1890s, a Dutch physician by the name of C. Eijkman noticed that chickens fed polished rice developed paralysis, which could be reversed by feeding

Fruits contain many vitamins.

them whole-grain rice. Noting the high incidence of beriberi, which results in extensive nerve damage, among hospital patients fed polished rice, he hypothesized that a highly refined diet was the main cause of beriberi. We now know that whole-grain rice, with its nutrient-rich bran layer, contains the vitamin thiamin and that thiamin deficiency results in beriberi. Similarly, in the early 1900s, it was observed that Japanese children living in fishing villages rarely developed a type of blindness common among Japanese children who did not eat fish. Experiments soon showed that cod liver oil, chicken liver, and eel fat prevented the disorder. We now know that each of these foods contains vitamin A, which is essential for healthy vision.

Such observations were followed by years of laboratory research before nutritionists came to fully accept the idea that very small amounts of substances present in food are critical to good health. In 1906, the term *accessory factors* was coined by the English scientist F. G. Hopkins; we now categorize these accessory factors as vitamins and minerals.

How Are Vitamins Classified?

Vitamins are carbon-containing compounds that regulate a wide range of body processes. Of the 13 vitamins recognized as essential, humans can synthesize only small amounts of vitamins D and K, so we must consume virtually all of the vitamins in our diets. Almost everyone who eats a varied and healthful diet can readily meet his or her vitamin needs from foods alone. The exceptions to this will be discussed shortly.

Fat-Soluble Vitamins

Vitamins A, D, E, and K are fat-soluble vitamins **(Table 1)**. They are found in the fatty portions of foods

Avocados are a source of fat-soluble vitamins.

(butterfat, cod liver oil, corn oil, and so on) and are absorbed along with dietary fat. Fat-containing meats, dairy products, nuts, seeds, vegetable oils, and avocados are all sources of one or more fat-soluble vitamins.

In general, the fat-soluble vitamins are readily stored in the body's adipose tissue; thus, we do not need to consume them every single day. While this may simplify day-to-day menu planning, there is also a disadvantage to our ability to store these nutrients. When we consume more of them than we can use, they build up in the adipose tissue, liver, and other tissues and can reach toxic levels. Symptoms of fat-soluble vitamin toxicity, described in Table 1, include damage to our hair, skin, bones, eyes, and nervous system. Overconsumption of vitamin supplements is the most common cause of vitamin toxicity in North America; rarely do our dietary choices lead to toxicity. Of the four fat-soluble vitamins, vitamins A and D are the most toxic; megadosing with ten or more times the recommended intake of either can result in irreversible organ damage and even death.

Even though our bodies can store the fat-soluble vitamins, deficiencies can occur, especially in people who have a disorder that reduces their ability to absorb dietary fat. In addition, people who are "fat phobic," or eat very small amounts of dietary fat, are at risk for a deficiency. The consequences of fat-soluble vitamin deficiencies, described in Table 1, include osteoporosis, the loss of night vision, and even death in the most severe cases.

TABLE 1 Fat-Soluble Vitamins

Vitamin Name	Primary Functions	Recommended Intake*	Reliable Food Sources	Toxicity/Deficiency Symptoms
A (retinol, retinal, retinoic acid)	Required for ability of eyes to adjust to changes in light Protects colour vision Assists cell differentiation Required for sperm production in men and fertilization in women Contributes to healthy bone Contributes to healthy immune system	RDA: Men = 900 µg Women = 700 µg UL = 3000 µg/day	Preformed retinol: beef and chicken liver, egg yolks, milk Carotenoid precursors: spinach, carrots, mango, apricots, cantaloupe, pumpkin, yams	*Toxicity:* fatigue; bone and joint pain; spontaneous abortion and birth defects of fetuses in pregnant women; nausea and diarrhea; liver damage; nervous system damage; blurred vision; hair loss; skin disorders *Deficiency:* night blindness, xerophthalmia; impaired growth, immunity, and reproductive function
D (cholecalciferol)	Regulates blood calcium levels Maintains bone health Assists cell differentiation	RDA Adults aged 19 to 70 years = 15 µg /day Adults aged >70 years = 20 µg /day UL = 100 µg/day	Canned salmon and mackerel, milk, fortified cereals	*Toxicity:* hypercalcemia *Deficiency:* rickets in children; osteomalacia and/or osteoporosis in adults
E (tocopherol)	As a powerful antioxidant, protects cell membranes, polyunsaturated fatty acids, and vitamin A from oxidation Protects white blood cells Enhances immune function Improves absorption of vitamin A	RDA: Men = 15 mg/day Women = 15 mg/day UL = 1000 mg/day	Sunflower seeds, almonds, vegetable oils, fortified cereals	*Toxicity:* rare *Deficiency:* hemolytic anemia; impairment of nerve, muscle, and immune function
K (phylloquinone, menaquinone, menadione)	Serves as a coenzyme during production of specific proteins that assist in blood coagulation and bone metabolism	AI: Men = 120 µg/day Women = 90 µg/day	Kale, spinach, turnip greens, Brussels sprouts	*Toxicity:* none known *Deficiency:* impaired blood clotting; possible effect on bone health

*Abbreviations: RDA, Recommended Dietary Allowance; UL, upper limit; AI, Adequate Intake.

Water-Soluble Vitamins

Vitamin C (ascorbic acid) and the B-complex vitamins (thiamin, riboflavin, niacin, vitamin B_6, vitamin B_{12}, folate, pantothenic acid, and biotin) are all water-soluble vitamins (Table 2). They are found in a wide variety of foods, including whole grains, fruits, vegetables, meats, and dairy products. They are easily absorbed through the intestinal tract directly into the bloodstream, where they then travel to target cells.

With the exception of vitamin B_{12}, our bodies do not store large amounts of water-soluble vitamins. Instead, our kidneys filter from our bloodstream any excess amounts and excrete them in urine.

Because we do not store large amounts of these vitamins in our tissues, toxicity is rare. When it does occur, however, it is often from the overuse of high-potency vitamin supplements. Toxicity can cause nerve damage and skin lesions.

Since most water-soluble vitamins are not stored in large amounts, they need to be consumed on a daily or weekly basis. Deficiency symptoms, including

Water-soluble vitamins can be found in a variety of foods.

TABLE 2 Water-Soluble Vitamins

Vitamin Name	Primary Functions	Recommended Intake*	Reliable Food Sources	Toxicity/Deficiency Symptoms
Thiamin (vitamin B_1)	Required as enzyme cofactor for carbohydrate and amino acid metabolism	RDA: Men = 1.2 mg/day Women = 1.1 mg/day	Pork, fortified cereals, enriched rice and pasta, peas, tuna, legumes	*Toxicity:* none known *Deficiency:* beriberi; fatigue, apathy, decreased memory, confusion, irritability, muscle weakness
Riboflavin (vitamin B_2)	Required as enzyme cofactor for carbohydrate and fat metabolism	RDA: Men = 1.3 mg/day Women = 1.1 mg/day	Beef liver, shrimp, milk and other dairy foods, fortified cereals, enriched breads and grains	*Toxicity:* none known *Deficiency:* ariboflavinosis; swollen mouth and throat; seborrheic dermatitis; anemia
Niacin, nicotin-amide, nicotinic acid	Required for carbohydrate and fat metabolism Plays role in DNA replication and repair and cell differentiation	RDA: Men = 16 mg/day Women = 14 mg/day UL = 35 mg/day	Beef liver, most cuts of meat/fish/poul-try, fortified cereals, enriched breads and grains, canned tomato products	*Toxicity:* flushing, liver damage, glucose intolerance, blurred vision differentiation *Deficiency:* pellagra; vomit-ing, constipation, or diarrhea; apathy
Pyridoxine, pyridoxal, pyridoxamine (vitamin B_6)	Required as enzyme cofactor for carbohydrate and amino acid metabolism Assists synthesis of blood cells	RDA: Men and women aged 19 to 50 = 1.3 mg/day Men aged >50 and over = 1.7 mg/day Women aged >50 and over = 1.5 mg/day UL = 100 mg/day	Chickpeas (garbanzo beans), most cuts of meat/fish/poultry, fortified cereals, white potatoes	*Toxicity:* nerve damage, skin lesions *Deficiency:* anemia; seborrheic dermatitis; depression, confu-sion, and convulsions
Folate (folic acid)	Required as enzyme cofactor for amino acid metabolism Required for DNA synthesis Involved in metabolism of homo-cysteine	RDA: Men = 400 µg/day Women = 400 µg/day UL = 1000 µg/day	Fortified cereals, enriched breads and grains, spinach, legumes (lentils, chickpeas, pinto beans), greens (spinach, romaine lettuce), liver	*Toxicity:* masks symptoms of vitamin B12 deficiency, specifically signs of nerve damage *Deficiency:* macrocytic anemia; neural tube defects in a developing fetus; elevated homocysteine levels
Cobalamin (vitamin B_{12})	Assists with formation of blood Required for healthy nervous system function Involved as enzyme cofactor in metabolism of homocysteine	RDA: Men = 2.4 µg/day Women = 2.4 µg/day	Shellfish, all cuts of meat/fish/poultry, milk and other dairy foods, fortified cereals	*Toxicity:* none known *Deficiency:* pernicious anemia; tingling and numbness of extremities; nerve damage; memory loss, disorientation, and dementia
Pantothenic acid	Assists with fat metabolism	AI: Men = 5 mg/day Women = 5 mg/day	Meat/fish/poultry, shiitake mushrooms, for-tified cereals, egg yolk	*Toxicity:* none known *Deficiency:* rare
Biotin	Involved as enzyme cofactor in carbohydrate, fat, and protein metabolism	RDA: Men = 30 µg/day Women = 30 µg/day	Nuts, egg yolk	*Toxicity:* none known *Deficiency:* rare
Ascorbic acid (vitamin C)	Antioxidant in extracellular fluid and lungs Regenerates oxidized vitamin E Assists with collagen synthesis Enhances immune function Assists in synthesis of hormones, neurotransmitters, and DNA Enhances iron absorption	RDA: Men = 90 mg/day Women = 75 mg/day Smokers = 35 mg more per day than RDA UL = 2000 mg	Sweet peppers, citrus fruits and juices, broc-coli, strawberries, kiwi	*Toxicity:* nausea and diarrhea, nosebleeds, increased oxida-tive damage, increased forma-tion of kidney stones in people with kidney disease *Deficiency:* scurvy; bone pain and fractures, depression, and anemia

*Abbreviations: RDA, Recommended Dietary Allowance; UL, upper limit; AI, Adequate Intake.

diseases or syndromes, can arise fairly quickly, especially during fetal development and in growing infants and children. The signs of water-soluble vitamin deficiency vary widely and are identified in Table 2.

Same Vitamin, Different Names and Forms

Food and supplement labels, magazine articles, and even nutrition textbooks such as this often use simplified alphabetic (A, D, E, K) names for the fat-soluble vitamins. The letters reflect their order of discovery: vitamin A was discovered in 1916, whereas vitamin K was not isolated until 1939. These lay terms, however, are more appropriately viewed as "umbrellas" that unify a small cluster of chemically related compounds. For example, the term *vitamin A* refers to the specific compounds retinol, retinal, and retinoic acid. Similarly, *vitamin E* occurs naturally in eight forms, known as tocopherols, of which the primary form is alpha-tocopherol. Compounds with *vitamin D* activity include cholecalciferol and ergocalciferol, and the *vitamin K* "umbrella" includes phylloquinone and menaquinone. As you can see, most of the individual compounds making up a fat-soluble vitamin cluster have similar chemical designations (such as tocopherols and calciferols). Table 1 lists both the alphabetic and chemical terms for the fat-soluble vitamins.

Similarly, there are both alphabetic and chemical designations for water-soluble vitamins. In some cases, such as *vitamin C* and *ascorbic acid*, you may be familiar with both terms. But few people would recognize *cobalamin* as designating the same micronutrient as *vitamin B$_{12}$*. Some of the water-soluble vitamins, such as niacin and vitamin B$_6$, mimic the "umbrella" clustering seen with vitamins A, E, D, and K: the term *vitamin B$_6$* includes pyridoxal, pyridoxine, and pyridoxamine. If you read any of these three terms on a supplement label, you will know it refers to vitamin B$_6$.

Some vitamins exist in only one form. For example, thiamin is the only chemical compound known as *vitamin B$_1$*. There are no other related chemical compounds. Table 2 lists both the alphabetic and chemical terms for the water-soluble vitamins.

How Are Minerals Classified?

Minerals are naturally occurring inorganic (non-carbon-containing) substances such as calcium, iron, and zinc. All minerals are elements; that is, they are already in the simplest chemical form possible and are not digested or broken down prior to absorption. Furthermore, unlike vitamins, they cannot be synthesized in the laboratory or by any plant or animal, including humans. Minerals are the same wherever they are found, whether in soil, a car part, or the human body. The minerals in our foods ultimately come from the environment; for example, the selenium in soil and water is taken up into plants and then incorporated into the animals that eat the plants. Whether humans eat the plant foods directly or eat the animal products, all of the minerals in our food supply originate from Mother Earth!

Major Minerals

Major minerals are those that are required in amounts of at least 100 mg per day. In addition, these minerals are found in the human body in amounts of 5 g (5000 mg) or higher. There are seven major minerals: sodium, potassium, phosphorus, chloride, calcium, magnesium, and sulphur. **Table 3** summarizes the primary functions, recommended intakes, food sources, and toxicity/deficiency symptoms of these minerals.

Trace Minerals

Trace minerals are those we need to consume in amounts of less than

Plants absorb minerals from soil and water.

100 mg per day. They are found in the human body in amounts of less than 5 g (5000 mg). Currently, the Dietary Reference Intake (DRI) Committee recognizes eight trace minerals as essential for human health: selenium, fluoride, iodine, chromium, manganese, iron, zinc, and copper (IOM, 2001). **Table 4** identifies the primary functions, recommended intakes, food sources, and toxicity/deficiency symptoms of these minerals.

Same Mineral, Different Forms

Unlike most vitamins, which can be identified by either alphabetic designations or the more complicated chemical terms, minerals are known by one name only. Iron, calcium, sodium, and all other minerals are simply referred to by their chemical name. That said, minerals do often exist within different chemical compounds; for example, a supplement label might identify calcium as calcium lactate, calcium gluconate, or calcium citrate. These different chemical compounds, while all containing the same elemental mineral, may differ in their ability to be absorbed by the body.

TABLE 3 Major Minerals

Mineral Name	Primary Functions	Recommended Intake*	Reliable Food Sources	Toxicity/Deficiency Symptoms
Sodium	Fluid balance Acid–base balance Transmission of nerve impulses Muscle contraction	AI: Adults = 1.5 g/day (1500 mg/day)	Table salt, pickles, most canned soups, snack foods, cured luncheon meats, canned tomato products	*Toxicity:* water retention, high blood pressure, loss of calcium *Deficiency:* muscle cramps, dizziness, fatigue, nausea, vomiting, mental confusion
Potassium	Fluid balance Transmission of nerve impulses Muscle contraction	AI: Adults = 4.7 g/day (4700 mg/day)	Most fresh fruits and vegetables: potatoes, bananas, tomato juice, orange juice, melons	*Toxicity:* muscle weakness, vomiting, irregular heartbeat *Deficiency:* muscle weakness, paralysis, mental confusion, irregular heartbeat
Phosphorus	Fluid balance Bone formation Component of ATP, which provides energy for our bodies	RDA: Adults = 700 mg/day	Milk/cheese/yogurt, soy milk and tofu, legumes (lentils, black beans), nuts (almonds, peanuts and peanut butter), poultry	*Toxicity:* muscle spasms, convulsions, low blood calcium *Deficiency:* muscle weakness, muscle damage, bone pain, dizziness
Chloride	Fluid balance Transmission of nerve impulses Component of stomach acid (HCl) Antibacterial	AI: Adults = 2.3 g/day (2300 mg/day)	Table salt	*Toxicity:* none known *Deficiency:* dangerous blood acid–base imbalances, irregular heartbeat
Calcium	Primary component of bone Acid–base balance Transmission of nerve impulses Muscle contraction	AI: Adults aged 19 to 50 = 1000 mg/day Adults aged > 50 = 1200 mg/day UL = 2500 mg/day	Milk/yogurt/cheese (best-absorbed form of calcium), sardines, collard greens and spinach, calcium-fortified juices	*Toxicity:* mineral imbalances, shock, kidney failure, fatigue, mental confusion *Deficiency:* osteoporosis, convulsions, heart failure
Magnesium	Component of bone Muscle contraction Assists more than 300 enzyme systems	RDA: Men aged 19 to 30 = 400 mg/day Men aged >30 = 420 mg/day Women aged 19 to 30 = 310 mg/day Women aged >30 = 320 mg/day UL = 350 mg/day	Greens (spinach, kale, collard greens), whole grains, seeds, nuts, legumes (navy and black beans)	*Toxicity:* none known *Deficiency:* low blood calcium, muscle spasms or seizures, nausea, weakness, increased risk for chronic diseases, such as heart disease, hypertension, osteoporosis, and type 2 diabetes
Sulphur	Component of certain B vitamins and amino acids Acid–base balance Detoxification in liver	No DRI	Protein-rich foods	*Toxicity:* none known *Deficiency:* none known

*Abbreviations: RDA, Recommended Dietary Allowance; UL, upper limit; AI, Adequate Intake; DRI, Dietary Reference Intake.

How Do Our Bodies Use Micronutrients?

In Chapter 3, we investigated the truth behind the claim "You are what you eat." We found out that the body has to change food in order to use it.

This is also true for foods containing vitamins and minerals, because the micronutrients found in foods and supplements are not always in a chemical form that can be used by our cells. This discussion will highlight some of the ways in which our bodies modify the food forms of vitamins and minerals in order to maximize their absorption and utilization.

What We Eat Differs from What We Absorb

The most healthful diet is of no value to our bodies unless the nutrients can be absorbed and transported to the cells that need them. Unlike

TABLE 4 Trace Minerals

Mineral Name	Primary Functions	Recommended Intake*	Reliable Food Sources	Toxicity/Deficiency Symptoms
Selenium	Required for carbohydrate and fat metabolism	RDA: Adults = 55 µg/day UL = 400 µg/day	Nuts, shellfish, meat/fish/poultry, whole grains	*Toxicity:* brittle hair and nails, skin rashes, nausea and vomiting, weakness, liver disease *Deficiency:* specific forms of heart disease and arthritis, impaired immune function, muscle pain and wasting, depression, hostility
Fluoride	Development and maintenance of healthy teeth and bones	RDA: Men = 4 mg/day Women = 3 mg/day UL: 2.2 mg/day for children aged 4 to 8; children aged >8 = 10 mg/day	Fish, seafood, legumes, whole grains, drinking water (variable)	*Toxicity:* fluorosis of teeth and bones *Deficiency:* dental caries, low bone density
Iodine	Synthesis of thyroid hormones Temperature regulation Reproduction and growth	RDA: Adults = 150 µg/day UL = 1100 µg/day	Iodized salt, saltwater seafood	*Toxicity:* goitre *Deficiency:* goitre, hypothyroidism, cretinism in infant of mother who is iodine deficient
Chromium	Glucose transport Metabolism of DNA and RNA Immune function and growth	AI: Men aged 19 to 50 = 35 µg/day Men aged >50 = 30 µg/day Women aged 19 to 50 = 25 µg/day Women aged >50 = 20 µg/day	Whole grains, brewer's yeast	*Toxicity:* none known *Deficiency:* elevated blood glucose and blood lipids, damage to brain and nervous system
Manganese	Assists many enzyme systems Synthesis of protein found in bone and cartilage	AI: Men = 2.3 mg/day Women = 1.8 mg/day UL = 11 mg/day for adults	Whole grains, nuts, leafy vegetables, tea	*Toxicity:* impairment of neuromuscular system *Deficiency:* impaired growth and reproductive function, reduced bone density, impaired glucose and lipid metabolism, skin rash
Iron	Component of hemoglobin in blood cells Component of myoglobin in muscle cells Assists many enzyme systems	RDA: Adult men = 8 mg/day Women aged 19 to 50 = 18 mg/day Women aged >50 = 8 mg/day	Meat/fish/poultry (best-absorbed form of iron), fortified cereals, legumes, spinach	*Toxicity:* nausea, vomiting, and diarrhea; dizziness, confusion; rapid heartbeat, organ damage, death *Deficiency:* iron-deficiency microcytic (small red blood cells), hypochromic anemia
Zinc	Assists more than 100 enzyme systems Immune system function Growth and sexual maturation Gene regulation	RDA: Men 11 = mg/day Women = 8 mg/day UL = 40 mg/day	Meat/fish/poultry (best-absorbed form of zinc), fortified cereals, legumes	*Toxicity:* nausea, vomiting, and diarrhea; headaches, depressed immune function, reduced absorption of copper *Deficiency:* growth retardation, delayed sexual maturation, eye and skin lesions, hair loss, increased incidence of illness and infection
Copper	Assists many enzyme systems Iron transport	RDA: Adults = 900 µg/day UL = 10 mg/day	Shellfish, organ meats, nuts, legumes	*Toxicity:* nausea, vomiting, and diarrhea; liver damage *Deficiency:* anemia, reduced levels of white blood cells, osteoporosis in infants and growing children

*Abbreviations: RDA, Recommended Dietary Allowance; UL, upper limit; AI, Adequate Intake.

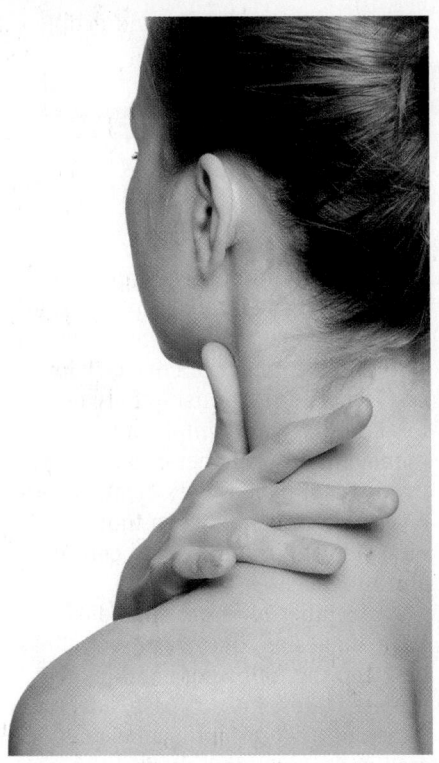

Minerals help maintain healthy skin and nails.

carbohydrates, fats, and proteins, which are efficiently absorbed (85%–99% of what is eaten makes it into the blood), some micronutrients are so poorly absorbed that only 3% to 10% of what is eaten ever arrives in the bloodstream.

The absorption of many vitamins and minerals depends on their chemical form. Dietary iron, for example, can be in the form of **heme iron** (found only in meats, fish, and poultry) or **non-heme iron** (found in plant and animal foods, as well as iron-fortified foods and supplements). Healthy adults absorb about 25% of heme iron but as little as 3% to 5% of non-heme iron.

In addition, the presence of other factors within the same food influences mineral absorption. For example, approximately 30% to 45% of the calcium found in milk and dairy products is absorbed, but the calcium in spinach, Swiss chard, seeds, and nuts is absorbed at a much lower rate because factors in these foods bind the calcium and prevent its absorption. Non-heme iron, zinc, vitamin E, and vitamin B$_6$ are other micronutrients

whose absorption can be reduced by various binding factors in foods.

The absorption of many vitamins and minerals is also influenced by other foods within the meal. For example, the fat-soluble vitamins are much better absorbed when the meal contains some dietary fat. Calcium absorption is increased by the presence of lactose, found in milk, and non-heme iron absorption can be doubled if the meal includes vitamin C–rich foods, such as red peppers, oranges, or tomatoes. On the other hand, high-fibre foods, such as whole grains, and foods high in oxalic acid, such as tea, spinach, and rhubarb, can decrease the absorption of zinc and iron. It may seem an impossible task to correctly balance your food choices to optimize micronutrient absorption, but the best approach, as always, is to eat a variety of healthful foods every day.

What We Eat Differs from What Our Cells Use

Many vitamins undergo one or more chemical transformations after they are eaten and absorbed into our bodies. For example, before they can go to work for our bodies, the B-complex vitamins must combine with other substances. For thiamine and vitamin B$_6$, a phosphate group is added. Vitamin D is another example: before cells can use it, the food form of vitamin D must have two hydroxyl (-OH) groups added to its structure. These combinations activate the vitamin; because they do not occur randomly, but only when the compound is needed, they help the body maintain control over its metabolic pathways.

While the basic nature of minerals does not change, minerals can undergo minor modifications that change their atomic structure. Iron (Fe) may alternate between Fe^{21} (ferrous) and Fe^{31} (ferric); copper (Cu) may exist as Cu^{11} or Cu^{21}. These are just two examples of how micronutrients can be modified from one form to another to help the body make the best use of dietary nutrients.

Foods high in oxalic acid, such as rhubarb, can decrease zinc and iron absorption.

Controversies in Micronutrient Metabolism

The science of nutrition continues to evolve, and our current understanding of vitamins and minerals will no doubt change over the next several years or decades. While some people interpret the term *controversy* as negative, nutrition controversies are exciting developments, proof of new information, and a sign of continued growth in the field.

Are Supplements Healthful Sources of Micronutrients?

Are the micronutrients in supplements any better or worse than those in foods? Do our bodies use the nutrients from these two sources any differently? These are issues

---

heme iron Iron that is a part of hemoglobin and myoglobin; found only in animal-based foods, such as meat, fish, and poultry.

non-heme iron The form of iron that is not a part of hemoglobin or myoglobin; found in animal- and plant-based foods.

that nutrition scientists and consumers continue to discuss.

The availability, or "usefulness," of micronutrients in foods depends in part on the food itself. The iron and calcium in spinach are poorly absorbed, whereas the iron in beef and the calcium in milk are absorbed efficiently. Because of these and other differences in the availability of micronutrients from different sources, it is difficult to generalize about the usefulness of supplements. Nevertheless, we can say a few things about this issue:

- In general, it is much easier to develop a toxic overload of nutrients from supplements than it is from foods. It is very difficult, if not impossible, to develop a vitamin or mineral toxicity through diet (food) alone.
- Some micronutrients consumed as supplements appear to be harmful to the health of certain consumers. Recent research has shown that the use of high-potency supplements of vitamins A, C, and E may actually increase rates of death (Bjelakovic et al., 2007).

  Earlier, it had been shown that high-potency beta-carotene supplements increased death rates among male smokers. Alcoholics are more susceptible to the potentially toxic effects of vitamin A supplements and should avoid their use unless specifically prescribed by a healthcare provider. There is also some evidence that high intake of vitamin A increases risk for osteoporosis and hip fracture in older adults (Penniston and Tanumihardjo, 2006).
- Most minerals are better absorbed from animal food sources than they are from supplements, except calcium citrate-malate, used in calcium-fortified juices.
- Enriching a low-nutrient food with a few vitamins and/or minerals does not turn it into a healthful food. For example, soft drinks fortified with micronutrients are still basically soft drinks.
- Eating a variety of healthful foods provides you with many more nutrients, phytochemicals, and

other dietary factors than supplements alone. Nutritionists are not even sure they have identified all the essential nutrients; the list of essential micronutrients may, in the future, expand. Supplements provide only those nutrients that the manufacturer puts in; foods provide nutrients that have been identified as well as yet-unknown factors.
- Foods often provide a balance of micronutrients and other factors that work in concert with one another. The whole food is more healthful than its isolated individual nutrients, providing benefits not always seen with purified supplements or highly refined, highly enriched food products.
- A healthful diet, built from a wide variety of foods, offers social, emotional, and other benefits that are absent from supplements. Humans eat food, not nutrients.

In certain populations, micronutrient supplements can play an important role in promoting good health. These include pregnant women, children

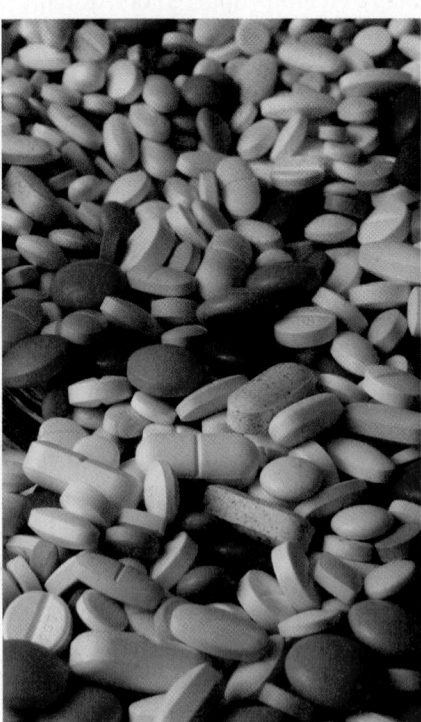

⬆ Thousands of supplements are marketed to consumers.

with poor eating habits, and people with certain illnesses.

Can Micronutrients Really Prevent or Treat Disease?

Nutritionists and other healthcare professionals clearly accept the role that dietary fat plays in the prevention and treatment of coronary heart disease. The relationship between total carbohydrate intake and the management of diabetes is also firmly established. Less clear, however, are the links between individual vitamins and minerals and certain chronic diseases.

A number of research studies have suggested, but not proven, links between the following vitamins and disease states. In each case, adequate intake of the nutrient has been associated with lower disease risk.

- Vitamin C and cataracts
- Vitamin D and colon cancer
- Vitamin E and complications of diabetes
- Vitamin K and osteoporosis

Other studies have examined relationships between minerals and chronic diseases. Again, in each case, the nutrient seems to be protective against the disease listed.

- Calcium and high blood pressure (hypertension)
- Chromium and type 2 diabetes in older adults
- Magnesium and muscle wasting (sarcopenia) in older adults
- Selenium and certain types of cancer

As consumers, it is important to critically evaluate any claims that are made regarding the protective or disease-preventing ability of a specific vitamin or mineral. Supplements that provide megadoses of micronutrients are potentially harmful, and vitamin/mineral therapies should never replace more traditional, proven methods of disease treatment. Current, reputable information can provide updates as the research into micronutrients continues.

Do More Essential Micronutrients Exist?

Nutrition researchers continue to explore the potential of a variety of substances to qualify as essential micronutrients. Vitamin-like factors, such as carnitine, and trace minerals, such as boron, nickel, and silicon, seem to have beneficial roles in human health, yet additional information is needed to fully define their metabolic roles. Until more research is done, we cannot classify such substances as essential micronutrients.

Another subject of controversy is the question "What is the appropriate intake of each micronutrient?" Contemporary research suggests that the answer to this question is to be found in each individual's genetic profile. As you learned in the Nutrition Debate in Chapter 1, the science of *nutrigenomics* blends the study of human nutrition with that of genetics. It is becoming clear that some individuals, for example, require much higher intakes of folate to achieve optimal health. Researchers have identified a specific genetic variation in a subset of the population that increases their need for dietary folate (Stover, 2006). Future studies may identify other examples of how a person's genetic profile influences his or her individual need for vitamins and minerals.

As explained in Chapter 1, the DRI Committees rely on Adequate Intake (AI) guidelines to suggest appropriate nutrient intake levels when research has not clearly defined an Estimated Average Requirement (EAR). As the science of nutrition continues to evolve, the next 50 years will be an exciting time for micronutrient research. Who knows? Within a few decades, we all might have personalized micronutrient prescriptions matched to our gender, age, and DNA!

NutriTools

Visit MasteringNutrition to access interactive animations including:

- Know Your Calcium Food Sources
- Know Your Iron Food Sources
- Let's Go to Lunch (for fat-soluble vitamins, water-soluble vitamins, and minerals)
- Vitamin or Mineral?

Web Resources

www.fda.gov
U.S. Food and Drug Administration

Select "Food" and then "Dietary Supplements" on the menu for information on how to evaluate dietary supplements.

www.ars.usda.gov/ba/bhnrc/ndl
Nutrient Data Laboratory Home Page

Click on "Search" and then type "Nutrients Lists" to find information on food sources of selected vitamins and minerals.

www.nal.usda.gov/fnic
The Food and Nutrition Information Center

Click on "Dietary Supplements" to obtain information on vitamin and mineral supplements.

www.dietary-supplements.info.nih.gov
Office of Dietary Supplements

This site provides summaries of current research results and helpful information about the use of dietary supplements.

http://.lpi.oregonstate.edu
Linus Pauling Institute of Oregon State University

This site provides up-to-date information on vitamins and minerals that promote health and lower disease risk.

Nutrients Involved in Fluid and Electrolyte Balance

7

CHAPTER OBJECTIVES

After reading this chapter you will be able to:

1. Identify four nutrients that function as electrolytes in our body, p. 229.

2. List three functions of water in our body, p. 230.

3. Describe how electrolytes assist in the regulation of healthful fluid balance, pp. 231–232.

4. Discuss the physical changes that trigger our thirst mechanism, pp. 233–234.

5. Describe the sources of fluid intake and output in our body, pp. 234–235.

6. Compare and contrast hypernatremia and hyponatremia, pp. 240–241.

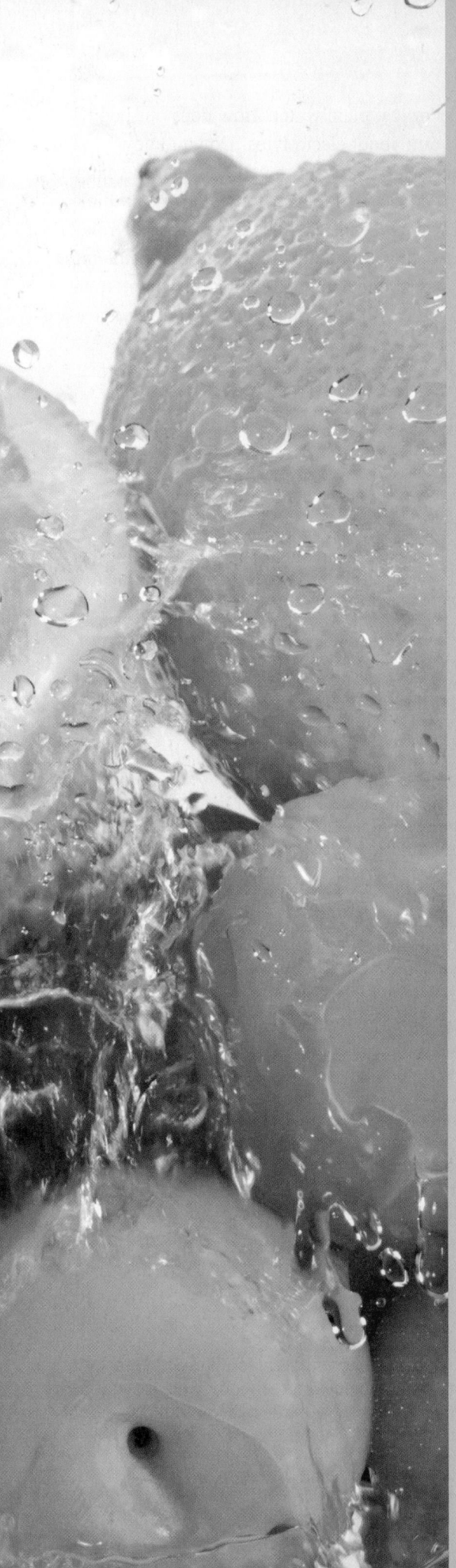

I

t's safe to assume that when you hear the word Vitaminwater™, you picture an image of a bottle of water full of fruits and vegetables, or at least of something that is good for you. However, if Vitaminwater™ had a slogan describing what it really was, it might be called "Non-carbonated sugar-water" instead. In one regular 500 millilitre bottle of Vitaminwater™, there is almost 40 mL or 8 teaspoons of sugar (32.5 grams). In one can of pop, there is a little over 45 mL or 9 teaspoons of sugar (39 grams). Does that change your opinion of these supposedly good-for-you beverages? Would you still buy Vitaminwater™ because it has added vitamins? It is marketed with health buzz words like "endurance," "energy," "defense," and "restore," so why wouldn't it be a smart beverage choice? The problem with calling it Vitaminwater™ is that the name itself is missing the third key ingredient: sugar. With several celebrity endorsements for Vitaminwater™, their branding of the product as being "packed with vitamins" did not escape the attention of the Centre for Science in the Public Interest (CSPI), an influential science-based organization in the United States who recently won the right to pursue a lawsuit against the company. As you learned in Chapter 2, health and nutrient claims are regulated by the government, and the CSPI argues that the company's use of the word "healthy" violates regulations on vitamin-fortified foods. According to the CSPI, those 40 mL or 8 teaspoons of sugar in each bottle "do more to promote obesity, diabetes, and other health problems than the vitamins in the drinks do to perform the advertised benefits listed on the bottles."

Do you drink these fortified drinks or just plain water? How does our body even use water, and what is so important about electrolytes? Do you know how to properly hydrate your body during physical activity? Are you aware of the dangers of dehydration and low blood sodium (also called *hyponatremia*)? Do you think it is possible to ever drink too much water? In this chapter, we explore the role of fluids and electrolytes in keeping our bodies adequately hydrated and maintaining the functions of our nerves and muscles. Immediately following this chapter, we take an ***In Depth*** look at some disorders that occur when fluids and electrolytes are out of balance.

What Are Fluids and Electrolytes, and What Are Their Functions?

Of course, you know that orange juice, blood, and shampoo are all fluids, but what makes them so? A **fluid** is characterized by its ability to move freely, adapting to the shape of the container that holds it. This might not seem very important, but as you will learn in this chapter, the fluid composition of your cells and tissues is critical to your body's ability to function.

Body Fluid Is the Liquid Portion of Our Cells and Tissues

Between 50% and 70% of a healthy adult's body weight is fluid. When we cut a finger, we can see some of this fluid dripping out as blood, but the fluid in the bloodstream cannot account for such a large percentage. So where is all this fluid hiding?

About two-thirds of an adult's body fluid is held within the walls of cells and is therefore called **intracellular fluid** (**Figure 7.1a**). Every cell in our body contains fluid. When our cells lose their fluid, they quickly shrink and die. On the other hand, when cells take in too much fluid, they swell and burst apart. This is why appropriate fluid balance—which we'll discuss throughout this chapter—is so critical to life.

The remaining third of body fluid is referred to as **extracellular fluid** because it flows outside our cells (Figure 7.1a). There are two types of extracellular fluid:

1. *Tissue fluid* (sometimes called *interstitial fluid*) flows between the cells that make up a particular tissue or organ, such as muscle fibres or the liver (Figure 7.1b). Other extracellular fluids, such as cerebrospinal fluid, mucus, and synovial fluid within joints, are also considered tissue fluid.
2. *Intravascular fluid* is found within blood and lymphatic vessels. Plasma is the fluid portion of blood that transports red blood cells through blood vessels. Plasma also contains proteins that are too large to leak out of blood vessels into the surrounding tissue fluid. As you learned in Chapter 6, protein concentration plays a major role in regulating the movement of fluids into and out of the bloodstream (Figure 7.1c).

Not every tissue in our body contains the same amount of fluid. Lean tissues, such as muscle, are more than 70% fluid by weight, whereas fat tissue is only between 10% and 20% fluid. This is not surprising, considering the water-repellent nature of lipids (see Chapter 5).

Body fluid levels also vary according to gender and age. Compared to females, males have more lean tissue and thus a higher percentage of body weight as fluid. The amount of body fluid as a percentage of total weight decreases with age. About 75% of an infant's body weight is water, whereas the total body water of an elderly person is generally less than 50% of body weight. This decrease in total body water is the result of the loss of lean tissue that typically occurs as people age.

As we age, our body water content decreases: approximately 75% of an infant's body weight is composed of water, while an elderly adult's body weight is only 50% water (or less).

fluid A substance composed of molecules that move past one another freely. Fluids are characterized by their ability to conform to the shape of whatever container holds them.

intracellular fluid The fluid held at any given time within the walls of the body's cells.

extracellular fluid The fluid outside the body's cells, either in the body's tissues or as the liquid portion of blood, called plasma.

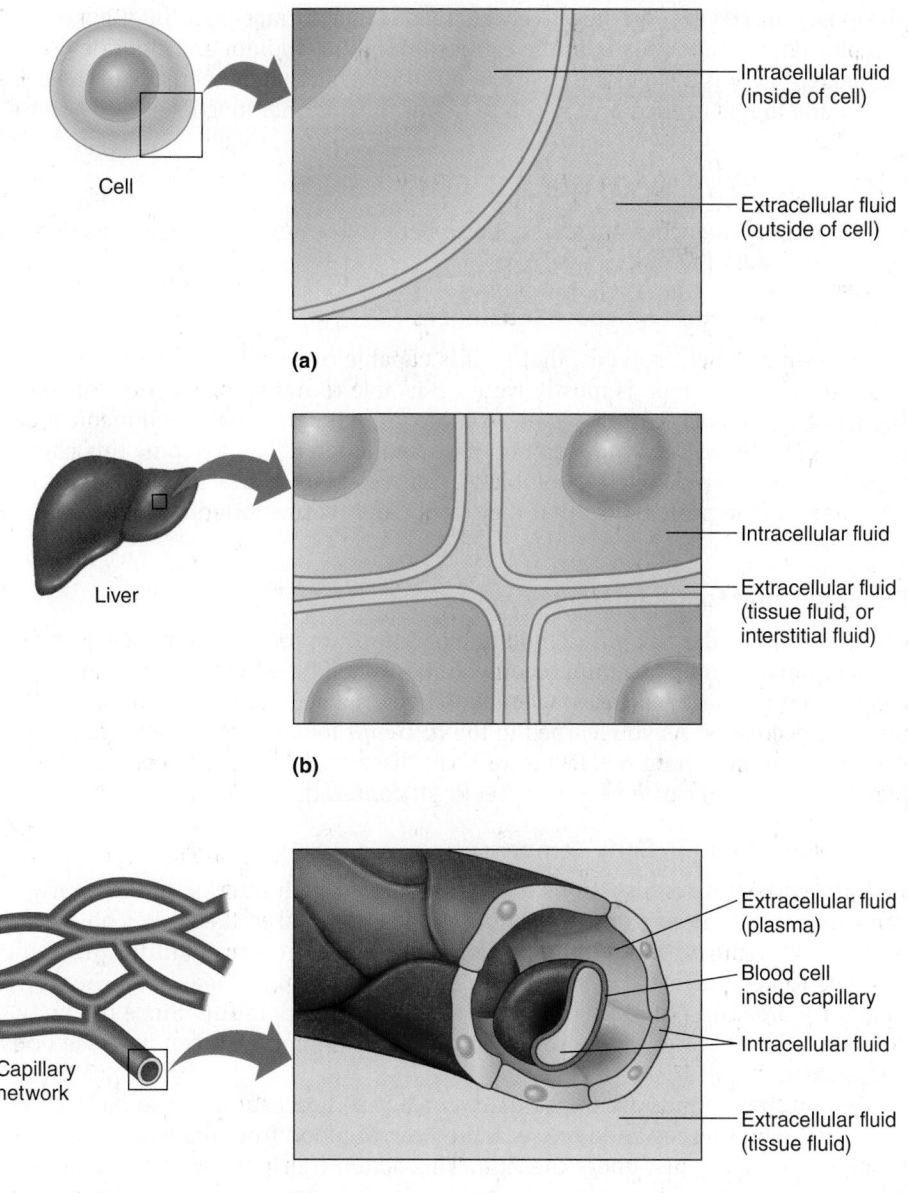

Figure 7.1 The components of body fluid. **(a)** Intracellular fluid is contained inside the cells that make up our body tissues. **(b)** Extracellular fluid is external to cells. Tissue fluid is external to tissue cells. **(c)** Another form of extracellular fluid is intravascular fluid—that is, fluid contained within vessels. Plasma is the fluid in blood vessels and is external to blood cells.

Body Fluid Is Composed of Water and Salts Called Electrolytes

Water is made up of molecules consisting of two hydrogen atoms bound to one oxygen atom (H_2O). You might think that pure water would be healthful, but we would quickly die if our cell and tissue fluids contained only pure water. Instead, within the body fluids are a variety of dissolved substances (called *solutes*) critical to life. These include four major minerals: sodium, potassium, chloride, and phosphorus. We consume these minerals in compounds called *salts,* including table salt, which is made of sodium and chloride.

These mineral salts are called **electrolytes,** because when they dissolve in water, the two component minerals separate and form charged particles called **ions,** which are capable of carrying an electrical current. The electrical charge, which can be positive or negative, is the "spark" that stimulates nerves and causes muscles to contract, making electrolytes critical to body functioning.

Of the four major minerals just mentioned, sodium (Na^+) and potassium (K^+) are positively charged, whereas chloride (Cl^-) and phosphorus (in the form of hydrogen

electrolyte A substance that disassociates in solution into positively and negatively charged ions and is thus capable of carrying an electrical current.

ion An electrically charged particle, either positively or negatively charged.

A hiker must consume adequate amounts of water to prevent heat illness in hot and dry environments.

phosphate, or HPO_4^{2-}) are negatively charged. In the intracellular fluid, potassium and phosphate predominate. In the extracellular fluid, sodium and chloride predominate. There is a slight difference in electrical charge on either side of the cell's membrane that is needed for the cell to perform its normal functions.

Fluids Serve Many Critical Functions

Water not only quenches our thirst; it also performs a number of functions that are critical to sustain life.

Fluids Dissolve and Transport Substances

Water is an excellent **solvent**; that is, it is capable of dissolving a wide variety of substances. Since blood is mostly water, it is able to transport a variety of solutes—such as amino acids, glucose, water-soluble vitamins, minerals, and medications—to body cells. In contrast, fats do not dissolve in water. To overcome this chemical incompatibility, lipids and fat-soluble vitamins are either attached to or surrounded by water-soluble proteins, so that they, too, can be transported in the blood to the cells.

Fluids Account for Blood Volume

Blood volume is the amount of fluid in blood; thus, appropriate fluid levels are essential to maintaining healthful blood volume. When blood volume rises inappropriately, blood pressure increases; when blood volume decreases inappropriately, blood pressure decreases. As you learned in the *In Depth* following Chapter 5, high blood pressure is an important risk factor for heart disease and stroke. In contrast, low blood pressure can cause people to feel tired, confused, or dizzy.

Fluids Help Maintain Body Temperature

Just as overheating is disastrous to a car engine, a high internal temperature can cause our body to stop functioning. Fluids are vital to the body's ability to maintain its temperature within a safe range. Two factors account for the ability of fluids to keep us cool. First, water has a relatively high capacity for heat: in other words, it takes a lot of energy to raise its temperature. Since the body contains a lot of water, only prolonged exposure to high heat can increase body temperature.

Second, body fluids are our primary coolant. When heat needs to be released from the body, there is an increase in the flow of blood from the warm body core to the vessels lying just under the skin. This action transports heat from the body core out to the periphery, where it can be released from the skin. At the same time, sweat glands secrete more sweat from the skin. As this sweat evaporates off of the skin's surface, heat is released and the skin and underlying blood are cooled **(Figure 7.2)**. This cooler blood flows back to the body's core and reduces internal body temperature.

Fluids Protect and Lubricate Our Tissues

Water is a major part of the fluids that protect and lubricate tissues. The cerebrospinal fluid that surrounds the brain and spinal cord protects them from damage, and a fetus in a mother's womb is protected by amniotic fluid. Synovial fluid lubricates joints, and tears cleanse and lubricate the eyes. Saliva moistens the food we eat and the mucus lining the walls of the GI tract eases the movement of food through the stomach and intestines. Finally, pleural fluid covering the lungs allows their friction-free expansion and retraction within the chest cavity.

solvent A substance that is capable of mixing with and breaking apart a variety of compounds. Water is an excellent solvent.

blood volume The amount of fluid in blood.

RECAP Our body fluids consist of water plus a variety of dissolved substances, including electrically charged minerals called electrolytes. Water serves many important functions in our bodies, including dissolving and transporting substances, accounting for blood volume, regulating body temperature, and protecting and lubricating body tissues.

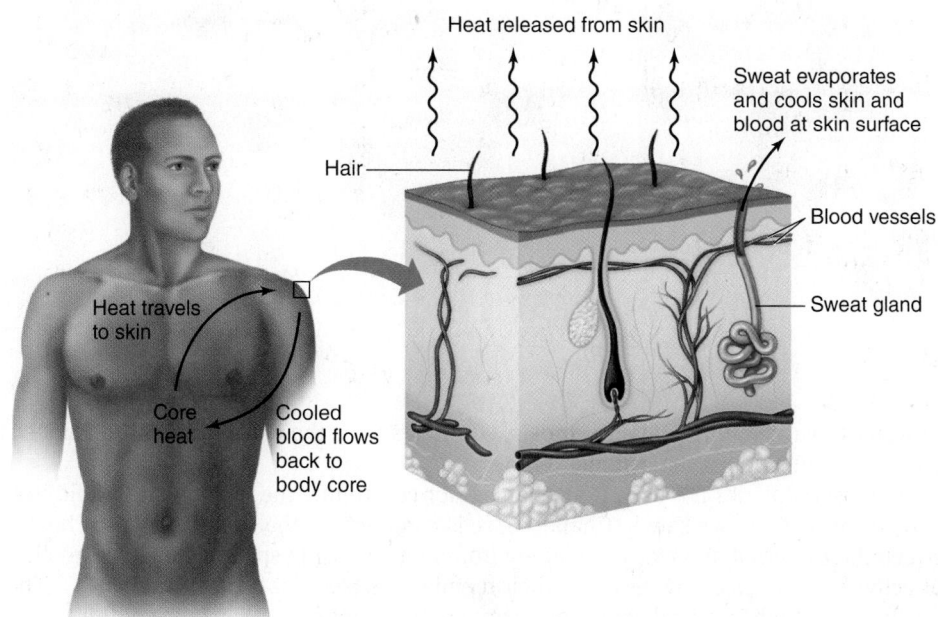

Heat released from skin

Hair

Heat travels to skin

Core heat

Cooled blood flows back to body core

Sweat evaporates and cools skin and blood at skin surface

Blood vessels

Sweat gland

Figure 7.2 Evaporative cooling occurs when heat is transported from the body core through the bloodstream to the surface of the skin. The water evaporates into the air and carries away heat. This cools the blood, which circulates back to the body core, reducing body temperature.

Electrolytes Support Many Body Functions

Now that you know why fluid is so essential to the body's functioning, we are ready to explore the critical roles of the electrolytes.

Electrolytes Help Regulate Fluid Balance

Cell membranes are *permeable* to water, meaning water flows easily through them. Cells cannot voluntarily regulate this flow of water and thus have no active control over the balance of fluid between the intracellular and extracellular environments. In contrast, cell membranes are *not* freely permeable to electrolytes. Sodium, potassium, and the other electrolytes stay where they are, either inside or outside a cell, unless they are actively transported across the cell membrane by special transport proteins. So how do electrolytes help cells maintain their fluid balance? To answer this question, a short review of chemistry is needed.

Imagine that you have a special filter with the same properties as cell membranes; in other words, this filter is freely permeable to water but not permeable to electrolytes. Now imagine that you insert this filter into a glass of pure distilled water to divide the glass into two separate chambers **(Figure 7.3a)**. Of course, the water levels on both sides of the filter would be identical, because the filter is freely permeable to water. Now imagine that you add a teaspoon of salt (which contains the electrolytes sodium and chloride) to the water on only one side of the filter (Figure 7.3b). Immediately, you would see the water on the "pure water" side of the glass begin to flow through the filter to the "salt water" side of the glass (Figure 7.3c). Why would this movement of water occur? It is because water always moves from areas where solutes, such as sodium and chloride, are low in concentration to areas where they are high in concentration. To put it another way, solutes *attract* water toward areas where they are more concentrated. This movement

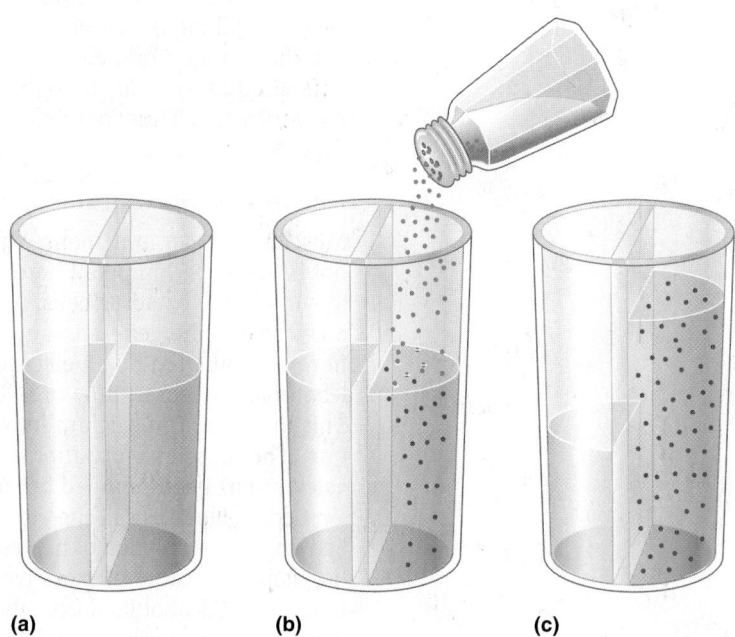

(a)   (b)   (c)

Figure 7.3 Osmosis. **(a)** A filter that is freely permeable to water is placed in a glass of pure water. **(b)** Salt is added to only one side of the glass. **(c)** Drawn by the high concentration of electrolytes, pure water flows to the "salt water" side of the filter. This flow of water into the concentrated solution will continue until the concentration of electrolytes on both sides of the membrane is equal.

▶ **Figure 7.4** The health of our body's cells depends on maintaining the proper balance of fluids and electrolytes on both sides of the cell membrane. **(a)** The concentration of electrolytes is the same on both sides of the cell membrane. **(b)** The concentration of electrolytes is much greater inside the cell, drawing water into the cell and making it swell. **(c)** The concentration of electrolytes is much greater outside the cell, drawing water out of the cell and making it shrink.

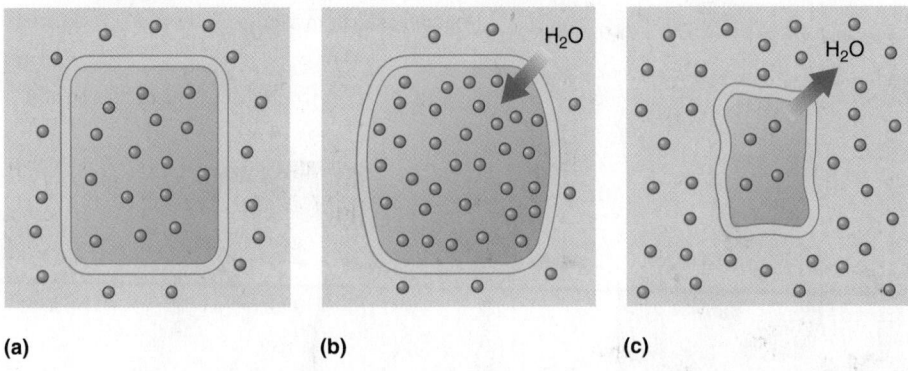

(a) (b) (c)

osmosis The movement of water (or any solvent) through a semi-permeable membrane from an area where solutes are less concentrated to areas where solutes are highly concentrated.

of water toward solutes, called **osmosis,** continues until the concentration of solutes is equal on both sides of the cell membrane.

Osmosis provides the body a mechanism for controlling the movement of fluid into and out of cells. As we saw in Chapter 6, cells can regulate the balance of fluids between their internal and extracellular environments by using special transport proteins to actively pump electrolytes across their membranes (see Chapter 6, Figure 6.11). The health of the body's cells depends on maintaining an appropriate balance of fluid and electrolytes between the intracellular and extracellular environments **(Figure 7.4a)**. If the concentration of electrolytes is much higher inside cells as compared to outside, water will flow into the cells in such large amounts that the cells can burst (Figure 7.4b). On the other hand, if the extracellular environment contains too high a concentration of electrolytes, water flows out of the cells, and they can dry up (Figure 7.4c).

Electrolytes Enable Our Nerves to Respond to Stimuli

In addition to their role in maintaining fluid balance, electrolytes are critical in allowing our nerves to respond to stimuli. Nerve impulses are initiated at the membrane of a nerve cell in response to a stimulus—for example, the touch of a hand or the clanging of a bell. Stimuli prompt changes in membranes that allow an influx of sodium into the nerve cell, causing the cell to become slightly less negatively charged. This is called *depolarization*. If enough sodium enters the cell, an electrical impulse is generated along the cell membrane **(Figure 7.5)**. Once this impulse has been transmitted, the cell membrane returns to its normal electrical state through the release of potassium to the outside of the cell. This return to the initial electrical state is termed *repolarization*. Thus, both sodium and potassium play critical roles in ensuring that nerve impulses are generated, transmitted, and completed.

Electrolytes Signal Our Muscles to Contract

Muscles contract in response to a series of complex physiological changes that will not be described in detail here. Simply stated, muscle contraction occurs in response to stimulation of nerve cells. As described previously, sodium and potassium play a key role in the generation of nerve impulses, or electrical signals. When a muscle fibre is stimulated by an electrical signal, changes occur in the cell membrane that lead to an increased flow of calcium into the muscle from the extracellular space. This movement of calcium into the muscle provides the stimulus for muscle contraction. The muscles relax after a contraction once the electrical signal is complete and calcium has been pumped out of the muscle cell.

Certain illnesses can threaten the delicate balance of fluid inside and outside the cells and impair the function of nerves and muscles. You may have heard of someone being hospitalized because of excessive diarrhea and/or vomiting. When this happens, the body loses a great deal of fluid from the intestinal tract and extracellular environment. This large fluid loss causes the extracellular electrolyte concentration to become very high. In response, a great deal of intracellular fluid flows out of the cells (see Figure 7.4c). This imbalance in fluid and electrolytes changes the flow of electrical impulses through the nerve and muscle cells of the heart, causing an irregular heart rate, which can eventually lead to death if left untreated. Food poisoning and eating disorders involving repeated vomiting and diarrhea can also result in death from life-threatening fluid and electrolyte imbalances.

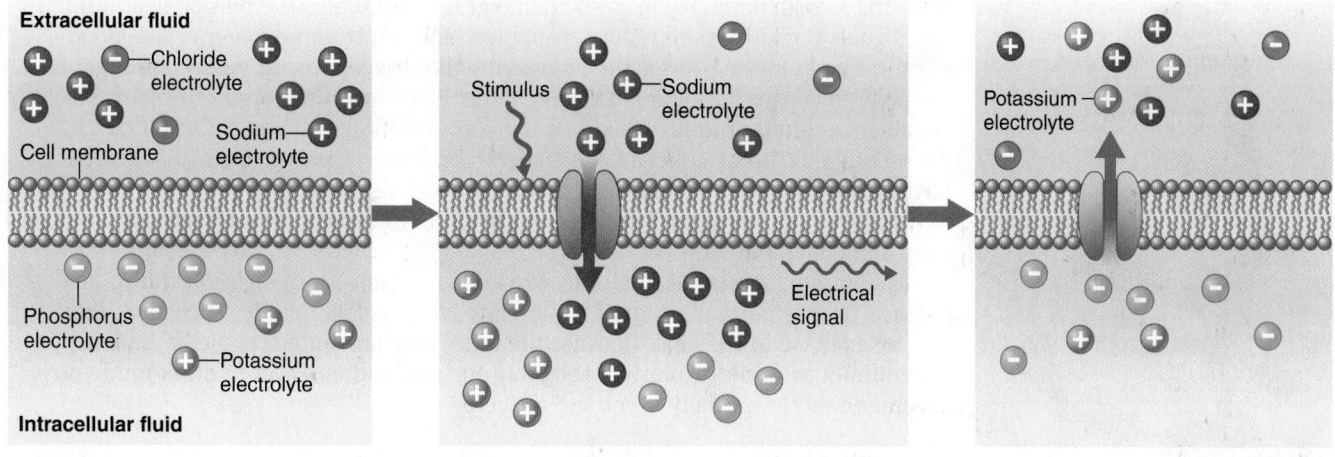

(a) Resting state   **(b) Depolarization**   **(c) Repolarization**

🔺 **Figure 7.5** The role of electrolytes in conduction of a nerve impulse. **(a)** In the resting state, the intracellular fluid has slightly more electrolytes with a negative charge. **(b)** A stimulus causes changes to occur that prompt the influx of sodium into the interior of the cell. Sodium has a positive charge, so when this happens, the charge inside the cell becomes slightly positive. This is called depolarization. If enough sodium enters the cell, an electrical signal is transmitted to adjacent regions of the cell membrane. **(c)** Release of potassium to the exterior of the cell allows the first portion of the membrane almost immediately to return to the resting state. This is called repolarization.

RECAP Electrolytes help regulate fluid balance by controlling the movement of fluid into and out of cells. Electrolytes, specifically sodium and potassium, play a key role in generating nerve impulses in response to stimuli. Calcium is an electrolyte that stimulates muscle contraction.

How Does Our Body Maintain Fluid Balance?

The proper balance of fluid is maintained in the body by a series of mechanisms that prompt us to drink and retain fluid when we are dehydrated and to excrete fluid as urine when we consume more than we need.

Our Thirst Mechanism Prompts Us to Drink Fluids

Imagine that, at lunch, you ate a ham sandwich and a bag of salted potato chips. Now it is almost time for your afternoon seminar to end and you are very thirsty. The last five minutes of class are a torment, and when the instructor ends the session you dash to the nearest drinking fountain. What prompted you to suddenly feel so thirsty?

The body's command centre for fluid intake is in the hypothalamus, part of the forebrain. Recall from Chapter 3 that a cluster of cells in the hypothalamus triggers hunger. Similarly, a group of hypothalamic cells, collectively referred to as the **thirst mechanism**, causes you to consciously desire fluids. The thirst mechanism prompts us to feel thirsty whenever it is stimulated by the following:

- An increased concentration of sodium and other dissolved substances in our blood. Remember that ham sandwich and those potato chips? Both these foods are salty, and eating them increased the blood's sodium concentration.
- A reduction in blood volume and blood pressure. This can occur when fluids are lost because of profuse sweating, blood loss, vomiting, or diarrhea or simply when fluid intake is too low.
- Dryness in the tissues of the mouth and throat. Tissue dryness reflects a lower amount of fluid in the bloodstream, which causes a reduced production of saliva.

thirst mechanism A cluster of nerve cells in the hypothalamus that stimulate our conscious desire to drink fluids in response to an increase in the concentration of salt in our blood or a decrease in blood pressure and blood volume.

Fruits and vegetables are delicious sources of water.

metabolic water The water formed as a by-product of our body's metabolic reactions.

sensible water loss Water loss that is noticed by a person, such as through urine output and visible sweating.

Once the hypothalamus detects such changes, it stimulates the release of a hormone that signals the kidneys to reduce urine flow and return more water to the bloodstream. The kidneys also secrete an enzyme that triggers blood vessels throughout the body to constrict, helping it retain water. Water is drawn out of the salivary glands in an attempt to further dilute the concentration of blood solutes; this causes the mouth and throat to become even drier. Together, these mechanisms prevent a further loss of body fluid and help the body avoid dehydration.

Although the thirst mechanism can trigger an increase in fluid intake, this mechanism alone is not always sufficient: people tend to drink until they are no longer thirsty, but the amount of fluid they consume may not be enough to achieve fluid balance. This is particularly true when body water is lost rapidly, such as during intense exercise in the heat. Because the thirst mechanism has some limitations, it is important to drink regularly throughout the day and not wait to drink until you become thirsty, especially if you are active.

We Gain Fluids by Consuming Beverages and Foods and Through Metabolism

We obtain the fluid we need each day from three primary sources: beverages, foods, and the body's production of metabolic water. Of course, you know that beverages are mostly water, but it is not as easy to see the water content in the foods we eat. For example, iceberg lettuce is almost 96% water, and even almonds contain a small amount of water (Figure 7.6).

Metabolic water is the water formed from the body's metabolic reactions. This water contributes about 10%–14% of the water the body needs each day.

We Lose Fluids Through Urine, Sweat, Evaporation, Exhalation, and Feces

We can perceive—or sense—water loss through urine output and sweating, so we refer to this as **sensible water loss**. Most of the water we consume is excreted through the kidneys in the form of urine. When we consume more water than we need, the kidneys process and excrete the excess in the form of dilute urine.

The second type of sensible water loss is via sweat. Our sweat glands produce more sweat during exercise or when we are in a hot environment. The evaporation of sweat from the skin releases heat, which cools the skin and reduces the body's core temperature.

Lettuce, iceberg	96%
Cucumbers, with peel, raw	95%
Peaches, raw	89%
Pineapple, raw	86%
Olives, ripe, canned	80%
Sweet potato, baked	76%
Pork chop, lean, broiled	61%
Almonds 5%	

0 10 20 30 40 50 60 70 80 90 100

Percent water content (%)

Figure 7.6 Water content of different foods. Much of your daily water intake comes from the foods you eat.
Data from U.S. Department of Agriculture, Agricultural Research Service. 2009. USDA Nutrient Database for Standard Reference, Release 22. Nutrient Data Laboratory Home Page. www.ars.usda.gov/ba/bhnrc/ndl.

Water is continuously evaporated from the skin, even when a person is not visibly sweating, and water is continuously exhaled from the lungs during breathing. Water loss through these routes is known as **insensible water loss**, as we do not perceive it. Under normal resting conditions, insensible water loss is less than 1 L of fluid each day; during heavy exercise or in hot weather, a person can lose up to 2 L of water per hour from insensible water loss.

Under normal conditions, only about 150 to 200 mL of water is lost each day in feces. The gastrointestinal tract typically absorbs much of the fluid that passes through it each day.

In addition to these five avenues of regular fluid loss, certain situations can cause a significant loss of fluid from our body:

- Illnesses that involve fever, coughing, vomiting, diarrhea, and a runny nose significantly increase fluid loss. For instance, when someone suffers from extreme diarrhea, water loss via bowel elimination alone can be as high as several litres per day. This is one reason that doctors advise people to drink plenty of fluids when they are ill.
- Traumatic injury, internal bleeding, blood donation, and surgery also increase loss of fluid because of the blood loss involved.
- Exercise increases fluid loss via sweat and respiration; although urine production typically decreases during exercise, fluid losses increase through the skin and lungs.
- Certain environmental conditions increase fluid loss. One of these is low humidity, such as in a desert or an airplane. When the water content of the environment is low, water from the body more easily evaporates into the surrounding dry air. High altitudes increase fluid loss, because we breathe faster to compensate for the lower oxygen pressure. This results in greater fluid loss via the lungs. Hot and cold environments also increase fluid loss. We have mentioned sensible losses from sweating in the heat, but cold temperatures can trigger hormonal changes that also increase fluid loss.
- Pregnancy increases fluid loss for the mother because fluids are continually diverted to the fetus and amniotic fluid.
- Breastfeeding requires a tremendous increase in fluid intake to make up for the loss of fluid as breast milk.
- Consumption of **diuretics**—substances that increase fluid loss via the urine— can result in dangerously excessive fluid loss. Diuretics include certain prescription medications, alcohol, and many over-the-counter weight-loss remedies. In the past, it was believed that caffeine acted as a diuretic, but recent research suggests that caffeinated drinks do not significantly influence fluid status in healthy adults.

Drinking beverages that contain alcohol causes an increase in water loss, because alcohol is a diuretic.

RECAP A healthy fluid level is maintained by balancing intake and excretion. The primary sources of fluids are water and other beverages, foods, and the production of metabolic water in the body. Fluid losses occur through urination, sweating, feces, exhalation from the lungs, and insensible evaporation from the skin.

A Profile of Nutrients Involved in Hydration and Neuromuscular Function

The nutrients involved in maintaining hydration and neuromuscular function are water and the minerals sodium, potassium, chloride, and phosphorus **(Table 7.1)**. As discussed in Chapter 1, these minerals are classified as *major minerals*, as the body needs more than 100 mg of each per day.

insensible water loss The loss of water not noticeable by a person, such as through evaporation from the skin and exhalation from the lungs during breathing.

diuretic A substance that increases fluid loss via the urine. Common diuretics include alcohol, some prescription medications, and many over-the-counter weight-loss pills.

TABLE 7.1 Overview of Nutrients Involved in Hydration and Neuromuscular Function

To see the full profile of nutrients involved in hydration and neuromuscular function, see **In Depth**, Vitamins and Minerals: Micronutrients with Macro Powers, pages 216–225.

Nutrient	Recommended Intake
Sodium	1.5 g/day* (1500 mg/day or 65 mmol/day)
Potassium	4.7 g/day* (4700 mg/day or 120 mmol/day)
Chloride	2.3 g/day* (2300 mg/day or 65 mmol/day)
Phosphorus	700 mg/day† (22.6 mmol/day)

*Adequate Intake (AI).
†Recommended Dietary Allowance (RDA).

Calcium and magnesium also function as electrolytes and influence our body's fluid balance and neuromuscular function. However, because of their critical importance to bone health, they are discussed in Chapter 9.

Water

Water is essential for life. Although we can live weeks without food, we can survive only a few days without water, depending on the environmental temperature. The human body does not have the capacity to store water, so we must continuously replace the water lost each day.

How Much Water Should We Drink?

Our need for water varies greatly, depending on our age, body size, health status, physical activity level, and exposure to environmental conditions. It is important to pay attention to how much our need for water changes under various conditions, so that we can avoid dehydration.

Fluid requirements are very individualized. For example, a highly active male athlete training in a hot environment may require up to 10 L of fluid per day to maintain a healthy fluid balance, while an inactive, petite woman who lives in a mild climate and works in a temperature-controlled office building may only require about 3 L of fluid per day.

The DRI for adult men aged 19 to 50 years is 3.7 L of total water per day. This includes approximately 3.0 L (13 cups) as beverages, including water. The DRI for adult women aged 19 to 50 years is 2.7 L of total water per day, including about 2.2 L (9 cups) as beverages (Institute of Medicine, 2004).

Figure 7.7 shows the amount and sources of water intake and output for a woman expending 10 500 kJ (2500 kcal) per day. Based on current recommendations, this woman needs about 3000 mL (3 L) of fluid per day. As shown,

- Water from metabolism provides 300 mL of water.
- The foods she eats provide her with an additional 500 mL of water each day.
- The beverages she drinks provide the remainder of the water she needs, which is equal to 2200 mL.

An 8 oz. glass of fluid is equal to 240 mL. In this example, the woman would need to drink 9 glasses of fluid to meet her needs. You may have read or heard that drinking 8 glasses of fluid each day is recommended for most people. Remember, however, that this recommendation is a general guideline. You may need to drink a different amount to meet your individual fluid needs.

Athletes and other people who are active, especially those working in very hot environments, may require more fluid than the current recommendations. The amount of sweat lost during exercise is very individualized and depends on body size, exercise intensity, level of personal fitness, environmental temperature, and humidity. A recent study reported that professional football players lose almost 7 litres of sweat per day when practicing in a hot, humid environment (Godek et al., 2008).

◀ Vigorous exercise causes significant water loss, which must be replenished to optimize performance and health.

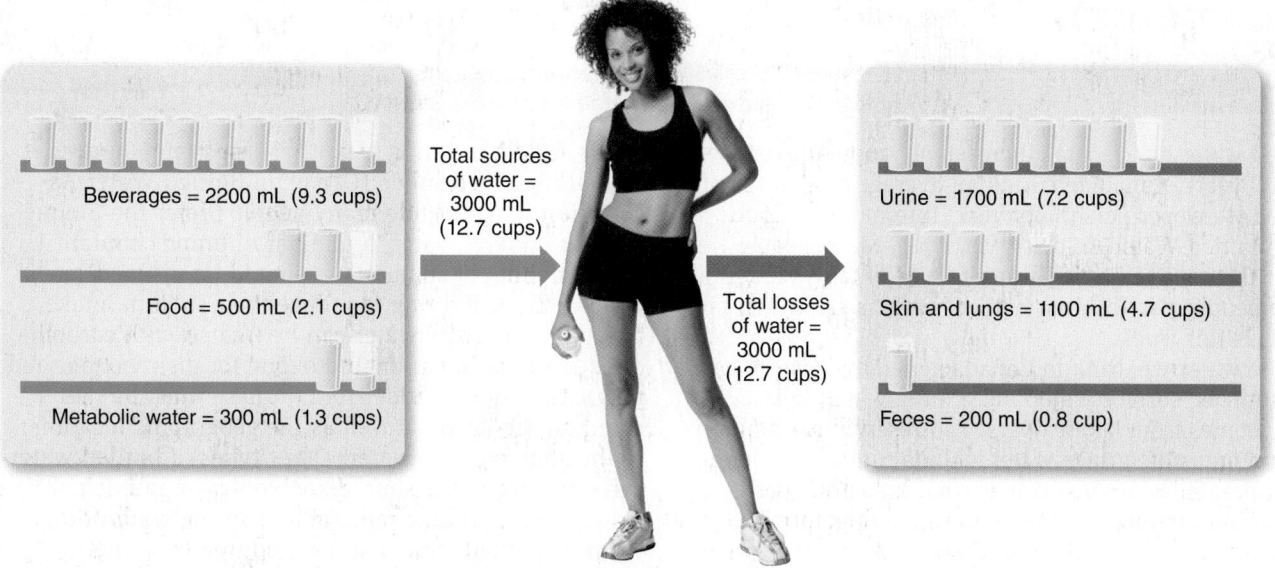

Beverages = 2200 mL (9.3 cups)

Food = 500 mL (2.1 cups)

Metabolic water = 300 mL (1.3 cups)

Total sources of water = 3000 mL (12.7 cups)

Total losses of water = 3000 mL (12.7 cups)

Urine = 1700 mL (7.2 cups)

Skin and lungs = 1100 mL (4.7 cups)

Feces = 200 mL (0.8 cup)

Figure 7.7 Amount and sources of water intake and output for a woman expending 10 500 kJ (2500 kcal) each day.

Thus, these individuals need to drink more to replace the fluid they lose. Sodium is the major electrolyte lost in sweat; some potassium and small amounts of minerals such as iron and calcium are also lost in sweat.

Because of their high fluid and electrolyte losses during exercise, some athletes drink sports beverages instead of plain water to help them maintain fluid balance. Recently, sports beverages have also become popular with recreationally active people and non-athletes. Is it really necessary for people to consume these beverages if they are not highly active? See the Nutrition Debate on sports beverages on page 246 to learn whether they are right for recreationally active people and non-athletes.

Sources of Drinking Water

One of the major changes in the beverage industry over the past 20 years has been the marketing of bottled water. The meteoric rise in bottled water production and consumption is most likely due to the convenience of drinking bottled water, to the health messages related to drinking more water, and to the public's fears related to the safety of tap water. Is bottled water safer than tap water? Refer to the Nutrition Myth or Fact box on bottled water to find the answer to this question.

What Happens If We Drink Too Much Water?

Drinking too much water and becoming overhydrated is very rare, but it can occur. Certain illnesses can cause excessive reabsorption, or retention, of water by the kidneys. When this occurs, overhydration and dilution of blood sodium result. Marathon runners and other endurance athletes who drink large amounts of fluid can overhydrate and dangerously dilute their blood sodium concentration. This condition, called *hyponatremia*, is discussed in more detail shortly.

What Happens If We Don't Drink Enough Water?

Dehydration results when we do not drink enough water or are unable to retain the water we consume. It is one of the leading causes of death around the world. Dehydration is generally due to some form of illness or gastrointestinal infection that causes diarrhea and vomiting. The impact of dehydration on health is discussed *In Depth* immediately following this chapter.

Numerous varieties of drinking water are available to consumers.

NUTRITION MYTH OR FACT

Bottled Water Is No Safer Than Tap Water

Bottled water has become increasingly popular over the past 20 years. Canadians drink an average of 47 litres of bottled water per person per year (International Council of Bottled Water Associations, n.d.). Many people prefer the taste of bottled water to that of tap water. Some people also feel that bottled water is safer than tap water. Is this true?

The water we drink in Canada generally comes from two sources: surface water and ground water. Surface water comes from lakes, rivers, and reservoirs. Common contaminants of surface water include runoff from highways, pesticides, animal wastes, and industrial wastes. Ground water comes from underground rock formations called aquifers. About 26% of Canadians, mostly people who live in rural areas or small towns, rely on ground water pumped from wells (Natural Resources Canada, 2009). Hazardous substances leaking from waste sites, dumps, landfills, and oil and gas pipelines can contaminate ground water.

Tap water is rigorously monitored. The regulation and oversight of tap water is shared between the provincial, territorial, federal, and municipal governments. The day-to-day responsibility of providing safe drinking water to the public generally rests with the provinces and territories, while municipalities usually oversee the day-to-day operations of the treatment facilities. Most municipal water treatment facilities use chlorine to kill contaminants. Some cities use ozone because ozonation does not produce the trihalomethane by-products that result when chlorine and organic matter react together (Health Canada, 2006). Small amounts of chlorine still need to be added during ozonation, because ozone breaks down quickly (Health Canada, 2006).

Bottled water is considered a food and is regulated under Canada's Food and Drugs Act and monitored by federal inspectors from the Canadian Food Inspection Agency (Health Canada, 2011). Most bottling plants use an ozone treatment instead of chlorine to disinfect water, and many people feel this process leaves the water tasting better than tap water treated with chlorine.

There are two categories of bottled water: mineral and spring water, and other bottled waters. Both mineral water and spring water come from protected underground sources (not a public water supply). Mineral water contains 500 mg per litre or more dissolved solids, whereas spring water has less than 500 mg per litre of dissolved solids (Canadian Bottled Water Association, n.d.). While many people prefer the unique taste of mineral water, a number of brands contain high amounts of sodium and should be avoided by people who are trying to reduce their sodium intake. Mineral and spring water can be treated with carbon dioxide for carbonation and ozone for disinfection, and may have fluoride added. All of these must be indicated on the label, as well as the geographic location of the source of the water. Other types of bottled water can come from any source, including the municipal water supply. Unlike mineral and spring water, other types of bottled water can be modified from their original composition; some are distilled to remove dissolved minerals, can be carbonated, or have minerals added. The labels must indicate how the bottled water has been treated—carbonated, demineralized, distilled, filtered, etc.

Although bottled water may taste better than tap water, there is no evidence that it is safer to drink (Health Canada, 2010). Bottled water (except spring or mineral water) may come directly from the tap! Some types of bottled water may contain more minerals than tap water, but there are no other additional nutritional benefits in drinking bottled water. Most brands of bottled water do not contain fluoride.

Health Canada has the following advice for consumers of bottled water:

- don't refill old bottles—buy new ones
- look on the label for the best-before date
- avoid bottles with broken seals
- look for the type of treatment (ozonated, etc.)
- don't keep bottled water past its two-year shelf life
- don't share bottles
- always refrigerate opened bottles

For more information on drinking water safety, go to Health Canada's website at www.hc-sc.gc.ca/ewh-semt/water-eau/drink-potab/index_e.html.

Source: Adapted from Health Canada, www.hc-sc.gc.ca/fn-an/securit/facts-faits/bottle_water-eau_embouteillee-eng.php (accessed February 2012).

RECAP Fluid intake needs are highly variable and depend on body size, age, physical activity, health status, and environmental conditions. Drinking too much water can lead to overhydration and dilution of blood sodium. Drinking too little water leads to dehydration, one of the leading causes of death around the world.

Sodium

Many people think of salt when they hear the word sodium, but the terms should not be used interchangeably. Salt, or sodium chloride (its chemical name) is about 40% sodium and 60% chloride by weight. One teaspoon (5 mL) of salt weighs 5 grams and contains about 2300 mg of sodium (IFICF, 2005).

Over the last 20 years, researchers have linked high sodium intake to an increased risk for high blood pressure among some groups of individuals. Because of this link, many people have come to believe that sodium is harmful to the body. This oversimplification, however, is just not true: sodium is a valuable nutrient that is essential for survival.

Functions of Sodium

Sodium has a variety of functions. As discussed earlier in this chapter, it is the major positively charged electrolyte in the extracellular fluid. Its exchange with potassium across cell membranes allows cells to maintain proper fluid balance, blood pressure, and acid–base balance.

Sodium also assists with the transmission of nerve signals and aids in muscle contraction. To review, the release of sodium from inside to outside the cell stimulates the spread of nerve signals within nervous tissue. The stimulation of muscles by nerve impulses provides the impetus for muscle contraction.

How Much Sodium Should We Consume?

The AI for sodium is 1.5 g per day (1500 mg per day or 65 mmol per day) for adult men and women aged 19 to 50 years (Institute of Medicine, 2004). The Tolerable Upper Intake Level (UL) is 2.3 g per day (2300 mg or 100 mmol). A recent study reported that most Canadians, including infants, children, adolescents and adults, consume more than the UL (Tanase et al., 2011). Over 90% of males aged 9–30 years had sodium intakes over the UL.

Beyond Table Salt: Sneaky Sources of Sodium

Sodium is found naturally in many whole foods, but most dietary sodium comes from processed foods and restaurant foods, which typically contain large amounts of added sodium. Try to guess which of the following foods contains the most sodium: 250 mL (1 cup) of tomato juice, 30 g (1 oz.) of potato chips, or 4 saltine crackers. Now look at **Table 7.2** to find the answer. This table shows foods that are high in sodium and gives lower-sodium alternatives. Are you surprised to find out that, of the tomato juice, potato chips and saltine crackers, the tomato juice has the most sodium?

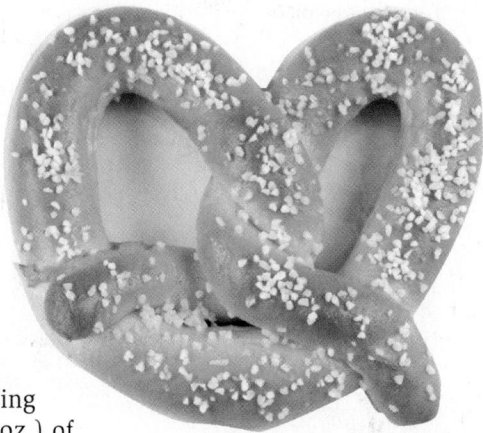

Many popular snack foods are high in sodium.

TABLE 7.2 High-Sodium Foods and Lower-Sodium Alternatives

High-Sodium Food	Portion	Sodium (mg)	Lower-Sodium Food	Portion	Sodium (mg)
Dill pickle	1 large, 10 cm (4 in.)	1731	Low-sodium dill pickle	1 large, 10 cm (4 in.)	23
Ham, cured, roasted	90 g (3 oz.)	1023	Pork, loin roast	90 g (3 oz.)	54
Turkey pastrami	90 g (3 oz.)	913	Roasted turkey, cooked	90 g (3 oz.)	54
Tomato juice, regular	250 mL (8 fl. oz.)	877	Tomato juice, lower sodium	250 mL (8 fl. oz.)	24
Macaroni and cheese	250 mL (1 cup)	800	Spanish rice	250 mL (1 cup)	5
Ramen noodle soup (chicken flavour)	1 pkg 85 g	1960	Ramen noodle soup made with sodium-free chicken bouillon	250 mL (8 fl. oz.)	0
Teriyaki chicken	250 mL (1 cup)	3210	Stir-fried pork/rice/vegetables	250 mL (1 cup)	575
Tomato sauce, canned	125 mL (0.5 cup)	741	Fresh tomato	1 medium	11
Creamed corn, canned	250 mL (1 cup)	730	Cooked corn, fresh	250 mL (1 cup)	28
Tomato soup, canned	250 mL (8 fl. oz.)	695	Lower-sodium tomato soup, canned	250 mL (8 fl. oz.)	480
Potato chips, salted	30 g (1 oz.)	168	Baked potato, unsalted	1 medium	14
Saltine crackers	4 crackers	156	Saltine crackers, unsalted	4 crackers	100

Data from U.S. Department of Agriculture. 2009. USDA Nutrient Database for Standard Reference, Release 22. Nutrient Data Laboratory Home Page. www.ars.usda.gov/ba/bhnrc/ndl.

Eating Right All Day

Breakfast
Whole-grain waffle with jam instead of a ham & cheese omelette!

Lunch
Spinach salad instead of pastrami submarine sandwich!

Dinner
Veggie pizza instead of pepperoni!

Snack
Unsalted almonds instead of corn chips!

Because sodium is so abundant, it is easy to overdo it. See the Quick Tips feature on page 241 for ways to reduce your sodium intake.

What Happens If We Consume Too Much Sodium?

High blood pressure is typically more common in people who consume high-sodium diets. This strong relationship between high-sodium diets and high blood pressure has prompted many health organizations to recommend lower sodium intakes; however, the question of whether high-sodium diets actually cause high blood pressure is a matter of considerable debate. Consuming excess sodium can cause an increased urinary excretion of calcium in some people, which in turn may increase their risk for bone loss. The relationship between sodium intake and bone health is also controversial; however, a number of recent studies suggest that a reduction in sodium intake improves bone status, particularly in older adults (Frassetto et al., 2008).

Hypernatremia refers to an abnormally high blood sodium concentration. Although theoretically it could be caused by a rapid intake of high amounts of sodium—for instance, if a shipwrecked sailor resorted to drinking seawater—consuming too much sodium does not usually cause hypernatremia in a healthy person, as the kidneys are able to excrete excess sodium in the urine. But people with congestive heart failure or kidney disease are not able to excrete sodium effectively, making them more prone to the condition. Hypernatremia is dangerous because it causes an abnormally high blood volume, again, by pulling water from the intracellular environment to dilute the sodium in the extracellular tissue spaces and vessels. This leads to edema (swelling) of tissues and elevation of blood pressure to unhealthy levels.

What Happens If We Don't Consume Enough Sodium?

Because the dietary intake of sodium is so high among Canadians, deficiencies of sodium are extremely rare, except in individuals who sweat heavily or consume little or no sodium in the diet. Nevertheless, certain conditions can cause dangerously low blood sodium levels.

Hyponatremia, or abnormally low blood sodium levels, can occur in people engaged in strenuous physical activity who drink large volumes of water and fail to replace sodium. This is discussed further in the accompanying Nutrition Myth or Fact? box on page 242. Severe diarrhea, vomiting, or excessive prolonged sweating can also cause hyponatremia. Symptoms include headaches, dizziness, fatigue, nausea, vomiting, and muscle cramps. If hyponatremia is left untreated, it can lead to seizures, coma, and death. Treatment for hyponatremia includes replacement of the lost minerals by consuming liquids and foods high in sodium and other minerals. It may be necessary to administer electrolyte-rich solutions intravenously if the person has lost consciousness or is not able to consume

◆ Condiments can add sodium to your diet.

hypernatremia A condition in which blood sodium levels are dangerously high.

hyponatremia A condition in which blood sodium levels are dangerously low.

beverages and foods by mouth.

Potassium

As we discussed previously, potassium is the major positively charged electrolyte in the intracellular fluid. It is a major constituent of all living cells and is found in both plants and animals.

Functions of Potassium

Potassium and sodium work together to maintain proper fluid balance and regulate the transmission of nerve impulses and the contraction of muscles. And in contrast to a high-sodium diet, a diet high in potassium actually helps maintain a lower blood pressure.

How Much Potassium Should We Consume?

Potassium is found in abundance in many fresh foods, especially fresh fruits and vegetables. Processed foods generally have less potassium than fresh foods.

The AI for potassium is 4.7 g/day (4700 mg or 120 mmol) (see Table 7.1). A recent study reported that most Canadians do not consume the recommended amount of potassium, including 68.5% of children aged

---

QUICK TIPS

Reducing the Sodium in Your Diet

- Put away the salt shaker—keep it off the table and train your taste buds to prefer foods with less salt.
- Follow a diet that is high in fruits, vegetables, whole grains, and lean protein foods. The more you include fresh, whole foods in your diet, the less sodium you will be eating.
- Look for the words "low sodium" when buying processed foods. Use the Nutrition Facts table to find foods that contain 5% or less of the daily value for sodium or less than 200 mg per serving.
- Look for hidden salt content on food labels; for example, both monosodium glutamate and sodium benzoate are forms of sodium.
- Compare the labels of various name brands of the same food, since products can vary greatly in their sodium content.
- Choose fresh or frozen vegetables (without added sauces), as they are usually much lower in sodium than canned vegetables. Alternatively, choose salt-free canned vegetables.
- Stay away from prepared stews, canned and dried soups, gravies, and pasta sauces, as well as packaged pasta, rice, and potato dishes that are high in sodium.
- Choose low-sodium versions of pickles, olives, three-bean salad, and salad dressings.
- Choose low-sodium versions of cheese, smoked meats and fish, and nuts.
- Snack on fruits and vegetables instead of salty snack foods. If you do buy pretzels, chips, and other snack items, choose low-sodium versions.
- When cooking, experiment with commercial salt substitutes, herbs, spices, lemon juice, and possibly cooking wine to flavour your food. Products that end in the word salt, such as garlic salt or celery salt, are high in sodium and should be avoided.
- Rinse canned legumes, such as black, navy, garbanzo, or kidney beans, with cold water to lower the sodium content before heating and consuming them.
- Reduce the amounts of condiments you use. Condiments such as ketchup, mustard, pickle relish, and soy sauce can add a considerable amount of sodium to your foods. Again, check the labels of these items.
- When eating out, look for entrées labelled "heart healthy" or "lower in sodium"; if nutrition information is provided, compare foods to select those with lower amounts of sodium.
- Check the labels on your medications. Many medications, including aspirin, are high in sodium.
- Check the labels of the beverages you consume as well; fluids are often a "hidden" source of dietary sodium.

1–3 years and 98.8% of women aged 71 years and older (Tanase et al., 2011). By avoiding processed foods and eating more fresh fruits, vegetables, legumes, whole grains, and dairy foods, you will increase your potassium intake and decrease your sodium intake, achieving a more healthful diet.

Sources of Potassium: Potatoes, Bananas, and More

As more and more people rely on processed foods, their sodium intake increases and their potassium intake decreases. Many researchers think that this sodium–potassium imbalance is a major factor contributing to the increased incidence of hypertension in North America. Thus, fresh foods, particularly fresh fruits and vegetables, should be included in every meal. **Figure 7.8** identifies foods that are high in potassium. See the Quick Tips on page 243 for information on how to increase your dietary potassium.

What Happens If We Consume Too Much Potassium?

People with healthy kidneys are able to excrete excess potassium effectively. However, people with kidney disease are not able to regulate their blood potassium levels. **Hyperkalemia**, or high blood potassium levels, occurs when potassium is not excreted efficiently from the body. Because of potassium's role in cardiac muscle

Tomato juice is an excellent source of potassium. Make sure you choose the low-sodium variety!

hyperkalemia A condition in which blood potassium levels are dangerously high.

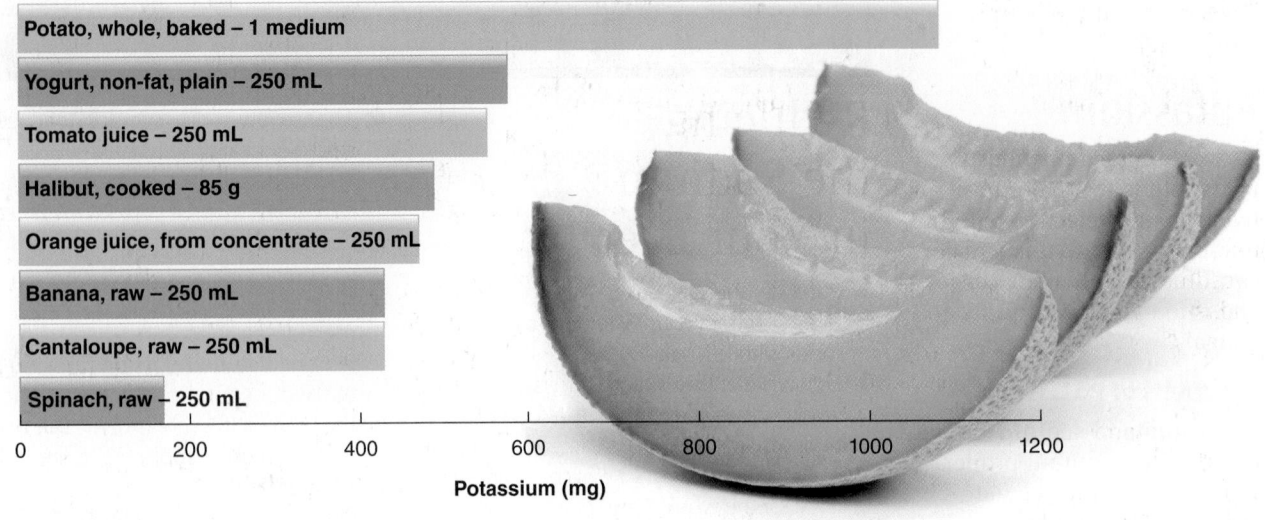

Potato, whole, baked – 1 medium

Yogurt, non-fat, plain – 250 mL

Tomato juice – 250 mL

Halibut, cooked – 85 g

Orange juice, from concentrate – 250 mL

Banana, raw – 250 mL

Cantaloupe, raw – 250 mL

Spinach, raw – 250 mL

Potassium (mg)

0   200   400   600   800   1000   1200

Figure 7.8 Common food sources of potassium. The AI for potassium is 4.7 g (4700 mg or 120 mmol) per day. (1 mmol = 40 mg potassium)
Data from U.S. Department of Agriculture, Agricultural Research Service. 2009. USDA Nutrient Database for Standard Reference, Release 22. Nutrient Data Laboratory Home Page. www.ars.usda.gov/ba/bhnrc/ndl.

contraction, severe hyperkalemia can alter the normal rhythm of the heart, resulting in heart attack and death. People with kidney failure must monitor their potassium intake very carefully to prevent complications from hyperkalemia. Individuals at risk for hyperkalemia should avoid consuming salt substitutes, as these products are high in potassium.

NUTRITION MYTH OR FACT?

Can Fluids Provide Too Much of a Good Thing?

It is well known that people participating in distance events, such as marathons (42.2 km or 26.2 miles), need to drink enough fluid to stay hydrated. But what has not been recognized until recently is that some runners, especially novice runners, can drink *too much* water and other fluids and develop hyponatremia, or abnormally low blood sodium levels.

A recent scientific review of what is now termed "exercise-associated hyponatremia," or EAH, found that major risk factors included longer race times, a slow pace of running, and intake of large amounts of water or other fluids during the race (Hew-Butler et al., 2008). The researchers speculate that less experienced athletes run more slowly, increasing the total time that they are competing; at the same time, they consume very large amounts of fluids, including water, to

Consuming too much water can deplete blood sodium levels.

avoid dehydration. The longer these individuals run, the more fluids they drink and the more diluted their blood sodium levels become. Many hyponatremic runners need to be hospitalized to prevent life-threatening complications.

A study of long-distance triathletes (competing in swimming, cycling, and running) found that about 18% of these athletes suffered from hyponatremia (Speedy et al., 1999). Thus, individuals competing in various long-distance events or activities are at risk for this disorder.

Hyponatremia is a dangerous and potentially fatal condition. Moderating total fluid intake during marathons and other long-distance activities and developing a personal plan of action with your healthcare provider can help prevent it.

What Happens If We Don't Consume Enough Potassium?

Because potassium is widespread in many foods, a dietary potassium deficiency is rare. However, potassium deficiency is not uncommon among people who have serious medical disorders. Kidney disease, a complication of poorly controlled diabetes known as diabetic acidosis, and other illnesses can lead to potassium deficiency.

In addition, people with high blood pressure who are prescribed diuretic medications are at risk for potassium deficiency. Diuretics promote the excretion of fluid as urine through the kidneys and some also increase the excretion of potassium. People who are taking diuretic medications should have their blood potassium monitored regularly and should

QUICK TIPS

Increasing Your Potassium Intake

▶ Avoid processed foods that are high in sodium and low in potassium. Check the Nutrition Facts table of the food before you buy it!

▶ For breakfast, look for cereals containing bran and/or wheat germ.

▶ Sprinkle wheat germ on yogurt and top with banana slices.

▶ Add wheat germ to baked goods, such as homemade pancakes and muffins.

▶ Drink milk! If you do not like milk, try one of the new drinkable yogurts. Many brands of soy milk are also good sources of potassium.

▶ Make a smoothie by blending ice cubes and low-fat vanilla ice cream or yogurt with a banana.

▶ Pack a can of low-sodium vegetable or tomato juice in your lunch in place of a soft drink.

▶ Serve avocado or bean dip with veggie slices.

▶ Replace the meat in your sandwich with thin slices of avocado or marinated tofu.

▶ Replace the meat in tacos and burritos with black or pinto beans.

▶ For a healthful alternative to french fries, toss slices of sweet potato in olive oil, place on a cookie sheet, and oven bake at 400° for 10–15 minutes.

▶ Toss a banana, some dried apricots, or a bag of sunflower seeds into your lunch bag.

▶ Make a fruit salad with apricots, bananas, cantaloupe, honeydew melon, mango, or papaya.

▶ Bake and enjoy a fresh pumpkin pie!

eat foods that are high in potassium to prevent **hypokalemia**, or low blood potassium levels (clinically defined as less than 3.8 milliequivalent per litre of blood). This is not a universal recommendation, however, because some diuretics are specially formulated to spare potassium; therefore, people taking this type of diuretic should not increase their dietary potassium above recommended levels.

Extreme dehydration, vomiting, and diarrhea can also cause hypokalemia. People who abuse alcohol or laxatives are also at risk for hypokalemia. Symptoms include confusion, loss of appetite, and muscle weakness. Severe cases of hypokalemia result in fatal changes in heart rate; many deaths attributed to extreme dehydration or eating disorders are caused by abnormal heart rhythms due to hypokalemia.

hypokalemia A condition in which blood potassium levels are dangerously low.

Chloride

Chloride should not be confused with *chlorine*, which is a poisonous gas used to kill bacteria and other germs in our water supply. Chloride is a negatively charged ion that is obtained almost exclusively in our diet from sodium chloride, or table salt.

Functions of Chloride

Coupled with sodium in the extracellular fluid, chloride assists with the maintenance of fluid balance. Chloride is also a part of hydrochloric acid (HCl) in the stomach, which aids in preparing food for further digestion (see Chapter 3). Chloride works with the white blood cells of our body during an immune response to help kill bacteria, and it assists in the transmission of nerve impulses.

How Much Chloride Should We Consume?

The AI for chloride for adult men and women aged 19 to 50 years is 2.3 g/day (2300 mg or 65 mmol per day; see Table 7.1). Our primary dietary source of chloride is salt in our foods. Chloride is also found in some fruits and vegetables.

Since virtually all dietary chloride is in the form of sodium chloride, consuming excess amounts of this mineral over a prolonged period leads to hypertension in salt-sensitive individuals. There is no other known toxicity symptom for chloride (Institute of Medicine, 2004).

Because of the relatively high dietary salt intake in Canada, most people consume more than enough chloride. Even when a person consumes a low-sodium diet,

⬆ Almost all chloride is consumed through table salt.

⬥ Milk is a good source of phosphorus.

phytic acid The form of phosphorus stored in plants.

chloride intake is usually adequate. A chloride deficiency can occur, however, during conditions of severe dehydration and frequent vomiting. For example, it can develop in people with eating disorders who regularly vomit to rid their bodies of unwanted calories.

Phosphorus

Phosphorus is the major intracellular negatively charged electrolyte. In the body, phosphorus is most commonly found in the form of phosphate, PO_4^{2-}. Phosphorus is an essential constituent of all cells and is found in both plants and animals.

Functions of Phosphorus

Phosphorus works with potassium inside cells to maintain proper fluid balance. It also plays a critical role in bone formation, as it is a part of the mineral complex of bone (see Chapter 9). In fact, about 85% of our body's phosphorus is stored in our bones.

As a primary component of adenosine triphosphate (ATP), phosphorus plays a key role in creating energy for our body. It also helps regulate many biochemical reactions by activating and deactivating enzymes. Phosphorus is a part of deoxyribonucleic acid (DNA) and ribonucleic acid (RNA), and it is a component in cell membranes (as phospholipids) and lipoproteins.

How Much Phosphorus Should We Consume?

The RDA for phosphorus is 700 mg/day (22.6 mmol; see Table 7.1). Phosphorus is widespread in many foods and is found in high amounts in foods that contain protein. Milk, meats, and eggs are good sources, and phosphorus deficiency is rare in North America. **Figure 7.9** shows the phosphorus content of various foods.

It is important to note that phosphorus from animal sources is absorbed more readily than that from plant sources. The phosphorus in plant foods such as beans, cereals, and nuts is found in the form of **phytic acid**, a plant storage form of phosphorus. Our body does not produce enzymes that can break down phytic acid, but we are still able to absorb up to 50% of the phosphorus found in plant foods because

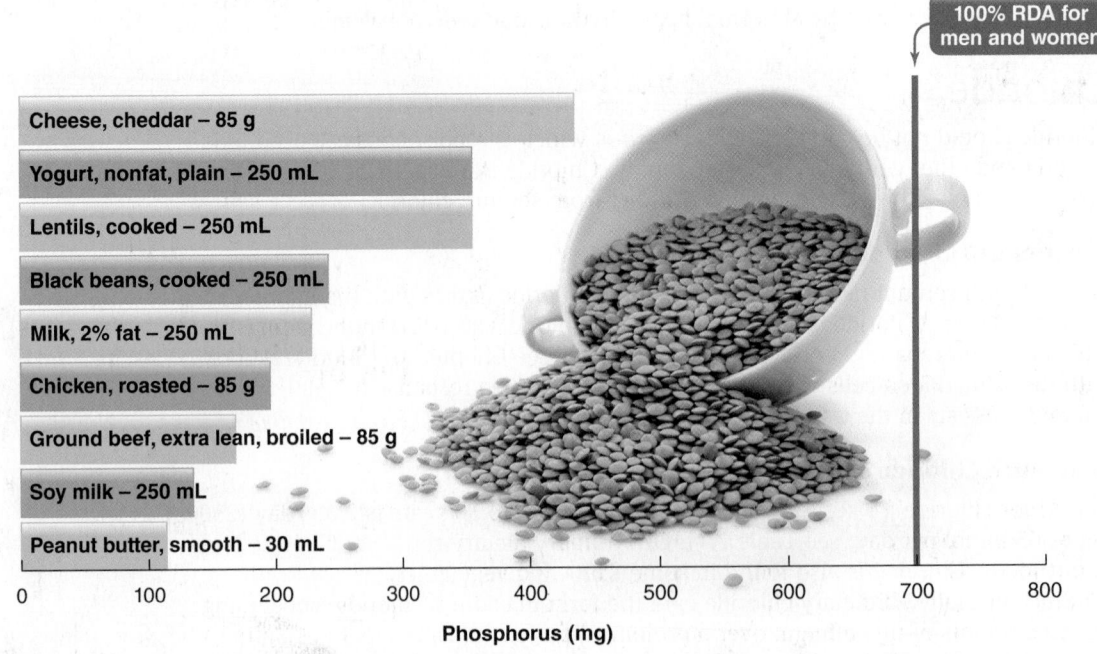

100% RDA for men and women

Cheese, cheddar – 85 g

Yogurt, nonfat, plain – 250 mL

Lentils, cooked – 250 mL

Black beans, cooked – 250 mL

Milk, 2% fat – 250 mL

Chicken, roasted – 85 g

Ground beef, extra lean, broiled – 85 g

Soy milk – 250 mL

Peanut butter, smooth – 30 mL

0   100   200   300   400   500   600   700   800

Phosphorus (mg)

⬥ **Figure 7.9** Common food sources of phosphorus. The RDA for phosphorus is 700 mg/day (22.6 mmol). 1 mmol = 31 mg phosphorus (/)
Data from U.S. Department of Agriculture, Agricultural Research Service. 2009. USDA Nutrient Database for Standard Reference, Release 22. Nutrient Data Laboratory Home Page. www.ars.usda.gov/ba/bhnrc/ndl.

other foods and the bacteria in our large intestine can break down phytic acid. Soft drinks are another common source of phosphorus in our diet.

People suffering from kidney disease and people taking too many vitamin D supplements or too many phosphorus-containing antacids can suffer from high blood phosphorus levels. Severely high levels of blood phosphorus cause muscle spasms and convulsions.

As mentioned previously, deficiencies of phosphorus are rare. People who may suffer from low blood phosphorus levels include premature infants, elderly people with poor diets, and people who abuse alcohol. People with vitamin D deficiency, those with hyperparathyroidism (oversecretion of parathyroid hormone), and those who overuse antacids that bind with phosphorus may also have low blood phosphorus levels.

RECAP The four electrolytes critical for hydration and neuromuscular function are sodium, potassium, chloride, and phosphorus. Most Canadians consume too much sodium and often get too little potassium; intakes of chloride and phosphorus are almost always adequate but not excessive. Electrolyte imbalances can result in heart failure, seizures, and death.

Nutrition DEBATE

Sports Beverages: Help or Hype?

Once considered specialty items used exclusively by elite athletes, sports beverages have become popular everyday beverage choices for both active and non-active people. This surge in popularity leads us to ask three important questions:

- Do these beverages benefit highly active athletes?
- Do these beverages benefit recreationally active people?
- Do non-athletes need to consume sports beverages?

The first question is relatively easy to answer. Sports beverages were originally developed to meet the unique fluid, electrolyte, and carbohydrate needs of competitive athletes. Highly active people need to replenish both fluids and electrolytes to avoid either dehydration or hyponatremia. For example, endurance athletes are able to exercise longer, maintain a higher intensity, and improve performance times when they drink a sports beverage during exercise (Manore et al., 2009). The carbohydrates in sports beverages may also help athletes consume more energy than they could by eating solid foods and water alone. Some competitive athletes train for 6 to 8 hours each day on a regular basis: it is virtually impossible to consume enough solid foods to support this level of exercise.

Do recreationally active people need to consume sports beverages? Most probably do not, but if they exercise for periods longer than 1 hour, they can benefit from consuming the carbohydrates and electrolytes in sports beverages during exercise. Any person who exercises in high temperatures also will benefit from the fluid and electrolyte replacement benefits of sports beverages (Sawka et al., 2007).

If you are active, how do you know whether you should consume a sports beverage? The answer depends on the duration and intensity of exercise, the environmental conditions, and your unique characteristics. Here are some situations in which drinking a sports beverage is appropriate (Manore et al., 2009):

- during exercise or physical work in high heat and/or high humidity or if you have recently experienced diarrhea or vomiting
- during exercise at high altitude and in cold environments; these conditions increase fluid and electrolyte losses
- after exercise for rapid rehydration or between exercise bouts, such as between multiple soccer matches during a tournament
- during long-duration exercise when blood glucose levels get low; sports beverages may be needed to maintain energy levels and to provide the fluid necessary to prevent dehydration
- during exercise sessions if you have poor glycogen stores prior to exercise or are not well fed prior to exercise

Interestingly, sports beverages have become very popular with people who do little or no regular exercise. Are there any benefits or negative consequences for inactive or lightly active people who regularly consume these drinks? There does not appear to be any evidence that people who do not exercise derive any benefits from consuming sports beverages. Even if these individuals live in a hot environment, they should be able to replenish the fluid and electrolytes they lose during sweating by drinking water and other beverages and eating a normal diet.

One common negative consequence when inactive people drink sports beverages is weight gain, contributing to obesity. As an example, drinking 360 mL (12 fl. oz.) of Gatorade adds 380 kJ (90 kcal) to a person's daily energy intake. Many inactive people consume two to three times this amount each day, adding 750 to 1130 kJ (180 to 270 kcal) to their diet. With obesity rates at an all-time high, it is important that we attempt to consume only the foods and beverages necessary to support our health. Sports beverages are not designed to be consumed by inactive people, and they do not contribute to the overall health of inactive or lightly active people.

⬆ Sports beverages were originally designed to meet the needs of competitive athletes.

Chapter Review

Test Yourself ANSWERS

1. False. Recent research suggests that caffeine intake has virtually no effect on fluid balance.

2. False. Most of the sodium consumed by Canadians is from processed and restaurant foods.

3. False. Our thirst mechanism signals that we need to replenish fluids, but it is not sufficient to ensure that we are completely hydrated.

Find the Quack

Libby is shopping for groceries with her 10-year-old daughter, Jen. When they turn into the beverage aisle, Jen exclaims over a colourful display offering a free hot-pink Frisbee with the purchase of a six-pack of a new vitamin-fortified sparkling water. The poster above the display shows a family in a park playing Frisbee together while drinking or holding a bottle of the new water. A banner above the photograph proclaims "Part of Your Healthy Life!"

"Mom, can we get some?" Jen asks.

Libby reads the product packaging, which describes the beverage as follows:

- "Lightly carbonated delicious sparkling water!"
- "All natural flavour and colour!"
- "Packed with vitamins!"
- A 360 mL (12 fl. oz.) serving of the water contains 10% of the Daily Value (DV) for vitamins E, B_6, B_{12}, and niacin.
- No other vitamins or minerals are listed.
- A serving contains 540 kJ (128 calories) and 32 g of carbohydrate.
- The product is sweetened with high-fructose corn syrup.
- The cost is $4.99 per six-pack.

Libby can't decide whether to give in and buy the water or not. "I don't know, honey," she tells her daughter. "It looks healthy, but $4.99 seems like a lot to pay for a Frisbee and some vitamins!"

1. The product packaging claims that the beverage is "Packed with vitamins!" Evaluate this statement by checking out the label of a multivitamin supplement either at home or at a market. How many vitamins does it contain, and at what percentage of the DV? Which provides more nutrients: the fortified water or a glass of plain water plus a multivitamin tablet? Calculate the difference in cost per serving.

2. It's summer, and Jen plays children's soccer two mornings a week on an unshaded field. Would Libby be smarter to purchase a sports beverage, such as Gatorade, for her daughter to drink during her soccer matches or this new vitamin-fortified water, or should she give Jen plain water to drink? Explain. (Hint: See the Nutrition Debate on page 246.)

3. Check out the nutrition information on a carton of milk. Which contains the greater variety of nutrients, and at what cost: the fortified water or the milk?

4. The vitamin-fortified water is sweetened with high-fructose corn syrup and contains 540 kJ (128 kcal) per serving. This is about equivalent to a can of grape soft drink. The promoters characterize the beverage as "Part of Your Healthy Life." Do you agree or disagree? Why?

Answers can be found in the study area of MasteringNutrition.

 **NutriTools**   Visit MasteringNutrition to access interactive animations, including:

- Nutrient Functionality

Review Questions

1. Which of the following is a characteristic of potassium?
   a. It is the major positively charged electrolyte in the extracellular fluid.
   b. It can be found in fresh fruits and vegetables.
   c. It is a critical component of the mineral complex of bone.
   d. It is the major negatively charged electrolyte in the extracellular fluid.

2. Which of the following people probably has the greatest percentage of his or her weight as body fluid?
   a. A female adult who is slightly overweight and vomits nightly after eating dinner.
   b. An elderly male of average weight who has low blood pressure.
   c. An overweight football player who has just completed a practice session in high heat.
   d. A healthy infant of average weight.

3. Plasma is one example of
   a. extracellular fluid.
   b. intracellular fluid.
   c. tissue fluid.
   d. metabolic water.

4. Which of the following is true of the cell membrane?
   a. It is freely permeable to all electrolytes.
   b. It is freely permeable to water and all solutes.
   c. It is freely permeable only to fats.
   d. It is freely permeable to water but not to solutes.

5. We lose fluids through
   a. sweat.
   b. breath.
   c. feces.
   d. all of the above.

6. What are diuretics?
   a. Substances that increase urine output and therefore increase fluid loss.
   b. Medications that control blood pressure in people with hypertension.
   c. Substances that cause vomiting and increase fluid loss.
   d. Substances that are used to purify water for drinking.

7. Which one of the following foods contains the most sodium per serving?
   a. Roast pork
   b. Baked salmon
   c. Baked ham
   d. Roast chicken

8. Which one of the following foods is the best source of potassium?
   a. French fries
   b. White bread
   c. Cola soft drinks
   d. Baked potato

9. Explain why chronic diarrhea in a young child can lead to death from abnormal heart rhythms.

10. After winning a cross-country relay race, you and your teammates celebrate with a trip to the local pub for a few beers. That evening, you feel shaky and disoriented, and you have a "pins and needles" feeling in your hands and feet. What could be going on that is contributing to these feelings?

11. For lunch today, your choices include: (a) chicken soup, a ham sandwich, and a can of tomato juice; or (b) potato salad, a tuna sandwich, and a bottle of mineral water. You have hockey practice in mid-afternoon. Which lunch should you choose, and why?

12. Your cousin, who is breastfeeding her three-month-old daughter, confesses to you that she has resorted to taking over-the-counter weight-loss pills to help her lose the weight she gained during pregnancy. What would you advise her?

13. It is winter in Manitoba, and Cheyenne is freezing cold. She remembers her gym teacher's advice to drink 10 cups of fluid a day, so she makes sure to stop by the coffee shop and grab a skim milk latte on her walk to and from school and at lunchtime. She also has a cup of warm apple cider during her spare period and refills her water bottle several times throughout the day. At dinner she guzzles a couple of glasses of cranberry juice, and before bedtime she enjoys a big mug of tea to warm up. Cheyenne is excited that she's followed her teacher's advice—but she could do without having to go the bathroom so much.

    Is the advice Cheyenne received sound? Does every person have the same fluid requirement? Do you think that Cheyenne is making the best choices of fluids? Why does she have to use the bathroom so often? After learning about hydration, what suggestions would you give her to improve her fluid intake?

Case Study

Michel works in a winery in the Okanagan, where the temperatures reach 35°C (95°F) during the growing season. He is used to working in the fields in these temperatures and drinks lots of water, but lately he's been complaining of feeling weak and sick to his stomach. He says, "It's probably just my high blood pressure acting up again."

a. What do you think might be wrong with Michel?

b. If you learned that he was following a low-sodium diet prescribed to manage his high blood pressure, would this information argue for or against your theory, and why?

c. What would you advise Michel to do differently in the fields tomorrow?

Answers to Review Questions can be found at the back of this text.

Web Resources

www.hc-sc.gc.ca/ewh-semt/water-eau/drink-potab/ index-eng.php
Health Canada

Visit this website for information on drinking water safety in Canada.

www.cbwa.ca
Canadian Bottled Water Association

Find current information about bottled water from this trade association, which represents the bottled water industry.

www.mayoclinic.com
Mayo Clinic

Search for "hyponatremia" to learn more about this potentially fatal condition.

www.nih.gov
The National Institutes of Health (NIH)

Search this site to learn more about dietary approaches to reducing hypertension.

www.nephrologychannel.com/electrolytes
HealthCommunities.com: Electrolyte Imbalances

Visit this website to learn more about hyponatremia, hypernatremia, hypokalemia, and hyperkalemia.

MasteringNutrition®

Assignments

Animations Role of Electrolytes in Water Balance • Intracellular & Extracellular Fluid • Water Balance

Study Area

Video: Using the Functional Approach to Understand Fluid & Electrolyte Balance • Practice Tests • Diet Analysis • eText

Fluid Imbalance

WANT TO FIND OUT...

- **why people get dehydrated?**

- **how to tell if you're adequately hydrated?**

- **what you should do if you or a friend is "feeling the heat"?**

READ ON.

On a Monday in late July, 2001, 27-year-old Korey Stringer, offensive tackle for the Minnesota Vikings, collapsed on the field during training because of exhaustion in the sweltering heat. The next morning, he was determined to make it through practice and failed to consult his trainer, even though he vomited three times during drills in temperatures over 30°C. After retiring to an air-conditioned trailer during break, he passed out and was rushed to the hospital. His body temperature was 42°C, or 108.8°F, about 5C° above normal. Despite expert treatment by more than a dozen medical specialists, his kidneys failed, then his lungs, and finally his heart. With his teammates at his bedside, he died shortly after midnight without ever regaining consciousness.

Stringer's is one of dozens of heat-related deaths among high school, varsity, and professional athletes. But athletes are not the only victims. Soldiers have died during basic training as well as while serving in hot climates, as have manual labourers working long hours in sweltering temperatures. The truth is, anyone whose body must contend with the combination of inadequate fluids and high heat is at risk for a number of potentially fatal disorders. Let's review some of these now.

Dehydration

Dehydration is a serious health problem that results when fluid excretion exceeds fluid intake. It most commonly occurs as a result of heavy exercise or hard physical labour in high environmental temperatures, when the body loses significant amounts of water through increased sweating and breathing.

Other common causes of dehydration include the following:

- *Diarrhea:* As discussed in Chapters 3 and 7, when excess fluid is quickly drawn into the lumen of the GI tract, diarrhea develops, leading to rapid expulsion of watery stools. Significant amounts of water can be lost via frequent, loose bowel movements.
- *Vomiting:* The risk for dehydration

is especially significant when the person cannot tolerate even small amounts of liquid without vomiting. In such cases, intravenous fluids may be necessary.

- *Fever:* Dehydration can develop when a high fever causes significant sweating.
- *Burn (including sunburn):* Normal, intact skin keeps tissue fluid inside the body. In people with severe burns, including sunburns over a large surface area of the body, fluid loss through the skin can be profound.
- *Poorly controlled diabetes:* When blood glucose levels are high, some of the glucose "spills" into the urine. Osmosis prompts water to follow the glucose, diluting the urine but leaving the person dehydrated.
- *Abuse of diuretics or laxatives:* These products cause excessive loss of body fluid and should be used only under medical supervision, as they significantly increase the risk for dehydration.

Older adults and infants are at a higher risk for dehydration than are healthy young and middle-aged adults. The elderly are at increased risk because they have a lower total amount of body water, thus a smaller "margin of error." Their thirst mechanism is less effective than that of a younger person, too, so they are less likely to meet their fluid needs. Infants, on the other hand, excrete urine at a higher rate, cannot tell us when they are thirsty, and have a greater ratio of body surface area to body core, causing them to respond more dramatically to heat and cold and to lose more body water than an older child.

Classifying Dehydration

Dehydration is classified in terms of

the percentage of weight loss that is exclusively due to the loss of fluid **(Table 1)**:

- Relatively small losses in body water, equal to a 1%–2% change in body weight, result in symptoms such as thirst, dry mouth, discomfort, and loss of appetite. For a person weighing 73 kg (160 pounds), these symptoms occur after a rapid loss of 0.5 to 2 kg (1 to 4 pounds) of body water.
- More severe water losses, equal to 3%–5% body weight, result in symptoms that include sleepiness, nausea, flushed skin, and inability to concentrate.
- Severe losses of body water, greater than 8% of body weight (about 6 kg or 13 pounds of water for someone weighing 73 kg or 160 pounds), can result in delirium, coma, and death because the rapid loss of body fluid leads to a dangerous increase in body temperature, which results in organ failure.

Preventing Dehydration During and After Physical Activity

We discussed in Chapter 7 the importance of fluid replacement in preventing dehydration. If you are physically active, how can you tell whether you are drinking enough fluid before, during, and after your exercise or training sessions? First, you can hop on the scale before

▲ Dehydration occurs when fluid excretion exceeds fluid intake.

▲ National Football League all-star Korey Stringer died in 2001 as a result of heat stroke.

---

dehydration The depletion of body fluid that results when fluid excretion exceeds fluid intake.

TABLE 1 Percentages of Body Fluid Loss Correlated with Weight Loss and Symptoms

Body Water Loss (%)	Weight Lost If You Weigh 75 kg (165 lb.)	Weight Lost If You Weigh 60 kg (132 lb.)	Symptoms
1–2	0.75–1.5 kg	0.6–1.2 kg	Strong thirst, loss of appetite, feeling uncomfortable
3–5	2.25–3.75 kg	1.8–3 kg	Dry mouth, reduced urine output, greater difficulty working and concentrating, flushed skin, tingling extremities, impatience, sleepiness, nausea, emotional instability
6–8	4.5–6 kg	3.6–4.8 kg	Increased body temperature that does not decrease, increased heart rate and breathing rate, dizziness, difficulty breathing, slurred speech, mental confusion, muscle weakness, blue lips
9–11	6.75–8.25 kg	5.4–6.6 kg	Muscle spasms, delirium, swollen tongue, poor balance and circulation, kidney failure, decreased blood volume and blood pressure

Data from Nutrition and Aerobic Exercise, edited by D. K. Layman. © 1986 American Chemical Society. (Converted to metric.)

and after each session, ideally when unclothed or just wearing under-clothes. If you weighed in at 73 kg (160 lb.) before basketball practice, and immediately afterward you weigh 72 kg (158 lb.), then you have lost approximately 1 kg or 2 pounds of body weight. This is equal to 1.3% of your body weight prior to practice. As you can see in Table 1, you would most likely experience strong thirst and diminished appetite, and you might even feel generally uncomfortable.

If you find you have lost weight during a session of physical activity, what should you do about it? Your goal is to consume enough water and other fluids to bring back your body weight to what it was before the session—and to do this prior to your next exercise session. Fortunately, this is not difficult: for instance, a weight loss of 1kg would require an intake of 1 L of fluid. In general, by following the daily fluid intake recommendations in Chapter 7, plus replacing fluids lost during sessions of physical activity, you should be able to avoid becoming dehydrated.

If you do not have time to weigh yourself before and after every workout, don't despair! A simpler method of monitoring your fluid levels is to observe the colour of your urine (**Figure 1**). If you are properly hydrated, your urine should be clear to pale yellow in colour, similar to diluted lemonade. Urine that is medium to dark yellow in colour, similar to apple juice, indicates an inadequate fluid intake. Very dark or brown urine, such as the colour of a cola beverage, is a sign of

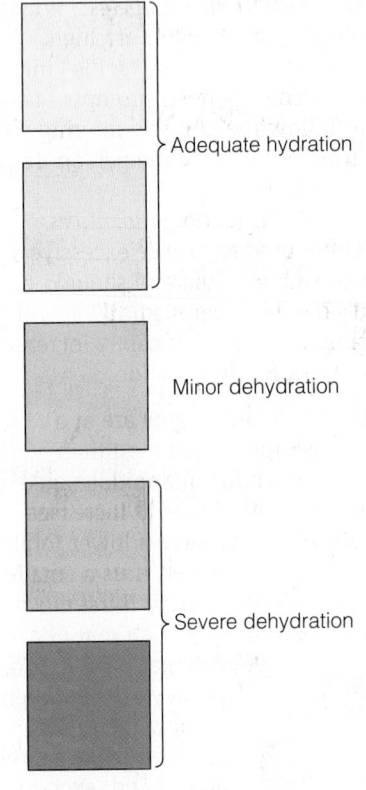

> Adequate hydration

> Minor dehydration

> Severe dehydration

Figure 1 Urine colour chart. Colour variations indicate levels of hydration.

severe dehydration and indicates potential muscle breakdown and kidney damage. Your goal should be to maintain a urine colour that is clear or pale yellow.

Heat Illnesses

Three common types of heat illness are closely linked to dehydration: in order of severity, these are heat cramps, heat exhaustion, and heat stroke.

Heat Cramps

Heat cramps are painful muscle cramps, usually in the abdomen, arms, or legs, that develop during sessions of vigorous physical activity in the heat. The spasms can last for several seconds or even minutes and are caused by a fluid and electrolyte imbalance, such as hypernatremia. The muscles may also feel weak and their functioning may be impaired.

If you ever experience muscle cramps during a workout or athletic event, the first thing you must do is stop your activity immediately! Go to a cool place, rest, and sip a sports beverage, juice, or—if these are not available—plain water. You can also sprinkle a dash of salt into a full glass of water. If heat cramps do not subside within an hour, seek medical attention. Finally, be aware that heat cramps may signal a more serious condition—heat exhaustion—discussed next.

Heat Exhaustion

Like heat cramps, **heat exhaustion** typically occurs when people are engaging in vigorous physical activity

heat cramps Involuntary, spasmodic, and painful muscle contractions that are caused by electrolyte imbalances occurring as a result of strenuous physical activity in high environmental heat.

heat exhaustion A serious condition, characterized by heavy sweating, paleness, nausea and vomiting, dizziness, and moderately elevated body temperature, that develops from dehydration in high heat.

in a hot environment. In such conditions, fluid losses via sweating are excessive and may quickly exceed the person's fluid intake. Heat exhaustion can also develop after several days in high temperatures when fluid intake is inadequate.

Signs and symptoms typically include increased thirst; weakness; muscle cramps; nausea and vomiting; dizziness and possibly fainting; and possibly elevated blood pressure and pulse. In a person with heat exhaustion, the sweat mechanism still functions; in fact, the person is typically sweating heavily. The skin is cool, damp, and pale. While body temperature is above normal, it does not exceed 40°C or 105°F.

A person with heat exhaustion should be taken indoors or placed in a shaded area and given a sports beverage to drink. Loosen the person's clothing and/or partially remove it, and cool the person off with water from a hose, shower, or bath. If those are not available, have the person hold an ice pack on areas of the body where blood circulating close to the surface can be quickly cooled: the neck, the armpits, and the groin. If symptoms do not subside within one

⬆ Treatment of heat illnesses includes replacing lost fluids and electrolytes by drinking a sports beverage rather than plain water.

hour, seek medical attention. It is critical to treat heat exhaustion promptly and aggressively to prevent it from progressing to heat stroke.

Heat Stroke

Heat stroke is a potentially fatal heat illness characterized by a failure of the body's heat-regulating mechanisms. It should be viewed as a medical emergency. Symptoms include rapid pulse; hyperventilation; high core body temperature (above 40°C or 105°F); and hallucinations or loss of consciousness. The skin is hot and dry, not sweaty, because the body's normal sweat mechanism has failed.

Anyone who engages in strenuous physical activity in hot weather is vulnerable to heat stroke. As we discussed at the beginning of this essay, National Football League all-star player Korey Stringer died of complications from heat stroke after training for several hours on a hot July morning. The high humidity that day was also a factor, as the body's ability to dissipate heat via evaporation of sweat is extremely limited in a humid environment. In addition, Stringer's tightly fitting uniform, which trapped warm air close to his body, was a factor in his death. His large body size (1.9 m, 150 kg; or 6'4", 330 pounds) also played a role: the larger the individual and the greater the

muscle mass, the more heat the body produces. In addition, excess body fat adds an extra layer of insulation, which makes it even more difficult to dissipate body heat.

Similar deaths have also occurred among high school and varsity athletes. These deaths have prompted international attention and resulted in strict guidelines requiring regular fluid breaks and the cancellation of training and competition or a change in the time of the event to avoid periods of high heat and humidity.

Any person who is active in a hot environment should stop exercising if dizziness, light-headedness, disorientation, or nausea set in. Heat stroke can be avoided by maintaining a healthy fluid balance before, during, and after exercise and by avoiding strenuous activity in hot and humid environmental conditions.

If you suspect that someone has heat stroke, provide cooling as quickly and effectively as possible while seeking immediate expert medical care: immerse the person in cool water if possible (keeping the head out of water). Alternatively, wet the person with wet washcloths or a hose and fan the person's body aggressively. If running water is not available, place ice or cold packs on areas of high circulation, such as the neck, armpits, and groin.

Web Resources

www.acsm.org
American College of Sports Medicine

Check out this website for information on heat illness and youth sports.

---

heat stroke A potentially fatal response to high temperature characterized by failure of the body's heat-regulating mechanisms; also commonly called sunstroke.

Nutrients 8 Involved in Antioxidant Function

CHAPTER OBJECTIVES

After reading this chapter you will be able to:

1. Define the term *free radicals* and explain how they can damage cells, pp. 257–258.

2. Define the term *antioxidant enzyme systems* and identify the minerals involved in these systems, p. 259.

3. Discuss the interrelated roles of vitamins E and C in protecting cells from oxidative damage, pp. 259–266.

4. Explain how vitamin C helps maintain bone, skin, tendons, and other tissues, pp. 262–263.

5. Describe the relationship between beta-carotene and vitamin A, p. 266.

6. Discuss the role of vitamin A in vision, pp. 269, 271–272.

M ika, a first-year student at a university eight hours away from home, just opened another care package from her mom. As usual, it contained an assortment of healthful snacks, a box of chamomile tea, and several types of supplements: echinacea extract to ward off colds, powdered papaya for good digestion, and antioxidant vitamins. "Wow, Mika!" her roommate laughed. "Can you let your mom know I'm available for adoption?"

"I guess she just wants me to stay healthy," Mika sighed. She wondered what her mother would think if she ever found out how much junk food Mika had been eating since she'd started college, or that she'd been binge-drinking most weekends, or that she'd been smoking since high school. "Still," Mika reminded herself, "at least I take the vitamins she sends."

What do you think of Mika's current lifestyle? Can a poor diet, binge-drinking, and smoking cause cancer or other health problems, and can the use of dietary supplements provide some protection? What are antioxidant vitamins, and why do you think Mika's mom included a bottle of these in her care package? If your health food store were promoting an antioxidant supplement, would you buy it?

It is not easy to sort fact from fiction when it comes to antioxidants—especially when they are in the form of supplements. Internet ads and articles in fitness and health magazines tout their benefits, yet some researchers claim that antioxidant supplements do not protect us from diseases and in some cases may even be harmful. In this chapter, you will learn what antioxidants are and how they work in the body. We'll discuss how antioxidants consumed in foods protect cells from damage that can lead to cancer and cardiovascular disease, and how consuming antioxidants in supplements may work against us. And as we profile each antioxidant nutrient, we'll identify additional roles it plays in protecting and maintaining our health.

What Are Antioxidants, and How Does Our Body Use Them?

Antioxidants are compounds that protect our cells from the damage caused by oxidation. *Anti* means "against," and antioxidants work *against,* or *prevent,* oxidation. Before we can go further in our discussion of antioxidants, we need to learn what oxidation is and how it damages cells.

Oxidation Is a Chemical Reaction in Which Atoms Lose Electrons

A review of some basic chemistry will help you understand the process of oxidation. In Chapter 3, we said that our body is made up of atoms, tiny units of matter that cannot be broken down by natural means. Hydrogen, carbon, and iron are unique because their atoms are unique. Every atom of carbon, for example, is identical to every other atom of carbon, whether it is present in coal or in cheese. We also said that atoms join together to form molecules, such as saccharides and amino acids, which are the smallest *physical units* of a substance. Some molecules, such as hydrogen gas (H_2), contain only one type of atom—in this case, hydrogen. Most molecules, however, are *compounds*—they contain two or more different types of atoms (such as water, H_2O). Our body is constantly breaking down compounds of food, water, and air into their component atoms, then rearranging these freed atoms to build the different substances our body needs.

Atoms Are Composed of Particles

We just said that atoms cannot be broken down by natural means, but during the twentieth century, physicists learned how to split atoms into their components, which they called *particles*. As you can see in **Figure 8.1**, this research revealed that all atoms have a central core, called a **nucleus**, which is positively charged. Orbiting around this nucleus at close to the speed of light are one or more **electrons**, which are negatively charged. The opposite attraction between the positive nucleus and the negative electrons keeps an atom together by making the atom stable, so that its electrons remain with it and do not veer off toward other atoms.

During Metabolism, Atoms Exchange Electrons

As you recall from Chapter 1, the process by which our body breaks down and builds up molecules is called *metabolism*. During metabolism, atoms may lose electrons (**Figure 8.2a**). We call this loss of electrons **oxidation**, because it is fuelled by oxygen. Atoms are capable of gaining electrons during metabolism as well. We call this

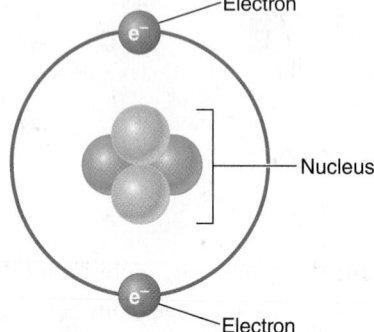

Figure 8.1 An atom consists of a central nucleus and orbiting electrons. The nucleus exerts a positive charge, which keeps the negatively charged electrons in its vicinity. Notice that this atom has an even number of electrons in orbit around the nucleus. This pairing of electrons results in the atom being chemically stable.

antioxidant A compound that has the ability to prevent or repair the damage caused by oxidation.

nucleus The positively charged, central core of an atom. It is made up of two types of particles—protons and neutrons—bound tightly together. The nucleus of an atom contains essentially all of its atomic mass.

electron A negatively charged particle orbiting the nucleus of an atom.

oxidation A chemical reaction in which molecules of a substance are broken down into their component atoms. During oxidation, the atoms involved lose electrons.

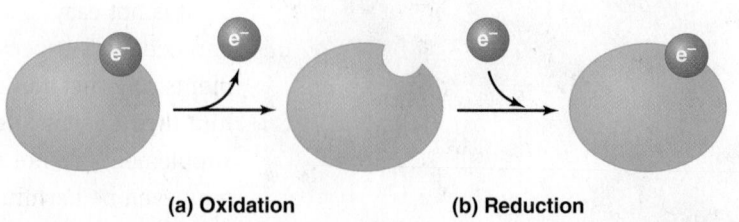

(a) Oxidation   **(b) Reduction**

Figure 8.2 The exchange reaction. Exchange reactions consist of two parts. **(a)** During oxidation, atoms lose electrons. **(b)** In the second part of the reaction, called reduction, atoms gain electrons.

process *reduction* (Figure 8.2b). This loss and gain of electrons typically results in an even exchange of electrons. Scientists call this loss and gain of electrons an *exchange reaction.*

Oxidation Sometimes Results in the Formation of Free Radicals

Stable atoms have an even number of electrons orbiting in pairs at successive distances (called *shells* or *rings*) from the nucleus. When a stable atom loses an electron during oxidation, it is left with an odd number of electrons in its outermost shell. In other words, it now has an *unpaired electron.* In most exchange reactions, unpaired electrons immediately pair up with other unpaired electrons, making newly stabilized atoms, but in some cases, atoms with unpaired electrons in their outermost shell remain unpaired. Such atoms are highly unstable and are called **free radicals**.

Free radicals are formed as a normal by-product of many of our body's fundamental physiologic processes. Still, excessive production of free radicals can cause serious damage to our cells and other body components. Let's look at the most common way they arise. Our body uses oxygen and hydrogen to generate the energy (ATP) it needs (**Figure 8.3**). We are constantly inhaling air into our body, thereby providing the oxygen needed to fuel this reaction. At the same time, we generate the necessary hydrogen as a result of digesting food. As shown in **Figure 8.4**, occasionally during metabolism, oxygen accepts a single electron that was released during this process. When it does so, the oxygen atom becomes an unstable free radical because of the added unpaired electron.

Free radicals are also formed from other physiologic processes, such as when the immune system produces inflammation to fight allergens or infections. Other factors that cause free radical formation include exposure to air pollution, ultraviolet (UV) rays from the sun, other types of radiation, tobacco smoke, industrial chemicals, and asbestos. Continual exposure to these factors leads to uncontrollable free radical formation, cell damage, and disease, as discussed next.

free radical A highly unstable atom with an unpaired electron in its outermost shell.

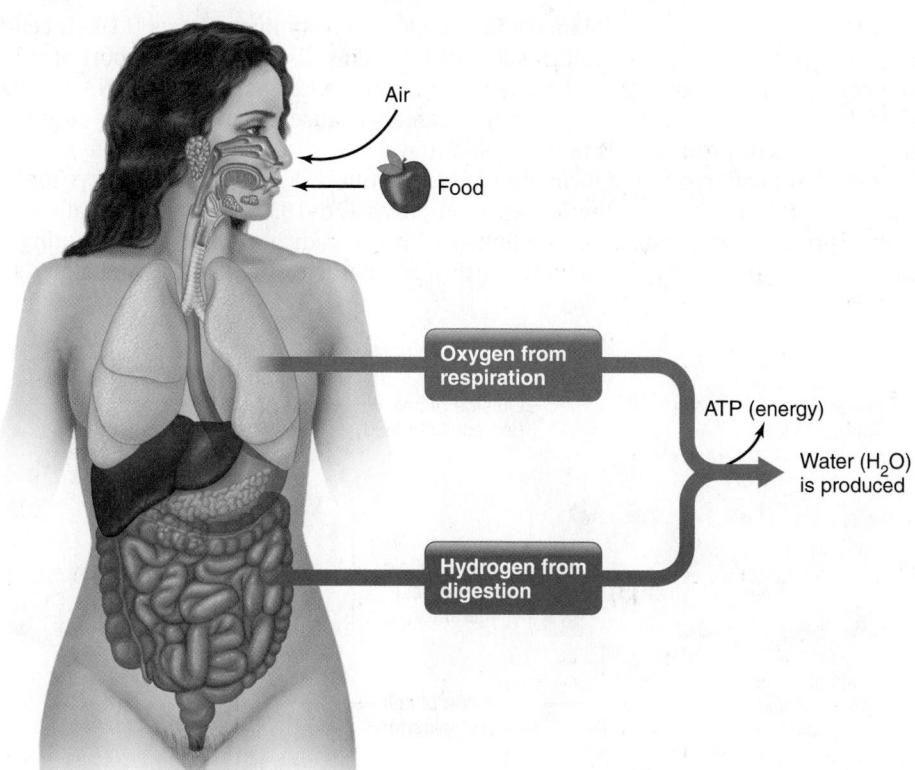

◀ **Figure 8.3** Oxygen (O) enters our body when we inhale air. Hydrogen (H) is released through the process of metabolizing food. As a result of exchange reactions during metabolism, electrons are freed to contribute to the production of the energy molecule ATP in body cells. The hydrogen and oxygen then recombine to form water (H_2O).

Air

Food

Oxygen from respiration

ATP (energy)

Water (H_2O) is produced

Hydrogen from digestion

Figure 8.4 Normally, an oxygen atom contains eight electrons. Occasionally, oxygen will accept an unpaired electron during the oxidation process. This acceptance of a single electron causes oxygen to become an unstable atom called a free radical.

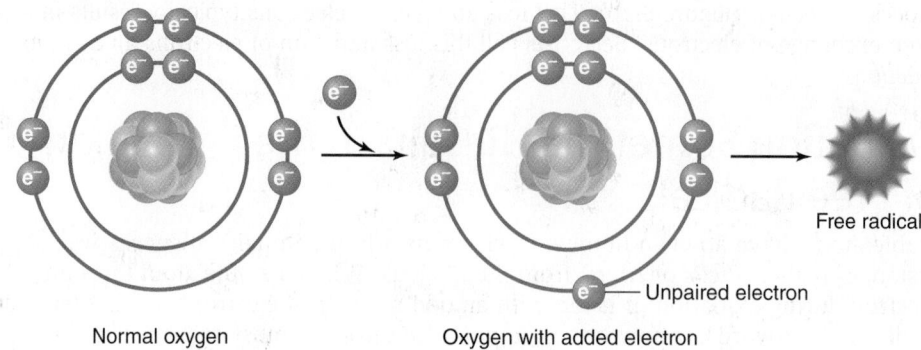

Normal oxygen

Oxygen with added electron

Unpaired electron

Free radical

Free Radicals Can Destabilize Other Molecules and Damage Our Cells

Why are we concerned with the formation of free radicals? Simply put, it is because of their destabilizing power. If you were to think of paired electrons as a married couple, a free radical would be an extremely seductive outsider. Its unpaired electron exerts a powerful attraction toward all stable atoms and molecules around it. In an attempt to stabilize itself, a free radical will "steal" an electron from these stable neighbours, in turn generating more unstable free radicals. This is a dangerous chain reaction, since the free radicals generated can damage or destroy our cells.

One of the most significant sites of free radical damage is the cell membrane. As shown in **Figure 8.5a**, free radicals that form within the phospholipid bilayer of cell membranes steal electrons from the stable lipid heads. Recall from Chapter 5 that lipids are insoluble in water, so a stable line-up of lipid heads allows cell membranes to keep water out. When these lipid heads are destroyed, the cell membrane can no longer repel water. With the cell membrane's integrity lost, its ability to regulate the movement of fluids and nutrients into and out of the cell is also lost. This loss of cell integrity causes damage to the cell and to all systems affected by the cell.

Other sites of free radical damage include low-density lipoproteins (LDLs), cell proteins, and DNA. Damage to LDLs and cell proteins disrupts the transport of substances into and out of cells and alters cell function, whereas defective DNA results in faulty protein synthesis. These changes can also cause harmful changes (mutations) in cells or prompt cells to die prematurely. Free radicals also promote blood vessel inflammation and the formation of clots, both of which are risk factors for cardiovascular disease (see the *In Depth* on pages 176–183 for more information). Not surprisingly, many diseases are linked with free radical production, including cancer, heart disease, type 2 diabetes, arthritis, cataracts, and kidney, Alzheimer's, and Parkinson's diseases.

Exposure to pollution from car exhaust and industrial waste increases our production of free radicals.

Figure 8.5 (a) The formation of free radicals in the lipid portion of our cell membranes can cause a dangerous chain reaction that damages the integrity of the membrane and can cause cell death. **(b)** Vitamin E is stored in the lipid portion of our cell membranes. By donating an electron to free radicals, it protects the lipid molecules in our cell membranes from themselves being oxidized and stops the chain reaction of oxidative damage.

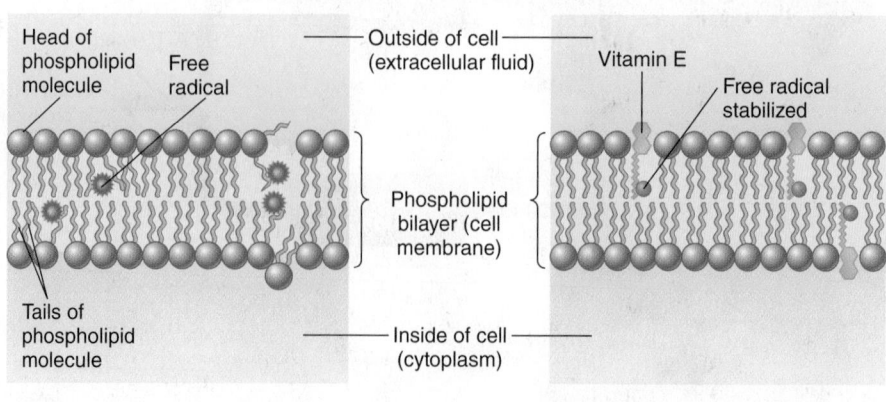

Head of phospholipid molecule

Free radical

Outside of cell (extracellular fluid)

Vitamin E

Free radical stabilized

Phospholipid bilayer (cell membrane)

Tails of phospholipid molecule

Inside of cell (cytoplasm)

(a)

(b)

Antioxidants Work by Stabilizing Free Radicals or Opposing Oxidation

How does our body fight free radicals and repair the damage they cause? These actions are performed by antioxidant vitamins, minerals, and phytochemicals and other compounds. These antioxidants perform their role in three ways:

1. Antioxidant vitamins work independently by donating their electrons or hydrogen atoms to free radicals to stabilize them and reduce the damage caused by oxidation (Figure 8.5b).
2. Antioxidant minerals, including selenium, copper, iron, zinc, and manganese, act as **cofactors**, substances required to activate enzymes so that they can do their work. These minerals function within complex *antioxidant enzyme systems* that convert free radicals to less damaging substances that are excreted by our body. They also work to break down fatty acids that have become oxidized, thereby destroying the free radicals associated with them. Antioxidant enzyme systems also make more vitamin antioxidants available to fight other free radicals. Examples of these antioxidant enzyme systems are superoxide dismutase, catalase, and glutathione peroxidase.
3. Other compounds, such as beta-carotene and other phytochemicals, help stabilize free radicals and prevent damage to cells and tissues.

In summary, free radical formation is generally kept safely under control by certain vitamins, minerals working within antioxidant enzyme systems, and phytochemicals. Next, we take a look at the specific vitamins and minerals involved. Phytochemicals are discussed *In Depth* following Chapter 2.

RECAP An atom is an extremely small and unique unit of matter having a nucleus and orbiting electrons. Atoms join together to form molecules. During metabolism, molecules break apart and their atoms gain, lose, or exchange electrons; loss of electrons is called oxidation. Free radicals are highly unstable atoms with an unpaired electron in their outermost shell. A normal by-product of oxidation reactions, they can damage our LDLs, cell proteins, and DNA and are associated with many diseases. Antioxidant vitamins and phytochemicals donate electrons or hydrogen atoms to free radicals to stabilize them and reduce oxidative damage. Antioxidant minerals are part of antioxidant enzyme systems that convert free radicals to less damaging substances.

A Profile of Nutrients That Function as Antioxidants

Our body cannot form antioxidants spontaneously. Instead, we must consume them in our diet. Nutrients that appear to have antioxidant properties or are part of our protective antioxidant enzyme systems include vitamins E, C, and A; beta-carotene (a phytochemical that is a precursor to vitamin A); and the mineral selenium (Table 8.1). The minerals copper, iron, zinc, and manganese play a peripheral role in fighting oxidation and are only mentioned briefly in this chapter. Let's review each of these nutrients now and learn more about their functions in the body.

Vitamin E

Vitamin E is one of the fat-soluble vitamins; thus, dietary fats carry it from our intestines through the lymphatic system and eventually transport it to our cells. As you remember, our body stores the fat-soluble vitamins: about 90% of the vitamin E in our body is stored in our adipose tissue. The remaining vitamin E is found in cell membranes.

Vitamin E is actually two separate families of compounds, *tocotrienols* and **tocopherols**. None of the different tocotrienol compounds appear to play an active role in our body. The four tocopherol compounds—alpha, beta, gamma, and delta—are the biologically active forms. Of these, the most active, or potent, vitamin E compound found in

cofactor A mineral or other substance that is needed to allow enzymes to function properly.

tocopherol The active form of vitamin E in our body.

TABLE 8.1 Nutrients Involved in Antioxidant Function

To see the full profile of nutrients involved in energy metabolism, turn to **In Depth**, Vitamins and Minerals: Micronutrients with Macro Powers, pages 216–225.

Nutrient	Recommended Intake
Vitamin E (fat soluble)	RDA: Women and men = 15 mg alpha-tocopheral
Vitamin C (water soluble)	RDA: Women = 75 mg Men = 90 mg Smokers = 35 mg more per day than RDA
Beta-carotene (fat-soluble provitamin for vitamin A)	None at this time
Vitamin A (fat soluble)	RDA: Women: 700 µg Men: 900 µg
Selenium (trace mineral)	RDA: Women and men = 55 µg

food and supplements is *alpha-tocopherol*. The RDA for vitamin E is expressed as milligrams of alpha-tocopherol equivalents per day (mg α-tocopherol/day). Food labels and vitamin and mineral supplements may express vitamin E in units of alpha-tocopherol equivalents (α-TE), milligrams, or International Units (IU). For conversion purposes

- one α-TE is equal to 1 mg of active vitamin E
- in supplements containing natural sources of vitamin E, 1 IU is equal to

$$0.67 \text{ mg } \alpha\text{-TE}$$

- in supplements containing synthetic sources of vitamin E, 1 IU is equal to

$$0.45 \text{ mg } \alpha\text{-TE}$$

Functions of Vitamin E

The primary function of vitamin E is as an antioxidant: it donates an electron to free radicals, stabilizing them and preventing them from destabilizing other molecules. Once vitamin E is oxidized, it is either excreted from the body or recycled back into active vitamin E through the help of other antioxidant nutrients, such as vitamin C.

Because vitamin E is prevalent in our adipose tissues and cell membranes, its action specifically protects polyunsaturated fatty acids (PUFAs) and other fatty components of our cells and cell membranes from being oxidized (Figure 8.5b). Vitamin E also protects our LDLs from being oxidized, thereby lowering our risk for heart disease. In addition to protecting our PUFAs and LDLs, vitamin E protects the membranes of our red blood cells from oxidation and plays a critical role in protecting the cells of our lungs, which are constantly exposed to oxygen and the potentially damaging effects of oxidation. Vitamin E's role in protecting PUFAs and other fatty components also explains why it is added to many oil-based foods and skincare products—by preventing oxidation in these products, it reduces rancidity and spoilage.

Vitamin E serves many other roles essential to human health. It is critical for normal fetal and early childhood development of nerves and muscles, as well as for maintenance of their functions. It protects white blood cells and other components of our immune system, thereby helping the body defend against illness and disease. It also improves the absorption of vitamin A if the dietary intake of vitamin A is low.

How Much Vitamin E Should We Consume?

Considering the importance of vitamin E to our health, you might think that you need to consume a huge amount daily. In fact, the RDA is modest: 15 mg alpha-tocopherol per day (see Table 8.1) (Institute of Medicine, 2000). The tolerable upper intake level (UL) is 1000 mg alpha-tocopherol per day. Remember that one of the primary roles of vitamin E is to protect PUFAs from oxidation. Thus, our need for vitamin E increases as we eat more oils and other foods that contain PUFAs. Fortunately, these foods also

Vegetable oils, nuts, and seeds are good sources of vitamin E.

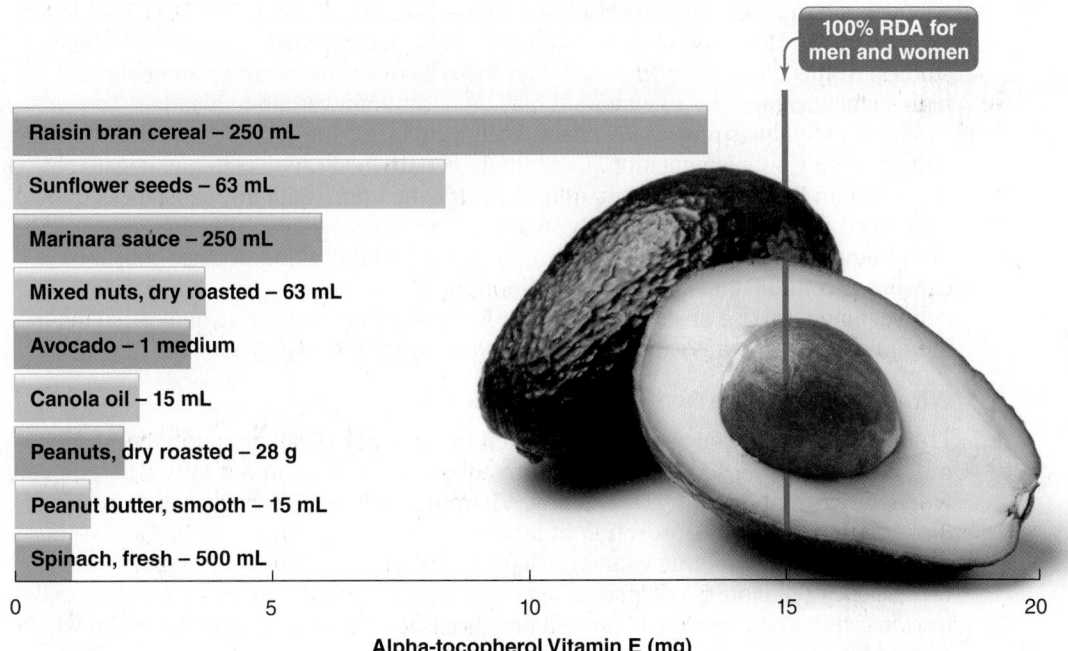

100% RDA for men and women

Raisin bran cereal – 250 mL

Sunflower seeds – 63 mL

Marinara sauce – 250 mL

Mixed nuts, dry roasted – 63 mL

Avocado – 1 medium

Canola oil – 15 mL

Peanuts, dry roasted – 28 g

Peanut butter, smooth – 15 mL

Spinach, fresh – 500 mL

Alpha-tocopherol Vitamin E (mg)

0   5   10   15   20

Figure 8.6 Common food sources of vitamin E. The RDA for vitamin E is 15 mg alpha-tocopherol per day for men and women.
Data from U.S. Department of Agriculture, Agricultural Research Service, 2009. USDA Nutrient Database for Standard Reference, Release 22. Nutrient Data Laboratory Home Page, www.ars.usda.gov/ba/bhnrc/ndl.

contain vitamin E, so we typically consume enough vitamin E within them to protect their PUFAs from oxidation.

Vitamin E: The Vegetarian Vitamin

Vitamin E is widespread in foods from plant sources **(Figure 8.6)**. Much of the vitamin E that we consume comes from products such as spreads, salad dressings, and mayonnaise made from vegetable oils, including safflower oil, sunflower oil, canola oil, and soybean oil. Nuts, seeds, soybeans, and some vegetables—including spinach, broccoli, and avocados—also contribute vitamin E to our diet. Although no single fruit or vegetable contains very high amounts of vitamin E, eating the recommended amounts of fruits and vegetables each day will help ensure adequate intake of this nutrient. Cereals are often fortified with vitamin E, and other grain products contribute modest amounts to our diet. Animal and dairy products are poor sources.

Vitamin E is destroyed by exposure to oxygen, metals, ultraviolet light, and heat. Although raw (uncooked) vegetable oils contain vitamin E, heating these oils destroys vitamin E. Thus, fried foods contain little vitamin E. This includes most fast foods. See the Quick Tips for increasing your intake of vitamin E.

Raw almonds are an appetizing way to help meet your vitamin E needs.

What Happens If We Consume Too Much Vitamin E?

Until recently, standard supplemental doses (one to eighteen times the RDA) of vitamin E were not associated with any adverse health effects. However, a 2005 study found that, among adults 55 years of age or older with vascular disease or diabetes, a daily intake of 268 mg of vitamin E per day (about eighteen times the RDA) for approximately seven years

QUICK TIPS

Eating More Vitamin E

- Eat cereals high in vitamin E for breakfast or as a snack.
- Add sunflower seeds to salads and trail mixes, or just have them as a snack.
- Add sliced almonds to salads, granola, and trail mixes to boost vitamin E intake.

- Pack a peanut butter sandwich for lunch.
- Eat veggies throughout the day—for snacks, for sides, and in main dishes.
- When dressing a salad, use vitamin E–rich oils, such as sunflower, safflower, or canola.
- Enjoy some fresh, homemade guacamole: mash a ripe avocado with a squeeze of lime juice and a sprinkle of garlic salt.

resulted in a significant increase in heart failure (The HOPE and HOPE-TOO Trial Investigators, 2005). However, these results have not been confirmed by additional research studies. At this time, it is unclear whether these adverse effects are an anomaly or if high supplemental doses of vitamin E may be harmful for certain individuals.

Some individuals report side effects such as nausea, intestinal distress, and diarrhea with vitamin E supplementation. In addition, certain medications interact negatively with vitamin E. The most important of these are the *anticoagulants,* substances that stop blood from clotting excessively. Aspirin is an anticoagulant, as is the prescription drug Coumadin. Vitamin E supplements can augment the action of these substances, causing uncontrollable bleeding. In addition, new evidence suggests that, in some people, long-term use of standard vitamin E supplements may cause hemorrhaging in the brain, leading to a type of stroke called *hemorrhagic stroke* (Sesso et al., 2008).

What Happens If We Don't Consume Enough Vitamin E?

True vitamin E deficiencies are uncommon in humans. This is primarily because vitamin E is fat soluble, so we typically store adequate amounts in our fatty tissues, even when our current dietary intake is low. Vitamin E deficiencies are usually a result of diseases that cause malabsorption of fat.

Despite the rarity of true vitamin E deficiencies, they do occur. One vitamin E–deficiency symptom is *erythrocyte hemolysis,* or the rupturing (*lysis*) of red blood cells (*erythrocytes*). The rupturing of our red blood cells leads to *anemia,* a condition in which our red blood cells cannot carry and transport enough oxygen to our tissues, leading to fatigue, weakness, and a diminished ability to perform physical and mental work. We discuss anemia in more detail in Chapter 10. Premature babies can suffer from vitamin E–deficiency anemia; if born too early, the infant does not receive vitamin E from its mother since the transfer of this vitamin from mother to baby occurs during the last few weeks of the pregnancy.

Other symptoms of vitamin E deficiency include loss of muscle coordination and reflexes, leading to impairments in vision, speech, and movement. Vitamin E deficiency can also impair immune function, especially when body stores of the mineral selenium are low.

In adults, vitamin E deficiencies are usually caused by diseases, particularly diseases that cause malabsorption of fat, such as those that affect the liver, gallbladder, and pancreas. As reviewed in Chapter 3, the liver makes bile, which is necessary for the absorption of fat. The bile travels to the gallbladder, where it is concentrated and stored. The gallbladder delivers the bile into our intestines, where it facilitates digestion of fat. The pancreas makes fat-digesting enzymes. Thus, when the liver, gallbladder, or pancreas are not functioning properly, fat and the fat-soluble vitamins, including vitamin E, cannot be absorbed, leading to their deficiency.

RECAP Vitamin E protects our cell membranes from oxidation, enhances immune function, and improves our absorption of vitamin A if dietary intake is low. The RDA for vitamin E is 15 mg alpha-tocopherol per day for men and women. Vitamin E is found primarily in vegetable oils and nuts. Toxicity is uncommon, but taking very high doses can cause excessive bleeding. A genuine deficiency is rare, but symptoms include anemia and impaired vision, speech, and movement.

Vitamin C

Vitamin C is a water-soluble vitamin. We must therefore consume it on a regular basis, as any excess is excreted (primarily in our urine) rather than stored. There are two active forms of vitamin C: ascorbic acid and dehydroascorbic acid **(Figure 8.7)**. Interestingly, most animals can make their own vitamin C from glucose. Humans and guinea pigs are two groups that cannot synthesize their own vitamin C and must consume it in the diet.

Functions of Vitamin C

Vitamin C is probably most well known for its role in preventing scurvy, a disease that ravaged sailors on long sea voyages centuries ago. In fact, the name *ascorbic acid* is derived from the combined Latin terms *a* (meaning "without") and *scorbic* (meaning

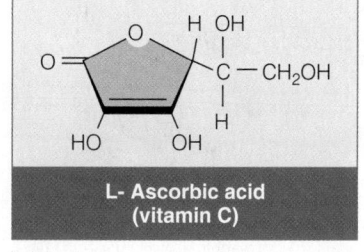

(a)

(b)

◆ **Figure 8.7** Chemical structure of (a) L-ascorbic acid and (b) dehydroascorbic acid.

"having scurvy"). Scurvy was characterized by bleeding tissues, especially of the gums, and is thought to have caused more than half of the deaths that occurred at sea. During these long voyages, the crew ate all of the fruits and vegetables early in the trip, then had only grain and animal products available until they reached land to resupply. In 1740 in England, Dr. James Lind discovered that citrus fruits can prevent scurvy. This is due to their high vitamin C content. Fifty years after the discovery of the link between citrus fruits and scurvy prevention, the British Navy finally required all ships to provide daily lemon juice rations for each sailor to prevent the onset of scurvy. A century later, sailors were given lime juice rations, earning them the nickname "limeys." It was not until 1930 that vitamin C was discovered and identified as a nutrient.

Many fruits, such as these yellow tomatoes, are high in vitamin C.

One reason that vitamin C prevents scurvy is that it assists in the synthesis of collagen. Collagen, a protein, is a critical component of all connective tissues in the body, including bone, teeth, skin, tendons, and blood vessels. Collagen assists in preventing bruises, and it ensures proper wound healing, as it is a part of scar tissue and a component of the tissue that mends broken bones. Without adequate vitamin C, the body cannot form collagen, and tissue hemorrhage, or bleeding, occurs. Vitamin C may also be involved in the synthesis of other components of connective tissues, such as elastin and bone matrix.

In addition to connective tissues, vitamin C assists in the synthesis of DNA, bile, neurotransmitters (such as serotonin, which helps regulate mood), and carnitine, which transports long-chain fatty acids from the cytosol into the mitochondria for energy production. Vitamin C also helps ensure that appropriate levels of thyroxine, a hormone produced by the thyroid gland, are produced to support basal metabolic rate and to maintain body temperature. Other hormones that are synthesized with assistance from vitamin C include epinephrine, norepinephrine, and steroid hormones.

Vitamin C also acts as an antioxidant. Because it is water soluble, it is an important antioxidant in the extracellular fluid. Like vitamin E, it donates electrons to free radicals, thus preventing the damage of cells and tissues. It also protects LDL-cholesterol from oxidation, which may reduce the risk for cardiovascular disease. Vitamin C acts as an important antioxidant in the lungs, helping protect us from the damage caused by ozone and cigarette smoke (Yeomans, Linseisen, and Wolfram, 2005). Vitamin C also regenerates vitamin E after it has been oxidized by donating an electron. This enables vitamin E to continue to protect our cell membranes and other tissues. It also enhances immune function by protecting white blood cells from the oxidative damage that occurs in response to fighting illness and infection. But contrary to popular belief, it is not a miracle cure (see the Nutrition Myth or Fact? box on vitamin C, page 264). In the stomach, vitamin C reduces the formation of *nitrosamines*, cancer-causing agents found in foods such as cured and processed meats. We discuss the role of vitamin C and other antioxidants in preventing some forms of cancer in the *In Depth* on pages 279–285.

Eating Right All Day

Breakfast
Grapefruit juice instead of sweetened coffee!

Lunch
Vegetable soup instead of chicken noodle!

Dinner
Spring rolls instead of sweet & sour pork!

Snack
Grapes instead of M&Ms!

NUTRITION MYTH OR FACT?
Can Vitamin C Prevent the Common Cold?

What do you do when you feel a cold coming on? If you are like many people, you drink a lot of orange juice or take vitamin C supplements to ward it off. Do these tactics really help prevent a cold?

It is well known that vitamin C is important for a healthy immune system. A deficiency of vitamin C can seriously weaken the immune cells' ability to detect and destroy invading microbes, increasing susceptibility to many diseases and illnesses—including the common cold. Many people have taken vitamin C supplements to prevent the common cold, basing their behaviour on its actions of enhancing our immune function. Interestingly, scientific studies do not support this action. A recent review of many of the studies of vitamin C and the common cold found that people taking vitamin C regularly in an attempt to ward off the common cold experienced as many colds as people who took a placebo. However, the *duration* of their colds was reduced—by 8% in adults and 13.6% in children (Hemilä et al., 2007). Timing appeared to be important, though: taking vitamin C after the onset of cold symptoms did not reduce either the duration or the severity of the cold. Interestingly, taking vitamin C

supplements regularly did reduce the number of colds experienced in marathon runners, skiers, and soldiers participating in exercises done under extreme environmental conditions.

The amount of vitamin C taken in these studies was at least 200 mg per day, with many using doses as high as 4000 mg per day (more than 40 times the RDA), with no harmful effects noted in those studies that reported adverse events.

It appears that, for most people, taking vitamin C supplements regularly will not prevent colds but may reduce their duration. Consuming a healthful diet that includes excellent sources of vitamin C will also help you maintain a strong immune system. Taking vitamin C after the onset of cold symptoms does not appear to help, so next time you feel a cold coming on, you may want to think twice before taking extra vitamin C.

Vitamin C also enhances the absorption of iron. It is recommended that people with low iron stores consume vitamin C–rich foods along with iron sources to improve absorption of the iron. For people with high iron stores, however, this practice can be dangerous and lead to iron toxicity.

How Much Vitamin C Should We Consume?

Although popular opinion suggests that our need for vitamin C is quite high, we really require amounts that are easily obtained when we eat the recommended amounts of fruits and vegetables daily. The RDA for vitamin C is 90 mg per day for men and 75 mg per day for women (see Table 8.1) (Institute of Medicine, 2000). The tolerable upper intake level (UL) is 2000 mg per day for adults. Smoking increases a person's need for vitamin C; thus, the RDA for smokers is 35 mg more per day than for non-smokers. This equals 125 mg per day for men and 110 mg per day for women. Other situations that may increase the need for vitamin C include healing from a traumatic injury, surgery, or burns and the use of oral contraceptives among women; there is no consensus on how much extra vitamin C is needed in these circumstances.

Vitamin C: Citrus and More

Fruits and vegetables are the best sources of vitamin C. Because heat and oxygen destroy vitamin C, fresh sources of these foods have the highest content. Cooking foods, especially boiling them, leaches their vitamin C, which is then lost when we strain them. The forms of cooking that are least likely to compromise the vitamin C content of foods are steaming, microwaving, and stir-frying.

As indicated in **Figure 8.8**, many fruits and vegetables are high in vitamin C. Citrus fruits (such as oranges, lemons, and limes), potatoes, strawberries, tomatoes, kiwi fruit, broccoli, spinach and other leafy greens, cabbage, green and red peppers, and cauliflower are excellent sources of vitamin C. Fortified beverages and cereals are also good sources. Dairy foods, meats, and non-fortified cereals and grains provide little or no vitamin C. With such a wide variety of foods to choose

100% RDA for women

100% RDA for men

Strawberries, fresh – 250 mL

Grapefruit juice, unsweetened – 250 mL

Kiwifruit – 1 medium

Orange – 1 medium

Cauliflower, cooked – 125 mL

Broccoli, cooked – 125 mL

Sweet potato, baked, with skin – 1

Bell peppers, green, raw – 250 mL

Pineapple, fresh – 1 slice

Tomatoes, fresh – 5 slices

0   20   40   60   80   100

Vitamin C (mg)

Figure 8.8 Common food sources of vitamin C. The RDA for vitamin C is 90 mg/day for men and 75 mg/day for women.
Data from U.S. Department of Agriculture, Agricultural Research Service, 2009. USDA Nutrient Database for Standard Reference, Release 22. Nutrient Data Laboratory Home Page, www.ars.usda.gov/ba/bhnrc/ndl.

from, it is easy to eat right all day! See Eating Right All Day on page 263 for some simple menu choices that are high in vitamin C. In addition, some tips for increasing your intake of vitamin C follow.

megadose A dose of a nutrient that is 10 or more times greater than the recommended amount.

What Happens If We Consume Too Much Vitamin C?

Because vitamin C is water soluble, we usually excrete any excess. Consuming excess amounts in food sources does not lead to toxicity, and only supplements can lead to toxic doses. Taking a **megadose** of vitamin C is not fatally harmful. However, side effects of doses exceeding 2000 mg/day for a prolonged period include nausea, diarrhea, nosebleeds, and abdominal cramps.

There are rare instances in which consuming even moderately excessive doses of vitamin C can be harmful. As mentioned in the Nutrition Myth or Fact box, vitamin C enhances the absorption of iron. This action is beneficial to people who need to increase iron absorption. It can be harmful, however, to people with a disease

QUICK TIPS

Selecting Foods High in Vitamin C

▶ Mix strawberries, kiwi fruit, cantaloupe, and oranges for a tasty fruit salad loaded with vitamin C.
▶ Include tomatoes on salads, wraps, and sandwiches for more vitamin C.
▶ Make your own fresh-squeezed orange or grapefruit juice!
▶ Add your favourite vitamin C–rich fruits, such as strawberries, to smoothies.
▶ Buy ready-to-eat vegetables, such as baby carrots and cherry tomatoes, and toss some in a zip-lock bag to take to school or work.
▶ Put a few slices of romaine lettuce on your sandwich.
▶ Throw a small container of orange slices, fresh pineapple chunks, or berries into your backpack for an afternoon snack.

▶ Store some 100% juice boxes in your freezer to pack with your lunch. They'll thaw slowly, keeping the rest of your lunch cool, and many brands contain a full day's supply of vitamin C in just 175 mL (6 fl. oz.).
▶ Enjoy raw bell peppers with low-fat dip for a crunchy snack.
▶ Serve reduced-salt corn chips with fresh salsa.
▶ Make gazpacho! In a blender, combine 250–750 mL (1–3 cups) of tomato juice, chunks of green pepper and red onion, a cucumber with seeds removed (no need to peel), the juice of one lime, a garlic clove, a splash each of red-wine vinegar and olive oil, a half teaspoon each of basil and cumin, and salt and pepper to taste. Seed and dice two to three fresh tomatoes and add to blended ingredients. Chill for several hours and serve cold, topped with a dollop of plain yogurt.

Fresh vegetables are good sources of vitamin C and beta-carotene.

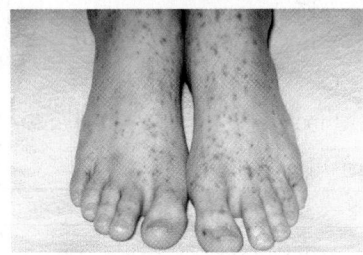

Figure 8.9 Petechiae seen in scurvy.

called *hemochromatosis,* which causes an excess accumulation of iron in the body. Such iron toxicity can damage our tissues and lead to a heart attack. In people who have pre-existing kidney disease, taking excess vitamin C can lead to the formation of kidney stones. This does not appear to occur in healthy individuals.

Critics of vitamin C supplementation claim that taking the supplemental form of the vitamin is "unbalanced" nutrition and leads vitamin C to act as a pro-oxidant. A **pro-oxidant**, as you might guess, is a nutrient that promotes oxidation. It does this by pushing the balance of exchange reactions toward oxidation, which promotes the production of free radicals. Although the results of a few studies suggest that vitamin C acts as a pro-oxidant, these studies were found to be flawed or irrelevant for humans. At the present time, there appears to be no strong scientific evidence that vitamin C, from either food or dietary supplements, acts as a pro-oxidant in humans.

What Happens If We Don't Consume Enough Vitamin C?

Vitamin C deficiencies are rare in developed countries but can occur in developing countries. Scurvy is the most common vitamin C–deficiency disease. The symptoms of scurvy appear after about one month of a vitamin C–deficient diet and include bleeding gums, hemorrhages around the hair follicles of the arms and legs (tiny purplish spots called *petechiae* shown in **Figure 8.9**), loose teeth, wounds that fail to heal, swollen ankles and wrists, bone pain and fractures, diarrhea, weakness, and depression. Anemia can also result from vitamin C deficiency. The people most at risk are those who eat few fruits and vegetables, including impoverished or homebound individuals, and people who abuse alcohol and drugs.

RECAP Vitamin C scavenges free radicals and regenerates vitamin E after it has been oxidized. It also assists in the synthesis of collagen, hormones, neurotransmitters, and DNA. Vitamin C also enhances iron absorption. The RDA for vitamin C is 90 mg per day for men and 75 mg per day for women; the RDA is 35 mg higher for people who smoke. Many fruits and vegetables are high in vitamin C, and our requirements are modest. Toxicity is uncommon; symptoms include nausea, diarrhea, and nosebleeds. Deficiency can result in scurvy or anemia.

Beta-Carotene

Although beta-carotene is not considered an essential nutrient, it is a *provitamin* found in many fruits and vegetables. **Provitamins** are inactive forms of vitamins that the body cannot use until they are converted to their active form. Our body converts beta-carotene to the active form of vitamin A, or *retinol;* thus, beta-carotene is a precursor of retinol. It takes two units of beta-carotene to make one unit of active vitamin A. Not surprisingly, we express the units of beta-carotene in a food as Retinol Activity Equivalents, or RAE. This measurement tells us how much active vitamin A is available to the body after it has converted the beta-carotene in the food.

Beta-carotene is classified as a **carotenoid**, a class of phytochemicals (see the *In Depth* on pages 68–71). As you might guess from their name, carotenoids are a group of plant pigments that are the basis for the orange, red, and deep yellow colours of many fruits and vegetables, including carrots. (Even dark-green leafy vegetables contain plenty of carotenoids, but the green pigment, chlorophyll, masks their colour!) Although there are more than 600 carotenoids found in nature, only about 50 are in the typical human diet. The six most common carotenoids found in human blood are alpha-carotene, beta-carotene, beta-cryptoxanthin, lutein, lycopene, and zeaxanthin. Of these, the body can convert only alpha-carotene, beta-carotene, and beta-cryptoxanthin to retinol. These are referred to as *provitamin A carotenoids.* We are just beginning to learn more about how carotenoids function in our body and how they may affect our health.

Functions of Beta-Carotene

Beta-carotene and some other carotenoids are recognized to have antioxidant properties. Like vitamin E, they are fat soluble and fight the harmful effects of oxidation in the lipid portions of our cell membranes and in our LDLs; however, compared to

pro-oxidant A nutrient that promotes oxidation and oxidative cell and tissue damage.

provitamin An inactive form of a vitamin that the body can convert to an active form. An example is beta-carotene.

carotenoid A fat-soluble plant pigment that the body stores in the liver and adipose tissues. The body is able to convert certain carotenoids to vitamin A.

vitamin E, beta-carotene is a relatively weak antioxidant. In fact, other carotenoids, such as lycopene and lutein, may be stronger antioxidants.

Carotenoids play other important roles in our body. Specifically, they

- enhance our immune system and boost our ability to fight illness and disease;
- protect our skin from the damage caused by the sun's ultraviolet rays; and
- protect our eyes from damage, preventing or delaying age-related vision impairment.

Carotenoids are also associated with a decreased risk for certain types of cancer.

We discuss the roles of carotenoids and other antioxidants in cancer in the *In Depth* on pages 279–285.

Foods that are high in carotenoids are easy to recognize by their bright colours.

How Much Beta-Carotene Should We Consume?

Nutritional scientists do not consider beta-carotene and other carotenoids to be essential nutrients, as they play no known essential roles in our body and are not associated with any deficiency symptoms. Thus, no RDA for these compounds has been established. It has been suggested that consuming 6 to 10 mg of beta-carotene per day from food sources can increase the beta-carotene levels in our blood to amounts that may reduce our risks for some diseases, such as cancer and heart disease (Burri, 1997). Supplements containing beta-carotene have become very popular, and supplementation studies have prescribed doses of 15 to 30 mg of beta-carotene. Refer to the Nutrition Debate on page 275 to learn more about how antioxidant supplementation, including beta-carotene, may affect your risk for cancer and cardiovascular disease.

Beta-Carotene: Beyond Carrots

Not only carrots, but most vegetables—and fruits—that are red, orange, yellow, or deep green are high in beta-carotene and other carotenoids, such as lutein and lycopene. Tomatoes, sweet potatoes, leafy greens (such as kale and spinach), apricots, cantaloupe, and pumpkin are good sources. Eating the recommended amounts of fruits and vegetables each day ensures an adequate intake of carotenoids. Because of its colour, beta-carotene is used as a natural colouring agent for many foods, including margarine, yellow cheddar cheese, cereal, cake mixes, gelatines, and soft drinks. However, these foods are not significant sources of beta-carotene. **Figure 8.10** identifies common foods that are high in beta-carotene.

We generally absorb only between 20% and 40% of the carotenoids present in the foods we eat. In contrast to vitamins E and C, carotenoids are absorbed better from cooked foods. Carotenoids are bound in the cells of plants, and the process of lightly cooking these plants breaks chemical bonds and can rupture cell walls, which humans do not digest. These actions result in more of the carotenoids being released

Pumpkin, canned – 250 mL

Sweet potato, baked, with skin – 1

Spinach, frozen, cooked – 250 mL

Kale, frozen, cooked – 250 mL

Carrots, raw – 250 mL

Cantaloupe, fresh – 250 mL

Spinach, raw – 500 mL

Broccoli, cooked – 500 mL

0   2   4   6   8   10   12   14   16   18   20

Beta-carotene (mg)

Figure 8.10 Common food sources of beta-carotene. There is no RDA for beta-carotene.
Data from U.S. Department of Agriculture, Agricultural Research Service. USDA—NCC Carotenoid Database for U.S. Foods, 2009. USDA Nutrient Database for Standard Reference, Release 22. Nutrient Data Laboratory Home Page, www.ars.usda.gov/ba/bhnrc/ndl.

QUICK TIPS

Boosting Your Beta-Carotene

- Start your day with an orange, grapefruit, pear, banana, apple, or slice of canta-loupe. All are good sources of beta-carotene.
- Pack a zip-lock bag of carrot slices or dried apricots in your lunch.
- Instead of french fries, think orange! Slice raw sweet potatoes, toss the slices in olive or canola oil, and bake.

- Add veggies to homemade pizza.
- Add shredded carrots to cake and muffin batters.
- Taking dessert to a potluck? Make a pump-kin pie! It's easy if you use canned pumpkin and follow the recipe on the can.
- Go green, too! The next time you have a salad, go for the dark-green leafy vegeta-bles instead of iceberg lettuce.
- Add raw spinach or other green leafy veg-etables to wraps and sandwiches.

from the plant. For instance, 250 mL (1 cup) of raw carrots contains approximately 10 mg of beta-carotene, whereas the same amount of cooked carrots contains approximately 13 mg (USDA, 2009). See Quick Tips for some tips for increasing your intake of beta-carotene.

What Happens If We Consume Too Much Beta-Carotene?

Consuming large amounts of beta-carotene or other carot-enoids in foods does not ap-pear to cause toxic symptoms. However, your skin can turn yellow or orange if you consume large amounts of foods that are high in beta-carotene. This condition is referred to as *carotenosis* or *carotenoderma*, and it appears to be both reversible and harmless. Taking beta-carotene supplements is not generally recommended, because we can get adequate amounts of this nutrient by eating more fruits and vegetables, and supplements may be harmful in certain populations.

What Happens If We Don't Consume Enough Beta-Carotene?

There are no known deficiency symptoms of beta-carotene or other carotenoids apart from beta-carotene's function as a precursor for vitamin A.

RECAP Beta-carotene is a carotenoid and a provitamin of vitamin A. It protects the lipid portions of cell membranes and LDL-cholesterol from oxidative damage. It also enhances immune function and protects vision. There is no RDA for beta-carotene. Orange, red, and deep green fruits and vegetables are good sources of beta-carotene. There are no known toxicity or deficiency symptoms, but yellowing of the skin can occur if too much beta-carotene is consumed.

Vitamin A: Much More than an Antioxidant Nutrient

As early as AD 30, the Roman writer Aulus Cornelius Celsus described in his medi-cal encyclopedia, *De Medicina,* a condition called night blindness and recommended as a cure the consumption of liver. We now know that night blindness is due to a deficiency of vitamin A, a fat-soluble vitamin stored primarily in the liver of animals. When we consume vitamin A, we store 90% in our liver, and the remainder in our adipose tissue, kidneys, and lungs. Because fat-soluble vitamins cannot dissolve in our blood, they require proteins that can bind with and transport them through the bloodstream to target tissues and cells. *Retinol-binding protein* is one such carrier protein for vitamin A. Retinol-binding protein carries one form of vitamin A, retinol, from the liver to the cells that require it.

There are three active forms of vitamin A in our body: **retinol** is the alcohol form, **retinal** is the aldehyde form, and **retinoic acid** is the acid form. These three forms are collectively referred to as the *retinoids* (**Figure 8.11**). Of the three, retinol has the starring role in maintaining our body's physiologic functions. Remember from the previous section that beta-carotene is a precursor to vitamin A. When we eat foods that contain beta-carotene, it is converted to retinol in the wall of our small intestine.

The unit of expression for vitamin A is Retinol Activity Equivalents (RAE). You may still see the expression Retinol Equivalents (RE) or International Units (IU) for vitamin A on food labels and dietary supplements. The conversions to RAE from

retinol An active, alcohol form of vitamin A that plays an important role in healthy vision and immune function.

retinal An active, aldehyde form of vitamin A that plays an important role in healthy vision and immune function.

retinoic acid An active, acid form of vitamin A that plays an important role in cell growth and immune function.

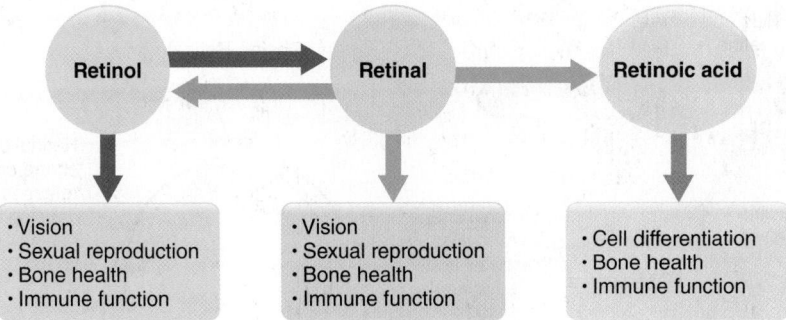

Figure 8.11 The three active forms of vitamin A in our body are retinol, retinal, and retinoic acid. Retinol and retinal can be converted interchangeably; retinoic acid is formed from retinal, and this process is irreversible. Each form of vitamin A contributes to many of our bodily processes.

various forms of retinol are 1 RAE = 1 microgram (µg) retinol, 12 µg beta-carotene, 24 µg alpha-carotene or beta-cryptoxanthin, 1 RE, and 3.3 IU.

Functions of Vitamin A

The known functions of vitamin A are numerous, and researchers speculate that many are still to be discovered.

Vitamin A May Act as an Antioxidant   Limited research indicates that vitamin A may act as an antioxidant (Gutteridge and Halliwell, 1994; Larsson et al., 2007; Livrea et al., 1995). Like vitamins E and C, it appears to scavenge free radicals and protect our LDLs from oxidation. As you might expect, adequate vitamin A levels in the blood are associated with lower risks for some forms of cancer and heart disease. However, the role of vitamin A as an antioxidant is not strongly established and is still under investigation.

Vitamin A Is Essential to Sight   A critical role of vitamin A in our body is certainly in the maintenance of healthy vision. Specifically, vitamin A affects our sight in two ways: it enables us to react to changes in the brightness of light, and it enables us to distinguish between various wavelengths of light—in other words, to see different colours. Let's take a closer look at this process.

Light enters our eyes through the cornea, travels through the lens, and then hits the **retina**, which is a delicate membrane lining the back of the inner eyeball **(Figure 8.12)**. You might already have guessed how *retinal* got its name: it is found in—and is integral to—the retina. In the retina, retinal combines with a protein called *opsin* to form **rhodopsin**, a light-sensitive pigment. Rhodopsin is found in the *rod cells*, which are cells that react to dim light and interpret black-and-white images.

When light hits the retina, a reaction occurs in which rhodopsin is split into retinal and opsin. This causes the rod cells to lose their colour. It also causes both retinal and opsin to change shape. These changes in turn result in the transmission of a signal to the brain that is interpreted as a black-and-white image. This process goes on continually, allowing our eyes to adjust continuously to subtle changes in our surroundings or in the level of light. Most of the retinal is recycled and combines with opsin to form rhodopsin again. However, some of the retinal is lost with each cycle and must be replaced by retinol from the bloodstream. At the same time, the *cone cells* of the retina, which are effective only in bright light, use retinal to interpret different wavelengths of light as different colours.

In summary, our abilities to adjust to dim light, recover from a bright flash of light, and see in colour are all critically dependent on adequate levels of retinal in our eyes.

Vitamin A Contributes to Cell Differentiation   Another important role of vitamin A is its contribution to **cell differentiation**, the process by which immature cells develop into highly specialized cells that perform unique functions. Obviously, this process is critical to the development of healthy organs and effectively functioning body systems. For example, specialized cells lining the trachea and bronchi, intestines, stomach, bladder, cornea of the eye, and other organs produce mucus, which lubricates the tissue and helps us propel substances out of our body tissues (for example, when we

Eating plenty of fruits and vegetables can help prevent vitamin A deficiency.

retina The delicate, light-sensitive membrane lining the inner eyeball and connected to the optic nerve. It contains retinal.

rhodopsin A light-sensitive pigment found in the rod cells that is formed by retinal and opsin.

cell differentiation The process by which immature, undifferentiated stem cells develop into highly specialized functional cells of discrete organs and tissues.

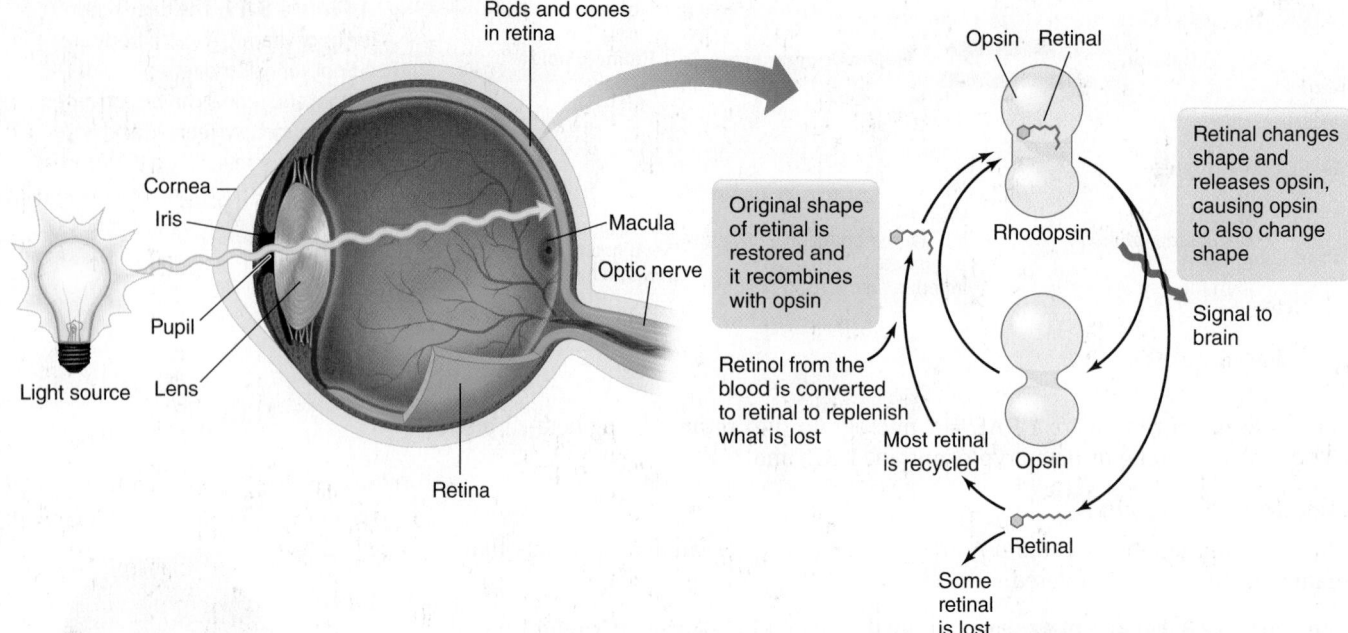

Figure 8.12 Vitamin A is necessary to maintain healthy vision. Light enters the eye through the cornea, travels through the lens, and hits the retina located in the back of the eye. In the rod cells of the retina, retinal is combined with opsin to form rhodopsin. As light hits the rod cells, they lose colour, and the components of rhodopsin, retinal and opsin, split and change shape. These changes cause transmission of a signal to the brain that allows us to see.

Liver, cantaloupe, and carrots all contain preformed vitamin A, or beta-carotene, that can be converted to vitamin A in our bodies.

cough up secretions or empty our bladder). When vitamin A levels are insufficient, these cells fail to differentiate appropriately, and we lose these functions. Vitamin A is also critical to the differentiation of specialized immune cells called *T-lymphocytes*, or *T-cells*, which fight infections. You can now see why vitamin A deficiency can lead to infections and other disorders of the lungs and respiratory tract, urinary tract, vagina, and eyes.

Other Functions of Vitamin A Vitamin A is involved in reproduction. Although its exact role is unclear, it appears necessary for sperm production in men and for fertilization to occur in women. It also contributes to healthy bone growth by assisting in breaking down old bone, so that new, longer, and stronger bone can develop. As a result of a vitamin A deficiency, children suffer from stunted growth and wasting. Finally, two popular treatments for acne contain derivatives of vitamin A.

How Much Vitamin A Should We Consume?

Vitamin A toxicity can occur readily because it is a fat-soluble vitamin, so it is important to consume only the amount recommended for your gender and age range. The RDA for vitamin A is 900 µg (RAE) per day for men and 700 µg (RAE) per day for women (see Table 8.1) (Institute of Medicine, 2001). The UL is 3000 µg (RAE) per day of preformed vitamin A in men and women (including those pregnant and lactating).

The most common sources of dietary preformed vitamin A are animal foods, such as beef liver, chicken liver, eggs, and whole-fat dairy products. Vitamin A is also found in fortified reduced-fat milks, margarine, and some breakfast cereals **(Figure 8.13)**. The other sources of the vitamin A we consume are foods high in beta-carotene and other carotenoids that can be converted to vitamin A. As discussed earlier in this chapter, dark-green, orange, and deep yellow fruits and vegetables are good sources of beta-carotene, and thus of vitamin A. Carrots, spinach, mango, cantaloupe, and tomato juice are excellent sources of vitamin A because they contain beta-carotene.

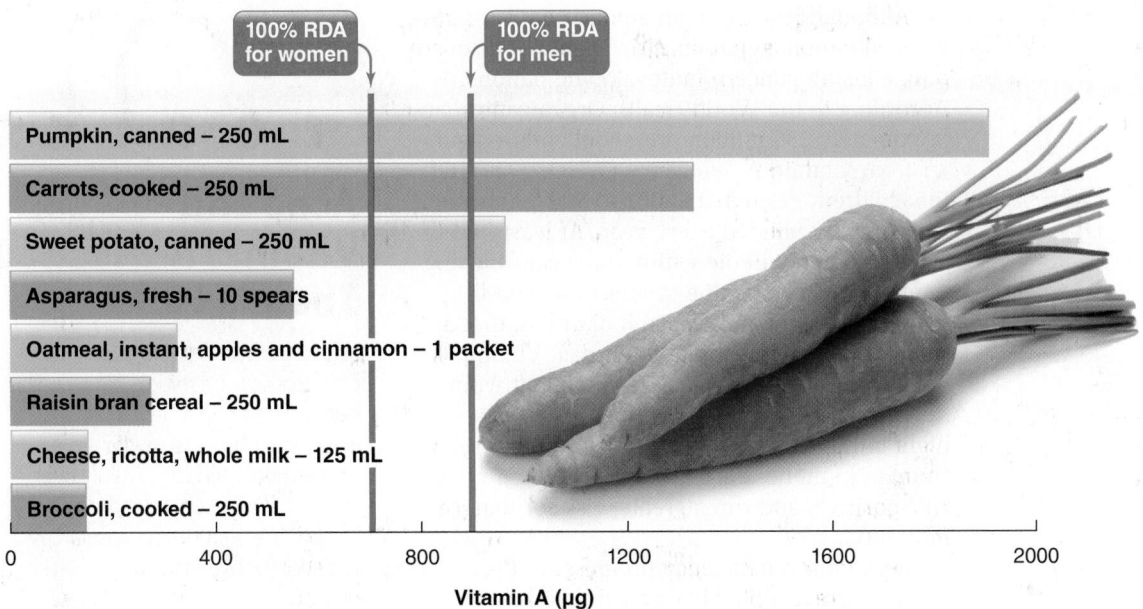

100% RDA for women

100% RDA for men

- Pumpkin, canned – 250 mL
- Carrots, cooked – 250 mL
- Sweet potato, canned – 250 mL
- Asparagus, fresh – 10 spears
- Oatmeal, instant, apples and cinnamon – 1 packet
- Raisin bran cereal – 250 mL
- Cheese, ricotta, whole milk – 125 mL
- Broccoli, cooked – 250 mL

0   400   800   1200   1600   2000

Vitamin A (µg)

Figure 8.13 Common food sources of vitamin A. The RDA for vitamin A is 900 µg/day for men and 700 µg/day for women.

Data from U.S. Department of Agriculture, Agricultural Research Service, 2009. USDA Nutrient Database for Standard Reference, Release 22. Nutrient Data Laboratory Home Page, www.ars.usda.gov/ba/bhnrc/ndl.

What Happens If We Consume Too Much Vitamin A?

Vitamin A is highly toxic, and toxicity symptoms develop after consuming only three to four times the RDA. Toxicity rarely results from food sources; however, vitamin A supplementation is known to have caused severe illness and even death. In pregnant women, it can cause serious birth defects and spontaneous abortion. Other toxicity symptoms include fatigue, loss of appetite, blurred vision, hair loss, skin disorders, bone and joint pain, abdominal pain, nausea, diarrhea, and damage to the liver and nervous system. If caught in time, many of these symptoms are reversible once vitamin A supplementation is stopped. However, permanent damage can occur to the liver, eyes, and other organs.

What Happens If We Don't Consume Enough Vitamin A?

Night blindness and colour blindness can result from vitamin A deficiency. Night blindness is characterized by an inability to adjust to dim light, as well as the failure to regain sight quickly after a bright flash of light (**Figure 8.14**). How severe a problem is night blindness?

night blindness A vitamin A deficiency disorder that results in loss of the ability to see in dim light.

Normal light adjustment   Slow light adjustment

Figure 8.14 A deficiency of vitamin A can result in poor night vision and difficulty in adjusting from bright light to dim light.

Although less common among people of developed nations, vitamin A deficiency is a severe public health concern in developing nations. According to the World Health Organization, approximately 250 million preschool children suffer from vitamin A deficiency (WHO, 2009). Of the children affected, 250 000 to 500 000 become permanently blinded every year. At least half of these children will die within one year of losing their sight. Death is due to infections and illnesses, including measles and diarrhea, that are easily treated in wealthier countries. Vitamin A deficiency is also a tragedy for pregnant women in these countries. These women suffer from night blindness, are more likely to transmit HIV (human immunodeficiency virus) to their child if HIV-positive, and run a greater risk for maternal mortality.

If vitamin A deficiency progresses, it can result in irreversible blindness due to hardening of the cornea (the transparent membrane covering the front of the eye), a condition called *xerophthalmia.* The prefix of this word, *xero-*, comes from a Greek word meaning "dry." Lack of vitamin A causes the cells of the cornea to lose their ability to produce mucus, causing the eye to become very dry. This leaves the cornea susceptible to damage, infection, and hardening. Once the cornea hardens in this way, the resulting blindness is irreversible. This is why it is critical to catch vitamin A deficiency in its early stages and treat it either with the regular consumption of fruits and vegetables that contain beta-carotene or with vitamin A supplementation.

Other deficiency symptoms include impaired immunity, increased risk for illness and infections, reproductive system disorders, and failure of normal growth. Individuals who are at risk for vitamin A deficiency include elderly people with poor diets, newborn or premature infants (due to low liver stores of vitamin A), young children with inadequate vegetable and fruit intakes, and alcoholics. Any condition that results in fat malabsorption can also lead to vitamin A deficiency. Children with cystic fibrosis and individuals with Crohn's disease, celiac disease, or diseases of the liver, pancreas, or gallbladder are at risk for vitamin A deficiency.

RECAP The role of vitamin A as an antioxidant is still under investigation. Vitamin A is critical for maintaining our vision. It is also necessary for cell differentiation, reproduction, and growth. The RDA for vitamin A is 900 µg per day for men and 700 µg per day for women. Animal liver, dairy products, and eggs are good animal sources of vitamin A; fruits and vegetables are high in beta-carotene,

HOT TOPIC

Acne and Vitamin A—Is There a Link?

Search the internet and you will find plenty of sites claiming a direct link between vitamin A deficiency and acne, and insisting that vitamin A supplements can successfully treat acne. Should you believe the hype?

In 2006, a study reported an association between low blood levels of vitamin A and the presence of acne: the more severe the acne, the lower the levels of vitamin A (El-akawi et al., 2006). Although these findings may seem suggestive, this study was conducted with a very small number of participants who were not randomly selected. Also, plasma levels of vitamin A were assessed to indicate vitamin A status; however, the Institute of Medicine, 2001 states that plasma levels of vitamin A are not necessarily an indicator of vitamin A status. To date, these results have not been replicated by other researchers, and there appears to be no evidence that vitamin A deficiency causes acne.

Interestingly, two effective treatments for acne are synthetic derivatives of vitamin A. Retin-A, or tretinoin, is a treatment applied to the skin. Accutane, or isotretinoin, is taken orally. These medications should be used carefully and only under the supervision of a licensed physician. Although they are relatively less toxic forms of vitamin A, they can cause birth defects in the developing fetus if used while a woman is pregnant and can lead to other toxicity problems in some individuals. It is recommended that these medications be stopped at least two years prior to conceiving. Contrary to what you might read on the Internet, vitamin A itself has no effect on acne; thus, vitamin A supplements are not recommended in its treatment.

which our body uses to synthesize vitamin A. Supplementation can be dangerous, as toxicity is reached at levels of only three to four times the RDA. Toxicity symptoms include birth defects, spontaneous abortion, blurred vision, and liver damage. Deficiency symptoms include night blindness, impaired immune function, and growth failure.

Selenium

Selenium is a trace mineral, and it is found in varying amounts in soil and thus in the food grown there. Keep in mind that although we need only minute amounts of trace minerals they are just as important to our health as the major minerals.

Functions of Selenium

It is only recently that we have learned about the critical role of selenium as a nutrient in human health. In 1979, Chinese scientists reported an association between a heart disorder called **Keshan disease** and selenium deficiency. This disease occurs in children in the Keshan province of China, where the soil is depleted of selenium. The scientists found that Keshan disease can be prevented with selenium supplementation.

The selenium in our body is contained in amino acids. Two amino acid derivatives contain most of the selenium in our body: *selenomethionine* is the storage form for selenium, while *selenocysteine* is the active form of selenium. Selenium is a critical component of the glutathione peroxidase antioxidant enzyme system mentioned earlier (page 259). Thus, selenium helps spare vitamin E and prevents oxidative damage to our cell membranes.

Like vitamin C, selenium is needed for the production of thyroxine, or thyroid hormone. By this action, selenium is involved in the maintenance of our basal metabolism and body temperature. Selenium appears to play a role in immune function, and poor selenium status is associated with higher rates of some forms of cancer.

How Much Selenium Should We Consume?

The content of selenium in foods is highly variable. As it is a trace mineral, we need only minute amounts to maintain health. The RDA for selenium is 55 μg per day for both men and women (see Table 8.1) (Institute of Medicine, 2000). The UL is 400 μg per day.

Selenium is present in both animal and plant food sources but in variable amounts. Because it is stored in the tissues of animals, selenium is found in reliably consistent amounts in animal foods. Organ meats, such as liver and kidneys, as well as pork and seafood, are particularly good sources **(Figure 8.15)**.

In contrast, the amount of selenium in plants is dependent on the selenium content of the soil in which the plant is grown. Many companies marketing selenium supplements warn that the agricultural soils in the United States are depleted of selenium and inform us that we need to take selenium supplements. In reality, the selenium content of soil varies greatly across North America, and because we obtain our food from a variety of geographic locations, few people in the United States suffer from selenium deficiency. This is especially true for people who eat even small quantities of meat or seafood.

What Happens If We Consume Too Much Selenium?

Selenium toxicity does not result from eating foods high in selenium. However, supplementation can cause toxicity. Toxicity symptoms include brittle hair and nails that can eventually break and fall off. Other symptoms include skin rashes, vomiting, nausea, weakness, and liver disease.

What Happens If We Don't Consume Enough Selenium?

As discussed previously, selenium deficiency is associated with a form of heart disease called Keshan disease. Selenium deficiency does not cause the disease, but

Keshan disease A heart disorder caused by selenium deficiency. It was first identified in children in the Keshan province of China.

Seafood is a rich source of selenium.

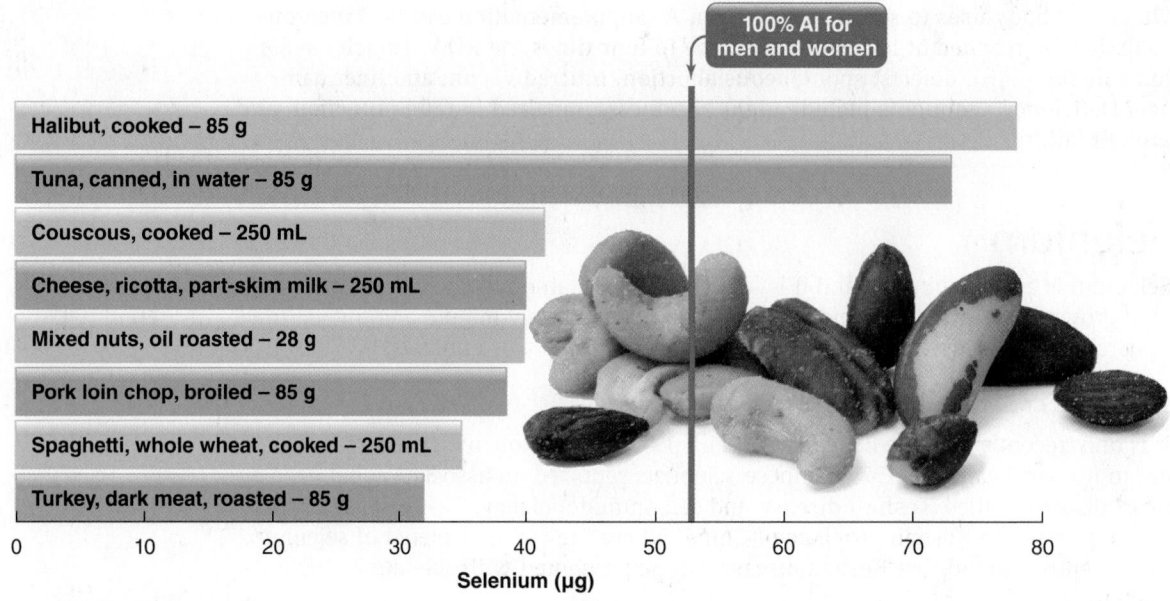

Figure 8.15 Common food sources of selenium. The RDA for selenium is 55 µg/day.
Data from U.S. Department of Agriculture, Agricultural Research Service, 2009. USDA Nutrient Database for Standard Reference, Release 22. Nutrient Data Laboratory Home Page, www.ars.usda.gov/ba/bhnrc/ndl.

Figure 8.17 Selenium deficiency can lead to deforming arthritis called Kashin-Beck disease.

selenium is necessary to help the immune system effectively fight the virus that causes the disease. Another deficiency disease is *Kashin-Beck disease*, a deforming arthritis also found in selenium-depleted areas in China and Tibet **(Figure 8.17)**.

Other deficiency symptoms include impaired immune responses, increased risk for viral infections, infertility, depression, hostility, impaired cognitive function, and muscle pain and wasting. Deficiencies of both selenium and iodine in pregnant women can cause a form of *cretinism* in the infant (discussed in Chapter 10).

Copper, Iron, Zinc, and Manganese Assist in Antioxidant Function

As discussed earlier, there are numerous antioxidant enzyme systems in our body. Copper, zinc, and manganese are cofactors for the superoxide dismutase antioxidant enzyme system. Iron is a part of the structure of catalase. In addition to their role in protecting against oxidative damage, these minerals play major roles in the optimal functioning of many other enzymes in our body. Copper, iron, and zinc help us maintain the health of our blood, and manganese is an important cofactor in carbohydrate metabolism. The functions, requirements, food sources, and deficiency and toxicity symptoms of these nutrients are discussed in detail in Chapter 10, which focuses on the nutrients involved in energy metabolism and blood health.

RECAP Selenium is part of the glutathione peroxidase antioxidant enzyme system. It indirectly spares vitamin E from oxidative damage, and it assists with immune function and the production of thyroid hormone. Organ meats, pork, and seafood are good sources of selenium, as are nuts, wheat, and rice. The selenium content of plants is dependent on the amount of selenium in the soil in which they are grown. Toxicity symptoms include brittle hair and nails, vomiting, nausea, and **liver cirrhosis**. Deficiency symptoms and side effects include Keshan disease, Kashin-Beck disease, impaired immune function, infertility, and muscle wasting. Copper, zinc, and manganese are cofactors for the superoxide dismutase antioxidant enzyme system. Iron is a cofactor for the catalase antioxidant enzyme. These minerals play critical roles in blood health and energy metabolism.

Nutrition DEBATE
Antioxidants: Food or Supplements?

As you have learned in this chapter, antioxidant nutrients play an important role in reducing free radical damage, which can in turn reduce the risk for chronic diseases such as cancer and cardiovascular disease (CVD). Despite this, research studies on the effects of antioxidant supplements on risks for cancer and CVD show inconsistent results.

The results of the Alpha-Tocopherol Beta-Carotene (ATBC) Cancer Prevention Study and the Beta-Carotene and Retinol Efficacy Trial (CARET) were particularly surprising (Albanes et al., 1995; Omenn et al., 1996). The ATBC Cancer Prevention Study was conducted in Finland from 1985 to 1993 with the purpose of determining the effects of beta-carotene and vitamin E supplements on the rates of lung cancer and other forms of cancer among male smokers between the ages of 50 and 69 years. Almost 30 000 men participated in the study for an average of six years. The participants were given daily a beta-carotene supplement, a vitamin E supplement, a supplement containing both, or a placebo.

Contrary to expectations, the male smokers who took beta-carotene supplements experienced an *increased* number of deaths during the study. More men in this group died of lung cancer, and there were higher rates of prostate and stomach cancers. Also, more men died of CVD. This negative effect appeared to be particularly strong in men who had a higher alcohol intake.

CARET began as a pilot study in the United States in 1985 and included more than 18 000 men and women who were smokers, former smokers, or workers who had been exposed to asbestos. The participants were randomly assigned to take daily supplements of beta-carotene and retinol (vitamin A) or a placebo. After a four-year follow-up period, the incidence of lung cancer was 28% higher among those taking the beta-carotene and retinol supplement. This significant finding, in addition to the results from the ATBC Cancer Prevention Study, prompted researchers to end the CARET study early and recommend that participants discontinue the supplements (Omenn et al., 1996).

The reasons that beta-carotene increased lung cancer risk in this population are not clear. However, the results of this study suggest that, for certain people, supplementation with beta-carotene may be harmful.

As with the research conducted on cancer, the studies of antioxidants and CVD show inconsistent results. Two large-scale surveys conducted in the United States show that men and women who eat more fruits and vegetables have a significantly reduced risk of CVD (Joshipura et al., 2001; Liu et al., 2001). And in the ATBC Cancer Prevention Study, vitamin E was found to lower the number of deaths

▲ The flavonoids in black tea might reduce the risk for CVD.

due to heart disease. However, it had no overall effect on the risk for stroke (The ATBC Study Group, 1994). In another study, vitamin E had no impact on the risk for CVD in people at high risk for heart attack and stroke (The HOPE and HOPE-TOO Trial Investigators, 2005). And recently, other large intervention studies conducted in the United States have shown no reductions in major cardiovascular events in men and women taking vitamins E or C (Lee et al., 2005; Sesso et al., 2008). Thus, there is growing evidence that antioxidant supplements do not reduce our risk for CVD.

Why might foods high in antioxidants be beneficial in reducing our risks for cancer and CVD, whereas supplements are not? It is important to note that other compounds (besides antioxidants) found in fruits, vegetables, and whole grains can reduce our risk for cancer and CVD. Here are just a few examples: dietary fibre has been shown to reduce the risk for colon and rectal cancers, decrease blood pressure, lower total cholesterol levels, and improve blood glucose and insulin levels. Folate, a B-vitamin found in fortified cereals, green leafy vegetables, and some other plant foods, is known to reduce blood levels of the amino acid homocysteine, and a high concentration of homocysteine is a known risk factor for CVD. Flavonoids are a group of phytochemicals found in many plant foods, including black tea. A recent study has shown that individuals who drank more than three cups of black tea per day had a lower rate of heart attacks than non–tea drinkers (Geleijnse et al, 2002). Thus, it appears that any number of nutrients and other components in fruits, vegetables, and whole-grain foods may be protective against cancer and CVD. As you can see, there is still much to learn about how people respond to foods high in antioxidant nutrients as compared to antioxidant supplementation.

Chapter Review

Test Yourself ANSWERS

1. True. Free radicals are highly unstable atoms that can destabilize neighbouring atoms or molecules and harm our cells; however, they are produced as a normal by-product of human physiology.

2. False. Overall, the research on vitamin C and colds does not show strong evidence that taking vitamin C supplements reduces our risk of suffering from the common cold.

3. True. Carrots are an excellent source of beta-carotene, a precursor for vitamin A, which helps maintain good vision.

Find the Quack

When Bruce and Tina got married, they assumed they'd have no problem becoming parents. But two years later, they're still trying. So when Tina comes home from a doctor's appointment and tells Bruce she has some bad news, he doesn't know what to expect. "Bruce," she says, "I know you're not going to like this, but the doctor says you should quit smoking. She says that smoking reduces your sperm count and could be one reason we haven't conceived. And besides, your own doctor has tried to get you to quit because of your high blood pressure." Bruce feels his spirits sink. It's true he has hypertension, and his dad died of a heart attack at age 45. But he's tried to quit smoking before, and the withdrawal symptoms have always been more than he could handle.

That evening he goes onto the internet and searches under "smoking" and "withdrawal symptoms." He finds a website promoting a supplement called "Quit Calm" that sounds promising, offering relief from the anxiety, sleeplessness, and cravings of nicotine withdrawal. Here is what the site states:

- "Quit Calm offers an all-natural blend of herbs that work together to decrease cravings, eliminate your anxiety, promote your sleep, heal your respiratory tissues, and purge harmful toxins from your body."
- "Ingredients include licorice root, peppermint, ginger, and slippery elm in a proprietary blend that soothes the body's tissues as they recover from nicotine addiction."

- "Independent studies have confirmed the beneficial effects of our patented formula."
- "Take one capsule three times a day 30 minutes before meals."
- "If you order now, a 30-day supply (90 capsules) costs just $29.99. Why wait? Think of all the money you'll be saving by not smoking, and order today!"

1. Bruce finds the statement "Independent studies have confirmed the beneficial effects of our patented formula" reassuring. Do you? Why or why not?

2. Look up licorice root in the "Herbs at a Glance" section of the website of the National Center for Complementary and Alternative Medicine (http://nccam.nih.gov). Would you recommend that Bruce take a supplement containing licorice root? Why or why not?

3. Comment on the advertisement's final bullet urging consumers to "think of all the money you'll be saving by not smoking, and order today!"

4. Instead of a supplements website, where online might Bruce have found reliable help in his quest to quit smoking? What other resources should he consult?

Answers can be found in the study area of MasteringNutrition.

 **NutriTools**

Visit MasteringNutrition to access interactive animations, including:

- Nutrient Functionality

Review Questions

1. Which of the following is a characteristic of vitamin E?
   a. It enhances the absorption of iron.
   b. It can be manufactured from beta-carotene.
   c. It is a critical component of the glutathione peroxidase system.
   d. It is destroyed by exposure to high heat.

2. Oxidation is best described as a process in which
   a. radiation causes a mutation in a cell's DNA.
   b. an atom loses an electron.
   c. an element loses an atom of oxygen.
   d. a compound loses a molecule of water.

3. Which of the following disorders is linked with the production of free radicals?
   a. cardiovascular disease
   b. carotenosis
   c. ulcers
   d. malaria

4. Which of the following function as a cofactor in antioxidant enzyme systems?
   a. iron
   b. zinc
   c. copper
   d. all of the above

5. Taking daily doses of three to four times the RDA of which of the following nutrients may cause death?
   a. vitamin A
   b. vitamin C
   c. vitamin E
   d. selenium

6. Which best describes the danger of free radicals?
   a. They impair eye sight.
   b. They destabilize our cells.
   c. They cause hemorrhaging.
   d. They are associated with Kashin-Beck disease.

7. Vitamin C helps regenerate
   a. vitamin A.
   b. vitamin E.
   c. beta-carotene.
   d. selenium.

8. Which is not a good source of selenium?
   a. Pork
   b. Seafood
   c. Nuts
   d. Legumes

9. Elena has had a heart attack in the past and her doctor has since prescribed her aspirin. She has turned a new leaf since her attack and is doing much better now with daily exercise in addition to proper nutrition. In being more health conscious, Elena has thought about taking vitamin supplements and asks her health care provider for advice. Which vitamin supplement should Elena be careful with?

10. In four months, Natalie and William are welcoming their first child. Being a doting husband, William has tirelessly run to the grocery store every time Natalie has had a craving. For the past two weeks, she has been craving fried beef liver and pumpkin puree almost every day. Should William be worried? What toxicity symptoms should he be looking for?

11. Explain how free radicals damage cell membranes and lead to cell death.

12. Describe the process by which cancer occurs, beginning with initiation and ending with metastasis of the cancer to widespread body tissues.

13. Explain why people taking anticoagulants should avoid vitamin E supplementation.

14. Discuss the contribution of trace minerals, such as selenium, to the prevention of oxidation.

15. Explain how vitamin E reduces our risk for heart disease.

Answers to Review Questions can be found at the back of this text.

Web Resources

www.cancer.ca
The Canadian Cancer Society

Click on "Prevention" for more information on ways you can reduce your risk of cancer. To learn about different types of cancers, click on "About Cancer." For descriptions of cancer research underway in Canada, click on "Cancer Research."

www.heartandstroke.com
Heart and Stroke Foundation of Canada

Find out about your own personal risk profile by taking the Heart and Stroke Risk Assessment™. This profile will also provide a free, confidential, customized action plan for healthy living.

www.cnib.ca
The Canadian National Institute for the Blind

Find out more about common causes of vision loss in Canada and the support services available.

www.ffb.ca
The Foundation Fighting Blindness—Canada

Learn more about age-related macular degeneration.

healthycanadians.ca/pr-rp/billC-51_e.html
Healthy Canadians, Health Canada

Visit this site to learn more about the federal government regulations for natural health products.

www.who.int
World Health Organization (WHO)

Click on "Health Topics" and search for "vitamin A deficiency" to find out more about vitamin A deficiency around the world.

www.fda.gov
U.S. Food and Drug Administration (FDA)

This site provides information on how to make informed decisions and evaluate information related to dietary supplements.

www.nal.usda.gov/fnic
The Food and Nutrition Information Center (FNIC)

Click on the Dietary Supplements button to obtain information on vitamin and mineral supplements, including consumer reports and industry regulations.

www.dietary-supplements.info.nih.gov
Office of Dietary Supplements

Go to this site to obtain current research results and reliable information about dietary supplements.

MasteringNutrition®

Assignments

Animations Free Radical Formation • Vitamin A and Epithelial Tissue • Vitamin A and the Visual Cycle

Study Area

Video: Using the Functional Approach to Understand Fluid & Electrolyte Balance • Practice Tests • Diet Analysis • eText

Cancer

WANT TO FIND OUT...

- how your lifestyle can influence your risk for cancer?

- about the link between antioxidants and cancer?

- if antioxidant supplements can reduce your risk for cancer?

READ ON.

The Canadian Cancer Society estimates that "every hour of every day, an average of 20 people will be diagnosed with some type of cancer and eight people will die from cancer" (Canadian Cancer Society, 2012a).

With such alarming statistics, it is not surprising that television commercials, internet sites, and health and fitness publications are filled with product claims promising to reduce your risk of developing cancer. Many of these claims tout the benefits of antioxidants.

In opposition to these claims, some research evidence suggests that taking antioxidant supplements may actually increase the risk of cancer for certain people (refer back to the Nutrition Debate on page 275). In this *In Depth*, we'll take a closer look at the group of diseases collectively known as cancer. We'll explore how it begins and spreads and identify the factors that most significantly increase our risk. We'll also review what is currently known about the role of antioxidant nutrients in cancer and identify other strategies for reducing your risk.

What Is Cancer?

Before we explore how antioxidants affect the risk for cancer, let's take a closer look at precisely what cancer is and how it spreads. **Cancer** is actually a group of diseases that are all characterized by cells that grow "out of control." By this we mean that cancer cells reproduce spontaneously and independently, and they are not inhibited by the boundaries of tissues and organs. Thus, they can aggressively invade tissues and organs far away from those in which they originally formed.

Most forms of cancer result in one or more **tumours**, which are newly formed masses of undifferentiated cells that are immature and have no physiologic function. Although the word *tumour* sounds frightening, it is important to note that not every tumour is *malignant*, or cancerous. Many are *benign* (not harmful to us) and are made up of cells that will not spread widely.

Cancer Progresses in Three Stages

Figure 1 shows how changes to normal cells prompt a series of other changes that can progress

cancer A group of diseases characterized by cells that reproduce spontaneously and independently and may invade other tissues and organs.

tumour Any newly formed mass of undifferentiated cells.

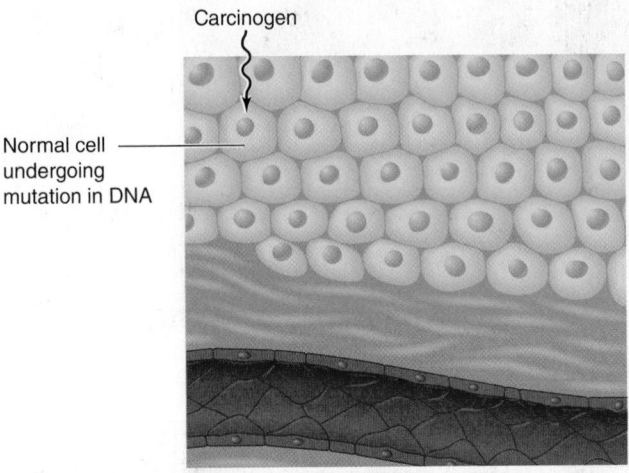

Carcinogen

Normal cell undergoing mutation in DNA

a **Initiation**: a carcinogen causes a mutation in the DNA of a normal cell.

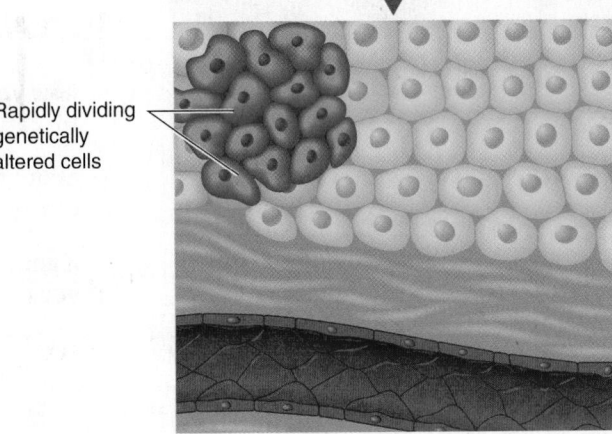

Rapidly dividing genetically altered cells

b **Promotion**: cell with mutation in DNA divides repeatedly.

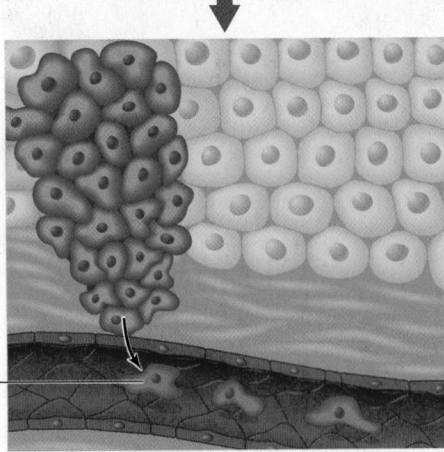

Cancer cell transported in blood vessel

c **Progression**: cancer cells invade surrounding tissues and spread to other sites in the body.

Figure 1 **(a)** Cancer cells develop as a result of a genetic mutation in the DNA of a normal cell. **(b)** The mutated cell replicates uncontrollably, eventually resulting in a tumour. **(c)** If not destroyed or removed, the cancerous tumour metastasizes and spreads to other parts of the body.

into cancer. There are three primary stages of cancer development: initiation, promotion, and progression. They occur as follows:

1. *Initiation.* The initiation of cancer occurs when a cell's DNA is *mutated* (changed). This mutation causes permanent changes in the cell.
2. *Promotion.* During this phase, the genetically altered cell is stimulated to divide. A single mutated cell divides in two, and these double to four, and so on. The mutated DNA is locked into each new cell's genetic instructions. Because the enzymes that normally work to repair damaged cells cannot detect alterations in the DNA, the cells can continue to divide uninhibited. Typically, it takes many years for a mutated cell to double repeatedly into a tumour mass large enough to be detectable (about the size of a grape), and promotion is the longest stage in cancer development (McConnell, 2007).
3. *Progression.* During this phase, the cancerous cells reproduce out of control. They grow their own blood vessels, which supply them with blood and nutrients, and invade adjacent tissues. In this early stage of progression, the immune system can sometimes detect these cancerous cells and destroy them. However, if the cells continue to grow, they develop into malignant tumours, disrupting body functioning at their primary site and invading the circulatory and lymphatic systems to *metastasize* (spread) to distant sites in the body.

We noted earlier that cancer is often fatal; however, a majority of people who develop cancer survive. Based on data from 2004 to 2006, the Canadian Cancer Society reports that the five-year survival rate for all cancers was 62% (Canadian Cancer Society, 2012b). Of course, cancers can be more or less aggressive, some are more readily detectable than others, and some tissues and organs are more vulnerable to cancer. These factors all influence the overall mortality rate associated with different cancers. The type of cancer with the highest mortality rate is lung cancer, with over 20 000 deaths estimated in 2011. Breast cancer ranks second for women (14% of cancer mortality), cancer of the colon and/or rectum ranks third for women and second for men (12% of all cancer deaths). For men, prostate cancer ranks third, with an estimated 4100 deaths in 2011.

A Variety of Factors Influence Cancer Risk

Researchers estimate that about half of all men and one-third of all women will develop cancer during their lifetime (American Cancer Society, 2009). But what factors cause cancer? Are you and your loved ones at risk? The answer depends on several factors, including your family history of cancer, your exposure to environmental agents, and various lifestyle choices.

Heredity can play a role in the development of cancer, because inherited "cancer genes," such as the BRC genes for breast cancer, increase the risk that an individual with those genes will develop cancer. However, only about 5% of all cancers are strongly hereditary (American Cancer Society, 2009). In addition, it is important to bear in mind that a family history of cancer does not guarantee you will get cancer, too. It just means that you are at an increased risk and should take all preventive actions available to you. While some risk factors are out of your control, others are modifiable, which means that you can take positive steps to reduce your risk.

▲ Using tobacco is a risk factor for cancer.

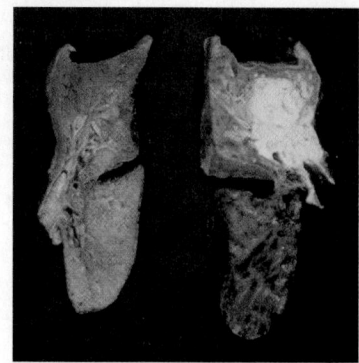

▲ **Figure 2** Cigarette smoking significantly increases our risk for lung and other types of cancer. The risk for lung cancer is 22.4 times higher in men who smoke and 12 times higher in women who smoke. **(a)** A normal, healthy lung; **(b)** the lung of a smoker. Notice the deposits of tar as well as the areas of tumour growth.

The Canadian Cancer Society identifies five modifiable risk factors that have been shown to have the greatest impact on an individual's cancer risk: tobacco, nutrition and fitness, alcohol, UV radiation, and vitamin D; the first four are discussed in this *In Depth*, along with infectious agents. Vitamin D is discussed in Chapter 9.

Tobacco Use

More than 40 compounds in tobacco and tobacco smoke are **carcinogens**, or substances that can cause cancer. Using tobacco increases the risk for cancers of the lung, larynx, mouth, and esophagus **(Figure 2)**. In Canada, it is estimated that smoking is responsible for 30% of all cancer deaths and is related to more than 85% of lung cancer cases (Canadian Cancer Society, 2011). Smoking can also cause heart disease, stroke, and emphysema. The positive news is that tobacco use is a modifiable risk factor. If you smoke or use smokeless tobacco, you can reduce your risk for cancer considerably by quitting.

Nutrition and Fitness

Researchers estimate that one-third of cancer deaths are related to overweight or obesity, poor nutrition, and physical activity and thus could be prevented.

carcinogen Any substance capable of causing the cellular mutations that lead to cancer.

HOT TOPIC

Disorders Linked to Tobacco Use

Many people use smokeless tobacco or smoke cigarettes or cigars. The use of these products can lead to serious health consequences that together reduce life expectancy by more than 13 years in males and 14 years in females (American Cancer Society, 2009). Tobacco use is a risk factor in the development of numerous types of cancers, including lung, larynx, mouth (**Figure 3**), pharynx, esophagus, bladder, pancreas, uterus, kidney, stomach, and some leukemias. Tobacco use is also a risk factor for heart disease, bronchitis, emphysema, stroke, and erectile dysfunction.

Maternal smoking can cause miscarriage, preterm delivery, stillbirth, infant death, and low birth weight. In addition, smoking causes a variety of other problems, such as the premature wrinkling and coarsening of the skin shown in Figure 3. Smoking also causes bad breath, yellowing of the fingernails and hair, and bad-smelling clothes, hair, and living quarters. Second-hand smoke is another concern, especially for those who live or work with smokers. Non-smokers who are exposed to second-hand smoke at home or work increase their risk of developing heart disease by 25%–30% and increase their risk of developing lung cancer by 20%–30%. Research indicates that there is no risk-free level of exposure to second-hand smoke (USDHHS, 2004).

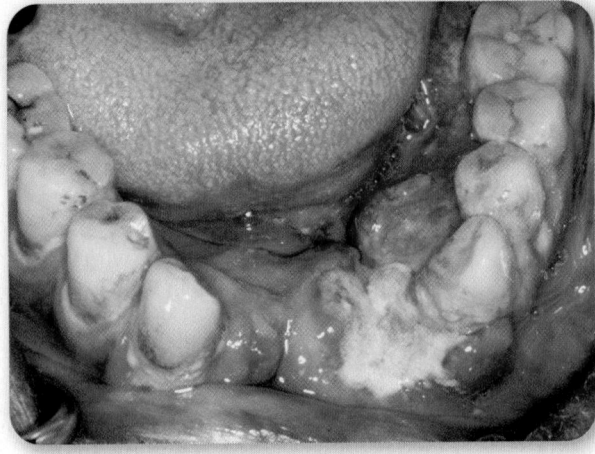

(a)

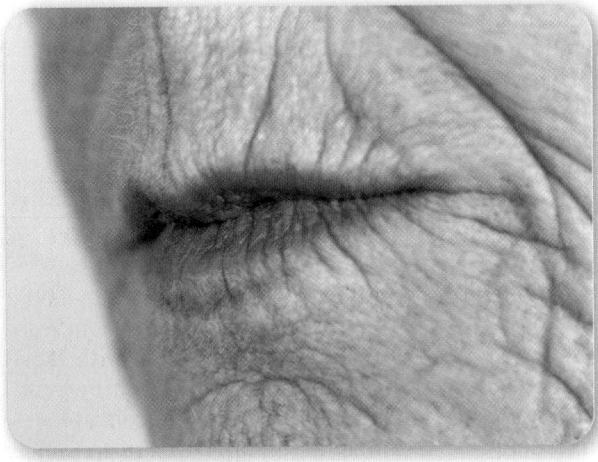

(b)

Figure 3 Effects of tobacco use. In addition to increasing your risk for lung cancer and cardiovascular disease, **(a)** using tobacco increases your risk for mouth cancer, and **(b)** smoking results in premature wrinkling of the skin, especially around the mouth.

Being overweight or obese increases your risk of cancer, particularly breast, colorectal, esophageal, kidney, pancreatic, and uterine cancer. A healthy diet high in fruits, vegetables, and fibre; low in saturated fat and sugar; and accompanied by regular physical activity can help maintain a healthy body weight. Research also shows that physical activity reduces the risk of colon cancer, and may reduce the risk of breast and uterine cancer (Canadian Cancer Society, 2011). Nutritional factors that protect against cancer include the consumption of foods rich in antioxidants, fibre, and phytochemicals. Diets high in saturated fats and low in fruits and vegetables increase the risk for overweight and obesity, which are associated with cancers of the esophagus, colon, breast, and prostate. A diet high in red meat and processed meat can also increase the risk for cancer.

A sedentary lifestyle increases the risk for colon cancer and possibly other forms of cancer (Thune and Furberg, 2001). At the same time, a recent review of several studies has found that moderately intense and vigorous physical activity is associated with a 20% to 30% reduction in our overall risk for cancer (Thune and Furberg, 2001). A clear protective effect of exercise was found specifically for breast and colon cancers. At this time, we do not know how exercise reduces the overall risk for cancer or for certain types of cancers. What about you? Are you making dietary and activity choices that help reduce your risk for cancer and other chronic diseases? Check out the What About You? quiz and find out!

Alcohol

Consuming alcohol increases your risk of many types of cancer, specifically cancers of the breast, colon and rectum, esophagus, larynx, liver, mouth, and pharynx. All forms of alcohol are included: beer, wine, and spirits. The less you drink, the lower your risk.

Staying physically active may help reduce the risk for some cancers.

What About You?

Are You Living Smart?

Cancer often seems to strike apparently healthy people "out of the blue." Because genetic and certain environmental factors are beyond your control, you may be wondering how your diet and level of physical activity might be influencing your risk. If so, take the following quiz and see for yourself! Answer each question Yes or No. Then keep reading to see how you can keep living smart!

▶ I eat at least five servings of vegetables and fruits every day.	Yes/No
▶ I eat at least three servings of whole-grain bread, rice, pasta, and cereal every day.	Yes/No
▶ I drink reduced-fat or fat-free milk and yogurt, and I seldom eat high-fat cheeses.	Yes/No
▶ I rarely eat processed and red meat like bacon, hot dogs, sausage, steak, ground beef, pork, or lamb.	Yes/No
▶ I take it easy on high-calorie baked goods such as pies, cakes, cookies, sweet rolls, and doughnuts.	Yes/No
▶ I rarely add butter, margarine, oil, sour cream, or mayonnaise to foods when I'm cooking or at the table.	Yes/No
▶ I rarely (less than twice a week) eat fried foods.	Yes/No
▶ I try to maintain a healthful weight.	Yes/No
▶ I get at least 30 minutes of moderate to vigorous physical activity on five or more days of the week.	Yes/No
▶ I usually take the stairs instead of waiting for an elevator.	Yes/No
▶ I try to spend most of my time being active, instead of watching television or sitting at the computer.	Yes/No
▶ I never, or only occasionally, drink alcohol.	Yes/No

How Do You Rate?

Zero to 4 "Yes" answers: Diet Alert!

Your diet is probably too high in fat and too low in plant foods like vegetables, fruits, and grains. You may want to take a look at your eating habits and find ways to make some changes. Trying to watch your intake of saturated fat? See the Quick Tips in Chapter 5 on page 170. Need to increase your vegetables and fruits? See the Quick Tips in on pages 261, 265, and 268.

5 to 8 "Yes" answers: Not bad! You're Halfway There!

You still have a way to go. Look at your "No" answers to help you decide which areas of your diet need to be improved, or whether your physical activity level should be increased. Check out the Quick Tips on page 285, and see Chapter 12 for ways to increase your level of physical activity.

9 to 12 "Yes" answers: Great Job! You're Living Smart!

Keep up the good habits and keep looking for ways to improve.

Data from American Cancer Society. Living Smart. Available at www.cancer.org/healthy/toolsandcalculators/quizzes/app/nutrition-activity-quiz.

Infectious Agents

Infectious agents account for 18% of cancers worldwide. For example, infection of the female cervix with the sexually transmitted virus *Human papillomavirus* is linked to cervical cancer **(Figure 4)**, and infection with the bacterium *Helicobacter pylori* is linked not only to ulcers but also to stomach cancer. Infection with HIV can cause many cancers. As microbial research advances, it is thought that more cancers will be linked to infectious agents.

Ultraviolet Radiation

Non-melanoma skin cancer is the most common form of cancer in the Canada, accounting for 74 100 out of 177 800 cases of cancer in 2011 (Canadian Cancer Society, 2011). Melanoma accounted for 5500 out of 177 800 cases of cancer (Canadian Cancer Society, 2011). Most cases of skin cancer are linked to exposure to ultraviolet (UV) rays from the sun and indoor tanning

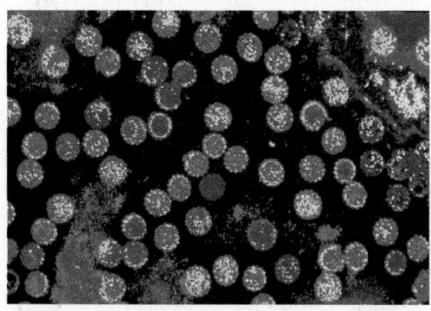

▲ **Figure 4** Human papillomavirus (HPV) is an infectious agent that can cause cancer.

▲ Arctic explorers wear special clothing to protect themselves from the cold as well as the high levels of ultraviolet rays from the sun.

beds. UV rays damage the DNA of immature skin cells, which then reproduce uncontrollably. Research has shown that a person's risk for skin cancer doubles if he or she has had five or more sunburns; however, your risk for skin cancer still increases with UV exposure even if you do not get sunburned (Pfahlberg, Kolmel, and Gefeller, 2002). Exposure to tanning beds before age 35 increases your risk of developing the most invasive form of skin cancer by 75% (Heinonen et al., 2007).

Skin cancer includes the non-melanoma cancers (basal cell and squamous cell cancers), which are not typically invasive, and malignant melanoma, which is one of the most deadly of all types of cancer **(Figure 5)**. Limiting your exposure to sunlight to no more than 20 minutes between 10 a.m. and 4 p.m. can help reduce your risk for skin cancer while allowing your body to synthesize adequate vitamin D. Beyond that, wear sunscreen with at least a 15 sun protection factor (SPF) rating and protective clothing.

Cancer Prompts a Variety of Signs and Symptoms

The signs and symptoms of cancer vary according to the structures affected, how large the tumour is, and how widely it has metastasized. Here, we discuss the most common signs and symptoms that people diagnosed

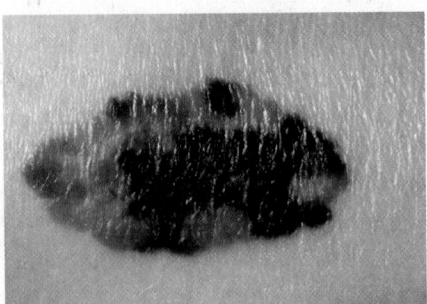

Figure 5 A lesion associated with malignant melanoma is characterized by asymmetry; uneven or blurred borders; mixed shades of tan, brown, black, and sometimes red or blue; and a diameter larger than a pencil eraser (6 mm).

with cancer typically report. However, it is important to bear in mind that these also occur with many other illnesses and even non-illness conditions. Also, having just one or two of these symptoms rarely means that a person has cancer. Still, the Canadian Cancer Society publishes a list of warning signs you should not ignore:

- a new or unusual lump or swelling in the breast, testicles, or any other part of the body
- any sore that does not heal anywhere on your body or in your mouth
- obvious change in the shape, size, or colour of a mole or wart
- a nagging cough, hoarseness, or a croaky voice
- difficulty swallowing
- blood in the urine, stool, or phlegm
- unusual bleeding or discharge of any sort from the nipple or vagina
- any change in bladder habits, such as pain or difficulty urinating
- any change in bowel habits (constipation or diarrhea) that lasts more than a few weeks
- persistent indigestion
- unexplained weight loss, fever, or fatigue
- unexplained aches and pains
- any new growth on the skin, or patches of skin that bleed, itch, or become red

How Is Cancer Treated?

Physicians typically evaluate signs and symptoms of cancer using a variety of blood tests and diagnostic scans, such as ultrasound, CT, and MRI scans. Once a diagnosis is made, the patient is often referred to the care of an oncologist, a physician who specializes in cancer treatment (*onco-* means "tumour").

The three major types of cancer treatment are surgery, radiation, and chemotherapy. Surgery is most effective when it can entirely remove the mass. Radiation therapy delivers high-energy x-rays, gamma rays, electron beams, or photons to tumour cells to kill them outright or damage their DNA so that they can no longer reproduce.

Chemotherapy is drug therapy, and any of more than 100 different drugs can be combined for different patient needs. For cancers that are localized—that is, confined to a limited area, with no metastasis—surgery may be the only treatment advised. Other cancers may require surgery followed by radiation and/or chemotherapy. Diffuse cancers, such as blood cancers and tumours in locations that cannot be accessed safely with surgery, such as head and neck tumours, may be considered inoperable, and radiation and/or chemotherapy may be prescribed. In some cases, a large tumour is first radiated, with the goal of shrinking it prior to surgery.

Can Cancer Be Prevented?

Some types of cancer can be prevented. For instance, vaccines, the appropriate use of antibiotics, and behavioural changes can prevent certain cancers known to be caused by infectious agents. Most cancers, however, are multifactorial—we cannot link them to only one cause. This means that there is no way to guarantee that you—or anyone else—will not get cancer.

Regular screening examinations can allow for the detection and removal of precancerous tissues. For instance, a test called a Pap smear can detect subtle changes in the cells lining a woman's cervix (the entrance to the uterus) that, if

These vegetables provide antioxidant nutrients, fibre, and phytochemicals, all of which reduce the risk for some cancers.

allowed to progress, could result in cervical cancer. Women with a Pap smear indicating these changes typically return to their physician for a quick outpatient procedure in which the layer of precancerous cells is removed. Similarly, colonoscopies allow for the detection and removal of precancerous polyps. Regular skin checks allow for suspicious lesions to be removed—and cell samples sent to a lab—to evaluate for skin cancer. Screening can also allow for detection at an early stage, when cancer is most treatable. For example, a mammogram may be able to detect a breast mass that is too small for the woman to feel.

Antioxidants Play a Role in Preventing Cancer

A large and growing body of evidence suggests that antioxidants play an important role in cancer prevention. But how? The following are some proposed mechanisms:

- Enhancing the immune system, which assists in the destruction and removal of precancerous cells from the body
- Inhibiting the growth of cancer cells and tumours
- Preventing oxidative damage to the cells' DNA by scavenging free radicals and stopping the formation and subsequent chain reaction of oxidized molecules

Eating whole foods that are high in antioxidants—especially fruits, vegetables, and whole grains—is consistently shown to be associated with decreased cancer risk (Greenwald, Clifford, and Milner, 2001). In addition, populations eating diets low in antioxidant nutrients have a higher risk for cancer. These studies show a strong association between level of dietary antioxidants and cancer risk, but they do not prove cause and effect. Nutrition experts agree that there are important interactions between antioxidant nutrients and other substances in foods, such as fibre and phytochemicals, which work

QUICK TIPS

Reducing Your Cancer Risk

▶ Lose weight or maintain your current healthful weight. Obesity appears to increase the risk for cancers of the breast, colon, prostate, endometrium (the lining of the uterus), cervix, ovary, kidney, gallbladder, liver, pancreas, rectum, and esophagus. The exact links between obesity and increased cancer risk are not clear but may involve hormonal changes associated with fat cells.

▶ Avoid heterocyclic amines in cooked meat. These carcinogenic chemicals are formed when meat is cooked at high temperatures, such as during broiling, barbecuing, and frying.

▶ Avoid nitrites and nitrates in cured meats. These compounds, which are found in some sausages, hams, bacon, and lunch meats, bind with amino acids to form nitrosamines, which are potent carcinogens.

▶ Eat a diet low in saturated fat. Diets high in saturated fat have been associated with increased risk for many cancers, including prostate and breast. However, not all studies support this association.

▶ Eat a diet rich in vegetables and fruits. These foods are high in antioxidants and in fibre, which some studies link to a reduced risk for certain cancers.

▶ Select foods containing phytoestrogens (plant estrogens). These compounds, found in soy-based foods and some vegetables and grains, may decrease the risk for breast, endometrial, and prostate cancers.

▶ Make sure to consume adequate omega-3 fatty acids (see Chapter 5). Consuming foods high in omega-3 fatty acids is associated with reduced rates of breast, colon, and rectal cancers.

together to reduce the risk for many types of cancers. Studies are now being conducted to determine whether eating foods high in antioxidants directly causes lower rates of cancer.

As we noted on page 275, the link between taking antioxidant supplements and reducing cancer risk is not clear. Laboratory animal and test tube studies show that the individual nutrients reviewed in this chapter act as antioxidants in various situations. However, supplementation studies in humans do not consistently show benefits of taking antioxidant supplements in the prevention of cancer and other diseases, and some suggest an increased risk.

Why do antioxidant supplements appear to work in some studies and for some cancers but not in others? The human body is very complex, as is the development and progression of the numerous forms of cancer. People differ substantially in their susceptibility and response to carcinogens, as well as to protective factors. These complexities cloud the relationship between nutrition and cancer. In any research study it is impossible to control all the factors that may increase the risk for cancer. Thus, many unknown factors can affect study outcomes. It has also been speculated

that antioxidants taken in supplemental form may act as pro-oxidants in some situations, whereas antioxidants consumed in foods may be more balanced. Many studies currently being conducted are examining the impact of whole foods and antioxidant supplements on the risk for various forms of cancer. The results of these studies will provide important insights into the link between whole foods, individual nutrients, and cancer.

Web Resources

www.cancer.ca
The Canadian Cancer Society

Click on "Prevention" for more information on ways you can reduce your risk of cancer. To learn about different types of cancers, click on "About Cancer." For descriptions of cancer research underway in Canada, click on "Cancer Research."

www.cancer.org
The American Cancer Society

Get recommendations for smoking cessation, nutrition, sun exposure, and physical activity for cancer prevention.

www.cancer.gov
The National Cancer Institute

Learn more about the nutritional factors that can influence your risk for cancer.

Nutrients Involved in Bone Health

9

O

ne fall could change your life. Falls account for almost 62% of injury-related hospitalizations for older adults, according to the Public Health Agency of Canada PHAC, 2009. Further, falls cause more than 90% of all hip fractures in older adults, and 20% of those injured die within a year of the fracture. The implications of injuries from falls can be significant, and affect older adults in different ways. Their daily lives can change emotionally, physically, socially, and economically after a fall. Imagine your lifestyle as an older adult—how do you think it would change if you were injured from a fall?

Maintaining bone mass is an important consideration at any age, both to help prevent serious injuries later in life and to prevent *osteoporosis*, which means "porous bone." When bones are not very dense, they are more likely to break, and osteoporosis can indeed cause bones to break during even minor weight-bearing activities. The need for calcium and vitamin D throughout life is crucial in building strong bones, but do you know how they do this, or how much you need? If calcium and vitamin D are good for building our bones, are there also foods that break them down? How dense are your bones—and how can you tell if you are going to be at risk for osteoporosis? In this chapter, we discuss the nutrients and lifestyle factors that play a critical role in maintaining bone health.

How Does Our Body Maintain Bone Health?

Contrary to what most people think, our skeleton is not an inactive collection of bones that simply supports our body. Bones are living organs that contain several tissues, including two types of bone tissue, cartilage, and connective tissue. Nerves and blood vessels run within channels in bone tissue, supporting its activities. Bones have many important functions in our body, some of which might surprise you **(Table 9.1)**. For instance, did you know that most of your blood cells are formed deep within your bones?

Given the importance of bones, it is critical that we maintain their health. Bone health is achieved through complex interactions among nutrients, hormones, and environmental factors. To better understand these interactions, we first need to learn about how bone structure and the constant activity of bone tissue influence bone health throughout our lifetime.

The Composition of Bone Provides Strength and Flexibility

We tend to think of bones as totally rigid, but if they were, how could we twist and jump our way through a basketball game or even carry an armload of books up a flight of stairs? Our bones need to be both strong and flexible, so that they can resist the compression, stretching, and twisting that occur throughout our daily activities. Fortunately, the composition of bone is ideally suited for its complex job: about 65% of bone tissue is made up of an assortment of minerals (mostly calcium and phosphorus) that provide hardness, but the remaining 35% is a mixture of organic substances that provide strength, durability, and flexibility. The most important of these substances is a fibrous protein called collagen. You might be surprised to learn that collagen fibres are actually stronger than steel fibres of similar size! Within our bones, the minerals form tiny crystals (called *hydroxyapatite*) that cluster around the collagen fibres. This design enables bones to bear our weight while responding to our demands for movement.

If you examine a bone very closely, you will notice two distinct types of tissue **(Figure 9.1)**: cortical bone and trabecular bone. **Cortical bone**, which is also called **compact bone**, is very dense. It constitutes approximately 80% of our skeleton. The outer surface of all bones is cortical; plus, many small bones of the body, such as the bones of the wrists, hands, and feet, are made entirely of cortical bone. Although cortical bone looks solid to the naked eye, it actually contains many microscopic openings, which serve as passageways for blood vessels and nerves.

In contrast, **trabecular bone** makes up only 20% of our skeleton. It is found within the ends of the long bones (such as the bones of the arms and legs), the spinal vertebrae, the sternum (breastbone), the ribs, most bones of the skull, and the pelvis.

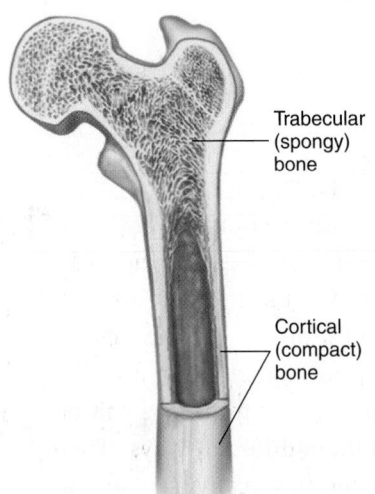

Trabecular (spongy) bone

Cortical (compact) bone

🔺 **Figure 9.1** The structure of bone. Notice the difference in density between the trabecular (spongy) bone and the cortical (compact) bone.

cortical bone (compact bone) A dense bone tissue that makes up the outer surface of all bones as well as the entirety of most small bones of the body. It makes up 80% or our skeleton.

trabecular bone (spongy bone) A porous bone tissue that makes up only 20% of our skeleton and is found within the ends of the long bones, inside the spinal vertebrae, inside the flat bones (sternum, ribs, and most bones of the skull), and inside the bones of the pelvis.

TABLE 9.1 **Functions of Bone in the Human Body**	
Functions Related to Structure and Support	**Functions Related to Metabolic Processes**
Bones provide physical support for organs and body segments. Bones protect vital organs; for example, the rib cage protects the lungs, the skull protects the brain, and the vertebrae of the spine protect the spinal cord. Bones work with muscles and tendons to allow movement—muscles attach to bones via tendons, and their contraction produces movement at the body's joints.	Bone tissue acts as a storage reservoir for many minerals, including calcium, phosphorus, and fluoride. The body draws upon such deposits when these minerals are needed for various body processes; however, this can reduce bone mass. Most blood cells are produced in the bone marrow.

Trabecular bone is sometimes referred to as **spongy bone** because to the naked eye it looks like a sponge, with cavities and no clear organization. The microscope reveals that trabecular bone is, in fact, aligned in a precise network of columns that protects the bone from stress. You can think of trabecular bone as the scaffolding inside the bone that supports the outer cortical bone.

Cortical and trabecular bone also differ in their rate of turnover—that is, in how quickly the bone tissue is broken down and renewed. Trabecular bone has a faster turnover rate than cortical bone. This makes trabecular bone more sensitive to changes in hormones and nutritional deficiencies. It also accounts for the much higher rate of age-related fractures in the spine and pelvis (including the hip)—both of which contain a significant amount of trabecular bone. Let's investigate how bone turnover influences bone health.

The Constant Activity of Bone Tissue Promotes Bone Health

Our bones develop through a series of three processes: bone growth, bone modelling, and bone remodelling **(Figure 9.2)**. Bone growth and modelling begin during the early months of fetal life, when our skeleton is forming, and continue until early adulthood. Bone remodelling predominates during adulthood; this process helps us maintain a healthy skeleton as we age.

Bone Growth and Modelling Determine the Size and Shape of Our Bones

Through the process of *bone growth,* the size of our bones increases. The first period of rapid bone growth is from birth to age 2, but growth continues in spurts throughout childhood and into adolescence. Most girls reach their adult height by age 14, and boys generally reach adult height by age 17 (USDA, 2008). In the later decades of life, some loss in height usually occurs because of decreased bone density in the spine.

Bone modelling is the process by which the shape of our bones is determined, from the round "pebble" bones that make up our wrists, to the uniquely shaped bones of our face, to the long bones of our arms and legs. Even after bones stop growing in length, they can still increase in thickness if they are stressed by engaging in repetitive exercise, such as weight training, or by being overweight or obese.

Although the size and shape of our bones do not change significantly after puberty, our **bone density**, or the compactness of our bones, continues to develop into early adulthood. *Peak bone density* is the point at which our bones are strongest because they are at their highest density. The following factors are associated with a lower peak bone density (Chevalley et al, 2005; Ho and Kung, 2005):

- late pubertal age in boys and late onset of menstruation in girls
- inadequate calcium intake
- low body weight
- physical inactivity during adolescence

About 90% of a woman's bone density has been built by 17 years of age, whereas the majority of a man's has been built by his twenties. However, male or female, before we reach the age of 30 years, our bodies have reached peak bone mass,

bone density The degree of compactness of bone tissue, reflecting the strength of the bones. Peak bone density is the point at which a bone is strongest.

Bone growth	Bone modeling	Bone remodeling
• Determines bone size • Begins in the womb • Continues until early adulthood	• Determines bone shape • Begins in the womb • Continues until early adulthood	• Maintains integrity of bone • Replaces old bone with new bone to maintain mineral balance • Involves bone resorption and formation • Occurs predominantly during adulthood

◀ **Figure 9.2** Bone develops through three processes: bone growth, bone modelling, and bone remodelling.

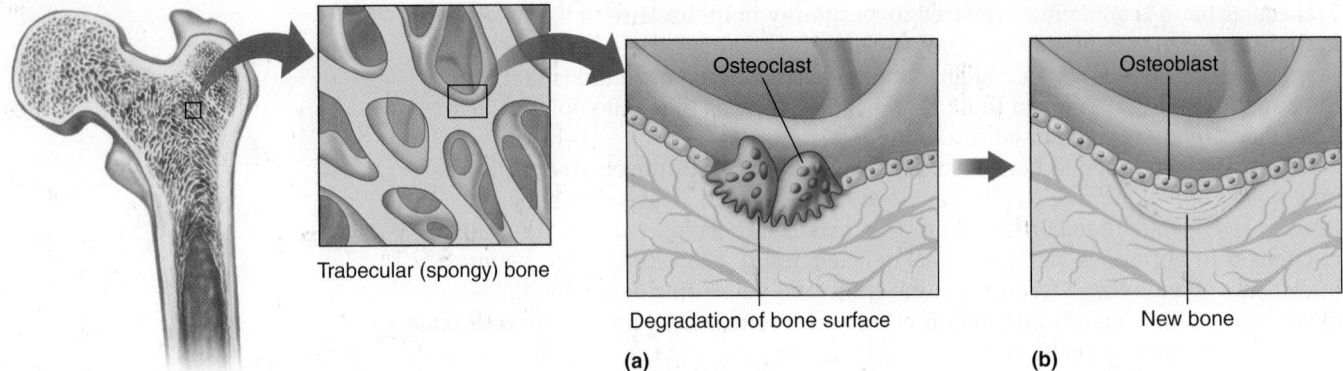

Trabecular (spongy) bone

Osteoclast

Degradation of bone surface

(a)

Osteoblast

New bone

(b)

Figure 9.3 Bone remodelling involves resorption and formation. **(a)** Osteoclasts erode the bone surface by degrading its components, including calcium, other minerals, and collagen; these components are then transported to the bloodstream. **(b)** Osteoblasts work to build new bone by filling the pit formed by the resorption process with new bone.

and we can no longer significantly add to our bone density. In our thirties, our bone density remains relatively stable, but by age 40, it has begun its irreversible decline.

Bone Remodelling Maintains a Balance Between Breakdown and Repair

Although our bones cannot increase their peak density after our twenties, bone tissue still remains very active throughout adulthood, balancing the breakdown of older bone tissue and the formation of new bone tissue. This bone recycling process is called **remodelling**. Remodelling is also used to repair fractures and to strengthen bone regions that are exposed to higher physical stress. The process of remodelling involves two steps: resorption and formation.

Bone is broken down through a process referred to as **resorption** (Figure 9.3a). During resorption, cells called **osteoclasts** erode the bone surface by secreting enzymes and acids that dig grooves into the bone matrix. Their ruffled surface also acts somewhat like a scrubbing brush to assist in the erosion process. One of the primary reasons the body regularly breaks down bone is to release calcium into the bloodstream. As discussed in more detail later in this chapter, calcium is critical for many physiologic processes, and bone is an important calcium reservoir. The body also breaks down bone that is fractured and needs to be repaired. Resorption at the injury site smooths the rough edges created by the break. Bone may also be broken down in areas away from the fracture site to obtain the minerals that are needed to repair the damage. Regardless of the reason, once bone is broken down, the resulting products are transported into the bloodstream and used for various body functions.

New bone is formed through the action of cells called **osteoblasts**, or "bone builders" (see Figure 9.3b). These cells work to synthesize new bone matrix by laying down the collagen-containing organic component of bone. Within this substance, the hydroxyapatite crystallizes and packs together to create new bone where it is needed.

In young, healthy adults, the processes of bone resorption and formation are equal, so that just as much bone is broken down as is built, maintaining bone mass. Around 40 years of age, bone resorption begins to occur more rapidly than bone formation, and this imbalance results in an overall loss in bone density. Because this affects the vertebrae of the spine, we also tend to lose height as we age. As we will discuss shortly, achieving a high peak bone mass through proper nutrition and exercise when we are young provides us with a stronger skeleton before the loss of bone begins. It can therefore reduce our risk for *osteoporosis*, a disorder characterized by low-density bones that fracture easily. Osteoporosis is discussed *In Depth* on pages 314–321.

remodelling The two-step process by which bone tissue is recycled; includes the breakdown of existing bone and the formation of new bone.

resorption The process by which the surface of bone is broken down by cells called osteoclasts.

osteoclasts Cells that erode the surface of bones by secreting enzymes and acids that dig grooves into the bone matrix.

osteoblasts Cells that prompt the formation of new bone matrix by laying down the collagen-containing component of bone, which is then mineralized.

RECAP Bones are organs that contain metabolically active tissues composed primarily of minerals and a fibrous protein called collagen. Of the two types of bone, cortical bone is more dense; trabecular bone is more porous. Trabecular bone is also more sensitive to hormonal and nutritional factors and turns over more rapidly than cortical bone. The three types of bone activity are growth, modelling, and remodelling. Bones reach their peak bone mass by the late teenage years into the twenties; bone mass begins to decline around age 40.

How Do We Assess Bone Health?

Over the past 40 years, technological advancements have led to the development of a number of affordable methods for measuring bone health. **Dual energy x-ray absorptiometry (DXA or DEXA)** is considered the most accurate assessment tool for measuring bone density. This method can measure the density of the bone mass over the entire body. Software is also available that provides an estimation of percentage body fat.

The DXA procedure is simple, painless, and non-invasive, and it is considered to be of minimal risk. It takes just 15 to 30 minutes to complete. The person participating in the test remains fully clothed but must remove all jewelry and other metal objects. The participant lies quietly on a table, and bone density is assessed through the use of a very low level of x-ray **(Figure 9.4)**.

DXA is a very important tool in determining a person's risk for osteoporosis. It generates a bone density score, which is compared to the average peak bone density of a healthy 30-year-old. Doctors use this comparison, which is known as a **T-score**, to assess the risk for fracture and determine whether the person has osteoporosis. If bone density is normal, the T-score ranges between +1 and −1 of the value for a healthy 30-year-old. A negative T-score between −1 and −2.5 indicates low bone mass and an increased risk for fractures. If the T-score is more negative than −2.5, the person has osteoporosis.

DXA tests are generally recommended for postmenopausal women because they are at highest risk for osteoporosis and fracture. Men and younger women may also be recommended for a DXA test if they have significant risk factors for osteoporosis (see the *In Depth* on osteoporosis immediately following this chapter).

dual energy x-ray absorptiometry (DXA or DEXA) Currently, the most accurate tool for measuring bone density.

T-score A comparison of an individual's bone density to the average peak bone density of a 30-year-old healthy adult.

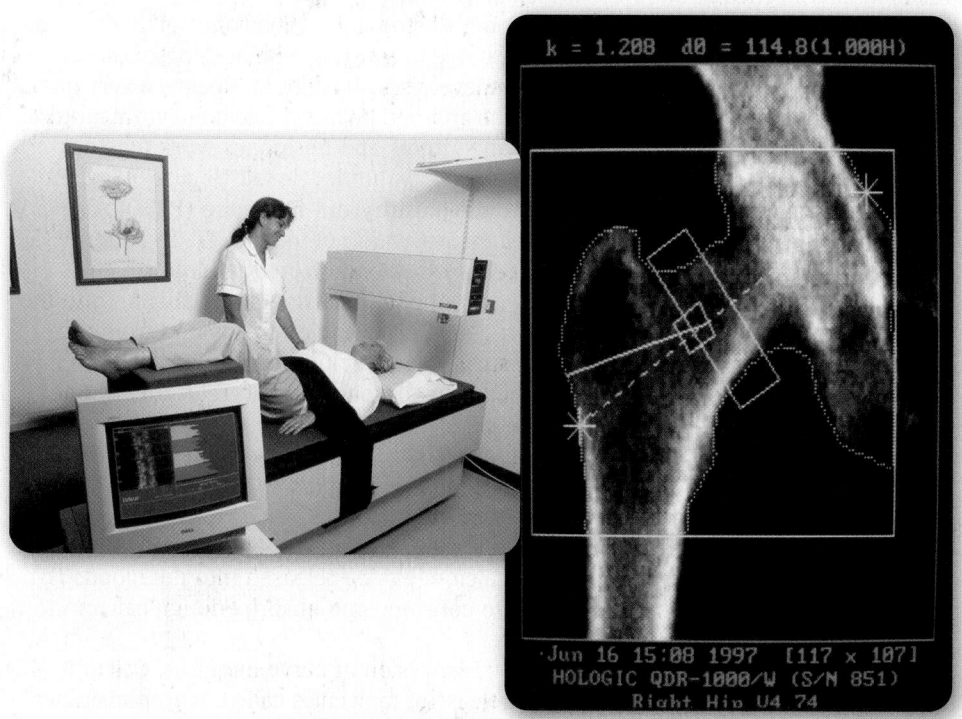

◀ **Figure 9.4** Dual energy x-ray absorptiometry is a safe and simple procedure that assesses bone density.

k = 1.208   d0 = 114.8(1.000H)

Jun 16 15:08 1997 [117 x 107]
HOLOGIC QDR-1000/W (S/N 851)
Right Hip U4 74

Other technologies have been developed to measure bone density. These use ultrasound or different forms of x-ray technology to measure the density of bone in the heel or another more peripheral part of the body. These technologies are frequently used at health fairs because the machines are portable and provide scores faster than the traditional DXA.

RECAP Dual energy x-ray absorptiometry (DXA or DEXA) is the gold standard measurement of bone mass. It is a simple, painless, and minimal-risk procedure. The result of a DXA is a T-score, which is a comparison of a person's bone density with that of a healthy 30-year-old. A T-score between +1 and −1 is normal; a score between −1 and −2.5 indicates poor bone density; and a score more negative than −2.5 indicates osteoporosis.

A Profile of Nutrients That Maintain Bone Health

Calcium is the most recognized nutrient associated with bone health; however, vitamins D and K, phosphorus, magnesium, and fluoride are also essential for strong bones, and the roles of other vitamins, minerals, and phytochemicals are currently being researched.

Calcium

Recall from Chapter 1 that the major minerals are those required in our diet in amounts greater than 100 mg per day. Calcium is by far the most abundant major mineral in our body, constituting about 2% of our entire body weight! Not surprisingly, it plays many critical roles in maintaining overall function and health.

Functions of Calcium

One of the primary functions of calcium is to provide structure to our bones and teeth. About 99% of the calcium found in our body is stored in the hydroxyapatite crystals built up on the collagen foundation of bone. As noted earlier, the combination of crystals and collagen provides both the characteristic hardness of bone and the flexibility needed to support various activities.

The remaining 1% of calcium in our body is found in the blood and soft tissues. Calcium is alkaline, or basic, and plays a critical role in assisting with acid–base balance. We cannot survive for long if our blood calcium level rises above or falls below a very narrow range; therefore, our body maintains the appropriate blood calcium level at all costs.

Figure 9.5 illustrates how various organ systems and hormones work together to maintain blood calcium levels. When blood calcium levels fall (Figure 9.5a), the parathyroid glands are stimulated to produce **parathyroid hormone (PTH)**. Also known as parathormone, PTH stimulates the activation of vitamin D. Together, PTH and vitamin D stimulate the kidneys to reabsorb calcium from the bloodstream. They also stimulate osteoclasts to break down bone, releasing more calcium into the bloodstream. In addition, vitamin D increases the absorption of calcium from the intestines. Through these three mechanisms, blood calcium levels increase.

When blood calcium levels are too high, the thyroid gland secretes a hormone called **calcitonin**, which inhibits the actions of vitamin D (Figure 9.5b). Thus, calcitonin prevents the reabsorption of calcium in the kidneys, limits calcium absorption in the intestines, and inhibits the osteoclasts from breaking down bone.

As just noted, the body must maintain blood calcium levels within a very narrow range. Thus, when an individual does not consume or absorb enough calcium from the diet, osteoclasts erode bone, so that calcium can be released into the blood. To maintain healthy bone density, we need to consume and absorb enough calcium to balance the calcium taken from our bones.

Calcium is also critical for the normal transmission of nerve impulses. Calcium flows into nerve cells and stimulates the release of molecules called neurotransmitters,

◀ One major role of calcium is to form and maintain bones and teeth.

parathyroid hormone (PTH)
A hormone secreted by the parathyroid gland when blood calcium levels fall. Also known as parathormone, it increases blood calcium levels by stimulating the activation of vitamin D, increasing reabsorption of calcium from the kidneys, and stimulating osteoclasts to break down bone, which releases more calcium into the bloodstream.

calcitonin A hormone secreted by the thyroid gland when blood calcium levels are too high. Calcitonin inhibits the actions of vitamin D, preventing reabsorption of calcium in the kidneys, limiting calcium absorption in the small intestine, and inhibiting the osteoclasts from breaking down bone.

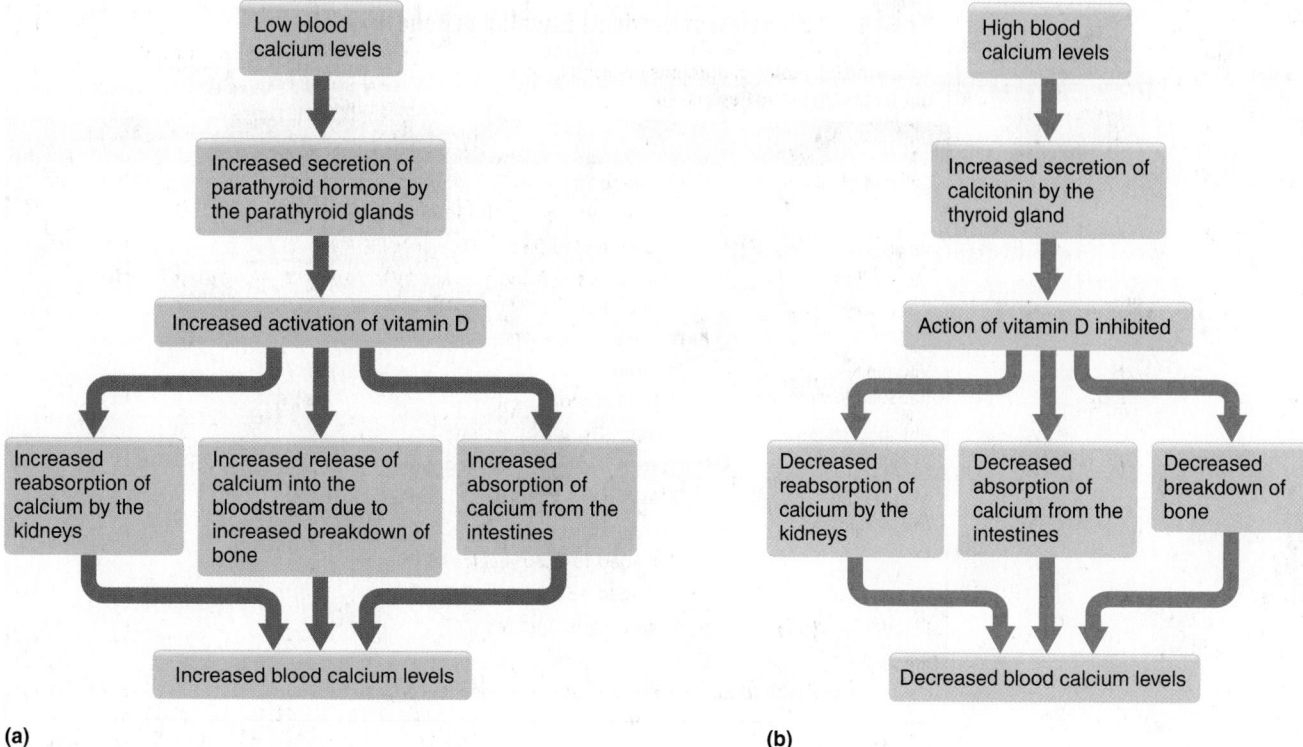

Figure 9.5 Regulation of blood calcium levels by various organs and hormones. **(a)** Low blood calcium levels stimulate the production of parathyroid hormone and activation of vitamin D, which in turn cause an increase in blood calcium levels. **(b)** High blood calcium levels stimulate the secretion of calcitonin, which in turn causes a decrease in blood calcium levels.

which transfer the nerve impulses from one nerve cell (neuron) to another. Without adequate calcium, our nerves' ability to transmit messages is inhibited. Not surprisingly, when blood calcium levels fall dangerously low, a person can experience convulsions.

A fourth role of calcium is to assist in muscle contraction, which is initiated when calcium flows into muscle cells. Conversely, muscles relax when calcium is pumped back outside of muscle cells. If calcium levels are inadequate, normal muscle contraction and relaxation are inhibited, and the person may suffer from twitching and spasms. This is referred to as **calcium tetany**. High levels of blood calcium can cause **calcium rigor**, an inability of muscles to relax, which leads to a hardening or stiffening of the muscles. These problems affect the function not only of skeletal muscles but also of heart muscle and can cause heart failure.

Other functions of calcium include the maintenance of healthy blood pressure, the initiation of blood clotting, and the regulation of various hormones and enzymes.

How Much Calcium Should We Consume?

There are no RDA values for calcium. The Adequate Intake (AI) varies according to age and gender. Adult values are listed in **Table 9.2**. Values for adults over age 50 are higher (1200 mg/day), and pre-teens and teens have the highest calcium requirements (1300 mg/day). Many people of all ages fail to consume enough calcium to maintain bone health.

A nutrient's **bioavailability** is the degree to which our body can absorb and use that nutrient. The bioavailability of calcium depends in part on our age and our calcium need. For example, infants, children, and adolescents can absorb more than 60% of the calcium they consume, as calcium needs are very high during these stages of life. In addition, pregnant and lactating women can absorb about 50% of dietary calcium. In contrast, healthy young adults absorb only about 30% of the calcium consumed in the diet. When our calcium needs are high, our body can generally increase

calcium tetany A condition in which muscles experience twitching and spasms as a result of inadequate blood calcium levels.

calcium rigor A failure of muscles to relax, which leads to a hardening or stiffening of the muscles; caused by high levels of blood calcium.

bioavailability The degree to which our body can absorb and utilize any given nutrient.

TABLE 9.2 Overview of Nutrients Essential to Bone Health

To see the full profile of nutrients involved in bone health, turn to **In Depth**, Vitamins and Minerals: Micronutrients with Macro Powers.

Nutrient	Recommended Intake
Calcium (major mineral)	Adequate Intake (AI): Women and men aged 19 to 50 years = 1000 mg/day
	Women and men aged >50 years = 1200 mg/day
Vitamin D (fat-soluble vitamin)	Recommended Dietary Allowance (RDA):*
	Children, women and men aged 9 to 70 years = 15 µg /day; Tolerable Upper Intake Level (UL) per day = 100 µg/day
	Women and men aged >70 years = 20 µg /day; UL per day = 100 µg/day
Vitamin K (fat-soluble vitamin)	AI: Women: 90 µg/day
	Men: 120 µg/day
Phosphorus (major mineral)	RDA:
	Women and men = 700 mg/day
Magnesium (major mineral)	RDA: Women aged 19 to 30 years = 310 mg/day
	Women aged >30 years = 320 mg/day
	Men aged 19 to 30 years = 400 mg/day
	Men aged >30 years = 420 mg/day
Fluoride (trace mineral)	AI: Women: 3 mg/day
	Men: 4 mg/day

*Based on the assumption that a person does not get adequate sun exposure.

its absorption of calcium from the small intestine. Although older adults have a high need for calcium, the ability to absorb calcium diminishes as we age and can be as low as 25%. These variations in bioavailability and absorption capacity were taken into account when calcium recommendations were determined.

The bioavailability of calcium also depends on how much calcium we consume throughout the day or at any one time. When our diet is generally high in calcium, absorption of calcium is reduced. In addition, our body cannot absorb more than 500 mg of calcium at any one time (Nelms et al., 2007), and as the amount of calcium in a single meal or supplement increases, the fraction that we absorb decreases. This explains why it is critical to consume calcium-rich foods throughout the day rather than relying on a single, high-dose supplement. Conversely, when dietary intake of calcium is low, the absorption of calcium is increased.

Dietary factors can also affect our absorption of calcium. Binding factors, such as phytates and oxalates, occur naturally in some calcium-rich seeds, nuts, grains, and vegetables, such as spinach and Swiss chard. Such factors bind to the calcium in these foods and prevent its absorption from the small intestine into the bloodstream. Additionally, consuming calcium with iron, zinc, magnesium, or phosphorus can interfere with the absorption and utilization of all these minerals. Despite these potential interactions, the Institute of Medicine (2010) has concluded that there is not sufficient evidence to suggest that these interactions cause deficiencies of calcium or other minerals in healthy individuals.

Finally, because vitamin D is necessary for the absorption of calcium, a lack of vitamin D severely limits the bioavailability of calcium. We'll discuss this and other contributions of vitamin D to bone health shortly.

Foods Rich in Calcium: Dairy, Greens, and More

Dairy products are among the most common sources of calcium in the Canadian diet. Skim milk, low-fat cheeses, and non-fat yogurt are nutritious sources of calcium **(Figure 9.6)**. Ice cream, regular cheese, and whole milk also contain a relatively high amount of calcium, but these foods should be eaten in moderation because of their high fat and energy content. Cottage cheese is one dairy product that is a relatively poor source of calcium, as the processing of this food removes a great deal of the

Although spinach contains high levels of calcium, binding factors in the plant prevent much of its absorption.

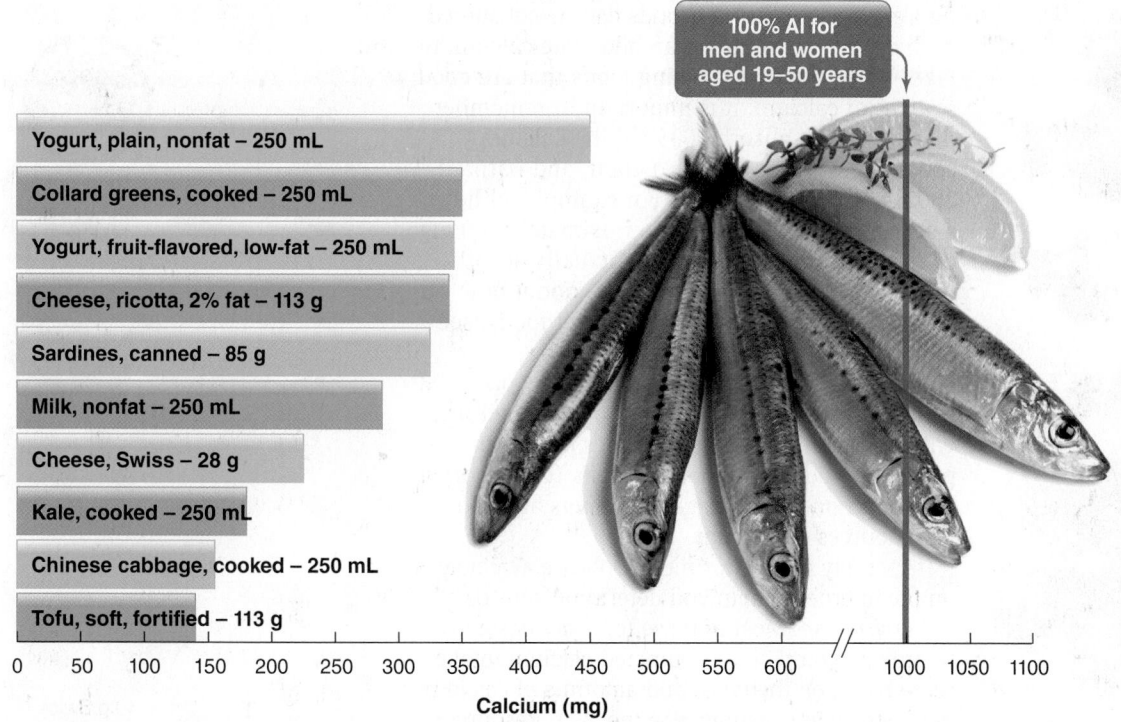

Yogurt, plain, nonfat – 250 mL

Collard greens, cooked – 250 mL

Yogurt, fruit-flavored, low-fat – 250 mL

Cheese, ricotta, 2% fat – 113 g

Sardines, canned – 85 g

Milk, nonfat – 250 mL

Cheese, Swiss – 28 g

Kale, cooked – 250 mL

Chinese cabbage, cooked – 250 mL

Tofu, soft, fortified – 113 g

100% AI for men and women aged 19–50 years

0   50   100   150   200   250   300   350   400   450   500   550   600   1000 1050 1100

Calcium (mg)

Figure 9.6 Common food sources of calcium. The AI for adult men and women aged 19 to 50 years is 1000 mg of calcium per day. For men and women older than 50 years of age, the AI increases to 1200 mg of calcium per day.
Data from U.S. Department of Agriculture, Agricultural Research Service. 2009. USDA Nutrient Database for Standard Reference, Release 22. Nutrient Data Laboratory Home Page. www.ars.usda.gov/ba/bhnrc/ndl.

calcium. One cup of low-fat cottage cheese contains approximately 150 mg of calcium, while the same serving of low-fat milk contains almost 300 mg.

Other good sources of calcium are green leafy vegetables, such as kale, collard greens, turnip greens, broccoli, cauliflower, green cabbage, Brussels sprouts, and Chinese cabbage (bok choy). The bioavailability of the calcium in these vegetables is relatively high compared to spinach, as these vegetables contain low levels of oxalates. Many packaged foods are now available fortified with calcium. For example, you can buy calcium-fortified orange juice, soy milk, rice milk, and tofu processed with calcium. Some dairies have even boosted the amount of calcium in their brand of milk!

Figure 9.7 illustrates serving sizes of various calcium-rich foods that contain the same amount of calcium as one glass (250 mL or 8 fl. oz.) of skim milk. As you can see from this

QUICK TIPS

Capitalizing on Calcium

▶ At the grocery store, stock up on calcium-fortified juice, soy milk, and rice milk. Look for single-serving portable "juice boxes" with calcium-fortified juice, milk, or chocolate milk.

▶ For quick snacks, purchase single-serving cups of yogurt, individually wrapped "cheese sticks," or calcium-fortified protein bars.

▶ Keep on hand shredded parmesan or any other hard cheese, and sprinkle it on hot soups, chili, salads, pasta, and other dishes.

▶ In any recipe, replace sour cream or mayonnaise with non-fat plain yogurt.

▶ Add non-fat dry milk powder to hot cereals, soups, chili, recipes for baked goods, coffee, and hot cocoa. One-third of a cup of

non-fat dry milk powder provides the same amount of calcium as a whole cup of non-fat milk.

▶ Make a yogurt smoothie by blending non-fat plain or flavoured yogurt with fresh or frozen fruit.

▶ At your favourite cafe, instead of black coffee, order a skim milk latte. Instead of black tea, order a cup of chai—spiced Indian tea brewed with milk.

▶ At home, brew a cup of strong coffee; then add 125 mL or half a cup of warm milk for a café au lait.

▶ When eating out, order skim or 1% milk instead of a soft drink with your meal.

▶ If you do not consume enough dietary calcium, consider taking a calcium supplement. Refer to the **In Depth** on osteoporosis following this chapter to learn how to choose a calcium supplement that is right for you.

◆ Kale and broccoli are a good source of calcium.

◆ Some soy milks are fortified with calcium and vitamin D. Be sure to shake the containers well to make sure the calcium does not settle as sediment on the bottom of the container.

figure, a wide variety of foods can be consumed each day to contribute to an adequate calcium intake. When you are selecting foods that are good sources of calcium, it is important to remember that we do not absorb 100% of the calcium contained in foods (Keller, Lanou, and Barnard, 2002; Nusser et al., 1996). For example, although a serving of milk contains approximately 300 mg of calcium, our body does not actually absorb this entire amount. To learn more about how calcium absorption rates vary for select foods, see the Nutrition Label Activity (page 300).

In general, meats and fish are not good sources of calcium. An exception is canned fish with bones (for example, sardines or salmon), providing you eat the bones. Fruits (except dried figs) and non-fortified grain products are also poor sources of calcium.

A variety of quick, simple tools are available on the internet to help you determine your daily calcium intake. Most of these tools are designed to provide you with an estimated calcium intake score based on the types and amounts of calcium-rich foods you consume. See the Web Resources at the end of this chapter. In addition, following the tips shown in the previous page can add more calcium to your bone bank.

As you can see, it is easy to increase your calcium intake by making smart menu choices throughout the day. Eating Right All Day (page 298) shows menu choices high in calcium. Notice that these are also low in fat and energy (calories).

What Happens If We Consume Too Much Calcium?

In general, consuming too much calcium from foods does not lead to significant toxicity symptoms in healthy individuals. Much of the excess calcium we consume is excreted in the feces. However, an excessive intake of calcium from supplements can lead to health problems (Institute of Medicine, 2010). One concern with consuming too much calcium is that it can lead to various mineral imbalances because, as we mentioned earlier, calcium interferes with the absorption of other minerals, including iron, zinc, and magnesium. In some people, the formation of kidney stones is associated with high intakes of calcium, oxalates, protein, and vegetable fibre. However, more studies need to be done to determine whether high intakes of calcium actually cause kidney stones.

Various diseases and metabolic disorders can alter our ability to regulate blood calcium. **Hypercalcemia** is a condition in which our blood calcium levels reach abnormally high concentrations. Hypercalcemia can be caused by cancer and by the overproduction of parathyroid hormone

hypercalcemia A condition marked by an abnormally high concentration of calcium in the blood.

1500 mL
lima beans
1255 kcal

169 mL plain,
non-fat yogurt
86 kcal

40 g Swiss
cheese
151 kcal

=

250 mL
non-fat milk
306 mg Ca
83 kcal

79 g canned
sardines
165 kcal

255 g, soft,
with calcium
165 kcal

219 mL cooked
collard greens
(from frozen)
54 kcal

◆ **Figure 9.7** Serving sizes and energy content of various foods that contain the same amount of calcium as a 250 mL (8 fl. oz.) glass of skim milk.

HIGHLIGHT

Calcium Supplements: Which Ones Are Best?

We know that calcium is a critical nutrient for bone health. Ideally, people should try to consume the recommended amount of calcium in their daily diet. But for vegans and people who avoid dairy products, it may be difficult to get sufficient calcium from the diet. Small or inactive people who eat less to maintain a healthy weight may not be able to consume enough food to provide adequate calcium, and older adults may need more calcium than they can obtain in their normal diets. In these circumstances, calcium supplements may be warranted.

There are an abundance of calcium supplements available to consumers, but which one is best? Most supplements come in the form of calcium carbonate, calcium citrate, calcium lactate, or calcium phosphate. Our bodies are able to absorb about 30% of the calcium from these various forms. Calcium citrate malate, which is the form of calcium used in fortified juices, is slightly more absorbable at 35%. Many antacids are also good sources of calcium, and it appears these are safe to take as long as you only consume enough to get the recommended level of calcium.

What is the most cost-effective form of calcium? In general, supplements that contain calcium carbonate tend to have more calcium per pill than other types. Thus, you are getting more calcium for your money when you buy this type. However, be sure to read the label of any calcium supplement you are considering taking to determine just how much calcium it contains. Some very expensive calcium supplements, such as coral calcium, do not contain a lot of calcium per pill, and you could be wasting your money. Coral calcium is advertised as being more absorbable than regular calcium supplements and having special curative properties, including reversing cancer (Barrett, 2004). However, it is simply calcium carbonate and, furthermore, some samples have been contaminated with lead. The curative claims have not been substantiated and have been prohibited by the U.S. Federal Trade Commission (Barrett, 2004).

Chelated forms of calcium supplements are sometimes touted as the best supplements available. Chelate refers to a claw-shaped protein that protects the calcium. Chelated calcium is easier to absorb, as the chelate protects the calcium from inhibitors, such as phytates and oxalates, that can bind with calcium in our intestine and make it harder to absorb. However, chelated calcium products are typically much more expensive and improve the absorption of calcium only by about 5% to 10%.

The lead content of calcium supplements is an important public health concern. Calcium supplements made from "natural" sources, such as oyster shell, bone meal, and dolomite (a type of rock containing calcium magnesium carbonate), are known to be higher in lead. In fact, many of these products can contain dangerously high levels of lead and should be avoided. Calcium supplements that include refined sources of calcium carbonate were considered to be very low in lead. However, a study conducted on 22 calcium supplements found that 8 (or 36%) of the supplements tested were unacceptably high in lead; this was true for oyster shell supplements and refined calcium carbonate (Ross, Szabo, and Tebbett, 2000). Shockingly, the supplement with the highest lead content was a popular, nationally recognized brand-name supplement! How can we avoid taking supplements that contain too much lead? Unfortunately, the lead content of supplements is not reported on the label. However, there are some supplements available that claim to be lead-free; in the study by Ross et al., (2000), the supplements claiming to be lead-free were found to have no detectable levels of lead. In addition, most supplements not made from oyster shell and other natural products are generally very low in lead.

How should we take our supplements? Recall that too much calcium from supplements can interfere with the body's absorption of iron, magnesium, phosphorus, and zinc and lead to mineral imbalances. So taking a calcium supplement along with a multivitamin and mineral supplement is not a good idea. Remember that our bodies cannot absorb more than 500 mg of calcium at any given time. Thus, taking a supplement that contains 1000 mg will be no more effective than one that contains 500 mg calcium. If at all possible, try to consume calcium supplements in small doses throughout the day. In addition, we absorb calcium better with meals, as the calcium stays in our intestinal tract longer during a meal and more calcium can be absorbed. However, it is better to take one calcium supplement outside of meals than to do nothing. By consuming foods high in calcium every day, we can minimize our need for calcium supplements. When we cannot consume enough calcium in our diets, there are many inexpensive, safe, and effective supplements available. The best supplement for you is the one you can tolerate, is affordable, and is readily available when you need it.

(PTH). As we noted earlier, PTH stimulates osteoclasts to break down bone and release more calcium into the bloodstream. Symptoms of hypercalcemia include fatigue, loss of appetite, constipation, and mental confusion, and it can lead to coma and possibly death. Hypercalcemia can also result in an accumulation of calcium deposits in the soft tissues, such as the liver and kidneys, causing failure of these organs.

Eating Right All Day

Breakfast
Skim-milk chai tea instead of a black coffee!

Lunch
Bean & cheese burrito instead of a beef burrito!

Dinner
Pasta with broccoli and grated cheese instead of meat sauce!

Snack
Non-fat fruit yogurt instead of Oreos!

What Happens If We Don't Consume Enough Calcium?

There are no short-term symptoms associated with consuming too little calcium. Even when we do not consume enough dietary calcium, our body continues to tightly regulate blood calcium levels by taking the calcium from bone. A long-term repercussion of inadequate calcium intake is osteoporosis. This disease is discussed *In Depth* immediately following this chapter.

Hypocalcemia is an abnormally low level of calcium in the blood. Hypocalcemia does not result from consuming too little dietary calcium, but is caused by various diseases, including kidney disease, vitamin D deficiency, and diseases that inhibit the production of PTH. Symptoms of hypocalcemia include muscle spasms and convulsions.

RECAP Calcium is the most abundant mineral in the human body and a significant component of our bones. Calcium is necessary for normal nerve and muscle function. Blood calcium is maintained within a very narrow range, and bone calcium is used to maintain normal blood calcium if dietary intake is inadequate. The AI for calcium is highest for pre-teens and teens. Dairy products, canned fish with bones, and some green leafy vegetables are good sources of calcium. The most common long-term effect of inadequate calcium consumption is osteoporosis.

Vitamin D

Vitamin D is like other fat-soluble vitamins in that we store excess amounts in our liver and adipose tissue. But vitamin D is different from other nutrients in two ways. First, vitamin D does not always need to come from the diet. This is because our body can synthesize vitamin D using energy from exposure to sunlight. However, when we do not get enough sunlight, we must consume vitamin D in our diet. Second, in addition to being a nutrient, vitamin D is considered a *hormone* because it is made in one part of the body, yet it regulates various activities in other parts of the body.

Figure 9.8 illustrates how our body makes vitamin D by converting a cholesterol compound in our skin to **calcitriol**, the active form of vitamin D that we need to function properly. When the ultraviolet rays of the sun hit our skin, they react with 7-dehydrocholesterol. This cholesterol compound is converted into a precursor of vitamin D, cholecalciferol, which is also called provitamin D$_3$. This inactive form is then converted to calcidiol in the liver. Calcidiol travels to the kidneys, where it is converted into calcitriol, which is considered the primary active form of vitamin D in our body. Calcitriol then circulates to various parts of the body, performing its many functions.

hypocalcemia A condition characterized by an abnormally low concentration of calcium in the blood.

calcitriol The primary active form of vitamin D in the body.

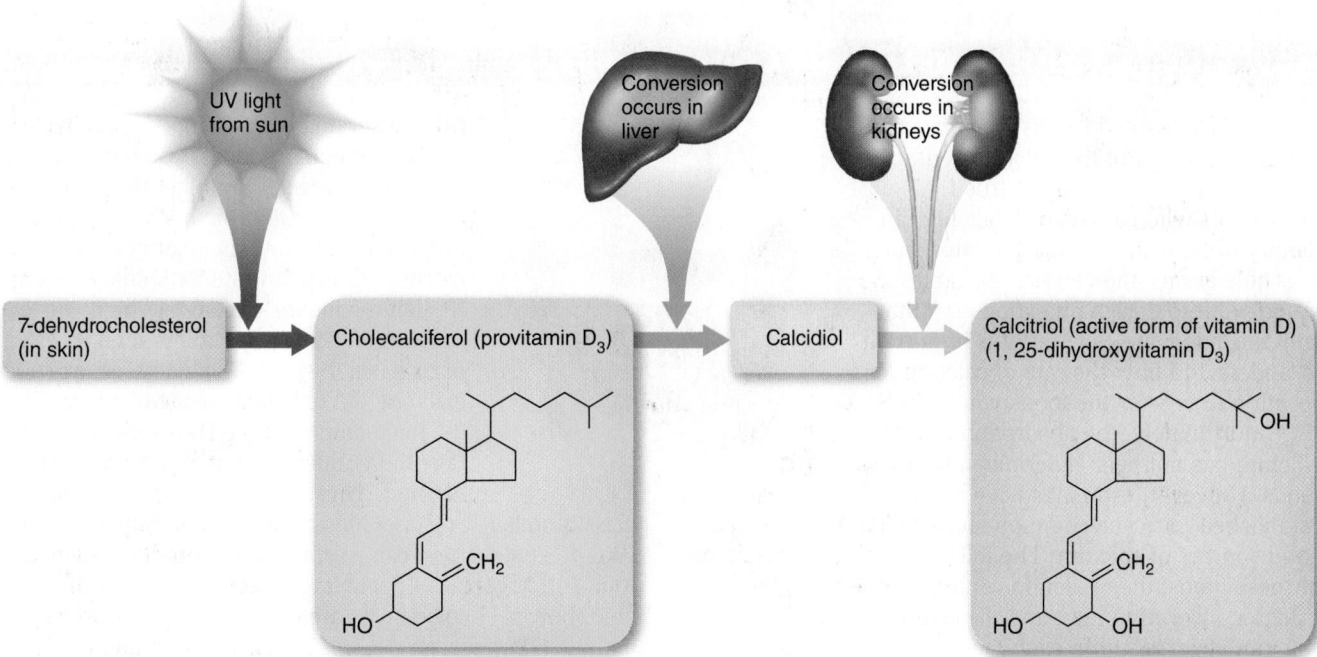

Figure 9.8 The process of converting sunlight into vitamin D in our skin. When the ultraviolet rays of the sun hit our skin, they react with 7-dehydrocholesterol. This compound is converted to cholecalciferol, an inactive form of vitamin D also called provitamin D_3. Cholecalciferol is then converted to calcidiol in the liver. Calcidiol travels to the kidneys, where it is converted into calcitriol, which is considered the primary active form of vitamin D in our body.

Functions of Vitamin D

Vitamin D (as calcitriol), PTH, and calcitonin all work together continuously to regulate blood calcium levels, which in turn maintains bone health. They do this by regulating the absorption of calcium and phosphorus from the small intestine, causing more to be absorbed when our needs for them are higher and less when our needs are lower. Vitamin D regulates calcium and phosphorus absorption by controlling genes that code for intestinal calcium transport proteins. In other words, vitamin D can "turn on" the genes that code for proteins to transport calcium across the intestinal wall; more transport proteins mean that more calcium can move from the lumen of the intestine into the bloodstream. They also decrease or increase blood calcium levels by signalling the kidneys to excrete more or less calcium in our urine. Finally, vitamin D affects gene expression in bone cells and works with PTH to stimulate osteoclasts to break down bone when calcium is needed elsewhere in the body.

Vitamin D is also necessary for the normal calcification of bone; this means it assists the process by which minerals such as calcium and phosphorus are crystallized. Similar to vitamin A, vitamin D appears to play a role in cell differentiation in various tissues.

Vitamin D may play some role in decreasing the formation of some cancerous tumours, as it can prevent certain types of cells from growing out of control. A study published in the *American Journal of Clinical Nutrition* in 2007 caused a great deal of excitement (Lappe et al., 2007). This randomized, double-blind, placebo-controlled trial followed approximately 1200 postmenopausal women for four years to determine the effects of a placebo, a calcium supplement (1400–1500 mg), and a combined calcium and vitamin D supplement with 1100 International Units (IU) of vitamin D. The results showed that the group receiving vitamin D and calcium had a 60% to 80% lower risk of all cancers compared with the placebo. However, since this trial was conducted to examine fractures and cancer was a secondary outcome, additional clinical trials are required to examine vitamin D supplements and cancer risk.

Other research suggests that vitamin D deficiency may play a role in cardiovascular disease, multiple sclerosis, and rheumatoid arthritis (IFIC Foundation, 2007).

NUTRITION LABEL ACTIVITY

How Much Calcium Am I Really Consuming?

As you have learned in this chapter, we do not absorb 100% of the calcium contained in foods. This is particularly true for individuals who eat lots of foods high in dietary fibre, oxalates, and phytates, such as whole grains and certain vegetables. So if you want to design an eating plan that contains adequate calcium, it is important to understand how the rate of calcium absorption differs for the foods you include.

Unfortunately, the absorption rate of calcium has not been determined for most foods. However, estimates have been established for some common foods that are considered good sources of calcium. The following table shows some of these foods, their calcium content per serving, the calcium absorption rate, and the estimated amount of calcium absorbed from each food.

As you can see from this table, many dairy products have a similar calcium absorption rate, just over 30%. Interestingly, many green leafy vegetables have a higher absorption rate of around 60%; however, because many times a serving of these foods contains less calcium than dairy foods, you would have to eat more vegetables to get the same calcium as you would from a standard serving of dairy foods. Note the relatively low calcium absorption rate for spinach, even though it contains a relatively high amount of calcium. This is due to the high levels of oxalates in spinach, which bind with calcium and reduce its bioavailability.

Remember that the DRIs for calcium take these differences in absorption rate into account. Thus, the 300 mg of calcium in a glass of milk counts as 300 mg toward your daily calcium goal. In general, you can trust that dairy products such as milk and yogurt (but not cottage cheese) are good, absorbable sources of calcium, as are most dark green leafy vegetables. Other dietary sources of calcium with good absorption rates are calcium-fortified orange juice, soy milk and rice milk, and tofu processed with calcium. Armed with this knowledge, you will be better able to select foods that can optimize your calcium intake and support bone health.

Food	Serving Size	Calcium per Serving (mg)*	Absorption Rate (%)†	Estimated Amount of Calcium Absorbed (mg)
Yogurt, plain skim milk	250 mL (8 fl. oz.)	452	32	145
Milk, skim	250 mL (8 fl. oz.)	306	32	98
Milk, 2%	250 mL (8 fl. oz.)	285	32	91
Kale, frozen, cooked	250 mL (1 cup)	179	59	106
Turnip greens, boiled	250 mL (1 cup)	197	52	103
Broccoli, frozen, chopped, cooked	250 mL (1 cup)	61	61	37
Cauliflower, boiled	250 mL (1 cup)	20	69	14
Spinach, frozen, cooked	250 mL (1 cup)	291	5	14

*Data from U.S. Department of Agriculture, Agricultural Research Service. 2009. USDA National Nutrient Database for Standard Reference, Release 22. www.ars.usda.gov/ba/bhnrc/ndl.
†Data from Weaver, C. M., W. R. Proulx, and R. Heaney, 1999. Choices for achieving adequate dietary calcium with a vegetarian diet. Am. J. Clin. Nutr. 70(suppl.):543S–548S; Weaver, C. M., and K. L. Plawecki, 1994. Dietary calcium: adequacy of a vegetarian diet. Am. J. Clin. Nutr. 59(suppl.):1238S–1241S.

Several European studies have found that infants receiving vitamin D supplements had significantly lower risks of developing type 1 diabetes.

How Much Vitamin D Should We Consume?

The new RDA for vitamin D is based on the assumption that an individual does not get adequate sun exposure (see Table 9.2). An Institute of Medicine (2010) report states that there are no additional health benefits associated with vitamin D intakes above the level of the new RDA. Total vitamin D intake should remain below the level of the new UL to avoid possible adverse effects.

If your exposure to the sun is adequate, then you do not need to consume any vitamin D in your diet. But how do you know whether you are getting enough sun? Of the many factors that affect your ability to synthesize vitamin D from sunlight, latitude and time of year are the most significant **(Table 9.3)**. Individuals living in very sunny climates relatively close to the equator, such as the southern United States and Mexico,

TABLE 9.3 Factors Affecting Sunlight-Mediated Synthesis of Vitamin D in the Skin

Factors That Enhance Synthesis of Vitamin D	Factors That Inhibit Synthesis of Vitamin D
Season—Most vitamin D is produced during summer months, particularly June and July	Season—Exposure in winter months (October through February) results in little or no vitamin D production
Latitude—Locations closer to the equator get more sunlight throughout the year	Latitude—Locations that are more north of 40°N and more south than 40°S get inadequate sun
Time of day—Generally, between the hours of 9:00 a.m. and 3:00 p.m. (dependent on latitude and time of year)	Time of day—Early morning, late afternoon, and evening hours
Age—Younger	Age—Older, due to reduced skin thickness with age
Limited or no use of sunscreen	Use of sunscreen with SPF 8 or greater
Sunny weather	Cloudy weather
Exposed skin	Protective clothing
Lighter skin pigmentation	Darker skin pigmentation
	Obesity—May negatively affect metabolism and storage of vitamin D
	Glass and plastics—Windows and other barriers made of glass or plastic (such as Plexiglas) block the sun's rays

may synthesize enough vitamin D from the sun to meet their needs throughout the year—as long as they spend time outdoors. However, vitamin D synthesis from the sun is not possible during most of the winter months for people living in places located at a latitude of more than 40°N or more than 40°S. This is because at these latitudes in winter the sun never rises high enough in the sky to provide the direct sunlight needed.

Researchers in the Canadian Multicentre Osteoporosis Study (CaMos) have collected data on the bone health and vitamin D status of over 9000 Canadians in nine regions across the country for 15 years (CaMos, 2012). Results from a sample of 188 men and women in Calgary showed that 34% of participants had low levels of vitamin D (vitamin D insufficiency) in at least one season of the year, most commonly fall or winter (Rucker et al., 2002). Calgary is said to have more hours of sunshine than any other Canadian city; however, at 51°N latitude, the sun's ultraviolet rays are not strong enough to produce sufficient vitamin D_3 (cholecalciferol) in the skin of many people. Thus, Canadians cannot rely on sun exposure for vitamin D synthesis from October to April, and an adequate intake of vitamin D from diet and supplements becomes essential during those months.

Other factors influencing vitamin D synthesis include the time of day, skin colour, traditional clothing in some cultures, age, and obesity status:

- More vitamin D can be synthesized when the sun's rays are strongest, generally between 10 a.m. and 3 p.m. (Holick, 2004). On overcast days, or days when there are high levels of air pollution, we may synthesize little or no vitamin D.
- Research has shown that people with darker skin pigmentations, such as Asians, Blacks, and Aboriginal people, have lower levels of vitamin D in their blood, regardless of the latitude or season. They require more sun exposure to synthesize vitamin D compared with lighter-skinned people.
- Women belonging to some cultural groups wear traditional clothing that covers most of their bodies, and they keep their infants fully clothed as well. Their avoidance of direct sunlight puts the mothers and their babies at high risk for vitamin D deficiency (Holick, 2004).
- People 65 years of age or older experience a fourfold decrease in their capacity to synthesize vitamin D from the sun (Holick, Matsuoka, and Wortsman, 1989; Need et al., 1993).
- Obesity is associated with lower levels of circulating vitamin D, possibly because of lower bioavailability of cholecalciferol from adipose tissue, decreased exposure to sunlight due to limited mobility or time spent outdoors with skin exposed, and alterations in vitamin D metabolism in the liver (Florez et al., 2007; Holick, 2005).

Two other factors influencing vitamin D synthesis in the skin are aging and the use of sunscreens. The best times of the day for vitamin D synthesis are when exposure to ultraviolet rays may be discouraged to prevent skin cancers. Many adults routinely apply sunscreens to themselves and their children to protect against the sun's ultraviolet rays. However, a sunscreen with a sun protection factor (SPF) of 8 will reduce vitamin D production in the skin by 95%, while an SPF 15 sunscreen reduces synthesis by 98% (Holick, 2004). More research is needed to determine the best practices in using sunscreens, so that the skin is able to synthesize vitamin D but is protected from too much sun and the risk of skin cancers. The current recommendation is to expose (with no sunscreen) your arms and legs or your hands, arms, and face to sunlight between 10 a.m. and 3 p.m. for about five to ten minutes, two or three times a week (Holick, 2004), with longer times needed for individuals with dark skin pigmentation.

Vitamin D: Fish, Fortified Foods, Supplements, or Sunlight

There are many forms of vitamin D, but only two can be converted into calcitriol. Vitamin D$_2$, also called *ergocalciferol*, is found exclusively in plant foods, whereas vitamin D$_3$, or *cholecalciferol,* is found in animal foods. Recall that cholecalciferol is also the form of vitamin D we synthesize from the sun.

Most foods naturally contain very little vitamin D. Thus, our primary source of vitamin D in the diet is from fortified milk. Currently, fluid cow's milk and goat's milk have approximately 100 IU of vitamin D added per 250 mL (8 fl. oz.), but yogurt, buttermilk, cottage cheese, and most cheeses are not fortified with vitamin D. Given that many Canadians have insufficient levels of vitamin D in their bodies, the government has proposed changes to both the levels of vitamin D added to foods and the types of foods fortified. One of the proposed changes is to increase the amount of vitamin D added to fluid cow's milk and goat's milk up to 1.3 µg (53 IU) per 100 mL. It is also proposed that breakfast cereals be fortified with vitamin D and calcium, as they are in the United States.

Since plants naturally contain very little vitamin D, vegans need to obtain their vitamin D from fortified foods such as fortified soy milks, from sun exposure, or from supplements. When reading the labels of fortified foods and supplements, you will see the amount of vitamin D expressed in units of either µg or IU. For conversion purposes, 1 µg of vitamin D is equal to 40 IU of vitamin D.

What Happens If We Consume Too Much Vitamin D?

We cannot get too much vitamin D from sun exposure, as our skin has the ability to limit its production. As just noted, foods contain little natural vitamin D. Thus, the only way we can consume too much vitamin D is through supplementation.

Consuming too much vitamin D from supplements causes hypercalcemia, or high blood calcium concentrations. As discussed in the section on calcium, symptoms of hypercalcemia include weakness, loss of appetite, constipation, mental confusion, vomiting, excessive urine output, and extreme thirst. Hypercalcemia also leads to the formation of calcium deposits in soft tissues, such as the kidneys, liver, and heart. In addition, toxic levels of vitamin D lead to increased bone loss because calcium is then pulled from the bones and excreted more readily from the kidneys.

What Happens If We Don't Consume Enough Vitamin D?

The primary deficiency associated with inadequate vitamin D is loss of bone mass. In fact, when vitamin D levels are inadequate, our small intestine can absorb only 10%–15% of the calcium we consume. Vitamin D deficiencies occur most often in individuals who have diseases that cause intestinal malabsorption of fat and thus the fat-soluble vitamins. People with liver disease, kidney disease, Crohn's disease, celiac disease, cystic fibrosis, or Whipple's disease may suffer from vitamin D deficiency and require supplements.

Reduced calcium absorption also means that fewer minerals are deposited on the collagen matrix, or bone tissue, produced by the osteoblasts. The pliable collagen matrix gets its strength and structure from deposits of minerals. When there is inadequate mineralization, the collagen becomes hydrated and expands outward, putting pressure on the sheath covering the bone (periosteal covering) and the many pain sensors in this sheath. This very painful condition is called **rickets** in children and **osteomalacia** in adults.

◆ Vitamin D synthesis from the sun is not possible during most of the winter months for people living in high latitudes. Therefore, many people need to consume vitamin D in their diet, particularly during the winter.

◆ Fatty fish contain vitamin D.

rickets A vitamin D–deficiency disease in children. Signs include deformities of the skeleton, such as bowed legs and knocked knees. Severe rickets can be fatal.

osteomalacia A vitamin D–deficiency disease in adults, in which bones become soft, weak, and prone to fractures.

In rickets, the bones are poorly mineralized and therefore soft. The weak bones may not support the weight of the growing child, and bone deformities are common. The legs may bow outward or the knees may "cave in," but either way the child experiences a great deal of pain and difficulty walking and running. Arms may look twisted, heads may be too large, and rib cages may protrude forward (Figure 9.9).

Severe cases of rickets can be fatal. Rickets is not common in North America, where milk is fortified with vitamin D, but children with illnesses that cause fat malabsorption or who drink no milk and get limited sun exposure are at increased risk. A review of reported cases of rickets among children in the United States found that approximately 83% were African American and that 95% had been breastfed (Holick, 2006; Weisberg, Scanlon, and Cogswell, 2004). Breast milk contains very little vitamin D, and fewer than 5% of the breastfed children were reported to have received vitamin D supplementation. Thus, rickets appears to occur more commonly in children with darker skin (their need for adequate sun exposure is higher than that of light-skinned children) and in breastfed children who do not receive adequate vitamin D supplementation.

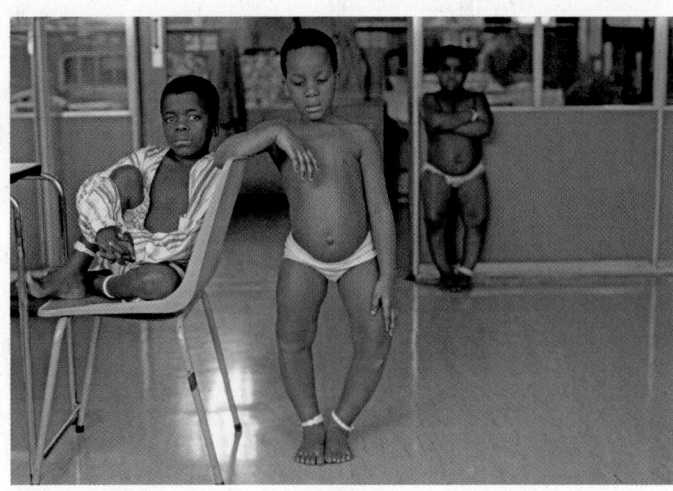

Figure 9.9 Typical presentation of children with rickets. These children, being treated at a hospital in Soweto, South Africa, have severe muscle weakness and bone deformities, including bowed legs and knocked knees.

Rickets is still a significant nutritional problem for children in other parts of the world, especially in countries where fish is not commonly consumed and where milk is not fortified with vitamin D. The most vulnerable age group is six months to three years of age. After the age of three, rickets cannot be completely reversed, but vitamin D treatment can be beneficial.

Vitamin D–deficiency disease in adults is called osteomalacia, a term meaning "soft bones." With osteomalacia, bones become weak and prone to fractures because they have a lower mineral content. People with osteomalacia often complain of aching bones, and some have bowed legs.

In contrast, people with osteoporosis have less whole bone tissue. That is, they lose the soft bone matrix (produced by the osteoblasts and destroyed by osteoclasts) and thus have less surface area for minerals to be deposited. Bone density is reduced because there is less bone matrix and less mineralization, resulting in porous and fragile bones. The vertebrae in the spine may compress, leading to a loss of height or a dowager's hump, but there may be few other symptoms of this bone disease until a fracture occurs. Osteoporosis, discussed *In Depth* on pages 314–321, can also result from a vitamin D deficiency.

As discussed earlier, recent studies suggest that Canadians may be more at risk for vitamin D insufficiency or deficiency than previously thought. Raiten and Picciano Raiten and Picciano (2004) have suggested some possible reasons for the current prevalence of low blood levels of vitamin D in North Americans. These include the fact that many people do not drink milk because of lactose intolerance or concerns about fat intakes and body weight. As well, the increased use of sunscreens, greater air pollution, and the avoidance of sunlight, especially among some cultural groups, have contributed to less skin synthesis of vitamin D among some groups. Young adults who work long hours indoors every day and get little or no sun exposure and older adults who are institutionalized may be at risk. Individuals with diseases that cause fat and fat-soluble vitamins to be poorly absorbed from the intestine are also at risk of vitamin D deficiencies.

Various medications can also alter the metabolism and activity of vitamin D. For instance, glucocorticoids, which are medications used to reduce inflammation, can cause bone loss by inhibiting our ability to absorb calcium through the actions of vitamin D. Anti-seizure medications, such as phenobarbital and Dilantin, alter vitamin D metabolism. Thus, people who are taking such medications may need to increase their vitamin D intake.

RECAP Vitamin D is a fat-soluble vitamin and a hormone. It can be made in the skin using energy from sunlight. Vitamin D regulates blood calcium levels and maintains bone health. Foods contain little vitamin D, with fortified milk being the primary source. Vitamin D toxicity causes hypercalcemia. Vitamin D deficiency can result in osteoporosis; rickets is vitamin D deficiency in children, whereas osteomalacia is vitamin D deficiency in adults.

Vitamin K

Vitamin K, a fat-soluble vitamin stored primarily in the liver, is actually a family of compounds known as quinones. *Phylloquinone,* which is the primary dietary form of vitamin K, is also the form found in plants; *menaquinone* is the animal form of vitamin K produced by bacteria in the large intestine.

The primary function of vitamin K is to assist in the production of *prothrombin,* a protein that plays a critical role in blood clotting. This is discussed in more detail in Chapter 10. Vitamin K also assists in the production of *osteocalcin,* a protein associated with bone turnover.

We can obtain vitamin K from our diet, and we absorb the vitamin K produced by bacteria in our large intestine. These two sources usually provide adequate amounts of this nutrient to maintain health, and there is no RDA or UL for vitamin K. AI recommendations are listed in Table 9.2.

Only a few foods contribute substantially to our dietary intake of vitamin K. Green leafy vegetables, including kale, spinach, collard greens, turnip greens, and lettuce, are good sources, as are broccoli, Brussels sprouts, and cabbage. Vegetable oils, such as soybean oil and canola oil, are also good sources. **Figure 9.10** identifies the amount of vitamin K in micrograms (μg) per serving for these foods.

Based on our current knowledge, for healthy individuals there appear to be no side effects associated with consuming large amounts of vitamin K (Institute of Medicine, 2002). This appears to be true for both supplements and food sources.

Vitamin K deficiency is associated with a reduced ability to form blood clots, leading to excessive bleeding; however, primary vitamin K deficiency is rare in humans. People with diseases that cause malabsorption of fat, such as celiac disease, Crohn's disease, and cystic fibrosis, can suffer secondarily from a deficiency of vitamin K.

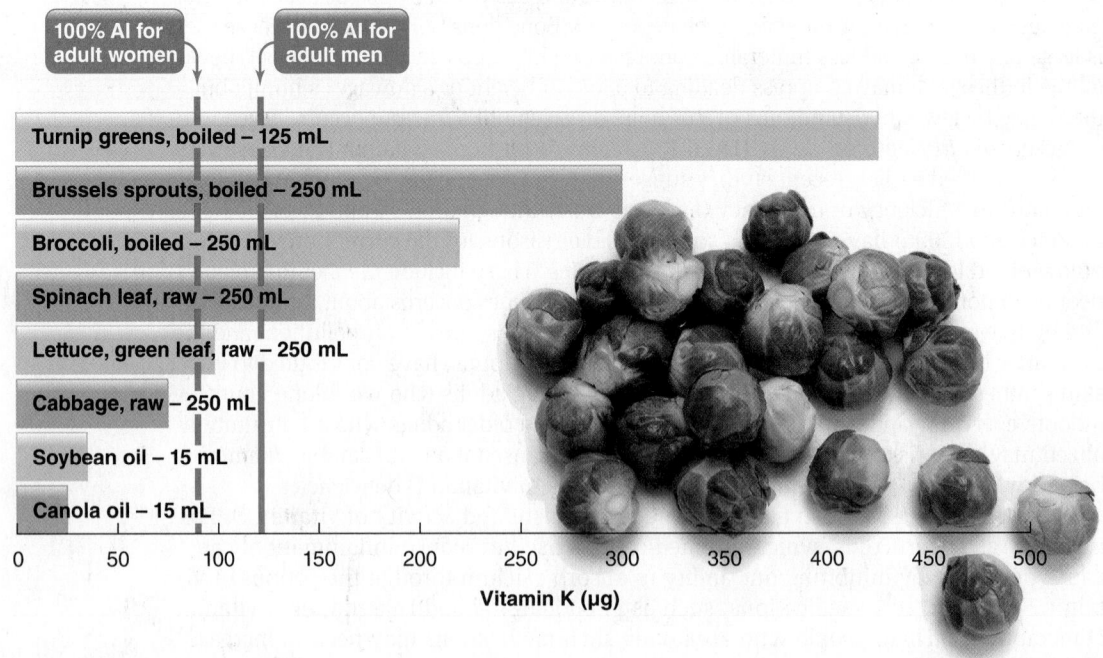

Figure 9.10 Common food sources of vitamin K. The AIs for adult men and women are 120 μg per day and 90 μg per day, respectively.

Data from U.S. Department of Agriculture, Agricultural Research Service. 2009. USDA Nutrient Database for Standard Reference, Release 22. Nutrient Data Laboratory Home Page. www.ars.usda.gov/ba/bhnrc/ndl.

Newborns are typically given an injection of vitamin K at birth, as they lack the intestinal bacteria necessary to produce this nutrient.

The impact of vitamin K deficiency on bone health is controversial. A study of vitamin K intake and a risk for hip fractures found that women who consumed the least amount of vitamin K had a higher risk for bone fractures than women who consumed relatively more vitamin K. Despite the results of this study, there is not enough scientific evidence to support the contention that vitamin K deficiency leads to osteoporosis (Institute of Medicine, 2002). In fact, there is no significant impact on overall bone density in people who take anticoagulant medications that result in a relative state of vitamin K deficiency.

Green leafy vegetables, including Brussels sprouts are good sources of vitamin K.

RECAP Vitamin K is a fat-soluble vitamin and coenzyme that is important for blood clotting and bone metabolism. We obtain vitamin K largely from bacteria in our large intestine. Green leafy vegetables and vegetable oils contain vitamin K. There are no known toxicity symptoms for vitamin K in healthy individuals. Vitamin K deficiency is rare and may lead to excessive bleeding.

Phosphorus

As discussed in Chapter 7, phosphorus is the major intracellular negatively charged electrolyte. In our body, phosphorus is most commonly found combined with oxygen in the form of phosphate (PO_4^{3-}). Phosphorus is an essential constituent of all cells and is found in both plants and animals.

Functions of Phosphorus

Phosphorus plays a critical role in bone formation, as it is a part of the mineral complex of bone. As discussed earlier in this chapter, calcium and phosphorus crystallize to form hydroxyapatite crystals, which provide the hardness of bone. About 85% of our body's phosphorus is stored in our bones, with the rest stored in soft tissues, such as muscles and organs.

The role of phosphorus in maintaining proper fluid balance was examined in detail in Chapter 7. Phosphorus also helps activate and deactivate enzymes, and it is a component of lipoproteins, cell membranes, DNA and RNA, and several energy molecules, including adenosine triphosphate (ATP).

How Much Phosphorus Should We Consume?

The details of phosphorus recommendations, food sources, and deficiency and toxicity symptoms were discussed in Chapter 7. The RDA for phosphorus is listed in Table 9.2. In general, phosphorus is widespread in many foods and is found in high amounts in foods that contain protein. Milk, meats, and eggs are good sources. See Figure 7.9 (page 244) for a review of the phosphorus content of various foods.

Phosphorus is also found in many processed foods as a food additive, where it enhances smoothness, binding, and moisture retention. Moreover, in the form of phosphoric acid, it is added to soft drinks to give them a sharper, or more tart, flavour and to slow the growth of moulds and bacteria. Our society has increased its consumption of processed foods and soft drinks substantially over the past 30 years, resulting in an estimated 10%–15% increase in phosphorus consumption (Institute of Medicine, 1997).

Nutrition and medical professionals have become increasingly concerned that heavy consumption of soft drinks may be detrimental to bone health. Studies have shown that consuming soft drinks is associated with reduced bone mass or an increased risk for fractures in both youth and adults (Wyshak, 2000; Wyshak and Frisch, 1994; Wyshak et al., 1989). Researchers have proposed three theories to explain why the consumption of soft drinks may be detrimental to bone health:

- Consuming soft drinks in place of calcium-containing beverages, such as milk, leads to a deficient intake of calcium.
- The phosphoric acid content of soft drinks causes an increased loss of calcium because calcium is drawn from bone into the blood to neutralize the excess acid.
- The caffeine found in many soft drinks causes increased calcium loss through the urine.

Phosphorus, in the form of phosphoric acid, is a major component of soft drinks.

Dr. Susan Whiting, of the University of Saskatchewan, and her colleagues have examined the levels, sources, and seasonality of calcium intakes in Saskatchewan and found that fluid milk provides approximately 44% of the calcium in the diets of adolescents (Iuliano-Burns et al., 1999). However, adolescent girls appear to have low calcium intakes, with about 50% of their Calories from beverages coming from soft drinks rather than milk, and this puts teen girls at more risk for suboptimal bone development than boys (Vatanparast et al., 2006). Whiting and her colleagues have, in fact, shown that the high amounts of soft drinks, coupled with the inadequate calcium intakes, are resulting in less than optimum bone accrual for adolescent girls (Whiting et al., 2001). Later, in Ireland, another study that used more than 10 times as many subjects showed a similar impact on bone mineral density in adolescents (McGartland et al., 2003). In both studies, girls had less bone accrual when intakes of soft drinks were high, while boys were spared an adverse effect on bone accrual (McGartland et al., 2003; Whiting et al., 2001). Whiting urges that, because females lose bone mineral mass faster than males later in life, it is especially important for females to achieve their maximal bone accrual and peak bone mass during adolescence (Whiting et al., 2004).

This work by these research teams strongly suggests that the direct substitution of soft drinks for milk beverages is the likely cause of the suboptimal bone health observed in teen girls, but this is difficult to prove conclusively. Other factors may cloud the picture, including smoking (perhaps the girls drinking soft drinks are also teen smokers?), overall poor diet quality (maybe less calcium-rich vegetables and legumes are consumed?), and low activity levels (a sedentary lifestyle may lead to less bone accrual).

What Happens If We Consume Too Much Phosphorus?

As discussed in Chapter 7, people with kidney disease and those who take too many vitamin D supplements or too many phosphorus-containing antacids can suffer from high blood phosphorus levels. Severely high levels of blood phosphorus can cause muscle spasms and convulsions.

What Happens If We Don't Consume Enough Phosphorus?

Phosphorus deficiencies are rare but can occur in people who abuse alcohol, in premature infants, and in elderly people with poor diets. People with vitamin D deficiency, people with hyperparathyroidism (oversecretion of parathyroid hormone), and those who overuse antacids that bind with phosphorus may also have low blood phosphorus levels.

RECAP Phosphorus is the major negatively charged electrolyte inside of the cell. It helps maintain fluid balance and bone health. It also assists in regulating chemical reactions, and it is a primary component of ATP, DNA, and RNA. Phosphorus is commonly found in high-protein foods. Excess phosphorus can lead to muscle spasms and convulsions, whereas phosphorus deficiencies are rare.

Magnesium

Magnesium is a major mineral. Our total body magnesium content is approximately 25 g. About 50%–60% of our body's magnesium is found in our bones, with the rest located in our soft tissues.

Functions of Magnesium

Magnesium is one of the minerals that make up the structure of bone. It is also important in the regulation of bone and mineral status. Specifically, magnesium influences the formation of hydroxyapatite crystals through its regulation of calcium balance and its interactions with vitamin D and parathyroid hormone.

Magnesium is a critical *cofactor* for more than 300 enzyme systems. Recall from Chapter 8 that a cofactor is a compound that is needed for an enzyme to be active. Magnesium is necessary for the production of ATP, and it plays an important role in DNA and protein synthesis and repair. Magnesium supplementation has been shown to improve insulin sensitivity, and there is epidemiological evidence that a high magnesium intake is associated with a decrease in the risk for colorectal cancer (Larsson,

Bergkvist, and Wolk, 2005; Paolisso et al, 1992).Magnesium supports normal vitamin D metabolism and action and is necessary for normal muscle contraction and blood clotting.

How Much Magnesium Should We Consume?

As magnesium is found in a wide variety of foods, people who are adequately nourished generally consume enough magnesium in their diet. The RDA for magnesium is identified in Table 9.2. There is no UL for magnesium for food and water; the UL for magnesium from supplements and drugs is 350 mg per day.

Magnesium is found in green leafy vegetables, such as spinach. It is also found in whole grains, seeds, and nuts. Other good food sources of magnesium include seafood, beans, and some dairy products. Refined and processed foods are low in magnesium. **Figure 9.11** shows many foods that are good sources of magnesium.

The magnesium content of drinking water varies considerably. The "harder" the water, the higher its content of magnesium. This variability makes it impossible to estimate how much our drinking water may contribute to the magnesium content of our diet.

The ability of the small intestine to absorb magnesium is reduced when one consumes a diet that is extremely high in fibre and phytates, because these substances bind with magnesium. Even though seeds and nuts are relatively high in fibre, they are excellent sources of absorbable magnesium. Overall, our absorption of magnesium should be sufficient if we consume the recommended amount of fibre each day (20–35 g per day). In contrast, higher dietary protein intakes enhance the absorption and retention of magnesium.

What Happens If We Consume Too Much Magnesium?

There are no known toxicity symptoms related to consuming excess magnesium in the diet. The toxicity symptoms that result from pharmacologic overuse of magnesium include diarrhea, nausea, and abdominal cramps. In extreme cases, large doses can result in acid–base imbalances, massive dehydration, cardiac arrest, and death. High blood magnesium levels, or **hypermagnesemia**, occur in individuals with impaired kidney function who consume large amounts of non-dietary magnesium, such as antacids. Side effects include the impairment of nerve, muscle, and heart function.

Trail mix with chocolate chips, nuts, and seeds is one common food source of magnesium.

hypermagnesemia A condition marked by an abnormally high concentration of magnesium in the blood.

Figure 9.11 Common food sources of magnesium. For adult men 19 to 30 years of age, the RDA for magnesium is 400 mg per day; the RDA increases to 420 mg per day for men 31 years of age and older. For adult women 19 to 30 years of age, the RDA for magnesium is 310 mg per day; this value increases to 320 mg per day for women 31 years of age and older.
Data from U.S. Department of Agriculture, Agricultural Research Service. 2009. USDA Nutrient Database for Standard Reference, Release 22. Nutrient Data Laboratory Home Page. www.ars.usda.gov/ba/bhnrc/ndl.

What Happens If We Don't Consume Enough Magnesium?

Hypomagnesemia, or low blood magnesium, results from magnesium deficiency. This condition may develop secondary to kidney disease, chronic diarrhea, or chronic alcohol abuse. Elderly people seem to be at particularly high risk for low dietary intakes of magnesium because they have a reduced appetite and blunted senses of taste and smell. In addition, the elderly face challenges related to shopping and preparing meals that contain foods high in magnesium, and their ability to absorb magnesium is reduced.

Low blood calcium levels are a side effect of hypomagnesemia. Other symptoms of magnesium deficiency include muscle cramps, spasms or seizures, nausea, weakness, irritability, and confusion. Considering magnesium's role in bone formation, it is not surprising that long-term magnesium deficiency is associated with osteoporosis. Magnesium deficiency is also associated with many other chronic diseases, including heart disease, high blood pressure, and type 2 diabetes (Institute of Medicine, 1997).

RECAP Magnesium is a major mineral found in fresh foods, including spinach, nuts, seeds, whole grains, and meats. It is important for bone health, energy production, and muscle function. The RDA for magnesium varies with age and gender. Hypermagnesemia can result in diarrhea, muscle cramps, and cardiac arrest. Hypomagnesemia causes hypocalcemia, muscle cramps, spasms, and weakness. Magnesium deficiencies are also associated with osteoporosis, heart disease, high blood pressure, and type 2 diabetes.

Fluoride

Fluoride, a trace mineral, is the ionic form of the element fluorine. As discussed in Chapter 1, trace minerals are minerals that our body needs in amounts less than 100 mg per day; the amount of trace minerals in our body is less than 5 g. About 99% of the fluoride in our body is stored in our teeth and bones.

Functions of Fluoride

Fluoride assists in the development and maintenance of our teeth and bones. During the development of both our baby and permanent teeth, fluoride combines with calcium and phosphorus to form *fluorohydroxyapatite,* which is more resistant to destruction by acids and bacteria than is hydroxyapatite. Even after all of our permanent teeth are in, treating them with fluoride, whether at the dentist's office or with fluoridated toothpaste, gives them more protection against dental caries (cavities) than teeth that have not been treated. That is because fluoride enhances tooth mineralization, decreases and reverses tooth demineralization, and inhibits the metabolism of the acid-producing bacteria that cause tooth decay.

Fluoride also stimulates new bone growth, and it is being researched as a potential treatment for osteoporosis, both alone and in combination with other medications (American Dietetic Association, 2005; Ringe et al., 2005; USDHHS, 1991). While early results are promising, more research needs to be conducted to determine if fluoride is an effective treatment for osteoporosis (American Dietetic Association, 2005; Pak et al., 1995; Reginster et al., 2003; Ringe et al., 2005).

How Much Fluoride Should We Consume?

Our need for fluoride is relatively small. Most Canadians get adequate amounts of fluoride every day through dental products, foods we eat that naturally contain fluoride in trace amounts, foods made with fluoridated water, and fluoridated water supplies. Health Canada, the Canadian Public Health Association, the Canadian Dental Association, the Canadian Medical Association, and the World Health Organization recommend the addition of fluoride to municipal drinking water to prevent tooth decay. About 40% of Canadians live in communities with fluoridated water (Health Canada, 2008b). Health Canada allows a maximum concentration of 1.5 mg fluoride per litre of water, and the Federal-Provincial–Territorial Committee on Drinking Water recommends 0.8 to 1.0 mg/L. Health Canada convened an expert panel on fluoride in January 2007 to review the latest science on the safety and efficacy of water fluoridation. The panel's

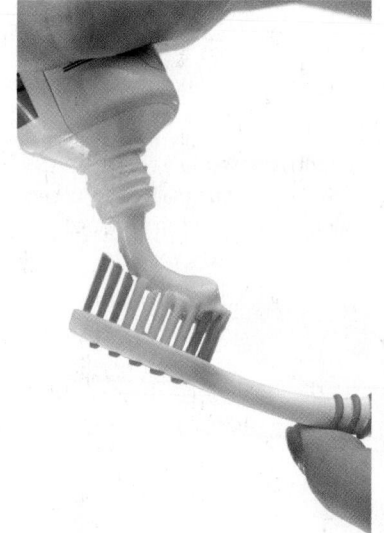
Fluoride is readily available in many communities in Canada through fluoridated water and dental products.

hypomagnesemia A condition characterized by an abnormally low concentration of magnesium in the blood.

findings were released in April 2008 and include the recommendation to slightly reduce the concentration of fluoride to 0.7 mg/L in drinking water (Health Canada, 2008a).

There is no RDA for fluoride. The AI for fluoride (see Table 9.2) for children aged 4 to 8 years is 1 mg per day; this value increases to 2 mg per day for boys and girls aged 9 to 13 years. The AI for boys and girls aged 14 to 18 years is 3 mg per day. The AI for adults is 4 mg per day for adult men and 3 mg per day for adult women. The UL is 2.2 mg per day for children aged 4 to 8 years; the UL for everyone older than 8 years of age is 10 mg per day.

Fluoride is readily available in many communities in Canada through fluoridated water and dental products. Fluoride is absorbed directly in the mouth into the teeth and gums, and it can be absorbed from the gastrointestinal tract once it is ingested. In the early 1990s, there was considerable concern that our intake of fluoride was too high due to the consumption of fluoridated water and fluoride-containing toothpastes and mouthwashes; it was speculated that this high intake could be contributing to an increased risk for cancer, bone fractures, kidney and other organ damage, infertility, and Alzheimer's disease. After reviewing the potential health hazards of fluoride, Health Canada supports fluoride in drinking water; however, some communities (e.g., Waterloo Region) are removing it from drinking water.

There are concerns that individuals who consume bottled water exclusively may be getting too little fluoride and increasing their risk for dental caries, as most bottled waters do not contain fluoride. However, these individuals may still consume fluoride through other beverages that contain fluoridated water and through fluoridated dental products. Toothpastes and mouthwashes that contain fluoride are widely marketed and used by the majority of consumers in Canada, and these products can contribute as much if not more fluoride to our diet than fluoridated water. Fluoride supplements are available only by prescription, and they are generally given only to children who do not have access to fluoridated water. Incidentally, tea is a good source of fluoride: one 8 oz. cup provides about 20%–25% of the AI.

What Happens If We Consume Too Much Fluoride?

Consuming too much fluoride increases the protein content of tooth enamel, resulting in a condition called **fluorosis**. Because increased protein makes the enamel more porous, the teeth become stained and pitted **(Figure 9.12)**. Teeth seem to be at highest risk for fluorosis during the first eight years of life, when the permanent teeth are developing. To reduce the risk for fluorosis, children should not swallow oral care products that are meant for topical use only, and Health Canada (2008b) advises against giving fluoride supplements and fluoridated mouthwash to children whose permanent teeth have not yet appeared (usually at about the age of six or seven years). Mild fluorosis generally causes white patches on the teeth, and it has no effect on tooth function. Moderate and severe fluorosis cause greater discoloration of the teeth, and there may be tooth pain that affects chewing but no other adverse effect on tooth function (Health Canada, 2008b).

Excess consumption of fluoride can also cause fluorosis of our skeleton. Mild skeletal fluorosis results in an increased bone mass and stiffness and pain in the joints. Moderate and severe skeletal fluorosis can be crippling, but it is extremely rare.

fluorosis A condition marked by staining and pitting of the teeth; caused by an abnormally high intake of fluoride.

What Happens If We Don't Consume Enough Fluoride?

The primary result of fluoride deficiency is dental caries. Adequate fluoride intake appears necessary at an early age and throughout our adult life to reduce our risk for tooth decay. Inadequate fluoride intake may also be associated with lower bone density, but there is not enough research available to support the widespread use of fluoride to prevent osteoporosis.

RECAP Fluoride is a trace mineral whose primary function is to support the health of teeth and bones. Primary sources of fluoride are fluoridated dental products and fluoridated water. Fluoride toxicity causes fluorosis of the teeth and skeleton, while fluoride deficiency causes an increase in tooth decay.

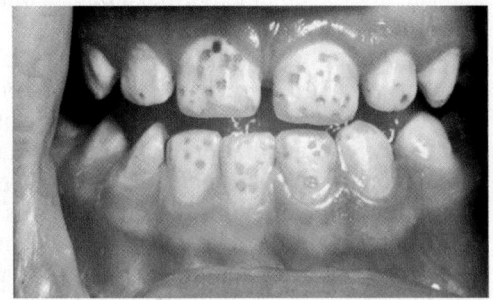

◄ **Figure 9.12** Consuming too much fluoride causes fluorosis, leading to staining and pitting of the teeth.

Nutrition DEBATE

Should Governments Pay for Blood Tests to Screen for Vitamin D Insufficiency?

With all the hype around vitamin D, many people have requested tests to determine their blood levels. This has resulted in a 2500% increase in testing in Ontario over the past five years (CBC News, 2010). Ontario is now considering restrictions that may prevent vitamin D testing unless it is for a serious medical condition, such as osteoporosis, rickets, osteopenia, renal (kidney) disease, and malabsorption syndromes (Crohn's disease, cystic fibrosis, liver disease). At least five other provinces (British Columbia, Alberta, Saskatchewan, Manitoba, and Newfoundland and Labrador) reportedly have done the same. The test costs range from $32 to $93 in labs across the country. Online test kits can be purchased for about US$70; however, these tests are not regulated by Health Canada and there is no guarantee the results are accurate.

What do you think? Is a vitamin D test necessary for healthy individuals? Is there adequate evidence to support this health care cost? Should doctors be recommending vitamin D supplements without a blood test? Let's discuss this issue further.

As we have learned in this chapter, vitamin D is a fat-soluble vitamin that acts as a hormone to regulate calcium levels in the blood and in bones. It is created in our bodies from sunlight when skin is exposed to UV rays, and can also be obtained through our diet (cod liver oil, fatty fish, fortified milk, and other fortified products) or supplements. Recent evidence has shown that vitamin D may also play a role in cell differentiation, immune stimulation, regulation of blood pressure, and regulation of insulin production (Dietitians of Canada, 2008). This means that optimal vitamin D status could be important in preventing chronic diseases such as diabetes and cancer, autoimmune disease such as multiple sclerosis, and infections such as tuberculosis.

Results from the 2007 to 2009 Canadian Health Measures Survey suggest that approximately 10%, or 3 million Canadians, aged 6 to 79 years were considered to have suboptimal levels of vitamin D (blood levels below 37.5 nmol/L); this included an estimated 1.1 million who were categorized as having vitamin D deficiency (blood levels less than 27.5 nmol/L) (Langlois et al., 2010). More men than women were found to have insufficient levels of vitamin D. However, there is some debate over the cut-off values that should be used for these tests, and some researchers propose that 75 nmol/L should be considered an optimal blood level; at this level, only one-third of Canadians would have optimal levels of vitamin D (Langlois et al., 2010).

Dr. Reinhold Vieth is a Professor in the Department of Nutritional Sciences, and Department of Laboratory Medicine at the University of Toronto, he is also the Director of the Bone and Mineral Laboratory at Mount Sinai Hospital, Toronto. He has worked in the vitamin D field for over 30 years and his research has focused on clinical trials of Vitamin D for optimal bone health. Dr. Vieth points out that some patients take vitamin D supplements and still do not absorb enough as a result of the many factors that affect absorption, discussed earlier in this chapter. Without the tests he worries that doctors will be guessing on the amounts of supplements to prescribe to their patients.

What do you think? Should vitamin D tests be regulated? Should the money spent on testing be used for treatment of chronic diseases? Or is this money a worthwhile investment for the promotion of health and prevention of diseases? Should there be an option for the public to pay out of their pockets for tests? Are you concerned about your vitamin D status? The sunshine vitamin is definitely creating a lot of controversy; hopefully the answers to these dilemmas will become clearer with further research.

Chapter Review

1. False. There are many good sources of calcium besides milk, yogurt, and cheese, including calcium-fortified juices, soy/rice beverages, and green leafy vegetables, such as kale, broccoli, and collard greens.

2. True. Our body can convert a cholesterol compound in our skin into vitamin D.

3. True. Too much calcium from supplements can interfere with the body's absorption of iron, zinc, phosphorus, and magnesium.

Find the Quack

Wyn just got some bad news: her mom phoned to say that a DXA scan ordered by her physician shows that she has osteoporosis. Wyn decides to go online to see if she can learn more about osteoporosis. When she discovers the importance of calcium and vitamin D, she searches on "calcium supplements." That's when she finds a site promoting "a unique form of calcium from Pacific sea coral." She reads that this form of "coral calcium" is derived from remnants of coral that have broken off from coral reefs and are mined from ocean beds. The manufacturer makes the following claims for coral calcium:

- "Coral calcium is absorbed into the body within 20 minutes, rather than within 6–8 hours, like other calcium supplements."
- "The calcium carbonate in coral calcium is 100% absorbable, whereas the calcium in milk is only 17% absorbable."
- "The most important daily habits people can adopt to preserve their health are to consume coral calcium and get a minimum of 2 hours of sunlight on their face, without sunscreen."
- "Calcium deficiency not only causes osteoporosis but also makes the body acidic and leads to a host of other diseases, including heart disease, multiple sclerosis, and cancer. People who live on the Japanese island of Okinawa never experience cancer because there is coral calcium in their drinking water, which keeps their body alkaline and cancels out disease-causing acids."

- "Coral calcium is only $19.95 for a 30-day supply."

1. Recall what you learned about digestion in Chapter 3. Do you think it is likely that coral calcium is absorbed into the body within 20 minutes? Why or why not?

2. Do you accept the claim that the calcium in milk is 17% absorbable but the calcium carbonate in coral calcium is 100% absorbable? Why or why not? If necessary, review the information on calcium absorption in this chapter.

3. Comment on the statement "The most important daily habits people can adopt to preserve their health are to consume coral calcium and get a minimum of 2 hours of sunlight on their face, without sunscreen."

4. Comment on the statement that calcium deficiency causes a host of diseases, such as heart disease, multiple sclerosis, and cancer, and that Okinawans "never experience cancer because there is coral calcium in their drinking water, which keeps their body alkaline and cancels out disease-causing acids."

Answers can be found in the study area of MasteringNutrition.

 **NutriTools**   Visit MasteringNutrition to access interactive animations, including:

- Nutrient Functionality

Review Questions

1. Hydroxyapatite crystals are predominantly made up of
   a. calcium and phosphorus.
   b. hydrogen, oxygen, and titanium.
   c. calcium and vitamin D.
   d. calcium and magnesium.

2. On a DXA test, a T-score of −0.5 indicates that the patient
   a. has osteoporosis.
   b. is at greater risk of fractures than an average, healthy person of the same age, sex, and race.
   c. has normal bone density as compared with an average, healthy 30-year-old of the same age, sex, and race.
   d. has slightly lower bone density than an average, healthy person of the same age, sex, and race.

3. Which of the following statements about trabecular bone is true?
   a. It accounts for about 80% of our skeleton.
   b. It forms the core of almost all the bones of our skeleton.
   c. It is also called compact bone.
   d. It provides the scaffolding for cortical bone.

4. Which of the following individuals is most likely to require vitamin D supplements?
   a. A dark-skinned child living and playing outdoors in Hawaii.
   b. A fair-skinned construction worker living in Florida.
   c. A fair-skinned retired teacher living in a nursing home in northern Manitoba.
   d. A dark-skinned postal worker walking a route in California.

5. Calcium is necessary for several body functions, including
   a. demineralization of bone, nerve transmission, and immune responses.
   b. cartilage structure, nerve transmission, and muscle contraction.
   c. structure of bone, nerve, and muscle tissue, immune responses, and muscle contraction.
   d. structure of bone, nerve transmission, and muscle contraction.

6. We can get vitamin D toxicity symptoms from
   a. too much exposure to the sun.
   b. eating too many milk products, including yogurt and cheese.
   c. taking high amounts of calcium in supplements.
   d. taking high amounts of vitamin D in supplements.

7. In addition to dietary sources, vitamin K is produced in our
   a. skin.
   b. stomach.
   c. small intestine.
   d. large intestine.

8. Give two reasons why adults over the age of 65 years may be more at risk for vitamin D deficiency than younger adults.

9. Explain the differences between osteoporosis and osteomalacia.

10. Explain how a person with breast cancer or prostate cancer may develop osteoporosis.

11. Explain why people with diseases that cause a malabsorption of fat may suffer from deficiency of vitamins D and K.

12. Most people reach their peak height by the end of adolescence, maintain that height for several decades, and then start to lose height in their later years. Describe the two processes behind this phenomenon.

13. Your best friend has fair skin and lives in Montreal. How much time does your friend need to spend out of doors with exposed skin on summer days to avoid the need for vitamin D from supplements? Should your friend take vitamin D supplements anyway?

14. Sinead's children are trying to convince her to have a DXA test to check her bone density. She is a 68-year-old woman living by herself, and she is refusing to go and see her doctor. She tells her children that she is much too young to have osteoporosis, and that she has always watched her weight and goes for walks at least three times a week. Her children argue that she's always had a penchant for diet pop and rarely drinks milk, so her bones must be in poor shape. What risk factors for osteoporosis apply to Sinead? What lifestyle factors are helping to reduce her risk for osteoporosis? Would you suggest that Sinead have the DXA test?

Case Study

Chloe and Andrea are at the convenience store, looking for something to quench their thirst. Andrea reaches for a big carton of chocolate milk and Chloe comments that there are tons of calories and sugar in that. Instead, Chloe grabs a big bottle of diet pop. She explains that diet pop has fewer calories and no real sugar in it, making it the healthier choice. Andrea exchanges her milk for a diet pop and the two girls head back to school.

a. Was Chloe's diet pop really a healthier choice than Andrea's chocolate milk? Why or why not?

b. How do you think schools and parents could help persuade children to choose milk over soft drinks?

Answers to Review Questions can be found at the back of this text.

Web Resources

www.cda-adc.ca
Canadian Dental Association

Visit this site for more information about dental care, new techniques, and cosmetic procedures.

www.osteoporosis.ca
Osteoporosis Canada

This charitable organization provides information and advice for individuals with osteoporosis, the general public, and health professionals. Try the Calcium Calculator to see if you are getting enough calcium in your diet.

www.dairycouncilofca.org/Tools/CalciumQuiz
Dairy Council of California's Calcium Quiz

Use this online interactive quiz to estimate your calcium intake.

www.nlm.nih.gov/medlineplus
Medline Plus Health Information

Search for rickets or osteomalacia to learn more about these vitamin D–deficiency diseases.

www.mouthhealthy.org
American Dental Association

Look for "Fluoride" under "A–Z Topics" to learn more about the fluoridation of water and the use of fluoride-containing products.

MasteringNutrition®

Assignments

Animations Activation of Vitamin D • Calcium Metabolism

Study Area

Video: Using the Functional Approach to Understand Antioxidant Function • Practice Tests • Diet Analysis • eText

Osteoporosis

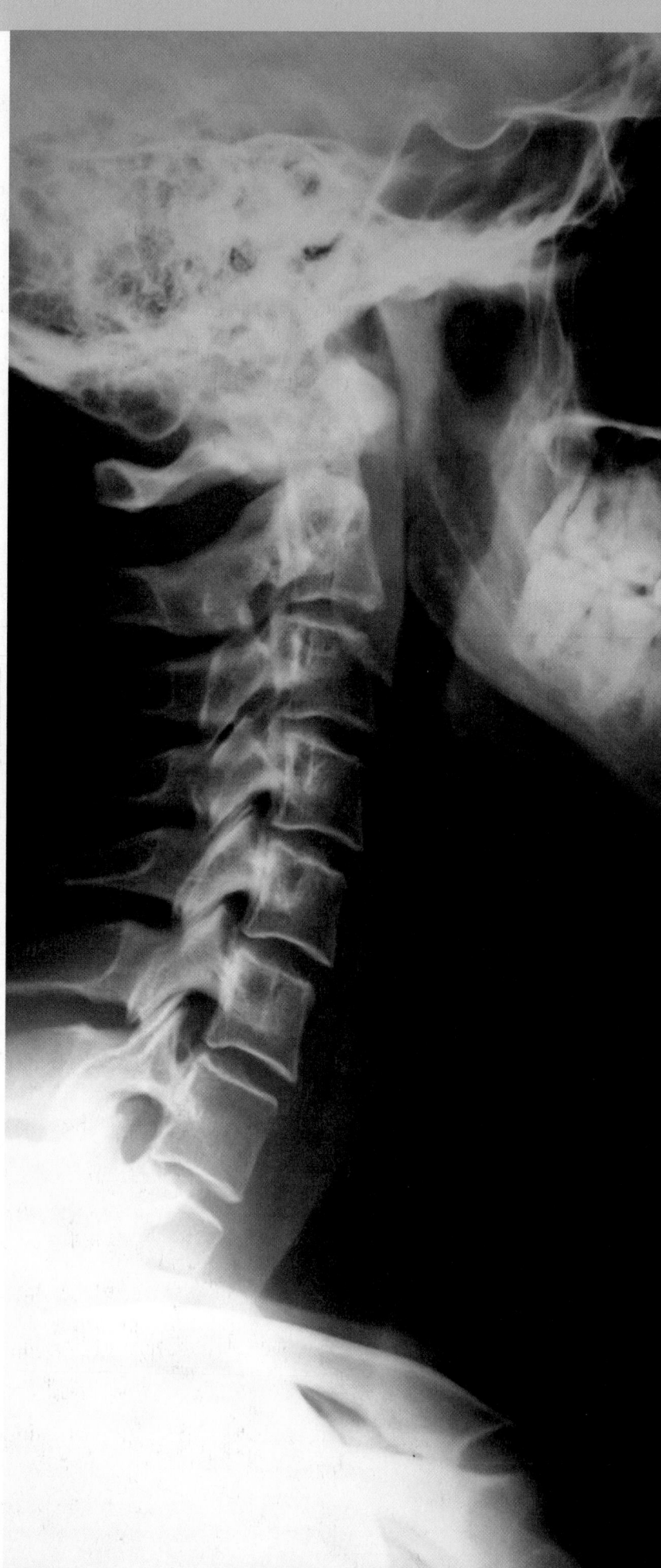

WANT TO FIND OUT...

- how a bone can break spontaneously—without any trauma at all?

- about the link between what you eat when you're young and your risk for osteoporosis later?

- if calcium supplements can reduce your risk for osteoporosis?

READ ON.

As a young woman, Erika Goodman leapt across the stage in leading roles with the Joffrey Ballet, one of the premier dance companies in the world. But at the age of 59, she died after falling in her Manhattan apartment. Goodman had a disease called *osteoporosis,* which means "porous bone." As we noted in Chapter 9 this chapter, the less dense the bone, the more likely it is to break; in fact, osteoporosis can cause bones to break during even minor weight-bearing activities, such as carrying groceries. In advanced cases, bones in the hip and spine can fracture spontaneously, merely from the effort of holding the body erect.

In this *In Depth*, we'll take a closer look at the disease of osteoporosis. We'll explore the impact of osteoporosis on a person's health and longevity and identify the factors that most significantly increase our risk. We'll also review what is currently known about the role of prescription medications in treating osteoporosis and identify other strategies for reducing your risk.

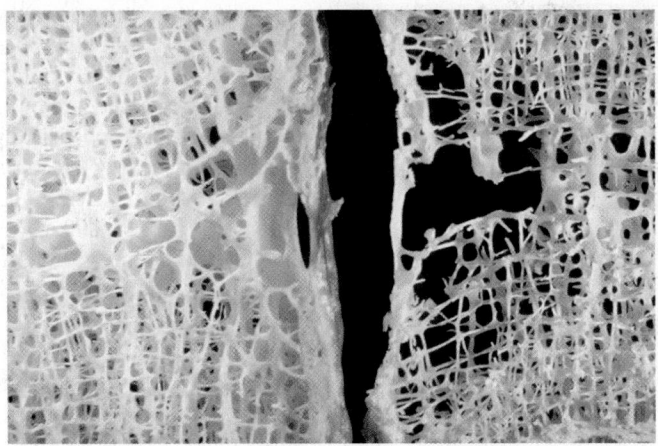

◆ **Figure 1** The vertebrae of a person with osteoporosis (right) are thinner and more collapsed than the vertebrae of a healthy person (left), in which the bone is more dense and uniform.

What Is Osteoporosis?

Of the many disorders associated with poor bone health, the most prevalent in North America is **osteoporosis,** a disease characterized by low bone mass. The bone tissue of a person with osteoporosis deteriorates over time, becoming thinner and more porous than that of a person with healthy bone. These structural changes weaken the bone, leading to a significantly reduced ability of the bone to bear weight **(Figure 1)**. This greatly increases the person's risk for a fracture (a broken bone). In 2009, 19.2% of Canadian women and 3.4% of men aged 50 or older reported that a health professional had diagnosed them with osteoporosis. For those

aged 71 years or older, the rates were higher: 31.1% of women and 6.4% of men (Garriguet, 2011).

Since the hip and the vertebrae of the spinal column are common sites of osteoporosis, it is not surprising that osteoporosis is the single most common cause of fractures of the hip and spine in older adults **(Figure 2)**. These fractures are extremely painful and can be debilitating, with many individuals requiring nursing home care. In addition, they increase the person's risk for infection and other related illnesses that can lead to premature death. In fact, about 20% of older adults who suffer a hip fracture die within one year after the fracture occurs, and among those who survive, half will have some type of permanent disability. Because men are typically older at the time of fracture, death rates are higher for men than for women (International Osteoporosis Foundation, 2007). Osteoporosis

Canada (2007b) notes that there are an estimated 25 000 hip fractures in Canada each year, and 70% of these are associated with osteoporosis. Canada spends an estimated $1.3 billion annually to treat osteoporosis and osteoporosis-related fractures (Osteoporosis Canada, 2007b). Osteoporosis of the spine also causes a generalized loss of height, which can be both disfiguring and painful: gradual compression fractures in the vertebrae of the upper back lead to a shortening and hunching of the spine called *kyphosis*, commonly referred to as *dowager's hump* **(Figure 3)**. Moreover, back pain from collapsed or fractured vertebrae can be severe. However, especially in the early stages,

---

osteoporosis A disease characterized by low bone mass and deterioration of bone tissue, leading to increased bone fragility and fracture risk.

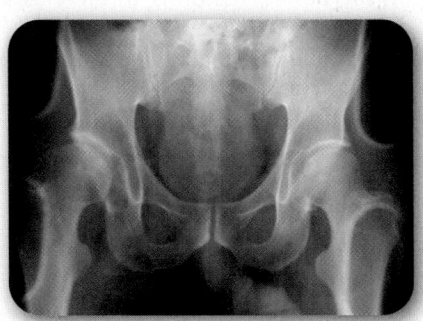

(a) Healthy hip bone

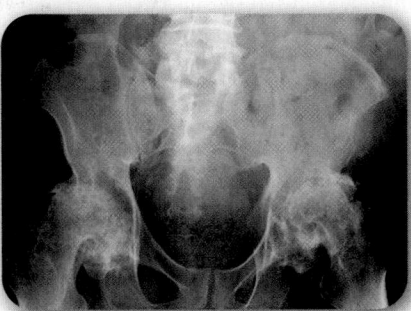

(b) Osteoporotic hip bone

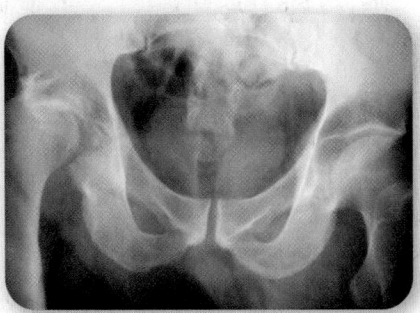

(c) Fractured hip bone

◆ **Figure 2** These x-rays reveal the progression of osteoporosis in hip bones. **(a)** Healthy bone. **(b)** A hip bone weakened by osteoporosis. **(c)** An osteoporotic bone that has fractured.

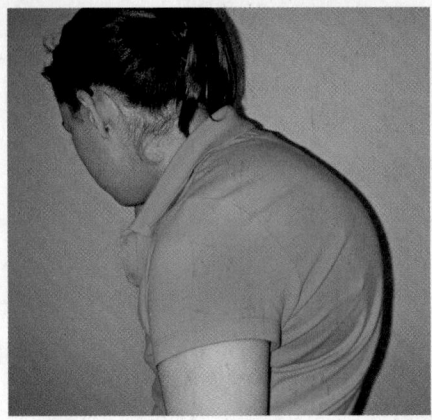

Figure 3 Osteoporosis of the spine causes kyphosis, marked by shortening and hunching of the spine.

osteoporosis can be a silent disease: the person may have no awareness of the condition until a fracture occurs.

What Influences Osteoporosis Risk?

The factors that influence the risk for osteoporosis are age, gender, genetics, nutrition, and physical activity **(Table 1)**. Let's review these factors and identify lifestyle changes that reduce the risk for osteoporosis.

Aging Increases Osteoporosis Risk

Because bone density declines with age, low bone mass and osteoporosis

are significant health concerns for older adults. By the year 2041 an estimated 25% of the Canadian population will be over the age of 65. The incidences of osteoporosis and low bone mass are expected to dramatically rise as people live longer (Osteoporosis Canada, 2007d). Hormonal changes that occur with aging have a significant impact on bone loss. Average bone loss is approximately 0.3%–0.5% per year after 30 years of age; however, during menopause in women, levels of the hormone estrogen decrease dramatically and cause bone loss to increase to about 3% per year during the first five years of menopause. Both estrogen and testosterone play important roles in promoting the deposition of new bone and limiting the activity of osteoclasts. Thus, men can also suffer from osteoporosis, caused by age-related decreases in testosterone. In addition, reduced levels of physical activity in older people and a decreased ability to metabolize vitamin D with age exacerbate the hormone-related bone loss.

Gender and Genetics Affect Osteoporosis Risk

Osteoporosis disproportionately affects women: 19% of Canadian women aged 50 years and older have osteoporosis, compared with 3% of Canadian men (Garriguet, 2011). There are three primary reasons for this:

- Women have a lower absolute bone density than men. From birth through puberty, bone mass is the same in girls as in boys. But during puberty, bone mass increases more in boys, probably because of their prolonged period of accelerated growth. This means that, when bone loss begins around age 40, women have less bone stored in their skeleton; thus, the loss of bone that occurs with aging causes osteoporosis sooner and to a greater extent in women.
- The hormonal changes that occur in men as they age do not have as dramatic an effect on bone density as those in women. The hormones in oral contraceptives may also have an effect on bone density. The CaMos study (2004) found that women in the 25- to 45-year age category who used oral contraceptives had lower bone density than women who did not use oral contraceptives.
- On average, women live longer than men, and because risk increases with age, more elderly women suffer from this disease.

A secondary factor that is gender-specific is the social pressure on girls to be thin. Extreme dieting is particularly harmful in adolescence, when bone mass is building and an adequate consumption of calcium and other nutrients is critical. In many girls, weight loss causes both a loss of estrogen and reduced weight-bearing stress on the bones. In contrast, men experience pressure to "bulk up," typically by lifting weights. This puts healthful stress on the bones, resulting in increased density.

Some individuals have a family history of osteoporosis, which increases their risk for this disease. Particularly at risk are Caucasian women of low body weight who have a first-degree relative (such as a mother or sister) with osteoporosis. Asian women are at higher risk than other non-Caucasian groups. Although we cannot change our gender or genetics, we can modify the lifestyle factors that affect our risk for osteoporosis.

TABLE 1 Risk Factors for Osteoporosis

Modifiable Risk Factors	Non-modifiable Risk Factors
Smoking	Older age (elderly)
Low body weight	Caucasian or Asian race
Low calcium intake	History of fractures as an adult
Low sun exposure	Family history of osteoporosis
Alcohol abuse	Gender (female)
History of amenorrhea (failure to menstruate) in women with inadequate nutrition	History of amenorrhea (failure to menstruate) in women with no recognizable cause
Estrogen deficiency (females)	
Testosterone deficiency (males)	
Repeated falls	
Sedentary lifestyle	

Data from Milot, JJ et al. "Osteoporosis: Evaluation and Treatment" in "Comprehensive Therapy" (2000) 26: 183–189, table 1. With kind permission from Springer Science+Business Media B.V.; p. 319: Courtesy of International Osteoporosis Foundation.

Tobacco, Alcohol, and Caffeine Influence Osteoporosis Risk

Cigarette smoking is known to decrease bone density because of its effects on the hormones that influence bone formation and resorption. For this reason, cigarette smoking increases the risk for osteoporosis and resulting fractures.

Chronic alcohol abuse is detrimental to bone health and is associated with high rates of fractures. In contrast, numerous research studies have shown that bone density is higher in people who are *moderate* drinkers (Felson et al., 1995; Feskanich et al., 1999; Holbrook and Barrett-Connor, 1993; Laitinen, Valimaki, and Keto, 1991; Rapuri et al., 2000). Despite the fact that moderate alcohol intake may be protective for bone, the dangers of alcohol abuse on overall health warrant caution in considering any dietary recommendations. As is consistent with the alcohol intake recommendations related to heart disease, people should not start drinking if they are non-drinkers, and people who do drink should do so in moderation. That means no more than two drinks per day for men and one drink per day for women.

Osteoporosis affects more women than men.

Smoking increases the risk for osteoporosis and resulting fractures.

Some researchers consider excess caffeine consumption to be detrimental to bone health. Caffeine is known to increase calcium loss in the urine, at least over a brief period of time. Younger people are able to compensate for this calcium loss by increasing absorption of calcium from the intestine. However, older people are not always capable of compensating to the same degree. Although the findings have been inconsistent, recent research now indicates that the relative amounts of caffeine and calcium consumed are critical factors affecting bone health. In general, elderly women do not appear to be at risk for increased bone loss if they consume adequate amounts of calcium and moderate amounts of caffeine (less than two cups of coffee, four cups of tea, or six 355 mL (12 fl. oz. cans of caffeine-containing soft drinks per day) (Massey, 2001). Elderly women who consume high levels of caffeine (more than three cups of coffee per day) have much higher rates of bone loss than women with low intakes (Rapuri et al., 2001). Thus, it appears important to bone health that we moderate our caffeine intake and consume an adequate amount of calcium.

Nutritional Factors Influence Osteoporosis Risk

In addition to their role in reducing the risk for heart disease and cancer, diets high in fruits and vegetables are also associated with improved bone health (Tucker et al., 1999; Tucker et al., 2002). This is most likely due to the fact that fruits and vegetables are good sources of the nutrients that play a role in bone and collagen health, including magnesium, vitamin C, and vitamin K. The effects of protein, calcium, vitamin D, and sodium on bone health have been the subject of extensive research.

Protein

The effect of high dietary protein intake on bone health is controversial. High protein intakes have been shown to have both a negative and a positive impact on bone health. Although it is well established that high protein intake increases calcium loss, protein is a critical component of bone tissue and is necessary for bone health. The key to this mystery appears to be adequate calcium intake. In one study, older adults taking calcium and vitamin D supplements and eating higher-protein diets were able to significantly increase bone mass over a three-year period, whereas those eating more protein and not taking supplements lost bone mass over the same time period (Dawson-Hughes and Harris, 2002). Low protein intakes are also associated with bone loss and increased risk for osteoporosis and fractures in elderly people. Thus, there appears to be an interaction between dietary calcium and protein, in that adequate amounts of each nutrient are needed together to support bone health.

Calcium and Vitamin D

Of the many nutrients that help maintain bone health, calcium and vitamin D have received the most attention for their role in the prevention of osteoporosis. Research studies conducted with older adults have shown that taking calcium and vitamin D supplements reduces bone loss and fracture risk. If people do not consume enough of these two nutrients over a prolonged period of time, their bone density is lower and they have a higher risk for bone fractures.

Because bones reach peak density when people are young, it is very important that children and

🔺 Regularly engaging in weight-bearing exercises, such as jogging, can help to increase and maintain your bone mass.

adolescents consume a high-quality diet that contains the proper balance of calcium, vitamin D, protein, and other nutrients to allow for optimal bone growth. Young adults also require a proper balance of these nutrients to maintain bone mass. In older adults, diets rich in calcium and vitamin D can help minimize bone loss.

Sodium

Higher intakes of sodium are known to increase the kidneys' excretion of calcium in the urine. One study found an association between high urinary sodium excretion and increased bone loss from the hip in postmenopausal women (Devine et al., 1995). However, there is no direct evidence that a high-sodium diet causes osteoporosis. The Institute of Medicine (1997) states that there is insufficient evidence to warrant different calcium recommendations based on dietary salt intake.

female athlete triad A condition characterized by the coexistence of three disorders in some athletic females: an eating disorder, amenorrhea, and osteoporosis.

Regular Physical Activity Reduces Osteoporosis Risk

Regular exercise is highly protective against bone loss and osteoporosis. Athletes are consistently shown to have denser bones than non-athletes, and regular participation in weight-bearing exercises (such as walking, jogging, tennis, and strength training) can help increase and maintain bone mass. When we exercise, our muscles contract and pull on our bones; this stresses bone tissue in a healthful way that stimulates increases in bone density. In addition, carrying weight during activities such as walking and jogging stresses the bones of the legs, hips, and lower back, resulting in a healthier bone mass in these areas. It appears that people of all ages can improve and maintain bone health through consistent physical activity.

Can exercise ever be detrimental to bone health? Yes, when the body is not receiving the nutrients it needs to rebuild the hydroxyapatite and collagen broken down in response to physical activity. Thus, active people who are chronically malnourished, including people who are impoverished and those who suffer from eating disorders, are at increased fracture risk. Research has confirmed this association among nutrition, physical activity, and bone loss in the **female athlete triad**, a condition characterized by the coexistence of three (a *triad* of) clinical conditions in some physically active females: low energy availability (with or without eating disorders), a complete loss of menstrual function, and osteoporosis. In the female athlete triad, inadequate food intake and regular strenuous exercise together result in a state of severe energy drain that causes a multitude of hormonal changes, including a reduction in estrogen production. These hormonal changes can result in the complete loss of menstrual function, called amenorrhea. Estrogen is important in maintaining healthy bone in women, so the loss of estrogen leads to osteoporosis in young women. The female athlete triad is discussed **In Depth** in Chapter 12.

Cancer Treatment and Bone Loss

Bone resorption (by osteoclasts) may outpace bone formation (by osteoblasts) when hormone levels are reduced, such as when estrogen levels drop during menopause in women. Hormonal changes are also part of some cancers, or they may be caused by some cancer treatments. Many breast cancers are associated with estrogen, for example, and cancer treatments may involve the use of drugs to reduce estrogen production. These treatments then lead to bone loss and the potential for bones to fracture. Similarly, androgen deprivation therapy (ADT) may be used to treat prostate cancer in men; however, it increases the risk of osteoporosis. Health professionals are being encouraged to consider the longer-term consequences of cancer treatment on bone remodelling and bone health, since osteoporosis is often not diagnosed until bone fractures occur (Osteoporosis Canada, 2007a). Some guidelines suggest regular DXA bone mineral density screening for men receiving ADT for prostate cancer, and for pre- and postmenopausal women who have received breast cancer therapy. It is estimated that only 3% to 32% of high-risk cancer patients currently have their bone mineral densities assessed. The use of bisphosphonates, discussed in the next section, is also encouraged to prevent bone loss in women receiving breast cancer treatment (Osteoporosis Canada, 2007a).

Now that we have identified the factors that influence a person's risk for osteoporosis, you may be wondering what your own risk is. If so, check out the What About You? feature box ahead.

How Is Osteoporosis Treated?

Although there is no cure for osteoporosis, a variety of treatments can slow and even reverse bone loss. First, individuals with osteoporosis

What About You?

Are You at Risk for Osteoporosis?

One in three women and one in five men will develop osteo-porosis in their lifetime (National Osteoporosis Foundation, 2008). But if you know you are at risk, you can take the steps such as increasing your amount of weight-bearing exercise and making sure you get enough calcium and vitamin D, to maintain the maximum amount of bone mass possible. That is why it is important to assess your risk. Below is the International Osteoporosis Foundation's One-Minute Osteoporosis Risk Test.

The more Yes answers you have, the greater the likelihood that you are in a higher-risk group than the general population.

If you answered Yes to any of these questions, it does not mean you have osteoporosis. Positive answers simply mean that you have clinically proven risk factors that may lead to osteoporosis and fractures. Discuss your results with your doctor, who can advise you on whether a bone density test is recommended.

1. Has either of your parents broken a hip after a minor bump or fall?	Yes/No
2. Have you broken a bone after a minor bump or fall?	Yes/No
3. Have you taken corticosteroid tablets (such as cortisone or prednisone) for more than three months?	Yes/No
4. Have you lost more than 3 cm (just over 1 in.) in height?	Yes/No
5. Do you regularly drink heavily (in excess of safe drinking limits)?	Yes/No
6. Do you smoke more than 20 cigarettes a day?	Yes/No
7. Do you suffer frequently from diarrhea (caused by problems such as celiac disease or Crohn's disease)?	Yes/No
For women:	Yes/No
8. Did you undergo menopause before the age of 45?	Yes/No
9. Have your periods stopped for 12 months or more (other than because of pregnancy)?	Yes/No
For men:	Yes/No
10. Have you ever suffered from impotence, lack of libido, or other symptoms related to low testosterone levels?	Yes/No

Data from International Osteoporosis Foundation. 2009. Are You at Risk of Osteoporosis? Take the One-Minute Osteoporosis Risk Test. www.osteofound.org. Courtesy of International Osteoporosis Foundation.

are encouraged to consume adequate calcium and vitamin D and to exercise regularly. Studies have shown that the most effective exercise programs include weight-bearing exercises, such as jogging, stair climbing, and resistance training (South-Pal, 2001).

In addition, several medications are available:

- bisphosphonates, such as alen-dronate (brand name Fosamax), which decrease bone loss and can increase bone density and reduce the risk for spinal and non-spinal fractures

  Health Canada recently ap-proved a new bisphosphonate, Zoledronic acid (brand name Aclasta), which is given by a 15-minute intravenous infusion once a year. This new medication has been shown to cut the risk of spinal fractures and hip fractures by 70% and 41%, respectively (Osteoporosis Canada, 2007c).

It is estimated that from 40% to 60% of patients taking weekly or daily doses of bisphosphonates do not take their medications regularly, and a once-yearly medication may help to solve this problem.

- selective estrogen receptor modu-lators, such as raloxifene (brand name Evista)

  Raloxifene (brand name Evis-ta) is a selective estrogen receptor modulator that was developed to mimic the beneficial effects of

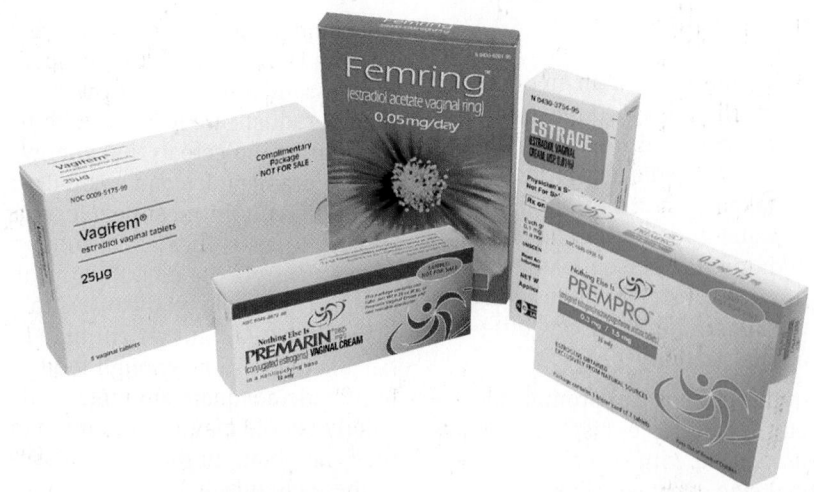

Hormone replacement medications come in a variety of forms.

estrogen without the potential risks and is used for the prevention and treatment of osteoporosis. It increases bone mass and reduces the risk of spinal fractures while apparently reducing the risk of some forms of breast cancer. It may even reduce the risk of heart disease and stroke in women who have a high risk for these diseases. Side effects are not common and include hot flashes and the formation of blood clots in the veins.

- calcitonin, a thyroid hormone
  Calcitonin (brand name Miacalcin) is a hormone that occurs naturally in our bodies and assists in the regulation of calcium and in bone metabolism. When used in the treatment of osteoporosis, calcitonin slows bone loss, increases the bone density of the spine, and reduces the risk for spinal fractures. Calcitonin is a protein; thus, it cannot be taken orally or it would be digested in our intestinal tract. It therefore must be injected or inhaled through a nasal spray. Side effects of injected calcitonin include allergic reactions, flushing of the face and hands, skin rash, increased need to urinate, and nausea. Side effects of nasal calcitonin include nasal irritation, bloody nose, headaches, and backaches.
- hormone replacement therapy (HRT), which combines estrogen with a hormone called progestin, and can reduce bone loss, increase bone density, and reduce the risk for hip and spinal fractures
  These drugs must be taken in the morning on an empty stomach, at least 30 minutes before eating, drinking, or taking any other medications, and must be taken with 250 mL (8 fl. oz.) of water and no other liquid. In addition, the person taking these drugs must stay upright during the 30 minutes following drug administration.

All of these drugs can prompt side effects. For example, bisphosphonates are associated with several gastrointestinal side effects, including abdominal pain, constipation, diarrhea, heartburn, irritation of the esophagus, and difficulty swallowing. Side effects of HRT include breast tenderness, changes in mood, vaginal bleeding, and an increased risk for gallbladder disease.

Until recently, it was believed that HRT protected women against heart disease. However, a study found that one type of HRT actually increases a woman's risk for heart disease, stroke, and breast cancer (Writing Group for the Women's Health Initiative Investigators, 2002). As a result, hundreds of thousands of women have stopped taking HRT as a means to prevent or treat osteoporosis. However, despite the associated risks, it is recognized that HRT is still an effective treatment and prevention option for osteoporosis. It also reduces the risk for colorectal cancer. Thus, women should work with their physician to weigh these benefits against the increased risks for breast cancer and heart disease when considering HRT as a treatment option for osteoporosis.

Can Osteoporosis Be Prevented?

Although some risk factors for osteoporosis cannot be changed, such as age, gender, race, and family history, there is a great deal you can do to try to prevent osteoporosis.

Consider Supplements

Consuming adequate calcium and vitamin D throughout the life span is an essential first step. Now that so many products are fortified with these nutrients, from cereals and energy bars to orange juice and soy milk, it is not difficult for most people, even vegans, to get sufficient calcium and vitamin D from the diet. Still, small or inactive people who eat less to maintain a healthful weight may not be able to consume enough food to provide adequate amounts, and elderly people may need more than they can obtain in their normal diet. In these circumstances, supplements may be warranted.

Calcium

By consuming foods high in calcium throughout the day, you can avoid the need for calcium supplements. But if you cannot consume enough calcium in your diet, many inexpensive, safe, and effective supplements are available. The best supplement for you is the one that you can tolerate, is affordable, is lead-free, and is readily available when you need it. See the Highlight in Chapter 9: Calcium Supplements: Which Ones Are Best?

Vitamin D

A recent review study of 12 trials involving thousands of patients suggests that taking a daily vitamin D supplement reduces the risk for fractures in people age 65 and older (Bischoff-Ferrara et al., 2009). The participants who took 482 to 770 IU per day of vitamin D cut their fracture risk by 18%–20%. These effects were not tied to participants also taking calcium supplements. So it seems that, at least for older adults, taking supplemental vitamin D is a smart preventive measure. *Eating Well with Canada's Food Guide* advises men and women over the age of 50 to consume the recommended servings of food groups and take a daily vitamin D supplement of 10 µg (400 IU).

When it comes to vitamin D supplements, are some better than others? The Office of Dietary Supplements at the National Institutes of Health (2009) states that vitamin D_3 is more than three times as effective as vitamin D_2 in raising and maintaining blood levels of vitamin D. Because vitamin D is a fat-soluble vitamin, it is important to stay below the UL of 100 µg (4000 IU) per day.

Other Preventive Measures

Another important strategy for preventing osteoporosis is engaging in regular physical activity throughout life. It is especially important to participate in weight-bearing activities. Examples include brisk walking, dancing, jogging, step-aerobics, hiking, tennis, tai chi, yoga, and

Because hiking requires your bones to bear your body weight plus the weight of your pack, it's a great form of exercise to reduce your risk for osteoporosis.

resistance training. All of these activities help preserve bone density because they appropriately stress your bones and muscles.

It is also important to avoid becoming underweight. Remember Erika Goodman, the dancer we discussed at the beginning of this *In Depth* essay? The factor that probably contributed most significantly to her early-onset osteoporosis was the drastic food restriction she practiced throughout her career. Appropriate body weight stresses the bones, and an adequate, balanced diet provides the nutrients to keep them healthy. In short, maintaining a healthy body weight is essential for preventing osteoporosis.

Other preventive measures include avoiding smoking and quitting if you are currently a smoker. It is also important to avoid alcohol abuse. Finally, increasing sun exposure safely will allow your body to synthesize adequate vitamin D and help prevent osteoporosis.

Web Resources

www.osteoporosis.ca
Osteoporosis Canada

This charitable organization provides information and advice for individuals with osteoporosis, the general public, and health professionals. Try the Calcium Calculator to see if you are getting enough calcium in your diet.

www.nof.org
National Osteoporosis Foundation

Learn more about the causes, prevention, detection, and treatment of osteoporosis.

www.osteofound.org
International Osteoporosis Foundation

Find out more about this foundation and its mission to increase awareness and understanding of osteoporosis worldwide.

www.niams.nih.gov/bone
National Institutes of Health: Osteoporosis and Related Bone Diseases—National Resource Center

Access this site for additional resources and information on metabolic bone diseases, including osteoporosis.

10
Nutrients Involved in Energy Metabolism and Blood Health

Dr. Leslie Bernstein looked in astonishment at the 80-year-old man in his office. Dr. Bernstein was a leading gastroenterologist and professor of medicine at Albert Einstein College of Medicine in New York City, and he had admired Pop Katz for years as one of his most healthy patients, a strict vegetarian and athlete who just weeks before had been going on 3 mile runs as if he were 40 years younger. Now he could barely stand. He was confused, cried easily, was wandering away from the house partially clothed, and had lost control of his bladder. Tests showed that he was not suffering from Alzheimer's disease, had not had a stroke, did not have a tumour or an infection, and had no evidence of exposure to pesticides, metals, drugs, or other toxins. Blood tests were normal, except that his red blood cells were slightly enlarged. Bernstein consulted with a neurologist, who diagnosed "rapidly progressive dementia of unknown origin."

Bernstein was unconvinced: "In a matter of weeks, a man who had not been sick for 80 years suddenly became demented. 'Holy smoke!' I thought, 'I'm an idiot! The man's been a vegetarian for 38 years. No meat. No fish. No eggs. No milk. He has not had any animal protein for decades. He has to be B_{12} deficient!'" Bernstein immediately tested Katz's blood, then gave him an injection of B_{12}. The blood test confirmed Bernstein's hunch: the level of B_{12} in Katz's blood was too low to measure. The morning after his injection, Katz could sit up without help. Within a week of continuing treatment, he could read, play card games, and hold his own in conversations. Unfortunately, the delay in diagnosis left some permanent neurologic damage, including alterations in his personality and an inability to

⬆ Vitamins do not provide energy directly, but the B vitamins help our body create the energy we need from the foods we eat.

concentrate. Bernstein notes, "A diet free of animal protein can be healthful and safe, but it should be supplemented periodically with B_{12} by mouth or by injection (Bernstein, 2000)."

It was not until 1906—when the English biochemist F. G. Hopkins discovered what he called *accessory factors*—that scientists began to appreciate the many critical roles of micronutrients in maintaining human health. Vitamin B_{12}, for instance, was not isolated until 1948! In Chapters 7 through 9, we explored several key roles of vitamins and minerals, including regulation of fluids and nerve-impulse transmission, protection against the damage caused by oxidation, and maintenance of healthy bones. In this chapter, we conclude our exploration of the micronutrients with a discussion of two final roles: their contribution to the metabolism of carbohydrates, fats, and proteins and their role in the formation and maintenance of our blood.

How Does Our Body Regulate Energy Metabolism?

We explored the digestion and metabolism of carbohydrates, fats, and proteins in Chapters 3 through 6 of this text. In those chapters, you learned that the regulation of energy metabolism is a complex process involving numerous biological substances and chemical pathways. Here, we describe how the micronutrients we consume in our diet assist us in generating energy from the carbohydrates, fats, and proteins we eat along with them.

Our Body Requires Vitamins and Minerals to Produce Energy

Although vitamins and minerals do not directly provide energy, we are unable to generate energy from the macronutrients without them. The B vitamins are particularly important in assisting us with energy metabolism. They include thiamin, riboflavin, vitamin B_6, niacin, folate, vitamin B_{12}, pantothenic acid, and biotin.

The primary role of the B vitamins is to act as coenzymes. Recall that an *enzyme* is a protein that accelerates the rate of chemical reactions but is not used up or changed during the reaction. A **coenzyme** is a molecule that combines with an enzyme to activate it and help it do its job. **Figure 10.1** illustrates how coenzymes

coenzyme A molecule that combines with an enzyme to activate it and help it do its job.

▶ **Figure 10.1** Coenzymes combine with enzymes to activate them, ensuring that the chemical reactions that depend on these enzymes can occur.

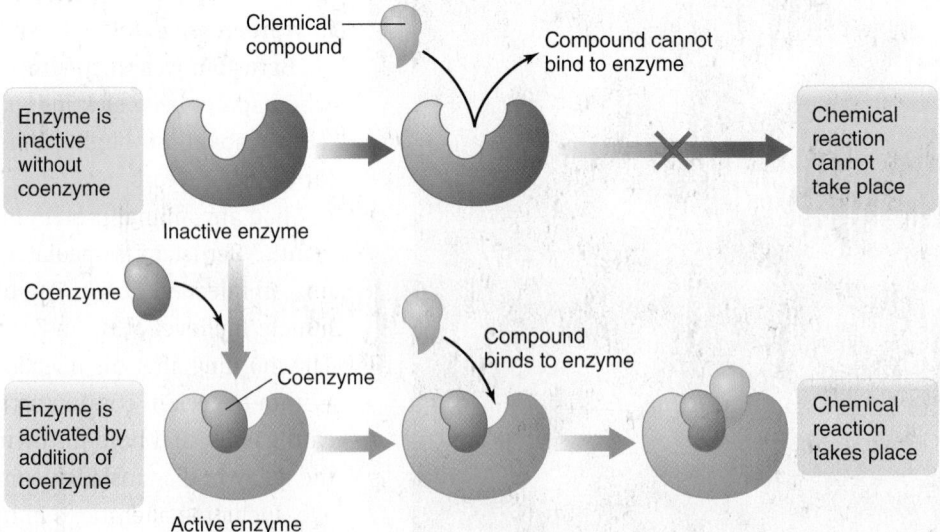

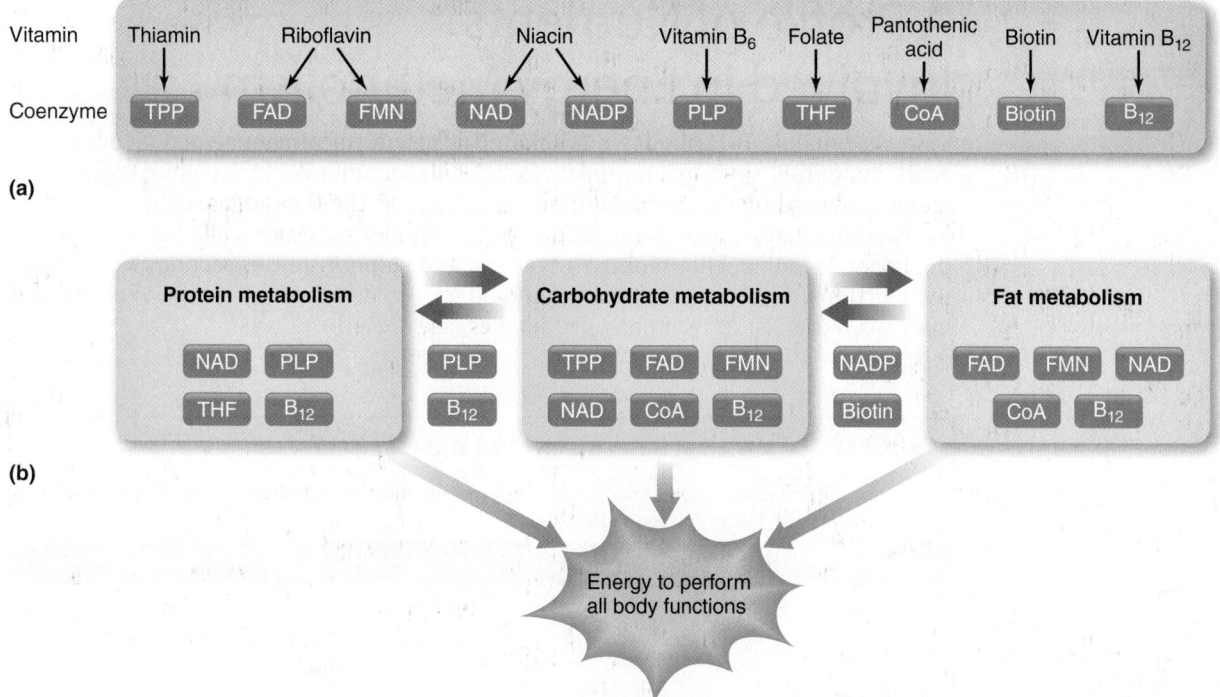

(a)

(b)

🔺 **Figure 10.2** The B vitamins play many important roles in the reactions involved in energy metabolism. **(a)** B vitamins and the coenzymes they are a part of. **(b)** This chart illustrates many of the coenzymes essential for various metabolic functions; however, this is only a small sample of the thousands of roles that the B vitamins serve in our body.

work. Without coenzymes, we would be unable to produce the energy necessary for sustaining life and supporting daily activities.

Figure 10.2 provides an overview of how some of the B vitamins act as coenzymes to promote energy metabolism. For instance, thiamin is part of the coenzyme thiamin pyrophosphate, or TPP, which assists in the breakdown of glucose. Riboflavin is a part of two coenzymes, flavin mononucleotide (FMN) and flavin adenine dinucleotide (FAD), which help break down both glucose and fatty acids. The specific functions of each B vitamin are described in detail shortly.

Some Micronutrients Assist with Nutrient Transport and Hormone Production

Some micronutrients promote energy metabolism by facilitating the transport of nutrients into the cells. For instance, the mineral chromium helps improve glucose uptake into cells. Other micronutrients assist in the production of hormones that regulate metabolic processes; the mineral iodine, for example, is necessary for the synthesis of thyroid hormones, which regulate our metabolic rate and promote growth and development. The details of these processes and their related nutrients are discussed in the following section.

RECAP Vitamins and minerals are not direct sources of energy, but they help generate energy from carbohydrates, fats, and proteins. Acting as coenzymes, nutrients such as the B vitamins assist enzymes in metabolizing nutrients to produce energy. Minerals such as chromium and iodine assist with nutrient uptake into the cells and with regulating energy production and cell growth.

A Profile of Nutrients Involved in Energy Metabolism

Thiamin (vitamin B_1), riboflavin (vitamin B_2), niacin (nicotinamide and nicotinic acid), vitamin B_6 (pyridoxine), folate (folic acid), vitamin B_{12} (cobalamin), pantothenic acid, and biotin are the nutrients identified as the B vitamins. Other nutrients involved in energy metabolism include a vitamin-like substance called choline and the minerals iodine, chromium, manganese, and sulphur. In this section, we discuss the functions, food sources, toxicity, and deficiency symptoms for these vitamins and minerals. For a list of recommended intakes, see **Table 10.1**.

TABLE 10.1 Overview of Nutrients Involved in Energy Metabolism

To see the full profile of nutrients involved in energy metabolism, turn to **In Depth**, Vitamins and Minerals: Micronutrients with Macro Powers, pages 216–225.

Nutrient	Recommended Intake
Thiamin (vitamin B_1)	RDA for 19 years and older: Women = 1.1 mg/day Men = 1.2 mg/day
Riboflavin (vitamin B_2)	RDA for 19 years and older: Women = 1.1 mg/day Men = 1.3 mg/day
Niacin (nicotinamide and nicotinic acid)	RDA for 19 years and older: Women = 14 mg/day Men = 16 mg/day
Vitamin B_6 (pyridoxine)	RDA for 19 to 50 years of age: Women and men = 1.3 mg/day RDA for 51 years and older: Women = 1.5 mg/day Men = 1.7 mg/day
Folate (folic acid)	RDA for 19 years and older: Women and men = 400 µg/day
Vitamin B_{12} (cobalamin)	RDA for 19 years and older: Women and men = 2.4 µg/day
Pantothenic acid	AI for 19 years and older: Women and men = 5 mg/day
Biotin	AI for 19 years and older: Women and men = 30 µg/day
Choline	AI for 19 years and older: Women = 425 mg/day Men = 550 mg/day
Iodine	RDA for 19 years and older: Women and men = 150 µg/day
Chromium	RDA for 19 to 50 years of age: Women = 25 µg/day Men = 35 µg/day RDA for 51 years and older: Women = 20 µg/day Men = 30 µg/day
Manganese	AI for 19 years and older: Women = 1.8 mg/day Men = 2.3 mg/day

Thiamin (Vitamin B₁)

Thiamin-deficiency disease is called **beriberi** and it comes in two forms: wet, where the cardiovascular system is affected, and dry **(Figure 10.3)**, where the nervous system is affected (Shils et al., 1999).

The symptoms have been described throughout recorded history. But it was not until the nineteenth century, when steam-powered mills began removing the outer shell of grains, especially rice, that the disease became widespread, especially in Southeast Asia. At the time, it was thought that milling grain improved the quality of the grain and made it more acceptable to consumers. What was not known was that the outer layer of the grain contained the highest concentrations of B vitamins, especially thiamin (Bates, 2006). Thus, most of the B vitamins were being removed and discarded as the grain was milled or the rice polished. In 1885, Dr. Kanehiro Takaki, a Japanese naval surgeon, discovered that he could prevent beriberi by improving the quality of the diets of seamen. Then in 1906, Dr. Christiaan Eijkman, a Dutch physician living in Java, and his colleague, Dr. Gerrit Grijns, described how they could produce beriberi in chickens or pigeons by feeding them polished rice and could cure them by feeding back the rice bran that was removed during polishing (Bates, 2006; McCollum, 1957). In 1911, Polish chemist Casimir Funk was able to isolate the water-soluble nitrogen-containing compound in rice bran that was responsible for the cure. He referred to this compound as a "vital amine" and called it thiamin. Because it was the first B vitamin discovered, it is designated vitamin B₁ (Bates, 2006).

Thiamin is part of the coenzyme thiamin pyrophosphate, or TPP. As a part of TPP, thiamin plays a critical role in the breakdown of glucose for energy and acts as a coenzyme in the metabolism of the essential amino acids leucine, isoleucine, and valine, also referred to as the *branched-chain amino acids*. These amino acids are metabolized primarily in the muscle and can be used to produce glucose if necessary. TPP also assists in producing DNA and RNA and plays a role in the synthesis of *neurotransmitters*, chemicals important in the transmission of messages throughout the nervous system.

Good food sources of thiamin include enriched cereals and grains, whole-grain products, wheat germ and yeast extracts, ready-to-eat cereals, ham and other pork products, organ meats of most animals, and some green vegetables, including peas, asparagus, and okra **(Figure 10.4)**. Overall, whole grains are some of the best sources of thiamin, while more processed foods, such as refined sugars and fats, are the lowest sources. Unless milled grains are fortified (that is, the thiamin is added back), they are poor sources.

Because thiamin is involved in energy-generating processes, the symptoms of beriberi include a combination of fatigue, apathy, muscle weakness, and detriments in cognitive function. The body's inability to metabolize energy or synthesize neurotransmitters also leads to muscle wasting, nerve damage, and the characteristic paralysis; in later stages, patients may be unable to move at all. The heart muscle may also be affected, and the patient may die of heart failure.

Beriberi is seen in countries in which unenriched, processed grains are a primary food source; for instance, beriberi was widespread in China when rice was processed and refined, and it still occurs in refugee camps and other settlements dependent on poor-quality food supplies. Beriberi is also seen in industrialized countries in people with heavy alcohol consumption and limited food intake. Chronic alcohol abuse is associated with a host of neurologic symptoms, collectively called **Wernicke-Korsakoff syndrome**, in which thiamin intake is decreased and absorption and utilization impaired (Bates, 2006). Although thiamin supplementation has been the treatment of choice for beriberi for nearly 100 years, there is still uncertainty about

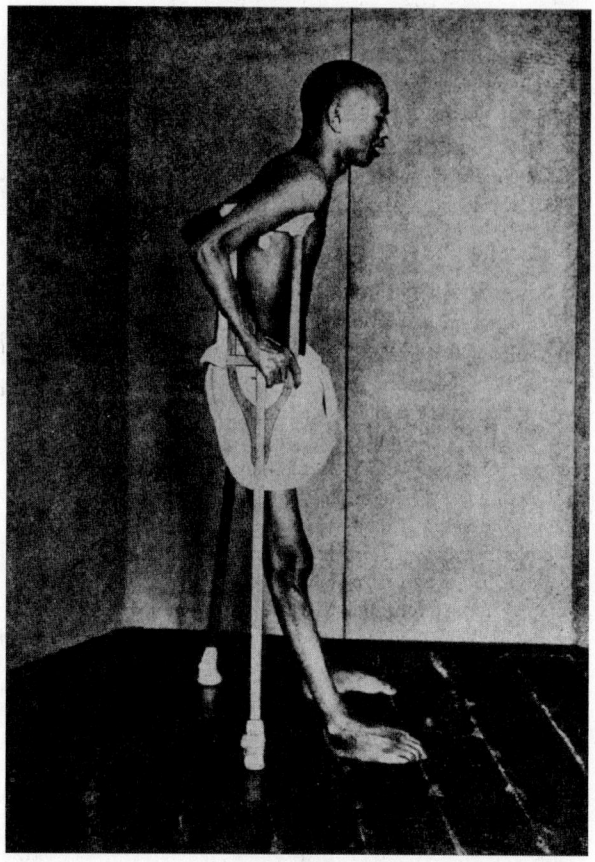

▲ **Figure 10.3** Dry beriberi with wasting and nerve damage.

▲ Ready-to-eat cereals are a good source of thiamin and other B vitamins.

beriberi A disease of muscle wasting and nerve damage caused by thiamin deficiency.

Wernicke-Korsakoff syndrome A form of thiamin deficiency seen in chronic alcoholics that results in mental confusion and a loss of memory.

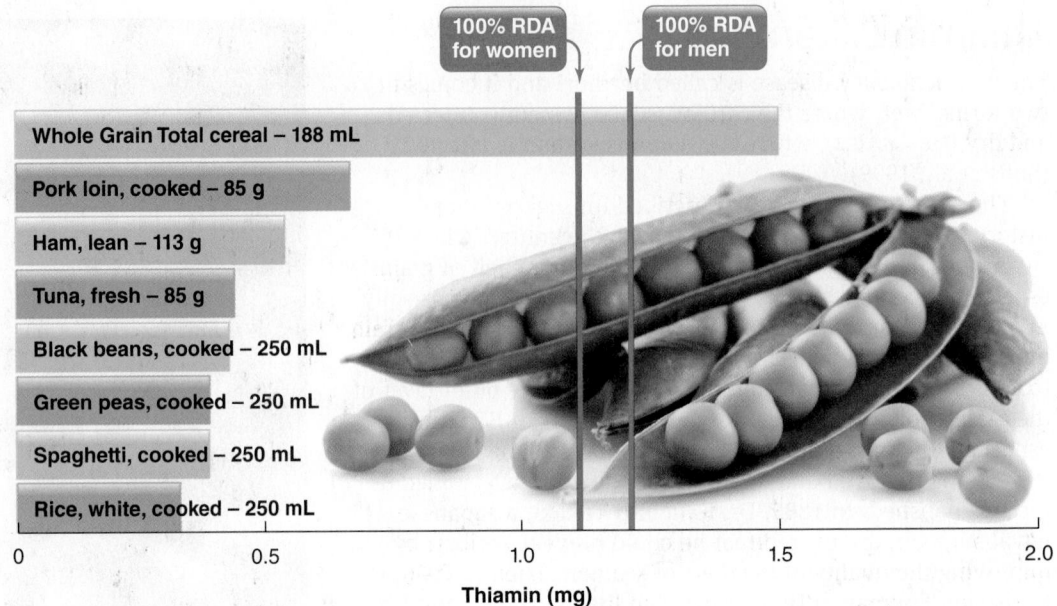

▲ **Figure 10.4** Common food sources of thiamin. The RDA for thiamin is 1.2 mg/day for men and 1.1 mg/day for women 19 years and older.

Data from U.S. Department of Agriculture, Agricultural Research Service. 2009. USDA Nutrient Database for Standard Reference, Release 22. Nutrient Data Laboratory Home Page. www.ars.usda.govba/bhnrc/ndl.

▲ Milk is a good source of riboflavin and is stored in opaque containers to prevent the destruction of riboflavin by light.

ariboflavinosis A condition caused by riboflavin deficiency.

the appropriate dose and duration of supplementation (Day et al., 2004). There are no known adverse effects from consuming excess amounts of thiamin.

Riboflavin (Vitamin B₂)

The theory that there might be more than one vitamin in rice bran was first proposed in the early 1900s after researchers noticed that rats fed diets of polished rice had poor growth (McCollum, 1957). Finally, in 1917 researchers found that there were at least two vitamins in the extracts of rice polishing, one that cured beriberi and another that stimulated growth. The latter substance was first called vitamin B₂ and then named riboflavin for its ribose-like side chain and the yellow colour it produced in water (*flavus* means "yellow" in Latin) (McCormick, 2005).

Riboflavin is an important component of coenzymes that are involved in chemical reactions occurring within the energy-producing metabolic pathways. These coenzymes, flavin mononucleotide (FMN) and flavin adenine dinucleotide (FAD), are involved in the metabolism of carbohydrates and fat. Riboflavin is also a part of the antioxidant enzyme glutathione peroxidase, thus assisting in the fight against oxidative damage.

Milk is a good source of riboflavin; however, riboflavin is destroyed when it is exposed to light. Thus, milk is generally stored in opaque containers to prevent the destruction of riboflavin. Other good food sources include yogurt, enriched grain products, ready-to-eat-cereals, and organ meats. However, green vegetables, such as broccoli, asparagus, and spinach, are also good sources. Finally, although whole grains are relatively low in riboflavin, fortification and enrichment of grains have increased the intake of riboflavin from these sources, especially ready-to-eat cereals and energy bars, which can provide 25%–100% of the Daily Value (DV) for riboflavin in 1 serving (**Figure 10.5**).

There are no known adverse effects from consuming excess amounts of riboflavin. Because coenzymes derived from riboflavin are so widely distributed in metabolism, riboflavin deficiency, referred to as **ariboflavinosis**, lacks the specificity seen with other vitamins. However, riboflavin deficiency can have profound effects on energy production, which result in "nondescript" symptoms such as fatigue and muscle weakness. More advanced riboflavin deficiency can result in lips that are dry and scaly, inflammation and ulcers of the mucous membranes of the mouth and throat, irritated patches on the skin, changes in the cornea, anemia, and in some cases personality changes (Rivlin, 2006). It is now known that cataract formation can be decreased

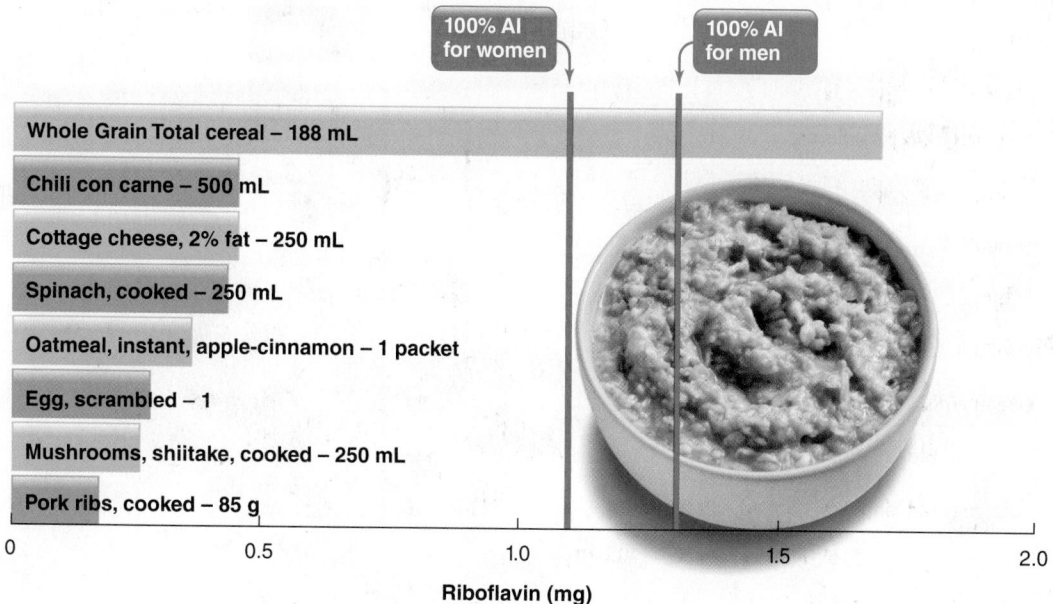

Whole Grain Total cereal – 188 mL

Chili con carne – 500 mL

Cottage cheese, 2% fat – 250 mL

Spinach, cooked – 250 mL

Oatmeal, instant, apple-cinnamon – 1 packet

Egg, scrambled – 1

Mushrooms, shiitake, cooked – 250 mL

Pork ribs, cooked – 85 g

100% AI for women

100% AI for men

Riboflavin (mg)

0   0.5   1.0   1.5   2.0

Figure 10.5 Common food sources of riboflavin. The RDA for riboflavin is 1.3 mg/day for men and 1.1 mg/day for women 19 years and older.
Data from U.S. Department of Agriculture, Agricultural Research Service. 2009. USDA Nutrient Database for Standard Reference, Release 22. Nutrient Data Laboratory Home Page, www.ars.usda.gov/ba/bhnrc/ndl.

by higher riboflavin intakes (Jacques et al., 2005). In addition, riboflavin is important in the metabolism of four other vitamins: folic acid, vitamin B_6, vitamin K, and niacin (Rivlin, 2006). Thus, a deficiency in riboflavin can affect a number of body systems.

pellagra A disease that results from severe niacin deficiency.

Niacin

Pellagra, the deficiency of niacin, was first described in the 1700s in northern Spain but was also seen widely across the United States, Western and Eastern Europe, and the Middle East, where corn or maize was the dietary staple (McCollum, 1957). The term *pellagra* literally means "raw skin" (Jacob, 2006). The four characteristic symptoms—dermatitis, diarrhea, dementia, and death—are referred to as the *four Ds*. Individuals who develop the disease first complain of inflammation and soreness in the mouth, followed by red, raw skin (dermatitis) on areas exposed to sunlight **(Figure 10.6)**. The disease then progresses to the digestive and nervous systems. The symptoms of this stage of the disease are diarrhea, vomiting, and dementia. At the present time, pellagra is rarely seen in industrialized countries, except in cases of chronic alcoholism. Pellagra is still found in impoverished areas of some developing nations. (For more information on pellagra, see the Nutrition Myth or Fact? box in Chapter 1.)

Corn-based diets are low in niacin and the amino acid tryptophan, which can be converted to niacin in the body. The term *niacin* actually refers to two compounds, nicotinamide and nicotinic acid, which are converted to active coenzymes that assist in the metabolism of carbohydrates and fatty acids for energy. Niacin also plays an important role in DNA replication and repair and in the process of cell differentiation. Thus, it is not surprising that a deficiency of niacin can disrupt so many systems in the body.

Niacin is widely distributed in foods, with good sources being yeast, meats (including fish and poultry), cereals, legumes, and seeds **(Figure 10.7)**. Other foods such as milk, leafy vegetables, coffee, and tea can also add appreciable amounts of niacin to the diet (Jacob, 2006). As with riboflavin, enriched or fortified breads, ready-to-eat cereals, and energy bars frequently provide 25%–100% of the Daily Value for niacin.

Halibut is a good source of niacin.

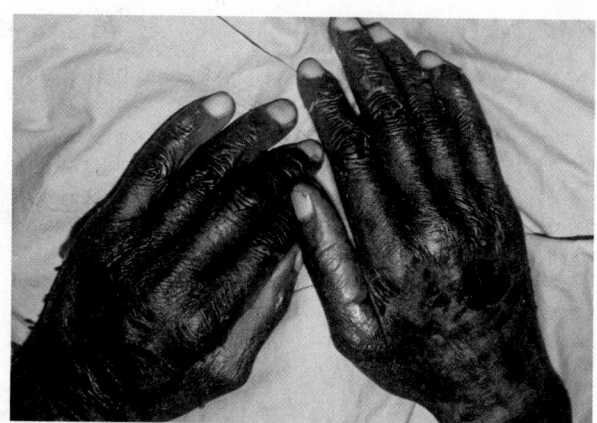

Figure 10.6 Pellagra is characterized by dermatitis in areas of the skin exposed to sunlight.

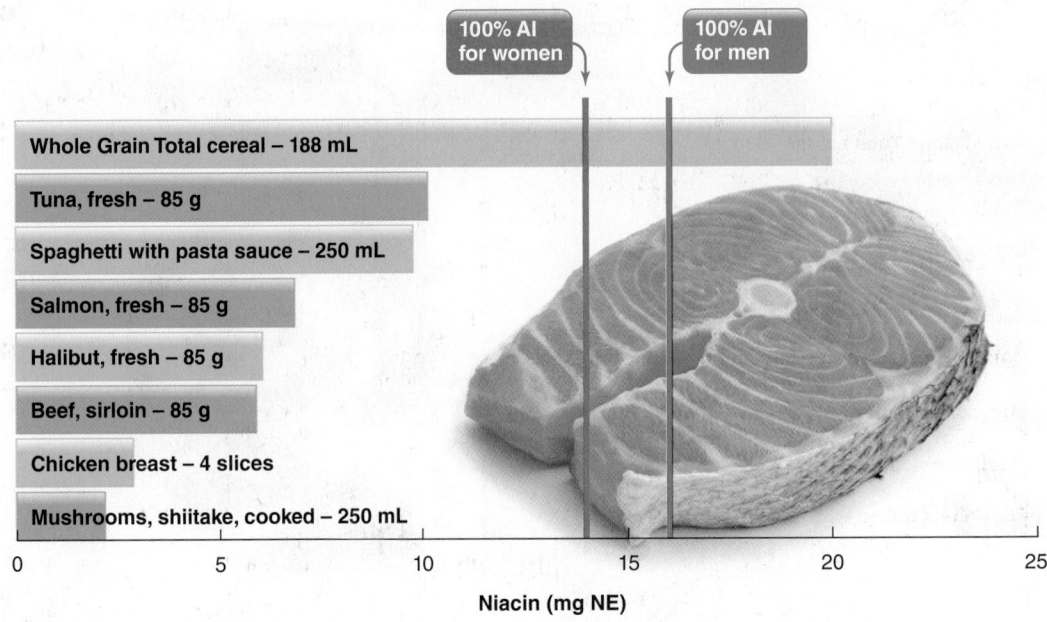

Figure 10.07 Common food sources of niacin. The RDA for niacin is 16 mg niacin equivalents (NE)/day for men and 14 mg NE/day for women 19 years and older.
Data from U.S. Department of Agriculture, Agricultural Research Service. 2009. USDA Nutrient Database for Standard Reference, Release 22. Nutrient Data Laboratory Home Page, www.ars.usda.gov/ba/bhnrc/ndl.

Niacin can cause toxicity symptoms when taken in supplement form. These symptoms include *flushing*, which is defined as burning, tingling, and itching sensations accompanied by a reddened flush primarily on the face, arms, and chest. Liver damage, glucose intolerance, blurred vision, and edema of the eyes can be seen with very large doses of niacin taken over long periods of time.

RECAP The B vitamins include thiamin, riboflavin, niacin, vitamin B_6 (pyridoxine), folate, vitamin B_{12} (cobalamin), pantothenic acid, and biotin. Thiamin plays critical roles in the metabolism of glucose and the branched-chain amino acids. Whole grains are good sources. Thiamin-deficiency disease is called beriberi. Riboflavin is an important coenzyme involved in the metabolism of carbohydrates and fat. Milk, meats, and green vegetables are good sources. Riboflavin-deficiency disease is called ariboflavinosis. Niacin assists in the metabolism of carbohydrates and fatty acids. It also plays an important role in DNA replication and repair and in cell differentiation. Corn-based diets can be low in niacin and can result in the deficiency disease pellagra.

Vitamin B_6 (Pyridoxine)

Researchers discovered vitamin B_6 by ruling out a deficiency of other B vitamins as the cause of a scaly dermatitis in rats (McCollum, 1957). They then discovered that B_6 deficiency was associated with convulsions in birds and later that infants fed formulas lacking B_6 also had convulsions and dermatitis (Jukes, 1990).

Functions of Vitamin B_6

The term *vitamin B_6* can actually refer to any of six related compounds: pyridoxine (PN), pyridoxal (PL), pyridoxamine (PM), and the phosphate forms of these three compounds. A coenzyme for more than 100 enzymes, vitamin B_6 is involved in many metabolic processes within the body, including the following:

- *Amino acid metabolism.* Vitamin B_6 is important for the metabolism of amino acids because it plays a critical role in transamination, which is a key process in making non-essential amino acids (see Chapter 6). Without adequate vitamin B_6, all amino acids become essential, as our body cannot make them in sufficient quantities.

- *Neurotransmitter synthesis.* Vitamin B_6 is a cofactor for enzymes involved in the synthesis of several neurotransmitters, which is also a transamination process. Because of this, vitamin B_6 is important in cognitive function and normal brain activity. Abnormal brain waves have been observed in both infants and adults in vitamin B_6–deficient states (Mackey, Davis, and Gregory, 2006).
- *Carbohydrate metabolism.* Vitamin B_6 is a coenzyme for an enzyme that breaks down stored glycogen to glucose. Thus, vitamin B_6 plays an important role in maintaining blood glucose during exercise. It is also important for the conversion of amino acids to glucose.
- *Heme synthesis.* The synthesis of heme, required for the production of hemoglobin and thus the transport of oxygen, requires vitamin B_6. Chronic vitamin B_6 deficiency can lead to small red blood cells with inadequate amounts of hemoglobin (Mackey, Davis, and Gregory, 2006).
- *Immune function.* Vitamin B_6 plays a role in maintaining the health and activity of lymphocytes and in producing adequate levels of antibodies in response to an immune challenge. The depression of immune function seen in vitamin B_6 deficiency may also be due to a reduction in the vitamin B_6–dependent enzymes involved in DNA synthesis.
- *Metabolism of other nutrients.* Vitamin B_6 also plays a role in the metabolism of other nutrients, including niacin, folate, and carnitine (Mackey, Davis, and Gregory, 2006).
- *Reduction of cardiovascular disease (CVD) risk.* As discussed later in this chapter, high blood levels of homocysteine are considered an independent risk factor for CVD (Boushey et al., 1995). **Homocysteine** is a metabolic by-product of the metabolism of methionine, an essential amino acid. The enzymes involved in homocysteine metabolism require three key vitamins: folate, vitamin B_6, and vitamin B_{12} (Joubert and Manore, 2006). If they are not available to completely metabolize methionine, blood levels of homocysteine increase. Adequate intakes of folate, vitamin B_6, and vitamin B_{12} can help keep blood levels of homocysteine low.

Tuna is a good source of vitamin B_6.

homocysteine An amino acid that requires adequate levels of folate, vitamin B_6, and vitamin B_{12} for its metabolism. High levels of homocysteine in the blood are associated with an increased risk for vascular diseases, such as cardiovascular disease.

How Much Vitamin B_6 Should We Consume?

The recommended intakes for vitamin B_6 are listed in Table 10.1. Rich sources of vitamin B_6 are meats, fish, poultry, eggs, dairy products, and peanut butter **(Figure 10.8)**.

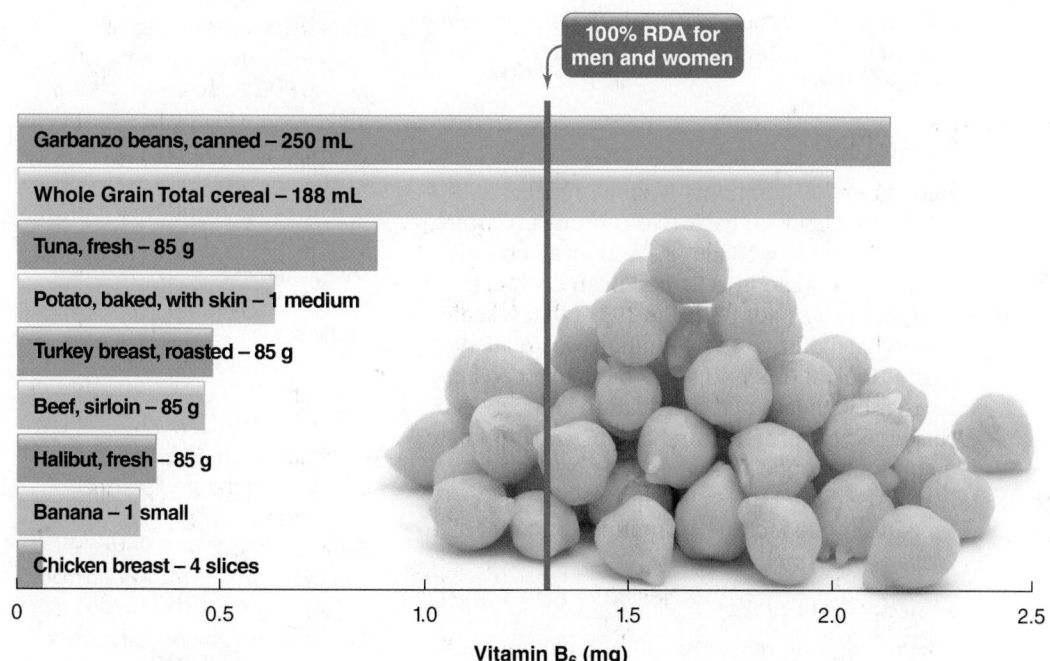

Figure 10.8 Common food sources of vitamin B_6. The RDA for vitamin B_6 is 1.3 mg/day for men and women 19–50 years.

Data from U.S. Department of Agriculture, Agricultural Research Service, 2009, USDA Nutrient Database for Standard Reference, Release 22. Nutrient Data Laboratory Home Page, www.ars.usda.gov/ba/bhnrc/ndl.

Headaches, anxiety, irritability, tension, and depression are common symptoms of PMS.

Many vegetables, such as asparagus, potatoes, and carrots; fruits, especially bananas; and whole-grain cereals are also good sources of vitamin B_6. As with the other B vitamins discussed in this chapter, fortified or enriched grains, cereals, and energy bars can provide 25%–100% of the Daily Value in 1 serving. Little vitamin B_6 is lost in the storage or handling of foods, except the milling of grains; however, vitamin B_6 is sensitive to both heat and light, so it can easily be lost in cooking.

Vitamin B_6 supplements have been used to treat conditions such as premenstrual syndrome (PMS) and carpal tunnel syndrome. You need to use caution, however, when using such supplements. Whereas consuming excess vitamin B_6 from food sources does not cause toxicity, excess B_6 from supplementing can result in nerve damage and lesions of the skin. A condition called *sensory neuropathy* (damage to the sensory nerves) has been documented in individuals taking high-dose B_6 supplements. The symptoms of sensory neuropathy include numbness and tingling involving the face, neck, hands, and feet, with difficulty manipulating objects and walking.

The symptoms of vitamin B_6 deficiency include anemia, convulsions, depression, confusion, and inflamed, irritated patches on the skin. Deficiency of vitamin B_6 has also been associated with a decreased ability to metabolize the amino acid methionine and a resultant increased risk for cardiovascular, cerebrovascular, and peripheral vascular disease. This condition also occurs with a deficiency of folate and vitamin B_{12}, and is discussed in more detail in the next section.

Folate

Reports of the symptoms we now recognize as folate deficiency go back two centuries (Carmel, 2006). By the late 1800s, a disorder associated with large red blood cells had been characterized, but it was not until the 1930s that researchers understood that the condition was related to diet. It took another 40 years before researchers more fully understood the relationship between this blood abnormality and a deficiency of folate, a substance found in many foods, especially leafy green vegetables. The name *folate* originated from the fact the vitamin is abundant in "foliage" (Carmel, 2006).

Functions of Folate

Folate-requiring reactions in the body are collectively called *1-C metabolism*. This means folate is involved in adding "one-carbon units" to other organic compounds during the synthesis of new compounds or the modification of existing ones.

Thus, the most basic cellular functions, such as the synthesis of DNA, require folate. The following are some of these functions:

- *Nucleotide synthesis.* Folate is required for the synthesis of nitrogen-containing compounds needed for DNA synthesis. For this reason folate is important for cell division. Adequate intake is especially critical during the first few weeks of pregnancy, when the combined sperm–egg cell multiplies rapidly to form the primitive tissues and structures of the human body. Folate continues to be important for tissue maintenance and repair throughout life. For example, low folate may predispose normal tissues to increased risk of transformation into cancer cells, while folate supplementation appears to suppress the development of tumours (Kim, 2006).
- *Amino acid metabolism.* Folate is involved in the metabolism of many of the amino acids, including serine, glycine, histidine, and methionine. And as mentioned earlier, folate, vitamin B_{12}, and vitamin B_6 are required for the metabolism of methionine.
- *Red blood cell synthesis.* Without adequate folate, the synthesis of normal red blood cells is impaired.

How Much Folate Should We Consume?

The recommended intakes for folate are listed in Table 10.1. The critical role of folate during the first few weeks of pregnancy and the fact that many women of childbearing age do not consume adequate amounts led to the mandatory fortification of wheat flour in Canada. Good food sources include breads, orange juice, lentils, oatmeal, asparagus, and leafy green vegetables, such as spinach and romaine lettuce **(Figure 10.9)**.

Because folate is sensitive to heat, it can be lost when foods are cooked. It can also leach out into cooking water, which may then be discarded.

What Happens If We Consume Too Much Folate?

Toxicity can occur when taking supplemental folate. One especially frustrating problem with folate toxicity is that it can mask a simultaneous vitamin B_{12} deficiency. This often results in failure to detect the B_{12} deficiency, and as you saw in the chapter-opening case, a delay in diagnosis of B_{12} deficiency can contribute to severe damage to the nervous system. There do not appear to be any clear symptoms of folate toxicity independent from its interaction with vitamin B_{12} deficiency.

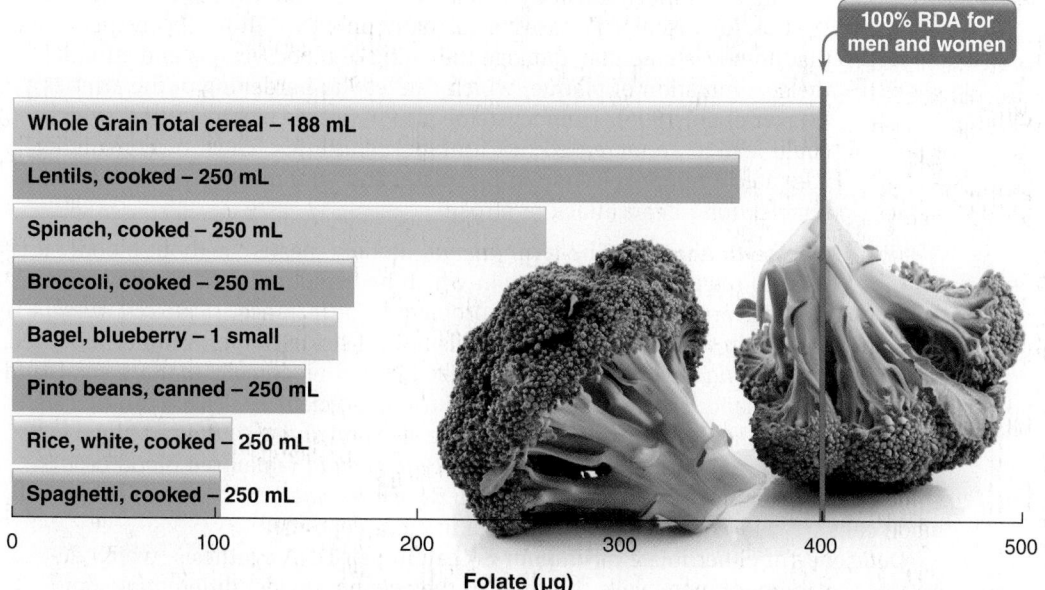

▲ **Figure 10.9** Common food sources of folate and folic acid. The RDA for folate is 400 µg/day for men and women.

Data from U.S. Department of Agriculture, Agricultural Research Service, 2009, USDA Nutrient Database for Standard Reference, Release 22. Nutrient Data Laboratory Home Page, www.ars.usda.gov/ba/bhnrc/ndl.

What Happens If We Don't Consume Enough Folate?

Folate deficiency can cause many adverse health effects, the three most significant of which are discussed here.

Neural Tube Defects   A woman's requirement for folate substantially increases during pregnancy. This is because of the high rates of cell development needed for enlargement of the uterus, development of the placenta, expansion of the mother's red blood cells, and growth of the embryo and fetus. Inadequate folate intake during pregnancy is associated with major birth defects.

neural tube defects The most common malformations of the central nervous system that occur during fetal development. A folate deficiency can cause neural tube defects.

Neural tube defects are the most common malformations of the central nervous system that occur during embryonic and fetal development. The neural tube is formed by the fourth week of pregnancy, and it eventually develops into the brain and the spinal cord of the fetus. In a folate-deficient environment, the tube will fail to fold and close properly. The resultant defect in the newborn depends on the degree of failure and can range from protrusion of the spinal cord outside of the spinal column to a partial absence of brain tissue. Some forms of neural tube defects are minor and can be surgically repaired, while other forms are fatal. Neural tube defects are described in more detail in Chapter 14. (For an illustration and a photo of the condition, see Figure 14.7.)

The challenging aspect of neural tube defects is that they occur very early in a woman's pregnancy, almost always before she knows she is pregnant. Thus, adequate folate intake is extremely important for all sexually active women of childbearing age, whether or not they intend to become pregnant. To prevent neural tube defects, it is recommended that all women capable of becoming pregnant consume 400 μg of folate daily from supplements, fortified foods, or both in addition to the folate they consume in their standard diet (Institute of Medicine, 1998).

Vascular Disease and Homocysteine   As mentioned earlier, folate, vitamin B_6, and vitamin B_{12} are necessary for the complete metabolism of the essential amino acid methionine **(Figure 10.10)**. When intakes of these nutrients are insufficient, the level of homocysteine, a by-product of methionine metabolism, increases in the blood. A thorough review of recent studies on this topic showed that elevated levels of homocysteine are associated with a 1.5 to 2 times greater risk for cardiovascular, cerebrovascular, and peripheral vascular diseases (Beresford and Boushey, 1997). These diseases substantially increase a person's risk for a heart attack or stroke.

The exact mechanism by which elevated homocysteine levels increase the risk for vascular diseases is currently unknown. It has been speculated that homocysteine may damage the lining of blood vessels and stimulate the accumulation of plaque, which can lead to hardening of the arteries (Mayer et al., 1996). Homocysteine also increases blood clotting, which could lead to an increased risk for blocked arteries. Thus, by consuming adequate amounts of vitamin B_6, folate, and vitamin B_{12}, we may decrease our risk for a heart attack or stroke.

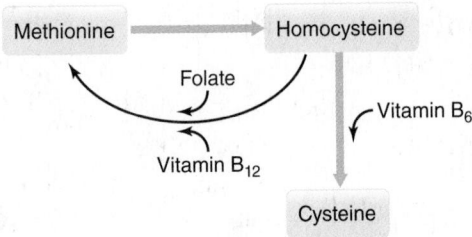

◄ Figure 10.10 The metabolism of methionine, an essential amino acid, to homocysteine. Homocysteine can then be converted back to methionine through a vitamin B_{12}–and folate-dependent reaction or to cysteine through a vitamin B_6–dependent reaction. Cysteine is a non-essential amino acid important for making other biological compounds. Without these B vitamins, blood levels of homocysteine can increase. High levels of homocysteine are a risk factor for cardiovascular disease.

Macrocytic Anemia   The term *anemia* literally means "without blood"; it is used to refer to any condition in which hemoglobin levels are low. Some anemias are caused by genetic problems. For instance, *sickle cell anemia* is a genetic disorder in which the red blood cells have a sickle shape. Another inherited anemia is *thalassemia,* a condition characterized by red blood cells that are small and short-lived. Other anemias are due to micronutrient deficiencies. These can be classified according to the general way they alter the size and shape of the red blood cells. Low iron, copper, and vitamin B_6 cause *microcytic anemia* (small red blood cells), while inadequate intakes of folate or vitamin B_{12} cause *macrocytic anemia* (large red blood cells). We discuss macrocytic anemia in more detail here.

Deficiency of either folate or vitamin B_{12} can impair DNA synthesis, which decreases the ability of blood cells to divide. If they cannot divide, differentiate, and mature, the cells remain large and immature precursors to red blood cells, known as *megaloblasts* (from *megalo,* meaning "large," and *blast,* meaning "a precursor cell"). These immature cells contain inadequate hemoglobin; thus, their ability to transport oxygen is diminished. The resulting condition is sometimes referred to as *megaloblastic anemia*, but is more commonly called **macrocytic anemia** (from *macro,* meaning "large," and *cyte,* meaning "cell"). Symptoms of macrocytic anemia are similar to those of other types of anemia, including weakness, fatigue, difficulty concentrating, irritability, headache, shortness of breath, and reduced exercise tolerance.

RECAP Vitamin B_6 is a coenzyme for more than 100 enzymes involved in processes such as the metabolism of amino acids and carbohydrates and the synthesis of neurotransmitters. It is widely found in meats, poultry, fish, dairy products, and certain fruits and vegetables. The most basic cellular functions, such as the synthesis of DNA as well as cell differentiation, require folate. Folate is widely found in green leafy vegetables and is added to breads, cereals, and other grain-based foods. Folate deficiency causes macrocytic anemia and can lead to neural tube defects in the developing fetus.

Vitamin B_{12} (Cobalamin)

In 1855, a clinician named Thomas Addison described a strange form of anemia in patients that left them feeling weak and exhausted (Carmel, 2006; Sabler, 2006). To our knowledge, this is the first report describing the often fatal course of vitamin B_{12} deficiency, later called **pernicious anemia** (the word *pernicious* means "causing great harm"). Several decades passed before an "animal protein factor" was associated with the cobalt-containing vitamin B_{12}. The first clinical experiments in humans were done by Drs. Minot and Murphy in the 1920s. They fed patients with pernicious anemia large doses of liver and documented the improvement in their red blood cells (Carmel, 2006). For this work they were awarded the Nobel Prize in 1934. Their work was extended by others who identified that some special "extrinsic factor" in the liver or meat was combined with an "intrinsic factor" in the stomach. When both of these factors were present, patients with pernicious anemia recovered. The final step in the identification of vitamin B_{12} as the extrinsic factor and in determining its structure was done by Dr. Dorothy Crowfoot Hodgkin, who was awarded the Nobel Prize for Chemistry in 1964 (Carmel, 2006).

Functions of Vitamin B_{12}

Vitamin B_{12} is a coenzyme for two enzymes in the body that are part of two very important metabolic pathways (Sabler, 2006). First, vitamin B_{12} is important for the metabolism of methionine, an essential amino acid, and assists in the synthesis of biological compounds such as creatine, phospholipids, neurotransmitters, DNA, and RNA. As with folate deficiency, a deficiency in vitamin B_{12} is most pronounced in rapidly dividing cells, such as the red blood cells, and results in a form of macrocytic anemia.

As noted earlier, adequate levels of folate, vitamin B_6, and vitamin B_{12} are necessary to prevent the buildup of homocysteine. A high level of homocysteine in the blood is related to an increased risk for heart disease.

The metabolic pathway involved in the metabolism of methionine also converts folate to its active form, which is a vitamin B_{12}–dependent process. Without vitamin B_{12}, folate becomes "trapped" in an inactive form and folate deficiency symptoms develop, even though adequate amounts of folate may be present in the diet.

Vitamin B_{12} is also important for the metabolism of certain abnormal fatty acids. When vitamin B_{12} is deficient in the diet, these abnormal fatty acids accumulate in the blood and are incorporated into cell membranes, including those in the nervous system, where they cause neurologic problems. Also, as you saw in the chapter-opening scenario, B_{12} is essential for healthy functioning of the nervous system because it helps maintain the myelin sheath that coats nerve fibres. When this sheath is damaged or absent, the conduction of nervous signals is slowed, causing numerous neurologic problems.

How Much Vitamin B_{12} Should We Consume?

The recommended intakes for vitamin B_{12} are listed in Table 10.1. Vitamin B_{12} is found primarily in animal products, such as meats, fish, poultry, dairy products, and

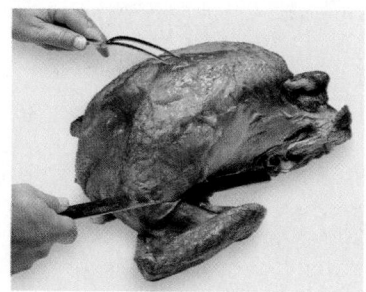
Turkey contains vitamin B_{12}.

macrocytic anemia A form of anemia manifested as the production of larger than normal red blood cells containing insufficient hemoglobin, which inhibits adequate transport of oxygen; also called megaloblastic anemia. Macrocytic anemia can be caused by a severe folate deficiency.

pernicious anemia A form of anemia that is the result of either insufficient intake of vitamin B_{12} or the inability to absorb the vitamin B_{12} consumed; often occurs at the end stage of a disorder that causes the loss of certain cells in the stomach.

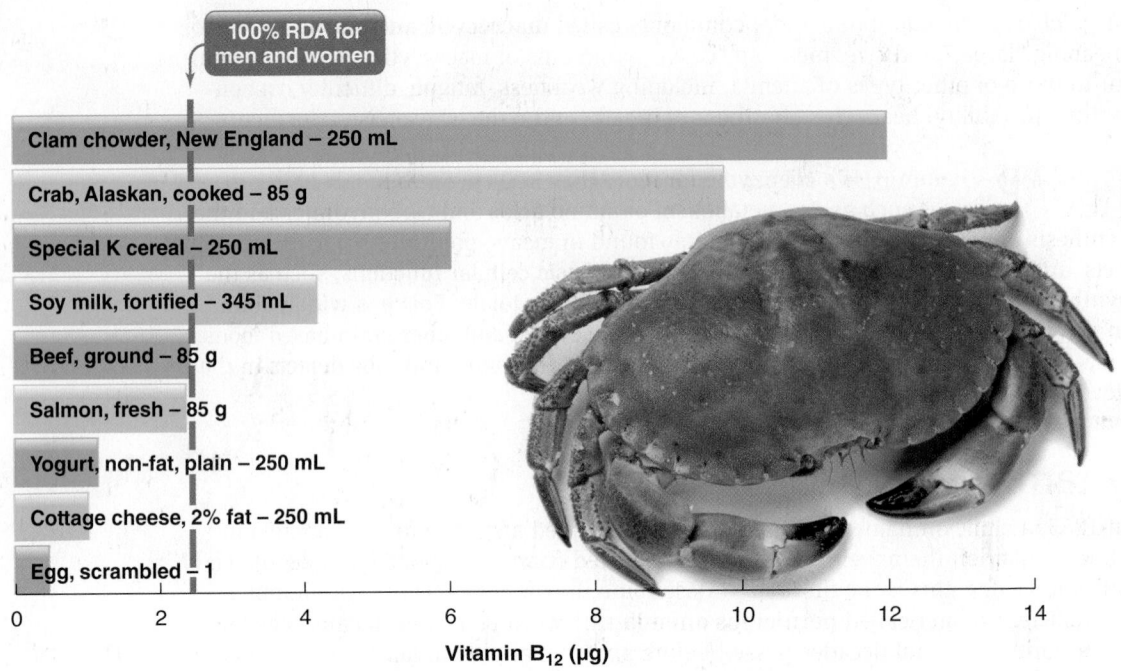

100% RDA for men and women

Clam chowder, New England – 250 mL

Crab, Alaskan, cooked – 85 g

Special K cereal – 250 mL

Soy milk, fortified – 345 mL

Beef, ground – 85 g

Salmon, fresh – 85 g

Yogurt, non-fat, plain – 250 mL

Cottage cheese, 2% fat – 250 mL

Egg, scrambled – 1

Vitamin B$_{12}$ (µg)

⬆ **Figure 10.11** Common food sources of vitamin B$_{12}$. The RDA for vitamin B$_{12}$ is 2.4 µg/day for men and women.

Data from U.S. Department of Agriculture, Agricultural Research Service, 2009, USDA Nutrient Database for Standard Reference, Release 22. Nutrient Data Laboratory Home Page, www.ars.usda.gov/ba/bhnrc/ndl.

eggs, and in fortified cereal products, such as ready-to-eat cereals (**Figure 10.11**). As discussed in Chapter 6, individuals consuming a vegan diet need to eat vegetable-based foods that are fortified with vitamin B$_{12}$ or take vitamin B$_{12}$ supplements or injections to ensure that they maintain adequate blood levels of this nutrient.

As we age, our sources of vitamin B$_{12}$ may need to change. Individuals younger than 51 years are generally able to meet the RDA for vitamin B$_{12}$ by consuming it in foods. However, it is estimated that about 10%–30% of adults older than 50 years have a condition referred to as **atrophic gastritis**, which results in low stomach acid secretion (Institute of Medicine, 1998). Since stomach acid separates food-bound vitamin B$_{12}$ from dietary proteins, if the acid content of the stomach is inadequate, then we cannot free up enough vitamin B$_{12}$ from food sources alone. Because atrophic gastritis can affect almost one-third of the older adult population, it is recommended that people older than 50 years of age consume foods fortified with vitamin B$_{12}$, take a vitamin B$_{12}$–containing supplement, or have periodic B$_{12}$ injections.

What Happens If We Consume Too Much Vitamin B$_{12}$?

There are no known adverse effects from consuming excess amounts of vitamin B$_{12}$ as either food or supplements (Institute of Medicine, 1998).

What Happens If We Don't Consume Enough Vitamin B$_{12}$?

The two primary causes of vitamin B$_{12}$ deficiency are insufficient intake and the inability to absorb the vitamin B$_{12}$ consumed. Either of these problems can result in the development of pernicious anemia. The most common cause of the vitamin B$_{12}$ deficiency seen with pernicious anemia is lack of a protein called **intrinsic factor**, which is normally secreted by certain cells in the stomach. Intrinsic factor binds to vitamin B$_{12}$ and aids its absorption in the small intestine. Without intrinsic factor, vitamin B$_{12}$ cannot cross the intestinal lining. Like atrophic gastritis, inadequate production of intrinsic factor occurs more commonly in older people, making them at higher risk for vitamin B$_{12}$ deficiency and pernicious anemia. Individuals who lack intrinsic factor may receive periodic vitamin B$_{12}$ injections, thus bypassing the need for B$_{12}$ absorption in the intestines. Pernicious anemia is also commonly seen in people with more

atrophic gastritis A condition that results in low stomach acid secretion; it is estimated to occur in about 10%–30% of adults older than 50 years.

intrinsic factor A protein secreted by cells of the stomach that binds to vitamin B$_{12}$ and aids its absorption in the small intestine.

generalized malabsorption disorders, such as celiac disease, as well as in people with tapeworm infestation of the gut, as the worms take up the vitamin B_{12} before it can be absorbed by the intestines. Pernicious anemia can also occur in people who consume little or no vitamin B_{12} in their diets, such as Mr. Katz in our chapter opener, who followed a strict vegan diet.

Symptoms of pernicious anemia include pale skin, reduced energy and exercise tolerance, fatigue, and shortness of breath. In addition, because nerve cells are destroyed, patients with pernicious anemia lose the ability to perform coordinated movements and maintain their body's positioning. Central nervous system involvement can lead to irritability, confusion, depression, and even paranoia. As we saw in the case of Mr. Katz, after onset, such symptoms can only be partially reversed, even with prompt administration of vitamin B_{12} injections.

Pantothenic Acid

The path leading to the discovery of pantothenic acid was similar to that for the other water-soluble vitamins. First, researchers established that pantothenic acid was important for the growth of certain bacteria and yeasts. Then they identified it as important for growth and the prevention of dermatitis in chickens. Finally, it was identified as essential for other animals and humans. The vitamin was named after the Greek word meaning "from everywhere," since the vitamin is widespread in the food supply (Miller, Rogers, and Rubker, 2006).

Pantothenic acid is a component of an important coenzyme that is required for all the energy-producing metabolic pathways. It is especially important for the breakdown and synthesis of fatty acids within the body. Thus, pantothenic acid assures that the foods we eat can be used for energy and that the excess energy we consume can be stored as fat.

The recommended intakes for pantothenic acid are listed in Table 10.1. Food sources include chicken, beef, egg yolks, potatoes, oat cereals, tomato products, whole grains, organ meats, and yeast **(Figure 10.12)**. There are no known adverse effects from consuming excess amounts of pantothenic acid. Deficiencies of pantothenic acid are very rare.

Shiitake mushrooms contain pantothenic acid.

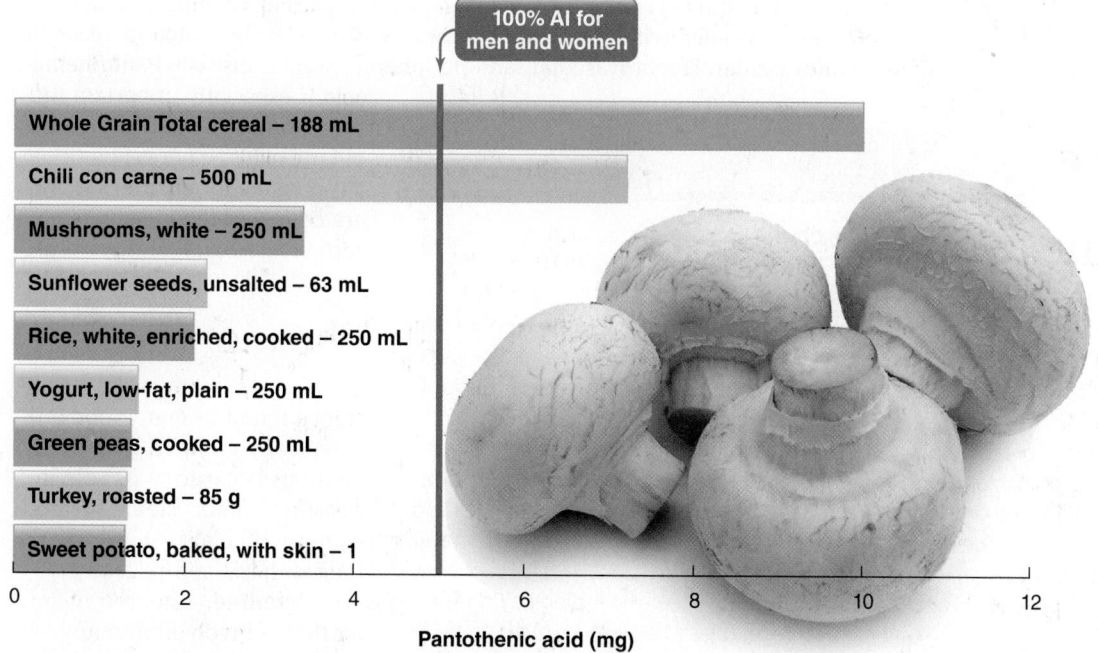

Figure 10.12 Common food sources of pantothenic acid. The AI for pantothenic acid is 5 mg/day for men and women.

Data from U.S. Department of Agriculture, Agricultural Research Service. 2009. USDA Nutrient Database for Standard Reference, Release 22. Nutrient Data Laboratory Home Page, www.ars.usda.gov/ba/bhnrc/ndl.

Biotin

Early in the 1900s, it was observed that rats could maintain normal growth while being fed a diet containing cooked egg whites as the sole source of protein. About the same time, other researchers observed that, if the egg whites were raw, rats developed diarrhea and skin problems (McCollum, 1957). The detrimental effects of feeding raw egg whites aroused great interest in the nutrition community. Could there be a toxic substance in raw egg whites that was not found in cooked egg whites? Experiments led to the discovery of biotin, which prevented the diarrhea and skin problems that occurred when raw egg whites were fed to rats. Raw egg whites contain a protein called avidin, which binds biotin in the gastrointestinal tract and prevents its absorption.

Biotin is a coenzyme for five enzymes that are critical in the metabolism of carbohydrate, fat, and protein. It also plays an important role in gluconeogenesis.

The recommended intakes for biotin are listed in Table 10.1. The biotin content has been determined for very few foods, and these values are not reported in food composition tables or dietary analysis programs. Biotin appears to be widespread in foods but is especially high in liver, egg yolks, and cooked cereals. Biotin is also produced by the intestinal flora in the gut, but its availability for absorption appears low.

There are no known adverse effects from consuming excess amounts of biotin. Biotin deficiencies are typically seen only in people who consume a large number of raw egg whites over long periods of time. Biotin deficiencies are also seen in people fed total parenteral nutrition (nutrients that are administered intravenously and bypass the gastrointestinal tract) that is not supplemented with biotin.

Symptoms include thinning of hair; loss of hair colour; development of a red, scaly rash around the eyes, nose, and mouth; depression; lethargy; and hallucinations.

As you have read about the B vitamins, you have probably noticed that many of them are susceptible to destruction on exposure to heat, light, and other factors in the environment. In fact, no matter how careful you are when storing and preparing foods, some vitamins will be lost. So how do you preserve the highest level of vitamins in the foods you eat (Combs, 2008)? Check out the Quick Tips below to find out more.

← Choline is widespread in foods and can be found in eggs and milk.

acetylcholine A neurotransmitter that is involved in many functions, including muscle movement and memory storage.

RECAP Vitamin B_{12} is essential for the metabolism of methionine and certain abnormal fatty acids. Deficiency leads to pernicious anemia, a type of macrocytic anemia, and nervous system damage. Low intakes of vitamin B_6, folate, and vitamin B_{12} are associated with elevated blood homocysteine levels, which increase the risk for cardiovascular, cerebrovascular, and peripheral vascular disease. Pantothenic acid is especially important for the breakdown and synthesis of fatty acids, whereas biotin is a coenzyme for enzymes that are critical in the metabolism of carbohydrate, fat, and protein.

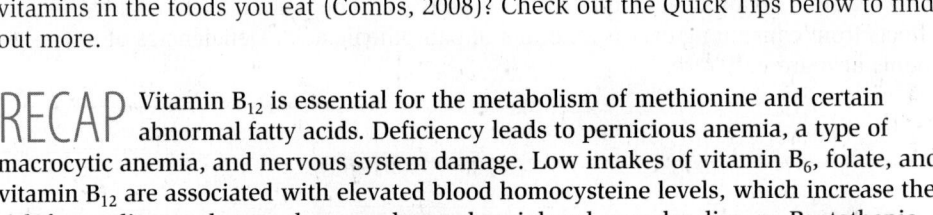

QUICK TIPS

Retaining the Vitamins in Foods

▶ Watch the water. Soak and cook foods in as little water as possible to minimize the loss of water-soluble vitamins. For the best possible outcome, steam vegetables in a steamer basket over half an inch of water.

▶ Lower the heat. Avoid high temperatures for long periods of time. Heat causes some loss of nutrients, especially vitamin C, thiamin, and riboflavin. Cook vegetables only until tender.

▶ Limit the light. Riboflavin is destroyed by light. Since milk is an excellent source of riboflavin, it is typically packaged in light-obstructing containers, such as coated cardboard or opaque bottles.

▶ Avoid air. Vitamins A, C, E, K, and B are destroyed by exposure to air. Ways to minimize losses are to cut fruits and vegetables in large pieces and store them in air-tight containers or covered with plastic wrap. Peel and cut produce immediately before cooking and eat them as soon after cooking as possible. Finally, eat vegetables and fruits whole, unpeeled, and raw whenever possible.

▶ Don't disturb the pH. Adding baking soda to vegetables to help them retain their colour is not smart. Baking soda makes cooking water alkaline, and thiamin, riboflavin, vitamin K, and vitamin C are destroyed.

Choline

Choline is a vitamin-like substance found in many foods. It is typically grouped with the B vitamins because of its role in assisting homocysteine metabolism. Choline also accelerates the synthesis and release of **acetylcholine**, a neurotransmitter that is involved in many functions, including muscle movement and memory storage. Choline is also necessary for the synthesis of phospholipids and other components of cell membranes; thus, choline plays a critical role in the structural integrity of cell membranes. Finally, choline plays an important role in the transport and metabolism of fats and cholesterol.

The recommended intakes for choline are listed in Table 10.1. The choline content of foods is not typically reported in nutrient databases. However, we do know that choline is widespread in foods, especially milk, liver, eggs, and peanuts. Inadequate intakes of choline can lead to increased fat accumulation in the liver, which eventually leads to liver damage. Excessive intake of supplemental choline results in various toxicity symptoms, including a fishy body odour, vomiting, excess salivation, sweating, diarrhea, and low blood pressure.

Iodine

Iodine is a trace mineral needed to support energy regulation. The heaviest metal required for human nutrition, it is responsible for just one function within the body, the synthesis of thyroid hormones (Freake, 2006). Our body requires thyroid hormones to regulate body temperature, maintain resting metabolic rate, and support reproduction and growth. The form of iodine found in the earth's environment is predominantly inorganic iodide, while iodine, the oxidized form of iodide, is the form of the nutrient most common in food. The iodine content of crops depends on the level of iodide in the soil. Iodide-deficient soils are common in mountainous areas and areas that have experienced frequent flooding. In general, the level naturally found in most foods and beverages is low.

While our body needs relatively little iodine, adequate amounts are necessary to maintain health. The recommended intakes are listed in Table 10.1. Very few foods naturally contain iodine. Saltwater fish and shrimp tend to have higher amounts because marine animals concentrate iodine from seawater. Interestingly, iodine is added to dairy cattle feed and used in sanitizing solutions in the dairy industry, so milk and other dairy foods are an important source. In addition, iodized salt and white and whole-wheat breads made with iodized salt and bread conditioners are an important source of iodine. Iodine has been added to salt in North America since the twentieth century to combat iodine deficiency resulting from poor iodine content of soils. For many people, iodized salt is their only source of iodine, and approximately 2 mL (1/2 tsp) meets the entire adult RDA for iodine.

Iodine toxicity, which generally occurs only with excessive supplementation, blocks the synthesis of thyroid hormones. As the thyroid attempts to produce more hormones, it may enlarge, a condition known as **goitre**. But since adequate levels of iodine are necessary for the synthesis of thyroid hormones, iodine deficiency also results in goitre. In fact, iodine deficiency is the primary cause of goitre worldwide. (Note that the term *goitre* refers only to the enlarged thyroid gland, regardless of its cause.)

A low level of circulating thyroid hormones is known as *hypothyroidism*. In addition to goitre, symptoms of hypothyroidism include decreased body temperature, inability to tolerate cold environmental temperatures, weight gain, fatigue, and sluggishness. If a woman experiences iodine deficiency during pregnancy, her infant has a high risk of being born with a form of mental impairment referred to as **cretinism**. In addition to mental impairment, these children may also suffer from stunted growth, deafness, and muteness.

Chromium

Chromium is a trace mineral that plays an important role in carbohydrate metabolism. You may be interested to learn that the chromium in your body is the same metal used in the chrome plating for cars.

Chromium enhances the ability of insulin to transport glucose from the bloodstream into cells. Chromium also plays important roles in the metabolism of RNA and DNA, in immune function, and in growth. Chromium supplements are marketed to reduce body fat and enhance muscle mass and have become popular with bodybuilders and other athletes interested in improving their body composition. The Nutrition Myth or Fact? box on page 340 investigates whether taking supplemental chromium is effective in improving body composition.

Saltwater fish, fresh or canned, provide iodine.

Goitre, or enlargement of the thyroid gland, develops as a result of iodine toxicity or deficiency.

goitre Enlargement of the thyroid gland; can be caused by either iodine toxicity or deficiency.

cretinism A form of mental retardation that occurs in children whose mothers experienced iodine deficiency during pregnancy.

▲ Our body contains very little chromium. Asparagus is a good dietary source of this trace mineral.

We have only very small amounts of chromium in our body. Whether the North American diet provides adequate chromium is controversial; our body appears to store less chromium as we age.

The recommended intakes for chromium are listed in Table 10.1. Foods that have been identified as good sources of chromium include mushrooms, prunes, dark chocolate, nuts, whole grains, cereals, asparagus, brewer's yeast, some beers, and red wine. Dairy products are typically poor sources of chromium.

There appears to be no toxicity related to consuming chromium naturally found in the diet or in most supplements. The chromium used for some industrial purposes can be toxic. Chromium deficiency appears to be uncommon in North America. When induced in a research setting, chromium deficiency inhibits the uptake of glucose by the cells, causing a rise in blood glucose and insulin levels. Chromium deficiency can also result in elevated blood lipid levels and in damage to the brain and nervous system.

Manganese

A trace mineral, manganese is a cofactor involved in energy metabolism and in the formation of urea, the primary component of urine. It also assists in the synthesis

NUTRITION MYTH OR FACT?
Can Chromium Supplements Enhance Body Composition?

Because athletes are always looking for a competitive edge, a multitude of supplements are marketed and sold to enhance exercise performance and body composition. Chromium supplements, predominantly in the form of chromium picolinate, are popular with bodybuilders and weight lifters. This popularity stems from the claims that chromium increases muscle mass and muscle strength and decreases body fat.

An early study of chromium supplementation was promising, in that chromium use in both untrained men and football players was found to decrease body fat and increase muscle mass (Evans, 1989). These findings caused a surge in the popularity of chromium supplements and motivated many scientists across the United States to test the reproducibility of these early findings. The next study of chromium supplementation found no effects of chromium on muscle mass, body fat, or muscle strength (Hasten et al., 1992).

These contradictory reports led experts to closely examine the two studies and to design more sophisticated studies to assess the effect of chromium on body composition. There were a number of flaws in the methodology of these early studies. One major concern was that the chromium status of the research participants prior to the study was not measured or controlled. It is possible that the participants were deficient in chromium; this deficiency could have caused a more positive reaction

to chromium than would be expected in people with normal chromium status.

A second major concern was that body composition was measured in these studies using the skinfold technique, in which calipers are used to measure the thickness of the skin and fat at various sites on the body. While this method gives a good general estimate of body fat in young, lean, healthy people, it is not sensitive to small changes in muscle mass. Thus, subsequent studies of chromium used more sophisticated methods of measuring body composition.

The results of research studies conducted over the past 15 years consistently show that chromium supplementation has no effect on muscle mass, body fat, or muscle strength in a variety of groups, including untrained college males and females, obese females, collegiate wrestlers, and older men and women (Campbell et al., 1999; Campbell et al., 2002; Diaz et al., 2008; Hallmark et al., 1996; Lukaski et al, 1996; Lukaski, Siders, and Penland, 2007; Pasman, Westerterp-Plantenga, and Saris, 1997; Volpe et al., 2001; Walker et al, 1998). Despite the overwhelming evidence to the contrary, many supplement companies still claim that chromium supplements enhance strength and muscle mass and reduce body fat. These claims result in millions of dollars of sales of supplements to consumers each year. Armed with this information, you can avoid being fooled by such an expensive nutrition myth.

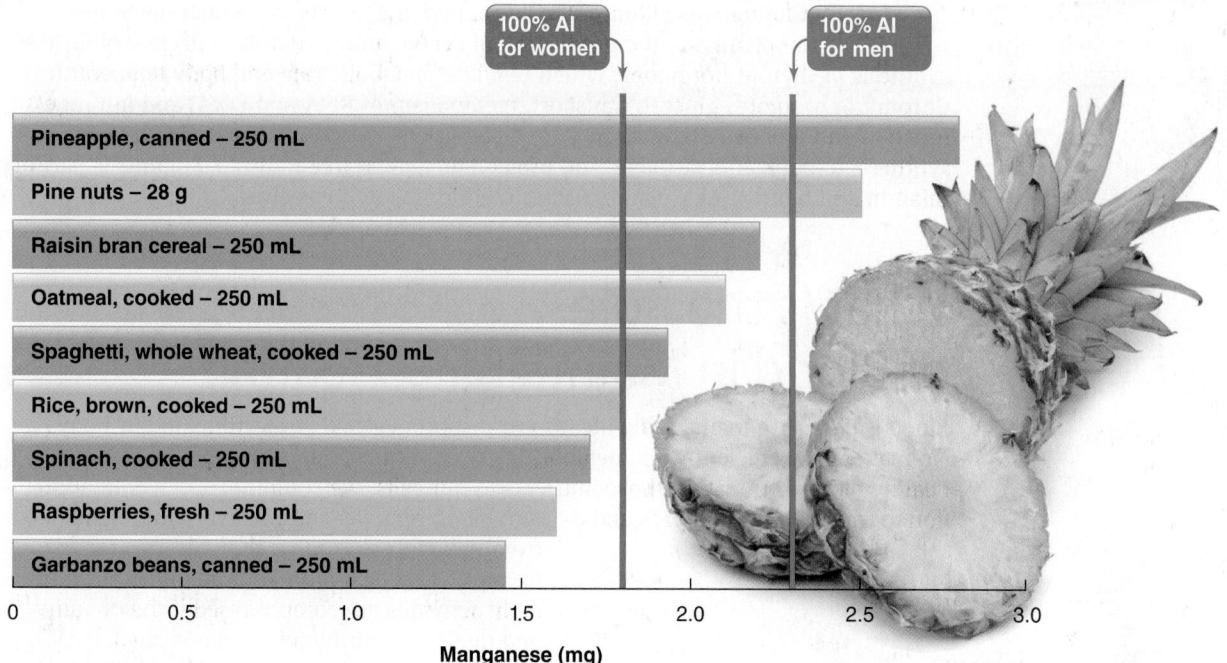

Figure 10.13 Common food sources of manganese. The AI for manganese is 2.3 mg/day for men and 1.8 mg/day for women.

Data from U.S. Department of Agriculture, Agricultural Research Service, 2009, USDA Nutrient Database for Standard Reference, Release 22. Nutrient Data Laboratory Home Page, www.ars.usda.gov/ba/bhnrc/ndl.

of the protein matrix found in bone tissue and in building cartilage, a tissue that supports joints. As reviewed in Chapter 8, manganese is also an integral component of superoxide dismutase, an antioxidant enzyme. Thus, manganese assists in the conversion of free radicals to less damaging substances, protecting our body from oxidative damage.

The recommended intakes for manganese are listed in Table 10.1. Manganese requirements are easily met, as this mineral is widespread in foods and is readily available in a varied diet. Whole-grain foods such as oat bran, wheat flour, whole-wheat spaghetti, and brown rice are good sources of manganese **(Figure 10.13)**. Other good sources include pineapple, pine nuts, okra, spinach, and raspberries.

Manganese toxicity can occur in occupational environments in which people inhale manganese dust; it can also result from drinking water high in manganese. Toxicity results in impairment of the neuromuscular system, causing symptoms similar to those seen in Parkinson's disease, such as muscle spasms and tremors. Manganese deficiency is rare in humans. Symptoms of manganese deficiency include impaired growth and reproductive function, reduced bone density and impaired skeletal growth, impaired glucose and lipid metabolism, and skin rash.

Raspberries are one of the many foods that contain manganese.

Sulphur

Sulphur is a major mineral and a component of the B vitamins thiamin and biotin. In addition, as part of the amino acids methionine and cysteine, sulphur helps stabilize the three-dimensional shapes of proteins. The liver requires sulphur to assist in the detoxification of alcohol and various drugs, and sulphur helps the body maintain acid–base balance.

We are able to synthesize ample sulphur from the protein-containing foods we eat; as a result, we do not need to consume sulphur in the diet, and there is no DRI for sulphur. There are no known toxicity or deficiency symptoms associated with sulphur.

RECAP Choline is a vitamin-like substance that assists in homocysteine metabolism and the production of acetylcholine. Iodine is necessary for the synthesis of thyroid hormones, which regulate metabolic rate and body temperature. Chromium promotes glucose transport, metabolism of RNA and DNA, and immune function and growth. Manganese is involved in energy metabolism, urea formation, synthesis of bone and cartilage, and protection against free radicals. Sulphur is part of thiamin and biotin and the amino acids methionine and cysteine.

What Is the Role of Blood in Maintaining Health?

Blood is critical to maintaining life, as it transports virtually everything in our body. No matter how efficiently we metabolize carbohydrates, fats, and proteins, without healthy blood to transport those nutrients to our cells, we could not survive. In addition to transporting nutrients and oxygen, blood removes the waste products generated from metabolism, so that they can be properly excreted. Our health and our ability to perform daily activities are compromised if the quantity and quality of our blood are diminished.

Blood is actually a tissue, the only fluid tissue in our body. It has four components **(Figure 10.14)**. **Erythrocytes**, or red blood cells, are the cells that transport oxygen. **Leukocytes**, or white blood cells, are the key to our immune function and protect us from infection and illness. **Platelets** are cell fragments that assist in the formation of blood clots and help stop bleeding. **Plasma** is the fluid portion of the blood, and it is needed to maintain adequate blood volume, so that the blood can flow easily throughout our blood vessels.

Certain micronutrients play important roles in the maintenance of blood health through their actions as cofactors, coenzymes, and regulators of oxygen transport. These nutrients are discussed in detail in the following section.

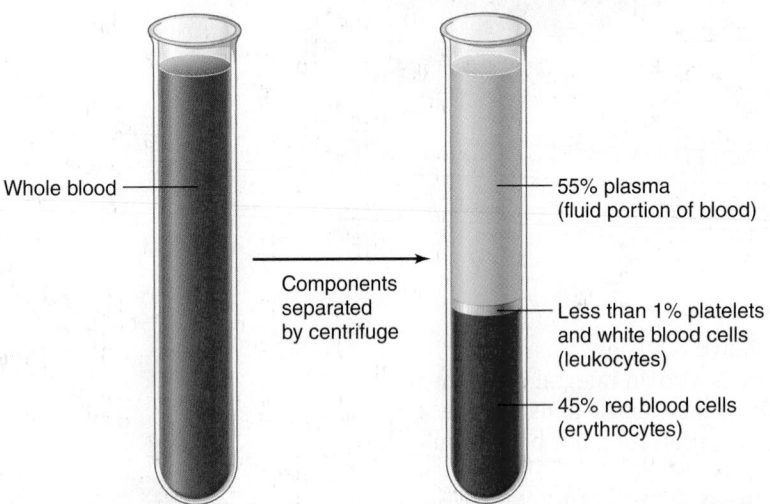

Whole blood

Components separated by centrifuge

55% plasma (fluid portion of blood)

Less than 1% platelets and white blood cells (leukocytes)

45% red blood cells (erythrocytes)

Figure 10.14 Blood has four components, which are visible when the blood is drawn into a test tube and spun in a centrifuge. The bottom layer is the erythrocytes, or red blood cells. The milky layer above the erythrocytes contains the leukocytes and platelets. The yellow fluid on top is the plasma.

A Profile of Nutrients That Maintain Healthy Blood

The nutrients recognized as playing a critical role in maintaining blood health are vitamin K, iron, zinc, and copper. Folate and vitamin B₁₂, already discussed, are also essential for blood health. A list of recommended intakes of these nutrients is provided in **Table 10.2**.

Vitamin K

Vitamin K is a fat-soluble vitamin important for both bone and blood health. The role of vitamin K in the synthesis of proteins involved in maintaining bone density was discussed in detail on page 304 in Chapter 9. In addition, vitamin K acts as a coenzyme that assists in the synthesis of a number of proteins that are involved in the coagulation of blood, including *prothrombin* and the *procoagulants, factors VII, IX, and X*. Without adequate vitamin K, blood does not clot properly: clotting time can be delayed, or clotting may even fail to occur. The failure of blood to clot can lead to increased bleeding from even minor wounds, as well as internal hemorrhaging.

erythrocytes The red blood cells, which are the cells that transport oxygen in our blood.

leukocytes The white blood cells, which protect us from infection and illness.

platelets Cell fragments that assist in the formation of blood clots and help stop bleeding.

plasma The fluid portion of the blood; needed to maintain adequate blood volume, so that the blood can flow easily throughout our body.

TABLE 10.2 Overview of Nutrients Essential to Blood Health

To see the full profile of nutrients involved in blood health, turn to **In Depth**, Vitamins and Minerals: Micronutrients with Macro Powers, pages 216–225.

Nutrient	Recommended Intake (RDA or AI and UL)
Iron	RDA: Women 19 to 50 years = 18 mg/day Men 19 to 50 years = 8 mg/day UL = 45 mg/day
Zinc	RDA: Women 19 to 50 years = 8 mg/day Men 19 to 50 years =11 mg/day UL = 40 mg/day
Copper	RDA for all people 19 to 50 years = 90 µg/day UL = 10 000 µg/day
Vitamin K	AI: Women 19 to 50 years = 90 µg/day Men 19 to 50 years = 120 µg/day UL = none determined
Folate (folic acid)	RDA for all people 19 to 50 years = 400 µg/day UL = 1000 µg/day
Vitamin B$_{12}$ (cyanocobalamin)	RDA for all people 19 to 50 years = 2.4 µg/day UL = not determined

Our needs for vitamin K are relatively small, but intakes of this nutrient are highly variable because vitamin K is found in few foods (Booth and Suttie, 1998). Green, leafy vegetables are good sources, as are soybean and canola oils. The recommended intakes for vitamin K are listed in Table 10.2. There is no upper limit (UL) established for vitamin K at this time (Institute of Medicine, 2001). Healthful intestinal bacteria produce vitamin K in our large intestine, providing us with an important non-dietary source of vitamin K.

There are no known side effects associated with consuming large amounts of vitamin K from supplements or from food (Institute of Medicine, 2001). In the past, a synthetic form of vitamin K was used for therapeutic purposes and was shown to cause liver damage; this form is no longer used.

Vitamin K deficiency inhibits our ability to form blood clots, resulting in excessive bleeding and even severe hemorrhaging in some cases. Although vitamin K deficiency is rare in humans, people with diseases that cause malabsorption of fat, such as celiac disease, Crohn's disease, and cystic fibrosis, can suffer secondarily from a deficiency of vitamin K. Newborns are typically given an injection of vitamin K at birth, as they lack the intestinal bacteria necessary to produce this nutrient.

As discussed in Chapter 9, the impact of vitamin K deficiency on bone health is controversial. Although a recent study found that low intakes of vitamin K were associated with a higher risk for bone fractures in women, there is not enough scientific evidence to state that vitamin K deficiency causes osteoporosis (Feskanich et al, 1999; Institute of Medicine, 2001).

RECAP Blood is a fluid tissue composed of erythrocytes, leukocytes, plasma, and platelets. It transports nutrients and oxygen to our cells to support life and removes the waste products generated from metabolism. Vitamin K is a fat-soluble vitamin and coenzyme that is important for blood clotting and bone metabolism. Bacteria manufacture vitamin K in our large intestine.

Iron

With few exceptions, iron is important for every known living organism. It is essential to cells but can be toxic in high doses. The body needs to regulate iron levels

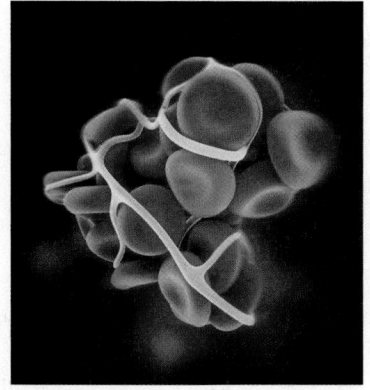
Without enough vitamin K, our blood will not clot properly.

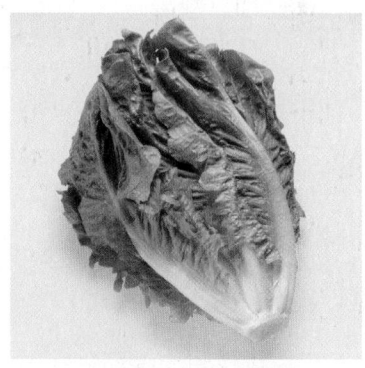
Green, leafy vegetables are a good source of vitamin K.

carefully to be sure adequate iron is supplied to cover the essential functioning of biological processes but prevent excess accumulation. Thus, iron is a trace mineral that is needed in very small amounts in our diets. Despite our relatively small need for iron, iron deficiency is the most common nutrient deficiency in the world.

Functions of Iron

Iron is a component of four primary iron-containing protein groups that carry out a number of important functions within the body. Two of these groups are oxygen-carrying proteins: hemoglobin and myoglobin. Almost two-thirds of all the iron in our body is found in **hemoglobin**, the oxygen-carrying protein in our red blood cells. As shown in **Figure 10.15**, the hemoglobin molecule consists of four polypeptide chains studded with four iron-containing **heme** groups. You know that we cannot survive for more than a few minutes without oxygen. Thus, hemoglobin's ability to transport oxygen throughout the body is absolutely critical to life. To carry oxygen, hemoglobin depends on the iron in its heme groups. Iron is able to bind with and release atoms such as oxygen, nitrogen, and sulphur very easily. It does this by transferring electrons to and from the other atoms as it moves between various oxidation states. In the bloodstream, iron acts as a shuttle, picking up oxygen from the environment, binding it during its transport in the bloodstream, and then dropping it off again in our tissues. Iron is also a component of **myoglobin**, a protein similar to hemoglobin but found in muscle cells. As a part of myoglobin, iron assists in the transport of oxygen into muscle cells.

Iron is also found in a number of enzymes involved in energy production. Iron-requiring enzymes called *cytochromes* are electron carriers within the metabolic pathways that result in the production of energy from carbohydrates, fats, and proteins. In the mitochondria alone there are more than 12 of these iron-requiring enzymes that help produce energy (Beard, 2006). Iron is also critical to the function of certain enzymes important to some immune cells and their communication pathways; thus, iron is required for humans to mount an effective immune response to pathogens (Beard, 2006). Finally, as you learned in Chapter 8, iron is a part of the antioxidant

hemoglobin The oxygen-carrying protein found in our red blood cells; almost two-thirds of all the iron in our body is found in hemoglobin.

heme The iron-containing molecule found in hemoglobin.

myoglobin An iron-containing protein similar to hemoglobin except that it is found in muscle cells.

▶ **Figure 10.15** Iron is contained in the heme portion of hemoglobin and myoglobin.

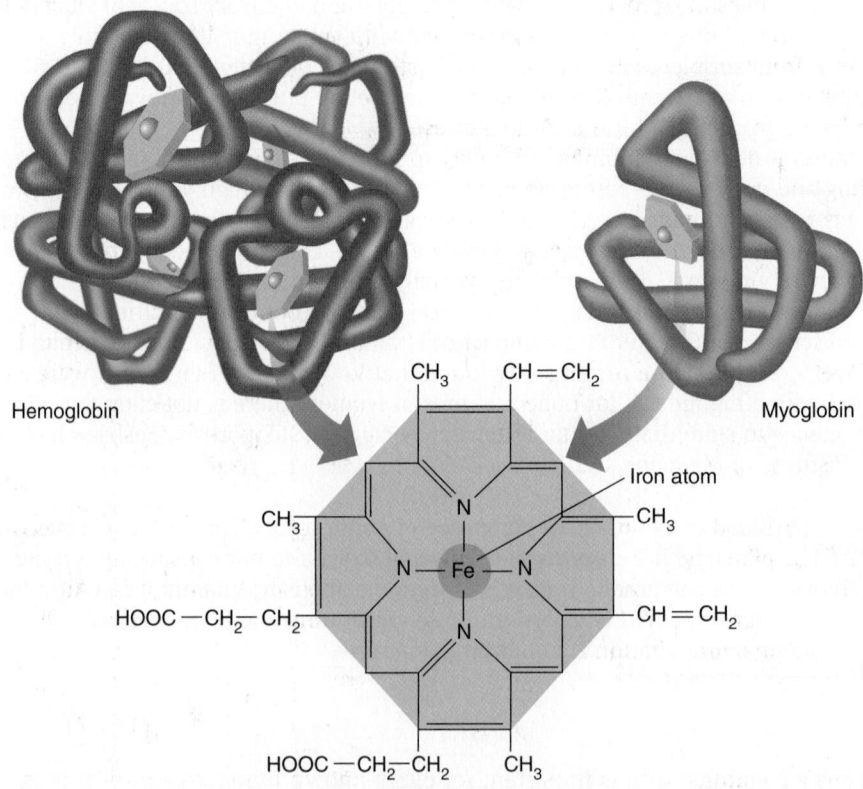

Heme portion containing iron (Fe)

enzyme system that assists in fighting free radicals. Interestingly, excess iron can also act as a pro-oxidant and promote the production of free radicals.

Research over the last 30 years has also documented the importance of iron in neuromuscular functions. Like vitamin B_{12}, iron is required for maintenance of the myelin sheath covering nerve fibres; as noted earlier, without adequate myelin, conduction of nerve impulses is slowed. Iron is also needed for the production of neurotransmitters, including serotonin, norepinephrine, and dopamine. Moreover, iron is important for muscle function. Individuals who have poor iron status complain of lethargy, apathy, and listlessness, which may be independent of iron's role in oxygen delivery. Some of these complaints might be due to the impact of iron deficiency on the brain or on fuel metabolism.

How Is Iron Absorbed?

Our body contains relatively little iron; men have less than 4 g of iron in their body, while women have just over 2 g. Our body is capable of storing excess iron in two storage forms, **ferritin** and **hemosiderin**. The most common areas of iron storage in our body are the liver, bone marrow, intestinal mucosa, and spleen. Because iron is so important for life, our body recycles the iron lost when aging cells are broken down, especially cells high in iron, such as red blood cells. The liver and spleen are responsible for breaking down old red blood cells and recycling the components, including the iron. This iron-recycling program reduces the body's reliance on dietary iron. Each day, about 85% of the iron released from hemoglobin breakdown is re-used by the body.

Our ability to absorb iron from the diet is influenced by a number of factors, including iron status, stomach acid content, the amount and type of iron in the foods we eat, and the presence of dietary factors that can either enhance or inhibit the absorption of iron. Absorption of iron is highest when our iron stores are low. Thus, people who have poor iron status, such as those with iron deficiency, pregnant women, and people who have recently experienced blood loss (including menstruation), have the highest iron absorption rates. In addition, adequate amounts of stomach acid are necessary for iron absorption. People with low levels of stomach acid, including many older adults, have a decreased ability to absorb iron.

The total amount of iron in your diet influences your absorption rate. People who consume low levels of dietary iron absorb more iron from their foods than those with higher dietary iron intakes. Our body can also detect when iron stores are high; when this occurs, less iron is absorbed from food.

The type of iron in the foods you eat is a major factor influencing your iron absorption. Two types of iron are found in foods: heme iron and non-heme iron. Heme iron is a part of hemoglobin and myoglobin and is found only in animal-based foods, such as meat, fish, and poultry. Non-heme iron is the form of iron that is not a part of hemoglobin or myoglobin. It is found in both plant-based and animal-based foods. Heme iron is much more absorbable than non-heme iron. Since the iron in animal-based foods is about 40% heme iron and 60% non-heme iron, animal-based foods are good sources of absorbable iron. Meat, fish, and poultry also contain a special **meat factor**, which enhances the absorption of non-heme iron. In contrast, all of the iron found in plant-based foods is non-heme iron, and no absorption-enhancing factor is present. However, any vitamin C (ascorbic acid) in the food itself or in an accompanying food or beverage will enhance the absorption of non-heme iron.

Dietary factors that impair iron absorption include phytates, polyphenols, vegetable proteins, and calcium. Phytates are found in legumes, rice, and whole grains. Polyphenols include tannins found in tea and coffee, and they are present in oregano and red wine. Soybean protein and calcium inhibit iron absorption. Because of the variability of iron absorption as a result of these dietary factors, it is estimated that the bioavailability of iron from a vegan diet is approximately 10%, while it averages 18% for a mixed Western diet (Institute of Medicine, 2001).

How Much Iron Should We Consume?

The variability of iron availability from food sources was taken into consideration when estimating dietary recommendations for iron, which are listed in Table 10.2.

Cooking foods in cast-iron pans significantly increases their iron content.

ferritin A storage form of iron in our body, found primarily in the intestinal mucosa, spleen, bone marrow, and liver.

hemosiderin A storage form of iron in our body, found primarily in the intestinal mucosa, spleen, bone marrow, and liver.

meat factor A special factor found in meat, fish, and poultry that enhances the absorption of non-heme iron.

TABLE 10.3 Special Circumstances Affecting Iron Status	
Circumstances That Improve Iron Status	**Circumstances That Diminish Iron Status**
• Use of oral contraceptives: use of oral contraceptives reduces menstrual blood loss in women. • Breastfeeding: breastfeeding delays resumption of menstruation in new mothers, so it reduces menstrual blood loss. It is therefore an important health measure, especially in developing nations. • Consumption of iron-containing foods and supplements.	• Use of hormone replacement therapy: use of hormone replacement therapy in postmenopausal women can cause uterine bleeding, increasing iron requirements. • Eating a vegetarian diet: vegetarian diets, particularly vegan diets, contain no sources of heme iron or meat factor. Due to the low absorbability of non-heme iron, vegetarians have iron requirements that are 1.8 times higher than those of non-vegetarians. • Intestinal parasitic infection: approximately 1 billion people suffer from intestinal parasitic infection. Many of these parasites cause intestinal bleeding and occur in countries in which iron intakes are inadequate. Iron-deficiency anemia is common in people with intestinal parasitic infection. • Blood donation: blood donors have lower iron stores than non-donors; people who donate frequently, particularly premenopausal women, may require iron supplementation to counter the iron losses that occur with blood donation. • Intense endurance exercise training: people engaging in intense endurance exercise appear to be at risk for poor iron status due to many factors, including suboptimal iron intake and increased iron loss in sweat and increased fecal losses.

Data from *Dietary Reference Intakes for Vitamin A, Vitamin K, Arsenic, Boron, Chromium, Copper, Iodine, Manganese, Molybdenum, Nickel, Silicon, Vanadium, and Zinc,* © 2002 by the National Academy of Sciences. Reprinted by permission.

Notice that the higher iron requirement for younger women is due to the excess iron and blood lost during menstruation.

A number of special circumstances can significantly affect iron requirements. These are identified in **Table 10.3**.

Finding Iron-Rich Foods

Good food sources of heme iron are meats, poultry, and fish **(Figure 10.16)**. Clams, oysters, and beef liver are particularly good sources. Many breakfast cereals and breads are enriched with iron; although this iron is the non-heme type and less absorbable, it is still significant because these foods are a major part of the North American diet. Some vegetables and legumes are also good sources of iron, and the absorption of their non-heme iron can be enhanced by eating them with even a small amount of meat, fish, or poultry, or with vitamin C–rich foods, such as citrus foods, red and green peppers, and broccoli.

Another way to increase your iron intake is to make smart menu choices throughout the day. The Eating Right All Day feature (page 348) shows menu choices high in iron. Some of these choices provide heme iron, whereas others are combination foods. For instance, the orange juice helps improve the absorption of the non-heme iron in the enriched bread. And see the Quick Tips on page 347 for other iron food sources.

What Happens If We Consume Too Much Iron?

Accidental iron overdose is the most common cause of poisoning deaths in children younger than six years of age in the United States (U.S. FDA, 1997). (No comparable data for Canada could be found.) It is important for parents to take the same precautions with dietary supplements as they would with other drugs, keeping them in a locked cabinet or well out of reach of children. Symptoms of iron toxicity include nausea, vomiting, diarrhea, dizziness, confusion, and rapid heartbeat. If iron toxicity

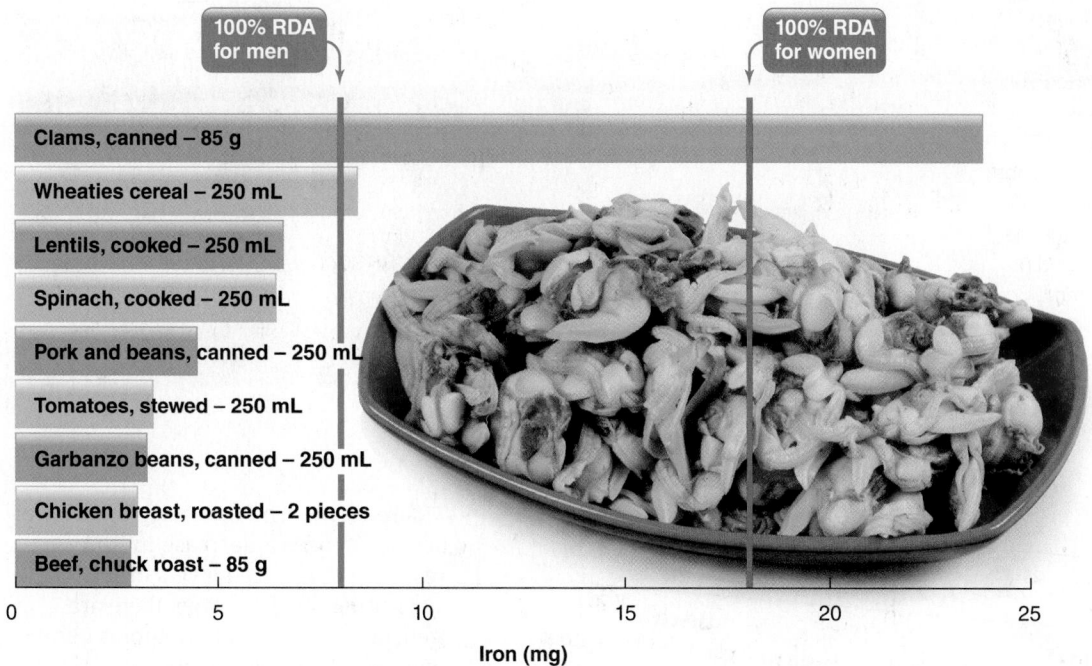

Figure 10.16 Common food sources of iron. The RDA for iron is 8 mg/day for men and 18 mg/day for women aged 19 to 50 years.

Data from U.S. Department of Agriculture, Agricultural Research Service, 2009, USDA Nutrient Database for Standard Reference, Release 22. Nutrient Data Laboratory Home Page, www.ars.usda.gov/ba/bhnrc/ndl.

is not treated quickly, significant damage to the heart, central nervous system, liver, and kidneys can result in death.

Adults who take iron supplements even at prescribed doses commonly experience constipation. Taking vitamin C with the iron supplement not only enhances absorption but also can help reduce constipation. Other gastrointestinal symptoms include nausea, vomiting, and diarrhea. As introduced in Chapter 8, some individuals suffer from a hereditary disorder called hemochromatosis. This disorder affects between 1 in 200 and 1 in 400 individuals of northern European descent (Bacon et al., 1999). Hemochromatosis is characterized by excessive absorption of dietary iron and altered iron storage. The accumulation of iron in these individuals over many years causes cirrhosis of the liver, liver cancer, heart attack and heart failure, diabetes, and arthritis. Men are more at risk for this disease than women due to the higher losses of iron in women through menstruation. Treatment includes reducing dietary intake of iron, avoiding high intakes of vitamin C, and withdrawing blood occasionally.

What Happens If We Don't Consume Enough Iron?

Iron deficiency is the most common nutrient deficiency in the world. People at particularly high risk for iron deficiency include infants and young children, adolescent girls, premenopausal women, and pregnant women.

Iron deficiency progresses through three stages

QUICK TIPS

Increasing Your Iron Intake

- Shop for iron-fortified breads and breakfast cereals. Check the Nutrition Facts table!
- Consume a food or beverage that is high in vitamin C along with plant or animal sources of iron. For instance, drink a glass of orange juice with your morning toast to increase the absorption of the non-heme iron in the bread. Or add chopped tomatoes to beans or lentils. Or sprinkle lemon juice on fish.
- Add small amounts of meat, poultry, or fish to baked beans, vegetable soups, stir-fried vegetables, or salads to enhance the absorption of the non-heme iron in the plant-based foods.
- Cook foods in cast-iron pans to significantly increase the iron content of foods: the iron in the pan will be absorbed into the food during the cooking process.
- Avoid drinking red wine, coffee, or tea when eating iron-rich foods, as the polyphenols in these beverages will reduce iron absorption.
- Avoid drinking cow's milk or soy milk with iron-rich foods, as both calcium and soybean protein inhibit iron absorption.
- Avoid taking calcium supplements or zinc supplements with iron-rich foods, as these minerals decrease iron absorption.

▶ **Figure 10.17** Iron deficiency passes through three stages. The first stage is identified by decreased iron stores, or reduced ferritin levels. The second stage is identified by decreased iron transport, or a reduction in transferrin. The final stage of iron deficiency is iron-deficiency anemia, which is identified by decreased production of normal, healthy red blood cells and inadequate hemoglobin levels.

Stage I, iron depletion

- Decreased iron stores
- Reduced ferritin level
- No physical symptoms

Stage II, iron-deficiency erythropoiesis

- Decreased iron transport
- Reduced transferrin
- Reduced production of heme
- Physical symptoms include reduced work capacity

Stage III, iron-deficiency anemia

- Decreased production of normal red blood cells
- Reduced production of heme
- Inadequate hemoglobin to transport oxygen
- Symptoms include pale skin, fatigue, reduced work performance, impaired immune and cognitive functions

Eating Right All Day

Breakfast
Whole-grain iron-fortified toast with orange juice instead of white toast with coffee!

Lunch
Pasta with clams and tomatoes instead of mac & cheese!

Dinner
Beef stew with vegetables instead of a burger with fries!

Snack
Low-cal nutrition bar instead of a chocolate bar!

(Figure 10.17). The first stage of iron deficiency causes a decrease in iron *stores*, resulting in reduced levels of ferritin.

During this first stage, there are generally no physical symptoms because hemoglobin levels are not yet affected. The second stage of iron deficiency causes a decrease in the *transport* of iron. This manifests as a reduction in the transport protein for iron, called **transferrin**. The production of heme also starts to decline during this stage, leading to symptoms of reduced work capacity. During the third and final stage of iron deficiency, **iron-deficiency anemia** results.

In iron-deficiency anemia, the production of normal, healthy red blood cells decreases. Red blood cells that are produced are smaller than normal and do not contain enough hemoglobin to transport adequate oxygen or to allow the proper transfer of electrons to produce energy. This type of anemia is often referred to as *microcytic anemia* (*micro*, meaning "small," and *cyte*, meaning "cell"). As normal cellular death occurs over time, more and more healthy red blood cells are replaced by these deficient cells, and the classic symptoms of oxygen and energy deprivation develop. These symptoms include impaired work performance, general fatigue, pale skin, depressed immune function, impaired cognitive and nerve function, and impaired memory. Pregnant women with severe anemia are at higher risk for low-birth-weight infants, premature delivery, and increased infant mortality.

transferrin The transport protein for iron.

iron-deficiency anemia A form of anemia that results from severe iron deficiency.

RECAP Iron is a trace mineral that, as part of the hemoglobin protein, plays a major role in the transportation of oxygen in our blood. Iron is also a coenzyme in many metabolic pathways involved in energy production. Meat, fish, and poultry are good sources of heme iron, which is more absorbable than non-heme iron. Toxicity symptoms for iron range from nausea and vomiting to organ damage and potentially death. If left untreated, iron deficiency eventually leads to iron-deficiency anemia.

Zinc

Zinc is a trace mineral that acts as a cofactor for approximately a hundred different enzymes. It thereby plays an important role in many physiologic processes in nearly every body system.

Functions of Zinc

As a cofactor, zinc assists in the production of hemoglobin, indirectly supporting the adequate transport of oxygen to our cells. Zinc is also part of the superoxide dismutase antioxidant enzyme system and thus helps fight the oxidative damage caused by free radicals. It assists enzymes in generating energy from carbohydrates, fats, and protein and in activating vitamin A in the retina of the eye.

Zinc also plays a role in facilitating the folding of proteins into biologically active molecules used in gene regulation. Thus, it is critical for cell replication and normal growth. In fact, zinc deficiency was discovered in the early 1960s, when researchers were trying to determine the cause of severe growth retardation, anemia, and poorly developed testicles in a group of Middle Eastern men. These symptoms of zinc deficiency illustrate its critical role in normal growth and sexual maturation (see **Figure 10.18**).

Zinc is vital for the proper development and functioning of the immune system. In fact, zinc has received so much attention for its contribution to immune system health that zinc lozenges have been formulated to fight the common cold. The Nutrition Debate at the end of this chapter explores the question of whether or not these lozenges are effective.

◆ **Figure 10.18** Growth retardation due to zinc deficiency. The boy on the right is 17 years old but is only four feet tall; his genitalia are like those of a six-year-old.

How Much Zinc Should We Consume?

As with iron, our need for zinc is relatively small, but our intakes are variable and absorption is influenced by a number of factors. Overall, zinc absorption is similar to that of iron, ranging from 10% to 35% of dietary zinc. People with poor zinc status absorb more zinc than individuals with optimal zinc status, and zinc absorption increases during times of growth, sexual development, and pregnancy.

Several dietary factors influence zinc absorption. High non-heme iron intakes can inhibit zinc absorption, which is a primary concern with iron supplements (which are non-heme), particularly during pregnancy and lactation. High intakes of heme iron appear to have no effect on zinc absorption. The phytates and fibre found in whole grains and beans strongly inhibit zinc absorption. In contrast, dietary protein, especially animal-based protein, enhances zinc absorption. It is not surprising, then, that the primary cause of the zinc deficiency in the Middle Eastern men just mentioned was their low consumption of meat and high consumption of beans and unleavened breads (also called *flat breads*). In leavening bread, the baker adds yeast to the dough. This not only makes the bread rise but also helps reduce the phytate content of the bread.

The recommended intakes for zinc are listed in Table 10.2. Good food sources of zinc include red meats, some seafood, whole grains, and enriched grains and cereals. The dark meat of poultry has a higher content of zinc than white meat. As zinc is significantly more absorbable from animal-based foods, zinc deficiency is a concern for people eating a vegan diet. **Figure 10.19** shows various foods that are relatively high in zinc.

◆ Zinc can be found in pork and beans.

What Happens If We Consume Too Much Zinc?

Eating high amounts of dietary zinc does not appear to lead to toxicity. Zinc toxicity can occur from consuming zinc in supplement form and in fortified foods. Toxicity symptoms include intestinal pain and cramps, nausea, vomiting, loss of appetite,

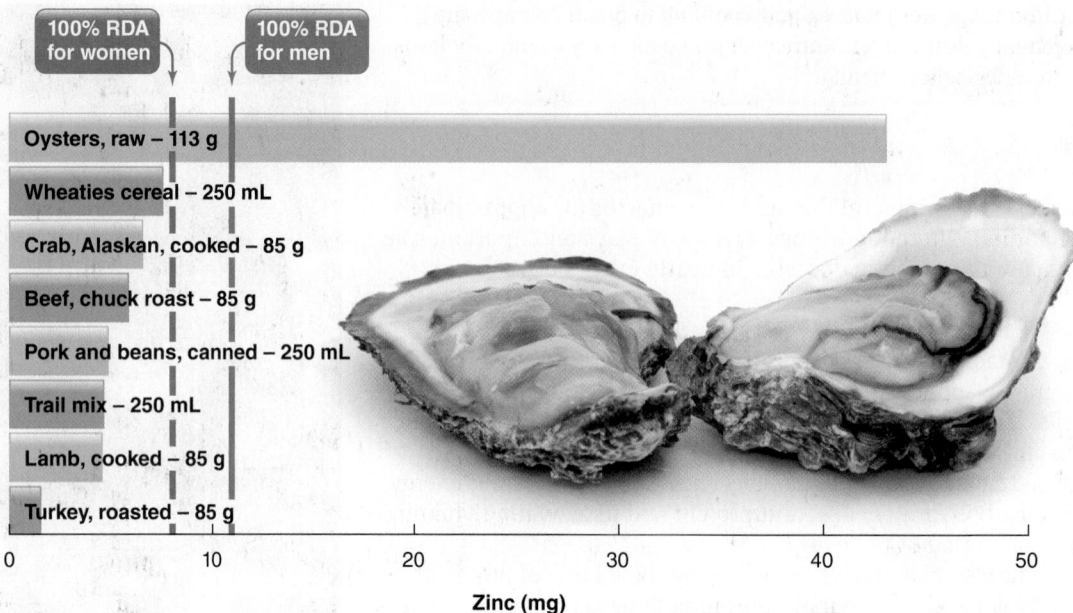

🔷 **Figure 10.19** Common food sources of zinc. The RDA for zinc is 11 mg/day for men and 8 mg/day for women.

Data from U.S. Department of Agriculture, Agricultural Research Service, 2009, USDA Nutrient Database for Standard Reference, Release 22. Nutrient Data Laboratory Home Page, www.ars.usda.gov/ba/bhnrc/ndl.

diarrhea, and headaches. Excessive zinc supplementation has also been shown to depress immune function and decrease high-density lipoprotein concentrations. High intakes of zinc can also reduce copper status, as zinc absorption interferes with the absorption of copper.

What Happens If We Don't Consume Enough Zinc?

Zinc deficiency is uncommon in North America but occurs more often in countries in which people consume predominantly grain-based foods. Symptoms of zinc deficiency include growth retardation, diarrhea, delayed sexual maturation and impotence, eye and skin lesions, hair loss, and impaired appetite. As zinc is critical to a healthy immune system, zinc deficiency also results in increased incidence of infections and illnesses.

Copper

Copper is a trace mineral that functions as a cofactor in many physiologic reactions. It functions as a cofactor in the metabolic pathways that produce energy, in the production of the connective tissues collagen and elastin, and as part of the superoxide dismutase enzyme system that fights the damage caused by free radicals. Copper is a component of *ceruloplasmin*, a protein that is critical for the proper transport of iron. If ceruloplasmin levels are inadequate, iron accumulation results, causing symptoms similar to those described with the genetic disorder hemochromatosis (page 347). Copper is also necessary for the regulation of certain neurotransmitters important to brain function.

As you can see in Table 10.2, our need for copper is small. Copper is widely distributed in foods, and people who eat a varied diet can easily meet their requirements. Good food sources of copper include organ meats, seafood, nuts, and seeds. Whole-grain foods are also relatively good sources. **Figure 10.20** identifies some foods relatively high in copper.

As we saw with iron and zinc, people with low dietary copper intakes absorb more copper than people with high dietary intakes. Also recall that high zinc intakes can reduce copper absorption and, subsequently, copper status. In fact, zinc supplementation is used to treat a rare disorder called Wilson's disease, in which copper toxicity occurs. High iron intakes can also interfere with copper absorption in infants.

🔷 Lobster is a food that contains copper.

100% RDA for
men and women

Oysters, fried – 85 g

Lobster, cooked – 85 g

Mushrooms, shiitake, cooked – 250 mL

Trail mix – 250 mL

Pork and beans, canned – 250 mL

Cashews, dry roasted – 28 g

Garbanzo beans, canned – 250 mL

Potato, baked, with skin – 1 small

Spinach, cooked – 250 mL

| 0 | 0.5 | 1.0 | 1.5 | 2.0 | 2.5 | 3.0 | 3.5 | 4.0 |

Copper (mg)

Figure 10.20 Common food sources of copper. The RDA for copper is 900 µg/day for men and women.
Data from U.S. Department of Agriculture, Agricultural Research Service, 2009, USDA Nutrient Database for Standard Reference, Release 22. Nutrient Data Laboratory Home Page, www.ars.usda.gov/ba/bhnrc/ndl.

The long-term effects of copper toxicity are not well studied in humans. Toxicity symptoms include abdominal pain and cramps, nausea, diarrhea, and vomiting. Liver damage occurs in the extreme cases of copper toxicity that occur with Wilson's disease and other health conditions associated with excessive copper levels.

Copper deficiency is rare but can occur in premature infants fed milk-based formulas and in adults fed prolonged formulated diets that are deficient in copper. Deficiency symptoms include anemia, reduced levels of white blood cells, and osteoporosis in infants and growing children.

RECAP Zinc is a trace mineral that is a part of almost a hundred enzymes that impact virtually every body system. It plays a critical role in hemoglobin synthesis, physical growth and sexual maturation, and immune function and assists in fighting oxidative damage. Copper is a trace mineral that functions as a cofactor in the metabolic pathways that produce energy, in the production of connective tissues, and as part of an antioxidant enzyme system. It is also a component of ceruloplasmin, a protein that is critical for the transport of iron.

Nutrition DEBATE

Do Zinc Lozenges Help Fight the Common Cold?

Approximately 1 billion colds occur in the United States each year (NIH, 2007); unfortunately we do not have data for Canada. Children suffer from six to ten colds each year, and adults average two to four. Although colds are typically benign, they result in significant absenteeism from work and cause discomfort and stress. Finding a cure for the common cold has been at the forefront of modern medicine for many years. It is estimated that more than 200 different viruses can cause a cold. Because of this variety, developing vaccines or other preventive measures for colds is extremely challenging.

The role of zinc in the health of our immune system is well known, but zinc has also been shown to inhibit the replication of some of the viruses that cause the common cold. These findings have led to speculation that taking zinc supplements may reduce the length and severity of colds (Jackson, Lesho, and Peterson, 2000; Prasad, 1996). Zinc lozenges were formulated as a means of providing potential relief from cold symptoms. These lozenges are readily found in a variety of formulations and dosages in most drugstores.

Does taking zinc in lozenge form actually reduce the length and severity of a cold? During the past 20 years, numerous research studies have been conducted to try to answer this question. Unfortunately, the results of these studies are inconclusive: about half have found that zinc lozenges do reduce the length and severity of a cold, whereas about half have found that zinc lozenges have no effect on cold symptoms or duration (Caruso, Prober, and Gwaltney, 2007). Some reasons that researchers have proposed to explain these different findings include the following:

- Researchers are unable to truly "blind" participants to the treatment. Because zinc lozenges have a unique taste, it may be difficult to keep the research participants uninformed about whether they are getting zinc lozenges or a placebo. Knowing what they are taking could lead participants to report biased results.
- Self-reported symptoms are subject to inaccuracy. Many studies had the research participants self-report changes in symptoms. Such self-reports may be inaccurate and influenced by emotional factors.
- A wide variety of viruses can cause a cold. We noted that more than 200 different viruses can cause a cold, and it is highly unlikely that zinc can combat all of these. It is possible that people who do not respond favourably to zinc lozenges are suffering from a cold virus that cannot be treated with zinc.
- Zinc dosages and formulations differ. The dosages of zinc consumed, the timing of consumption, and the formulation of the lozenge used differed across studies. For example, it is estimated that, for zinc to be effective, at least 80 mg of zinc should be consumed each day and that people should begin using zinc lozenges within 48 hours of the onset of cold symptoms, yet the studies followed a variety of dosing and timing protocols. Also, different sweeteners and flavourings found in different zinc-lozenge formulations may bind the zinc and inhibit its ability to be absorbed into the body, limiting its effectiveness.
- Supplements may provide excessive zinc and actually impair immune function! The level of zinc noted earlier as the effective dose—80 mg/day—is nearly ten times the RDA and can decrease the absorption of copper and iron if continued for long periods of time. In addition,

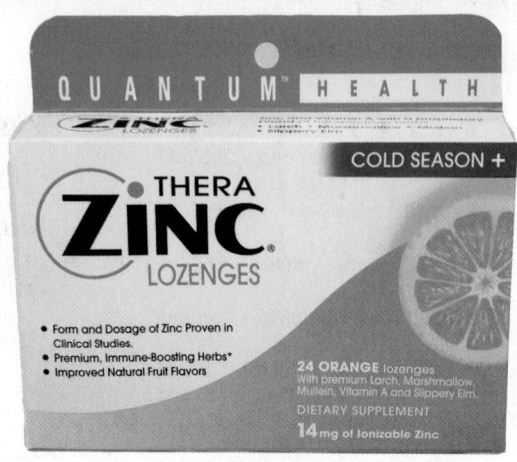

⬅ Zinc lozenges come in different formulations and dosages.

one experimental study showed that 300 mg/day of supplemental zinc *reduced* immune cell response and *decreased* destruction of bacteria (Chandra, 1984). This amount is about six tablets of a zinc gluconate pill that has 50 mg of elemental zinc.

- Measuring the compliance of test participants can be difficult. Typically, participants need to take one zinc lozenge every 2 to 3 hours while they are awake for the duration of the study, which can last 6 to 10 days. Unless the participants are monitored by research staff, researchers have to rely on the participants to self-report their compliance to the study protocol. Of course, different compliance rates can alter the outcomes of different studies.

In short, there is no conclusive evidence supporting or refuting the effectiveness of zinc lozenges in treating the common cold.

One word of caution: if you decide to use zinc lozenges, more is not better. Excessive or prolonged zinc supplementation can reduce immune function and cause other mineral imbalances. Check the label of the product you are using, and do not exceed its recommended dosage or duration of use.

Chapter Review

Test Yourself ANSWERS

1. False. B vitamins do not directly provide energy for our body. However, they play critical roles in ensuring that our body is able to generate energy from carbohydrates, fats, and proteins.

2. True. People who consume a vegan diet need to pay particularly close attention to consuming enough vitamin B$_{12}$,

iron, and zinc. In some cases, these individuals may need to take supplements to consume adequate amounts of these nutrients.

3. True. This deficiency is particularly common in infants, children, and women of childbearing age.

Find the Quack

Like many college students, Dionna maintains a full course load and works part-time. She also participates in aerobics and yoga classes four afternoons a week, is a member of her college math and chess clubs, and spends Saturday mornings volunteering at a local food bank. With so much going on in her life, she's had to stay up way past midnight almost every night for the past few weeks to finish homework assignments and study for exams. Coming out of aerobics class yesterday, she collapsed onto the bench in the locker room, feeling utterly exhausted. Her friend Addie asked what was wrong and, when Dionna explained, gave her a hug and opened her gym bag. "Here," she said, handing Dionna a bottle of supplements. The label said *Fatigue-Fighting Formula for Women*, and the ingredients list indicated that the supplement provided 100% of the Daily Value for all eight B vitamins, as well as iron, selenium, chromium, and manganese. "Start taking one of these every day, like I do, and you'll have all the energy you need!"

Dionna took a swig from her water bottle and swallowed a tablet. Then she read the back of the supplement label. It said:

- "If you experience fatigue, muscle weakness, difficulty concentrating, or depression, you may have a deficiency of the vitamins and minerals important in maintaining an adequate level of energy."

- "One tablet a day of *Fatigue-Fighting Formula for Women* may help restore your natural vitality."

- "Our average customer rating for this product is five stars! A typical satisfied customer: 'I used to feel so exhausted that I could barely drag myself through the days. *Fatigue-Fighting Formula for Women* has given me energy to spare!' —Tasha from Santa Monica."

Dionna asked her friend how much a bottle of the supplement—which included 60 tablets, or a two-month supply—cost. Addie said that she ordered them online for $23.99 and would be placing another order soon. "Want me to get a bottle for you?"

1. Read carefully the first two bulleted statements from the back of the supplement label. Do these assertions strike you as reasonable, exaggerated, misleading, or entirely false? Explain your answer.

2. What, if any, health concerns might the level of vitamins and minerals in this supplement raise?

3. Tasha from Santa Monica states that the supplement "has given me energy to spare." Comment on the implication of her statement that the micronutrients it provides give us energy.

4. Should Dionna have Addie order a bottle of the supplements for her? Why or why not?

Answers can be found in the study area of MasteringNutrition.

 **NutriTools**

Visit MasteringNutrition to access interactive animations including:

- Nutrient Functionality
- Metabolism: General Terms

Review Questions

1. The B vitamins include
   a. niacin, folate, and iodine.
   b. cobalamin, iodine, and chromium.
   c. manganese, riboflavin, and pyridoxine.
   d. thiamin, pantothenic acid, and biotin.

2. The micronutrient most closely associated with blood clotting is
   a. iron.
   b. vitamin K.
   c. zinc.
   d. vitamin B_{12}.

3. Which of the following statements about iron is true?
   a. Iron is stored primarily in the liver, the blood vessel walls, and the heart muscle.
   b. Iron is a component of hemoglobin, myoglobin, and certain enzymes.
   c. Iron is a component of red blood cells, platelets, and plasma.
   d. Excess iron is stored primarily in the form of ferritin, cytochromes, and intrinsic factor.

4. Homocysteine is
   a. a by-product of glycolysis.
   b. a trace mineral.
   c. an amino acid.
   d. a B vitamin.

5. Which of the following statements about choline is true?
   a. Choline is found exclusively in foods of animal origin.
   b. Choline is a B vitamin that assists in homocysteine metabolism.
   c. Choline is a neurotransmitter that is involved in muscle movement and memory storage.
   d. Choline is necessary for the synthesis of phospholipids and other components of cell membranes.

6. Which of the following is not a component of blood?
   a. Erythrocyte
   b. Leukocytes
   c. Biotin
   d. Plasma

7. Which trace mineral has no DRI, UL, or RDA?
   a. Sulphur
   b. Manganese
   c. Iodine
   d. Choline

8. Pernicious anemia is the primary effect of
   a. an iron deficiency.
   b. a zinc deficiency.
   c. a folate deficiency.
   d. a B_{12} deficiency.

9. Jackie was thrilled about her first pregnancy and was eager to share the news to her friends. As they chattered excitedly, they told her about seeing advice about folate supplements. Unfortunately, none of them were familiar with the details so Jackie consulted her health-care provider about it. What foods are good sources of folate? When should Jackie start taking folate supplements? Why is folate recommended for young women?

10. Copper toxicity may lead to
    a. beriberi.
    b. Wilson's disease.
    c. pellagra.
    d. cretinism.

11. In the chapter-opening story, Mr. Katz was given an injection of vitamin B_{12}. Why didn't his physician simply give him the vitamin in pill form?

12. Cassandra is 11 years old and has just begun menstruating. She and her family members are vegans (that is, they consume only plant-based foods). Explain why Cassandra's parents should be careful that their daughter consumes not only adequate iron but also adequate vitamin C.

13. Create a simple flow chart showing how loss of intrinsic factor in an older adult can lead to symptoms of dementia.

14. Avery is a lacto-ovo-vegetarian. His typical daily diet includes milk, yogurt, cheese, eggs, nuts, seeds, legumes, whole grains, and a wide variety of fruits and vegetables. He does not take any supplements. What, if any, micronutrients are likely to be inadequate in his diet?

15. Janine is 23 years old and engaged to be married. She is 18.2 kg (40 lb.) overweight, has hypertension, and her mother suffered a mild stroke recently, at age 45. For all these reasons, Janine is highly motivated to lose weight and has put herself on a strict low-carbohydrate diet recommended by a friend. She now scrupulously avoids breads, pastries, pasta, rice, and "starchy" fruits and vegetables. Identify two reasons why Janine should consider taking a folate supplement.

16. It has been three months since Eli's wife, Monica, lost her job. As they live in a small town in New Brunswick, the job market is tight and Monica feels hopeless. Eli is growing more concerned every day because his wife doesn't get out of bed, seems disoriented and confused, and constantly cries. Once an avid hockey player, Monica no longer skates or even goes outside. She claims that she is too tired to even get up and have dinner. After hearing that B vitamins increase your energy, Eli immediately goes to the nearest health food store and grabs every B vitamin supplement he can get his hands on. Is this claim that B vitamins increase energy true? After learning about Monica's situation, do you think that taking a B vitamin supplement would help? Why or why not? Does her situation give rise to any other concerns? What additional advice might you give her?

Case Study

During class, the topic of vitamin and mineral supplements comes up. Your teacher asks the students if anyone takes multivitamin and mineral supplements, and many volunteer to explain why they have chosen to take these supplements. Chantal swears by her vitamins to help her lose weight, and Jamal claims that his multivitamin and mineral supplement gives him more energy and focus. Li-Mei claims to take a supplement "just for insurance," and Muna simply says that for as long as she can remember, she's always taken a multivitamin and mineral capsule at breakfast, so she continues to do so because it's a habit.

All those who responded are healthy university students. Would you suggest that they all continue taking a supplement? Are the claims that the multivitamin and mineral supplements help reduce weight and enhance energy correct? Where do you think these students got their ideas, and what source of information would you suggest they turn to when seeking facts about multivitamin and mineral supplements?

Answers to Review Questions can be found at the back of this text.

Web Resources

www.ars.usda.gov
Nutrient Data Laboratory Home Page

Click on Search to find reports listing food sources for selected nutrients.

www.anemia.com
Anemia Lifeline

Visit this site to learn about anemia and its various treatments.

www.unicef.org/nutrition
UNICEF—Nutrition

This site provides information about micronutrient deficiencies in developing countries and the efforts to combat them.

www.thearc.org
The Arc

Search this site for "neural tube defects" and find a wealth of information on the development and prevention of these conditions.

MasteringNutrition®

Assignments

Animations Glycolysis • Cori Cycle • The Energy Currency: ATP • Vitamin B_{12} Absorption
Activities NutriTools

Study Area

Videos: Understanding Metabolism; Introduction to the Functional Approach & Understanding Energy Metabolism; Using the Functional Approach to Understand Blood Health & Immunity • Practice Tests • Diet Analysis • eText

Dietary Supplements: Necessity or Waste?

WANT TO FIND OUT...

- **if dietary supplements are as tightly regulated as drugs?**

- **how to spot a fraudulent supplement?**

- **whether or not you should take a multivitamin-mineral supplement?**

READ ON.
Marcus has type 2 diabetes and high blood pressure and is worried about his health. He attended a nutrition seminar in which the health benefits of various dietary supplements were touted. After attending this seminar, Marcus was convinced that he needed to take a supplement providing 200%–800% of the Daily Value for many vitamins and minerals, as well as an herbal preparation for "heart health." After a few months of taking these supplements on a daily basis, Marcus started to experience headaches, nausea, diarrhea, and tingling

Marcus was not an expert in nutrition, he suspected that he might be experiencing side effects related to nutrient toxicity. He decided to talk to his doctor about the supplements he was taking to determine whether they could be causing his symptoms.

Marcus's story is not unique. According to Health Canada (2012), in 2010 73% of Canadians have used products like vitamins and minerals, herbal products, and homeopathic medicines. A review of U.S. national opinion surveys found that a significant number of Americans regularly take dietary supplements, but they do not report the use of these products to their physicians because they feel their physicians have little knowledge of these products and may harbour a bias against their use (Blendon et al., 2001). Interestingly, many supplement users state that they would continue to use these products even if scientific studies found them to be ineffective!

Why do so many people take dietary supplements? Many people believe they cannot consume adequate nutrients in their diet, and they take a supplement as extra nutritional insurance. Others have been advised by their healthcare provider to take a supplement to address a given health concern. There are people, like Marcus, who believe that they can use certain supplements to treat their disease. Others use supplements in the hope that they will enhance their appearance or athletic performance.

*It's Your Health – Safe Use of Natural Health Products. Health Canada, 2004. Reproduced with the permission from the Minister of Health, 2012.

Are such uses wise? A waste of money? Dangerous? Who *should* be taking supplements? Here, we explore *In Depth* the answers to these questions and more.

What Are Natural Health Products?

In Canada, dietary supplements are part of a wider category of products called natural health products. According to Health Canada (2011a), "Natural health products (NHPs) are naturally occurring substances that are used to restore or maintain good health. They are often made from plants, but can also be made from animals, microorganisms, and marine sources. They come in a wide variety of forms like tablets, capsules, tinctures, solutions, creams, ointments and drops."

These include products often called "complementary" or "alternative" medicines, such as herbal remedies (see Figure 1), and products such as vitamins, minerals, probiotics, amino acids, essential fatty acids, and even certain toothpastes, antiperspirants, shampoos, and mouthwashes (Health Canada, 2011a).

How Are Natural Health Products Regulated?

In Canada, the Natural Health Products Directorate is responsible for regulating the sale of dietary supplements. As of 2004, Canadian regulations were changed to introduce and define natural health products as vitamins and minerals, herbal remedies, homeopathic medicines, traditional medicines such as traditional Chinese medicines, probiotics, and other products like amino acids and essential fatty acids (Health Canada, 2012)*. This was done to increase the safety of these products. Natural health products do not require a prescription, and are not regulated as drugs. Licensed natural

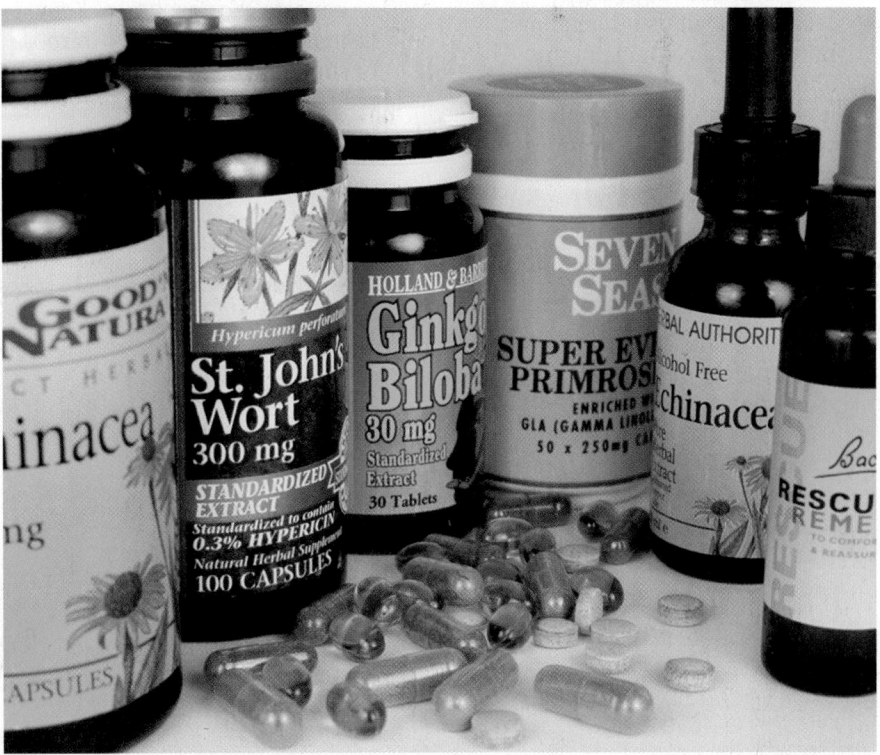

Figure 1 Dietary supplements can be pills, capsules, powders, or liquids and contain micronutrients, amino acids, herbs, or other substances.

health products have a natural product number (NPN) or a homeopathic medicine number (DIN-HM) on the label, followed by an eight-digit number (Health Canada, 2009).

Under these regulations, Health Canada evaluates the safety and effectiveness of products before approving them for sale as natural health products. The type and amount of evidence required is gauged based on the potential risk of the product. Types of evidence include "clinical trial data or references to published studies, journals, pharmacopoeias, and traditional resources" (Health Canada, 2011b). Manufacturers, packagers, labellers, and importers of NHPs are required to have a site license to ensure safety standards.

Health Canada's (2011b) website states that "All NHPs must meet specific labelling requirements, to help you make safe and informed choices about the NHPs you choose to use. Information required on NHP labels includes:

- product name
- product license number
- quantity of product in the bottle
- complete list of medicinal and non-medicinal ingredients
- recommended use (including purpose or health claim, route of administration and dose)
- any cautionary statements, warnings, contra-indications

and possible adverse reactions associated with the product

- any special storage conditions

How Can You Avoid Fraudulent or Dangerous Supplements?

Although many of the supplement products sold today are safe, some are not. In addition, some companies are less than forthright about the true content of ingredients in their supplements. How can you avoid purchasing fraudulent or dangerous supplements? See Quick Tips below.

Many supplements are also sold over the internet. Researchers suggest six criteria that can be used to evaluate dietary supplement websites (Dancho and Manore, 2001) Keep these criteria in mind each time you consider buying a dietary supplement over the Web:

1. What is the purpose of the website? Is it trying to sell a product or educate the consumer? Keep in mind that the primary purpose of supplement companies is to make money. Look for sites that provide educational information

about a specific nutrient or product and that do not just focus on selling the products.

2. Does the site contain accurate information? Accuracy of the information on the website is the most difficult thing for a consumer to determine. Testimonials are *not* reliable and accurate; claims supported by scientific research are most desirable. If what the company claims about its product sounds too good to be true, it probably is.

3. Does the site contain reputable references? References should be from articles published in peer-reviewed scientific journals. References should be complete and contain author names, article title, journal title, date, volume, and page numbers. This information allows the consumer to check original research for the validity of a company's claims about its product. Be cautious of sites that refer to claims that are "proven by research studies" but fail to provide a complete reference.

4. Who owns or sponsors the site? Full disclosure regarding sponsorship and possible sources of bias or conflict of interest should be included in the site's information.

5. Who wrote the information? Websites should clearly identify the

---

Vitamin C

"A factor in the maintenance of good health"

90 capsules

NPN 12345678

Figure 2 A licensed natural health product label showing the natural product number (NPN).

QUICK TIPS

Reducing Your Risk when Using Natural Health Products (Health Canada, 2006)*

▸ Tell your doctor what you are taking and why.
▸ Use products that are approved. Look for a DIN, NPN or DIN-HM on the label.
▸ Be sceptical about health-related claims for potentially serious conditions. Consult

your doctor about the appropriate use of these products. Do not rely on company advertisements or package information.
▸ Be aware of any reaction or interactions with other drugs you are taking. Report any adverse reaction to your doctor.
▸ Consult your health care provider before giving a natural health product to a child.
▸ Consult your health care provider before taking a health product if you are pregnant or breastfeeding, are a senior, have been diagnosed with a serious disease or significant medical condition, or are scheduled for an operation.

*Health Canada, 2012. Reproduced with the permission from the Minister of Health, 2012.

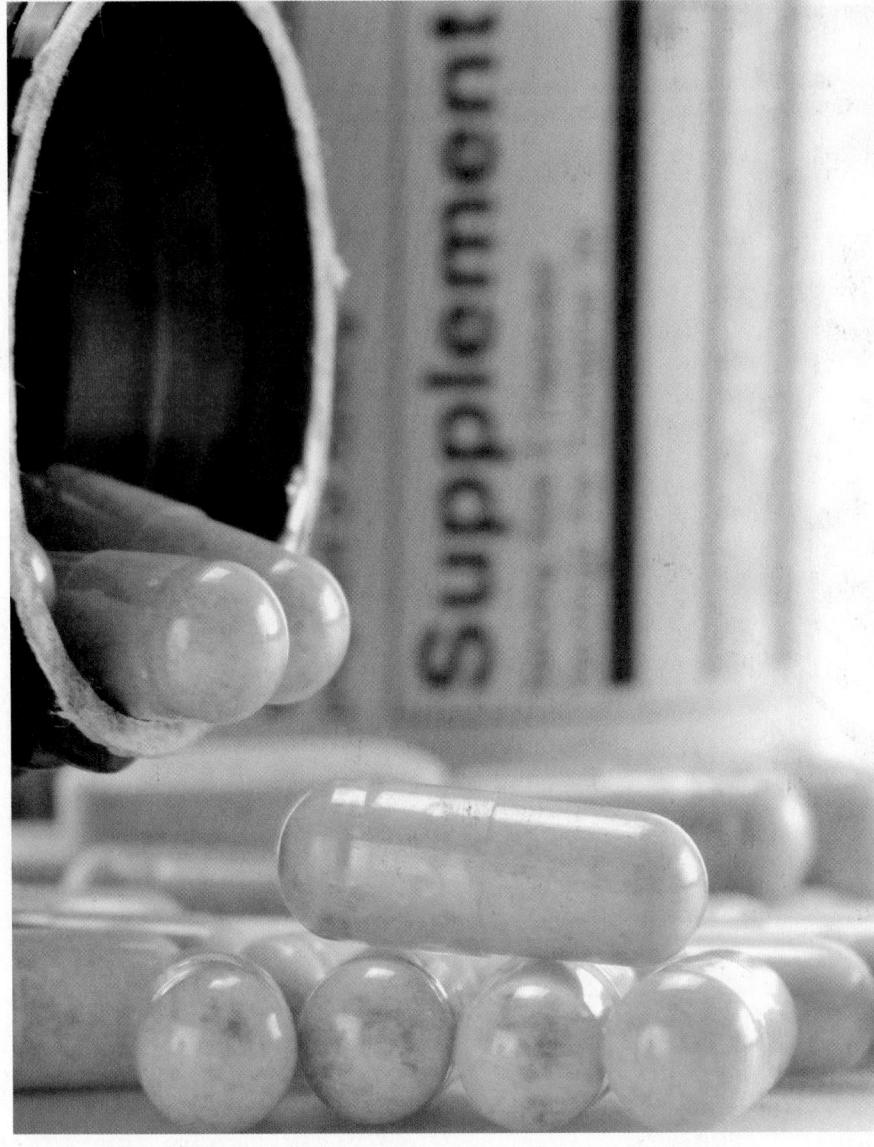

⬆ Always research a dietary supplement and its manufacturer before taking it.

echinacea, lavender, and many other herbs have been used by different cultures throughout the world for centuries to promote health and treat discomfort and disease. The National Center for Complementary and Alternative Medicine (NCCAM, 2004) defines an **herb** (also called a *botanical*) as a plant or plant part used for its scent, flavour, and/or therapeutic properties. As you would suspect, with a definition this broad there are hundreds of different herbs on the market.

It is clear that some herbs are effective medicines, but for what disorders, in what forms, and at what dosages? And are some herbs promoted as medicines ineffective, or even dangerous? To answer these questions about herbs you might be considering, NCCAM evaluates dozens of the most commonly used herbs in "Herbs at a Glance" fact sheets, available at its website (see the Web Resources at the end of this chapter). In addition, NCCAM recommends that you practice the Quick Tips listed earlier for all types of dietary supplements, as well as the following precautions, which are specific to the use of herbs.

The most essential of these precautions is to consult your healthcare provider before using any herbal supplement. Herbs can act the same way as drugs; therefore, they can cause medical problems if not used correctly or if taken in large amounts. In some cases, people have experienced negative effects even though they followed the instructions on a supplement label. It is especially important to check with your healthcare provider if you are taking any prescription medications. Some herbal supplements are known to interact with medications in ways that cause health problems.

author of the article and include the credentials of the author. Recognized experts include individuals with relevant health-related credentials, such as RD, PhD, MD, or MSc. Keep in mind that this person is responsible for the information posted in the article but may not be the creator of the website.

6. Is the information current and updated regularly? As information about supplements changes regularly, websites should be updated regularly, and the date should be clearly posted. All websites should also include contact information to allow consumers to ask questions about the information posted.

Are There Special Precautions for Herbal Supplements?

A common saying in India cautions that "A house without ginger is a sick house." Indeed, ginger,

herb A plant or plant part used for its scent, flavour, and/or therapeutic properties (also called a botanical).

⬥ Echinacea, commonly known as purple coneflower, has been used for centuries to prevent colds, flu, and other infections.

It is critical to avoid using herbs if you are pregnant or nursing, unless your physician has approved their use. Some can promote miscarriage or birth defects or can enter breast milk. This caution also applies to treating children with herbal supplements.

Finally, be aware that the active ingredients in many herbs and herbal supplements are not known. There may be dozens, even hundreds, of unknown compounds in an herbal supplement. Also, published analyses of herbal supplements have found differences between what is listed on the label and what is in the bottle. This means you may be taking less—or more—of the supplement than the label indicates or ingesting substances not mentioned on the label. Some herbal supplements have been found

to be contaminated with metals, unlabelled prescription drugs, microorganisms, and other substances.

Should You Take a Natural Health Product?

Contrary to what some people believe, the food supply is not void of nutrients, and all people do not need to supplement their diets all of the time. In fact, we now know that foods contain a diverse combination of compounds that are critical to our health, and vitamin and mineral supplements do not contain the same amount or variety of substances found in foods. Thus, dietary

supplements are not substitutes for whole foods. However, nutritional needs change throughout the life span, so you may benefit from taking a supplement at certain times for certain reasons. For instance, if you adopt a vegan diet in your college years, your healthcare provider might prescribe a supplement providing riboflavin, vitamin B_{12}, vitamin D, calcium, iron, and zinc. Animal products are high in these nutrients, so if you eliminate these foods, you might not get enough of these nutrients in the other foods you are eating. Or if you are a member of your college soccer team, your team's sports dietitian might advise taking a supplement specially formulated to provide micronutrients that support intense physical activity.

Natural health products, including vitamins and minerals and herbal supplements, consist of hundreds of thousands of products sold for many purposes, and it is impossible to discuss here all of the various situations in which their use may be advisable. So to simplify this discussion, let's focus on identifying the groups of people who may or may not benefit from taking vitamin and mineral supplements.

Table 1 lists groups of people who may benefit from supplementation. But even if you fall within one of these groups, it is still important to analyze your total diet to determine whether you might need to take the vitamin or mineral supplement indicated. It is also a good idea to check with your healthcare provider or a registered dietitian before taking any supplements, as supplements can interfere with some prescription and over-the-counter medications.

Of course, many people who do not need to take supplements do so, anyway. The following are instances in which taking vitamin and mineral supplements is unnecessary, or even harmful:

1. Providing fluoride supplements to children who already drink fluoridated water.
2. Taking supplements in the belief that they will cure a disease, such as cancer, diabetes, or heart disease.
3. Taking supplements with certain medications. For instance, people who take the blood-thinning drug Coumadin should not take vitamin E or K supplements, as this can cause excessive bleeding. People who take aspirin daily should check with their physician before taking vitamin E or K supplements, as aspirin also thins the blood (NIH, 2005).
4. Taking non-prescribed supplements if you have liver or kidney disease. Physicians may prescribe vitamin and mineral supplements for their patients because many nutrients are lost during treatment for these diseases. However, these individuals cannot properly metabolize certain supplements and should not take any that are not prescribed by their physician because of a high risk for toxicity.
5. Taking beta-carotene supplements if you are a smoker. There is evidence that beta-carotene supplementation increases the risk for lung and other cancers in smokers.
6. Taking vitamins and minerals in an attempt to improve physical appearance or athletic performance. There is no evidence that vitamin and mineral supplements enhance appearance or athletic performance in healthy adults who consume a varied diet with adequate energy.
7. Taking supplements to increase your energy level. Vitamin and mineral supplements do not provide energy, because they do not contain fat, carbohydrate, or protein (sources of calories).

TABLE 1 Individuals Who May Benefit from Dietary Supplementation

Type of Individual	Specific Supplements That May Help
Newborns	Routinely given a single dose of vitamin K at birth
Infants	Depends on age and nutrition; may need iron, vitamin D, or other nutrients
Children not drinking fluoridated water	Fluoride supplements
Children on strict vegetarian diets	Vitamin B_{12}, iron, zinc, vitamin D (if not exposed to sunlight)
Children with poor eating habits or overweight children on an energy-restricted diet	Multivitamin/multimineral supplement that does not exceed the RDA for the nutrients it contains
Pregnant teenagers	Iron and folic acid; other nutrients may be necessary if diet is very poor
Women who may become pregnant	Multivitamin or multivitamin/multimineral supplement that contains 0.4 mg of folic acid
Pregnant or lactating women	Multivitamin/multimineral supplement that contains iron, folic acid, zinc, copper, calcium, vitamin B_6, vitamin C, and vitamin D
People on prolonged weight-reduction diets	Multivitamin/multimineral supplement
People recovering from serious illness or surgery	Multivitamin/multimineral supplement
People with HIV/AIDS or other wasting diseases; people addicted to drugs or alcohol	Multivitamin/multimineral supplement or single-nutrient supplements
People who do not consume adequate calcium	Calcium supplements: for example, women need to consume 1000 to 1300 mg of dietary calcium per day; thus, supplements may be necessary
People whose exposure to sunlight is inadequate to allow synthesis of adequate vitamin D	Vitamin D
People eating a vegan diet	Vitamin B_{12}, riboflavin, calcium, vitamin D, iron, and zinc
People who have had portions of their intestinal tract removed; people who have a malabsorptive disease	Depends on the exact condition; may include various fat-soluble and/or water-soluble vitamins and other nutrients
People with lactose intolerance	Calcium supplements
Elderly people	Multivitamin/multimineral supplement, vitamin B_{12}

One of the best strategies for maintaining good health is to eat a diet that provides a rich variety of whole foods. If you do that, you probably won't need to take supplements.

Although many vitamins and minerals are necessary for us to produce energy, taking dietary supplements in place of eating food will not provide us with the energy necessary to live a healthy and productive life.

8. Taking single-nutrient supplements, unless a qualified healthcare practitioner prescribes a single-nutrient supplement for a diagnosed medical condition (for example, prescribing iron supplements for someone with anemia). These products contain very high amounts of the given nutrient, and taking them can quickly lead to toxicity.

If you eat a healthful diet that contains a variety of whole foods, you probably will not need to take vitamin and mineral supplements. And if you do use a supplement, select one that contains no more than 100% of the recommended levels for the nutrients it contains. Avoid taking single-nutrient supplements unless advised to do so by your healthcare practitioner. Finally, avoid taking supplements that contain substances that are known to cause illness or injuries. Some of these substances are listed in **Table 2**.

TABLE 2 Natural Health Product Ingredients Associated with Illnesses and Injuries

Ingredient	Potential Risks
Herbal Ingredients	
Chaparral	Liver disease
Kava (also known as kava kava)	Severe liver toxicity
Comfrey	Obstruction of blood flow to liver, possible death
Slimming/dieter's teas	Nausea, diarrhea, vomiting, stomach cramps, constipation, fainting, possible death
Ephedra (also known as ma huang, Chinese ephedra, and epitonin)	High blood pressure, irregular heartbeat, nerve damage, insomnia, tremors, headaches, seizures, heart attack, stroke, possible death
Germander	Liver disease, possible death
Lobelia	Breathing problems, excessive sweating, rapid heartbeat, low blood pressure, coma, possible death
Magnolia-Stephania preparation	Kidney disease, can lead to permanent kidney failure
Willow bark	Reye's syndrome (a potentially fatal disease that may occur when children take aspirin), allergic reaction in adults
Wormwood	Numbness of legs and arms, loss of intellectual processing, delirium, paralysis
Vitamins and Essential Minerals	
Vitamin A (when taking 25 000 IU or more per day)	Birth defects, bone abnormalities, severe liver disease
Vitamin B_6 (when taking more than 100 mg per day)	Loss of balance, injuries to nerves that alter our touch sensation
Niacin (when taking slow-release doses of 500 mg or more per day, or when taking immediate-release doses of 750 mg or more per day)	Stomach pain; nausea; vomiting; bloating; cramping; diarrhea; liver disease; damage to the muscles, eyes, and heart
Selenium (when taking 800 to 1000 µg per day)	Tissue damage
Other Ingredients	
Germanium (a non-essential mineral)	Kidney damage
L-tryptophan (an amino acid)	Eosinophilia-myalgia syndrome (a potentially fatal blood disorder that causes high fever)

Data from U.S. Food and Drug Administration. 2007. Dietary supplements. Warnings and safety information. Available at www.cfsan.fda.gov/~dms/ds-warn.html; and U.S. Food and Drug Administration. 1998. Supplements associated with illnesses and injuries. FDA Consumer Magazine, September/October. Available at www.fda.gov/fdac/features/1998/dietchrt.html.

Web Resources

http://www.hc-sc.gc.ca/dhp-mps/prod-natur/index-eng.php
Health Canada Natural Health Products

Follow the links to find out more about Natural Health Product Regulations and access the database of all licensed Natural Health Products available in Canada.

11
Achieving and Maintaining a Healthful Body Weight

CHAPTER OBJECTIVES

After reading this chapter you will be able to:

1. Describe what is meant by a healthful weight, p. 366.

2. Define the terms *underweight, overweight, obesity*, and the *three classes of obesity*, pp. 367–368.

3. List at least three methods that can be used to assess your body composition or risk for overweight, p. 370.

4. Identify and discuss the three components of energy expenditure, pp. 374–378.

5. List and describe at least two theories that link genetic influences to control of body weight, pp. 378–379.

6. Discuss at least two societal factors that influence our body weight, pp. 382–383.

7. Develop an action plan for healthful weight loss, pp. 383–390.

Test Yourself answers can be found at the end of the chapter.

Test Yourself

1. Ⓣ Ⓕ People who are moderately overweight and physically active should not be considered healthy.

2. Ⓣ Ⓕ Getting your body composition measured at the local fitness club will give you an accurate assessment of your body fat level.

3. Ⓣ Ⓕ By staying physically active as we get older, we can prevent some of the decline in our muscle mass and our basal metabolic rate.

D**o you know what Fat Talk is?** It is not about being overweight or obese; in fact, it may have nothing to do with your weight at all. Have you ever been with a group of friends and somehow the conversation switches to everyone sharing things that they don't like about themselves? Before long, everyone has contributed at least one, and while it may feel good for a minute or two to share your flaws amongst others, it is nothing more than unnecessarily negative thoughts about ourselves and our bodies. Often people choose to engage in Fat Talk as a coping mechanism, during social outings, or simply to hide their true feelings about self-worth, body image, and self-esteem. You can prevent Fat Talk by working hard at thinking positively about yourself and your lifestyle, and consciously correcting yourself if you hear any negative words come out of your mouth. Now that you know more about Fat Talk, can you recall anytime where you think you engaged in it? Are you happy with your weight, shape, body composition, and fitness? If not, what needs to change—your attitude, your diet, your level of physical activity? What role do diet and physical activity play in maintaining a healthful body weight? How much of your body size and shape is due to genetics?

What influence does society—including food advertising— have on your weight? And if you decide that you do need to lose weight, what's the best way to do it? In this chapter, we'll explore these questions and provide some answers.

⬥ Fashion model Emme Aronson's weight is healthful for her. She follows a nutritious diet and works out regularly.

How Can You Evaluate Your Body Weight?

As you begin to think about achieving and maintaining a healthful weight, it's important to make sure you understand what a healthful body weight actually is and the various methods you can use to figure out if your own weight is healthful.

Understand What a Healthful Body Weight Really Is

We can define a healthful weight as all of the following (Manore, Meyer, and Thompson, 2009):

- A weight that is appropriate for your age and physical development
- A weight that you can achieve and sustain without severely curtailing your food intake or constantly dieting
- A weight that is compatible with normal blood pressure, lipid levels, and glucose tolerance
- A weight that is based on your genetic background and family history of body shape and weight
- A weight that promotes good eating habits and allows you to participate in regular physical activity
- A weight that is acceptable to you

As you can see, a healthful weight is not one at which a person must be extremely thin or overly muscular. In addition, there is no one body type that can be defined as healthful. Thus, achieving a healthful body weight should not be dictated by the latest fad or current societal expectations of what is acceptable.

Various methods are available to help you determine whether you are currently maintaining a healthful body weight. Let's review a few of these methods.

Determine Your Body Mass Index (BMI)

body mass index (BMI) A measurement representing the ratio of a person's body weight to his or her height.

Body mass index (**BMI**, or *Quetelet's index*) is a commonly used index representing the ratio of a person's body weight to the square of his or her height. **Table 11.1** helps to interpret the resulting ratio. You can calculate your BMI using the following equation:

$$\text{BMI (kg/m}^2) = \text{weight (kg)/height (m)}^2$$

For those less familiar with the metric system, there is an equation to calculate BMI using weight in pounds and height in inches:

$$\text{BMI (kg/m}^2) = [\text{weight (lb)/height (in.)}^2] \times 703$$

A less exact but practical method is to use the graph in **Figure 11.1**, which shows approximate BMIs for your height and weight and whether your BMI is in a healthful

TABLE 11.1 Health Canada BMI Classifications and Risk of Developing Health Problems		
Classification	**BMI Category (kg/m²)**	**Risk of Developing Health Problems**
Underweight	<18.5	Increased
Normal Weight	18.5–24.9	Least
Overweight	25.0–29.9	Increased
Obese		
Class I	30.0–34.9	High
Class II	35.0–39.9	Very high
Class III	>40.0	Extremely high

Source: Canadian Guidelines for Body Weight Classification in Adults. Health Canada, © 2003. Reproduced with the permission of the Minister of Health, 2012.
Note: For persons 65 years and older, the "normal" range may begin slightly above BMI 18.5 and extend into the "overweight" range.

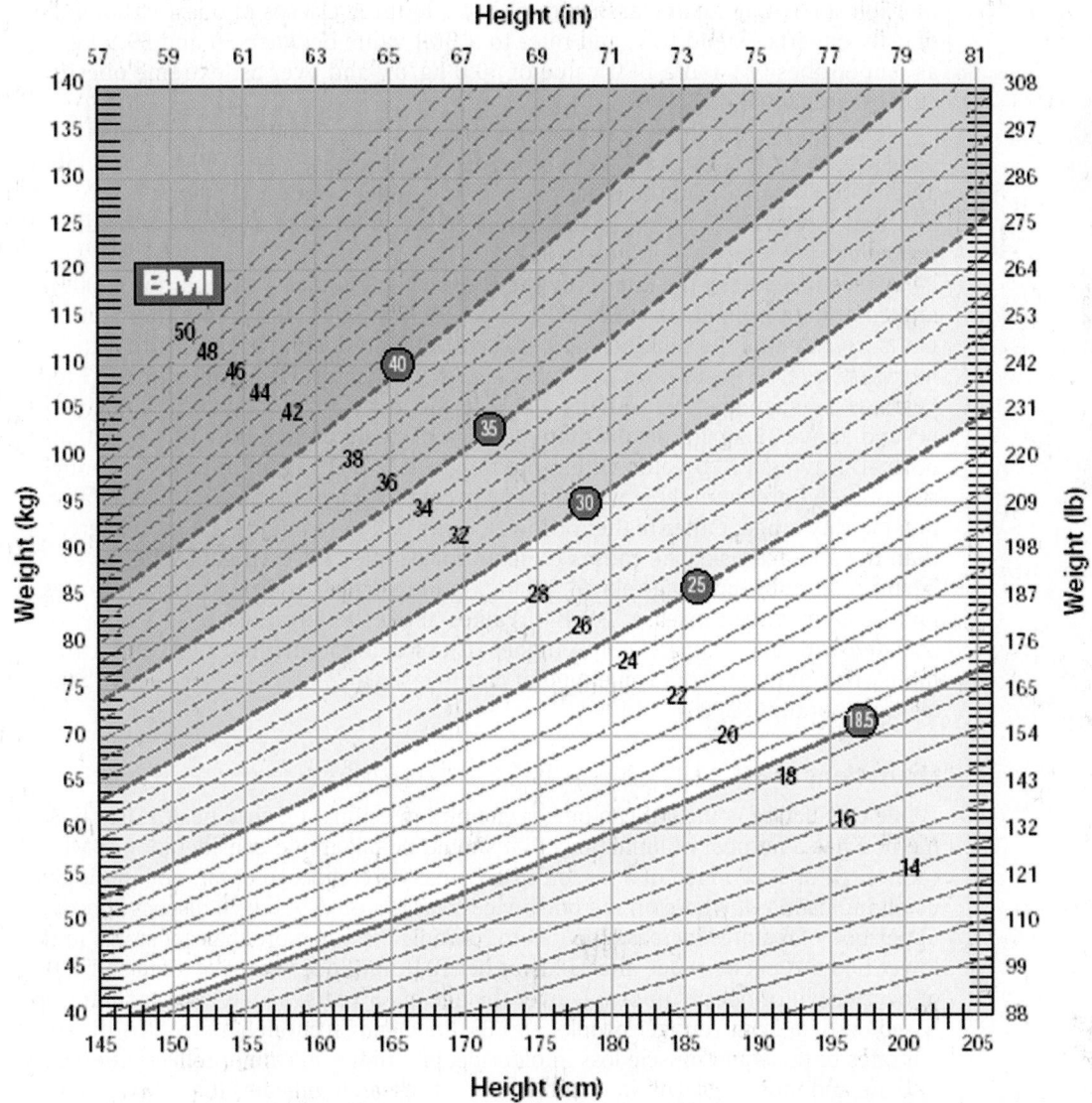

Height (in)

Height (cm)

Weight (kg)

Weight (lb)

BMI

➤ **Figure 11.1** Measure your body mass index (BMI) using this graph. To determine your BMI, find the value for your height on the left and follow this line to the right until it intersects with the value for your weight on the bottom axis. The area on the graph where these two lines intersect is your BMI.

Source: Canadian Guidelines for Body Weight Classification in Adults. Health Canada, ©2003. Reproduced with the permission of the Minister of Health, 2012.

range. You can also calculate your BMI on the internet using the BMI calculator found at www.nhlbisupport.com/bmi.

Why Is BMI Important?

Your body mass index provides an important clue to your overall health. Physicians, nutritionists, and other scientists define **underweight** as having too little body fat to maintain health, causing a person to have a weight that is below an acceptably defined standard for a given height. A person having a BMI less than 18.5 kg/m² is considered underweight. Normal weight ranges from 18.5 to 24.9 kg/m². **Overweight** is defined as having a moderate amount of excess body fat, resulting in a person having a weight that is greater than some accepted standard for a given height but is not considered obese. Having a BMI between 25 and 29.9 kg/m² indicates that a person is overweight. **Obesity** is defined as having an excess of body fat that adversely affects health, resulting in a person having a weight that is substantially greater than some accepted standard for a given height. A BMI value of 30 kg/m² and greater is consistent with obesity. As shown

underweight Having too little body fat to maintain health, causing a person to weigh less than an acceptably defined standard for a given height.

overweight Having a moderate amount of excess body fat, resulting in a person weighing more than an accepted standard for a given height, but not considered obese.

obesity Having an excess of body fat that adversely affects health, resulting in a person weighing substantially more than an accepted standard for a given height.

▲ A healthful weight is one that is appropriate for your age, physical development, heredity, and other factors.

in Table 11.1, Canadian classifications include three classes of obesity. Some obesity experts extend this, and refer to a BMI value between 50 and 59.9 kg/m^2 as 'super obesity', and a BMI value of 60.0 kg/m^2 and over as 'extreme obesity' (Buchwald, 2005).

Research studies show that a person's risk for type 2 diabetes, high blood pressure, heart disease, and many other diseases increases when BMI is at or above a value of 30 kg/m^2. On the other hand, being underweight and having a very low BMI, below 18.5 kg/m^2, is also associated with an increased risk for health problems.

A recent report in the *Lancet* by the Prospective Studies Collaboration (2009) looked at data from almost 900 000 people, in 57 studies, and across four continents, to examine the relationship between BMI and death. It confirms that the *mortality rate,* or death rate, from all diseases, and across age groups from 35 to 89 years, is a J-shaped curve. Having a BMI in the low-normal range of 18.5–22.5 kg/m^2 and above 25 kg/m^2 means that your risk of dying prematurely is higher than normal. Having a BMI value within the range of 22.5–25 kg/m^2 means that your risk of dying prematurely is within the expected average. If your BMI value falls outside this range, either higher or lower, your risk of dying prematurely is greater than the average risk. The causes of death for people with BMI values below 22.5 kg/m^2 tend to be smoking-related, including lung cancer and respiratory diseases, and ischaemic heart disease. For BMI values above 25 kg/m^2, each 5 kg/m^2 is associated with approximately 30% higher risk of dying from any cause, and a 40% higher risk of dying from some type of cardiovascular problem. (Prospective Studies Collaboration, 2009).

Limitations of BMI

While calculating your BMI can be very helpful in estimating your health risk, this method has a number of limitations that should be taken into consideration. BMI cannot tell us how much of a person's body mass is composed of fat, nor can it give us an indication of where on the body excess fat is stored. As we'll discuss shortly, upper-body fat stores increase the risk for chronic disease more than fat stores in the lower body. A person's age affects his or her BMI; BMI does not give a fair indication of overweight or obesity in people over the age of 65 years, as the BMI standards are based on data from younger people, and BMI does not accurately reflect the differential rates of bone and muscle loss in older people. BMI also cannot reflect differences in bone and muscle growth in children. Recent research indicates that BMI is more strongly associated with height in young people; thus, taller children are more likely

YOU DO THE MATH

Calculating Your Body Mass Index

Calculate your personal BMI value based on your height and weight. Let's use Matthew's values as an example:

$$BMI = weight\ (kg) \div height\ (m)^2$$

1. Matthew's weight is 200 pounds. To convert his weight to kg, divide his weight in pounds by 2.2 pounds per kg:

   200 pounds ÷ 2.2 pounds per kg = 90.91 kg

2. Matthew's height is 6 feet 8 inches, or 80 inches. To convert his height to metres, multiply his height in inches by 0.0254 metres per inch:

   80 inches × 0.0254 metres per inch = 2.03 metres

3. Find the square of his height in metres:

   2.03 m × 2.03 m = 4.13 m^2

4. Then, divide his weight in kg by his height in m^2 to get his BMI value:

   90.91 kg ÷ 4.13 m^2 = 22.01 kg/m^2

Is Matthew underweight according to this BMI value? As you can see in Figure 11.1, this value shows that he is maintaining a normal, healthy weight!

HIGHLIGHT

Dr. Linda McCargar: Sarcopenic Obesity: An Emerging Health Problem

Can a person have too little muscle and be over-fat? Do you know an older person who has lost a lot of muscle mass, but has ample body fat? Dr. Linda McCargar, a professor at the University of Alberta and the Director of the Human Nutrition Research Unit there, is a leading expert in body composition. Recently she's been interested in a condition called sarcopenic obesity. Literally, *sarco* means "muscle" and *penia* means "lack of"; sarcopenic obesity, therefore, refers to a condition of low muscle mass and high body fat (McCargar, 2007). A person may not necessarily look obese, but they have too little lean body mass relative to their fat mass. How can you tell if an individual has too little muscle and too much fat? The new imaging techniques available today can quantify the amount of fat and lean tissue fairly accurately. Dual energy x-ray absorptiometry (DEXA) is a simple, non-invasive technique that, according to McCargar (2007), "is rapidly becoming the method of choice for body composition research, because it is precise and overcomes some disadvantages of other commonly used methods." This technique has been widely used to measure bone density and mineral content, but it is also an excellent choice to measure whole body composition. It uses very low dose x-rays to identify and quantify soft tissue (lean and fat tissue) and bone separately.

As we learned already in this chapter, if you have a pear body shape and you carry much of your body fat in your hips and thighs, you don't have the same health risks as someone who has an apple body shape or a "spare tire" around their middle. In other words, the more fat deposited centrally (around your abdomen), the greater the health risks. McCargar's colleague and collaborator Dr. Geoff Ball, also from the University of Alberta, has shown that there can be significant differences in the amount of abdominal fat among 10-year-old children who have the same BMI values and are at the same stage of development. These findings may help health professionals to predict which children will be at

⬆ Dr. Linda McCargar is a leading expert in body composition

greatest risk for possible future health problems, such as type 2 diabetes.

Who is most at risk of sarcopenic obesity? Most of the research to date has examined the muscle wasting commonly seen in older adults. However, sarcopenia has also been seen in breast cancer survivors and patients with other types of cancer. McCargar notes that "recent studies have confirmed a unique pattern of weight gain often observed in breast cancer patients: usually fat gain with a loss or no change in lean tissue" (McCargar, 2007). This suggests that women recovering from breast cancer may benefit from following a healthy diet and an exercise regime that includes both aerobic and resistance training. A loss of lean body mass has also been observed in patients with colon cancer. An abnormal body composition may influence the distribution and efficacy of chemotherapy drugs in the body. In general, our population has become more obese and less active over the last two decades; thus an increased incidence of sarcopenic obesity may be seen in the future.

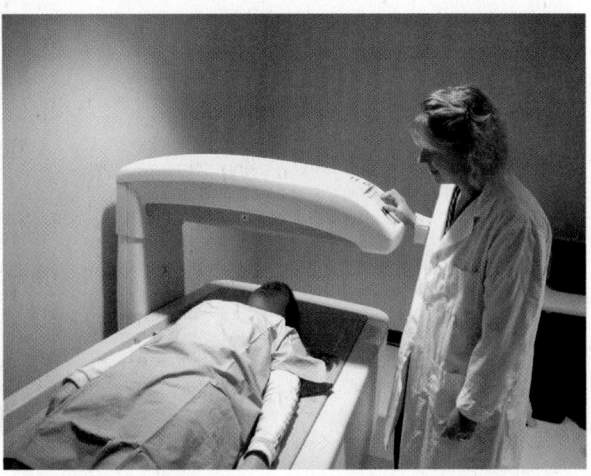

⬆ DEXA has been widely used to assess bone density, but it is also an excellent choice to measure whole body composition.

Method		Limitations
Underwater weighing: Considered the most accurate method. Estimates body fat within a 2%–3% margin of error. This means that if your underwater weighing test shows you have 20% body fat, this value could be no lower than 17% and no higher than 23%. Used primarily for research purposes.	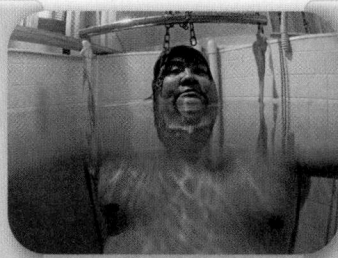	• Must be comfortable in water. • Requires trained technician and specialized equipment. • Does not work well with obese people. • Must abstain from food for at least 8 hours and from exercise for at least 12 hours prior to testing.
Skinfolds: Involves "pinching" a person's fold of skin (with its underlying layer of fat) at various locations of the body. The fold is measured using a specially designed caliper. When performed by a skilled technician, it can estimate body fat with an error of 3%–4%. This means that if your skinfold test shows you have 20% body fat, your actual value could be as low as 16% or as high as 24%.	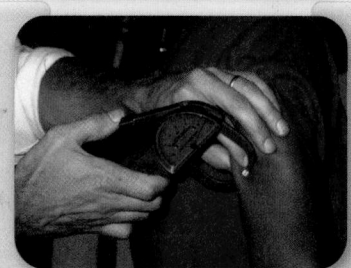	• Less accurate unless technician is well trained. • Proper prediction equation must be used to improve accuracy. • Person being measured may not want to be touched or to expose their skin. • Cannot be used to measure obese people, as their skinfolds are too large for the caliper.
Bioelectrical impedance analysis (BIA): Involves sending a very low level of electrical current through a person's body. As water is a good conductor of electricity and lean body mass is made up of mostly water, the rate at which the electricity is conducted gives an indication of a person's lean body mass and body fat. This method can be done while lying down, with electrodes attached to the feet, hands, and the BIA machine. Hand-held and standing models (which look like bathroom scales) are now available. Under the best of circumstances, BIA can estimate body fat with an error of 3%–4%.	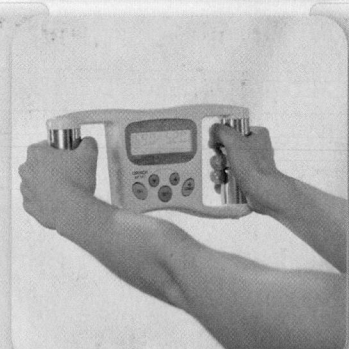	• Less accurate. • Body fluid levels must be normal. • Proper prediction equation must be used to improve accuracy. • Should not eat for 4 hours and should not exercise for 12 hours prior to the test. • No alcohol should be consumed within 48 hours of the test. • Females should not be measured if they are retaining water due to menstrual cycle changes.
Dual-energy x-ray absorptiometry (DXA): The technology is based on using very low level x-rays to differentiate among bone tissue, soft (or lean) tissue, and fat (or adipose) tissue. It involves lying for about 30 minutes on a specialized bed fully clothed, with all metal objects removed. The margin of error for predicting body fat ranges from 2% to 4%.	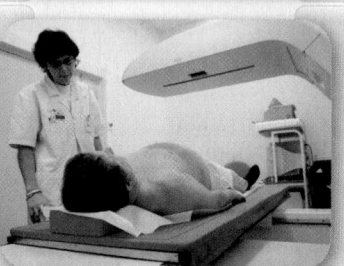	• Expensive; requires trained technician with specialized equipment. • Cannot be used to measure extremely tall, short, or obese people, as they do not fit properly within the scanning area.
Bod Pod: A machine that uses air displacement to measure body composition. This machine is a large, egg-shaped chamber made from fibreglass. The person being measured sits inside wearing a swimsuit. The door is closed and the machine measures how much air is displaced. This value is used to calculate body composition. It appears promising as an easier and equally accurate alternative to underwater weighing in many populations, but it may overestimate body fat in some African-American men.	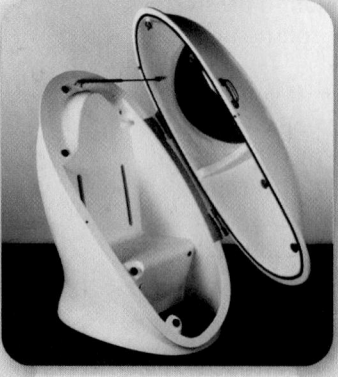	• Expensive. • Less accurate in some populations.

⬆ **Figure 11.2** Overview of various body composition assessment methods.

RECAP Body mass index, body composition, and the waist-to-hip ratio and waist circumference are tools that can help you evaluate the health of your current body weight. None of these methods is completely accurate, but most may be used appropriately as general health indicators.

What Makes Us Gain and Lose Weight?

Have you ever wondered why some people are thin and others are overweight, even though they seem to eat about the same diet? If so, you're not alone. For hundreds of years, researchers have puzzled over what makes us gain and lose weight. In this section, we'll explore some information and current theories that may shed some light on this question.

We Gain or Lose Weight when Our Energy Intake and Expenditure Are Out of Balance

Fluctuations in body weight are a result of changes in our **energy intake** (the food we eat) and our **energy expenditure** (the amount of energy we expend at rest and during physical activity). This relationship between what we eat and what we do is defined by the energy balance equation:

Energy balance occurs when energy intake = energy expenditure

This means that our energy is balanced when we consume the same amount of energy that we burn each day. **Figure 11.5** shows how our weight changes when we change either side of this equation. From this figure you can see that to lose body weight we must expend more energy than we consume. In contrast, to gain weight, we must consume more energy than we expend. Finding the proper balance between energy intake and expenditure allows us to maintain a healthful body weight.

Energy Intake Is the Food We Eat Each Day

Energy intake is equal to the amount of energy in the food we eat each day. This value includes all foods and beverages. Daily energy intake is expressed as *kilojoules per day* (kJ/day or kJ/d) or *kilocalories per day* (kcal/day or kcal/d). You can estimate your energy intake by using food composition tables or computerized dietary analysis programs. The energy content of each food is a function of the amount of carbohydrate, fat, protein, and alcohol that each food contains; vitamins and minerals have no energy value.

Remember that the energy value of carbohydrate and protein is 17 kJ/g (4 kcal/g) and the energy value of fat is 37 kJ/g (9 kcal/g). The energy value of alcohol is 29 kJ/g (7 kcal/g). By multiplying the energy value (in kJ or kcal per gram) by the amount of the nutrient (in g), you can calculate how much energy is in a particular food. For instance, 250 mL (1 cup) of quick oatmeal contains 6 g of protein, 25 g of carbohydrate, and 2 g of fat. Using the energy values for each nutrient, you can calculate the total energy content as follows:

6 g protein $\times$ 17 kJ/g (4 kcal/g) = 100 kJ (24 kcal) from protein

25 g carbohydrate $\times$ 17 kJ/g (4 kcal/g) = 420 kJ (100 kcal) from carbohydrate

2 g fat $\times$ 37 kJ/g (9 kcal/g) = 80 kJ (18 kcal) from fat

Total kcal for 250 mL (1 cup) oatmeal = 100 kJ (24 kcal) + 420 kJ (100 kcal)
+ 80 kJ (18 kcal) = (600 kJ) 142 kcal

Note, energy measured in kJ is usually rounded to the nearest 10 kJ, so the calculations are not exact.

When someone's total daily energy intake exceeds the amount of energy that person expends, he or she gains weight. An excess intake of approximately 14 640 kJ or 3500 kcal will result in a gain of approximately 0.5 kg (1 lb.). Without exercise, this gain will likely be fat.

The energy provided by a bowl of oatmeal is derived from its protein, carbohydrate, and fat content.

energy intake The amount of food a person eats; in other words, it is the amount of energy or number of kilocalories consumed.

energy expenditure The energy the body expends to maintain its basic functions and to perform all levels of movement and activity.

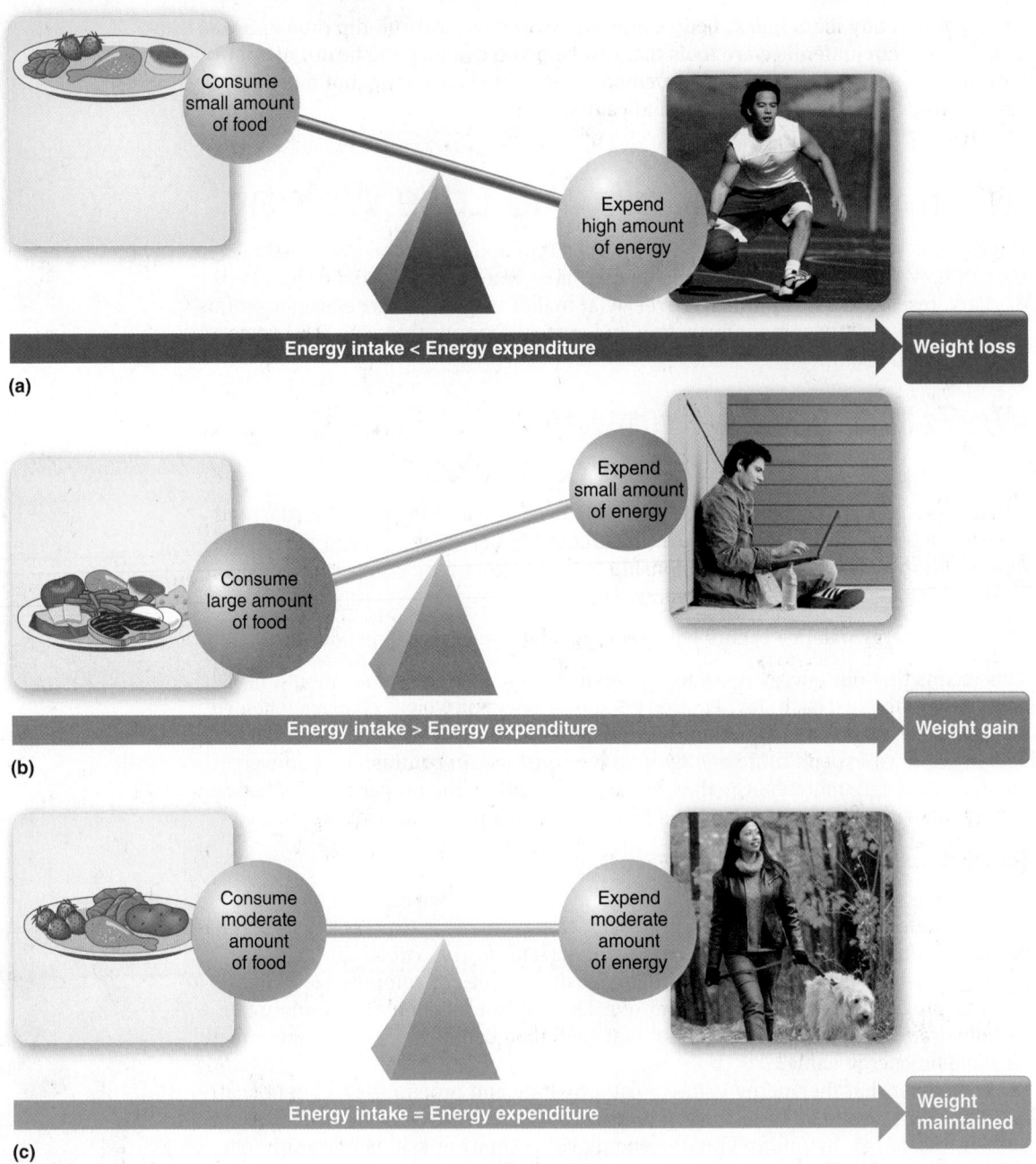

🔺 **Figure 11.5** Energy balance is the relationship between the food we eat and the energy we burn each day. **(a)** Weight loss occurs when food intake is less than energy output. **(b)** Weight gain occurs when food intake is greater than energy output. **(c)** We maintain our body weight when food intake equals energy output.

Energy Expenditure Includes More than Just Physical Activity

Energy expenditure (also known as energy output) is the energy our body expends to maintain its basic functions and to perform all levels of movement and activity. Total 24-hour energy expenditure is calculated by estimating the energy used during rest and as a result of physical activity. There are three components of energy expenditure: basal metabolic rate (BMR), thermic effect of food (TEF), and energy cost of physical activity **(Figure 11.6)**.

basal metabolic rate (BMR) The energy the body expends to maintain its fundamental physiologic functions.

Our Basal Metabolic Rate Is Our Energy Expenditure at Rest   Basal metabolic rate, or **BMR**, is the energy we expend just to maintain our body's *basal*, or *resting*, functions. These functions include respiration, circulation, body temperature, synthesis of new cells and tissues, secretion of hormones, and nervous system activity. The majority of our energy output each day (about 60%–75%) is a result of our BMR. This means that 60%–75% of our energy output goes to fuel the basic activities of staying alive, aside from any physical activity.

BMR varies widely among people. The primary determinant of our BMR is the amount of lean body mass we have. People with a higher lean body mass have a higher BMR, as lean body mass is more metabolically active than body fat. Thus, it takes more energy to support this active tissue. One common assumption is that obese people have a depressed BMR. This is usually not the case. Most studies of obese people show that the amount of energy they expend for every kilogram of lean body mass is similar to that of a non-obese person. In general, people who weigh more also have more lean body mass and consequently have a *higher* BMR. See **Figure 11.7** for an example of how lean body mass can vary for people with different body weights and body fat levels.

BMR decreases with age, approximately 3%–5% per decade after age 30. This age-related decrease results partly from hormonal changes, but much of this change is due to the loss of lean body mass resulting from physical inactivity. Thus, a large proportion of this decrease can be prevented with regular physical activity. There are other factors that can affect a person's BMR, and some of these are listed in **Table 11.3**.

How can you estimate the amount of energy you expend for your BMR? Of the many equations that can be used, one of the simplest ways to estimate your BMR is to multiply your body weight in kilograms by 4.2 kJ or 1.0 kcal per kilogram of body weight per hour for men or by 3.8 kJ or 0.9 kcal per kilogram of body weight per hour for women. A little later in this chapter, you'll have an opportunity to calculate your BMR and determine your total daily energy needs.

The Thermic Effect of Food Is the Energy Expended to Process Food   The **thermic effect of food (TEF)** is the energy we expend as a result of processing the food we eat. A certain amount of energy is needed to digest, absorb, transport, metabolize, and store the nutrients we need. The TEF is equal to about 5%–10% of the energy content of a meal, a relatively small amount. Thus, if a meal contains 2100 kJ

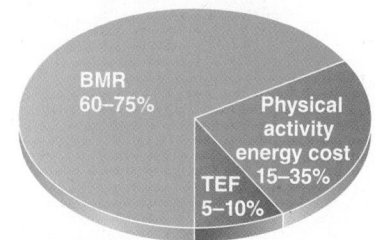

Components of energy expenditure

Figure 11.6 The components of energy expenditure are basal metabolic rate (BMR), the thermic effect of food (TEF), and the energy cost of physical activity. BMR accounts for 60%–75% of our total energy output, whereas TEF and physical activity together account for 25%–40%.

thermic effect of food (TEF) The energy expended as a result of processing food consumed.

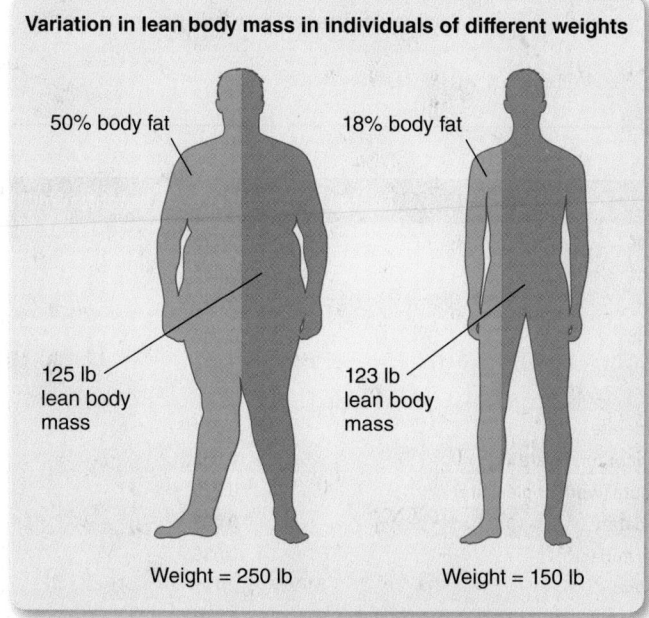

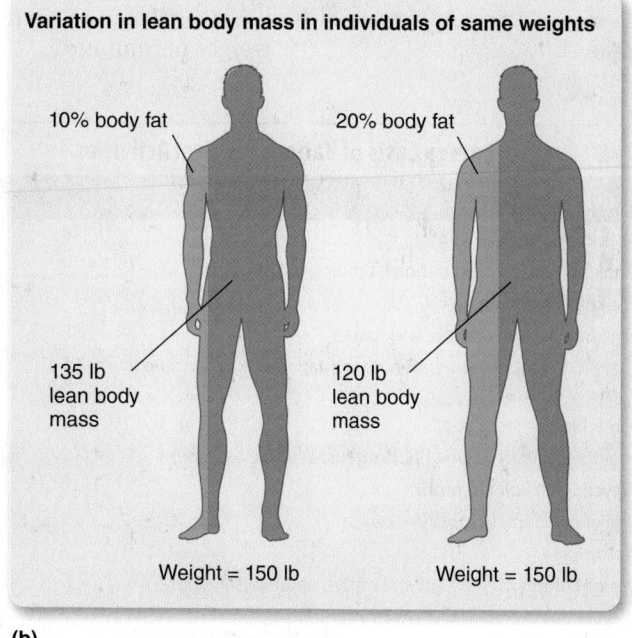

(a)   (b)

Figure 11.7 Lean body mass varies in people with different body weights and body fat levels. **(a)** The person on the left has greater body weight, body fat, and lean body mass than the person on the right. **(b)** The two people are the same weight, but the person on the right has more body fat and less lean body mass than the person on the left.

TABLE 11.3 Factors Affecting Basal Metabolic Rate (BMR)

Factors that Increase BMR	Factors that Decrease BMR
Higher lean body mass	Lower lean body mass
Greater height (more surface area)	Lower height
Younger age	Older age
Elevated levels of thyroid hormone	Depressed levels of thyroid hormone
Stress, fever, illness	Starvation or fasting
Male gender	Female gender
Pregnancy and lactation	Certain drugs, such as stimulants, caffeine, and tobacco

(500 kcal), the thermic effect of processing that meal is about 105 to 210 kJ (25–50 kcal). These values apply to eating what is referred to as a mixed diet, or a diet containing a mixture of carbohydrate, fat, and protein. Most of us eat some combination of these nutrients throughout the day. Individually, the processing of each nutrient takes a different amount of energy. While fat requires very little energy to digest, transport, and store in our cells, protein and carbohydrate require relatively more energy to process.

The Energy Cost of Physical Activity Is Highly Variable   The **energy cost of physical activity** represents about 15%–35% of our total energy output each day. This is the energy we expend due to any movement or work above basal levels. This includes both lower-intensity activities, such as sitting, standing, and walking, and higher-intensity activities, such as running, skiing, and bicycling. One of the most obvious ways to increase how much energy we expend as a result of physical activity is to do more activities for a longer period of time.

energy cost of physical activity
The energy that is expended on body movement and muscular work above basal levels.

Table 11.4 lists the energy costs for certain activities. As you can see, activities such as running, swimming, and cross-country skiing, which involve moving our larger muscle groups (or more parts of the body), require more energy. The amount of energy we expend during activities is also affected by our body size, the intensity of the activity, and how long we perform the activity. That is why the values in Table 11.4 are expressed as kilocalories of energy per kilogram of body weight per minute.

TABLE 11.4 Energy Costs of Various Physical Activities

Activity	Intensity	Energy Cost (kcal/kg body weight/min)
Sitting, knitting/sewing	Light	0.026
Cooking or food preparation (standing or sitting)	Light	0.035
Walking, shopping	Light	0.040
Walking, 3.2 kph (2 mph, slow pace)	Light	0.044
Cleaning (dusting, straightening up, vacuuming, changing linen, carrying out trash)	Moderate	0.044
Stretching—hatha yoga	Moderate	0.044
Weight lifting (free weights, Nautilus, or universal type)	Light or moderate	0.052
Bicycling 16 kph (10 mph)	Leisure (work or pleasure)	0.070
Walking, 6.5kph (4 mph, brisk pace)	Moderate	0.088
Aerobics	Low impact	0.088
Weight lifting (free weights, Nautilus, or universal type)	Vigorous	0.105
Bicycling, 19 to 22 kph (12–13.9 mph)	Moderate	0.140
Running, 8 kph, 7.5 minutes per km (5 mph)	Moderate	0.140
Running, 9.5 kph, 6.3 minutes per km (6 mph)	Moderate	0.175
Running, 13.8 kph, 4.3 minutes per km (8.6 mph)	Vigorous	0.245

Data from Ainsworth, B. E., W. L. Haskell, M. C. Whitt, M. L. Irwin, A. M. Swartz, S. J. Strath, W. L. O'Brien, D. R. Bassett, Jr., K. H. Schmitz, P. O. Emplaincourt, D. R. Jacobs, Jr., and A. S. Leon, 2000. Compendium of physical activities: an update of activity codes and MET intensities. Med. Sci. Sports Exerc. 32: S498–S516. Lippincott, Williams & Wilkins. Reprinted with permission.

YOU DO THE MATH
Calculating BMR and Total Daily Energy Needs

You can estimate how much energy you need each day by recording your total food and beverage intake for a defined period of time, such as 3 or 7 days. You can then use a food composition table or computerized dietary assessment program to estimate the amount of energy you eat each day. Assuming that your body weight is stable over this period of time, your average daily energy intake should represent how much energy you need to maintain your present weight.

Unfortunately, many studies of energy intake in humans have shown that dietary records estimating energy needs are not very accurate. Most studies show that people underestimate the amount of energy they eat by 10%–30%. Overweight people tend to underestimate by an even higher margin, at the same time overestimating the amount of activity they do. This means that someone who really eats about 8370 kJ (2000 kcal) per day may record eating only 5860 to 7530 kJ (1400–1800 kcal) per day. So one reason many people are confused about their ability to lose weight is that they are eating more than they realize.

A simpler and more accurate way to estimate your total daily energy needs is to calculate your BMR and then add the amount of energy you expend as a result of your activity level. Refer to the following example to learn how to do this. Because the energy cost for the thermic effect of food is very small, you don't need to include it in your calculations.

1. *Calculate your BMR.* If you are a man, you will need to multiply your body weight in kilograms by 1 kcal per kilogram body weight per hour. Assuming you weigh 175 pounds, your body weight in kilograms is 175 lb ÷ 2.2 lb/kg = 79.5 kg. Next, multiply your weight in kilograms by 1 kcal per kilogram body weight per hour:

   1 kcal/kg body weight/hour × 79.5 kg = 79.5 kcal/hour

   Calculate your BMR for the total day (24 hours):

   79.5 kcal/hour × 24 hours/day
   = 1909 kcal or 8020 kJ per day

   (If you are a woman, multiply your body weight in kg by 0.9 kcal/kg body weight/hour.)

2. *Estimate your activity level by selecting the description that most closely fits your general lifestyle.* The energy cost of activities is expressed as a percentage of your BMR. Refer to the values in the following table when estimating your own energy output.

3. *Multiply your BMR by the decimal equivalent of the lower and higher percentage values for your activity level.* Let's use the man referred to in step 1. He is a college student who lives on campus. He walks to classes located throughout campus, carries his book bag, and spends most of his time reading and writing. He does not exercise on a regular basis. His lifestyle would be defined as lightly active, meaning he expends 50%–70% of his BMR each day in activities. You want to calculate how much energy he expends at both ends of this activity level. How many kcal does this equal?

   1909 kcal/day × 0.50 (50%) = 955 kcal (4010 kJ) per day
   1909 kcal/day × 0.70 (70%) = 1336 kcal (5610 kJ) per day

   These calculations show that this man expends about 955 – 1336 kcal (4010 to 5610 kJ) per day doing daily activities.

4. *Calculate total daily energy output by adding together BMR and the energy needed to perform daily activities.* In this man's case, his total daily energy output is

   1909 kcal/day + 955 kcal/day = 2864 kcal (12 030 kJ) per day

   or

   1909 kcal/day + 1336 kcal/day = 3245 kcal (13 630 kJ) day

Assuming this man is maintaining his present weight, he requires between 2864 and 3245 kcal (12 030 to 13 630 kJ) per day to stay in energy balance!

	Men	Women
Sedentary/Inactive Involves mostly sitting, driving, or very low levels of activity	25%–40%	25%–35%
Lightly Active Involves a lot of sitting; may also involve some walking, moving around, and light lifting	50%–70%	40%–60%
Moderately Active Involves work plus intentional exercise, such as an hour of walking or cycling 4 or 5 days per week; may have a job requiring some physical labour	65%–80%	50%–70%
Heavily Active Involves a great deal of physical labour, such as roofing, carpentry work, and/ or regular heavy lifting and digging	90%–120%	80%–100%
Exceptionally Active Involves a lot of physical activities for work and intentional exercise; also applies to athletes who train for many hours each day, such as triathletes and marathon runners or other competitive athletes performing heavy, regular training	130%–145%	110%–130%

Brisk walking expends energy.

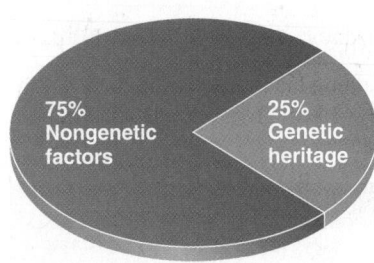

75% Nongenetic factors

25% Genetic heritage

Percent (%) contribution to body fat

Figure 11.8 Research indicates that about 25% of our body fat is accounted for by our genetic heritage. However, non-genetic factors, such as diet and exercise, play a much larger role.

thrifty gene theory The theory that some people possess a gene (or genes) that causes them to be energetically thrifty, resulting in their expending less energy at rest and during physical activity.

set-point theory The theory that the body raises or lowers energy expenditure in response to increased or decreased food intake and physical activity. This action maintains an individual's body weight within a narrow range.

Using the energy value for running at 9.5 km (6 miles) per hour (or a 10-minute-per-mile running pace) for 30 minutes, let's calculate how much energy Matthew would expend doing this activity:

- Matthew's body weight (in kg) = 200 lb ÷ 2.2 lb/kg = 90.91 kg.
- Energy cost of running at 9.5 kph = 0.175 kcal/kg body weight/min.
- At Matthew's weight, the energy cost of running per minute = 0.175 kcal/kg body weight/min × 90.91 kg = 15.91 kcal/min.
- If Matthew runs at this pace for 30 minutes, his total energy output = 15.91 kcal/min × 30 min = 477 kcal or approx. 2000 kJ.

Given everything we've discussed so far, you're probably asking yourself, "How many kilocalories do I need each day to maintain my current weight?" This question is not always easy to answer, as our energy needs fluctuate from day to day according to our activity level, the environmental conditions, and other factors, such as the amount and type of food we eat and our intake of caffeine, which temporarily increases our BMR. However, you can get a general estimate of how much energy your body needs to maintain your present weight. The You Do the Math box on page 377 describes how you can estimate your total daily energy needs.

RECAP The energy balance equation relates food intake to energy expenditure. Eating more energy than you expend causes weight gain, while eating less energy than you expend causes weight loss. The three components of energy expenditure are basal metabolic rate, the thermic effect of food, and the energy cost of physical activity.

Genetic Factors Affect Body Weight

Our genetic background influences our height, weight, body shape, and metabolic rate. A classic study showed that the body weights of adults who were adopted as children are similar to the weights of their biological parents, not their adoptive parents (Stunkard et al., 1986). **Figure 11.8** shows that about 25% of our body fat is accounted for by genetic influences. Two theories linking genetics with our body weight are the thrifty gene theory and the set-point theory.

The Thrifty Gene Theory

The **thrifty gene theory** suggests that some people possess a gene (or genes) that causes them to be energetically thrifty. This means that at rest and even during active times these individuals expend less energy than people who do not possess this gene. The proposed purpose of this gene is to protect a person from starving to death during extreme food shortages. This theory has been applied to some Native American tribes, as these societies were exposed to centuries of feast or famine. Those with a thrifty metabolism survived when little food was available, and this trait was passed on to future generations. Although an actual thrifty gene (or genes) has not yet been identified, researchers continue to study this explanation as a potential cause of obesity.

If this theory were true, think about how people who possessed this thrifty gene would respond to today's environment. Low levels of physical activity, inexpensive food sources that are high in fat and energy, and excessively large serving sizes are the norm in our society. People with a thrifty metabolism would experience a great amount of weight gain, and their body would be more resistant to weight loss. Theoretically, having thrifty genetics would be advantageous during times of minimal food resources; however, this state could lead to very high levels of obesity in times of plenty.

The Set-Point Theory

The **set-point theory** suggests that our body is designed to maintain our weight within a narrow range, or at a "set point." In many cases, our body appears to respond in such a way as to maintain our present weight. When we dramatically reduce our energy intake (such as with fasting or strict diets), our body responds with physiologic changes that cause our BMR to drop. This causes a significant slowing of our energy output. In addition, being physically active while fasting or starving is difficult because we just don't have the energy for it. These two mechanisms of energy conservation may contribute to some of the rebound weight gain many dieters experience after they quit dieting.

Conversely, overeating in some people may cause an increase in BMR and is thought to be associated with an increased thermic effect of food, as well as an increase in spontaneous movements, or fidgeting. This in turn increases energy output and prevents weight gain. These changes may explain how some people fail to gain all of the weight expected from eating excess food. We don't eat exactly the same amount of food each day; some days we overeat, while other days we eat less. When you think about how much our daily energy intake fluctuates (about 20% above and below our average monthly intake), our ability to maintain a certain weight over long periods of time suggests that there is some evidence to support the set-point theory.

Can we change our weight set point? It appears that, when we maintain changes in our diet and activity level over a long period of time, weight change does occur. This is obvious in the case of obesity, since many people become obese during middle adulthood, and they are not able to maintain the lower body weight they had as a younger adult. Also, many people do successfully lose weight and maintain that weight loss over long periods of time. Thus, the set-point theory cannot entirely account for our body's resistance to weight loss.

A classic study done by researchers at Laval University in Quebec shows how genetics may affect our tendency to maintain a set point (Bouchard et al., 1990). Twelve pairs of male identical twins volunteered to stay in a dormitory, where they were supervised 24 hours a day for 120 consecutive days. Researchers measured how much energy each man needed to maintain his body weight at the beginning of the study. For 100 days, the subjects were fed 1000 kcal (4200 kJ) more per day than they needed to maintain body weight. Daily physical activity was limited, but each person was allowed to walk outdoors for 30 minutes each day, read, watch television and videos, and play cards and video games. The research staff stayed with these men to ensure that they did not stray from the study protocol.

The average weight gain this group of men experienced was almost 8.2 kg (18 lb.). Although they were all overfed enough energy to gain about 11.8 kg (26 lb.), the average weight gain was 3.6 kg (8 lb.) less than expected. These men gained mostly fat but also gained about 2.7 kg (6 lb.) of lean body mass. Interestingly, there was a very wide range of weight gained. One man gained only about 4.3 kg (9.5 lb.), while another man gained more than 13.2 kg (29 lb.)! Keep in mind that the food these men ate and the activities they performed were tightly controlled.

This study shows that, when people overeat by the same amount of food, they can gain very different amounts of weight and body fat. While each twin gained an amount similar to that of his brother, there was a lot of difference in how each set of twins responded. It is suggested that those who are more resistant to weight gain when they overeat have the ability to increase BMR, store more excess energy as lean body mass instead of fat, and increase spontaneous movements, such as fidgeting. Thus, genetic differences may explain why some people are better able to maintain a certain weight set point.

▲ Identical twins tend to maintain a similar weight throughout life.

RECAP Many factors affect our ability to gain and lose weight. Our genetic background influences our height, weight, body shape, and metabolic rate. The thrifty gene theory suggests that some people possess a thrifty gene, or set of genes, that causes them to expend less energy at rest and during physical activity than people who do not have this gene (or genes). The set-point theory suggests that our body is designed to maintain weight within a narrow range, also called a set point.

Physiologic Factors Influence Body Weight

Numerous physiologic factors affect body weight, including hypothalamic regulation of hunger and satiety, specific proteins, and other factors. Together, these contribute to the complexities of weight regulation.

▲ A balanced diet contains protein, carbohydrate, and fat.

Hunger and Satiety

As introduced in Chapter 3, *hunger* is the innate, physiologic drive or need to eat. Physical signals, such as a growling stomach and light-headedness, indicate when one is hungry. This drive for food is triggered by physiologic changes, such as low blood glucose, that affect chemicals in the brain. The hypothalamus plays an important role in hunger regulation. Special hypothalamic cells referred to as *feeding cells* respond to conditions of low blood glucose, causing hunger and driving a person to eat. Once one has eaten and the body has responded accordingly, other centers in the hypothalamus are triggered, and the desire to eat is reduced. The state reached in which there is no longer a desire to eat is referred to as *satiety*. Some people may have an insufficient satiety mechanism, which prevents them from feeling full after a meal, allowing them to overeat.

Proteins

Leptin is a protein; it is produced by adipose cells and functions as a hormone. The amounts found circulating in the blood are proportional to the amount of body fat (specifically white adipose tissue)—that is, the higher the body fat, the more leptin produced. First discovered in mice, leptin reduces food intake and increases physical activity and energy expenditure, and thus causes a decrease in body weight and body fat. A gene called the *ob* gene (obesity gene) codes for the production of leptin. When the ob gene is functioning normally, it produces leptin. When there is a genetic mutation of the ob gene, leptin is not secreted in sufficient amounts, food intake increases dramatically, energy expenditure is reduced, and weight gain occurs. Researchers believe that leptin is the hormone that relays information about fat cell and fat tissue metabolism and body weight to the appetite centres in the hypothalamus (Kieffer and Habener, 2000). They have found that mice bred to become obese (the ob/ob strain) are not only leptin deficient but also have type 2 diabetes. Several studies have demonstrated that these obese mice respond well to leptin injections, and not only do they lose weight, but their blood insulin levels also drop.

When these findings were first published, a great deal of excitement was generated about how leptin might decrease obesity in humans. Unfortunately, studies have shown that, although obese mice respond positively to leptin injections, obese humans do not. Instead, they tend to have very high amounts of leptin in their body and are insensitive to leptin's effects. In truth, we have just begun to learn about leptin and its role in the human body. Researchers are currently studying leptin's relation to diabetes, starvation, and overeating, and it might be involved in cardiovascular and kidney complications that result from obesity and related diseases.

In addition to leptin, numerous proteins affect the regulation of appetite and storage of body fat. Primary among these is **ghrelin**, a protein synthesized in the stomach. It acts as a hormone and plays an important role in appetite regulation through its actions in the hypothalamus. Ghrelin stimulates appetite and increases food intake. Ghrelin levels increase before a meal and fall within about one hour after a meal. This action indicates that ghrelin may be a primary contributor to both hunger and satiety. Ghrelin levels appear to increase after weight loss, and researchers speculate that this factor might explain why people who have lost weight have difficulty keeping it off (Cummings et al., 2002). We noted earlier that obese people seem to lose their sensitivity to leptin, but this is not true for ghrelin: obese people are just as sensitive to the effects of ghrelin as non-obese people (Druce et al., 2005). For this reason, potential mechanisms that can block the actions of ghrelin are currently a prime target of research into the treatment of obesity.

Peptide YY, or **PYY**, is a protein produced in the gastrointestinal tract. It is released after a meal, in amounts proportional to the energy content of the meal. In contrast with ghrelin, PYY decreases appetite and inhibits food intake in animals and humans (Batterham et al., 2002). Interestingly, obese individuals have lower levels of PYY when they are fasting and show less of an increase in PYY after a meal than non-obese individuals, which suggests that PYY may be important in the manifestation and maintenance of obesity (Batterham et al., 2003).

Uncoupling proteins have recently become the focus of research into body weight. These proteins are found in the inner membrane of mitochondria, which you may

leptin A hormone, produced by body fat, that acts to reduce food intake and increase physical activity and energy, thereby leading to a loss of body weight and body fat.

ghrelin A protein, synthesized in the stomach, that acts as a hormone and plays an important role in appetite regulation by stimulating appetite.

peptide YY (PYY) A protein, produced in the gastrointestinal tract, that is released after a meal in amounts proportional to the energy content of the meal; it decreases appetite and inhibits food intake.

recall from Chapter 3 are organelles present within cells that generate ATP, including skeletal muscle cells and adipose cells. Some research suggests that uncoupling proteins cause certain steps in ATP production to become disconnected or unlinked from one another; when this occurs, the process produces heat instead of ATP. This production of heat increases energy expenditure and results in less storage of excess energy. Thus, a person with more uncoupling proteins or a higher activity of these proteins would be more resistant to weight gain and obesity.

Three forms of uncoupling proteins have been identified: UCP1 is found exclusively in **brown adipose tissue**, a type of adipose tissue that has more mitochondria than white adipose tissue. It is found in significant amounts in animals and newborn humans. It was traditionally thought that adult humans had very little brown adipose tissue. However, recent evidence suggests that humans may have substantially more brown adipose tissue than previously assumed (Virtanen et al., 2009) and that people with higher BMI values have lower amounts of brown adipose tissue (Cypess et al., 2009). These findings suggest a possible role of brown adipose tissue in obesity. Two other uncoupling proteins, UCP2 and UCP3, are known to be important to energy expenditure and resistance to weight gain. These proteins are found in various tissues, including white adipose tissue and skeletal muscle. The roles of brown adipose tissue and uncoupling proteins in human obesity are currently being researched.

Other Physiologic Factors

The following are other physiologic factors known to increase satiety (or decrease food intake):

- The hormones serotonin and cholecystokinin (CCK); serotonin is made from the amino acid tryptophan, and CCK is produced by the intestinal cells and stimulates the gallbladder to secrete bile; this triggers satiety receptors in the brain
- An increase in blood glucose levels, such as that normally seen after the consumption of a meal
- Stomach expansion
- Nutrient absorption from the small intestine

The following are other physiologic factors that can decrease satiety (or increase food intake):

- Beta-endorphins, which are hormones that enhance a sense of pleasure while eating, increasing food intake
- Neuropeptide Y, an amino acid–containing compound produced in the hypothalamus; ghrelin triggers the secretion of neuropeptide Y, which in turn causes people to feel hungry and to eat
- Decreased blood glucose levels, such as the decrease that occurs after an overnight fast.

Cultural and Economic Factors Affect Food Choices and Body Weight

Both cultural and economic factors can contribute to obesity. As discussed in detail in Chapter 1, cultural factors (including religious beliefs and learned food preferences) affect our food choices and eating patterns. In addition, the customs of many cultures put food at the centre of celebrations of festivals and holidays, and overeating is tacitly encouraged. In addition, because both parents work outside the home in most Canadian families, more people are embracing the 'fast-food culture', preferring and almost exclusively choosing highly processed and high calorie (i.e., high calorie fast foods) fast foods from restaurants and grocery stores.

Coinciding with these cultural influences on food intake are cultural factors that promote inactivity. These include the shift from manual labour to more sedentary jobs and increased access to labour-saving devices in all areas of our lives. Even seemingly minor changes—such as texting someone in your dorm instead of walking down the hall to chat, or walking through an automated door instead of pushing a door open—add up to a lower expenditure of energy by the end of the day. Research

brown adipose tissue A type of adipose tissue that has more mitochondria than white adipose tissue, and which can increase energy expenditure by uncoupling oxidation from ATP production. It is found in significant amounts in animals and newborn humans.

with sedentary ethnic minority women in the United States indicates that other common barriers to increasing physical activity include lack of personal motivation, no physically active role models to emulate, acceptance of larger body size, exercise being considered culturally unacceptable, and fear for personal safety in both rural and urban settings (Eyler, Matson-Koffman, Rohm-Young et al., 2003; Eyler, Matson-Koffman, Vest et al., 2002). In short, cultural factors influence both food consumption and levels of physical activity and can contribute to weight gain.

Economic status is related to health status, particularly in developed countries, such as Canada and the United States: people of lower economic status have higher rates of obesity and related chronic diseases than people with higher incomes (Pickett, et al., 2005). In addition, economic factors strongly affect our food choices and eating behaviours. Refer to Chapter 2 for helpful information on designing healthful diets.

Psychological and Social Factors Influence Behaviour and Body Weight

In Chapter 3, we explored the concept that *appetite* can be experienced in the absence of hunger. Appetite may therefore be considered a psychological drive to eat, being stimulated by learned preferences for food and particular situations that promote eating. People may also follow social cues related to the timing and size of meals. Mood can also affect appetite, as some people will eat more or less if they feel depressed or happy. As you can imagine, appetite leads many people to overeat.

Some Social Factors Promote Overeating

Social factors—such as pressure from family and friends to eat the way they do—can encourage people to overeat. For instance, the pressure to overeat on holidays is high, as family members or friends offer extra servings of favourite holiday foods and follow a very large meal with a rich dessert.

Canadians also have numerous opportunities to overeat because of easy access throughout the day to foods high in fat and energy. Vending machines selling junk foods are everywhere: at some schools, in business offices, and even at fitness centres. Shopping malls are filled with fast-food restaurants, where inexpensive, large serving sizes are the norm. Food manufacturers are producing products in ever-larger serving sizes. Even some foods traditionally considered healthful, such as some brands of peanut butter and yogurt, are filled with added sugars and other ingredients that are high in energy. This easy access to large servings of high-energy meals and snacks leads many people to consume excess energy.

Some Social Factors Promote Inactivity

Social factors can also cause people to be less physically active. For instance, we don't even have to spend time or energy preparing food anymore, as everything either is ready to serve or requires just a few minutes to cook in a microwave oven. Other social factors restricting physical activity include living in an unsafe community; watching a lot of television; coping with family, community, and work responsibilities that do not involve physical activity; and living in an area with harsh weather conditions. Many overweight people identify such factors as major barriers to maintaining a healthful body weight, and research seems to confirm their influence.

Another social factor promoting inactivity in both children and adults is the increasing dominance of technology in our choices of entertainment. Instead of participating in sports or gathering for a dance at the community hall, we go to the movies or stay at home watching television, surfing the internet, and playing with video games and other hand-held devices. By reducing energy expenditure, these behaviours contribute to weight gain. For instance, a study of 11- to 13-year-old schoolchildren found that children who watched more than two hours of television per night were more likely to be overweight or obese than children who watched less than two hours of television per night. Similarly, adults who reported an increase in television watching of 20 hours per week (approximately three hours per day) over a nine-year period had a significant increase in waist circumference, indicating significant weight gain (Koh-Banerjee et al., 2003).

Fast foods may be inexpensive and filling, but they're usually high in saturated fat, salt, and sugar.

Social Pressures Can Promote Underweight

On the other hand, social pressures to maintain a lean body are great enough to encourage many people to undereat or to avoid foods that are perceived as "bad," especially fats. Our society ridicules and often ostracizes overweight people, many of whom face discrimination in many areas of their lives, including employment. A recent study found that children who are obese are 60% more likely to experience bullying than children of normal weight (Lumeng et al., 2010). Moreover, media images of waif-like fashion models and men in tight jeans with muscular chests and abdomens encourage many people—especially adolescents and young adults—to skip meals, resort to crash diets, and exercise obsessively. Even some people of normal body weight push themselves to achieve an unrealistic and unattainable weight goal, in the process threatening their health and even their lives (see the **In Depth** following Chapter 12 for the consequences of disordered eating).

It should be clear that how a person gains, loses, and maintains body weight is a complex matter. Most people who are overweight have tried several weight-loss programs but have been unsuccessful in maintaining long-term weight loss. A significant number of these people have consequently given up all weight-loss attempts. Some even suffer from severe depression related to their body weight. Should we condemn these people as failures and continue to pressure them to lose weight? Should people who are overweight but otherwise healthy (for example, having normal blood pressure, cholesterol, triglyceride, and glucose levels) be advised to lose weight? As we continue to search for ways to help people achieve and maintain a healthful body weight, our society must take measures to reduce the social pressures facing people who are overweight or obese.

◆ Behaviours learned as a child can affect weight and physical activity patterns.

RECAP The macronutrient composition of the diet influences the storage of body fat, and physiologic factors, such as hunger, leptin, ghrelin, peptide YY, uncoupling proteins, and various hormones, affect body weight by their effects on satiety, appetite, and energy expenditure. Cultural and economic factors can significantly influence the amounts and types of food we eat. Psychological and social factors influencing weight include the ready availability of large portions of high-energy foods and lack of physical activity. Social pressures on those who are overweight can drive people to use harmful methods to achieve an unrealistic body weight.

How Can You Achieve and Maintain a Healthful Body Weight?

Now that you understand what constitutes a healthful body weight, how are you feeling about yours? If you are feeling ready to make some changes to your lifestyle, then take heart. Losing weight and maintaining that weight loss are goals well within your reach using three primary strategies:

- Gradual reduction in energy intake
- Regular and appropriate physical activity
- Application of behaviour modification techniques

In this section, we'll first discuss popular diet plans that may or may not incorporate these strategies. We'll then explore how to design a personalized weight-loss program that includes all three of them.

If You Decide to Follow a Popular Diet Plan, Choose One Based on the Three Strategies

If you'd like to lose weight, the information on pages 386–387 will help you to design your own personalized diet plan. If you'd feel more comfortable following an established plan, however, many are available. How can you know whether it is based on sound dietary principles, and whether its promise of long-term weight loss will prove true for *you*? Look to the three strategies just identified: Does the plan promote gradual reductions in energy intake? Does it advocate increased physical activity? Does it include strategies for modifying your eating and activity-related behaviours? Reputable diet plans incorporate all of these strategies. Unfortunately, many dieters are drawn to fad diets, which do not.

Avoid Fad Diets

Beware of fad diets! They are simply what their name implies—fads that do not result in long-term, healthful weight changes. To be precise, fad diets are programs that enjoy short-term popularity and are sold based on a marketing gimmick that appeals to the public's desires and fears. Of the hundreds of such diets on the market today, most will "die" within a year, only to be born again as a 'new and improved' fad diet. The goal of the person or company designing and marketing a fad diet is to make money.

How can you tell if the program you are interested in qualifies as a fad diet? Here are some pointers to help you:

- The promoters of the diet claim that the program is new, improved, or based on some new discovery; however, no credible scientific data are available to support these claims.
- The program is touted for its ability to promote rapid weight loss or body fat loss, usually more than 1 kg or 2.2 lb. per week, and may claim that weight loss can be achieved with little or no physical exercise.
- The diet includes special foods and supplements, many of which are expensive and/or difficult to find or can be purchased only from the diet promoter. Common recommendations for these diets include avoiding certain foods, eating only a special combination of certain foods, and including 'magic' foods in the diet that 'burn fat' and 'speed up metabolism'.
- The diet may include a rigid menu that must be followed daily or may limit participants to eating a few select foods each day. Variety and balance are discouraged, and certain foods (such as fruits and vegetables) are restricted.
- Many programs promote supplemental foods and/or nutritional supplements that are described as critical to the success of the diet. They usually include claims that these supplements can cure or prevent a variety of health ailments or that the diet can stop the aging process.

In a world where many of us feel we have to meet a certain physical standard to be attractive and 'good enough', these types of diets flourish. Unfortunately, the only people who usually benefit from them are their marketers, who can become very wealthy promoting programs that are not effective for most people.

Diets Focusing on Macronutrient Composition May or May Not Work for You

It is well recognized that achieving a negative energy balance is the major factor in successful weight loss. The impact of the macronutrient composition of a diet is currently a topic of considerable debate. The three main types of weight-loss diets that have been most seriously and comprehensively researched all encourage increased consumption of certain macronutrients and restrict the consumption of others. Provided here is a brief review of these three main types and their general effects on weight loss and health parameters (Freedman, King, and Kennedy, 2001).

Diets High in Carbohydrate and Moderate in Fat and Protein
Balanced high-carbohydrate, moderate-fat and -protein diets typically contain 55%–60% of total energy intake as carbohydrate, 20%–30% of total energy intake as fat, and 15%–20% of energy intake as protein. These diets include *Weight Watchers*, *Jenny Craig*, and others that follow the general guidelines of *Canada's Food Guide*. All of these diet plans emphasize that weight loss occurs when energy intake is lower than energy expenditure. The goal is gradual weight loss, or about 0.5 to 1 kg (1 to 2 lb.) of body weight per week. Typical energy deficits are between 2100 and 4200 kJ or 500 and 1000 kcal per day. It is recommended that women eat no less than 4200 to 5020 kJ or 1000 to 1200 kcal per day and that men consume no less than 5020 to 5880 kJ or 1200 to 1400 kcal per day. Regular physical activity is encouraged.

To date, these types of low-energy diets have been researched more than any others. A substantial amount of high-quality scientific evidence (from randomized controlled trials) indicates that they are effective in decreasing body weight. In addition, the people who lose weight on these diets also decrease their LDL-cholesterol, reduce their blood triglyceride levels, and decrease their blood pressure. The diets are nutritionally adequate if the individual's food choices follow *Canada's Food Guide*. If the individual's food choices are not varied and balanced, the diet may be low in nutrients such as fibre, zinc, calcium, iron, and vitamin B_{12}. Under these circumstances, supplementation is needed.

Diets Low in Carbohydrate and High in Fat and Protein Low-carbohydrate, high-fat and -protein diets cycle in and out of popularity on a regular basis. By definition, these types of diets generally contain less than 100 g of carbohydrate per day, about 55%–65% of total energy intake as fat, and the balance of daily energy intake as protein. Examples of these types of diets are Dr. Atkins' Diet Revolution, the Carbohydrate Addict's Diet, Sugar Busters, and Protein Power. These diets minimize the role of restricting total energy intake on weight loss. They instead advise participants to restrict carbohydrate intake, proposing that carbohydrates are addictive and cause significant overeating, insulin surges leading to excessive fat storage, and an overall metabolic imbalance that leads to obesity. The goal is to reduce carbohydrates enough to cause ketosis, which will decrease blood glucose and insulin levels and can reduce appetite.

Countless people claim to have lost substantial weight on these types of diets; however, quality scientific studies of these diets are just beginning to be conducted. The current limited evidence suggests that individuals in both free-living and experimental conditions do lose weight with these diets (Gardner et al., 2007). In addition, it appears that people who lose weight may also experience positive metabolic changes, such as decreased blood lipid levels, decreased blood pressure, and decreased blood glucose and insulin (Clifton, Keogh, and Noakes, 2008; Shai et al., 2008). However, the amount of weight loss and improvements in metabolic health measured with these diets are no greater than those seen with higher-carbohydrate diets (Foster et al., 2010). Our current limited evidence of the effectiveness, along with concerns about long-term compliance, potential health risks, and side effects, has made these diets controversial. Some researchers have suggested that it may be more important to focus on the glycemic index, as there is evidence that low GI diets produce smaller increases in blood levels of insulin and more body fat oxidation (Lopes da Silva & de Cássia Gonçalves Alfenas, 2011). Others have suggested that it might be more useful to identify strategies to help people maintain their diets than to focus on the macronutrient content (Alhassan et al., 2008).

Low-Fat and Very-Low-Fat Diets Low-fat diets contain 11%–19% of total energy as fat, whereas very-low-fat diets contain less than 10% of total energy as fat. Both of these types of diets are high in carbohydrate and moderate in protein. Examples are Dr. Dean Ornish's Program for Reversing Heart Disease and the New Pritikin Program. These diets do not focus on total energy intake but emphasize eating foods higher in complex carbohydrates and fibre. Consumption of sugar and white flour is very limited. The Ornish diet is vegetarian, whereas the Pritikin diet allows 100 grams (3.5 oz.) of lean meat per day. Regular physical activity is a key component of these diets.

These programs were not originally designed for weight loss but, rather, were developed to decrease or reverse heart disease. Also, these diets are not popular with consumers, who view them as too restrictive and difficult to follow. Thus, there are limited data on their effects. However, high-quality evidence suggests that people following these diets do lose weight, and some data suggest that these diets may also decrease LDL-cholesterol, triglyceride, glucose, and insulin levels, as well as blood pressure. Few side effects have been reported on these diets; the most common is flatus (intestinal gas), which typically decreases over time. Low-fat diets are low in vitamin B_{12}, and very-low-fat diets are low in essential fatty acids, vitamins B_{12} and E, and zinc. Thus, supplementation is needed. These types of diets are not considered safe for people with diabetes who are insulin dependent (either type 1 or type 2) or for people with carbohydrate-malabsorption illnesses.

'Low-carb' diets may lead to weight loss, but there are few studies evaluating their effectiveness over the longer term.

Low-fat and very-low-fat diets emphasize eating foods higher in complex carbohydrates and fibre.

If You Decide to Design Your Own Diet Plan, Include the Three Strategies

As we noted earlier, a healthful and effective weight-loss plan involves making a modest reduction in your energy intake, incorporating physical activity into each day, and practicing changes in behaviour that can help you reduce your energy intake and increase your energy expenditure. Following are some guidelines for designing your own personalized diet plan that incorporates these strategies.

Set Realistic Goals

The first key to safe and effective weight loss is setting realistic goals related to how much weight to lose and how quickly to lose it. Although making gradual changes in body weight is frustrating for most people, this slower change is much more effective in maintaining weight loss over the long term. Ask yourself the question "How long did it take me to gain this extra weight?" If you are like most people, your answer is that it took one or more years, not just a few months. A fair expectation for weight loss is similarly gradual: experts recommend a pace of about 0.25 to 1 kg (0.5 to 2 lb.) per week. A weight-loss plan should never provide less than 5020 kJ or 1200 kcal per day unless you are under a physician's supervision. Your weight-loss goals should also take into consideration any health-related concerns you have. After checking with your physician, you may decide initially to set a goal of simply maintaining your current weight and preventing additional weight gain. After your weight has remained stable for several weeks, you might then write down realistic goals for weight loss.

Goals that are more likely to be realistic and achievable share the following characteristics:

- *They are specific.* Telling yourself "I will eat less this week" is not helpful because the goal is not specific. An example of a specific goal is "I will eat only half of my restaurant entrée tonight and take the rest home and eat it tomorrow for lunch."
- *They are reasonable.* If you are not presently physically active, it would be unreasonable to set a goal of exercising for 30 minutes every day. A more reasonable goal would be to exercise for 15 minutes per day, three days per week. Once you've achieved that goal, you can increase the frequency, intensity, and time of exercise according to the improvements in fitness that you have experienced.
- *They are measurable.* Effective goals are ones you can measure. An example is "I will lose at least half a pound by May 1st" or "I will substitute drinking water for my regular soft drink at lunch each day this week." Recording your specific, measurable goals will help you determine whether you are achieving them.

By monitoring your progress regularly, you can determine whether you are meeting your goals or whether you need to revise them based on accomplishments or challenges that arise.

QUICK TIPS

Controlling Portion Sizes

- Follow the serving sizes recommended in *Canada's Food Guide*. This requires understanding what constitutes a serving size and measuring foods to determine whether they meet or exceed the recommended serving size.
- To help increase your understanding of the portion sizes of packaged foods, measure out the amount of food that is identified as 1 serving on the Nutrition Facts Panel, and eat it from a plate or bowl instead of straight out of the box or bag.
- Try using smaller dishes, bowls, and glasses. This will make your portion appear larger, and you'll be eating or drinking less.
- When cooking at home, put a serving of the entrée on your plate; then freeze any leftovers in single-serving containers. This way, you won't be tempted to eat the whole batch before the food goes bad, and you'll have ready-made servings for future meals.
- To help you fill up, take second helpings of plain vegetables. That way, dessert may not seem so tempting!
- When buying snacks, go for single-serving, prepackaged items. If you buy larger bags or boxes, divide the snack into single-serving bags.
- When you have a treat, such as ice cream, measure out 125 mL or 1/2 cup, eat it slowly, and enjoy it!
- To test your understanding of what exactly constitutes a serving size, take the "Portion Distortion" interactive quiz from the National Institutes of Health (http://hp2010.nhlbihin.net/portion/index.htm).

Eat Smaller Portions of Lower-Fat Foods

The portion sizes of foods offered and sold in restaurants have expanded considerably over the past 40 years. One of the biggest challenges is understanding what a healthful portion size is and how to reduce the portion sizes of foods that we eat.

Recent studies indicate that, when children and adults are presented with large portion sizes of foods and beverages, they eat more energy (calories) overall and do not respond to cues of fullness or satiety (Ello-Martin, Ledikwe, and Rolls, 2005; Flood, Roe, and Rolls, 2006). Thus, it has been suggested that effective weight-loss strategies include reducing both the portion size and the energy density of foods consumed and replacing energy-dense beverages with low-calorie or non-caloric beverages (Flood, Roe, and Rolls, 2006).

What specific changes can you make to reduce your energy intake and stay healthy? The Weight-Control Information Network of the U.S. National Institutes of Health offers some helpful suggestions on their website: www.win.niddk.nih.gov/publications/just_enough.htm#home.

Now that you have your portion sizes under control, what can you do to reduce the energy content of the portions you *do* eat? This goal can be achieved by eliminating extra fats, such as butter, cheese sauces, mayonnaise, and snack foods (such as ice cream, doughnuts, and cakes). Save these foods as occasional special treats. Select lower-fat versions of the foods listed in *Canada's Food Guide*. This means selecting leaner cuts of meat (such as the white meat of poultry and extra-lean ground beef) and reduced-fat or skim dairy products, and selecting lower-fat preparation methods (such as baking and broiling instead of frying). It also means switching from a sugar-filled beverage to a low-calorie or non-caloric beverage during and between meals.

In addition, try to increase the number of times each day that you choose foods that are nutrient dense—that are relatively low in energy and high in nutrients and fibre. These include salads (with low-calorie or non-caloric dressings), fruits, vegetables, and broth-based soups. Because they contain relatively more water and fibre than more energy-dense foods, they can help you feel satiated without having to consume large amounts of energy.

Participate in Regular Physical Activity

Why is being physically active so important for achieving changes in body weight and for maintaining a healthful body weight? Of course, we expend extra energy during physical activity, but there's more to it than that because exercise alone (without a reduction of energy intake) does not result in dramatic decreases in body weight. Instead, one of the most important reasons for being regularly active is that it helps us maintain or increase our lean body mass and our BMR. In contrast, energy restriction alone causes us to lose lean body mass. As you've learned, the more lean body mass we have, the more energy we expend over the long term.

The U.S. National Weight Control Registry is an ongoing project documenting the habits of over 4000 people who have lost at least

QUICK TIPS

Overcoming Barriers to Physical Activity

▶ *I don't have enough time!* An active lifestyle doesn't have to consume all your free time. Try to do a minimum of 30 minutes of moderate activity most—preferably all—days of the week. If you can, do 45 minutes. But remember, you don't have to get in all of your daily activity in one go! Be active for a few minutes at a time throughout your day. Walk from your residence or apartment to classes, if possible. Instead of meeting friends for lunch, meet them for a lunchtime walk, jog, or workout. Break up study sessions with three minutes of jumping jacks. Skip the elevator and take the stairs. When you're talking on the phone, pace instead of sitting still.

▶ *I can't manage the details!* Bust this excuse by keeping clean clothes, shoes, water, and equipment for physical activity in a convenient place. If time management is an obstacle, enroll in a scheduled fitness class, yoga class, sports activity, walking group, or running club. Put it on your schedule of academic classes and make it part of your weekly routine.

▶ *I just don't like to work out!* You don't have to! Try dancing, roller blading, walking, hiking, swimming, tennis, or any other activity you enjoy.

▶ *I can't stay motivated.* Friends can help. Use the "buddy" system by exercising with a friend and calling each other when you need encouragement to stay motivated. Or keep a journal or log of your daily physical activity. Write your week's goal at the top of the page (such as "Walk to and from campus each day, and at least 10 minutes on campus at lunch"). Then track your progress.

Nutrition DEBATE

Is Bariatric Surgery Appropriate for Adolescents?

For most of Stephanie's life, she has struggled with obesity. Following surgery to remove a craniopharyngioma (a type of brain tumour) at age seven, Stephanie began to feel hungry all the time. Doctors had to remove a part of the hypothalamus, the part of the brain that controls appetite. Stephanie gained weight to the point that she had difficulty moving and walking. She felt isolated from her teenage peers. By 15, Stephanie was 1.5 m (5 feet) tall and 158 kg (348 lb) (SickKids, 2010).

How do you think Stephanie felt in her daily life? What do you think her options are? Do you think this is an appropriate case for bariatric surgery?

There are many different terms and definitions for severe obesity. In adults a body mass index (BMI) over 40 kg/m² is considered obese class III. However in children and adolescents, BMI is classified using a growth chart that looks at BMI-for-age. It is estimated that 3% of Canadian children aged 12–17 years have complex severe obesity defined as: (1) BMI greater than the 95th percentile for their age and gender, and an obesity-related condition requiring specialty care, or another co-existing significant chronic illness; or (2) a BMI greater than the 99th percentile (SickKids, 2010).

Some researchers suggest that bariatric surgery should be considered in these individuals when lifestyle changes and pharmacotherapy (use of prescribed weight loss medications) have not resulted in significant weight loss. Bariatric surgery has the potential to decrease morbidity (illness) and health care costs for these individuals by decreasing the risk factors for related chronic diseases. The weight loss from bariatric surgery reduces the risk of obesity-related conditions such as type 2 diabetes, non-alcoholic fatty liver disease, dyslipidemia, hypertension, obstructive sleep apnea, and orthopedic problems (Inge, Xanthakos, and Zeller, 2007). Recent evidence suggests that bariatric surgery can cause type 2 diabetes to go into "remission" indefinitely and may improve glucose metabolism in adolescents (Inge et al., 2009). This means, with early intervention, in certain adolescents there is the potential to prevent a lifelong chronic disease. It may also greatly reduce the amount of teasing and bullying of obese adolescents, a situation that may become so intolerable that obese teens stop going to school.

Opponents to bariatric surgery in adolescents caution that there is not enough evidence on the effectiveness to support the risks associated with surgery. The risks depend on the type of surgery and are discussed further below. As of yet, there is no evidence to show that bariatric surgery reduces early mortality. Few randomized control trials have been done in adolescents to determine the long term effectiveness of surgery. In addition, the long-term effects and risks are unknown. Bariatric surgery requires a lifetime commitment and compliance to a rigorous lifestyle change (Lynn & Miller, 2009), and some teens are not ready for such a commitment. Some pediatricians feel strongly that surgery that causes malabsorption (e.g., gastric bypass) will interfere with the growth and development of teens, and argue that only "restrictive" techniques (e.g., adjustable gastric banding) should be used.

The two main types of bariatric surgery that have been trialed during adolescence are Roux-en-Y gastric bypass and adjustable gastric banding.

Roux-en-Y gastric bypass is a procedure that attaches the lower part of the small intestine to the stomach, so that most of the food bypasses the stomach and small intestine (see Figure 2 in the *In Depth* section following this chapter). This results in significantly less intake and absorption of food. In gastric banding the stomach size is reduced using a constricting band, thus restricting food intake (see Figure 2c in the *In Depth*). This surgery is minimally invasive and reversible. Gastric bypass surgery is associated with a greater weight loss; however, it comes with more operative and post-operative complications compared to gastric banding (Puzziferri et al., 2008). Gastric bypass has a 1% mortality rate (Tsai, Inge, and Burd, 2007) and complications include wound infections, hernia, bowel obstruction, ulcers, stricture, and nutrient deficiencies.

A survey of the members of the International Pediatric Endosurgery Group (n = 125) asked what was the best surgery for adolescents: 59% chose the gastric band, 22% chose the Roux-en-Y gastric bypass, 14% chose gastric sleeve, 1% chose biliopancreatic diversion, and 3% chose other surgical treatments (Puzziferri et al., 2008).

The Canadian Obesity Network is a non-profit corporation that brings together health care professionals, researchers, policy makers, and stakeholders to reduce the mental, physical, and economic burden of obesity on Canadians. In 2006, the Canadian Obesity Network released Clinical Practice Guidelines for obesity that recommend that bariatric surgery in adolescents be limited to exceptional cases and only be carried out by experienced teams. However, this recommendation was based on anecdotal evidence.

Guidelines and criteria for bariatric surgery in adolescence have also been suggested by researchers; however, there does not seem to be a consensus between regulating bodies yet. One main consideration is whether the patient's health is being compromised by severe obesity. In 2007, Inge et al. suggested the following criteria for

Have attempted at least six months of an organized weight management program
Have attained or nearly attained physiologic maturity
Be very severely obese (>95th percentile) with serious obesity-related co-morbidities or have a BMI-for-age >99th percentile with less severe co-morbidities (other existing conditions related to obesity)
Demonstrate commitment to comprehensive medical and psychological evaluations both before and after surgery
Be capable of and willing to adhere to nutritional guidelines postoperatively
Provide informed assent to surgical treatment
Agree to avoid pregnancy for at least one year postoperatively
Demonstrate decisional capacity to make informed decisions (based on age or psychological assessment)
Have a supportive family environment

adolescents considering bariatric surgery. These guidelines are more rigorous then the guidelines used in adults.

There are also several contraindications to bariatric surgery such as a medical cause for obesity, recent drug or substance abuse, lactation, pregnancy or planned pregnancy within two years, or a medical, psychiatric, or cognitive impairment that would prevent them from following post-surgery guidelines.

Post-surgery diet progresses slowly from liquids, to pureed food, to solid food. Due to the restriction of the size of the stomach patients must continue to have small, low calorie, and low carbohydrate meals. Adequate protein, vitamins, and minerals are still required and vitamin/mineral supplementation is required. Research is required on the compliance of adolescences to dietary recommendations post-surgery. Adolescents should also be followed by a multidisciplinary team including a bariatric surgeon, pediatric obesity specialist, nurse, dietitian, and pediatric psychologist or psychiatrist during all stages of surgery and post-surgery maintenance.

In February 2010, the Hospital for Sick Children in Toronto announced the opening of a new centre called SickKids Team Obesity Management Program, or STOMP. STOMP offers a team of health care providers and support groups to help manage pediatric obesity; they also offer gastric banding for eligible patients as one aspect of their total care. This is the first centre to offer bariatric surgery in children aged 12–17 years in Canada. The team includes doctors, a dietitian, a psychologist, an exercise therapist, and a nurse practitioner to oversee the care of their patients. In the first year the program anticipated 50 patients and 10–15 gastric banding surgeries. Stephanie was the first to have the gastric banding surgery at SickKids. Three years later, the surgery, better eating habits, and regular exercise have enabled her to lose more than one-third of her body weight (Sick-Kids, 2010).

She says, "I don't think I ever really saw a future for myself, in general... When I got the [surgery], it was like a second chance at life" (Weeks, 2010).

Many members of the public are still apprehensive about bariatric surgery in adolescents. A poll in the *Globe and Mail* newspaper found that of the 250 votes that came in, 57% said they didn't think surgery was the right option for obese teens, while 37% said it was the right one, and 12% were undecided (CBC, 2010).

What do you think? Which type of bariatric surgery do you think is the better option? What are your suggestions for future research and guidelines?

SickKids, February 5th, 2010. February 5, 2010. New SickKids program helps teens STOMP out obesity. Retrieved May 27, 2011 from http://www.sickkids.ca/AboutSickKids/Newsroom/PastNews/2010/STOMp. html; CBC news, February 5th, 2010. Obese teens offered surgery option. Retrieved May 27th, 2011 from http://www.cbc.ca/news/health/story/2010/02/05/obesity-surgery-children.html; Weeks, C. February 5th, 2010. SickKids first to offer teens surgery for obesity. Retrieved May 27th, 2011 from http://www.theglobeandmail.com/life/health/sickkids-first-to-offer-teens-surgery-for-obesity/article1457031.

QUICK TIPS

Modifying Your Behaviours Related to Food

▶ Shop for food only when you're not hungry.

▶ Avoid buying problem foods—that is, foods that you may have difficulty eating in moderate amounts.

▶ Avoid purchasing high-fat, high-sugar food from vending machines and convenience stores.

▶ Avoid feelings of deprivation by eating small, regular meals throughout the day.

▶ Eat only at set times in one location. Do not eat while studying, working, driving, watching television, and so forth.

▶ Slow down while eating.

▶ Keep a log of what you eat, when, and why. As discussed in Chapter 3, try to identify social or emotional cues that cause you to overeat, such as getting a poor grade on an exam or feeling lonely. Then strategize about non-food-related ways to cope, such as phoning a sympathetic friend.

▶ Save high-fat, high-energy snack foods (such as ice cream, doughnuts, and cakes) for occasional special treats.

▶ Whether at home or dining out, share food with others.

▶ Prepare healthful snacks to take along with you, so that you won't be tempted by foods from vending machines and fast-food restaurants.

▶ Chew food slowly, taking at least 20 minutes to eat a full meal, stopping at once if you begin to feel full.

▶ Always use appropriate utensils.

▶ Leave food on your plate or store it for the next meal.

▶ Don't punish yourself for deviating from your plan (and you will—everyone does). Ask others to avoid responding to any slips you make.

13.6 kg (30 lb.) and kept their weight off for at least one year (Wing and Phelan, 2005). The members have lost an average of 33 kg and have maintained the minimum weight-loss (13.6 kg) for an average of more than five years. Members report engaging in high levels of physical activity (approximately one hour per day); eating a low-calorie, low-fat diet; eating breakfast regularly; self-monitoring weight; and maintaining a consistent eating pattern across weekdays and weekends.

In addition to expending energy and maintaining lean body mass and BMR, regular physical activity improves our mood, results in a higher quality of sleep, increases self-esteem, and gives us a sense of accomplishment (see Chapter 12 for more benefits of regular physical activity). All of these changes enhance our ability to engage in long-term healthful lifestyle behaviours.

RECAP Achieving and maintaining a healthful body weight involves gradual reductions in energy intake, such as by eating smaller portion sizes and limiting dietary fat; engaging in regular physical activity; and applying appropriate behaviour modification techniques. Fad diets do not use these strategies and do not result in long-term, healthful behaviour change. Diets based on an altered macronutrient composition (e.g., low carbohydrate, high protein and high fat) may promote short-term weight loss, but longer-term health effects and weight loss have not been well documented.

What About Underweight?

As defined earlier in this chapter, underweight occurs when a person has too little body fat to maintain health. People with a BMI of less than 18.5 kg/m² are typically considered underweight. Being underweight increases the risk for infections and illness and impairs the body's ability to recover. Some people are healthy but underweight because of their genetics and/or because they are very physically active and consume adequate energy to maintain their underweight status but not enough to gain weight. In others, underweight is due to heavy smoking; an underlying disease, such as cancer or HIV infection; or an eating disorder, such as anorexia nervosa (see the **In Depth** on eating disorders that follows Chapter 12).

With so much emphasis on obesity and weight loss, some find it surprising that many people are trying to gain weight. People looking to gain weight include those who are underweight to the extent that it is compromising their health and many athletes who are attempting to increase their strength and power for competition.

To gain weight, people must eat more energy than they expend. While overeating large amounts of foods high in saturated fats (such as bacon, sausage, and cheese) can cause weight gain, doing this without exercising is not considered healthful because most of the weight gained is fat, and high-fat diets can increase

◀ Eating frequent nutrient- and energy-dense snacks can help promote weight gain.

T O P I C

Using Dietary Supplements to Lose Weight— Should You Consider It?

As we explored **In Depth** following Chapter 10, dangerous or ineffective supplements can be marketed and sold online without meeting strict safety and quality standards. Moreover, many of the recalls of supplements are voluntary. So if you want to lose weight—should you consider an over-the-counter weight-loss supplement?

Consumers have a variety of weight-loss products to choose from. Some of the most common are the mineral chromium, spirulina (blue-green algae), ginseng (a root used in Chinese medicine), chitosan (derived from the exoskeleton of crustaceans), green tea, and psyllium (a source of fibre) (Allison et al., 2001; Saper, Eisenberg, and Phillips, 2004). These products are popular despite the fact that studies find insufficient evidence to support their use. Some products marketed for weight loss do indeed increase metabolic rate and decrease appetite; however, they create these effects because they contain stimulants, substances that speed up physiologic processes. Use of these substances is controversial and may be dangerous, as excessive increases in heart rate and blood pressure can occur.

our risks for cardiovascular and other diseases. Unless there are medical reasons to eat a high-fat diet, it is recommended that people trying to gain weight eat a diet that is relatively low in dietary fat (less than 30% of total calories) and relatively high in complex carbohydrates (55% of total calories). Recommendations for weight gain include:

- Eat a diet that includes about 2100–4200 kJ (500–1000 kcal) per day more than is needed to maintain present body weight. Although we don't know exactly how much extra energy is needed to gain 0.5 kg or 1 lb., estimates range from 12 600 to 14 700 kJ or 3000 to 3500 kcal. Thus, eating 2100–4200 kJ (500–1000 kcal) per day in excess should result in a gain of 0.5–1.0 kg (1–2 lb.) of weight each week.
- Eat frequently, including meals and numerous snacks throughout the day. Many underweight people do not take the time to eat often enough.
- Avoid the use of tobacco products, as they depress appetite and increase metabolic rate, and both of these effects oppose weight gain. Tobacco use also causes lung, mouth, and esophageal cancers.
- Exercise regularly and incorporate weight lifting or some other form of resistance training into your exercise routine. This form of exercise is most effective in increasing muscle mass. Performing aerobic exercise (such as walking, running, bicycling, or swimming) at least 30 minutes for three days per week will help you maintain a healthy cardiovascular system.

The key to gaining weight is to eat frequent meals throughout the day and to select energy-dense foods. When selecting foods that are higher in fat, make sure they are higher in polyunsaturated and monounsaturated fats (such as peanut butter, olive and canola oils, and avocados). For instance, smoothies and milkshakes made with lower-fat milk or yogurt are a great way to take in a lot of energy. Eating peanut butter with fruit or celery and including salad dressings on your salad are other ways to increase the energy density of foods. The biggest challenge to weight gain is setting aside time to eat; by packing a lot of foods to take with you throughout the day, you can increase your opportunities to eat more.

RECAP Weight gain can be achieved by eating about 2100–4200 kJ (500–1000 kcal) per day more than is needed to maintain present weight and by performing weight lifting and aerobic exercise. Eating frequent meals throughout the day, selecting healthy foods that are energy dense, and avoiding the use of tobacco products are strategies that can assist with healthy weight gain.

Chapter Review

Test Yourself ANSWERS

1. False. Health can be defined in many ways. An individual who is overweight but who exercises regularly and has no additional risk factors for various diseases, such as heart disease and type 2 diabetes, is considered a healthy person.

2. False. Body composition assessments can help give you a general idea of your body fat level, but most methods are not extremely accurate.

3. True. Staying physically active helps us to maintain our muscle mass, which in turn assists us in preventing a dramatic drop in our basal metabolic rate. These changes can help reduce our risk for becoming obese as we get older.

Find the Quack

Jeff is an account executive for a telecommunications business. His long hours leave him little time to exercise, and his frequent travel means too many fattening restaurant meals. Thus, his weight has been creeping steadily upward, and as a result, he has high blood pressure. He's shopping for groceries one evening when he notices a colourful display at the end of an aisle. Bright signs surrounding stacks of slender, elegant bottles are promoting a new soft drink called GingerSlim, which promises to increase body metabolism and burn calories. Intrigued, Jeff accepts the sample a saleswoman hands him, along with a pamphlet. While sipping the beverage, which tastes like a strong ginger ale, Jeff reads the following in the product brochure:

- "GingerSlim is a calorie-burning soft drink that works by increasing the body's basal metabolic rate (BMR). An increased BMR burns more calories."
- "On average, BMR increases 10% for one to three hours after consuming GingerSlim."
- "GingerSlim is itself almost completely calorie-free (17 kJ per 250 mL or 4 calories per 8 fl. oz. bottle). It is a patented blend of pure water, ginger, caffeine, a sugar substitute, and a private blend of herbs and spices that rev up your metabolism."
- "GingerSlim can be safely consumed up to three times a day to maintain your increased BMR."

When Jeff reads the fine print on the back of the brochure, he discovers that each 8 oz. bottle of GingerSlim contains 210 mg of caffeine. He also notices a small area of boxed text at the bottom. It reads: "These statements have not been evaluated by Health Canada. This product is not intended to diagnose, treat, cure, or prevent any disease." Jeff notes the price of GingerSlim on the display: it's "On Special" for $4.99 for a four-pack.

1. A 250 mL or 8 fl. oz. cup of brewed coffee contains an average of 85 mg of caffeine. Approximately how many cups of coffee does the amount of caffeine in a 250 mL or 8 fl. oz. bottle of GingerSlim represent?

2. If Jeff were to drink the recommended three bottles of GingerSlim per day, how much caffeine would he consume?

3. Jeff normally starts his day with one cup of brewed coffee. He then switches to bottled water, juices, and caffeine-free sodas. Predict how Jeff might feel if he starts consuming three bottles of GingerSlim per day. Predict the effects, if any, that the beverage might have on his long-term health and his weight.

4. Jeff's morning coffee, for which he uses canned coffee, costs him approximately 20¢ per 250 mL or 8 fl. oz. cup. How much would Jeff pay to brew coffee containing the same amount of caffeine as in a bottle of GingerSlim? (Reminder: one bottle of GingerSlim costs approximately $1.25 and contains 210 mg caffeine.) Do you think GingerSlim offers anything that is worth the increased price? Why or why not?

Answers can be found in the study area of MasteringNutrition.

Review Questions

1. The ratio of a person's body weight to height is represented as his or her
   a. body composition.
   b. basal metabolic rate.
   c. bioelectrical impedance.
   d. body mass index.

2. The body's total daily energy expenditure includes
   a. basal metabolic rate, thermal effect of food, and effect of physical activity.
   b. basal metabolic rate, movement, standing, and sleeping.
   c. effect of physical activity, standing, and sleeping.
   d. body mass index, thermal effect of food, and effect of physical activity.

3. All people gain weight when they
   a. eat a high-fat diet (>35% fat).
   b. take in more energy than they expend.
   c. fail to exercise.
   d. take in less energy than they expend.

4. The set-point theory proposes that
   a. people who are overweight have a gene not found in slender people that sets their weight at a point higher than a normal healthful weight.
   b. people who are overweight have a gene that causes them to be energetically thrifty.
   c. all people have a genetic set point for their body weight.
   d. all people have a hormone that regulates their weight so that it always hovers near a given set point.

5. Our innate, physiologic drive to eat is called
   a. hunger.
   b. appetite.
   c. satiety.
   d. our basal metabolic rate.

6. To lose 0.5 kg (approximately 1 lb.) of weight, you need to create a deficit of approximately
   a. 1000 kcal.
   b. 3500 kcal.
   c. 7000 kcal.
   d. 14 700 kcal.

7. What percentage of adult Canadians are estimated to be overweight or obese?
   a. 10%
   b. 25%
   c. 40%
   d. More than 50%

8. Which one of the following is *not* a component of a sound weight change plan?
   a. Make gradual changes in energy intake
   b. Incorporate regular physical activity
   c. Aim to lose more than 1 kg (approx. 2.2 lbs) per week
   d. Choose a variety of foods

9. As part of recovery from surgery, Sydney has been trying to put on some weight and muscle. However, he has not been listening to the dietitian. He hates going to the gym and has been eating high-caloric foods to gain instead. His doctor has been worried about Sydney since he has an apple-shaped pattern of body fat. What are the risks associated with apple-shaped fat patterning? What do you think the dietitian suggested Sydney do to gain weight?

10. Identify at least four characteristics of a healthy weight.

11. Describe a sound weight loss program, including recommendations for diet, physical activity, and behavioural modifications.

12. Can you increase your basal metabolic rate? Is it wise to try? Defend your answer.

13. Identify at least four societal factors that may have influenced the rise in obesity rates in North America. Think especially of the effect of advances in technology that have occurred in the last 40 years.

14. Your friend Misty joins you for lunch and confesses that she is discouraged about her weight. She says that she has been trying "really hard" for three months to lose weight, but that no matter what she does, she cannot drop below 67.2 kg (148 lb). Based on her height, you know Misty is not overweight, and she exercises regularly. What questions would you suggest she think about? How would you advise her?

15. Simon has always had a lean build, but recently he's finding it even harder to keep his weight up. Constantly playing hockey, soccer, and badminton for his high school teams, Simon is always on the go. His mom always makes him a big breakfast of bacon and eggs, and Simon makes sure to eat a couple of ham sandwiches at lunchtime. Dinner is usually a couple of hamburgers after soccer practice, and sometimes he'll have his favourite protein bar before bed. He's never hungry between meals, so he rarely snacks during the day. Simon would really like to beef up so he can be a little more intimidating on the field, but he feels this is impossible. Given what you've learned about energy balance and weight management, do you think there are any problems with Simon's food intake? What might you advise him to change about his food choices that could help stimulate his appetite? Are there any other suggestions you might give Simon to help him gain weight?

Case Study

While babysitting, you notice that Haruki, the youngest child, isn't playing in the wading pool. His older siblings and their friends are all having a great time escaping the heat, so you ask Haruki why he isn't joining them. You discover that he is constantly picked on in school, and he is always called names like "elephant" and "fatty." He tries not to show that it bothers him, but he confides to you that he often goes home and cries by himself. Haruki states that he will never put on his bathing suit, no matter how hot it gets. Instead of playing in the wading pool, he asks if he can go get an ice cream cone and sit on the bench.

    a. Think back to your own childhood. Were you ever teased for some aspect of yourself that you felt unable to change?

    b. Can Haruki change his weight? What kinds of obstacles does he face?

    c. As overweight children are often made to feel ashamed and worthless by their peers, how would you propose that adults increase their awareness of social stigmatization and reduce incidents of teasing and insensitivity?

Answers to Review Questions can be found at the back of this text.

Web Resources

www.eatrightontario.ca
Eat Right Ontario

Email or call a registered dietitian! Learn more about a Canadian service designed to help you improve your health through nutritious eating.

www.hc-sc.gc.ca/fn-an/food-guide-aliment/index-eng.php
Health Canada—Eating Well with Canada's Food Guide

See this site for information about *Canada's Food Guide.*

www.obesitynetwork.ca
Canadian Obesity Network

This is a network connecting researchers, health professionals, and 150 partner organizations concerned about obesity issues in Canada.

www.cdc.gov/healthyweight/index.html
Centres for Disease Control and Prevention. Healthy Weight—It's Not a Diet, It's a Lifestyle!

This is an interactive site from the CDC for consumers who want to change their lifestyle to achieve and maintain a healthy weight.

www.sneb.org
Society for Nutrition Education and Behavior

Click on Nutrition Resources and then Weight Realities Division Resource List for additional resources related to positive attitudes about body image and healthful alternatives to dieting.

www.eatright.org
Academy of Nutrition and Dietetics (formerly the American Dietetic Association)

Go to this site to learn more about fad diets.

women.webmd.com/fad-diets
WebMD—Spotting Fad Diets

Visit this site to learn about the dangers of fad diets and how to identify them.

www.ftc.gov
Federal Trade Commission (US)

Go to Consumer Protection tab, click on Consumer Information and then choose Weight Loss & Fitness under the Health category. Find out about how to avoid false weight loss claims.

www.eatracker.ca
Eat Tracker

This online tool by the Dietitians of Canada allows you to track your day's food intake and activity expenditure and compares them with Health Canada guidelines.

www2.niddk.nih.gov/HealthEducation/HealthNutrit
National Institute of Diabetes and Digestive and Kidney Diseases

Find out more about healthy weight loss.

hp2010.nhlbihin.net/portion/
National Institutes of Health Portion Distortion

Take the "Portion Distortion" quiz and find out how changing portion sizes influences body weight.

www.nhlbisupport.com/bmi/
National Heart, Lung, and Blood Institute BMI calculator

Calculate your body mass index (BMI) on the internet.

MasteringNutrition®

Assignments
Animations Reading Labels
Activities NutriTools

Study Area
Practice Tests • Diet Analysis • eText

Obesity

R EAD ON.
Our society espouses values of
tolerance and compassion toward
all people, despite their political
or religious beliefs, sexual orientation, racial
and ethnic background, age, or level of functioning. However, there seems to be at least
one group of people against whom prejudice
is still acceptable: obese people. They remain
the punch line of many jokes, are socially
ostracized, and experience widespread harass-
ment and embarrassment at school, at work,
and even when they visit their doctors! At
work, people who are obese are paid less
than their normal-weight colleagues and are
discriminated against during both the hiring
and promotion processes (American Obesity

Association, 2002). Even more alarming, many studies have documented a general stigma toward obesity among physicians: one recent study found that higher patient BMI correlated with lower physician respect (Huizinga et al., 2009).

Such disdain is unwarranted: just like diabetes, heart disease, and cancer, obesity is a **multifactorial disease**, meaning that there are many things that cause it. Although factors within an individual's control, such as overeating and doing too little exercise, are certainly part of the picture, genetics, physiology, and psychological and social factors also contribute. This multifactorial basis makes obesity extremely challenging to treat. In this *In Depth*, we first take a closer look at the health effects of obesity. We then explore the factors that contribute to obesity and identify the treatment options currently available.

Why Is Obesity Harmful?

As noted in Chapter 11, one of the characteristics of obesity is an excessive amount of body fat that adversely affects health. People with a BMI of 30 kg/m^2 and greater are considered obese. Health Canada uses three classes of obesity, with a BMI value of 40 and over associated with an extremely high risk of developing health problems.

Both overweight and obesity are considered an epidemic in North America. Results of the 2007–2009 Canada Health Measures Survey showed that 38% of adults fall in the healthy weight range, 1% are

*Fitness of Canadian adults: Results from the 2007–2009 Canadian Health Measures Survey, from the Statistics Canada publication "Health Reports", 2010, Catalogue 82-003, Vol. 21, No. 1, March, 2010, available at: http://www.statcan.gc.ca/cgi-bin/af-fdr.cgi?l = eng&loc = 2010001/article/11064-eng.pdf.

underweight, 37% are overweight, and 24% are obese (Statistics Canada, 2010).* This alarming rise in obesity is a major health concern because it is linked to many chronic diseases and complications:

- Hypertension
- Dyslipidemia, including elevated total cholesterol, triglycerides, and LDL-cholesterol and decreased HDL-cholesterol
- Type 2 diabetes
- Heart disease
- Stroke
- Gallbladder disease
- Osteoarthritis
- Sleep apnea
- Certain cancers, such as colon, breast, endometrial, and gallbladder
- Menstrual irregularities and infertility
- Gestational diabetes, premature fetal deaths, neural tube defects, and complications during labour and delivery
- Depression
- Alzheimer's disease, dementia, and cognitive decline

Abdominal obesity is also one of five risk factors collectively referred to as the **metabolic syndrome**. A diagnosis of metabolic syndrome, which is typically made if a person has three or more of the factors, increases one's risk for heart disease, type 2 diabetes, and stroke. According to the ATP III Guidelines (van den Hooven, Ploemacher, and Goodwin, 2006), the factors are:

- Abdominal (central) obesity, defined as a waist circumference greater than or equal to 102 cm (40 inches) for men and 88 cm (35 inches) for women

---

multifactorial disease Any disease that may be attributable to one or more of a variety of causes.

metabolic syndrome A cluster of risk factors that increase one's risk for heart disease, type 2 diabetes, and stroke, including abdominal obesity, higher than normal triglyceride levels, lower than normal HDL-cholesterol levels, higher than normal blood pressure (greater than or equal to 130/85 mm Hg), and elevated fasting blood glucose levels.

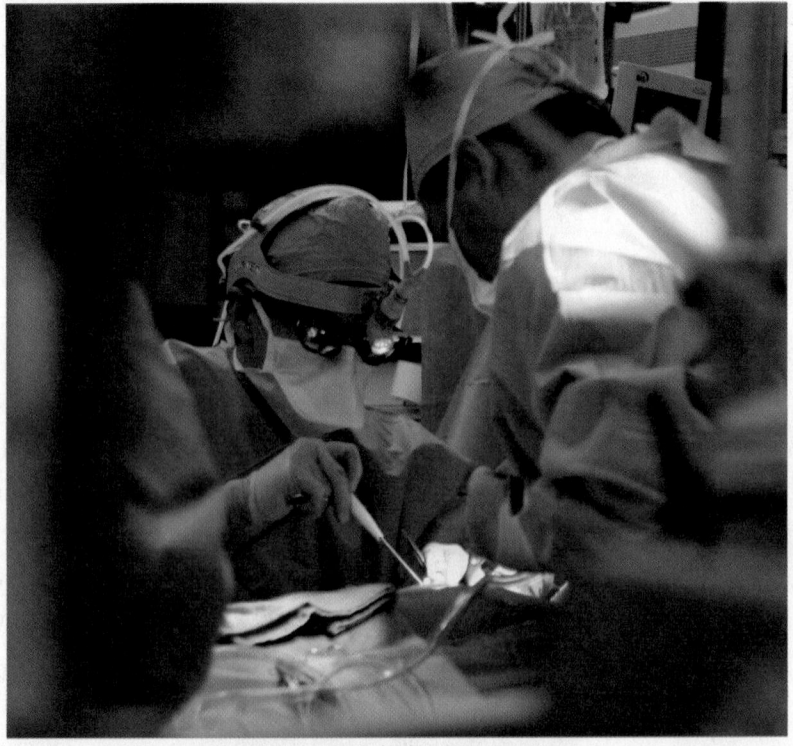

Obesity increases a person's risk of experiencing a heart attack, stroke, or other medical emergency.

- Higher-than-normal triglyceride levels, greater than or equal to 1.69 mmol/L

AND

- Lower-than-normal HDL-cholesterol levels (less than 1.04 mmol/L in men and 1.29 mmol/L in women)
- Higher than normal blood pressure (greater than or equal to 130/85 mm Hg)
- Fasting blood glucose levels greater than 6.1 mmol/L

People with metabolic syndrome are twice as likely to develop heart disease and five times as likely to develop type 2 diabetes than people without metabolic syndrome. About 25% of adults in the United States have metabolic syndrome (Department of Health and Human Services, 2010), but in Canada, the prevalence has not been well established. As we discussed in Chapter 1, several of the leading causes of death in Canada are associated with obesity.

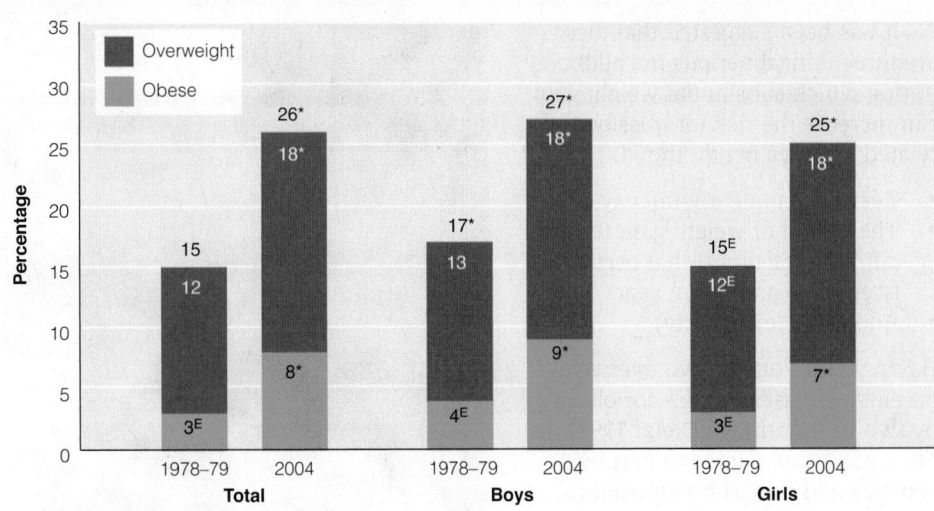

Figure 1 Overweight and obesity rates among Canadian children and adolescents aged 2 to 17, 1978–79 versus 2004.
*significantly higher than estimate for 1978–79 (p<0.05).
ᴱCoefficient of variation 16.6% to 33.3% (interpret with caution).
Source: From the Statistics Canada publication *Measured obesity, Overweight Canadian children and adolescents*, 2004, no. 1, Catalogue 82-620, July 6, 2005, page 23, available at: www.statcan.ca/46nglish/research/82-620-MIE/2005001/articles/child/cobesity.htm, accessed January 2006.

Why Do People Become Obese?

Although it is certainly true that obesity, like overweight, is caused by eating more energy than is expended, it is also true that some people are more susceptible to becoming obese than others. As we saw with the twin study in the chapter preceding this *In Depth*, different people consuming the same excessive energy and engaging in the same low level of physical activity will gain very different amounts of weight. Why? Research on the causes of obesity is ongoing, but let's explore some current theories.

Genetic and Physiologic Factors Influence Obesity Risk

Because a person's genetic background influences his or her height, weight, body shape, and metabolic rate, it can also affect a person's risk

for obesity. Some obesity experts point out that, if proved, the existence of a thrifty gene or genes (discussed in the preceding chapter) would show that obese people have a genetic tendency to expend less energy both at rest and during physical activity. Other researchers are working to determine whether the set-point theory can partially explain why many obese people are very resistant to weight loss. As we learn more about genetics, we will gain a greater understanding of the role it plays in the development and treatment of obesity.

We also discussed several physiologic factors that may influence an individual's experience of hunger and satiation. These include the proteins leptin, ghrelin, PYY, and uncoupling proteins. Other physiologic factors, such as beta-endorphins, neuropeptide Y, and decreased blood glucose, can reduce satiety or increase hunger, theoretically promoting overeating and weight gain.

Childhood Overweight and Obesity Are Linked to Adult Obesity

The prevalence of overweight in children and adolescents is increasing at

an alarming rate in Canada (**Figure 1**). There was a time when having extra "baby fat" was considered good for a child. We assumed that the condition was temporary and that the child would grow out of it. While it is important for children to have a certain minimum level of body fat to maintain health and to grow properly, researchers are now concerned that obesity is harming children's health and increasing their risk for obesity in adulthood.

Health data demonstrate that obese children are already showing signs of chronic disease while they are young, including elevated blood pressure, high cholesterol levels, and changes in insulin and glucose metabolism that may increase the risk for type 2 diabetes (formerly known as *adult onset diabetes*). In some communities, children as young as five years of age have been diagnosed with type 2 diabetes. Unfortunately, many of these children are maintaining these disease risk factors into adulthood.

Does being an obese child guarantee that obesity will be maintained during adulthood? Although some children who are obese grow up to have a normal body weight, about 70% of children who are obese maintain their higher weight as adults (Torgan, 2002). Obviously, this has important consequences for their health.

It has been suggested that there are three critical periods in childhood during which substantial weight gain can increase the risk for obesity and related diseases in adulthood:

- Gestation and early infancy
- The period of weight gain (called *adiposity rebound*) that occurs between five and seven years of age
- Adolescence (puberty)

Having either one or two overweight parents increases the risk for obesity by two to four times (Dietz, 1994). This may be explained in part by genetics and in part by unhealthful eating patterns or lack of physical activity within the family. We know that children who eat healthful diets that do not contain a lot of excess fat and sugar and are very physically active are unlikely to become obese. In contrast, children who eat a lot of foods that contain excess fat and sugar and spend most of their time on the computer or watching television are more likely to be obese. When these patterns are carried into adolescence and adulthood, the obesity is likely to persist.

Having a spouse, sibling, or friend who is obese may increase an individual's risk for obesity.

Adequate physical activity is instrumental in preventing childhood obesity.

Social Factors Appear to Influence Obesity Risk

Social factors, including poverty and a lower level of education, have been linked to obesity. One reason for this may be that high-calorie processed foods cost less and are easier to find and prepare than more healthful foods, such as fresh fruits and vegetables. Other reasons may include reduced access to safe places to walk, hike, or engage in other forms of physical activity, not to mention the cost of membership in a health club, gym, or commercial weight-loss program. Our social ties may also have a subtle influence on our risk for obesity. Although their data have been challenged, researchers from Harvard Medical School evaluated a social network of more than 12 000 people and concluded that an individual's risk of becoming obese increases significantly—by 37%–57%—if the person has a spouse, sibling, or friend who has become obese (Christakis and Fowler, 2007).

Physical Factors Can Contribute to Obesity

An abnormally low level of thyroid hormone, or an elevated level of the hormone cortisol, can lead to weight gain and obesity. A physician can check your blood for levels of these hormones. Certain prescription medications, including steroids used for asthma and other disorders, seizure medications, and some antidepressants, can slow basal metabolic rate or stimulate appetite, leading to weight gain (NIDDK, 2008).

Does Obesity Respond to Treatment?

Ironically, up to 40% of women and 25% of men are dieting at any given time. How can obesity rates be so high when there are so many people dieting? Although relatively few studies have tracked maintenance of weight loss, existing evidence suggests that only about 20% of obese people are successful at long-term weight loss (Wing and Phelan, 2005). In this study, success was defined as losing at least 10% of initial body weight and maintaining the loss for at least one year. These results suggest that about 80% of obese people who are dieting are somehow failing to lose weight or to keep it off. Why is permanent weight loss so challenging?

Although these statistics might suggest that obesity somehow resists intervention, that's not the case. Bearing in mind that 20% of people do succeed in long-term weight loss, the question becomes "How do they do it?"

Lifestyle Changes Can Help

The first line of defence in treating obesity is a low-energy diet and regular physical activity. Overweight and obese individuals should work with their healthcare practitioner to design and maintain a low-fat diet (less than 30% of total energy from fat) that has a deficit of 2100–4200 kJ (500–1000 kcal) per day. The chapter preceding this **In Depth** provides detailed information about dieting for weight loss.

Physical activity should be increased gradually, so that the person can build to a program in which he or she is exercising at least 30 minutes per day, five times per week. The Institute of Medicine (2002) concurs that 30 minutes a day, five times a week is the minimum amount of physical activity needed, but up to 60 minutes per day may be necessary for many people to lose weight and to sustain a body weight in the healthy range over the long term. We provided strategies for increasing your energy expenditure in Chapter 11, and more detailed information about physical activity is provided in Chapter 12.

Counselling and support groups can help people maintain these dietary and activity changes. Behavioural therapy can be particularly helpful in challenging clients to examine the underlying thought patterns, situations, and stressors that may be undermining their efforts at weight loss.

Weight Loss Can Be Enhanced with Prescribed Medications

The biggest complaint about the lifestyle recommendations for healthful weight loss is that they are difficult to maintain. Many people are looking for a "magic bullet" that will allow them to lose weight quickly and easily, requiring little sustained effort on their part to achieve their weight goals. Other people have tried to follow healthful weight-loss suggestions for years and have not been successful. In response to these challenges, prescription drugs have been developed to assist people with weight loss. These drugs typically act as appetite suppressants and may increase satiety.

Prescription Weight-Loss Medications Are Not for Everyone

Although the use of prescribed weight-loss medications is associated with side effects and a certain level of risk, they are justified for people who are obese. That's because the health risks

◀ Increased physical activity can help many obese people succeed in losing weight and keeping it off.

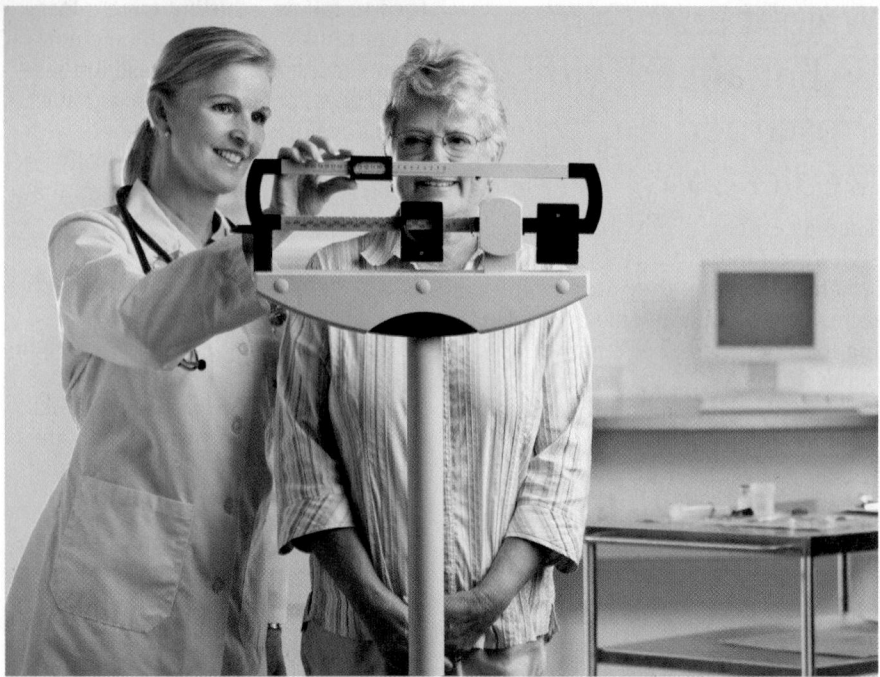

⬆ Some people find that combining lifestyle changes with prescription medications increases their success in losing weight.

of obesity override the risks of the medications. Specifically, prescription weight-loss medications are advised for people who have the following:

- A BMI greater than or equal to 30 kg/m^2
- A BMI greater than or equal to 27 kg/m^2 who also have other significant health risk factors, such as heart disease, high blood pressure, and type 2 diabetes

These medications should be used only while under a physician's supervision, so that progress and health risks can be closely monitored. They are most effective when combined with a program that supports energy restriction, regular exercise, and increased physical activity throughout the day.

Over-the-Counter Substances Used and Abused for Weight Loss

Over-the-counter (OTC) dietary and herbal supplements and prescription medications are also marketed for weight loss. A growing number of these products increase metabolic rate and suppress appetite due to one or several combined ingredients, including caffeine, ephedrine, and phenylpropanolamine (PPA). Ephedrine and PPA are commonly found in many cold remedies and allergy medications but have been banned by Health Canada as weight loss aids, as it is thought that abnormal increases in heart rate and blood pressure can occur and may be dangerous if used improperly (Health Canada, 2010; (2011).

Ephedrine, also known as ephedra, Chinese ephedra, or ma huang, is commonly found in products that claim to suppress appetite, promote weight loss, aid bodybuilding, and speed up metabolism. In addition to increasing stamina, ephedrine is claimed to aid in the reduction of body weight and body fat in sedentary women, which has piqued the interest of a growing number of Canadians. Those looking to find ephedrine as their answer for weight loss can find hundreds of aggressively marketed American fitness and weight loss ads on the internet, promoting ephedrine-containing products as "fat burners" and "rapid fat loss catalysts."

However, side effects of ephedrine include headaches, nausea, nervousness, anxiety, irregular heart rate, and high blood pressure. At least one death in Canada has been linked to the use of a product that combined large doses of ephedrine with caffeine, and at least 60 adverse events had been reported in Canada related to the use of ephedrine. Most such reactions involved the use or overuse of combination products, which combine ephedrine with caffeine (Health Canada, 2003).

Phenylpropanolamine (PPA) is another ingredient used in many OTC and prescription cough and cold medications as a decongestant and in OTC weight loss products. In 2000, both Canada and the United States banned PPA from the market when several women died of hemorrhagic stroke, or bleeding into the brain, after taking the prescribed dose. The increased risk of hemorrhagic stroke was detected among women using the drug for weight control within three days of starting to use the medication (USFDA, 2000).

As you can see, Canada has had a history of identifying and advising against weight loss aids. Clearly, using weight loss supplements can have dangerous consequences. Even the use of prescribed weight loss medications is associated with side effects and a certain level of risk. Recently, several Canadian provinces have seen a rise in the incidence of abuse of an illegal drug known as methamphetamine, more commonly known by its street name, crystal meth. Young adolescent females are vulnerable to use of the drug as a weight control measure. Sadly, many teenage girls begin taking this stimulant in an attempt to lose weight but end up highly addicted and faced with severe long-term effects. Side effects can include irritability, heart palpitations, confusion, severe anxiety, paranoia, violence, or psychosis. Long-term use may cause structural changes to the brain, memory loss, difficulty completing complex tasks, and permanent psychotic symptoms.

Surgery Can Be Used to Treat Obesity

For people who are obese, surgery may be recommended. Historically, surgery has been advised in people with a BMI greater than or equal to kg/m² or in people with a BMI greater than or equal to 35 kg/m² who have other life-threatening conditions, such as sleep apnea (NIH, 1998). The 2004 Consensus Conference of the American Society for Bariatric Surgery, intended to update the 1991 NIH Consensus Conference, called for extending bariatric surgery to patients with Class 1 obesity (BMI of 30–34.9 kg/m²) given recent evidence that some associated conditions (such as type 2 diabetes and sleep apnea) can be markedly improved when weight loss is large and sustained over time (Buchwald, 2005).

Two of the most common types of weight-loss surgery performed are gastric bypass Roux-En-Y and gastric banding **(Figure 2)**. Both can be done with laparoscopic surgery using incisions in the abdomen to allow surgical tools and tiny cameras to be inserted. Laparoscopic surgery is considered safer (with fewer wound complications and much faster recovery) than traditional surgery, where the abdomen is opened and internal organs are exposed (Buchwald, 2005).

- *Gastric bypass Roux-En-Y surgery* (RYGB) involves attaching the lower part of the small intestine to the stomach, so that food bypasses most of the stomach and the duodenum of the small intestine

(see Figure 2c). This results in both significantly less absorption of food in the intestine and a smaller stomach pouch, which holds about 30–60 mL (2–4 Tbsp), and that restricts food intake. Recall that the macronutrients that provide energy (e.g., fat) and most micronutrients are absorbed in the duodenum. When food bypasses this area because of a surgical procedure, absorption of both is greatly reduced. While this leads to weight loss, patients who do not follow the recommendations for micronutrient supplements can have severe deficiencies of vitamins and minerals that result in serious health consequences. Because food intake is also severely restricted, it is important that foods that are consumed are nutrient dense foods to help prevent nutrient deficiencies.

Thus the RYGB technique uses both restriction (of the stomach size) and malabsorption (because the duodenum is bypassed) to achieve weight loss. Patients can expect to lose 65%–70% of their excess body weight by two years post-surgery. Excess body weight is the amount of weight that is above what would be considered a normal weight for that individual. This procedure has the lowest

failure rate but the highest risk of complications (10%) from malabsorption. Some patients who have not taken their prescribed nutritional supplements have developed Beri Beri and iron deficiency anemia, and deaths have resulted.

- *Laparoscopic Adjustable Gastric Banding* (LAGB) is a relatively new procedure and considered to be in the pilot phase in some places (e.g., Ontario). It causes weight loss by restricting the capacity of the stomach with an adjustable band positioned where the lower esophagus meets the upper part of the stomach (see Figure 2d). A balloon is inserted on the inside of the band and it gets inflated, which constricts the stomach. This balloon is attached to a tube that sits near the surface of the skin in the abdominal area, and a needle can be used by the surgeon to adjust the inflation of the balloon, and thus the amount of constriction caused by the band. As a result, food passes through a very small area (about 7 mm), which means that patients have to chew their food very well and food choices may be limited. Patients can expect to lose about 50% of their excess weight by two years post-surgery. Because

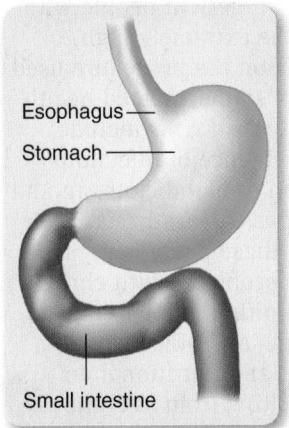

(a) Normal anatomy

Esophagus
Stomach
Small intestine

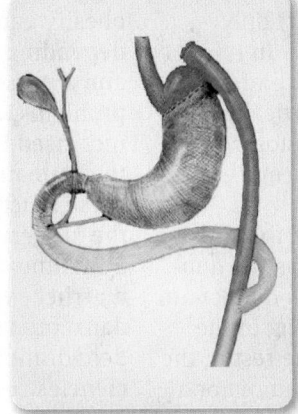

(b) Vertical banded gastroplasty

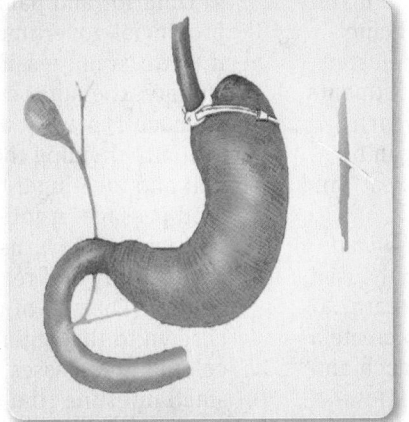

(c) Gastric bypass

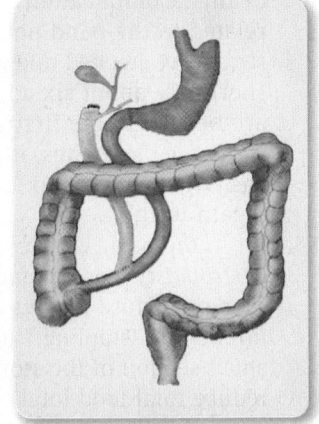

(d) Gastric banding

Figure 2 Various forms of surgery alter the normal anatomy **(a)** of the gastrointestinal tract to result in weight loss: Roux-en-Y gastric bypass **(b)**, Laparoscopic Adjustable Gastric banding **(c)**, and Duodenal Switch **(d)**.

Source: (Reprinted from Surgery for obesity and related diseases: official journal of the American Society for Bariatric Surgery, 1:3, Buchwald, Henry, Consensus Conference Statement, 371–382, 2005, with permission from Elsevier.)

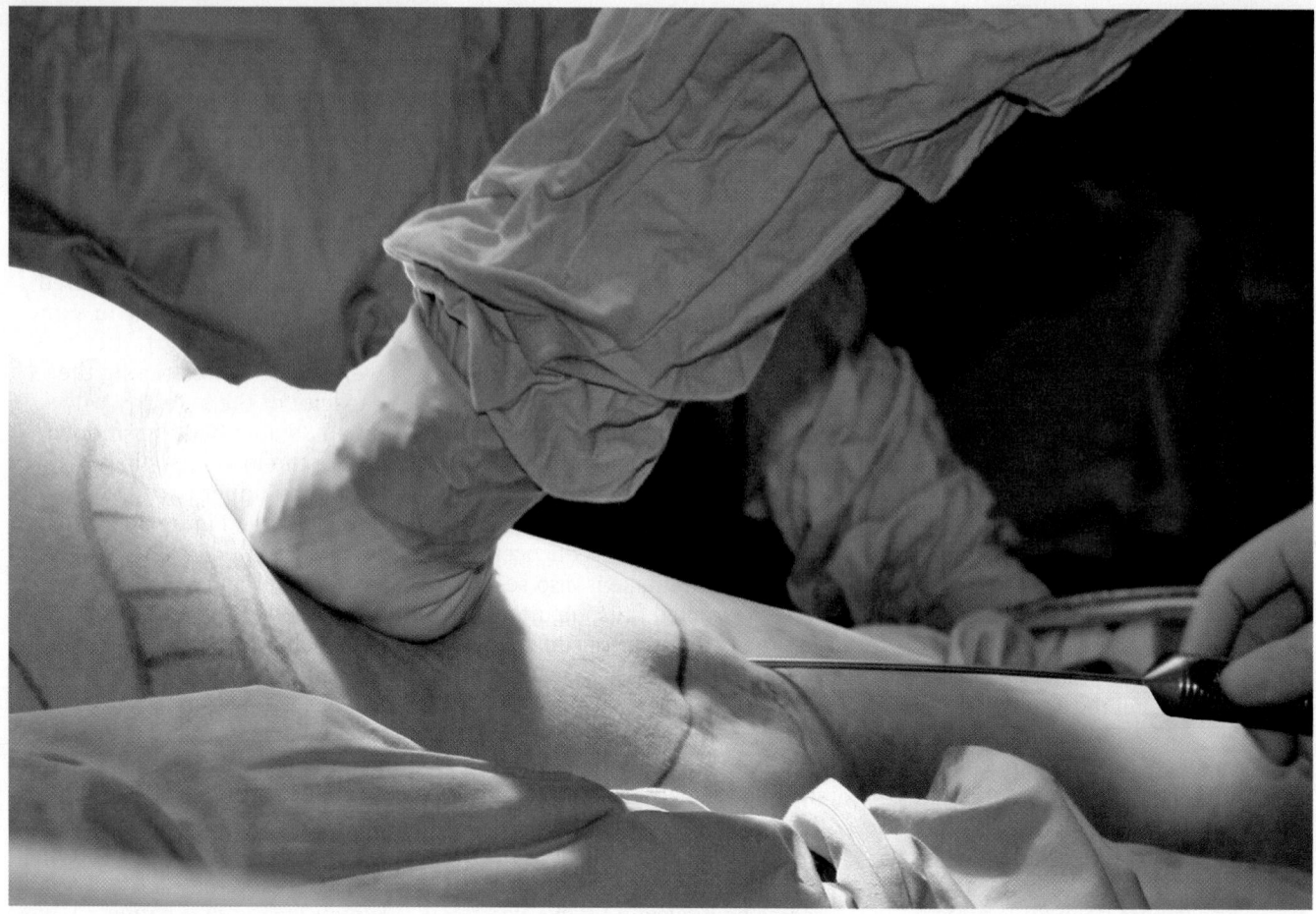

⬆ Liposuction removes fat cells from specific areas of the body.

this technique does not create malabsorption, there are few nutritional risks and very few deaths. Complications are mainly related to the band not being regularly checked and adjusted (normally about six adjustments are needed in the first year); if the area stretches, it can be easier for patients to "cheat" and regain weight.

In the past, *Vertical banded gastroplasty* was commonly used. This procedure involves partitioning, or "stapling," to create a small section of the stomach and reduce total food intake. However, only an estimated 20% of patients were able to maintain their weight loss, and this procedure has largely been replaced by the Laparoscopic Adjustable Gastric Band.

- A third type of laparoscopic surgery, called *Laparoscopic*

Sleeve Gastrectomy (LSG), has not yet been approved for adults in the United States but is used in Ontario (and paid for by the provincial government) only if RYGB is not feasible. In this surgery, the outer curve of the stomach is stapled vertically, essentially dividing the stomach in half and creating a "sleeve" for food passage. A fourth type, the *Duodenal Switch*, uses the sleeve gastrectomy and retains the duodenum. The end of the duodenum is sewn to the beginning of the colon and bypasses the rest of the small intestine (the jejunum and ileum). Like the gastric bypass, using both restriction and malabsorption, the duodenal switch is a complicated procedure and patients must take large amounts of vitamins and minerals, divided into five doses per day. However, the stomach pouch is larger than

in the gastric bypass—about 100–150 mL (4–5 Tbsp).

The risks of surgery in people with obesity can be extremely high, depending upon the procedure used and a person's other related health problems. Surgical risks include increased incidence of infections, the formation of blood clots, and adverse reactions to anesthesia. After the surgery, these people may face a lifetime of problems with chronic diarrhea, vomiting, intolerance to dairy products and other foods, dehydration, and nutritional deficiencies resulting from alterations in nutrient digestion and absorption that occur with bypass procedures. Thus, the potential benefits of the procedure must outweigh the risks. It is critical that each surgery candidate be carefully screened by a physician. If the immediate threat of serious disease and death is more dangerous than the risks associated with surgery, then the procedure is justified.

Are these surgical procedures successful in reducing obesity? About one-third to one-half of people who received obesity surgery lose significant amounts of weight and keep this weight off for at least five years. Some procedures, such as the LAGB, are reversible. Many obesity-related conditions can be resolved or improved, and people may even improve their ability to stay physically active over a prolonged period of time (Sjöström et al., 2004).

Liposuction is a cosmetic surgical procedure that removes fat cells from localized areas in the body. It is not recommended or typically used to treat obesity or morbid obesity. Instead, it is often used by normal-weight or mildly overweight people to "spot reduce" fat from various areas of the body. This procedure is not without risks; blood clots, skin and nerve damage, adverse drug reactions, and perforation injuries occur as a result of liposuction. It can also cause deformations in the area where the fat is removed. This procedure is not the solution to long-term weight loss, as the millions of fat cells that remain in the body after liposuction enlarge if the person continues to overeat. In addition, although liposuction may reduce the fat content of a localized area, it does not reduce a person's risk for the diseases that are more common among overweight or obese people. Only traditional weight loss with diet and exercise can reduce body fat and the risks for chronic diseases.

Web Resources

www.oa.org
Overeaters Anonymous

Visit this site to learn about ways to reduce compulsive overeating.

www.nhlbi.nih.gov/health/dci/ Diseases/obe/obe_treatments
National Heart, Lung, and Blood Institute Overweight and Obesity Site

Visit this site to find out more about various treatment options for overweight and obesity.

www.win.niddk.nih.gov
Weight-control Information Network

This site, from the National Institute of Diabetes and Digestive and Kidney Diseases (NIDDK), offers information, brochures, and other tools on obesity, weight control, physical activity, and related nutritional issues.

12

Nutrition and Physical Activity: Keys to Good Health

CHAPTER OBJECTIVES

After reading this chapter you will be able to:

1. Explain the differences between physical activity and exercise, p. 406.

2. Define the four components of fitness, p. 406.

3. List at least four health benefits of being physically active on a regular basis, pp. 406–407.

4. Describe the FIT principle and calculate your maximal and training heart rate range, pp. 410–412.

5. List and describe at least three processes we use to break down fuels to support physical activity, pp. 413–415.

6. Discuss at least three changes in nutrient needs that can occur in response to an increase in physical activity or vigorous exercise training, pp. 418–425.

7. Define the term *ergogenic aids* and discuss the potential benefits and risks of at least four ergogenic aids that are currently on the market , pp. 428–430.

Test Yourself

1. **T F** Despite the multitude of health benefits of participating in regular physical activity, half of all Canadians are insufficiently active.

2. **T F** It is important to eat extra protein in order to build muscle.

3. **T F** Most ergogenic aids are not effective, and many can be dangerous or cause serious health consequences.

Test Yourself answers can be found at the end of the chapter.

At the start of the 2010 Winter Olympic Games in Vancouver, British Columbia, the Vancouver Organizing Committee had already bought 36 540 eggs, 42 440 litres of 2% milk, 28 140 litres of skim milk, 77 800 pounds of bananas, 11 000 pounds of pasta, and over 150 000 apples. Athletes know just how important the proper fuel can be in terms of performance, and that gold medals can sometimes be won by a matter of mere hundredths of a second. Some athletes, particularly those competing in endurance events, need to consume a huge amount of energy (calories) just to replenish their body stores of glycogen and electrolytes. Even if you are not an Olympic athlete in competition mode, you can certainly learn from their dedication to high-quality fuel when engaging in physical activity, whatever the sport.

We all know that regular physical activity dramatically improves our strength, stamina, health, and longevity—but what qualifies as "regular physical activity"? In other words, how much do we need to do to reap the benefits? And if we do become more active, how should our diet change to accommodate the increased activity? If you think about it, could you perform at your best without the proper fuel? Healthy eating practices and regular physical activity go hand-in-hand in promoting overall wellness and preventing chronic diseases. In fact, the nutrition and physical activity recommendations for reducing your risk of heart disease also reduce your risk of high blood pressure, type 2 diabetes, obesity, and some forms of cancer! In this chapter, we define physical activity, identify its many benefits, and discuss the nutrients needed to maintain an active life.

With the help of a nutritious diet, many people are able to remain physically active—and even competitive—throughout adult life.

Why Engage in Physical Activity?

A lot of people are looking for a "magic pill" that will help them maintain weight loss, reduce their risk for diseases, make them feel better, and improve their quality of sleep. Although many people are not aware of it, regular physical activity is this magic pill. **Physical activity** is any movement produced by muscles that increases energy expenditure. Different categories of physical activity include occupational, household, leisure-time, and transportation (USDHHS, 1996). **Leisure-time physical activity** is any activity not related to a person's occupation and includes competitive sports, planned exercise training, and recreational activities such as hiking, walking, and bicycling. **Exercise** is therefore considered a subcategory of leisure-time physical activity and refers to activity that is purposeful, planned, and structured (Caspersen, Powell, and Christensen, 1985).

One of the most important benefits of regular physical activity is that it increases our physical fitness. **Physical fitness** is a state of being that arises largely from the interaction between nutrition and physical activity. It is defined as the ability to carry out daily tasks with vigour and alertness, without undue fatigue, and with ample energy to enjoy leisure-time pursuits and meet unforeseen emergencies (USDHHS, 1996). Physical fitness has several components **(Table 12.1)**, including (Heyward, 2006):

- Cardiorespiratory fitness is the ability of the heart, lungs, and circulatory system to efficiently supply oxygen and nutrients to working muscles.
- Musculoskeletal fitness involves fitness of both the muscles and bones. It includes *muscular strength*, the maximal force or tension level that can be produced by a muscle group, and *muscular endurance*, the ability of a muscle to maintain submaximal force levels for extended periods of time.
- Flexibility is the ability to move a joint fluidly through the complete range of motion, and *body composition* is the amount of bone, muscle, and fat tissue in the body.

Although many people are interested in improving their physical fitness, some are more interested in maintaining general fitness, while others are interested in achieving higher levels of fitness to optimize their athletic performance. Other benefits of regular physical activity include the following:

- It reduces the risks for, and complications of, heart disease, stroke, and high blood pressure. Regular physical activity increases high-density lipoprotein cholesterol (HDL, the "good" cholesterol) and lowers triglycerides in the blood, improves the strength of the heart, helps maintain healthy blood pressure, and limits the progression of atherosclerosis (hardening of the arteries).
- It reduces the risk for obesity. Regular physical activity maintains lean body mass and promotes more healthful levels of body fat, may help in appetite control, and increases energy expenditure and the use of fat as an energy source.
- It reduces the risk for type 2 diabetes. Regular physical activity enhances the action of insulin, which improves the cells' uptake of glucose from the blood, and it can improve blood glucose control in people with diabetes, which in turn reduces the risk for, or delays the onset of, diabetes-related complications.

physical activity Any movement produced by muscles that increases energy expenditure; includes occupational, household, leisure-time, and transportation activities.

leisure-time physical activity Any activity not related to a person's occupation; includes competitive sports, recreational activities, and planned exercise training.

exercise A subcategory of leisure-time physical activity; any activity that is purposeful, planned, and structured.

physical fitness The ability to carry out daily tasks with vigour and alertness, without undue fatigue, and with ample energy to enjoy leisure-time pursuits and meet unforeseen emergencies.

TABLE 12.1 The Components of Fitness

Fitness Component	Examples of Activities One Can Do to Achieve Fitness in Each Component
Cardiorespiratory	Aerobic-type activities, such as walking, running, swimming, cross-country skiing
Musculoskeletal fitness:	Resistance training, weight lifting, calisthenics, sit-ups, push-ups
Muscular strength	Weight lifting or related activities using heavier weights with few repetitions
Muscular endurance	Weight lifting or related activities using lighter weights with more repetitions
Flexibility	Stretching exercises, yoga
Body composition	Aerobic exercise, resistance training

- It reduces the risk for osteoporosis. Regular physical activity strengthens bones and enhances muscular strength and flexibility, thereby reducing the likelihood of falls and the incidence of fractures and other injuries when falls occur.
- It potentially reduces the risk for colon cancer. Although the exact role that physical activity may play in reducing colon cancer risk is still unknown, we do know that regular physical activity enhances gastric motility, which reduces the transit time of potential cancer-causing agents through the gut.

Regular physical activity is also known to improve sleep patterns, reduce the risk for upper respiratory infections by improving immune function, improve self-esteem, and reduce anxiety and mental stress. It also can be effective in treating mild and moderate depression. During pregnancy, regular physical activity helps maintain the mother's fitness and muscle tone and helps control weight gain. It is also associated with a reduced risk for pregnancy-related complications (Davidson, London, and Ladewig, 2008).

Despite the plethora of benefits derived from regular physical activity, most people find that this magic pill is not easy to swallow. Results from a 2011 survey show that 53.8% of Canadians aged 12 and older are physically active (Statistics Canada, 2012), meaning that 46.2% are not active. This is lower than the estimate of 51% who are not active from the 2004–2005 Canadian Community Health Survey (CCHS v.2) (Statistics Canada, 2009) and the estimate of 59% from the CCHS v.1 (Statistics Canada 2009). These rates suggest that Canadians may be getting more physically active. Inadequate physical activity is also a problem in young people. Although 54% of schools claimed to have a policy requiring daily physical education classes, only 16% of schools were actually offering these classes in 2001 (CIHI, 2004). On average, time allotted for physical activity ranged from 44 minutes (junior elementary school) to 60 minutes (senior secondary students) per week (Canadian Fitness and Lifestyle Research Institute, 2005). For the Canadian Fitness and Lifestyle Research Institute's *Canadian Physical Activity Levels Among Youth* (CANPLAY) *Study,* children and youth were given pedometers to wear. On average, children and youth between the ages of 5 and 19 took 11 356 steps a day. As **Figure 12.1** shows, children 5 to 10 years of age recorded the highest number of steps, and teens aged 15 to 19 recorded the fewest, with boys taking more steps than girls across all age categories (Canadian Fitness and Lifestyle Research Institute, 2005). Since our habits related to eating and physical activity are formed early in life, it is imperative that we provide opportunities for children and adolescents to engage in regular, enjoyable physical activity. An active lifestyle during childhood increases the likelihood of a healthier life as an adult.

Hiking is a leisure-time physical activity that can contribute to your physical fitness.

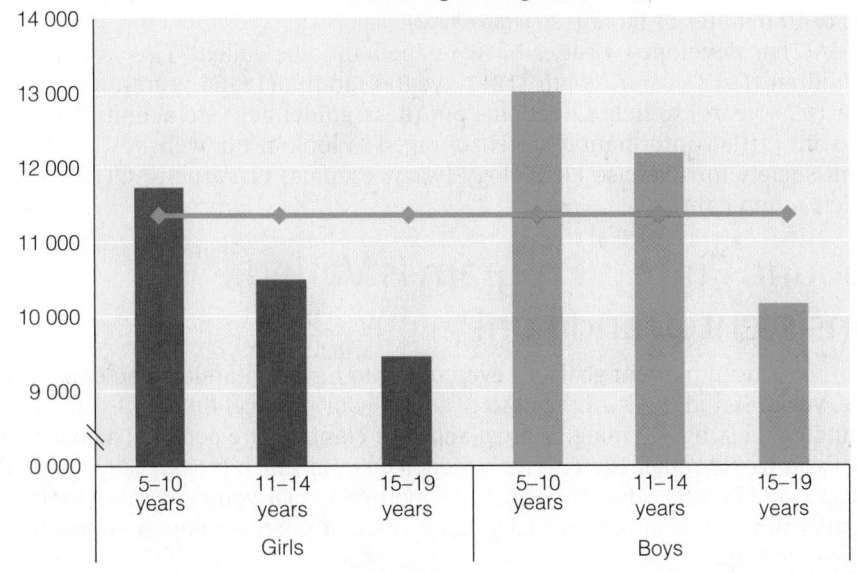

Mean number of steps for children and youth by child's age and gender

Figure 12.1 Mean number of steps a day for children and youth by child's age and gender.
Canadian Fitness and Lifestyle Research Institute, 2005, *Physical activity among Canadians: The current situation.* www.cflri.ca/eng/statistics/surveys/documents/pam2005_sec1.pdf. Reprinted with permission of the Canadian Fitness and Lifestyle Institute. www.cflri.ca.

RECAP Physical activity is any movement produced by muscles that increases energy expenditure. Physical fitness is the ability to carry out daily tasks with vigour and alertness, without undue fatigue, and with ample energy to enjoy leisure-time pursuits and meet unforeseen emergencies. Physical activity provides a multitude of health benefits, including reducing our risks for obesity and many chronic diseases, and relieving anxiety and stress. Despite the many health benefits of physical activity, approximately one-half of Canadians, including many children, are inactive.

What Is a Sound Fitness Program?

There are several widely recognized qualities of a sound fitness program, as well as guidelines to help you design one that is right for you. These are explored here. Keep in mind that people with heart disease, high blood pressure, diabetes, obesity, osteoporosis, asthma, or arthritis should get approval to exercise from their healthcare practitioner prior to starting a fitness program. In addition, a medical evaluation should be conducted before starting an exercise program for an apparently healthy but currently inactive man 40 years or older or woman 50 years or older.

A Sound Fitness Program Meets Your Personal Goals

A fitness program that may be ideal for you is not necessarily right for everyone. Before designing or evaluating any program, it is important to define your personal fitness goals. Do you want to prevent osteoporosis, diabetes, or another chronic disease that runs in your family? Do you simply want to increase your energy and stamina? Or do you intend to compete in athletic events? Each of these scenarios requires a unique fitness program.

For example, if you want to train for athletic competition, a traditional approach that includes planned, purposive exercise sessions under the guidance of a trainer or coach would probably be most beneficial. Or if you want to achieve cardiorespiratory fitness, participating in an aerobics class at least three times per week may be recommended.

In contrast, if your goal is to maintain your overall health, you might do better to follow new physical activity guidelines released by the Canadian Society for Exercise Physiology (2011) in consultation with the Public Health Agency of Canada (PHAC). These guidelines recommend that adults 18 to 64 years of age spend 2.5 hours or 150 minutes of moderate- to vigorous-intensity aerobic physical activity per week, in bouts of 10 minutes or more (see **Figure 12.2**).

PHAC has developed a series of two-page handouts called "Tips to Get Active" for children (5–11 years), youth (12–17 years), adults (18–64 years), and older adults (65+ years) to help Canadians put these guidelines into action. People who want further information are encouraged to look at the websites for the Canadian Society for Exercise Physiology (www.csep.ca) or ParticipACTION (www.participaction.com).

A Sound Fitness Program Is Varied, Consistent... and Fun!

One of the most important goals for everyone is to have fun; unless you enjoy being active, you will find it very difficult to maintain your physical fitness. If you enjoy the outdoors, hiking, camping, fishing, and rock climbing are potential activities for you. If you would rather exercise with friends on your lunch break, walking, climbing stairs, and bicycle riding may be more appropriate. Or you may prefer to use the programs and equipment at your local fitness club or purchase your own treadmill and free weights.

Moderate physical activity, such as gardening, helps maintain overall health.

Watching television or reading can provide variety while walking or running on a treadmill.

Canadian Physical Activity Guidelines

FOR ADULTS - 18 – 64 YEARS

Guidelines

 To achieve health benefits, adults aged 18–64 years should accumulate at least 150 minutes of moderate- to vigorous-intensity aerobic physical activity per week, in bouts of 10 minutes or more.

 It is also beneficial to add muscle and bone strengthening activities using major muscle groups, at least 2 days per week.

 More physical activity provides greater health benefits.

Let's Talk Intensity!

Moderate-intensity physical activities will cause adults to sweat a little and to breathe harder. Activities like:

- Brisk walking
- Bike riding

Vigorous-intensity physical activities will cause adults to sweat and be 'out of breath'. Activities like:

- Jogging
- Cross-country skiing

Being active for at least **150 minutes** per week can help reduce the risk of:

- Premature death
- Heart disease
- Stroke
- High blood pressure
- Certain types of cancer
- Type 2 diabetes
- Osteoporosis
- Overweight and obesity

And can lead to improved:

- Fitness
- Strength
- Mental health (morale and self-esteem)

Pick a time. Pick a place. Make a plan and move more!

☑ Join a weekday community running or walking group.
☑ Go for a brisk walk around the block after dinner.
☑ Take a dance class after work.
☑ Bike or walk to work every day.

☑ Rake the lawn, and then offer to do the same for a neighbour.
☑ Train for and participate in a run or walk for charity!
☑ Take up a favourite sport again or try a new sport.
☑ Be active with the family on the weekend!

Now is the time. Walk, run, or wheel, and embrace life.

www.csep.ca/guidelines

Figure 12.2 *Canadian Physical Activity Guidelines* for Adults 18–64 Years.

Source: (Canadian Physical Activity Guidelines, © 2011. Used with permission from the Canadian Society for Exercise Physiology, www.csep.ca/guidelines.)

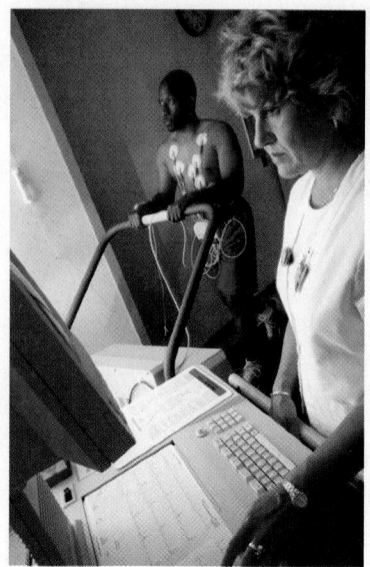

⬤ Testing in a fitness lab is the most accurate way to determine maximal heart rate.

resistance training Exercises in which our muscles act against resistance.

overload principle Placing an extra physical demand on your body to improve your fitness level.

FIT principle The principle used to achieve an appropriate overload for physical training; FIT stands for frequency, intensity, and time of activity.

frequency The number of activity sessions per week you perform.

intensity The amount of effort expended during the activity, or how difficult the activity is to perform.

low-intensity activities Activities that cause very mild increases in breathing, sweating, and heart rate.

moderate-intensity activities Activities that cause moderate increases in breathing, sweating, and heart rate.

vigorous-intensity activities Activities that produce significant increases in breathing, sweating, and heart rate; talking is difficult when exercising at a vigorous intensity.

maximal heart rate The rate at which your heart beats during maximal-intensity exercise.

Variety is critical to maintaining your fitness. While some people enjoy doing similar activities day after day, most of us get bored with the same fitness routine. Incorporating a variety of activities into your fitness program will help maintain your interest and increase your enjoyment while you are active. Variety can be achieved by engaging in different indoor and outdoor activities on different days of the week, taking a different route when you walk each day, or watching different TV programs or listening to music while you ride a stationary bicycle or work out on a rowing machine. This smorgasbord of activities can increase your activity level without leading to monotony and boredom.

It is important to understand that you cannot do just one activity to achieve overall fitness because every activity is specific to a certain fitness component. Refer back to Table 12.1, and notice the various activities listed as examples for the various components. For instance, participating in aerobic-type activities will improve cardiorespiratory fitness but will do little to improve muscular strength. To achieve that goal, we must participate in some form of **resistance training**, or exercises in which our muscles work against resistance. Flexibility is achieved by participating in stretching activities. By following the recommendations in the *Canadian Physical Activity Guidelines*, you can achieve physical fitness in all components.

A Sound Fitness Program Appropriately Overloads the Body

To improve your fitness, you must place an extra physical demand on your body. This is referred to as the **overload principle**. A word of caution is in order here: *the overload principle does not advocate subjecting your body to inappropriately high stress* because this can lead to exhaustion and injuries. In contrast, an appropriate overload on various body systems will result in healthy improvements in fitness.

To achieve an appropriate overload, you should consider three factors, collectively known as the **FIT principle**: *f*requency, *i*ntensity, and *t*ime of activity. You can use the FIT principle to design either a general physical fitness program or a performance-based exercise program. **Figure 12.3** shows how the FIT principle applies to a cardiorespiratory, musculoskeletal, and flexibility fitness program. Let's consider each of the FIT principle's three factors in more detail.

Frequency

Frequency refers to the number of activity sessions per week. Depending on your goals for fitness, the frequency of your activities will vary. To achieve cardiorespiratory fitness, you should train more than two days per week. On the other hand, training more than five days per week does not cause significant gains in fitness but can substantially increase your risk for injury. Training three to five days per week appears optimal to achieve and maintain cardiorespiratory fitness. In contrast, only two to three days are needed to achieve musculoskeletal fitness.

Intensity

Intensity refers to the amount of effort expended or to how difficult the activity is to perform. In general, **low-intensity activities** are those that cause very mild increases in breathing, sweating, and heart rate, while **moderate-intensity activities** cause moderate increases in these responses. **Vigorous-intensity activities** produce significant increases in breathing, sweating, and heart rate, so that talking is difficult when exercising.

Traditionally, heart rate has been used to indicate level of intensity during aerobic activities. You can calculate the range of exercise intensity that is appropriate for you by estimating your **maximal heart rate**, which is the rate at which your heart beats during maximal-intensity exercise (see the You Do the Math box on the 412). Maximal heart rate is estimated by subtracting your age from 220. The Centers for Disease Control and Prevention recommends that to achieve moderate-intensity physical activity, your target heart rate should be 50%–70% of your estimated maximal heart

	Frequency	Intensity	Time
Cardiorespiratory fitness 	3–5 days per week	64–90% maximal heart rate	At least 20 consecutive minutes
Muscular fitness 	2–3 days per week	70–85% maximal weight you can lift	1–3 sets of 8–12 lifts* for each set *A minimum of 8–10 exercises involving the major muscle groups such as arms, shoulders, chest, abdomen, back, hips, and legs is recommended.
Flexibility 	2–4 days per week	Stretching through full range of motion	2–4 repetitions per stretch* *Hold each stretch for 15–30 seconds.

Figure 12.3 Using the FIT principle to achieve cardiorespiratory and musculoskeletal fitness and flexibility.

rate; to achieve vigorous-intensity physical activity, your target heart rate should be 70%–85% of your estimated maximal heart rate (Centers for Disease Control and Prevention, 2010). People who are older or who have been inactive for a long time may want to exercise at the lower end of the moderate-intensity range. Those who are more physically fit or are striving for a more rapid improvement in fitness may want to exercise at the higher end of the vigorous-intensity range. Competitive athletes generally train at a higher intensity, around 80%–95% of their maximal heart rate.

Although the calculation *220 − age* has been used extensively for years to predict maximal heart rate, it was never intended to represent everyone's true maximal heart rate or to be used as the standard of aerobic training intensity. The most accurate way to determine your own maximal heart rate is to complete a maximal exercise test in a fitness laboratory; however, this test is not commonly conducted with the general public and can be very expensive. Although not completely accurate, the estimated maximal heart rate method can still be used to give you a general idea of your aerobic training range.

Time of Activity

Time of activity refers to how long each session lasts. To achieve general health, you can do multiple short bouts (10 minutes) of activity. However, to achieve higher levels of fitness, it is important that the activities be done for at least 20 to 30 consecutive minutes.

For example, let's say you want to compete in triathlons. To be successful during the running segment of the triathlon, you will need to be able to run for at least 5 miles. Thus, it is appropriate for you to train so that you can complete 5 miles

time of activity The period of time that an exercise session lasts.

YOU DO THE MATH
Calculating Your Maximal and Training Heart Rate Range

Judy was recently diagnosed with type 2 diabetes, and her healthcare provider has recommended she begin an exercise program. She is considered obese according to her body mass index, and she has not been regularly active since she was a teenager. Judy's goals are to improve her cardiorespiratory fitness and achieve and maintain a more healthful weight. Fortunately, Valley Hospital, where she works as a nurse's aide, recently opened a small fitness centre for the use of its employees. Judy plans to begin by either walking on the treadmill or riding the stationary bicycle at the fitness centre during her lunch break.

Judy needs to exercise at an intensity that will help her improve her cardiorespiratory fitness and lose weight. She is 38 years of age, is obese, has type 2 diabetes, and has been approved to do moderate-intensity activity by her healthcare provider. She does a lot of walking and lifting in her work as a nurse's aide, and her doctor has recommended that she start her program by setting her training heart rate range at 50%; once her fitness improves, she can work toward exercising at 75% of her maximal heart rate.

Let's calculate Judy's maximal heart rate values:

- Maximal heart rate: 220 – age = 220 – 38 = 182 beats per minute (bpm)
- Lower end of intensity range: 50% of 182 bpm = 0.50 × 182 bpm = 91 bpm
- Higher end of intensity range: 75% of 182 bpm = 0.75 × 182 bpm = 137 bpm

Because Judy is a trained nurse's aide, she is skilled at measuring a heart rate, or pulse. To measure your own pulse,

- Place your second (index) and third (middle) fingers on the inside of your wrist, just below the wrist crease and near the thumb. Press lightly to feel your pulse. Don't press too hard, or you will occlude the artery and be unable to feel its pulsation.
- If you can't feel your pulse at your wrist, try the carotid artery at your neck. This is located below your ear, on the side of your neck directly below your jaw. Press lightly against your neck under the jaw bone to find your pulse.
- Begin counting your pulse with the count of "zero," then count each beat for 15 seconds.
- Multiply that value by four to estimate heart rate over one minute.
- Do not take your pulse with your thumb, as it has its own pulse, which would prevent you from getting an accurate estimate of your heart rate.

As you can see from these calculations, when Judy walks on the treadmill or rides the bicycle, her heart rate should be between 91 and 137 bpm; this will put her in her aerobic training zone and allow her to achieve cardiorespiratory fitness. It will also help her lose weight.

---

during one session and still have enough energy to swim and bicycle during the race. You will need to consistently train at a distance of 5 miles; you will also benefit from running longer distances.

A Sound Fitness Plan Includes a Warm-Up and a Cool-Down Period

To properly prepare for and recover from an exercise session, warm-up and cool-down activities should be performed. **Warm-up**, which properly prepares muscles for exertion by increasing blood flow and temperature, includes general activities (such as stretching and aerobics) and specific activities that prepare you for the actual activity (such as jogging or swinging a golf club). The warm-up should be brief (5 to 10 minutes), gradual, and sufficient to increase muscle and body temperature, but it should not cause fatigue or deplete energy stores.

Cool-down activities are done after the exercise session. The cool-down should be gradual, allowing your body to recover slowly, with ample stretching as well as a lower-intensity version of some of the same activities you performed during the exercise session. Cool-down after exercise assists in the prevention of injury and may help reduce muscle soreness.

Simple Changes Can Boost Your Physical Activity

There are 1440 minutes in every day and 10 080 minutes in every week. Spend just 150 of those minutes each week in physical activity, and you will be taking an

◀ Stretching should be included in the warm-up before and the cool-down after exercise.

important step toward improving your health. Here are some tips from the Public Health Agency of Canada (2012) for working daily activity into your life:

If you have been inactive for a while, use a sensible approach by starting out slowly. Gradually build up the time you spend doing the activity by adding a few minutes every few days until you reach 150 minutes each week. As this becomes easier, gradually increase either the length of time you spend in activity, the intensity of the activities you choose, or both.

QUICK TIPS

Physical Activity Tips for Adults 18–64 Years

▶ **Choose a variety of physical activities you enjoy**. Try different activities until you find the ones that feel right for you.

▶ **Get into a routine**—go to the pool, hit the gym, join a spin class, or set a regular run and do some planned exercise. Make it social by getting someone to join you.

▶ **Limit the time you spend watching TV** or sitting in front of a computer during leisure time.

▶ **Move yourself**—use active transportation to get places. Whenever you can, walk, bike, or run instead of taking the car.

▶ **Spread your sessions of moderate to vigorous aerobic activity throughout the week**. Do at least 10 minutes of physical activity at a time.

▶ **Join a team**—take part in sports and recreation activities in groups. You'll make new friends and get active at the same time.

Source: Public Health Agency of Canada (2012). http://www.phac-aspc.gc.ca/hp-ps/hl-mvs/pa-ap/07paap-eng.php, accessed May 15, 2012.

RECAP A sound fitness program must meet your personal fitness goals. It should be fun and include variety and consistency to help you maintain interest and achieve fitness in all components. It must also place an extra physical demand, or an overload, on your body. To achieve appropriate overload, follow the FIT principle: *frequency* refers to the number of activity sessions per week; *intensity* refers to how difficult the activity is to perform, and *time* refers to how long each activity session lasts. Warm-up and cool-down activities help the body prepare for and recover from exertion.

What Fuels Our Activities?

To perform exercise, or muscular work, we must be able to generate energy. The common currency of energy for virtually all cells in the body is **adenosine triphosphate**, or ATP. As you might guess from its name, a molecule of ATP includes an organic compound called adenosine and three phosphate groups **(Figure 12.4)**. When one of the phosphates is cleaved, or broken away, from ATP, energy is released. The products remaining after this reaction are adenosine diphosphate (ADP) and an independent inorganic phosphate group (P_i). In a mirror image of this reaction, the body regenerates ATP by adding a phosphate group back to ADP. In this way, we continually provide energy to our cells.

The amount of ATP stored in a muscle cell is very limited; it can keep the muscle active for only about one to three seconds. Thus, we need to generate ATP from other sources to fuel activities for longer periods of time. Fortunately,

warm-up Activities that prepare you for an exercise bout, including stretching, aerobics, and movements specific to the exercise bout; also called preliminary exercise.

cool-down Activities done after an exercise session is completed; should be gradual and allow your body to slowly recover from exercise.

adenosine triphosphate (ATP) The common currency of energy for virtually all cells of the body.

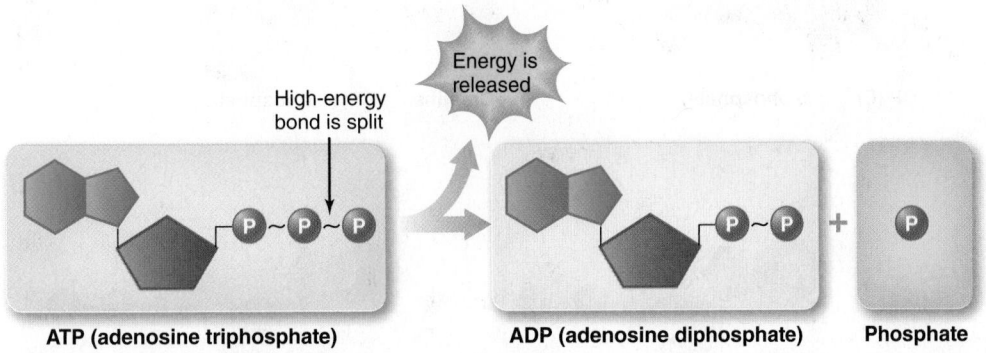

Figure 12.4 Structure of adenosine triphosphate (ATP). Energy is produced when ATP is split into adenosine diphosphate (ADP) and inorganic phosphate (P_i).

The amount of daily physical activity you should participate in is determined by your personal fitness goals.

creatine phosphate (CP) A high-energy compound that can be broken down for energy and used to regenerate ATP.

anaerobic Means "without oxygen"; the term used to refer to metabolic reactions that occur in the absence of oxygen.

glycolysis The breakdown of glucose; yields two ATP molecules and two pyruvic acid molecules for each molecule of glucose.

pyruvic acid The primary end product of glycolysis.

lactic acid A compound that results when pyruvic acid is metabolized in the presence of insufficient oxygen.

▶ **Figure 12.5** When the compound creatine phosphate (CP) is broken down into a molecule of creatine and an independent phosphate molecule, energy is released. This energy, along with the independent phosphate molecule, can then be used to regenerate ATP.

we are able to generate ATP from the breakdown of carbohydrate, fat, and protein, providing our cells with a variety of sources from which to receive energy. The primary energy systems that provide energy for physical activities are the adenosine triphosphate–creatine phosphate (ATP-CP) energy system and the anaerobic and aerobic breakdown of carbohydrates. Our body also generates energy from the breakdown of fats. As you will see, the type, intensity, and duration of the activities performed determine the amount of ATP needed and therefore the energy system that is used.

The ATP-CP Energy System Uses Creatine Phosphate to Regenerate ATP

As previously mentioned, muscle cells store only enough ATP to maintain activity for one to three seconds. When more energy is needed, a high-energy compound called **creatine phosphate (CP)** (also called *phosphocreatine*, or *PCr*) can be broken down to support the regeneration of ATP **(Figure 12.5)**. Because this reaction can occur in the absence of oxygen, it is referred to as an **anaerobic** (meaning "without oxygen") reaction.

Muscle tissue contains about four to six times as much CP as ATP, but there is still not enough CP available to fuel long-term activity. CP is used the most during very intense, short bouts of activity, such as lifting, jumping, and sprinting **(Figure 12.6)**. Together, our stores of ATP and CP can support a *maximal* physical effort for only about 3 to 15 seconds. We must rely on other energy sources, such as carbohydrate and fat, to support activities of longer duration.

The Breakdown of Carbohydrates Provides Energy for Both Brief and Long-Term Exercise

During activities lasting about 30 seconds to 3 minutes, our body needs an energy source that can be used quickly to produce ATP. The breakdown of carbohydrates, specifically glucose, provides this quick energy in a process called **glycolysis**. The most common source of glucose during exercise comes from glycogen stored in the muscles and glucose found in the blood. As shown in **Figure 12.7**, for every glucose molecule that goes through glycolysis, two ATP molecules are produced. The primary end product of glycolysis is **pyruvic acid**.

When oxygen availability is limited in the cell, pyruvic acid is converted to **lactic acid**. For years it was assumed that lactic acid was a useless, even potentially toxic, by-product of high-intensity exercise. We now know that lactic acid is an important intermediate of glucose breakdown and that it plays a critical role in supplying fuel

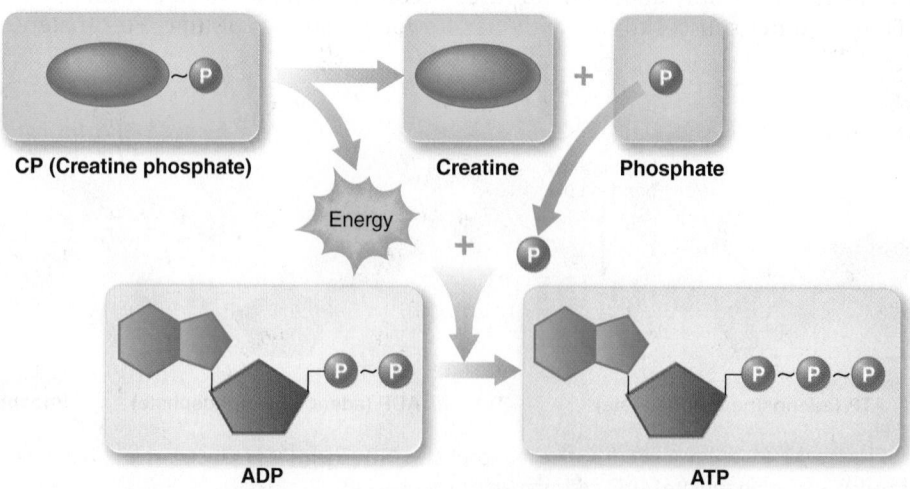

CP (Creatine phosphate)　　　Creatine　　　Phosphate

Energy

ADP　　　ATP

for working muscles, the heart, and resting tissues (see the Nutrition Myth or Fact box on page 416).

The major advantage of glycolysis is that it is the fastest way that we can regenerate ATP for exercise, other than the ATP–CP system. However, this high rate of ATP production can be sustained only briefly, generally less than three minutes. To perform exercise that lasts longer than three minutes, we must rely on the aerobic energy system to provide adequate ATP.

To generate even more ATP molecules, pyruvic acid can go through additional metabolic pathways in the presence of oxygen (see Figure 12.7). Although this process is slower than glycolysis occurring under anaerobic conditions, the breakdown of 1 glucose molecule going through aerobic metabolism yields 36 to 38 ATP molecules for energy, while the anaerobic process yields only 2 ATP molecules. Thus, this aerobic process supplies 18 times more energy! Another advantage of the aerobic process is that it does not result in the significant production of acids and other compounds that contribute to muscle fatigue, which means that a low-intensity activity can be performed for hours. Aerobic metabolism of glucose is the primary source of fuel for our muscles during activities lasting from three minutes to four hours (see Figure 12.6).

As you learned in Chapter 4, we can store only a limited amount of glycogen in our body. An average, well-nourished man who weighs about 70 kg (154 pounds) can store about 200 to 500 g of muscle glycogen, which is equal to 800 to 2000 kcal of energy. Although trained athletes can store more muscle glycogen than the average person, even their bodies do not have enough stored glycogen to provide an unlimited energy supply for long-term activities. Thus, we also need a fuel source that is very abundant and can be broken down under aerobic conditions, so that it can support activities of lower intensity and longer duration. This fuel source is fat.

Aerobic Breakdown of Fats Supports Exercise of Low Intensity and Long Duration

When we refer to fat as a fuel source, we mean stored triglycerides, which is the primary storage form of fat in our cells. As you learned in Chapter 5, a triglyceride molecule is composed of a glycerol backbone attached to three fatty acid molecules (see Figure 5.1 in Chapter 5). It is these fatty acid molecules that provide much of the energy we need to support long-term activity. Fatty acids are classified by their length—that is, by the number of carbons they contain. The longer the fatty acid, the more ATP that can be generated from its breakdown. For instance, palmitic acid is a fatty acid with 16 carbons. If palmitic acid is broken down completely, it yields 129 ATP molecules! Obviously, far more energy is produced from this one fatty acid molecule than from the aerobic breakdown of a glucose molecule.

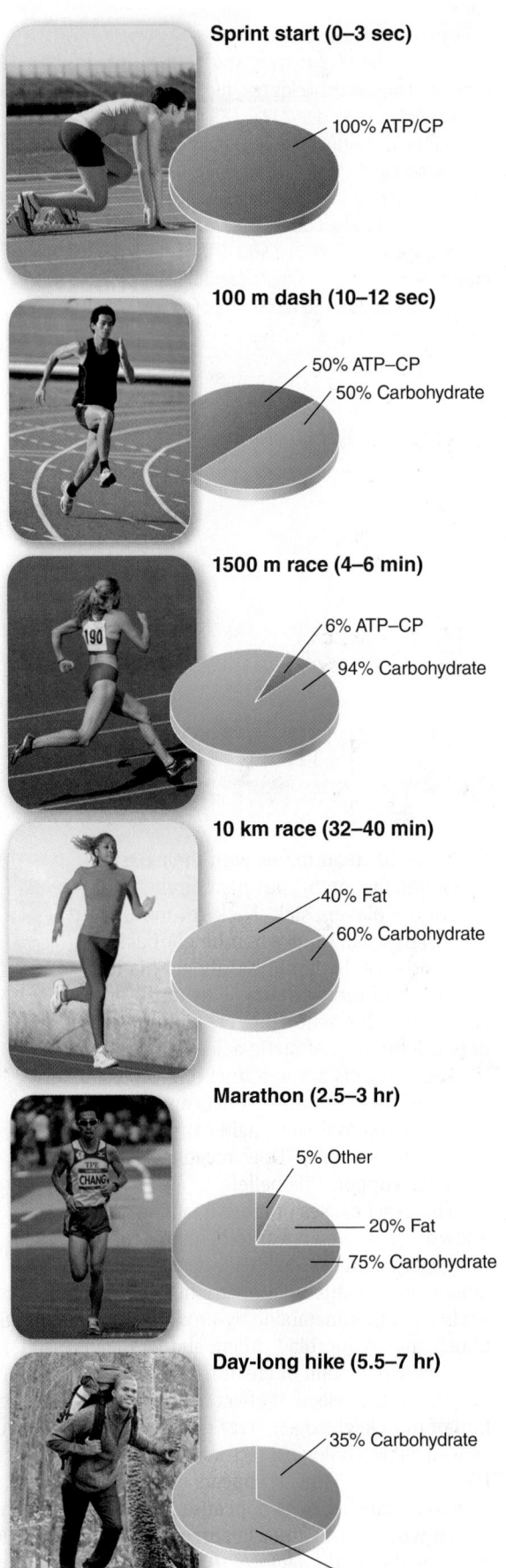

Sprint start (0–3 sec)
100% ATP/CP

100 m dash (10–12 sec)
50% ATP–CP
50% Carbohydrate

1500 m race (4–6 min)
6% ATP–CP
94% Carbohydrate

10 km race (32–40 min)
40% Fat
60% Carbohydrate

Marathon (2.5–3 hr)
5% Other
20% Fat
75% Carbohydrate

Day-long hike (5.5–7 hr)
35% Carbohydrate
65% Fat

Figure 12.6 The relative contributions of ATP–CP, carbohydrate, and fat to activities of various durations and intensities.

▶ **Figure 12.7** The breakdown of one molecule of glucose, or the process of glycolysis, yields two molecules of pyruvic acid and two ATP molecules. The further metabolism of pyruvic acid in the presence of insufficient oxygen (anaerobic process) results in the production of lactic acid. The metabolism of pyruvic acid in the presence of adequate oxygen (aerobic process) yields 36 to 38 molecules of ATP.

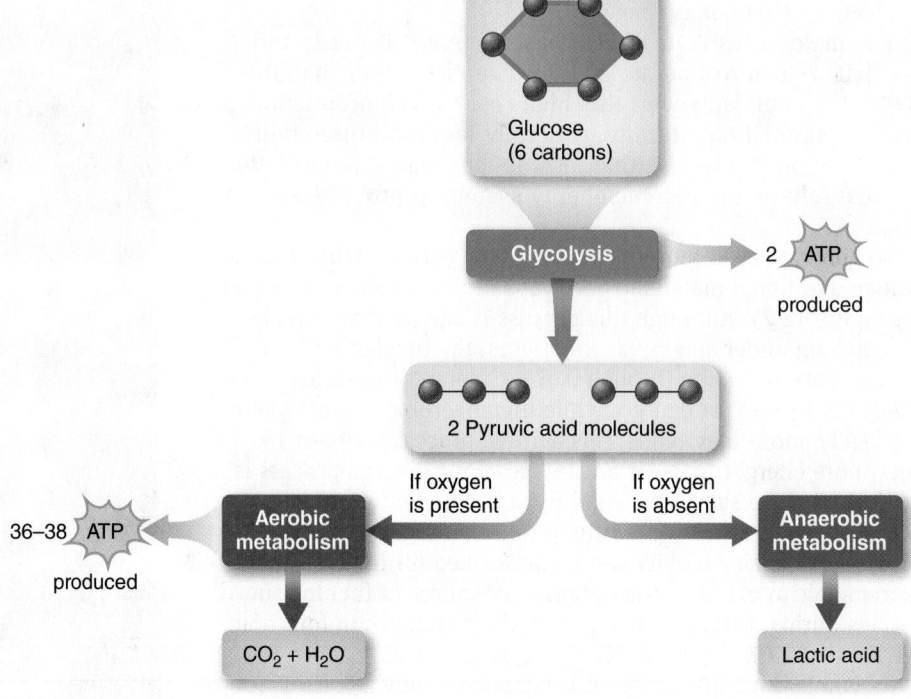

NUTRITION MYTH OR FACT?
Does Lactic Acid Cause Muscle Fatigue and Soreness?

Nick and his teammates won their basketball game last night, but just barely. With two of the players sick, Nick got more court time than usual, and when he got back to the residence, he could hardly get his legs to carry him up the stairs. This morning, Nick's muscles ache all over, and he wonders if a buildup of lactic acid is to blame.

Lactic acid is a by-product of glycolysis. For many years, both scientists and athletes believed that lactic acid caused muscle fatigue and soreness. Does recent scientific evidence support this belief?

The exact causes of muscle fatigue are not known, and there appear to be many contributing factors. Recent evidence suggests that fatigue may be due not only to the accumulation of many acids and other metabolic by-products, such as inorganic phosphate (Westerblad, Allen, and Lännergen, 2002), but also to the depletion of creatine phosphate and changes in calcium in the cells that affect muscle contraction. Depletion of muscle glycogen, liver glycogen, and blood glucose, as well as psychological factors, can all contribute to fatigue (Brooks, 2000). Thus, it appears that lactic acid only contributes to fatigue but does not cause fatigue independently.

So what causes muscle soreness? As with fatigue, there are probably many factors. It is hypothesized that soreness usually results from microscopic tears in the muscle fibres as a result of strenuous exercise. This damage triggers an inflammatory reaction, which causes an influx of fluid and various chemicals to the damaged area. These substances work to remove damaged tissue and initiate tissue repair, but they may also stimulate pain. However, it appears highly unlikely that lactic acid is an independent cause of muscle soreness.

Recent studies indicate that lactic acid is produced even under aerobic conditions! This means it is produced at rest as well as during exercise at any intensity. The reasons for this constant production of lactic acid are still being studied. What we do know is that lactic acid is an important fuel for resting tissues, for working cardiac and skeletal muscles, and even for the brain both at rest and during exercise (Brooks, 2009; Van Hall et al., 2009). That's right—skeletal muscles not only *produce* lactic acid but also *use* it for energy, both directly and after it is converted into glucose and glycogen in the liver. We also know that endurance training improves the muscles' ability to use lactic acid for energy. Thus, contrary to being a waste product of glucose metabolism, lactic acid is actually an important energy source for muscle cells during rest and exercise.

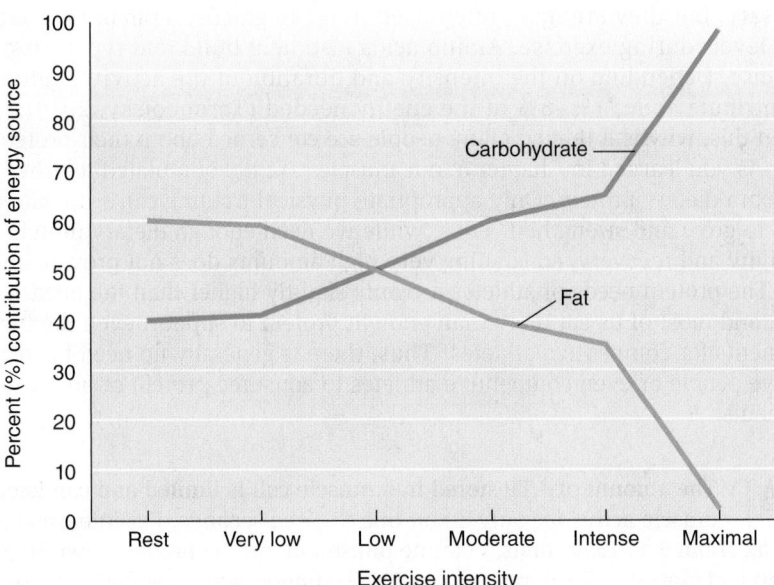

◀ **Figure 12.8** For most daily activities, including exercise, we use a mixture of carbohydrate and fat for energy. At lower exercise intensities, we rely more on fat as a fuel source. As exercise intensity increases, we rely more on carbohydrate for energy. Data from Brooks, G. A., and J. Mercier, 1994. Balance of carbohydrate and lipid utilization during exercise: the "crossover" concept. J. Appl. Physiol. 76(6):2253–2261.

There are two major advantages of using fat as a fuel. First, fat is an abundant energy source, even in lean people. For example, a man who weighs 70 kg (154 pounds) who has a body fat level of 10% has approximately 7 kg (15 lb.) of body fat, which is equivalent to more than 209 200 kJ (50 000 kcal) of energy! This is significantly more energy than can be provided by his stored muscle glycogen (3350 to 8370 kJ or 800 to 2000 kcal). Second, fat provides 37 kJ (9 kcal) of energy per gram, more than twice as much energy per gram as carbohydrate. The primary disadvantage of using fat as a fuel is that the breakdown process is relatively slow; thus, fat is used predominantly as a fuel source during activities of lower intensity and longer duration. Fat is also our primary energy source during rest, sitting, and standing in place.

What specific activities are primarily fuelled by fat? Walking long distances uses fat stores, as does hiking, long-distance cycling, and other low- to moderate-intensity forms of exercise. Fat is also an important fuel source during endurance events, such as marathons (42 km or 26.2 miles) and ultra-marathon races (80 km or 49.9 miles). Endurance exercise training improves our ability to use fat for energy, which may be one reason that people who exercise regularly tend to have lower body fat levels than people who do not exercise.

It is important to remember that we are almost always using some combination of carbohydrate and fat for energy. At rest, we use very little carbohydrate, relying mostly on fat. However this does not mean that we can reduce our body fat by resting and doing very little activity! As discussed in Chapter 11, to lose weight and reduce body fat, a person needs to exercise regularly and reduce energy intake, so that a negative energy balance results. During maximal exercise (at 90%–100% effort), we are using virtually all carbohydrate. However, most activities we do each day involve some use of both fuels **(Figure 12.8)**.

When it comes to eating properly to support regular physical activity or exercise training, the nutrient to focus on is carbohydrate. This is because most people store more than enough fat to support exercise, whereas our storage of carbohydrate is limited. It is especially important that we maintain adequate stores of glycogen for moderate to intense exercise. Dietary recommendations for fat, carbohydrate, and protein are reviewed later in this chapter.

Amino Acids Are Not Major Sources of Fuel During Exercise

Proteins, or more specifically amino acids, are not major energy sources during exercise. As discussed in Chapter 6, amino acids can be used directly for energy if necessary, but they are more often used to make glucose to maintain our blood glucose levels during exercise. Amino acids also help build and repair tissues after exercise. Depending on the intensity and duration of the activity, amino acids may contribute about 1%–6% of the energy needed (Tarnopolsky, 2010).

Given this, why is it that so many people are concerned about their protein intakes? As you learned in Chapter 6, our muscles are not stimulated to grow when we eat extra dietary protein. Only appropriate physical training can stimulate our muscles to grow and strengthen. Thus, while we need enough dietary protein to support activity and recovery, consuming very high amounts does not provide an added benefit. The protein needs of athletes are only slightly higher than the needs of nonathletes, and most of us eat more than enough protein to support even the highest requirements for competitive athletes! Thus, there is generally no need for recreationally active people or even competitive athletes to consume protein or amino acid supplements.

RECAP The amount of ATP stored in a muscle cell is limited and can keep a muscle active for only about one to three seconds. For intense activities lasting about 3 to 15 seconds, creatine phosphate can be broken down to provide energy and support the regeneration of ATP. To support activities that last from 30 seconds to 2 minutes, energy is produced from glycolysis. Fatty acids can be broken down aerobically to support activities of low intensity and longer duration. The two major advantages of using fat as a fuel are that it is an abundant energy source and it provides more than twice the energy per gram as compared with carbohydrate. Amino acids may contribute from 3% to 6% of the energy needed during exercise, depending on the intensity and duration of the activity. Amino acids help build and repair tissues after exercise.

🔺 Small snacks can be helpful to meet daily energy demands.

What Kind of Diet Supports Physical Activity?

Lots of people wonder, "Do my nutrient needs change if I become more physically active?" The answer to this question depends on the type, intensity, and duration of the activity in which you participate. It is not necessarily true that our requirement for every nutrient is greater if we are physically active.

People who are performing moderate-intensity daily activities for health can follow the dietary guidelines put forth in *Eating Well with Canada's Food Guide.* For smaller or less active people, the lower end of the range of recommendations for each food group may be appropriate. For larger or more active people, the higher end of the range is suggested. Modifications may be necessary for people who exercise vigorously every day, particularly for athletes training for competition. **Table 12.2** provides an overview of the nutrients that can be affected by regular, vigorous exercise training. Each of these nutrients is described in more detail in the following section (American College of Sports Medicine, American Dietetic Association and Dietitians of Canada, 2009).

Vigorous Exercise Increases Energy Needs

Athletes generally have higher energy needs than moderately physically active or sedentary people. The amount of extra energy needed to support regular training is determined by the type, intensity, and duration of the activity. In addition, the energy needs of male athletes are higher than those of female athletes because male athletes weigh more, have more muscle mass, and expend more energy during activity. This is relative, of course: a large woman who trains three to five hours each day will probably need more energy than a small man who trains one hour each day. The energy needs of athletes can range from only 7530 to

TABLE 12.2 Suggested Intakes of Nutrients to Support Vigorous Exercise

Nutrient	Functions	Suggested Intake
Energy	Supports exercise, activities of daily living, and basic body functions	Depends on body size and the type, intensity, and duration of activity. For many female athletes: 7530 to 14 650 kJ (1800 to 3500 kcal) per day For many male athletes: 10 460 to 31 380 kJ (2500 to 7500 kcal) per day
Carbohydrate	Provides energy, maintains adequate muscle glycogen and blood glucose; high complex carbohydrate foods provide vitamins and minerals	45%–65% of total energy intake Depending on sport and gender, should consume 6–10 g of carbohydrate per kg body weight per day
Fat	Provides energy, fat-soluble vitamins, and essential fatty acids; supports production of hormones and transport of nutrients	20%–35% of total energy intake
Protein	Helps build and maintain muscle; provides building material for glucose; energy source during endurance exercise; aids recovery from exercise	10%–35% of total energy intake Endurance athletes: 1.2–1.4 g per kg body weight Strength athletes: 1.2–1.7 g per kg body weight
Water	Maintains temperature regulation (adequate cooling); maintains blood volume and blood pressure; supports all cell functions	Consume fluid before, during, and after exercise Consume enough to maintain body weight Consume at least 2 litres (64 fl. oz.) of water daily to maintain regular health and activity Athletes may need up to 3–4 litres (170 fl. oz.) every day; more is required if exercising in a hot environment or high altitude
B-vitamins	Critical for energy production from carbohydrate, fat, and protein	May need slightly more (one to two times the RDA) for thiamin, riboflavin, and vitamin B_6
Calcium	Builds and maintains bone mass; assists with nervous system function, muscle contraction, hormone function, and transport of nutrients across cell membrane	Meet the current AI: 14–18 years: 1300 mg/day 19–50 years: 1000 mg/day 51 and older: 1200 mg/day
Iron	Primarily responsible for the transport of oxygen in blood to cells; assists with energy production	Consume at least the RDA: Males: 14–18 years: 11 mg/day 19 and older: 8 mg/day Females: 14–18 years: 15 mg/day 19–50 years: 18 mg/day 51 and older: 8 mg/day

8400 kJ (1800 to 2000 kcal) per day for a small female gymnast to more than 31 380 kJ (7500 kcal) per day for a male cyclist competing in the Tour de France cross-country cycling race!

Figure 12.9 shows a sample of meals that total 7530 kJ (1800 kcal) per day and 16 800 kJ (4000 kcal) per day, with the carbohydrate content of these meals meeting more than 60% of total energy intake. As you can see, athletes who require more than 16 800 kJ (4000 kcal) per day need to consume very large quantities of food. However, the heavy demands of daily physical training, work, school, and family responsibilities often leave these athletes with little time to eat adequately. Thus, many athletes meet their energy demands by planning regular meals and snacks and **grazing** (eating small meals throughout the day) consistently. They may also take advantage of the energy-dense snack foods and meal replacements specifically designed for athletes participating in vigorous training. These steps help athletes maintain their blood glucose and energy stores.

If an athlete is losing body weight, then his or her energy intake is inadequate. Conversely, weight gain may indicate that energy intake is too high.

grazing Consistently eating small meals throughout the day; done by many athletes to meet their high energy demands.

1800 kcal/day	4000 kcal/day
Breakfast: 375 mL Cheerios 125 mL skim milk 1 medium banana 250 mL orange juice	**Breakfast:** 750 mL Cheerios 250 mL skim milk 1 medium banana 2 slices whole-wheat toast 15 mL butter 500 mL orange juice

Lunch:
Turkey sandwich with:
  2 slices whole-wheat bread
  85 g turkey lunch meat
  28 g Swiss cheese slice
  1 leaf iceberg lettuce
  2 slices tomato
250 mL tomato soup
  (made with water)
	Lunch:
	Two turkey sandwiches with:
	  2 slices whole-wheat bread
	  85 g turkey lunch meat
	  28 g Swiss cheese slice
	  1 leaf iceberg lettuce
	  2 slices tomato
	500 mL tomato soup
	  (made with water)
	Two 250 mL containers of
	  low-fat fruit yogurt
	750 mL Gatorade

Dinner:
113 g grilled skinless
  chicken breast
375 mL mixed salad greens
15 mL French salad dressing
250 mL steamed broccoli
250 mL cooked brown rice
250 mL skim milk
	Dinner:
	170 g grilled skinless
	  chicken breast
	750 mL mixed salad greens
	45 mL French salad dressing
	500 mL cooked
	  spaghetti noodles
	250 mL spaghetti sauce
	  with meat
	500 mL skim milk

Figure 12.9 High-carbohydrate (approximately 60% of total energy) meals that contain approximately 7530 kJ (1800 kcal) per day (on left) and 16 800 kJ (4000 kcal) per day (on right). Athletes, particularly those with very high energy needs, must plan their meals carefully to meet energy demands.

Some athletes diet to meet a predefined weight category.

Weight maintenance is generally recommended to maximize performance. If weight loss is warranted, food intake should be lowered no more than 840 to 2100 kJ (200 to 500 kcal) per day, and athletes should try to lose weight prior to the competitive season, if at all possible. Weight gain may be necessary for some athletes and can usually be accomplished by consuming 2100 to 2940 kJ (500 to 700 kcal) per day more than needed for weight maintenance. The extra energy should come from a healthy balance of carbohydrate (45%–65% of total energy intake), fat (20%–35% of total energy intake), and protein (10%–35% of total energy intake).

Many athletes are concerned about their weight. Jockeys, boxers, wrestlers, judo athletes, and others are required to "make weight"—to meet a predefined weight category. Others, such as distance runners, gymnasts, figure skaters, and dancers, are required to maintain a very lean figure for performance and aesthetic reasons. These athletes tend to eat less energy than they need to support vigorous training, which puts them at risk for inadequate intakes of all nutrients. These athletes are also at a higher risk of suffering from health consequences resulting from poor energy and nutrient intake, including eating disorders, osteoporosis, menstrual disturbances, dehydration, heat and physical injuries, and even death.

Carbohydrate Needs Increase for Many Active People

As you know, carbohydrate (in the form of glucose) is one of the primary sources of energy needed to support exercise. Both endurance athletes and strength athletes require adequate carbohydrate to maintain their glycogen stores and provide quick energy.

How Much of an Athlete's Diet Should Be Carbohydrate?

You may recall from Chapter 4 that the AMDR for carbohydrates is 45%–65% of total energy intake. Athletes should consume carbohydrate within this recommended range. Although high-carbohydrate diets (greater than 60% of total energy intake) have been recommended in the past, this percentage value may not be appropriate for all athletes.

To illustrate the importance of carbohydrate intake for athletes, let's see what happens to Nick when he participates in a study designed to determine how carbohydrate intake affects glycogen stores during a period of heavy training. Nick was asked to go to the exercise laboratory at the university and ride a stationary bicycle for two hours a day for three consecutive days at 75% of his maximal heart rate. Before and after each ride, samples of muscle tissue were taken from his thighs to determine the amount of glycogen stored in the working muscles. Nick performed these rides under two different experimental conditions—once when he had eaten a high-carbohydrate diet (80% of total energy intake) and again when he had eaten a moderate-carbohydrate diet (40% of total energy intake). As you can see in **Figure 12.10**, Nick's muscle glycogen levels decreased dramatically after each training session. More important, his muscle glycogen levels did not recover to baseline levels over the three days when Nick ate the lower-carbohydrate diet. He was able to maintain his muscle glycogen levels only when he was eating the higher carbohydrate diet. Nick also told the researchers that completing the two-hour rides was much more difficult when he had eaten the moderate-carbohydrate diet as compared to when he ate the diet that was higher in carbohydrate.

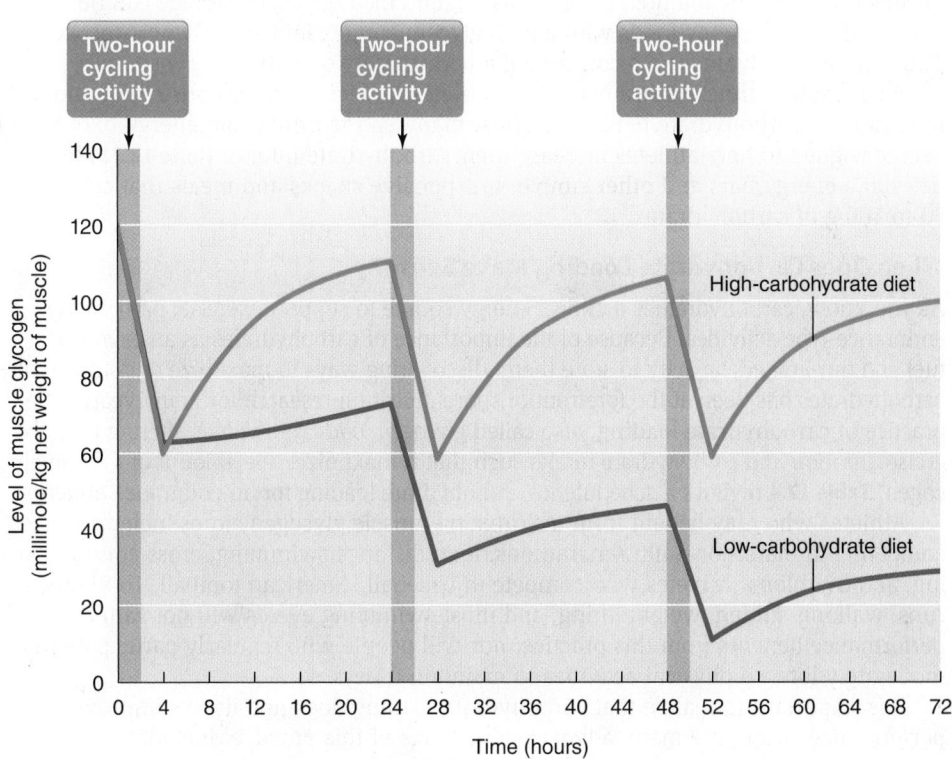

Figure 12.10 The effects of a low-carbohydrate diet on muscle glycogen stores. When a low-carbohydrate diet is consumed, glycogen stores cannot be restored during a period of regular vigorous training.
Data from Costill, D. L., and J. M. Miller, 1980. Nutrition for endurance sport: CHO and fluid balance. Int. J. Sports Med. 1:2–14. Copyright © 1980 Georg Thieme Verlag. Used with permission.

When Should Carbohydrates Be Consumed?

It is important for athletes not only to consume enough carbohydrate to maintain glycogen stores but also to time their intake optimally. Our body stores glycogen very rapidly during the first 24 hours of recovery from exercise, with the highest storage rates occurring during the first few hours (Burke, 2010). Higher carbohydrate intakes during the first 24 hours of recovery from exercise are associated with higher amounts of glucose being stored as muscle glycogen. A daily carbohydrate intake of approximately 6 to 10 g of carbohydrate per kg body weight will optimize muscle glycogen stores in many athletes. However, this need might be much greater in athletes who are training heavily daily, as they have less time to recover and require more carbohydrate to support both training and storage needs.

If an athlete has to perform or participate in training bouts that are scheduled less than eight hours apart, then he or she should try to consume enough carbohydrate in the few hours following training to allow for ample glycogen storage. However, with a longer recovery time (generally 12 hours or more), the athlete can eat when he or she chooses, and glycogen levels should be restored as long as the total carbohydrate eaten is sufficient.

Interestingly, studies have shown that muscle glycogen can be restored to adequate levels in the muscle whether the food is eaten in small, multiple snacks or in larger meals (Burke, 2010), although some studies show enhanced muscle glycogen storage during the first four to six hours of recovery when athletes are fed large amounts of carbohydrate every 15 to 30 minutes (Jentjens et al., 2001; van Loon et al., 2000). There is also evidence that consuming high glycemic index foods during the immediate post-recovery period results in higher glycogen storage than is achieved as a result of eating low glycemic index foods. This may be due to a greater malabsorption of the carbohydrate in low glycemic index foods, as these foods contain more indigestible forms of carbohydrate (Burke, 2010).

What Food Sources of Carbohydrates Are Good for Athletes?

What are good carbohydrate sources to support vigorous training? In general, complex, less processed carbohydrate foods, such as whole grains and cereals, fruits, vegetables, and juices, are excellent sources that also supply fibre, vitamins, and minerals. Guidelines recommend that intake of simple sugars be less than 10% of total energy intake, but some athletes who require very large energy intakes to support training may need to consume more. In addition, as previously mentioned, glycogen storage can be enhanced by consuming foods with a high glycemic index immediately post-recovery. Thus, there are advantages to consuming a wide variety of carbohydrate sources.

As a result of time constraints, many athletes have difficulties consuming enough food to meet carbohydrate demands. Thus, many sports drinks and energy bars have been designed to help athletes increase their carbohydrate intake. **Table 12.3**, identifies some energy bars and other simple, inexpensive snacks and meals that contain 50 to 100 g of carbohydrate.

When Does Carbohydrate Loading Make Sense?

As you know, carbohydrate is a critical energy source to support exercise, particularly endurance-type activities. Because of the importance of carbohydrates as an exercise fuel and our limited capacity to store them, discovering ways to maximize our storage of carbohydrates has been at the forefront of sports nutrition research for many years. The practice of **carbohydrate loading**, also called *glycogen loading,* involves altering both exercise duration and carbohydrate intake such that it maximizes the amount of muscle glycogen. **Table 12.4** reviews a schedule for carbohydrate loading for an endurance athlete.

Athletes who may benefit from maximizing muscle glycogen stores include those competing in marathons, ultra-marathons, long-distance swimming, cross-country skiing, and triathlons. Athletes who compete in baseball, American football, 10-kilometre runs, walking, hiking, weight lifting, and most swimming events will not gain any performance benefits from this practice, nor will people who regularly participate in moderately intense physical activities to maintain fitness.

It is important to realize that carbohydrate loading does not always improve performance. There are many adverse side effects of this practice, including extreme gastrointestinal distress, particularly diarrhea. We store water along with the extra

Fruit and vegetable juices can be a good source of carbohydrates.

Carbohydrate loading may benefit endurance athletes, such as cross-country skiers.

carbohydrate loading Also known as glycogen loading. A process that involves altering training and carbohydrate intake so that muscle glycogen storage is maximized.

TABLE 12.3 Carbohydrate and Total Energy in Various Foods

Food	Amount	Carbohydrate (g)	Energy from Carbohydrate (%)	Total Energy (kcal)
Sweetened applesauce	250 mL (1 cup)	50	97	207
Large apple with	1 each	50	82	248
Saltine crackers	8 each			
Whole-wheat bread	30 g (1-oz.) slice	50	71	282
with jelly	20 mL (4 tsp.)			
and skim milk	375 mL (12 fl. oz.)			
Spaghetti (cooked)	1 cup	50	75	268
with tomato sauce	65 mL (1/4 cup)			
Brown rice (cooked)	250 mL (1 cup)	100	88	450
with mixed vegetables	125 mL (1/2 cup)			
and apple juice	375 mL (12 fl. oz.)			
Grape-Nuts cereal	125 mL (1/2 cup)	100	84	473
with raisins	35 mL (1/8 cup)			
and skim milk	250 mL (8 fl. oz.)			
Clif Bar (chocolate chip)	69 g (2.4 oz.)	45	72	250
Power Bar (chocolate)	65 g (2.25 oz.)	42	75	225
PR Bar Ironman	58 g (2 oz.)	24	42	230

Source: Data from Manore, M. M., N. L. Meyer, and J. Thompson, 2009. Sport Nutrition for Health and Performance, 2nd ed. Champaign, IL: Human Kinetics.

glycogen in our muscles, which leaves many athletes feeling heavy and sluggish. Athletes who want to try carbohydrate loading should experiment prior to competition to determine whether it is an acceptable and beneficial approach for them.

Moderate Fat Consumption Is Enough to Support Most Activities

As you have learned, fat is an important energy source for both moderate physical activity and vigorous endurance training. When athletes reach a physically trained state, they are able to use more fat for energy; in other words, they become better "fat burners." This can also occur in people who are not athletes but who regularly participate in aerobic-type fitness activities. This training effect occurs for a number of reasons, including an increase in the number and activity of various enzymes involved in fat metabolism, improved ability of the muscle to store fat, and improved ability to extract fat from the blood for use during exercise. By using fat as a fuel, athletes can spare carbohydrate, so that they can use it during prolonged, intense training or competition.

Many athletes concerned with body weight and physical appearance believe they should eat less than 15% of their total energy intake as fat, but this is inadequate for

TABLE 12.4 Recommended Carbohydrate Loading Guidelines for Endurance Athletes

Days Prior to Event	Exercise Duration (minutes) at 70% Maximal Effort	Carbohydrate Content of Diet (g/kg of body weight)
6	90	5
5	40	5
4	40	5
3	20	10
2	20	10
1	Rest	10
Day of race	Competition	Precompetition food and fluid

Source: Data from Coleman, E. 2006. Carbohydrate and exercise. In: Dunford, M., ed. Sports Nutrition, 4th ed. Chicago, IL: The American Dietetic Association. Used with permission.

vigorous activity. Instead, a fat intake of 20%–35% of total energy intake is generally recommended for most athletes, with less than 10% of total energy intake as saturated fat.

These recommendations are also put forth for non-athletes. Recall from Chapter 5 that fat provides not only energy but also fat-soluble vitamins and essential fatty acids that are critical to maintaining general health. If fat consumption is too low, inadequate levels of these nutrients can eventually prove detrimental to training and performance. Athletes who have chronic disease risk factors, such as high blood lipids, high blood pressure, or unhealthful blood glucose levels, should work with their physician to adjust their intake of fat and carbohydrate according to their health risks.

Many Athletes Have Increased Protein Needs

The protein intakes suggested for competitive athletes and moderately active people are given in **Table 12.5**. Let's consider the terminology used in the table:

- Competitive male and female endurance athletes train five to seven days per week for more than an hour each day; many of these individuals may train for three to six hours per day. These athletes need significantly more protein than the current RDA of 0.8 g of protein per kg body weight.
- Resistance athletes focus on building and maintaining muscle mass and strength. Those who are already trained need less protein than those who are initiating training. Studies do not support the claim that consuming more than 2 g of protein per kg body weight improves protein synthesis, muscle strength, or performance (Tarnopolsky, 2010).
- Moderate-intensity endurance athletes are people exercising four or five times per week for 45 to 60 minutes each time; these individuals may compete in community races and other activities. Their protein needs are only modestly increased above the RDA.
- Recreational endurance athletes are people who exercise four or five times per week for 30 minutes at less than 60% of their maximal effort. These individuals have a protein need that is equal to or only slightly higher than the RDA.

As noted previously, most inactive people and many athletes in the United States consume more than enough protein to support their needs (Manore, Meyer, and Thompson, 2009). However, some athletes do not consume enough protein; these typically include individuals with very low energy intakes, vegetarians or vegans who do not consume high-protein food sources, and young athletes who are growing and are not aware of their higher protein needs.

In 1995, Dr. Barry Sears published *The Zone: A Dietary Road Map*, a book that claims numerous benefits of a high-protein, low-carbohydrate diet for athletes (Sears, 1995). Since that time, Sears has published several additional books espousing the same principles, which are still being recommended to both athletes and non-athletes. Unlike many of the current high-protein diets, the Zone Diet was developed and marketed specifically for competitive athletes. It recommends that athletes eat a 40–30–30 diet, or one composed of 40% carbohydrate, 30% fat, and 30% protein. Dr. Sears claims that high-carbohydrate diets impair athletic performance because of unhealthy effects of insulin. These claims have never been supported by research—in

TABLE 12.5 Estimated Protein Requirements for Athletes

Group	Protein Requirements (g/kg of body weight)
Competitive male and female athletes	1.4–1.6
Moderate-intensity endurance athletes	1.2
Recreational endurance athletes	0.8–1.0
Football, power sports players	1.4–1.7
Resistance athletes, weight lifters (early training)	1.5–1.7
Resistance athletes, weight lifters (steady-state training)	1.0–1.2

Data from Tarnopolsky, M, 2006. Protein and amino acid needs for training and bulking up. In Clinical Sports Nutrition, 3rd ed., edited by L. Burke and V. Deakin. New York: McGraw-Hill.

fact, many of Dr. Sears's claims are not consistent with human physiology. The primary problem with the Zone Diet for athletes is that it is too low in both energy and carbohydrate to support training and performance.

As described in Chapter 6, high-quality protein sources include lean meats, poultry, fish, eggs and egg whites, low-fat dairy products, legumes, and soy products. By following *Eating Well with Canada's Food Guide* and meeting energy needs, people of all fitness levels can consume more than enough protein without the use of supplements or specially formulated foods.

RECAP The type, intensity, and duration of activities a person participates in determine his or her nutrient needs. Carbohydrate needs may increase for some active people. In general, athletes should consume 45%–65% of their total energy as carbohydrate. Carbohydrate loading involves altering physical training and the diet such that the storage of muscle glycogen is maximized. Active people use more fat than carbohydrates for energy because they experience an increase in the number and activity of the enzymes involved in fat metabolism, and they have an improved ability to store fat and extract it from the blood for use during exercise. A dietary fat intake of 20%–35% is recommended for athletes, with less than 10% of total energy intake as saturated fat. Although protein needs can be higher for athletes, most people in Canada already consume more than their daily needs for protein.

Water is essential for maintaining fluid balance and preventing dehydration.

Regular Exercise Increases Our Need for Fluids

A detailed discussion of fluid and electrolyte balance is provided in Chapter 7. In this chapter, we will focus on the role of water during exercise.

Cooling Mechanisms

Heat production can increase 15 to 20 times during heavy exercise! The primary way in which we dissipate this heat is through sweating, which is also called **evaporative cooling**. When body temperature rises, more blood (which contains water) flows to the surface of the skin. Heat is carried in this way from the core of our body to the surface of our skin. By sweating, the water (and body heat) leaves our body, and the air around us picks up the evaporating water from our skin, cooling our body.

Dehydration and Heat-Related Illnesses

Heat illnesses occur because when we exercise in the heat, our muscles and skin constantly compete for blood flow. When there is no longer enough blood flow to provide adequate blood to both our muscles and our skin, muscle blood flow takes priority and evaporative cooling is inhibited. Exercising in heat plus humidity is especially dangerous because whereas the heat dramatically raises body temperature, the high humidity inhibits evaporative cooling; that is, the environmental air is already so saturated with water that it is unable to absorb the water in sweat. Body temperature becomes dangerously high, and heat illness is likely.

It is important to remember that dehydration significantly increases our risk for heat illnesses. In **Figure 12.11**, specific signs of dehydration during heavy exercise are listed. Review the **In Depth** following Chapter 7 for more information on specific heat-related illnesses in which fluid intake plays a role.

Guidelines for Proper Fluid Replacement

How can we prevent dehydration and heat illnesses? Obviously, adequate fluid intake is critical before, during, and after exercise. Unfortunately, our thirst mechanism cannot be relied upon to signal when we need to drink. If we rely only on our feelings of thirst, we will not consume enough fluid to support exercise.

General fluid replacement recommendations are based on maintaining body weight. As discussed in Chapter 7, athletes who are training and competing in hot environments should weigh themselves before and after the training session or event and should regain the weight lost over the subsequent 24-hour period. They should avoid losing more than 2%–3% of body weight during exercise, as performance can be impaired with fluid losses as small as 1% of body weight.

Drinking sports beverages during training and competition lasting more than one hour replaces fluid, carbohydrates, and electrolytes.

evaporative cooling Another term for sweating, which is the primary way in which we dissipate heat.

Symptoms of Dehydration During Heavy Exercise:
- Decreased exercise performance
- Increased level in perceived exertion
- Dark yellow or brown urine colour
- Increased heart rate at a given exercise intensity
- Decreased appetite
- Decreased ability to concentrate
- Decreased urine output
- Fatigue and weakness
- Headache and dizziness

Figure 12.11 Symptoms of dehydration during heavy exercise.

Table 12.6 reviews the guidelines for proper fluid replacement. For activities lasting less than one hour, plain water is generally adequate to replace fluid losses. However, for training and competition lasting longer than one hour in any weather, sports beverages containing carbohydrates and electrolytes are recommended. These beverages are also recommended for people who will not drink enough water because they

TABLE 12.6 Guidelines for Fluid Replacement

Activity Level	Environment	Fluid Requirements (litres per day)
Sedentary	Cool	2–3
Active	Cool	3–6
Sedentary	Warm	3–5
Active	Warm	5–10

Before Exercise or Competition:
- Drink adequate fluids during the 24 hours before event; should be able to maintain body weight.
- Slowly drink about 5–7 mL/kg (approx. 2–3 mL/lb.) body weight of water or a sports drink at least four hours prior to exercise or event to allow time for excretion of excess fluid prior to event.
- Consuming beverages with sodium and/or small amounts of salted snacks at a meal will help stimulate thirst and retain fluids consumed.

During Exercise or Competition:
- Drink early and regularly throughout event to sufficiently replace all water lost through sweating.
- Amount and rate of fluid replacement depend on individual sweating rate, exercise duration, weather conditions, and opportunities to drink.
- Fluids should be cooler than the environmental temperature and flavoured to enhance taste and promote fluid replacement.

During Exercise or Competition That Lasts More Than One Hour:
- Fluid replacement beverage should contain 6%–8% carbohydrate to maintain blood glucose levels; sodium and other electrolytes should be included in the beverage in amounts of 0.5–0.7 g of sodium per litre of water to replace the sodium lost by sweating.

Following Exercise or Competition:
- Consume at least 450–675 mL (16-24 fl. oz.) of fluid for each 0.5 kg or pound of body weight lost.
- Fluids after exercise should contain water to restore hydration status, carbohydrates to replenish glycogen stores, and electrolytes (for example, sodium and potassium) to speed rehydration.
- Consume enough fluid to permit regular urination and to ensure the urine colour is very light or light yellow in colour; drinking about 125%–150% of fluid loss is usually sufficient to ensure complete rehydration.

In General:
- Products that contain fructose should be limited, as these may cause gastrointestinal distress.
- Caffeine and alcohol should be avoided, as these products increase urine output and reduce fluid retention.
- Carbonated beverages should be avoided, as they reduce the desire for fluid intake due to stomach fullness.

Source: Data from Murray, R, 1997. Drink more! Advice from a world class expert. ACSM's Health and Fitness Journal 1:19–23; American College of Sports Medicine Position Stand, 2007. Exercise and fluid replacement. Med. Sci. Sports Exerc. 39(2):377–390; Casa, D. J., L. E. Armstrong, S. K. Hillman, S. J. Montain, R. V. Reiff, B. S. E. Rich, W. O. Roberts, and J. A. Stone, 2000. National Athletic Trainers' Association position statement: fluid replacement for athletes. J. Athlet. Train. 35:212–224; Dietitians of Canada, American College of Sports Medicine, American Dietetic Association. (2008) Joint Position Paper: Nutrition and Athletic Performance, www.dietitians.ca.

do not like the taste. If drinking these beverages will guarantee adequate hydration, they are appropriate to use. For more specific information about sports beverages, refer to Chapter 7, page 246.

Inadequate Intakes of Some Vitamins and Minerals Can Diminish Health and Performance

When individuals train vigorously for athletic events, their requirements for certain vitamins and minerals may be altered. Many highly active people do not eat enough food or a variety of foods that allows them to consume enough of these nutrients, yet it is imperative that active people do their very best to eat an adequate, varied, and balanced diet to try to meet the increased needs associated with vigorous training.

B-Vitamins

The B-vitamins are directly involved in energy metabolism (see pages 325–326). There is reliable evidence that the requirements of active people for thiamin, riboflavin, and vitamin B6 may be slightly higher than the current RDA due to increased production of energy in active people and inadequate dietary intake in some individuals (Manore, Meyer, and Thompson, 2009). However, these increased needs are easily met by consuming adequate energy and a lot of complex carbohydrates, fruits, and vegetables. Athletes and physically active people at risk for poor B-vitamin status are those who consume inadequate energy or who consume mostly refined carbohydrate foods, such as soda pop and sugary snacks. Vegan athletes and active individuals may be at risk for inadequate intake of vitamin B_{12}. Food sources enriched with this nutrient include soy and cereal products.

Calcium and the Female Athlete Triad

Calcium supports proper muscle contraction and ensures bone health (see pages 292–293). Calcium intakes are inadequate for most women in North America, including both sedentary and active women. This is most likely due to a failure to consume foods that are high in calcium, particularly dairy products. While vigorous training does not appear to increase our need for calcium, we need to consume enough calcium to support bone health. If we do not, stress fractures and severe loss of bone can result.

Some female athletes suffer from a syndrome known as the *female athlete triad.* This condition is discussed in the **In Depth** following this chapter. In the female athlete triad, nutritional inadequacies cause irregularities in the menstrual cycle and hormonal disturbances that lead to a significant loss of bone mass. Thus, for female athletes, consuming the recommended amounts of calcium is critical. For female athletes who are physically small and have lower energy intakes, calcium supplementation may be needed to meet current recommendations.

Iron

Iron is a part of the thiamin molecule and is critical for the transport of oxygen in our blood to our cells and working muscles. Iron also is involved in energy production. Research has shown that active individuals lose more iron in the sweat, feces, and urine than do inactive individuals and that endurance runners lose iron when their red blood cells break down in their feet due to the high impact of running (Weaver and Rajaram, 1992). Female athletes and non-athletes lose more iron than male athletes because of menstrual blood losses, and females in general tend to eat less iron in their diet. Vegetarian athletes and active people may also consume less iron. Thus, many athletes and active people are at higher risk for iron deficiency. Depending on its severity, poor iron status can impair athletic performance and our ability to maintain regular physical activity.

Not all athletes suffer from iron deficiency. A phenomenon known as *sports anemia* was identified in the 1960s. Sports anemia is not true anemia, but a transient decrease in iron stores that occurs at the start of an exercise program for some people, and it is seen in athletes who increase their training intensity. Exercise training increases the amount of water in our blood (called *plasma volume*); however, the amount of thiamin does not increase until later in the training period. Thus, the iron content in the blood appears to be low but instead is falsely depressed due to increases in plasma volume. Sports anemia, since it is not true anemia, does not affect performance.

The stages of iron deficiency are described on pages 347–348. In general, it appears that physically active females are at relatively high risk of suffering from the first stage of iron depletion, in which iron stores are low (Haymes, 1998; Haymes and Clarkson, 1998). Because of this, it is suggested that blood tests of iron stores and monitoring of dietary iron intake be done routinely for active females (Manore, Meyer, and Thompson, 2009). In some cases, iron needs cannot be met through the diet, and supplementation is necessary. Iron supplementation should be done with a physician's approval and proper medical supervision.

RECAP Regular exercise increases fluid needs. Fluid is critical to cool our internal body temperature and prevent heat illnesses. Dehydration is a serious threat during exercise in extreme heat and high humidity. Active people may need more thiamin, riboflavin, and vitamin B_6 than inactive people. Exercise itself does not increase our calcium needs, but most women, including active women, do not consume enough calcium. Some female athletes suffer from the female athlete triad, a condition that involves the interaction of low energy availability, osteoporosis, and amenorrhea. Many active individuals require more iron, particularly female athletes and vegetarian athletes.

Are Ergogenic Aids Necessary for Active People?

Many competitive athletes and even some recreationally active people search continually for that something extra that will enhance their performance. **Ergogenic aids** are substances used to improve exercise and athletic performance. For example, nutrition supplements can be classified as ergogenic aids, as can anabolic steroids and other pharmaceuticals. Interestingly, people report using ergogenic aids not only to enhance athletic performance but also to improve their physical appearance, prevent or treat injuries, treat diseases, and help them cope with stress. Some people even report using them because of peer pressure!

As you have learned in this chapter, adequate nutrition is critical to athletic performance and to regular physical activity, and products such as sports bars and beverages can help athletes maintain their competitive edge. However, as we will explore shortly, many of these products are not effective, some are dangerous, and most are very expensive. For the average consumer, it is virtually impossible to track the latest research findings for these products. In addition, many have not been adequately studied, and unsubstantiated false claims surrounding them are rampant. How can you become a more educated consumer about ergogenic aids?

New ergogenic aids are available virtually every month, and keeping track of these substances is a daunting task. It is therefore not possible to discuss every available product in this chapter. However, a brief review of a number of currently popular ergogenic aids is provided.

Anabolic Products Are Touted as Muscle and Strength Enhancers

Many ergogenic aids are said to be **anabolic**, meaning that they build muscle and increase strength. Most anabolic substances promise to increase testosterone, which is the hormone that is associated with male sex characteristics and that increases muscle size and strength. Although some anabolic substances are effective, they are generally associated with harmful side effects.

Anabolic Steroids

Anabolic steroids are testosterone-based drugs that have been used extensively by strength and power athletes. Anabolic steroids are known to be effective in increasing

ergogenic aids Substances used to improve exercise and athletic performance.

anabolic The term applied to a substance that builds muscle and increases strength.

Ergogenic Aids: Let the Buyer Beware?

The sale of ergogenic aids is a multibillion-dollar industry, and some companies resort to misleading claims to boost their share of the market. Beware of the following deceptive tactics used to market ergogenic aids:

1. Taking published research out of context, applying the findings in an unproven manner, or having inappropriate control over study results. Some companies claim that research has been done or is currently being done, but fail to provide specific information.

2. Paying celebrities to endorse products—remember that testimonials can be faked, bought, and exaggerated.

3. Stating that the product is patented and that this proves its effectiveness. Patents are granted to indicate differences among products.

4. Advertising through infomercials and mass-media marketing videos. Although Advertising Standards Canada regulates false claims in advertising, products may be investigated only if they appear to pose significant public danger.

5. Offering mail-order fitness evaluations or anabolic measurements. Most of these evaluations are inappropriate and inaccurate.

muscle size, strength, power, and speed. However, these products are illegal in Canada and the United States, and their use is banned by all major collegiate and professional sports organizations, in addition to the Canadian, U.S., and International Olympic Committees. The following are proven long-term and irreversible effects of steroid use:

- infertility
- early closure of the plates of the long bones, resulting in permanent shortened stature
- shrivelled testicles, enlarged breast tissue (that can be removed only surgically), and other signs of "feminization" in men
- enlarged clitoris, facial hair growth, and other signs of "masculinization" in women
- increased risk for certain forms of cancer
- liver damage
- unhealthful changes in blood lipids
- hypertension
- severe acne
- hair thinning or baldness
- disorders such as depression, delusions, sleep disturbances, and extreme anger (so-called "roid rage")

Androstenedione and Dehydroepiandrosterone

Androstenedione ("andro") and dehydroepiandrosterone (DHEA) are precursors of testosterone. Manufacturers of these products claim that taking them will increase testosterone levels and muscle strength. Androstenedione became very popular after baseball player Mark McGwire claimed he used it during the time he was breaking home run records. A U.S. national survey found that, in 2002, about one of every 40 high-school seniors had used it in the past year (FDA, 2004). Contrary to popular claims, studies have found that neither androstenedione nor DHEA increases testosterone levels, and androstenedione has been shown to increase the risk for heart disease in men aged 35 to 65 (Broeder et al., 2000). There are no studies that support claims that these products improve strength or increase muscle mass.

Gamma-Hydroxybutyric Acid

Gamma-hydroxybutyric acid, or GHB, has been promoted as an alternative to anabolic steroids for building muscle. The production and sale of GHB have never been approved in Canada or the United States; however, it was illegally produced

Anabolic substances are often marketed to people wishing to increase muscle size, but carry risks for harmful side effects.

and sold on the black market. For many users, GHB caused only dizziness, tremors, or vomiting, but others experienced severe side effects, including seizures. Many people were hospitalized and some died.

After GHB was banned, a similar product (gamma-butyrolactone, or GBL) was marketed in its place. This product was also found to be dangerous and was removed from the market. Recently, another replacement product called BD, or 1,4-butanediol, was banned because it has caused at least seventy-one deaths, with forty more under investigation. BD is an industrial solvent and is listed on ingredient labels as tetra-methylene glycol, butylene glycol, or sucol-B. Side effects include wild, aggressive behaviour; nausea; incontinence; and sudden loss of consciousness.

Creatine

Creatine is a supplement that has become wildly popular with strength and power athletes. Creatine, or creatine phosphate, is found in meat and fish and stored in our muscles. As described earlier in this chapter, we use creatine phosphate (CP) to regenerate ATP. It is hypothesized that, by taking creatine supplements, individuals have more CP available to replenish ATP, which will prolong their ability to train and perform in short-term, explosive activities, such as weight lifting and sprinting. Between 1994 and 2010, more than 1700 research articles related to creatine and exercise in humans were published. These studies indicate that creatine does not enhance performance in aerobic-type events, but it does enhance sprint performance in swimming, running, and cycling (Balsom et al., 1995; Broeder et al., 2000; Grindstaff et al., 1997; Kreider et al., 1998; Tarnopolsky and MacLennan, 2000). Other studies have shown that creatine increases the work performed and the amount of strength gained during resistance exercise (Kreider et al., 1998; Kreider et al., 1999; Volek et al., 1999). Currently, creatine is not banned by any sports governing bodies, and many collegiate sports programs readily provide creatine supplements for their athletes.

In January 2001, the *New York Times* (Reuters, 2001) reported that the French government had claimed that creatine use could lead to cancer. The news spread quickly across national and international news organizations and over the internet. These claims were subsequently found to be false, as there are no studies in humans that suggest an increased risk for cancer with creatine use. In fact, numerous studies show an anticancer effect for creatine (Ara et al, 1998; Jeong et al, 2000). Although side effects such as dehydration, muscle cramps, and gastrointestinal disturbances have been reported with creatine use, there is very little information on how the long-term use of creatine impacts health. Further research is needed to determine the effectiveness and safety of creatine use over prolonged periods of time.

Some Products Are Said to Optimize Fuel Use During Exercise

Certain ergogenic aids are touted as increasing energy levels and improving athletic performance by optimizing our use of fat, carbohydrate, and protein. The products reviewed here are caffeine, ephedrine, carnitine, chromium, and ribose.

Caffeine

Caffeine is a stimulant that makes us feel more alert and energetic, decreasing feelings of fatigue during exercise. Caffeine has been shown to increase the use of fat as a fuel during endurance exercise, which spares muscle glycogen and improves performance (Anderson et al., 2000; Spriet and Howlett, 2000). Energy drinks that contain high amounts of caffeine, such as Red Bull, have become popular with athletes and many college students. These drinks should be avoided during exercise, as severe dehydration can result due to the combination of fluid loss from exercise and caffeine consumption. It should be recognized that caffeine is a controlled or restricted drug in the athletic world, and athletes can be banned from Olympic competition if urine caffeine levels are too high. However, the amount of caffeine that is banned is quite high, and athletes would need to consume caffeine in pill form to reach this level. Side effects of caffeine use include increased blood pressure, increased heart rate, dizziness, insomnia, headache, and gastrointestinal distress.

Ephedrine

Ephedrine, also known as ephedra, Chinese ephedra, or *ma huang*, is a strong stimulant marketed as a weight-loss supplement and energy enhancer. In reality, many products sold as Chinese ephedra (or herbal ephedra) contain ephedrine from the laboratory and other stimulants, such as caffeine. The use of ephedra supplements does not appear to enhance performance, but supplements containing both caffeine and ephedra

Ephedrine is made from the herb *Ephedra sinica* (Chinese ephedra).

have been shown to prolong the amount of exercise that can be done until exhaustion is reached (Bucci, 2000). Ephedra is known to reduce body weight and body fat in sedentary women, but its impact on weight loss and body fat levels in athletes is unknown. Side effects of ephedra use include headaches, dizziness, nausea, reduced appetite, nervousness, anxiety, irregular or fast heart rate, high blood pressure, strokes, seizures, and death (Health Canada, 2011). Ephedra has been banned by the International Olympic Committee for many years, and Health Canada advises Canadians that the only approved use of ephedra is in nasal decongestants (Health Canada, 2008). Products containing ephedra for body building, weight loss, or increased physical energy are not approved for sale in Canada (Health Canada, 2008).

Carnitine

Carnitine (also known as L-carnitine and levocarnitine) is a compound made from amino acids (lysine and methionine) that is found in the mitochondrial membrane of our cells. Carnitine helps shuttle fatty acids into the mitochondria so that they can be used for energy. In theory, it has been proposed that exercise training depletes our cells of carnitine and that supplementation should increase the amount of carnitine in our cell membranes. By increasing cellular levels of carnitine, we should be able to improve our use of fat as a fuel source. Thus, carnitine is marketed not only as a performance-enhancing substance but also as a "fat burner." Research studies of carnitine supplementation do not support these claims, as neither the transport of fatty acids nor their oxidation appears to be enhanced with supplementation (Hawley, 2002; Heinonen, 1996). Use of carnitine supplements has not been associated with significant side effects.

Chromium

Chromium is a trace mineral that enhances insulin's action of increasing the transport of amino acids into the cell (see Chapter 10). It is found in whole-grain foods, cheese, nuts, mushrooms, and asparagus. It is theorized that many people are chromium deficient and that supplementation will enhance the uptake of amino acids into muscle cells, which will increase muscle growth and strength. Like carnitine, chromium is marketed as a fat burner, as it is speculated that its effect on insulin stimulates the brain to decrease food intake (Williams, 1998). Chromium supplements are available as chromium picolinate and chromium nicotinate. Early studies of chromium supplementation showed promise, but more recent, better-designed studies do not support any benefit of chromium supplementation to muscle mass, muscle strength, body fat, or exercise performance (Vincent, 2003).

Ribose

Ribose is a five-carbon sugar that is critical to the production of ATP. Ribose supplementation is claimed to improve athletic performance by increasing work output and promoting a faster recovery time from vigorous training. While ribose has been shown to improve exercise tolerance in patients with heart disease (Pliml et al., 1992), several studies have reported that ribose supplementation has no impact on athletic performance (Earnest et al., 2004; Hellsten, Skadhauge, and Bangsbo, 2004; Kreider et al., 2003).

From this review of ergogenic aids, you can see that most of these products are not effective in enhancing athletic performance or optimizing muscle strength or body composition. It is important to be a savvy consumer when examining these products to make sure you are not wasting your money or putting your health at risk by using them.

RECAP Ergogenic aids are substances used to improve exercise and athletic performance. Anabolic steroids are effective in increasing muscle size, power, and strength, but they are illegal and can cause serious health problems. Androstenedione and dehydroepiandrosterone are precursors of testosterone; neither of these products has been shown to effectively increase testosterone levels or to increase strength or muscle mass. Creatine supplements are popular and can enhance sprint performance in swimming, running, and cycling. Caffeine is a stimulant that increases the use of fat during exercise; its use in the athletic world is controlled. Ephedrine is a stimulant that has potentially fatal side effects. Carnitine, chromium, and ribose are marketed as ergogenic aids, but studies do not support their effectiveness.

Nutrition DEBATE

Can Exercise Become Addictive?

Do you know someone who turns down social invitations because he wants to go to the gym? Do you have friends who are exercising when they have sports injuries? Has a friend told you that she feels guilty when she misses a workout? Do you know someone who is at the gym twice a day, and insists that it is healthy behaviour? These may be symptoms of obsessive exercising.

Anorexia athletica (also called compulsive exercising, sports anorexia and hypergymnasia) is an addiction to exercise, and shares some similar characteristics as anorexia nervosa and bulimia nervosa. Some who suffer from this condition are female and between the ages of 12 and 19 years. They are not athletes, and may not even enjoy physical activity, yet they feel obligated to exercise and feel guilty when they do not exercise (Anorexia Report, 2012). More commonly, sufferers are serious athletes who "live to work out" (Anorexia Report, 2012), and who measure their self-worth by their athletic performance and achievements (Lein, 2012).

These athletes may show signs of disordered eating, such as restricting calories, but they generally are not diagnosed with anorexia nervosa or bulimia nervosa, which are distinctly different diagnoses, although all three conditions are along the spectrum of eating disorders. (See the **In Depth** at the end of this chapter for more on eating disorders.) In advanced cases, athletes with anorexia athletica deny their obsessive exercising is a problem, even when there are harmful social, physical, and psychological consequences that are obvious to their families and friends. At this point, professional treatment is warranted.

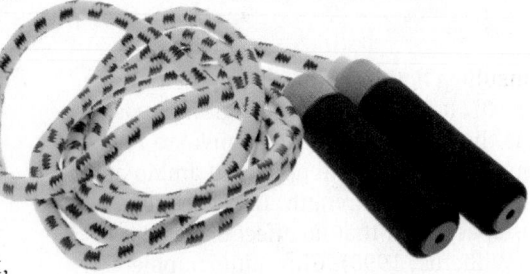

Warning Signs

Someone may be exercising compulsively if he or she:

- won't skip a workout, even if tired, sick, or injured

- doesn't enjoy exercise sessions, but feels obligated to do them
- seems anxious or guilty when missing even one workout
- does miss one workout and exercises twice as long the next time
- is constantly preoccupied with his or her weight and exercise routine
- doesn't like to sit still or relax because of worry that not enough calories are being burnt
- has lost a significant amount of weight
- exercises more after eating more
- skips seeing friends, gives up activities, and abandons responsibilities to make more time for exercise
- seems to base self-worth on the number of workouts completed and the effort put into training
- is never satisfied with his or her own physical achievements

It is important, too, to recognize the types of athletes who are more prone to compulsive exercise because their sports place a particular emphasis on being thin. Ice skaters, gymnasts, wrestlers, and dancers can feel even more pressure than most athletes to keep their weight down and their body toned. Runners also frequently fall into a cycle of obsessive workouts.

Getting Professional Help

If you recognize two or more warning signs of compulsive exercise in a friend or family member, urge the person to call his or her doctor. Because compulsive exercise is so often linked to an eating disorder, a community agency that focuses on treating these disorders might be able to offer advice or referrals.

Treating a compulsion to exercise is never a quick-fix process—it may take several months or even years. Therapy can help improve self-esteem and body image, as well as teaching a person how to deal with emotions. Sessions with a dietitian can help develop healthy eating habits.

Why Is Exercising Too Much a Bad Thing?

We all know that regular exercise is an important part of a healthy lifestyle. But few people realize that too much can cause physical and psychological harm:

- Excessive exercise can damage tendons, ligaments, bones, cartilage, and joints, and when minor injuries are not allowed to heal, they often result in long-term damage. Instead of building muscle, too much exercise actually destroys muscle mass, especially if the body is not getting enough nutrition, forcing it to break down muscle for energy.
- Females who exercise compulsively may disrupt the balance of hormones in their bodies. This can change their menstrual cycles (some adolescents or adult women lose their periods altogether, a condition known as amenorrhea) and increase the risk of premature bone loss (osteoporosis). And of course, working their bodies so hard leads to exhaustion and constant fatigue.
- An even more serious risk is the stress that excessive exercise can place on the heart, particularly when someone is also engaging in unhealthy weight-loss behaviours such as restricting intake, vomiting, and using diet pills or supplements. In extreme cases, the combination of anorexia and compulsive exercise can be fatal.
- Psychologically, exercise addicts are often plagued by anxiety and depression. They may have a negative image of themselves and feel worthless. Their social lives may suffer as they withdraw from friends and family to fixate on exercise.

Source: © 1995–2012. The Nemours Foundation/KidsHealth. Reprinted with Permission.

Chapter Review

1. True. About 51% of Canadians are insufficiently active.

2. False. Our muscles are not stimulated to grow when we eat extra protein, whether as food or supplements. Weight-bearing exercise appropriately stresses the body and produces increased muscle mass and strength.

3. True. Most ergogenic aids do not produce the results that are advertised. Many ergogenic aids, such as anabolic steroids and ephedrine, can actually cause serious health consequences, even death.

Find the Quack

When Brian joined the track team his first year in high school, he found his passion. Now in his third year of university, he's built a reputation as a winning distance runner, and he has several medals to prove it. One day his friend Jim, who is the track team's top sprinter, tells him about creatine supplements. Jim says that since he started using them several weeks ago, his performance times have improved. With a big event approaching, Brian is looking to improve his performance, so he goes online to check out the creatine supplements website Jim recommends. Here's what he learns:

- "Creatine is an amino acid synthesized by the body that plays a vital role in anaerobic energy production by regenerating ATP in skeletal muscle."
- "Creatine supplementation has been shown in several controlled studies to increase muscle stores of creatine and to improve performance in athletes whose sports rely heavily on the creatine phosphate anaerobic energy pathway." (The article cites six recent studies published in academic journals.)
- "Creatine supplementation is most effective for the performance of intense bursts of activity."
- "The manufacturer has on file more than 1000 testimonials from satisfied customers whose athletic performance improved after taking creatine supplements."

- "The recommended dosage for an athlete's 'loading phase' varies according to gender, weight, and other factors, but a general recommendation is to consume four or five doses of 5 g each per day, for 5 to 7 days. This will fill the muscles' creatine phosphate stores to capacity. After this, a reduced maintenance dose of approximately 2–5 g/day is recommended. Taken as recommended, the supplements cost as little as $1 a day!"

1. Explain what the website article means by "the creatine phosphate anaerobic energy pathway."

2. Brian is a distance runner. Would you recommend he purchase creatine supplements? Why or why not?

3. Brian's track teammate Jim is a sprinter. Do you think it's possible that he has experienced physiologic benefits from creatine supplementation, or do you think his increased performance times are due to the placebo effect? Explain.

4. Recall the Hot Topic on deceptive practices used to market ergogenic aids. How many of these were employed by the creatine supplements website? Is this website an example of quackery? Why or why not?

Answers can be found in the study area of MasteringNutrition.

Review Questions

1. Using the FIT principle for achieving and maintaining cardiorespiratory fitness, the intensity range typically recommended is
   a. 25% to 50% of your estimated maximal heart rate.
   b. 35% to 75% of your estimated maximal heart rate.
   c. 55% to 90% of your estimated maximal heart rate.
   d. 75% to 95% of your estimated maximal heart rate.

2. The amount of ATP stored in a muscle cell can keep a muscle active for about
   a. 1 to 3 seconds.
   b. 10 to 30 seconds.
   c. 1 to 3 minutes.
   d. 1 to 3 hours.

3. To support a long afternoon of gardening, the body predominantly uses which nutrient for energy?
   a. Carbohydrate
   b. Fat
   c. Amino acids
   d. Lactic acid

4. Creatine
   a. seems to enhance performance in aerobic-type events.
   b. appears to increase an individual's risk for bladder cancer.
   c. seems to increase strength gained in resistance exercise.
   d. is stored in our muscles.

5. What percents of dietary fat and carbohydrate are recommended for athletes?
   a. 15% to 25% fat and 55% to 60% carbohydrate
   b. 55% to 60% fat and 15% to 25% carbohydrate
   c. 25% to 35% fat and 45% to 50% carbohydrate
   d. 45% to 50% fat and 25% to 35% carbohydrate

6. What practice do long-distance athletes sometimes follow to maximize their race performance?
   a. Glycolysis loading
   b. Glucose loading
   c. Carbohydrate loading
   d. Mineral loading

7. What does FIT stand for?
   a. Frequency, interval, time
   b. Frequency, intensity, time
   c. Fast, interval, target heart rate
   d. Fitness, intensity, target heart rate

8. Catherine is an ultra-distance runner who has just started training for a 100-kilometre race. Being new to the event, Catherine has found the more intense training challenging. Although she is a vegetarian, Catherine makes sure she eats plenty of nuts and legumes to maintain her iron stores. However, during a routine blood test, one week into her training, the laboratory report indicated that Catherine's blood iron content was low. What do you think happened? List and explain the factors that put Catherine at risk for iron deficiency. Should Catherine begin iron supplementation?

9. Write a plan for a weekly activity/exercise routine that does the following:
   • meets your personal fitness goals
   • is fun for you to do
   • includes variety and consistency
   • uses all components of the FIT principle
   • includes a warm-up and cool-down period

10. Determine how many grams of carbohydrate, protein, and fat you need to consume daily to support the activity/exercise routine you described in the previous question.

11. You decide to start training for your school's annual marathon. After studying this chapter, which of the following preparation strategies would you pursue, and why?
    • use of B vitamin supplements
    • use of creatine supplements
    • use of sports beverages
    • carbohydrate loading

12. Your father is a slightly overweight couch potato. Would you advise him to begin a planned exercise program of low to moderate intensity? Why or why not? If so, what steps should he take before starting an exercise program?

13. Marisa and Conrad are students at the same city college. Marisa walks to and from school each morning from her home seven blocks away. Conrad lives in a suburb 19 kilometres (12 miles) away and drives to school. Marisa, an early childhood education major, covers the lunch shift, two hours a day, at the college's daycare centre, cleaning up the lunchroom and supervising the children in the playground. Conrad, an accounting major, works in his department office two hours a day, entering data into computer spreadsheets. On weekends, Marisa and her sister walk downtown and go shopping. Conrad goes to the movies with his friends. Neither Marisa nor Conrad participates in sports or scheduled exercise sessions. Marisa has maintained a normal, healthy weight throughout the school year, but in the same period, Conrad has gained several kilograms. Identify at least two factors that might play a role in Marisa's and Conrad's current weight.

14. While exercising at the gym, you notice a middle-aged woman on the treadmill next to you. Her shirt is soaked with sweat and she has no water bottle. Looking shaky, she breathlessly but proudly tells you that she's been running for 40 minutes straight on the second-highest level. Then she goes on to tell you that this is the first time she's exercised in 10 years! Five minutes later, she abruptly stops running and heads to the change room. How would you critique this woman's exercise routine? What is positive about her story? Is there anything about it that alarms you? What suggestions might you give this woman, keeping in mind that you don't want to discourage her?

Case Study

Dylan is preparing for the upcoming soccer season by hitting the gym every day. His coach advises him to see a dietitian to make sure that he's eating properly. After keeping a food record, he calculates that he eats an average of about 500 grams of carbohydrates and 150 grams of protein each day. Dylan is 1.83 metres (6') tall and about 82 kg (180 lbs.) during practice season. Working out, he's been feeling sluggish, sometimes dragging himself through practice. A trainer at the gym overhears Dylan commenting on his concern about consuming too little protein and suggests trying one of the protein powders sold by the gym.

a. Given what you know about the role of energy nutrients in vigorous physical activity, what do you think might be causing Dylan to feel exhausted?

b. Would you recommend that he try the protein powder offered by the gym?

c. What other strategies might Dylan consider?

Answers to Review Questions can be found at the back of this text.

Web Resources

www.phac-aspc.gc.ca/hp-ps/hl-mvs/pa-ap/index-eng.php
Physical Activity Unit, Public Health Agency of Canada

This site has all the physical activity guides (for adults, older adults, children, and youth) and good ideas about how to incorporate physical activity into your daily work and leisure activities.

www.caaws.ca
Canadian Association for the Advancement of Women and Sport and Physical Activity

Visit this site to learn more about the opportunities for girls and women to become active in sports and physical activity through such programs as Mothers in Motion and On the Move.

www.phecanada.ca/about-us
Physical & Health Education Canada

PHE Canada describes itself on its website as "Canada's premier professional organization for physical and health educators." Visit the site to learn more about its unique initiatives.

www.cflri.ca
Canadian Fitness and Lifestyle Research Institute

This research institute monitors the physical activity levels of Canadian adults and children on an annual basis.

www.csep.ca
Canadian Society for Exercise Physiology (CSEP)

Interested in becoming a certified fitness consultant or a professional fitness and lifestyle consultant? Visit this website to learn about the certification programs available.

www.acsm.org
American College of Sports Medicine

Look under Student Corner for career ideas in sports medicine and exercise science.

http://fnic.nal.usda.gov/dietary-supplements /ergogenic-aids
Food and Nutrition Information Center

Visit this site for links to detailed information about ergogenic aids and sports nutrition.

MasteringNutrition®

Assignments
Activities NutriTools

Study Area
Practice Tests • Diet Analysis • eText

Disordered Eating

WANT TO FIND OUT...

- **what is the leading cause of death in females age 15 through 24?**

- **whether men experience disordered eating?**

- **what's keeping some overweight people up all night?**

READ ON.
On August 2, 2006, Uruguayan fashion model Luisel Ramos collapsed during a fashion show. Just 22 years old, she was pronounced dead of heart failure brought on by *anorexia nervosa,* a condition of self-imposed starvation. Family members said that, in the months prior to her death, she had adopted a diet of lettuce leaves and Diet Coke, and at 1.7 m (5'9") tall, her weight had dropped to just 44.5 kg (98 pounds). The following month, Madrid's "Fashion Week" responded to Ramos's death by banning from its runway fashion models who could not meet a minimum

weight–height standard. A similar ruling was quickly adopted by the Milan fashion show, and several modelling agencies began to require prospective models to present medical records certifying that they are healthy. Although promising, such measures alone are clearly inadequate, and at least three more fashion models had died from self-starvation by the summer of 2008.

Do only models develop eating disorders, or can they occur in people like you? When does normal dieting cross the line into disordered eating? What early warning signs might tip you off that a friend was crossing that line? If you noticed the signs in a friend or family member, would you confront him or her? If so, what would you say? In the following pages, we explore *In Depth* some answers to these important questions.

Eating Behaviours Occur on a Continuum

Disordered eating is a general term used to describe a variety of atypical eating behaviours that people use to achieve or maintain a lower body weight. These behaviours may be as simple as going on and off diets or as extreme as refusing to eat any fat. Such behaviours do not usually continue for long enough to make the person seriously ill, nor do they significantly disrupt the person's normal routine.

In contrast, some people restrict their eating so much or for so long that they become dangerously underweight. These people have an **eating disorder**, a psychiatric condition that involves extreme body dissatisfaction and long-term eating patterns that negatively affect body functioning. The

⬆ A string of models have died because of eating disorders.

two more commonly diagnosed eating disorders are anorexia nervosa and bulimia nervosa. **Anorexia nervosa** is a potentially life-threatening eating disorder characterized by self-starvation, which eventually leads to a severe nutrient deficiency. In contrast, **bulimia nervosa** is characterized by recurrent episodes of extreme overeating and compensatory behaviours to prevent weight gain, such as self-induced vomiting, misuse of laxatives, fasting, excessive exercise, or several of these in combination. Both disorders will be discussed in more detail shortly.

When does normal dieting cross the line into disordered eating? Eating behaviours occur on a *continuum*, a spectrum that cannot be divided neatly into parts. One example of a continuum is a rainbow—where exactly does the red end and the orange begin? Thinking about eating behaviours as a continuum makes it easier to understand how a person can progress from relatively normal eating behaviours to a pattern that is disordered. Suppose

that for several years you have skipped breakfast in favour of a mid-morning snack, but now you find yourself avoiding the cafeteria until early afternoon. Is this normal? To answer that question, you would need to consider your feelings about food and your **body image**—the way you perceive your body.

Take a moment to take the self-test in the accompanying What About You? box. It will help you clarify how you feel about your body and about food and whether you are at risk for disordered eating.

Many Factors Contribute to Disordered Eating Behaviours

The factors that result in the development of disordered eating are very complex, but research indicates that a number of psychological, interpersonal, social, and biological factors may contribute in any particular individual.

disordered eating A variety of abnormal or atypical eating behaviours that are used to keep or maintain a lower body weight.

eating disorder A clinically diagnosed psychiatric disorder characterized by severe disturbances in body image and eating behaviours.

anorexia nervosa A serious, potentially life-threatening eating disorder characterized by self-starvation, which eventually leads to a deficiency in energy and the essential nutrients the body requires to function normally.

bulimia nervosa A serious eating disorder characterized by recurrent episodes of binge eating and recurrent inappropriate compensatory behaviours to prevent weight gain, such as self-induced vomiting, fasting, excessive exercise, or misuse of laxatives, diuretics, enemas, or other medications.

body image A person's perception of his or her body's appearance and functioning.

What About You?

Are You at Risk for Disordered Eating?

Take a look at the Eating Issues and Body Image Continuum figure **(Figure 1)**. Which of the five columns best describes your feelings about food and your body? If you find yourself identifying with the statements on the left side of the continuum, you probably have few issues with food or body image. Most likely, you accept your body size and view food as a normal part of maintaining your health and fuelling your daily physical activity.

As you progress to the right side of the continuum, food and body image become bigger issues, with food restriction becoming the norm. If you identify with the statements on the far right, you may be afraid of eating and dislike your body. If so, you should consult a healthcare professional as soon as possible. The earlier you seek treatment, the more likely it is you will succeed in taking ownership of your body and developing a more healthful approach to food.

FOOD IS NOT AN ISSUE	CONCERNED/WELL	FOOD PREOCCUPIED/ OBSESSED	DISRUPTIVE EATING PATTERNS	EATING DISORDERED
• I am not concerned about what others think regarding what and how much I eat. • When I am upset or depressed I eat whatever I am hungry for without any guilt or shame. • I feel no guilt or shame no matter how much I eat or what I eat. • Food is an important part of my life but only occupies a small part of my time. • I trust my body to tell me what and how much to eat.	• I pay attention to what I eat to maintain a healthy body. • I may weigh more than I like, but I enjoy eating and balance my pleasure with eating with my concern for a healthy body. • I am moderate and flexible in goals for eating well. • I try to follow Dietary Guidelines for healthy eating.	• I think about food a lot. • I feel I don't eat well most of the time. • It's hard for me to enjoy eating with others. • I feel ashamed when I eat more than others or more than I feel I should be eating. • I am afraid of getting fat. • I wish I could change how much I want to eat and what I am hungry for.	• I have tried diet pills, laxatives, vomiting, or extra time exercising to lose or maintain my weight. • I have fasted or avoided eating for long periods of time to lose or maintain my weight. • I feel strong when I can restrict how much I eat. • Eating more than I wanted to makes me feel out of control.	• I regularly stuff myself and then exercise, vomit, or use diet pills or laxatives to get rid of the food or calories. • My friends/family tell me I am too thin. • I am terrified of eating fat. • When I let myself eat, I have a hard time controlling the amount of food I eat. • I am afraid to eat in front of others.
BODY OWNERSHIP	**BODY ACCEPTANCE**	**BODY PREOCCUPIED/ OBSESSED**	**DISTORTED BODY IMAGE**	**BODY HATE/ DISASSOCIATION**
• Body image is not an issue for me. • My body is beautiful to me. • My feelings about my body are not influenced by society's concept of an ideal body shape. • I know that the significant others in my life will always find me attractive. • I trust my body to find the weight it needs to be at so I can move and feel confident about my physical body.	• I base my body image equally on social norms and my own self-concept. • I pay attention to my body and my appearance because it is important to me, but it only occupies a small part of my day. • I nourish my body so it has the strength and energy to achieve my physical goals. • I am able to assert myself and maintain a healthy body without losing my self-esteem.	• I spend a significant amount time viewing my body in the mirror. • I spend a significant amount time comparing my body to others. • I have days when I feel fat. • I am preoccupied with my body. • I accept society's ideal body shape and size as the best body shape and size. • I believe that I'd be more attractive if I were thinner, more muscular, etc.	• I spend a significant amount of time exercising and dieting to change my body. • My body shape and size keep me from dating or finding someone who will treat me the way I want to be treated. • I have considered changing or have changed my body shape and size through surgical means so I can accept myself. • I wish I could change the way I look in the mirror.	• I often feel separated and distant from my body—as if it belongs to someone else. • I hate my body and I often isolate myself from others. • I don't see anything positive or even neutral about my body shape and size. • I don't believe others when they tell me I look OK. • I hate the way I look in the mirror.

Figure 1 The Eating Issues and Body Image Continuum. The progression from normal eating (far left) to eating disorders (far right) occurs on a continuum.

Source: Data from Smiley, L., L. King, and H. Avery. University of Arizona Campus Health Service. Original Continuum, C. Shlaalak. Preventive Medicine and Public Health. Copyright ©1997 Arizona Board of Regents. Used with permission.

Influence of Genetic Factors

Overall, the diagnosis of anorexia nervosa and bulimia nervosa is several times more common in females, and in siblings and other blood relatives who also have the diagnosis, than in the general population (American Psychiatric Association, 1994). This observation might imply the existence of an "eating disorder gene"; however, it is difficult to separate the contribution of genetic from other biological and social factors (Treasure, Claudino, and Zucker, 2010).

Influence of Family

Research suggests that family conditioning, structure, and patterns of interaction can influence the development of an eating disorder. Based on observational studies, compared to families without a member with an eating disorder, families with an anorexic member show more rigidity in their family structure and less clear interpersonal boundaries, and they tend to avoid open discussions on topics of disagreement. Conversely, families with a member diagnosed with bulimia nervosa tend to have a less stable family organization and to be less nurturing, more angry,

and more disruptive (Vandereycken, 2002). In addition, childhood physical or sexual abuse can increase the risk for an eating disorder (Patrick, 2002).

Influence of Media

As media saturation has increased over the last century, so has the incidence of eating disorders among white women (Striegel-Moore and Smolak, 2002). Every day we are confronted with advertisements in which computer-enhanced images of lean, beautiful women promote everything from beer to cars (**Figure 2**). Most adult men and women understand that these images are unrealistic, but adolescents, who are still developing a sense of their identity and body image, lack the same ability to distance themselves from what they see (Steinberg, 2002). Because body image influences eating behaviours, it is not unlikely that the barrage of media models may be contributing to the increase in eating disorders. However, scientific evidence demonstrating that the media are *causing* increased eating disorders is difficult to obtain.

Influence of Social and Cultural Values

Eating disorders are significantly more common in white females in

developed Western societies than in other women worldwide (Treasure, Claudino, and Zucker, 2010). This may be due in part to the white Western culture's association of slenderness with health, wealth, and high fashion (**Figure 3**). In contrast, until recently, the prevailing view in developing societies has been that excess body fat is desirable as a sign of health and material abundance.

The members of society with whom we most often interact—our family members, friends, classmates, and co-workers—also influence the way we see ourselves. Their comments related to our body weight or shape can be particularly hurtful—enough so to cause some people to start down the path of disordered eating. For example, individuals with bulimia nervosa report that they perceived greater pressure from their peers to be thin than controls, while research shows that peer teasing about weight increases body dissatisfaction and eating disturbances (Stice, 2002). Thus, our comments to others regarding their weight do count.

Influence of Personality

A number of studies suggest that people with anorexia nervosa exhibit increased rates of obsessive-compulsive behaviours and perfectionism. They also tend to be socially inhibited, compliant, and emotionally restrained (Wonderlich, 2002). Unfortunately, many studies observe these behaviours only in individuals who are very ill and in a state of starvation, which may affect personality. Thus, it is difficult to determine if personality is a contributing factor or an effect of the disorder.

In contrast to people with anorexia nervosa, people with bulimia nervosa tend to be more impulsive, have low self-esteem, and demonstrate an extroverted, erratic personality style that seeks attention and admiration. In these people, negative moods are more likely to cause overeating than food restriction (Wonderlich, 2002).

Family environment often influences when, what, and how much we eat.

Figure 2 Photos of celebrities and models are often airbrushed or otherwise altered to "enhance" physical appearance. Unfortunately, many people regard these as accurate portrayals and strive to reach an unrealistic level of physical beauty.

Figure 3 The preferred look among runway models can require extreme emaciation, often achieved by self-starvation and/or drug abuse.

Anorexia Nervosa Is a Potentially Deadly Eating Disorder

According to the American Psychiatric Association (1994), 90%–95% of individuals with anorexia nervosa are young girls or women. A study conducted in Ontario estimated that 0.3% of men and 2.1% of women between the ages of 15 and 64 years had either anorexia nervosa or bulimia nervosa (Health Canada, 2002). People admitted to hospitals for eating disorders stay an average of 27.5 days, or almost one month, and the hospitalization rates are highest among adolescents aged 10 to 19 with eating disorders. Anorexia nervosa is the most common and deadly psychiatric disorder diagnosed in women and the leading cause of death in U.S. females between the ages of 15 and 24 years (Patrick, 2002). As the statistics indicate, anorexia nervosa also occurs in males, but the prevalence is much lower than in females (Robb and Dadson, 2002; Treasure, Claudino, and Zuker, 2010).

---

amenorrhea The absence of menstruation. In females who had previously been menstruating, it is defined as the absence of menstrual periods for three or more months.

Signs and Symptoms of Anorexia Nervosa

The classic sign of anorexia nervosa is an extremely restrictive eating pattern that leads to self-starvation **(Figure 4)**. These individuals may fast completely, restrict energy intake to only a few kilocalories per day, or eliminate all but one or two food groups from their diet. They also have an intense fear of weight gain, and even small amounts (such as 0.5–1.0 kg or 1–2 lb.) trigger high stress and anxiety.

In females, **amenorrhea** (no menstrual periods for at least three months) is a common feature of anorexia nervosa. It occurs when a young woman consumes insufficient energy to maintain normal body functions.

The American Psychiatric Association (2000) identifies the following conditions of anorexia nervosa:

- Refusal to maintain body weight at or above a minimally normal weight for age and height
- Intense fear of gaining weight or becoming fat, even though considered underweight by all medical criteria
- Disturbance in the way in which one's body weight or shape is experienced, undue influence of body weight or shape on self-evaluation, or denial of the seriousness of the current low body weight

Figure 4 People with anorexia nervosa experience an extreme drive for thinness, resulting in potentially fatal weight loss.

HOT TOPIC

Muscle Dysmorphia: The Male Eating Disorder?

Is there an eating disorder unique to men? Recently, experts have defined a disorder called muscle dysmorphia. Men with muscle dysmorphia perceive themselves as small and frail, even though they may actually be large and muscular. They spend long hours lifting weights, but no matter how "chiselled" they become, their biology cannot match their idealized body size and shape (Andersen, 2001).

A common behaviour of men with muscle dysmorphia is abuse of performance-enhancing drugs. Additionally, men with muscle dysmorphia tend to consume excessive amounts of high-protein foods and dietary supplements, such as protein powders.

Men with muscle dysmorphia share some characteristics with men and women with other eating disorders. For instance, they report "feeling fat" and express significant discomfort with the idea of exposing their bodies to others. They also have increased rates of mental illness (Pope, Phillips, and Olivardia, 2000).

Outward indications that someone is struggling with muscle dysmorphia include:

- Rigid and excessive weight training
- Strict adherence to a high-protein, muscle-enhancing diet
- Use of muscle-enhancing drugs or supplements
- Avoiding social engagements that might interfere with following a strict diet or training schedule
- Frequent and critical body self-evaluation

Muscle dysmorphia can cause distress and despair. Therapy can help.

⬆ Men are more likely than women to exercise excessively in an effort to control their weight.

- Amenorrhea in females who are past puberty; a woman is considered to have amenorrhea if her periods occur only when given hormones, such as estrogen or oral contraceptives

The signs of an eating disorder, such as anorexia nervosa, may be somewhat different in males. Females with eating disorders say they *feel* fat even though they typically are normal weight or even underweight before they develop the disorder. In contrast, males who develop eating disorders are more likely to have actually *been* overweight or even obese (Beals, 2004; Robb and Dadson, 2002). Thus, the male's fear of "getting fat again" is based on reality. In addition, males with disordered eating are less concerned with actual body weight (scale weight) than females but are more concerned with body composition (percentage of muscle mass compared to fat mass).

The methods that men and women use to achieve weight loss also appear to differ. Males are more likely to use excessive exercise as a means of weight control, whereas females tend to use severe energy restriction, vomiting, and laxative abuse. These weight-control differences may stem from socio cultural biases; that is, dieting is considered to be more acceptable for women, whereas the overwhelming socio cultural belief is that "real men don't diet" (Beals, 2004).

Health Risks of Anorexia Nervosa

Left untreated, anorexia nervosa eventually leads to a deficiency in energy and other nutrients that are required by the body to function normally. The body will then use stored fat and lean tissue (such as organ and muscle tissue) as an energy source to maintain brain tissue and vital body functions. The body will also shut down or reduce non-vital body functions to conserve energy. Electrolyte imbalances can lead to heart failure and death. **Figure 5** highlights many of the health problems that occur in people with anorexia nervosa. The best chance of recovery is when an individual receives intensive treatment early.

Bulimia Nervosa Is Characterized by Bingeing and Purging

Bulimia nervosa is an eating disorder characterized by repeated

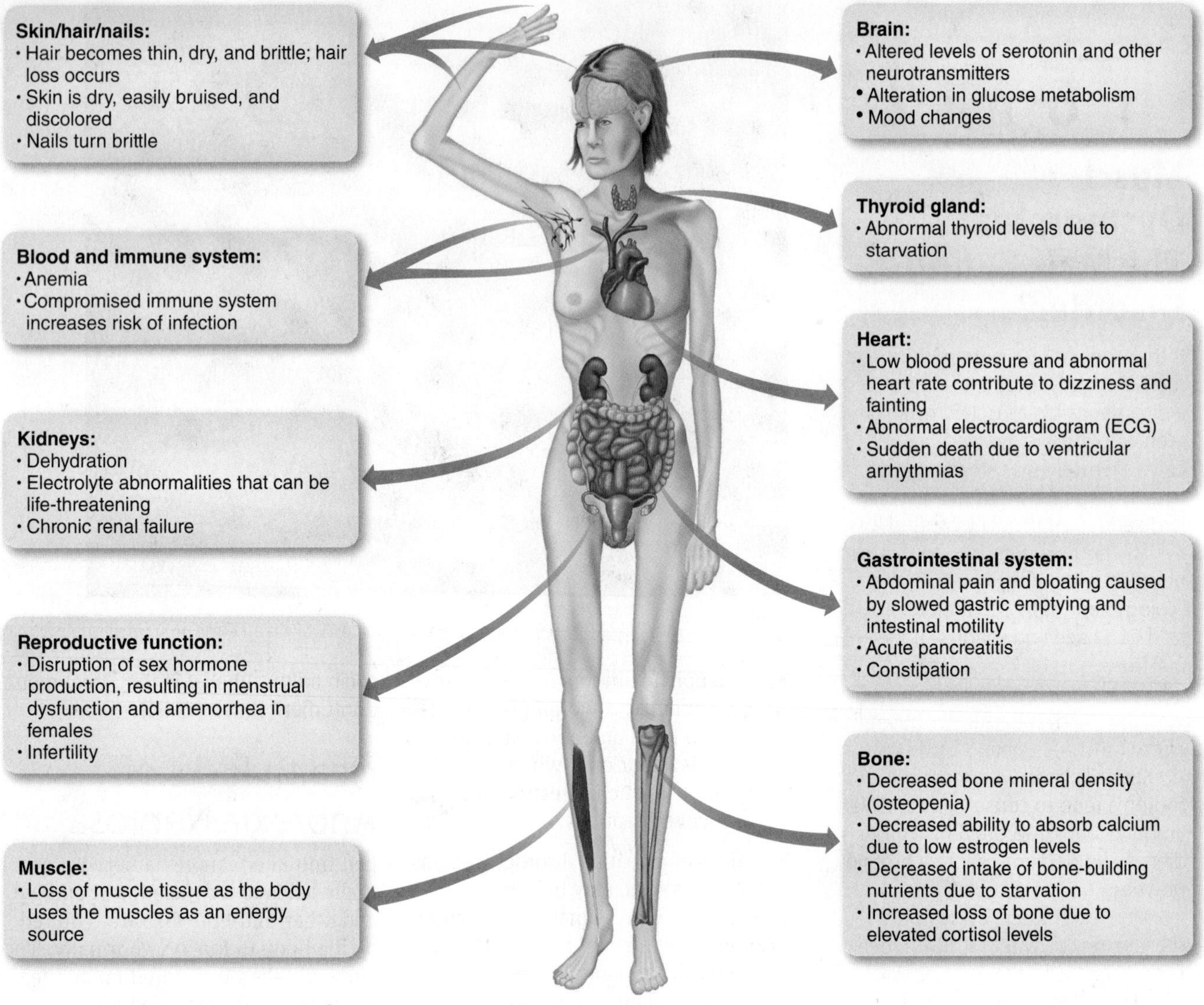

Skin/hair/nails:
- Hair becomes thin, dry, and brittle; hair loss occurs
- Skin is dry, easily bruised, and discolored
- Nails turn brittle

Blood and immune system:
- Anemia
- Compromised immune system increases risk of infection

Kidneys:
- Dehydration
- Electrolyte abnormalities that can be life-threatening
- Chronic renal failure

Reproductive function:
- Disruption of sex hormone production, resulting in menstrual dysfunction and amenorrhea in females
- Infertility

Muscle:
- Loss of muscle tissue as the body uses the muscles as an energy source

Brain:
- Altered levels of serotonin and other neurotransmitters
- Alteration in glucose metabolism
- Mood changes

Thyroid gland:
- Abnormal thyroid levels due to starvation

Heart:
- Low blood pressure and abnormal heart rate contribute to dizziness and fainting
- Abnormal electrocardiogram (ECG)
- Sudden death due to ventricular arrhythmias

Gastrointestinal system:
- Abdominal pain and bloating caused by slowed gastric emptying and intestinal motility
- Acute pancreatitis
- Constipation

Bone:
- Decreased bone mineral density (osteopenia)
- Decreased ability to absorb calcium due to low estrogen levels
- Decreased intake of bone-building nutrients due to starvation
- Increased loss of bone due to elevated cortisol levels

Figure 5 The impact of anorexia nervosa on the body.

episodes of **binge eating** followed by some form of **purging**. While binge eating, the person feels a loss of self-control, including an inability to end the binge once it has started (Garfinkel, 2002). At the same time, the person feels a sense of euphoria not unlike a drug-induced high. A "binge" is usually defined as a

quantity of food that is large for the person and for the amount of time in which it is eaten **(Figure 6)**. For example, a person may eat a dozen brownies with 2 litres of ice cream in 30 minutes.

The prevalence of bulimia nervosa is higher than that of anorexia nervosa and is estimated to affect 1%–4% of women. Like anorexia nervosa, bulimia nervosa is found predominately in women: six to ten females are diagnosed for every one male. The mortality rate is lower than for anorexia nervosa, with 1% of patients dying within 10 years of diagnosis (Patrick, 2002).

Although the prevalence of bulimia nervosa is much higher in

women, rates for men are significant in some predominantly "thin-build" sports in which participants are encouraged to maintain a low body weight (for instance, horse racing, wrestling, crew, and gymnastics). Individuals in these sports typically do not have all the characteristics of bulimia nervosa, however, and the purging behaviours they practice usually stop once the sport is discontinued.

An individual with bulimia nervosa typically purges after most episodes, but not necessarily on every occasion, and weight gain as a result of binge eating can be significant. Methods of purging include vomiting, laxative or diuretic abuse, enemas,

binge eating Consumption of a large amount of food in a short period of time, usually accompanied by a feeling of loss of self-control.

purging An attempt to rid the body of unwanted food by vomiting or other compensatory means, such as excessive exercise, fasting, or laxative abuse.

⬆ Men who participate in "thin-build" sports, such as jockeys, have a higher risk for bulimia nervosa than men who do not.

fasting, or excessive exercise. For example, after a binge, a runner may increase her daily mileage to equal the "calculated" energy content of the binge.

⬆ **Figure 6** People with bulimia nervosa can consume relatively large amounts of food in brief periods of time.

Symptoms of Bulimia Nervosa

As with anorexia nervosa, the American Psychiatric Association (2000) has identified conditions of bulimia nervosa:

- Recurrent episodes of binge eating, such as eating a large amount of food within a short period of time (about two hours).
- Recurrent inappropriate compensatory behaviour to prevent weight gain, such as self-induced vomiting; misuse of laxatives, diuretics, enemas, or other medications; fasting; or excessive exercise.
- Binge eating occurring on average at least twice a week for three months.
- Body shape and weight unduly influencing self-evaluation.
- The disturbance not necessarily occurring exclusively during episodes of anorexia nervosa. Some individuals will have periods of binge eating and then periods of starvation, which makes classification of their disorder difficult.

How can you tell if someone has bulimia nervosa? In addition to the recurrent and frequent binge eating and purging episodes, the National Institutes of Health have identified the following symptoms of bulimia nervosa:

- chronically inflamed and sore throat
- swollen glands in the neck and below the jaw
- worn tooth enamel and increasingly sensitive and decaying teeth as a result of exposure to stomach acids
- gastroesophageal reflux disorder
- intestinal distress and irritation from laxative abuse
- kidney problems from diuretic abuse
- severe dehydration from purging of fluids

Health Risks of Bulimia Nervosa

The destructive behaviours of bulimia nervosa can lead to illness and even death. The most common health consequences associated with bulimia nervosa are the following:

- Electrolyte imbalance typically caused by dehydration and the loss of potassium and sodium from the body from frequent vomiting. This can lead to irregular heartbeat and even heart failure and death.
- Gastrointestinal problems: inflammation, ulceration, and possible rupture of the esophagus and stomach from frequent bingeing and vomiting. Chronic irregular bowel movements and constipation may result in people with bulimia who chronically abuse laxatives.
- Dental problems: tooth decay and staining from stomach acids released during frequent vomiting

As with anorexia nervosa, the chance of recovery from bulimia nervosa increases, and the negative effects on health decrease, if the disorder is detected and treated at an early stage. Familiarity with the warning signs of bulimia nervosa can help you identify friends and family members who might be at risk.

Binge-Eating Disorder Can Cause Significant Weight Gain

When was the last time a friend or relative confessed to you about "going on an eating binge"? Most likely, the person explained that the behaviour followed some sort of stressful event, such as a problem at work, the break-up of a relationship, or a poor grade on an exam. Many people have one or two binge episodes every year or so, in response to stress. But in people with **binge-eating disorder**, the behaviour occurs an average of twice a week or more and is not usually followed by purging. This lack of compensation for the binge distinguishes binge-eating disorder from bulimia nervosa and explains why the person tends to gain a lot of weight.

The prevalence of binge-eating disorder is estimated to be 2%–3% of the

binge-eating disorder A disorder characterized by binge eating an average of twice a week or more, typically without compensatory purging.

adult population and 8% of the obese population (Grilo, 2002). In contrast to anorexia and bulimia, binge-eating disorder is also common in men. Our current food environment, which offers an abundance of good-tasting, cheap food any time of the day, makes it difficult for people with binge-eating disorder to avoid food triggers.

As you would expect, the increased energy intake associated with binge eating significantly increases a person's risk of being overweight or obese. In addition, the types of foods individuals typically consume during a binge episode are high in fat and sugar, which can increase blood lipids. Finally, the stress associated with binge eating can have psychological consequences, such as low self-esteem, avoidance of social contact, depression, and negative thoughts related to body size.

Night-Eating Syndrome Can Lead to Obesity

Night-eating syndrome was first described in a group of patients who were not hungry in the morning but spent the evening and night eating and reported insomnia. Like binge-eating disorder, it is associated with obesity because, although night eaters do not binge, they do consume significant energy in their frequent snacks, and they do not compensate for the excess energy intake.

Symptoms of Night-Eating Syndrome

The distinguishing characteristic of night-eating syndrome is the time during which most of the day's energy intake occurs. Night eaters eat relatively little during the day, consuming the majority of their energy between 8:00 p.m. and 6:00 a.m. They even get up in the night to eat. Night eating is also characterized by a depressed mood and insomnia. In short, night eaters appear to have a unique combination of three disorders: an eating disorder, a sleep disorder, and a mood disorder (Stunkard, 2002).

⬆ People with night-eating syndrome consume most of their daily energy between 8 p.m. and 6 a.m.

Health Risks of Night-Eating Syndrome

Night-eating syndrome is important clinically because of its association with obesity, which increases the risk for several chronic diseases, including heart disease, high blood pressure, stroke, type 2 diabetes, and arthritis. Obesity also increases the risk for sleep apnea, which can further disrupt the night eater's already abnormal sleeping pattern.

The Female Athlete Triad Consists of Three Disorders

The female athlete triad is a serious syndrome that consists of three clinical conditions in some physically active females: (1) low energy availability (such as inadequate energy intake to maintain menstrual function or to cover energy expended in exercise) with or without eating disorders, (2) amenorrhea (the absence of menstruation), and (3) osteoporosis (Nattiv et al., 2007) **(Figure 7)**. Certain sports

that strongly emphasize leanness or a thin body build may place a young girl or a woman at risk for the female athlete triad. These sports typically include figure skating, gymnastics, and diving; classical ballet dancers are also at increased risk for the disorder.

Components of the Female Athlete Triad

Active women experience the general social and cultural demands placed on women to be thin, as well as pressure from their coach, teammates, judges, and/or spectators to meet weight standards or body-size expectations for their sport. Failure to meet these standards can result in severe consequences, such as being cut from the team, losing an athletic scholarship, or decreased participation with the team.

As the pressure to be thin mounts, active women may restrict their energy intake, typically by engaging in disordered eating behaviours. Energy restriction combined with high levels of physical activity can disrupt the

⬆ Sports that emphasize leanness, or that require athletes to wear body-contouring clothing, increase the risk for female athlete triad.

night-eating syndrome A disorder characterized by intake of the majority of the day's energy between 8:00 p.m. and 6:00 a.m. Individuals with this disorder also experience mood and sleep disorders.

menstrual cycle and result in amenorrhea. Menstrual dysfunction can also occur in active women who are not dieting and do not have an eating disorder. These women are simply not eating enough to cover the energy costs of their exercise training and all the other energy demands of the body and daily living. Female athletes with menstrual dysfunction, regardless of the cause, typically have reduced levels of the reproductive hormones, such as estrogen and progesterone. When estrogen levels in the body are low, it is difficult for bone to retain calcium, and gradual loss of bone mass occurs. Thus, many female athletes develop premature bone loss (osteoporosis) and are at increased risk for fractures.d **Figure 7** The female athlete triad is a syndrome composed of three coexisting disorders: low energy availability (with or without eating disorders), menstrual dysfunction (such as amenorrhea), and osteoporosis. Energy availability is defined as dietary energy intake minus exercise energy expenditure.

Recognizing and Treating the Female Athlete Triad

Recognition of an athlete with one or more of the components of the female athlete triad can be difficult, especially if the athlete is reluctant to be honest when questioned about the symptoms. For this reason, familiarity with the early warning signs is critical. These include excessive dieting and/or weight loss, excessive exercise, stress fractures, and self-esteem that appears to be dictated by body weight and shape.

Treating an athlete requires a multidisciplinary approach. This means that the sports medicine team, sports dietitian, exercise physiologist, psychologist, coach, trainer, parents,

friends of the athlete, and athlete all must work together.

Treatment for Disordered Eating Requires a Multidisciplinary Approach

As with any health problem, prevention is the best treatment for disordered eating. People having trouble with eating and body image issues need help to deal with these issues before they develop into something more serious.

Treating anyone with disordered eating requires a multidisciplinary approach, which typically includes the physician and psychologist, a nutritionist, and family members. The severity of the eating disorder will dictate the treatment. Patients who are severely underweight, display signs of malnutrition, are medically unstable, or are suicidal may require immediate hospitalization. Conversely, patients who are underweight but are still medically stable may enter an outpatient program designed to meet their specific needs.

Do you have a friend you suspect has an eating disorder? Discussing a friend's eating behaviours can be difficult. It is important to choose an appropriate time and place to raise your concerns and to listen closely and with great sensitivity to your friend's feelings. It is also important to locate a health professional specializing in eating disorders whom you can recommend. If you are at a university or college, check with the student health centre to see what resources it has.

Menstrual dysfunction

Low bone density

Low energy availability

Web Resources

www.nedic.ca
National Eating Disorder Information Centre

This site provides information and resources on eating disorders and weight preoccupation. NEDIC is a program of the University Health Network in Toronto.

www.edfofcanada.com
Eating Disorders Foundation of Canada

This is a national non-government organization and a member of the Institute of Neurosciences, Mental Health and Addiction (INMHA), a division of the Canadian Institutes of Health Research (CIHR). It partners with university researchers and government agencies, and does fundraising to support the residential treatment facilities, new technology, evaluation, research, and support services associated with the treatment of eating disorders.

www.nimh.nih.gov
National Institute of Mental Health (NIMH) Office of Communications and Public Liaison

Search this site for "disordered eating" or "eating disorders" to find numerous articles on the subject.

www.anad.org
National Association of Anorexia Nervosa and Associated Disorders

Visit this site for information and resources about eating disorders.

www.nationaleatingdisorders.org
National Eating Disorders Association

This site is dedicated to expanding public understanding of eating disorders and promoting access to treatment for those affected and support for their families.

www.menstuff.org
Menstuff Eating Disorders

Search for "eating disorders" and find information about male anorexia and eating disorders in general, self-assessments, disordered eating statistics, and prevention information.

www.somethingfishy.org
Something Fishy Website on Eating Disorders

A comprehensive website about the dangers of eating disorders, eating disorder treatment, and signs of symptoms of disorders. This site includes first hand survivors' stories and online chats.

13

Food Safety and Technology: Impact on Consumers

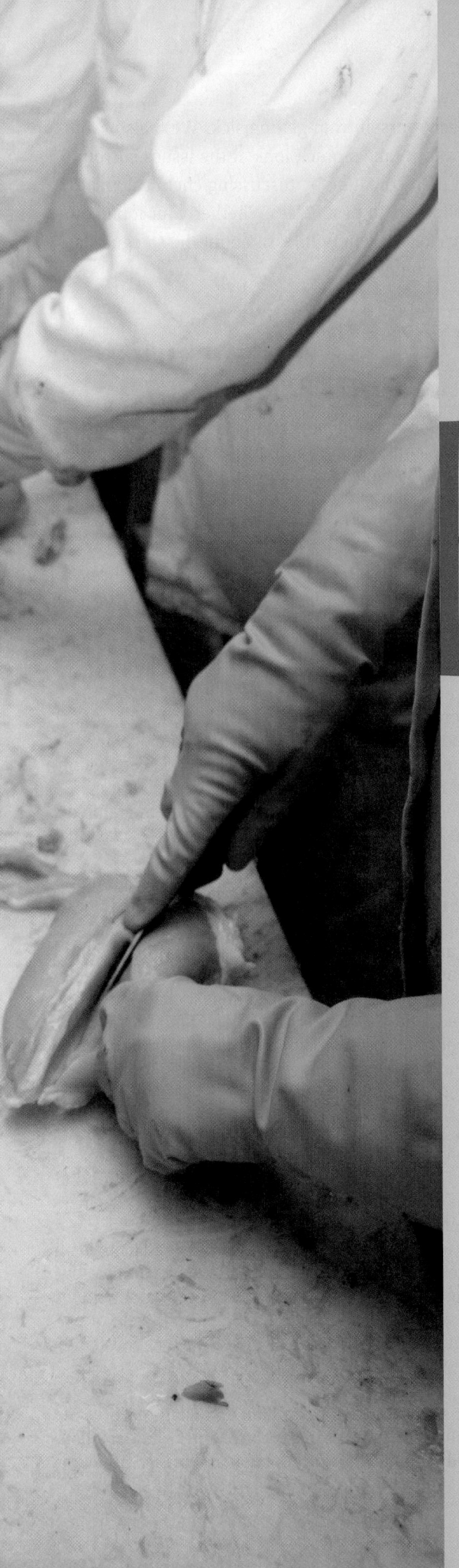

Test Yourself

1. (T) (F) Freezing destroys any microorganisms that might be lurking in your food.

2. (T) (F) The colour of hamburger is a good indicator of whether the meat is sufficiently cooked.

3. (T) (F) Mould is the most common cause of food poisoning.

Test Yourself answers can be found at the end of the chapter.

B efore the summer of 2008, did you know what listeriosis was? By August 2008, Maple Leaf Foods had issued a product recall of all 220 meat and deli items produced at one of its Toronto plants, as a result of tests confirming a link between those products and the listeriosis outbreak that hit Canada. Although it began as just a curious increase in reported cases of listeriosis in June, by August it had turned into a massive public health outbreak with 23 people dead and hundreds ill from consuming the products. While you may have heard of *Salmonella* or *E. coli* before, listeriosis was relatively unknown prior to the Maple Leaf Foods incident. *Listeria monocytogenes* are bacteria known to contaminate unpasteurized milk, soft cheeses, deli meats, hot dogs, and unwashed vegetables. Listeriosis is a food-borne illness that presents fever, diarrhea, vomiting, but in those very young or very old, it can be quite dangerous, leading to meningitis and encephalitis. Pregnant women are also at high risk for life-threatening complications because listeriosis can cause miscarriages and infect the growing fetus.

What do outbreaks like these tell us about the safety of our food supply? Are there any guarantees that our food is safe? Public health officials determined that the cause of the bacteria came from the slicing equipment in the Toronto plant, and the plant was shut down until cleared for production again. The deli meats and food products were fully cooked already, so consumers who purchased them would have had no way of eliminating the deadly bacteria unless they reheated the products.

We'll begin this chapter by considering the key reasons that food-borne illness has become a priority public health issue. We'll then identify the major culprits in food-borne illness and describe some simple ways to protect yourself from getting sick. We'll also examine information about food preservation, take a quick look at the issues surrounding genetically modified foods, and then conclude by discussing chemical residues that can affect food safety, from pollutants to pesticides. Whether your food comes from South America or your own backyard, you will learn about the safeguards that must be in place to ensure food safety.

Why Is Food-Borne Illness a Critical Concern?

Food-borne illness is a term generally used to encompass any symptom or illness that arises from ingesting food or water that contains an infectious agent or a toxic substance. Food-borne illness is commonly called *food poisoning.*

Food-Borne Illness Affects an Estimated 11 Million Canadians Each Year

An estimated 11 million Canadians get food-borne illnesses each year (CFIA, 2012a). The symptoms can include stomach cramps, nausea, vomiting, diarrhea, and fever, and many people mistakenly think they have the flu. Infants and young children, older adults, pregnant women, and people with weak immune systems are most at risk of becoming seriously ill and even dying from a food-borne illness.

Although these statistics may seem frightening, most experts consider our food supply safe. That is partly because not all cases of food contamination make all people sick; in fact, even virulent strains cause illness in only a small percentage of people. In the Peanut Corporation of American's (PCA) *Salmonella* case, although more than 500 people became ill, thousands are assumed to have eaten the tainted products. Moreover, modern science and technology have given us a wide array of techniques to preserve foods. We'll discuss these later in this chapter.

Food safety in Canada is monitored by several government agencies. The Canadian Food Inspection Agency (CFIA) is part of Agriculture and Agri-Food Canada, and reports to Health Canada. The agency is responsible for enforcing 14 federal acts related to food, plants, and animals and ensures that the food safety, animal health, and plant protection standards set out in those acts are followed. The CFIA inspects foods, plants, animals, restaurants, and food-service establishments; checks that food-labelling regulations are followed; and issues allergy alerts and food recalls.

At the municipal level, public health inspectors visit all eating and drinking establishments to ensure that the minimum standards for food temperatures, food handling, sanitation, dishwashing, and personal hygiene practices are being followed.

Food Production Is Increasingly Complex

Despite the safeguards, food-borne illness is emerging as a major public health issue because our food production systems are increasingly complex. More foods are mass-produced than ever before, with a combination of ingredients from a much greater number of sources, including fields, feedlots, and a variety of processing facilities all over the world. These various sources can remain hidden not only to consumers but even to food companies using the ingredients. Contamination can occur at any point from farm to table (**Figure 13.1**), and when it does, it can be difficult to trace. For example, in the PCA outbreak, many of the manufacturers of the recalled cookies and other products could not identify the source of their peanut ingredients.

RECAP Food-borne illness affects an estimated 11 million Canadians each year. Contamination can occur at any point from farm to table. The Canadian Food Inspection Agency monitors and regulates food production and preservation and helps to set standards to ensure food safety.

A nationwide food recall in the United States in early 2009 as a result of *Salmonella* contamination at the Peanut Corporation of America's (PCA) U.S. production plant included hundreds of products made from peanuts, many of which were distributed in Canada.

food-borne illness An illness transmitted through food or water, either by an infectious agent, a poisonous substance, or a protein that causes an immune reaction.

Farms

Animals raised for meat can harbour harmful micro-organisms, and crops can be contaminated with pollutants from irrigation, runoff from streams, micro-organisms or toxins in soil, or pesticides. Contamination can also occur during animal slaughter or from harvesting, sorting, washing, packing, and/or storage of crops.

Processing

Some foods, such as produce, may go from the farm directly to the market, but most foods are processed. Processed foods may go through several steps at different facilities. At each site, people, equipment, or environments may contaminate foods. Federal safeguards, such as cleaning protocols, testing, and training, can help prevent contamination.

Transportation

Foods must be transported in clean, refrigerated vehicles and containers to prevent multiplication of micro-organisms and microbial toxins.

Retail

Employees of food markets and restaurants may contaminate food during storage, preparation, or service. Conditions such as inadequate refrigeration or heating may promote multiplication of micro-organisms or microbial toxins. Establishments must follow Health Canada guidelines for food safety and pass local health inspections.

Table

Consumers may contaminate foods with unclean hands, utensils, or surfaces. They can allow the multiplication of micro-organisms and microbial toxins by failing to follow the food-safety guidelines for storing, preparing, cooking, and serving foods discussed in this chapter.

◀**Figure 13.1** Food is at risk for contamination at any of the five stages from farm to table, but following food-safety guidelines can reduce the risks.
Source: (Data from Iowa State University Extension, Food Safety and Quality Project. 2000. Safe Food: It's Your Job Too! www.extension.iastate.edu/foodsafety/ Lesson/?CFID=2587460&CFTOKEN=69223455. U.S. Food and Drug Administration (FDA). How Can I Prevent Foodborne Illness? www.cfsan.fda.gov/~dms/ qa-topfd.html; and Centers for Disease Control and Prevention (CDC), Division of Bacterial and Mycotic Diseases. Disease Information, Foodborne Illness. www.cdc.gov/ncidod/dbmd/diseaseinfo/ foodborneinfections_g.htm.)

What Causes Most Food-Borne Illness?

Microorganisms—that is, microscopic living organisms—and their toxins are responsible for most cases of food-borne illness. The consumption of food containing pathogenic microorganisms—those capable of causing disease—results in *food infections or food intoxications*. *Food intoxications* result from consuming food in which microorganisms have secreted harmful substances called *toxins*. Naturally occurring plant and marine toxins also contaminate food. Finally, chemical residues in foods, such as pesticides and pollutants in soil or water, can cause illness. Residues are discussed later in this chapter.

Several Types of Microorganisms Contaminate Foods

The microorganisms that most commonly cause food infections are bacteria and viruses (CDC, 2005); however, other tiny organisms and non-living particles can also contaminate foods.

Bacteria are microorganisms that lack a true nucleus and have a chemical called peptidoglycan in their cell walls **(Table 13.1)**. They make their way into food and water in a variety of ways, but many thrive naturally in the intestines of birds and mammals, including poultry, pigs, and cattle. Often, food-borne infection results from consuming undercooked or raw meats, foods contaminated with juices from raw meats, or milk or water contaminated with infected animal feces. Of the several species involved, *Campylobacter jejuni* is thought to be the most common culprit. Most cases result from eating foods or drinking milk or water contaminated with infected animal feces. The bacteria cause fever, pain, and bloody and frequent diarrhea (Bauman, 2009).

Salmonella is the second most common bacterial culprit in food infections. As with *Campylobacter*, most *Salmonella* infections result from eating food contaminated with animal feces. Poultry and eggs are commonly implicated but all foods, including fruits and vegetables, can become contaminated with *Salmonella*. Salmonellosis causes diarrhea, nausea, and vomiting, and cells of some strains of the bacteria can perforate the intestines and infect the blood. Approximately 6000 to 12 000 Canadians are diagnosed with Salmonellosis each year (Health Canada, 2006b). It is thought that a much larger number of people are affected but attribute their symptoms to the "stomach flu." *Salmonella* bacteria can be difficult to eradicate, as some strains have developed a resistance to commonly prescribed antibiotics (Health Canada, 2006b).

Escherichia coli, more commonly known as *E. coli*, are bacteria that are found in the intestines of cattle, poultry, and other animals. Although some strains are relatively harmless, other strains, such as *E. coli* O157:H7, can cause serious illness. One complication of an *E. coli* O157:H7 infection is hemolytic uremic syndrome (HUS). An infected person will experience bloody diarrhea, vomiting, abdominal cramping, and fever, usually commencing between two and four days after exposure to this bacterium. Interestingly, it takes only 10 to 100 colony-forming units (bacteria cells or parts of cells) for *E. coli* O157:H7 to become infectious, which is quite few compared with the 1 million to 100 million *E. coli* colony-forming units required for a person to become infected with traveller's diarrhea (University of Florida, 2002). Although the symptoms may resemble the flu, HUS is not to be taken lightly, as it can lead to permanent kidney damage, particularly in children younger than 5 years of age and adults over the age of 50. Of the children who become ill with this condition, upward of 80% will need blood transfusions and about 50% will require kidney dialysis (Kidney Foundation of Canada, 2002); some will need kidney transplants.

How does a person become infected by *E. coli* O157:H7? This bacterium can be transferred several ways: food to person, food to food, person to person, or person to food. Coming into contact with fecal matter from an infected person or animal can lead to infection. Hamburger meat may become contaminated through the slaughtering and grinding processes, and contamination is estimated to cost meat producers $5 billion

bacteria Microorganisms that lack a true nucleus and have a chemical called peptidoglycan in their cell walls.

TABLE 13.1 Common Bacterial Causes of Food-Borne Illness

Bacteria	Incubation Period	Duration	Symptoms	Foods Most Commonly Affected	Usual Sources of Contamination	Steps for Prevention
Campylobacter jejuni	1–7 days	7–10 days	Fever Headache and muscle pain followed by diarrhea (sometimes bloody) Nausea Abdominal cramps	Raw and undercooked meat, poultry, or shellfish Raw eggs Cake icing Untreated water Unpasteurized milk	Intestinal tracts of animals and birds Raw milk Untreated water and sewage sludge	Drink only pasteurized milk Cook foods properly Avoid cross-contamination
Salmonella (more than 2300 types)	12–24 hours	4–7 days	Diarrhea Abdominal pain Chills Fever Vomiting Dehydration	Raw or undercooked eggs, poultry, and meat Raw milk and dairy products Seafood Fruits and vegetables	Intestinal tract and feces of poultry *Salmonella enteritidis* in raw shell eggs	Cook foods thoroughly Avoid cross-contamination Use sanitary practices
Escherichia coli (O157:H7 and other strains that can cause human illness)	2–4 days	5–10 days	Diarrhea (may be bloody) Abdominal cramps Nausea Can lead to kidney and blood complications	Contaminated water Raw milk Raw or rare ground beef, sausages Unpasteurized apple juice or cider Uncooked fruits and vegetables	Intestinal tracts of cattle Raw milk Unchlorinated water	Cook meats thoroughly Avoid cross-contamination
Clostridium botulinum	12–36 hours	1–8 days	Nausea Vomiting Diarrhea Fatigue Headache Muscle paralysis; difficulty speaking, swallowing, and breathing	Improperly canned or vacuum-packed food Meats Sausage Fish Garlic in oil Honey	Widely distributed in nature In soil, in water, on plants, and in intestinal tracts of animals and fish Grows only in little or no oxygen	Properly can foods, following recommended procedures Cook foods properly Children under 16 months should not consume raw honey
Staphylococcus	1–6 hours	2–3 days	Severe nausea and vomiting Abdominal cramps Diarrhea	Custard- or cream-filled baked goods Ham Poultry Dressings, sauces, and gravies Eggs Mayonnaise-based salads	Human skin Infected cuts Pimples Noses and throats	Refrigerate foods Use sanitary practices
Listeria monocytogenes	2 days–3 weeks	None reported	Fever Muscle aches Nausea Diarrhea Headache, stiff neck, confusion, loss of balance, or convulsions if infection spreads to nervous system. Infections during pregnancy can lead to miscarriage or stillbirth	Uncooked meats and vegetables Soft cheeses Lunch meats and hot dogs Unpasteurized milk	Intestinal tract and feces of animals Soil and manure used as fertilizer Raw milk	Cook meats thoroughly Wash produce before eating Avoid cross-contamination Avoid unpasteurized milk and foods made with unpasteurized milk People at high risk should: • not eat hot dogs or lunch meats unless they are reheated until steaming hot • avoid getting fluid from hot dog packages on foods, utensils, and surfaces • wash hands after handling hot dogs or lunch meats • avoid eating refrigerated smoked seafood unless it is cooked

Data from Iowa State University Extension, Food Safety and Quality Project, 2000. Safe Food: It's Your Job Too! www.extension.iastate.edu/foodsafety/Lesson/?CFID=2587460&CFTOKEN=69223455. U.S. Food and Drug Administration (FDA). How Can I Prevent Foodborne Illness? www.cfsan.fda.gov/~dms/qa-topfd.html; and Centers for Disease Control and Prevention (CDC), Division of Bacterial and Mycotic Diseases. Disease Information, Foodborne Illness. www.cdc.gov/ncidod/dbmd/diseaseinfo/foodborneinfections_g.htm.

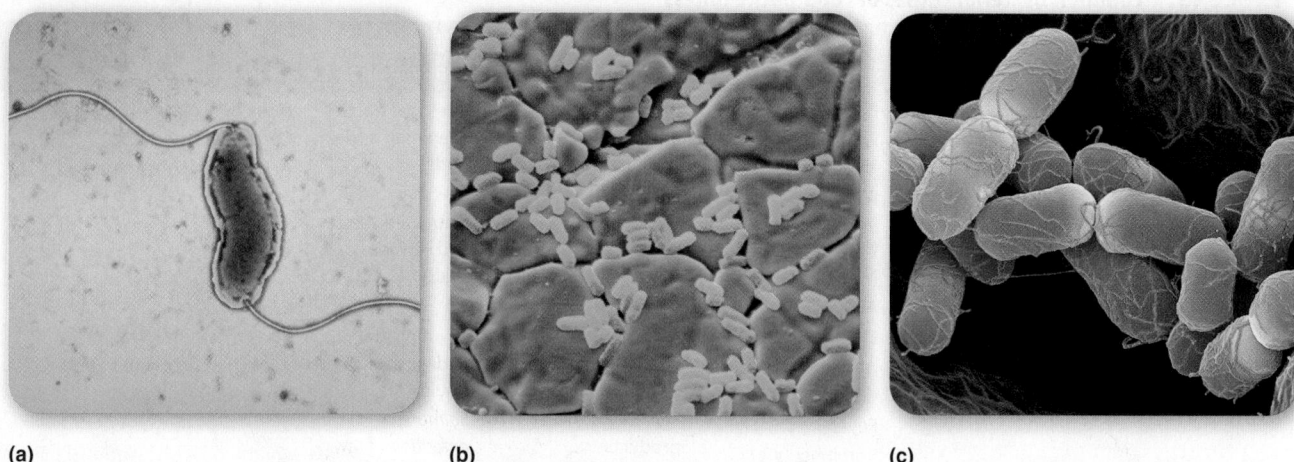

(a) (b) (c)

Figure 13.2 The three bacteria responsible for the majority of food-borne infections. **(a)** Infection with *Campylobacter jejuni* causes fever, cramping, abdominal pain, and diarrhea (which may be bloody). **(b)** Salmonellosis, the disease caused by eating food contaminated by *Salmonella*, causes fever, diarrhea, and abdominal cramps, and cells of some strains of *Salmonella* can perforate the intestines and invade the blood. Shown is *S. enteritidis*, one of more than 2000 strains. **(c)** The bacterial species called *Escherichia coli* (*E. coli*) includes strains that are harmless, but the strain shown here, *E. coli* O157:H7, can cause severe and bloody diarrhea and can lead to kidney failure and death.

viruses A group of infectious agents that are much smaller than bacteria, lack independent metabolism, and are incapable of growth or reproduction apart from living cells.

parasite A microorganism that simultaneously derives benefit from and harms its host.

helminth A multicellular microscopic worm.

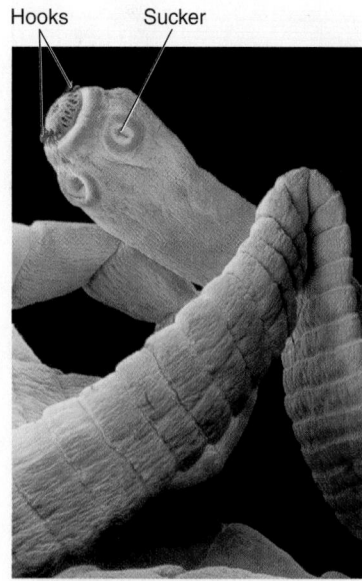

Hooks   Sucker

Figure 13.3 Tapeworms have long, worm-like bodies and hooks and suckers, which help them attach to human tissues.

annually (Canadian Institutes of Health Research, 2003). In fact, undercooked hamburger meat was responsible for two of the five biggest *E. coli* O157:H7 outbreaks on record (University of Florida, 2002), and HUS is often referred to as *hamburger disease*.

But vegetarians beware—this illness is not limited to meat. In fact, some large outbreaks have been caused by bean sprouts and alfalfa sprouts. Lettuce, salami, and unpasteurized milk, cider, and juice are other sources of infection. A shocking 50 000 North Americans become infected each year, and, of those, 500 cases are fatal (Canadian Institutes of Health Research, 2003).

Listeria monocytogenes is a bacterium that is commonly found in soil, plants, water, sewage, and manure. Humans and animals may carry it and not show any symptoms of ill health. When it is present in large amounts, pregnant women, the elderly, and people with poor immune systems are at high risk of a serious and sometimes fatal illness called listeriosis. Pregnant women may be 20 times more susceptible than women who are not pregnant, and their babies may be born early or seriously ill, or they may be stillborn.

Listeria is an unusual bacterium because it can live and grow slowly on refrigerated foods, and contaminated foods may appear safe and taste normal.

Although bacteria are the primary cause of food-borne infections, some food-borne **viruses** also cause disease. Viruses are infectious agents that are much smaller than bacteria, lack independent metabolism, and are incapable of growth or reproduction apart from living cells. Noroviruses are the most common cause of outbreaks of acute gastroenteritis worldwide (CDC, 2005). Gastroenteritis is inflammation of the lining of the stomach and intestines; it results in stomach cramps, vomiting, and diarrhea. Infected food-service workers can contaminate foods during preparation or serving if they have the virus on their hands. Hepatitis A and hepatitis E viruses also commonly contaminate foods during harvesting, processing, and preparation. They can cause acute liver damage and even death.

Parasites are microorganisms that simultaneously derive benefit from and harm their host. They include multicellular worms called helminths and single-celled organisms called protozoa. **Helminths**, which include tapeworms, flukes, and roundworms **(Figure 13.3)**, reproduce by releasing their eggs into the environment, such as in vegetation or water. Animals, including fish, then consume the contaminated matter. The eggs hatch inside their host, and larvae develop in the host's tissue. The larvae can survive in the flesh long after the host is killed for food. Thoroughly cooking beef, pork, and fish destroys the larvae. In contrast, people who eat contaminated meat or fish either raw or undercooked consume living larvae, which then mature into adult worms in their small intestine. Some worms cause mild symptoms, such as nausea and diarrhea, but others can grow large enough to cause intestinal obstruction and some can even cause death.

Unlike helminths, **protozoa** most commonly cause water-borne illness. One of the most common culprits worldwide is *Giardia duodenalis* (formerly called *Giardia lamblia*), which causes a diarrheal illness called *giardiasis* (USDA, 2001). *Giardia* lives in the intestines of infected animals and humans, and it is passed into the environment from their stools. People typically consume *Giardia* by swallowing contaminated water (this includes water in lakes, streams, rivers, swimming pools, hot tubs, and fountains) or by eating uncooked food contaminated with *Giardia*. It can also be transmitted by putting something in your mouth that has come in contact with the stool of an infected person or animal. Symptoms include diarrhea, loose or watery stools, stomach cramps, and upset stomach, but some people show no symptoms. The symptoms usually begin within one to two weeks of being infected and generally last two to six weeks.

Figure 13.4 Moulds rarely cause human illness, in part because they look so unappealing that we throw the food away.

Fungi are plantlike, spore-forming organisms that can grow either as single cells or multicellular colonies. Two types of fungi are yeasts, which are globular, and moulds, which are long and thin. The growth of fungi on foods rarely causes food infection. This is due in part to the fact that very few species of fungi cause serious disease in people with healthy immune systems, and those that do cause disease in humans are not typically food-borne (Bauman, 2009). In addition, unlike bacterial growth, which is invisible and often tasteless, fungal growth typically makes food look and taste so unappealing that we immediately discard it **(Figure 13.4)**.

A food-borne illness in beef cattle that has had front-page exposure in recent years is mad cow disease, or *bovine spongiform encephalopathy* (*BSE*). This neurologic disorder is caused by a **prion**, a proteinaceous infectious particle that is self-replicating. Prions are normal proteins of animal tissues that can misfold and become infectious. When they do, they can transform other normal proteins into abnormally shaped prions until they eventually cause illness. The human form of BSE can develop in people who consume contaminated meat or tissue. If you eat beef, are you at risk? Check out the Nutrition Myth or Fact? box on page 454.

Some Microorganisms Release Toxins

The microbes just discussed cause illness by directly infecting and destroying body cells. In contrast, other bacteria and fungi secrete chemicals, called **toxins**, that are responsible for serious and even life-threatening illnesses. These toxins bind to body cells and can cause a variety of symptoms, such as diarrhea, vomiting, organ damage, convulsions, and paralysis. Toxins can be categorized depending on the type of cell they bind to; the two primary types of toxins associated with food-borne illness are neurotoxins, which damage the nervous system and can cause paralysis, and enterotoxins, which target the gastrointestinal system and generally cause severe diarrhea and vomiting.

One of the most common and deadly toxins is produced by the bacterium *Clostridium botulinum* (see Table 13.1). The botulism toxin blocks nerve transmission to muscle cells and causes paralysis, including of the muscles required for breathing. Common sources of contamination are split or pierced, bulging cans; foods improperly canned at home; and any honey (raw or pasteurized). Health Canada warns parents not to put honey in infant food or on infant soothers because there is a chance that it can carry *Clostridium botulinum* spores, which are not killed by pasteurization. Infants under the age of one year do not have protective bacterial flora in their gastrointestinal tracts or bile acids to prevent the spores from germinating and producing neurotoxins (Health Canada, 2006a).

protozoa Single-celled, mobile microorganisms.

fungi Plantlike, spore-forming organisms that can grow either as single cells or multicellular colonies.

prion An infectious, self-replicating protein.

toxin A harmful substance; specifically, a chemical produced by a microorganism that harms tissues or causes adverse immune responses.

Some fungi produce poisonous chemicals called *mycotoxins*. (The prefix *myco-* means "fungus.") These toxins are typically found in grains stored in moist environments. In some instances, moist conditions in the field encourage fungi to reproduce and release their toxins on the surface of growing crops. Long-term consumption of mycotoxins can cause organ damage or cancer, and they can be fatal if consumed in large doses. A mycotoxin called *aflatoxin* is produced by the mould *Aspergillus flavus*. Aflatoxin has been associated with peanuts and other crops and, if ingested, can cause illness in livestock and humans.

Some Toxins Occur Independently of Microorganisms

Some toxins develop in foods independently of microorganisms. For example, a highly visible fungus that causes food intoxication is the poisonous mushroom. Most mushrooms are not toxic, but a few, such as the death cap mushroom (*Amanita phalloides*), can be fatal. Some poisonous mushrooms are quite colourful (**Figure 13.5**), a fact that helps explain why the victims of mushroom poisoning are often children (Bauman, 2009).

▲ **Figure 13.5** Some mushrooms, such as this fly agaric, contain toxins that can cause illness or even death.

NUTRITION MYTH OR FACT?

Mad Cow Disease: Is It Safe to Eat Beef?

Mad cow disease is a fatal brain disorder in cattle caused by a *prion*, which is an abnormally folded, infectious protein. Prions influence other proteins to mimic their abnormal shape, and these abnormal proteins then cause brain damage. Mad cow disease is also called *bovine spongiform encephalopathy (BSE)*. The disease eats away at a cow's brain, leaving it full of spongelike holes, and eventually the brain can no longer control vital life functions. Unfortunately, people who eat meat from infected cattle will also be infected. Symptoms may take years to appear, but eventually an infected person will develop the human form of mad cow disease, called *variant Creutzfeldt-Jakob disease (vCJD)*. This disease has killed at least 168 people in Great Britain, as well as people in France and other nations (International Society for Infectious Disease, 2010). So if you eat beef, are you at risk?

Scientists are not certain how the prions are introduced to cattle. They think that cattle become infected by eating feed containing tissue from the brains and spinal cords of other infected cattle. Decades ago in Great Britain and Europe, it was common practice to feed livestock with meal made from other animals. This practice there has since ceased.

The effect of mad cow disease on the European beef market has been staggering, with beef consumption

dropping 25%–70% in some countries, and ranchers have been forced to slaughter almost five million cattle.

For years, experts in North American believed that BSE was a problem limited to Europe. But from 2003 to 2006, eight cases of BSE were found in cows in Canada, and one in the United States. These discoveries prompted many countries to swiftly ban importation of Canadian and American beef. The CFIA took quick action to restore confidence in the beef supply. Steps included the destruction of potentially infected beef, as well as changes in feeding practices, including greater enforcement of a ban on livestock meal made with animal by-products. Since 1997 Canada and the United States have banned the use of rendered beef in cattle feed. And in Canada as of 2007, tissues that would contain the infectious agent in an infected animal, the brain and spinal cord, have been banned from all animal feed, pet feed, and fertilizers. These tissues are also removed from all cattle that are slaughtered for human consumption, to prevent the likelihood of an unknown case of BSE entering the human food chain.

So is it safe to eat beef? Canada's surveillance programs should detect any future cases of BSE, and the safeguards put in place will prevent infected animals from entering the animal or human food chains.

Fisheries and Oceans Canada issues red tide warnings for costal areas, warning residents not to harvest shellfish. Red tides are caused by an excessive production of certain species of toxic algae, whose bloom turns ocean waters red. Humans do not consume these marine toxins directly, but they can accumulate in mussels, clams, and other seafoods. When humans consume the seafood, which typically looks, smells, and tastes normal, they become ill (CDC, 2005).

Ciguatoxins are among the most common marine toxins. They are produced by microscopic sea plants called *dinoflagellates*, which are consumed by small fish. The toxins become progressively more concentrated as larger fish eat these small fish, and high concentrations can be present in grouper, sea bass, snapper, and a number of other large fish from tropical regions. Symptoms of ciguatoxin poisoning include nausea, vomiting, diarrhea, headache, itching, a "pins-and-needles" feeling, and even nightmares or hallucinations, but the illness is rarely fatal and typically resolves within a few weeks (CDC, 2005).

Potatoes that have turned green contain the toxin solanine, which forms during the greening process. The green colour is actually due to chlorophyll, a harmless pigment that forms when the potatoes are exposed to light. Although the production of solanine occurs simultaneously with the production of chlorophyll, the two processes are separate and unrelated (Pavlista, 2001). Although there is a potential for toxicity from consuming potatoes with a very high solanine content, because solanine formation occurs near the potato's skin, the green areas can be cut away to remove any toxins. A good guide is to taste a small piece of the potato after the green areas have been removed. If the potato tastes bitter, then throw it away. If you are in doubt, or if you are serving the potato to someone with allergies or compromised immunity, you should discard the potato. You can avoid the greening of potatoes by storing them for only short periods in a dark cupboard or brown paper bag in a cool area. Wash the potato to expose its colour, and cut away and discard any green areas. Cooked potatoes cannot turn green or produce solanine, but cooking green potatoes does not remove the chlorophyll or solanine that is formed prior to cooking.

The Body Responds to Contaminated Foods with Acute Illness

Many food-borne microbes are killed in the mouth by antimicrobial enzymes in saliva or in the stomach by hydrochloric acid. Any microbe that survives these chemical assaults will usually trigger vomiting and/or diarrhea as the gastrointestinal tract attempts to expel the offender. Simultaneously, the white blood cells of the immune system will be activated, and a generalized inflammatory response will cause the person to experience nausea, fatigue, fever, and muscle cramps. Depending on the state of one's health, the precise microbe involved, and the number of microbes ingested, the symptoms can range from mild to severe, including double vision, loss of muscle control, and excessive or bloody diarrhea. As noted earlier, some cases, if left untreated, can result in death.

To diagnose a food-borne illness, a specimen must be obtained and cultured. This means the specimen is analyzed in a laboratory setting in which the offending microorganisms are grown in a specific chemical medium. Stool (fecal) cultures are usually analyzed, especially if diarrhea is a symptom. Blood is cultured if the patient has a high fever. Treatment usually involves keeping the person hydrated and comfortable, as most food-borne illness tends to be self-limiting; the person's vomiting and/or diarrhea, although unpleasant, rid the body of the offending agent. In treating botulism, the patient's intestinal tract is flushed repeatedly to remove the microorganisms, and antibodies are injected to neutralize its deadly toxin.

In Canada, all levels of the public health system (local, provincial, territorial, and federal) collect information about diseases and food-borne illnesses. Some types of food-borne illnesses are "national notifiable diseases," which means that they must be reported by local public health departments to the Public Health Agency of Canada (PHAC, 2005). This enables public health authorities to analyze trends and issue alerts if necessary (PHAC, 2012).

▲ Sea bass may look appealing, but like several other large, predatory tropical fish, can be contaminated with a high concentration of marine toxins.

Certain Conditions Help Microorganisms Multiply in Foods

Given the correct conditions, microbes can thrive and multiply in many types of food. These growth-favouring conditions can be remembered with the acronym FAT-TOM. FATTOM stands for

- Food—bacteria like high-protein and high-carbohydrate foods;
- Acid—a mildly acidic environment with a pH of 4.6 to 7.0;
- Time—when conditions are ideal, bacteria can double their numbers every 15 to 30 minutes. In general, bacteria grow to sufficient numbers to cause illness in about four hours;
- Temperature—bacteria grow best between 5°C (41°F) and 60°C (140°F);
- Oxygen—some bacteria are aerobic and need oxygen, while others are anaerobic and cannot survive in the presence of oxygen;
- Moisture—many microbes require a high level of moisture, and thus foods like boxed dried pasta and rice do not make suitable microbial homes, although cooked pasta and cooked rice left at room temperature might prove hospitable.

As just noted, many microbes cannot tolerate acidic foods. For example, *Clostridium botulinum* cannot grow or produce its toxin in an acidic environment, so the risk of botulism is lower in citrus fruits, sauerkraut, and pickles. In contrast, more alkaline foods, such as eggs and canned mushrooms, are a magnet for *C. botulinum.*

In addition, microorganisms need an entryway into a food. Just as our skin protects our body from microbial invasion, the peels, rinds, and shells of many foods seal off access to the nutrients within. Eggshells are a good example of a natural food barrier. Once such a barrier is removed, however, the food loses its primary defence against contamination.

RECAP Food infections result from the consumption of food containing living microorganisms, such as bacteria, whereas food intoxications result from consuming food in which microbes have secreted toxins. Some foods develop toxins independently of microbes. The body has several defence mechanisms, such as saliva, stomach acid, vomiting, diarrhea, and the inflammatory response, which help rid us of offending microorganisms or their toxins. To reproduce in foods, microbes require a precise range of temperature, humidity, acidity, and oxygen content. Most bacteria prefer protein-rich or carbohydrate-rich foods and need about four hours to grow to numbers that cause illness.

How Can Food-Borne Illness Be Prevented?

Foods of animal origin are most commonly associated with food-borne illness. These include not only raw meat, poultry, and fish but also eggs, shellfish, and unpasteurized milk. Fruits and vegetables can also cause problems when they are consumed unwashed and raw. So how can you protect yourself when eating foods of animal origin and fresh fruits and vegetables? Here, we discuss food-safety tips for when you are preparing foods at home, eating out, or travelling to other countries.

When preparing foods at home, you can prevent food-borne illness by following four basic rules: clean, separate, chill, and cook (**Figure 13.6**):

1. Clean. Wash your hands and kitchen surfaces often.
2. Separate. Keep foods separated to prevent **cross-contamination**—that is, the spread of bacteria or other microbes from one food to another. This commonly occurs when raw, unwashed foods are cut on the same cutting board or served together on the same plate.
3. Chill. Refrigerate or freeze foods to prevent microbes from growing.
4. Cook. Cook foods to their proper temperatures.

Each of these rules is discussed in detail in the following sections.

Peels protect foods against contamination; however, you should still wash fruit before peeling.

cross-contamination Contamination of one food by another via the unintended transfer of microbes through physical contact.

◀ **Figure 13.6** The FightBAC! logo is the food-safety logo of the Canadian Partnership for Consumer Food Safety Education and the U.S. Department of Agriculture (see www.canfightbac.org).

Wash Your Hands and Kitchen Surfaces Often

One of the easiest and most effective ways to prevent food-borne illness is to wash your hands both before and after preparing food. Although you should wash dishes in hot water, it is too harsh for normal hand washing: it causes the surface layer of the skin to break down, increasing the risk that microbes will be able to penetrate your skin. Instead, use gentle soap under warm, running water. Scrub for at least 20 seconds (sing "Happy Birthday" or say the ABCs to time yourself). Pay special attention to the areas underneath your fingernails and between your fingers. Also, it is a good idea to remove rings and bracelets while cooking, as they can harbour bacteria. To prevent cross-contamination, always wash your hands after working with each raw food and before progressing to the next one.

A clean area and tools are also essential in reducing cross-contamination. Wash utensils, containers, and cutting boards in the dishwasher or with hot, soapy water before and after contact with food. If a cutting board, plate, countertop, or other surface has held raw meat, poultry, or seafood, sanitize it with a solution of 5 mL (1 tsp) of chlorine bleach to 1 litre (1 quart) of water, or use a commercial kitchen cleaning agent (USDA, 2006). It is also important to wash utensils, faucets, cabinet knobs, countertops, and other areas you have touched. Rinse; then air-dry or dry with fresh paper towels. For cutting foods, use a nonporous, smooth plastic or stone cutting board, because porous wood and scratched plastic can hold juices and harbour bacteria.

Dishtowels, cloths, and aprons should be washed in hot water often. It is a good idea to wash sponges in the dishwasher each time you run it and to replace them regularly. If you do not have a dishwasher, put sponges in boiling water for three minutes to sterilize them.

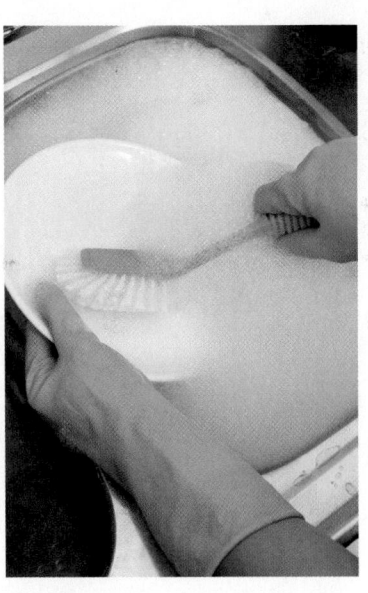

⬆ Washing dishes, utensils, and cutting boards reduces the chances for food contamination.

Separate Foods to Prevent Cross-Contamination

Raw meat, poultry, and seafood harbour an array of microbes and can easily contaminate other foods through direct contact, as well as by the juices they leave behind on surfaces (including hands). Avoid contact between foods that have already been cooked or that will not be cooked (such as salad ingredients) and raw foods or their juices. Also avoid placing cooked or ready-to-eat foods on a plate or other surface that previously held raw meat, seafood, or poultry. When preparing meals with a marinade, reserve some of the fresh marinade in a clean container; then add the raw ingredients to the remainder. In this way, some non-contaminated marinade will be available if needed later in the cooking process. Raw food should always be marinated in the refrigerator.

Store Foods in the Refrigerator or Freezer

Different microbes thrive in different environmental temperatures. The majority of the bacteria that cause food-borne illness grow best in temperatures at or above 4°C (40°F) (NDDIC, 2007). Because of this, refrigeration (keep your refrigerator at or below 4°C (40°F)) and freezing (keep your freezer at −20°C (0°F)) are two of the most reliable methods of diminishing the ability of bacteria to cause illness (NDDIC, 2007). Not all bacteria in cool environments are killed, but the rate at which they reproduce is drastically reduced. Also, naturally occurring enzymes that cause food decomposition are stopped at freezing temperatures.

Shopping for Perishable Foods

When shopping for food, pick up refrigerated and frozen foods last. Many grocery stores are designed so that these foods are in the last aisles. Put packaged meat, poultry, or fish into a plastic bag before placing it in your shopping cart (FDA, 2005). This prevents food drippings from coming into contact with the other foods in your cart.

When you are buying meats, poultry, seafood, and dairy products, look for the durable life information on their labels or on a poster near the food. The durable life of a food is the number of days that an unopened product will keep its freshness, taste, and nutritional value when stored properly (CFIA, 2012b). The best before (*meilleur avant*) date is another way of giving this information and is required on products that have a durable life of 90 days or less. It indicates the last day an unopened product will maintain its quality; proper storage instructions (e.g., "keep refrigerated") must also be provided. It is best to avoid buying foods past the best before date, even though they are generally still safe to eat. For foods that are packaged in the store, such as meat, fish, or poultry, the label must have a packaged-on date and durable life information (on the label or an accompanying poster); alternatively, the foods can carry a best before date and storage instructions (CFIA, 2012b). For less perishable foods, such as cereal and baking mixes, the "best if used by [or before]" dates indicate the shelf life of the product or the date at which the product is no longer at peak flavour, texture, and appearance. These foods can be safely eaten past the listed date if they have been stored properly, but they may not taste as good or be as nutritious as they were before this date. Proper storage for non-perishable items includes storage in a dry, clean, cool (less than 29°C or 85°F) cabinet or pantry.

Do not purchase foods with punctured or otherwise damaged packaging. Dented or bulging cans are especially dangerous, as they could harbour potentially deadly bacteria. Report any damaged packaging to the store manager.

Watch for unsanitary practices and conditions inside the store. For example, the unsafe displaying of food products, such as cooked shrimp on the same bed of ice as raw seafood, is illegal, as is trimming raw meat with the same knife used to slice cold cuts. Report such unsanitary practices or conditions to your local health authorities.

After purchasing perishable foods, get them home and into the refrigerator or freezer within one hour. If your trip home will take longer than an hour, take along a cooler to transport them.

Refrigerating Foods

Once you get home, put meat, poultry, and seafood in the coldest part of the refrigerator. Keep them wrapped in plastic, so that their juices do not drip onto any other foods. If you are not going to use ground beef, poultry, or fish within 48 hours, store them in the freezer (USDA, 2006). Remember that eggs are also perishable and should be kept refrigerated. Avoid overstocking your refrigerator or freezer, as air

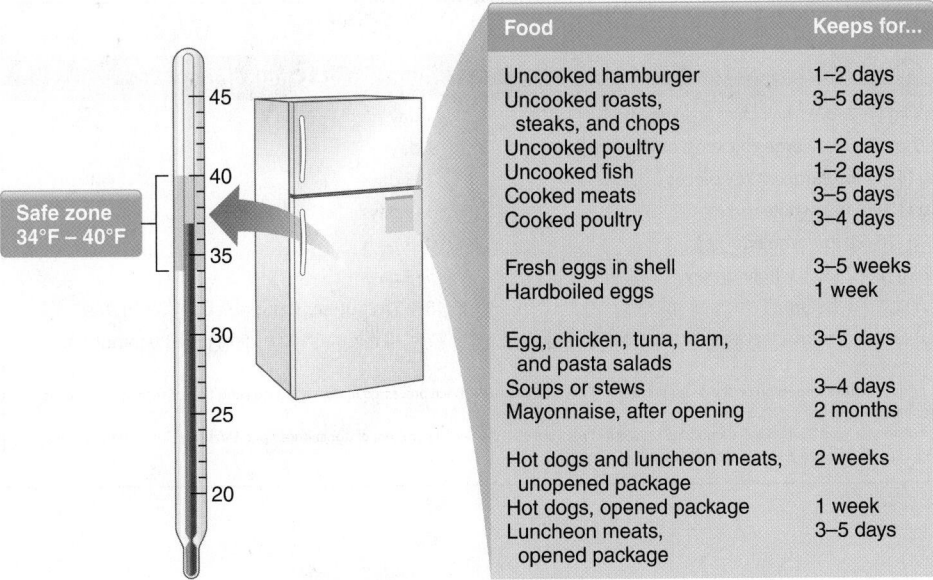

Food	Keeps for...
Uncooked hamburger	1–2 days
Uncooked roasts, steaks, and chops	3–5 days
Uncooked poultry	1–2 days
Uncooked fish	1–2 days
Cooked meats	3–5 days
Cooked poultry	3–4 days
Fresh eggs in shell	3–5 weeks
Hardboiled eggs	1 week
Egg, chicken, tuna, ham, and pasta salads	3–5 days
Soups or stews	3–4 days
Mayonnaise, after opening	2 months
Hot dogs and luncheon meats, unopened package	2 weeks
Hot dogs, opened package	1 week
Luncheon meats, opened package	3–5 days

Safe zone 34°F – 40°F

Figure 13.7 While it's important to keep a well-stocked refrigerator, it's also important to know how long foods will keep.
Data from U.S. Department of Agriculture, Food Safety and Inspection Service, 2009. Fact Sheets. Safe Food Handling. Refrigeration and Food Safety. (modified June 3, 2010): www.fsis.usda.gov/Fact_Sheets/Focus_On_Freezing/index.asp.

needs to circulate around food to cool it quickly and discourage microbial growth. Purchase a refrigerator thermometer and check it regularly to ensure that your refrigerator is at or below 4°C (40°F).

After a meal, promptly refrigerate leftovers—even if still hot—to discourage microbial growth. The standard rule for storing leftovers is *2 hours/2 inches/4 days*. Food should be refrigerated *within two hours* of serving. If the environmental temperature is 32°C (90°F) or higher, such as at a picnic, then foods should be refrigerated within one hour (USDA, 2006). Because a larger quantity of food takes longer to cool and will allow more microbes to thrive, food should be stored at a depth of no greater than five centimetres or *two inches*. The interior of deeper containers of foods can remain warm long enough to allow bacteria to multiply rapidly even when the surface of the food has cooled. Leftovers should only be refrigerated for *up to four days*. If you do not plan on using the food within four days, freeze it. A guide for storing foods in your refrigerator is provided in **Figure 13.7**.

Freezing and Thawing Foods

The temperature in your freezer should be set at −20°C (0°F) (USDA, 2006). Use a thermometer to check periodically that a freezing temperature is being maintained. If your electricity goes out, avoid opening the freezer until the power is restored. When the power does come back on, check to make sure the temperature on the top shelf of the freezer compartment is no warmer than 5°C (41°F). If it is warmer, you should inspect your freezer's contents and discard any items that are not firmly frozen.

When freezing items, remember that smaller packages will freeze more quickly. So rather than attempting to freeze an entire casserole or a whole batch of home-made spaghetti sauce, divide the food into multiple portions in freezer-safe containers; then freeze.

Sufficient thawing will ensure adequate cooking throughout, which is essential to preventing food-borne illness. Raw poultry is a good example of a food item that needs to be carefully contained as it thaws, so that its juices do not contaminate other foods. The perfect place to thaw poultry is on the bottom shelf of the refrigerator in a large bowl to catch any of its juices. **Table 13.2** shows recommended poultry thawing times based on weight. However, more research is needed to establish the safety of other methods, such as thawing in the microwave or in basins of cold water (Lacroix, Li, and Powell, 2003). Health Canada (2010) recommends that food thawed in a microwave be cooked immediately. Never thaw frozen meat, poultry, or seafood on a kitchen counter or in a basin of warm water. Room temperatures allow

TABLE 13.2 A Guide to Thawing Poultry

Method Needed	Size of Poultry	Approximate Length of Time
Refrigerator	0.5–1.5 kg (1–3 lb.), small chickens, pieces	1 day
	1.5–3.0 kg (3–6 lb.), large chickens, ducks, small turkeys	2 days
	2–6 kg (4–12 lb.), large turkey pieces	1–3 days
	6–8 kg (12–16 lb.), whole turkey	3–4 days
	8–10 kg (16–20 lb.), whole turkey	4–5 days
	10–12 kg (20–24 lb.), whole turkey	5–6 days
Microwave (read instructions)	0.5–1.5 kg (1–3 lb.), small chickens, pieces	8–15 minutes* (standing time 10 minutes)
	1.5–3.0 (3–6 lb.), large chickens, ducks, small turkeys	15–30 minutes* (standing time 20 minutes)

*Approximate; read microwave's instructions.

Note: Turkeys purchased stuffed and frozen with the USDA or state mark of inspection on the packaging are safe because they have been processed under controlled conditions. These turkeys should not be thawed before cooking. Follow package directions for handling.

Source: Data from Lacey, R. W. 1994. Hard to Swallow: A Brief History of Food. Cambridge: Cambridge University Press, pp. 85–187. U.S. Department of Agriculture, Food Safety and Inspection Service. 2005. Poultry Preparation. www.fsis.usda.gov/Fact_Sheets/Poultry_Preparation_Fact_Sheets/index.asp#talk_turkey.

the growth of bacteria on the surface of food, although the inside may still be frozen (Food Marketing Institute, 2003).

Dealing with Moulds in Refrigerated Foods

Have you ever taken cheese out of the refrigerator and noticed that it had a fuzzy, blue growth on it? This is mould, one of the two types of fungus. Interestingly, cool temperatures and high acidity do not slow the growth of some moulds; in fact, some prefer these conditions. For instance, when acidic foods, such as applesauce, yogurt, and spaghetti sauce, are refrigerated, they readily support the growth of mould. But how does mould get into a closed, refrigerated container? Mould spores are common in the atmosphere, and they randomly land on food, either in the processing plant or in open containers at your home. If the temperature and acidity of the food are hospitable, they will grow.

Most people throw away mouldy foods because they are so unappealing, but as we noted earlier, food-borne illnesses are not commonly caused by fungi. If the surface of a small portion of a solid food, such as hard cheese, becomes mouldy, it is generally safe to cut off that section down to about an inch and eat the unspoiled portion. If soft cheese, sour cream, yogurt, tomato sauce, applesauce, or another soft or fluid product becomes mouldy, discard it.

Some fungi are actually used in the food industry to create popular foods and beverages. The distinct flavour of Roquefort and blue cheeses can be attributed to the moulds used in their ripening process. Yeast, the globular form of fungi, gives a distinct flavour to fermented foods such as sourdough bread, miso, soy sauce, beer, wine, and distilled spirits. Even the production of chocolate requires the help of yeasts, which ferment the cacao seeds, causing them to lose their bitter taste.

Cook Foods Thoroughly

Thoroughly cooking food is a sure way to kill the intestinal worms discussed earlier and many other microbes. The proper internal temperatures for doneness of meat, poultry, seafood, and eggs vary, as shown in **Figure 13.8**.

The colour of cooked meat can be deceiving. Grilled meat and poultry often brown very quickly on the outside but may not be thoroughly cooked on the inside. The only way to be sure meat is thoroughly cooked is with a food thermometer. Test the food in several places to be sure it is cooked evenly, and remember to wash the thermometer after each use.

Microwave cooking is convenient, but you need to be sure your food is thoroughly cooked and there are no cold spots in the food where bacteria can thrive. For best results when microwaving, remember to cover food, stir often, rotate for

Food Safety Tips

Ground Meat — Recommended internal cooking temperature

Beef, pork, veal .... 71°C (160°F)
Chicken, turkey .... 74°C (165°F)

Fresh Beef

Rare .... 63°C (145°F)
Medium .... 71°C (160°F)
Well done .... 77°C (170°F)
Rolled beef roasts or steaks .... 71°C (160°F)
Beef minute steak .... 71°C (160°F)

Fresh Pork

Pork chops .... 71°C (160°F)
Roasts .... 71°C (160°F)
Fresh cured ham .... 71°C (160°F)
Cooked ham (to reheat) .... 60°C (140°F)

Poultry — Recommended internal cooking temperature

Chicken, turkey–whole, stuffed .... 85°C (185°F)
Chicken–whole, unstuffed .... 82°C (180°F)
Turkey–whole, unstuffed .... 77°C (170°F)
Chicken, turkey–pieces .... 74°C (165°F)

Stuffing

Cooked alone .... 74°C (165°F)

Eggs & Egg Dishes

Egg casseroles, sauces, custards .... 74°C (165°F)

Leftovers–reheated .... 74°C (165°F)

Figure 13.8 Based on cooking temperatures from Health Canada.

even cooking and allow "standing time" if it is recommended (Health Canada, 2010). "Standing time" helps to ensure the temperature inside the product is uniform. If you are microwaving meat or poultry, use a thermometer to check internal temperatures in several spots, since temperatures vary in different parts of food more in microwave cooking than in conventional ovens (Health Canada, 2010).

Raw and semi-raw (such as marinated or partly cooked) fish delicacies, such as sushi and sashimi, may be tempting, but their safety cannot be guaranteed. Always cook fish thoroughly. When done, fish should be opaque and flake easily with a fork. It is important to recognize that sushi restaurants cannot guarantee the safety of their food. Although freezing effectively kills any parasites that might be in the fish, it does not kill bacteria or viruses. Thus, eating raw seafood remains risky, and people with compromised immunity, children, pregnant women, and the elderly should avoid it.

You may have memories of licking the cake batter off a spoon when you were a kid, but such practices are no longer safe. That is because most cake batters contain raw eggs, which may be contaminated with *Salmonella*. For this reason, eggs should be cooked until the whites and yolks are firm. Scrambled eggs should not be runny. If you are using eggs in a casserole or custard, make sure that the internal temperature reaches at least 71°C (160°F) (CSPI, 2004).

Protect Yourself from Toxins in Foods

Killing microorganisms with heat is an important step in keeping food safe, but it will not protect people against the toxins. That is because toxins are unaffected by heat and are capable of causing severe illness even when the microbes that produce them have been destroyed.

For example, let's say you prepare a casserole for a team picnic. Too bad you forget to wash your hands before serving it to your teammates because you contaminate the casserole with the bacteria *Staphylococcus aureus,* which is commonly found on human skin (see Table 13.1). You and your friends go off and play soccer, leaving the food in the sun, and a few hours later you take the rest of the casserole home. At supper, you heat the leftovers thoroughly, thinking as you do so that this will kill any bacteria that might have multiplied while it was left out. That night you wake up with nausea, severe vomiting, and abdominal pain. What happened? While your food was left out, the bacteria from your hands multiplied in the casserole and produced a toxin (Figure 13.9). When you reheated the food, the microorganisms were killed, but their toxin was unaffected by the heat. When you then ate the food, the toxin made you sick. Fortunately, in the case of *S. aureus,* symptoms typically resolve on their own in healthy people in about 24 hours.

At a barbecue, it's essential to heat foods to the proper temperature.

When Eating Out

When choosing a place to eat out, avoid restaurants that do not look clean. Grimy tabletops and dirty restrooms indicate indifference to hygiene. On the other hand, the cleanliness of areas used by the public does not guarantee that the kitchen is clean. That is why health inspections are important.

Public health inspectors randomly visit and inspect the food preparation areas of all businesses that serve food, whether eaten in or taken out. You can usually find the results of these inspections in the local newspaper or by contacting your local health department. In some Canadian cities, these establishments are required to post the report of the inspection for consumers to see (see an example in **Figure 13.10**).

Another way to protect yourself when dining out is by ordering foods to be cooked thoroughly. If you order a hamburger that arrives pink in the middle, send it back and ask for it to be cooked longer. If you order scrambled eggs that arrive runny, send them back to be cooked thoroughly or order something else.

When Travelling to Other Countries

When planning a trip to another country, tell your physician your travel plans and ask about vaccinations needed or any medications that should be taken along in case you get sick. Also pack a waterless antibacterial hand cleanser, and use it frequently during the trip. When dining, select foods and beverages carefully. All raw food has the potential for contamination, especially in areas where hygiene and sanitation are inadequate. If fish is a local delicacy, be aware that some tropical species can contain marine toxins, even when well cooked.

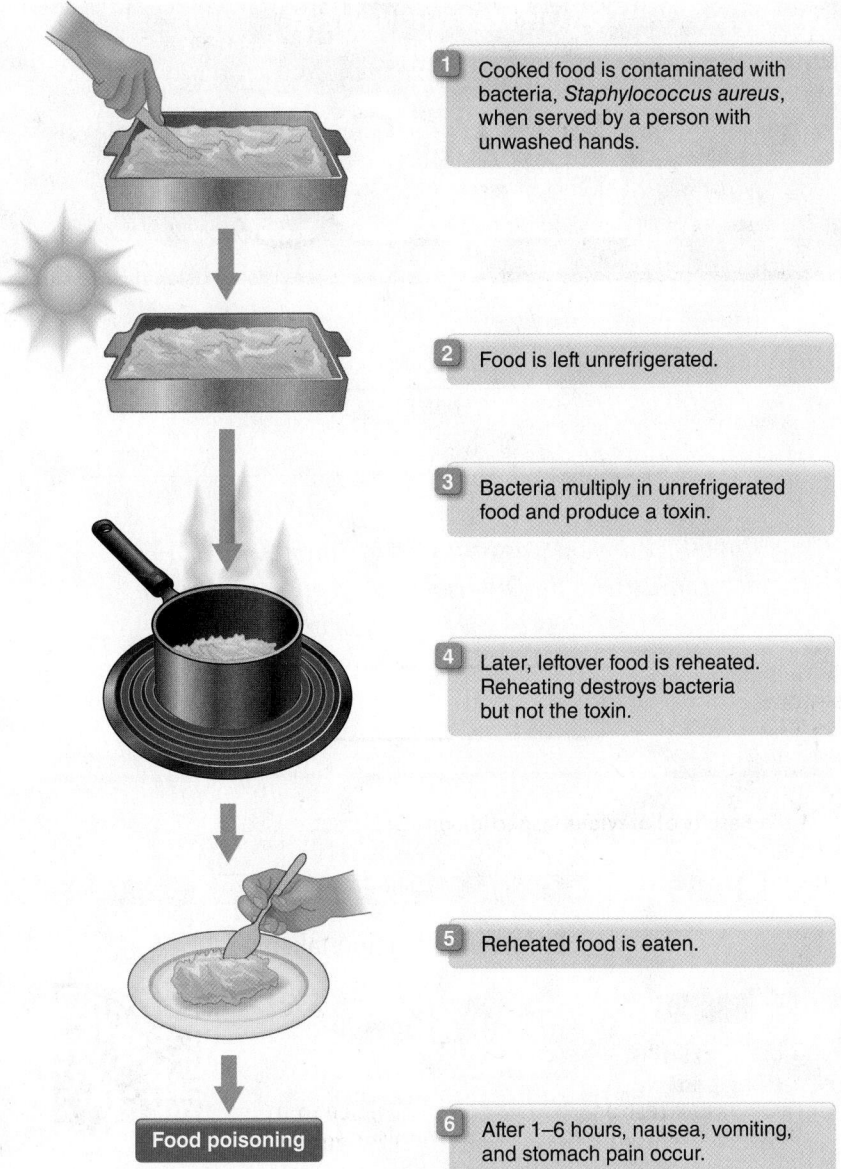

1. Cooked food is contaminated with bacteria, *Staphylococcus aureus*, when served by a person with unwashed hands.

2. Food is left unrefrigerated.

3. Bacteria multiply in unrefrigerated food and produce a toxin.

4. Later, leftover food is reheated. Reheating destroys bacteria but not the toxin.

5. Reheated food is eaten.

Food poisoning

6. After 1–6 hours, nausea, vomiting, and stomach pain occur.

Figure 13.9 Food intoxication can occur long after the microbe itself has been destroyed.

Tap water is seldom a safe option, even if chlorinated, as chlorine does not kill all the organisms that can cause disease. If you think the local water may be contaminated, do not even brush your teeth with it: use bottled water or boil the water for one minute; then allow it to return to room temperature before brushing. You can find more information about food and water safety when travelling by visiting the CDC's website (see Web Resources at the end of this chapter) or by contacting your local health department.

RECAP Food-borne illness can be prevented at home by following four tips. Clean: wash your hands and kitchen surfaces often. Separate: isolate foods to prevent cross-contamination. Chill: store foods in the refrigerator or freezer. Cook: heat foods long enough and at proper temperatures to ensure proper cooking. When eating out, avoid restaurants that do not look clean, and ask that all food be cooked thoroughly. When travelling, avoid all raw foods unless they are thoroughly washed in bottled or boiled water, and choose beverages that are boiled, bottled, or canned, without ice.

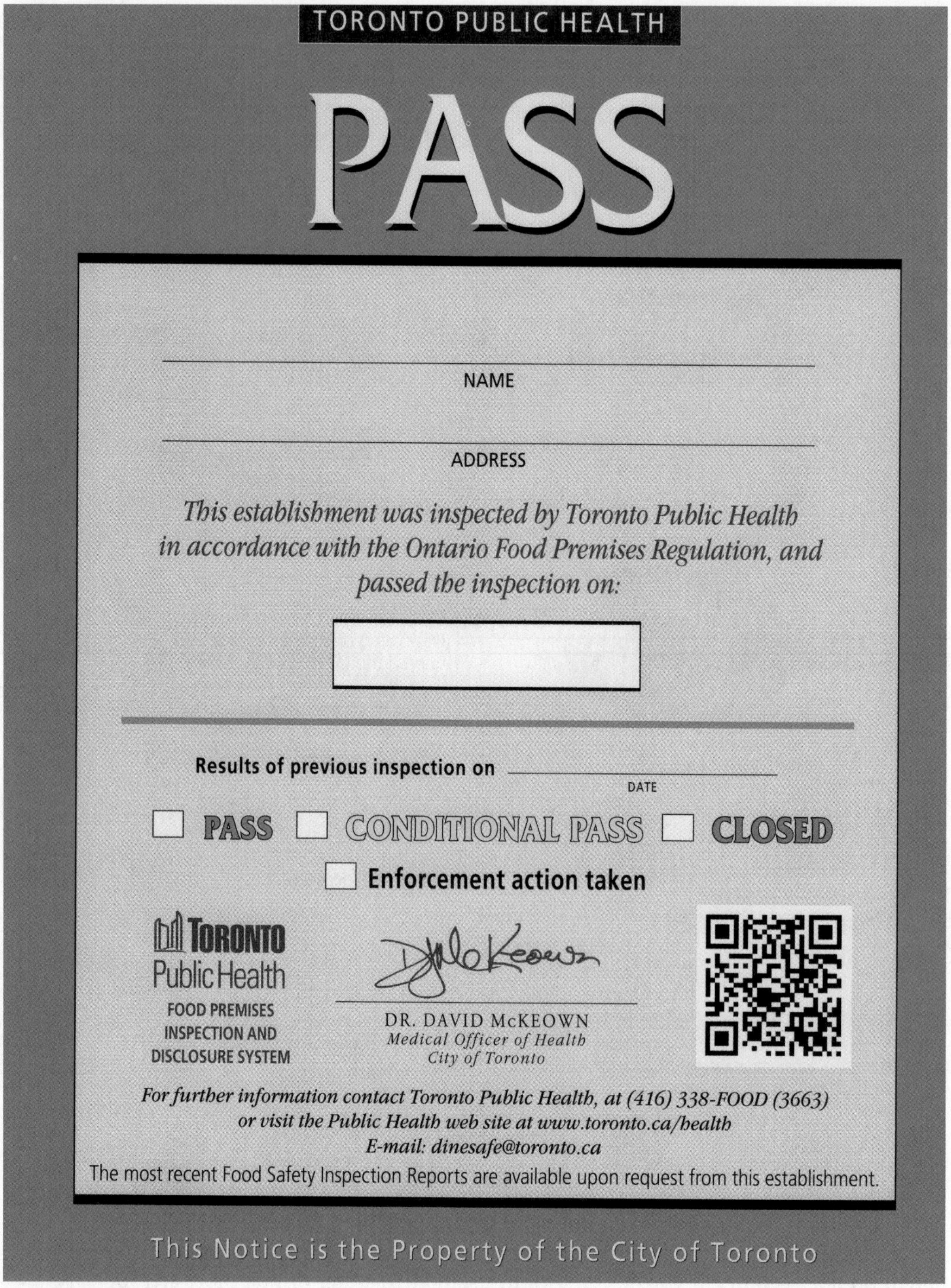
TORONTO PUBLIC HEALTH

PASS

NAME

ADDRESS

This establishment was inspected by Toronto Public Health in accordance with the Ontario Food Premises Regulation, and passed the inspection on:

Results of previous inspection on ______ DATE

☐ PASS ☐ CONDITIONAL PASS ☐ CLOSED

☐ **Enforcement action taken**

TORONTO Public Health
FOOD PREMISES INSPECTION AND DISCLOSURE SYSTEM

DR. DAVID McKEOWN
Medical Officer of Health
City of Toronto

For further information contact Toronto Public Health, at (416) 338-FOOD (3663) or visit the Public Health web site at www.toronto.ca/health
E-mail: dinesafe@toronto.ca

The most recent Food Safety Inspection Reports are available upon request from this establishment.

This Notice is the Property of the City of Toronto

Figure 13.10 An example of the Food Premises Inspection and Disclosure form used by Toronto Public Health. (Used with permission from Toronto Public Health.)

How Is Food Spoilage Prevented?

processed foods Foods that are manipulated mechanically or chemically during their production or packaging. Processed foods may or may not resemble the original ingredients in their final form.

Any food that has been harvested and that people are not ready to eat must be preserved in some way, or before long it will degrade enzymatically and become home to a variety of microorganisms. Even **processed foods**—foods that are manipulated mechanically or chemically—have the potential to spoil.

Spoilage makes food unsafe to eat: because decomposition of foods is accomplished in part by microorganisms, if you eat a food that has spoiled, you risk developing a food-borne illness. Fortunately, spoilage usually degrades the appearance, texture, and smell of food so much that we throw it away uneaten. Would you eat fish with a strong odour or a tomato that has turned to "mush"?

Modern science and technology have given us a wide array of techniques to produce, preserve, and transport food. But these advances have not eliminated the threat of food spoilage, which can occur at any point on the journey from farm to table. Any food that has been harvested and that people are not ready to eat must be preserved. Here, we look at some techniques that people have used for centuries to preserve food, as well as more modern techniques used in the food industry.

Traditional Methods Are Effective in Preserving Foods

Some methods of preserving foods have been used for thousands of years and employ naturally derived substances, such as salt, sugars, and smoke, or techniques such as drying and cooling.

- *Salting.* Salt preserves food by drawing the water out of the plant or animal cells by osmosis. This dehydrates the food, making it inhospitable to microbes. It also slows the action of enzymes that would otherwise degrade the food. Some meats are preserved with salt: a good example is Parma ham from Italy.
- *Sugaring.* Sugar has an osmotic effect similar to that of salt. However, foods preserved with sugar retain much of their shape, colour, and texture because some of the sugar is absorbed into the cells, replacing the water drawn out. The downside to using sugar is that fungi tend to flourish in sweet, acidic environments, such as jams.

Honey, a natural sweetener, is also an effective preserver. Thousands of years ago, long before the processing of white or cane sugar, honey was used to preserve meats and fruits (Shephard, 2000). Hams are often covered in honey to create an antibacterial coating to protect them during storage.

- *Drying.* Drying is an ancient method of preserving food that, like salting and sugaring, works by drawing water out of the food. Fish, poultry, beans, peas, and fruits are commonly preserved by drying. One drawback to drying is that it can change a food's colour, texture, and flavour and can decrease its vitamin content. A modern version, called *freeze-drying*, preserves colour, texture, and flavour: the food is first flash-frozen, so any water within it converts to fine ice crystals. These are evaporated in a vacuum and the product is immediately packaged. Freeze-dried foods have a shelf life of several years as long as the seal is not broken. Food manufacturers use freeze-drying for such products as coffee, tea, dried milk, gravy, and soup powders. This method is also used to make freeze-dried food products for camping and backpacking trips.

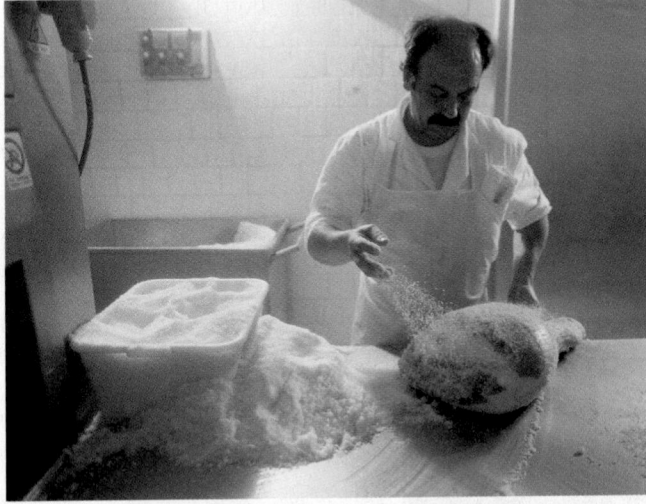

⬆ A worker salting a Parma ham.

- *Smoking.* Smoking has been used for centuries to preserve meats, poultry, and fish. Historically, if food did not dry well, it was hung near a campfire or chimney, so that the smoke of the fire permeated the food, further drying it. For short-term preservation, food can be *cold-smoked* at a temperature no higher than 29°C (85°F). The smoke will give a mild, smoky flavour to the food as it dries but will not actually cook the food. This method is good for meat or fish but will only preserve them for a limited time before they start to spoil. Cold-smoking is commonly used for foods that are eaten raw, such as beef fillets or smoked salmon.

  Hot-smoking uses temperatures above 55°C (130°F). It not only dries but also partially cooks the food. This process is used for such foods as venison, poultry, smoked trout, pork, lamb, and beef. Originally, heavy salting was used in conjunction with hot-smoking, but modern hot-smoked food uses much less salt.

◆ Before the modern refrigerator, an iceman delivered ice to homes and businesses.

The type of wood used to smoke foods contributes to the food's flavour. Birch, hickory, apple, juniper, mesquite, and willow are woods that have distinctive flavours. Smoked foods still need to be covered and stored in areas where air, heat, and insects cannot have easy access to them.

Unfortunately, smoking does not guarantee that a food is safe to eat. For example, *Listeria monocytogenes* is a type of bacterium that can survive in smoked fish (see Table 13.1).

- *Cooling.* As mentioned earlier, bacterial metabolism works best at temperatures at or above 15.5°C (60°F). As the temperature of a food is lowered, the bacteria's metabolism is slowed, and it becomes less able to reproduce or give off toxic by-products. So what did people use to cool and store foods before they had electric refrigerators?

For thousands of years, people have stored foods in underground cellars, caves, running streams, and even cold pantries—rooms of the house that were kept dark and unheated and often were stocked with ice. The use of icehouses to store food is discussed in records from second-century China. Thirteenth- and fourteenth-century Egyptian royalty were also storing food in icehouses, stocked with ice brought from the mountains of Lebanon (Shephard, 2000). The transport of freshly caught fish by using ice is also first attributed to the Chinese, and European merchants fascinated with the idea soon perfected the use of cold to design and build refrigerated vessels to transport all types of foods. Ice therefore became an important commodity. The forerunner of our refrigerator, the miniature icehouse, was developed in the early 1800s, and in cities and towns the local iceman would make rounds, delivering ice to homes.

Modern Techniques Improve Food Safety

To be successful, food producers have had to find ways to preserve the integrity of their products during the days, weeks, or months between harvesting and consumption. By the mid-twentieth century, technological advances in food preservation had given us canning, pasteurization, and preservative chemicals. However, in the past few decades, modern packaging techniques and irradiation have greatly expanded our food choices.

Industrial Canning

The French inventor Nicolas-François Appert first developed the canning process in the late 1700s, and modern techniques have contributed to the retention of flavour, texture, and nutrients in canned foods.

Producers of canned foods are required by law to ensure that all spores of *Clostridium botulinum* are eliminated from their goods. If the spores of this bacterium were to germinate inside a can of food, the food would soon become saturated with the deadly botulism toxin. The same process that destroys *C. botulinum* spores also kills other microorganisms that could contaminate the food. This process involves several steps:

◆ Canning food involves several steps to ensure that all microorganisms in the food are killed.

1. The food to be canned is sorted, and any spoiled food is removed.
2. The food is washed.
3. The food is blanched. Blanching involves the use of hot water or steam to parboil or scald the food, thereby stopping enzymatic processes and killing microorganisms on the food's surface. It can also be used to help remove skins from certain fruits and vegetables.
4. Cans are filled and heated, air is siphoned out, and they are sealed.
5. The sealed cans are heated to a very high temperature by steam under pressure and then cooled in a water bath.

The U.S. Army has found canned meats, vegetables, and jam in "excellent states of preservation" after 46 years. However, long storage of canned foods is not recommended. Canned food has an average shelf life of two years from the date of purchase. It is recommended that all canned food be stored in moderate temperatures (24°C or 75°F and below). When buying canned foods, look for cans that have no dents, cracks, or bulging lids or sides.

Pasteurization

Pasteurization was developed in 1864 by Louis Pasteur to destroy microorganisms that spoiled wine. The technique involves the quick use of heat to eliminate pathogens, typically in fluids—for example, 72°C (162°F) for 15 seconds pasteurizes milk. This barely alters the taste or quality of the product, making pasteurization particularly useful in the dairy and juice industries. Pasteurization does not eliminate all microbes but significantly decreases the numbers of heat-sensitive microorganisms, which tend to be the most harmful.

A newer technique called *flash pasteurization* uses higher temperatures and shorter times to destroy pathogens. It is commonly used with fruit juices, cider, and milk because it helps to maintain the nutrients and the flavour of the product. Beverages in tetra boxes or pouches have likely used flash pasteurization so that they can sit at room temperature on grocery shelves.

Louis Pasteur.

Innovations in Packaging Techniques

Many different packaging techniques have arisen over the past several decades:

- *Aseptic packaging* is probably most easily recognized as "juice boxes." Foods and beverages are first sterilized in a flash-heating and cooling process, then placed in a sterile container, which is formulated to provide a unique barrier against light and oxygen. Nutrient quality, as well as overall food quality, remain high as long as the package seals are not broken. The process uses less energy than traditional canning (Aseptic Packaging Council, 2005).
- *Modified atmosphere packaging* is a process in which the oxygen in a package of food is replaced with an inert gas, such as nitrogen or carbon dioxide. This slows the growth of bacteria that require oxygen, as well as the oxidation reactions that commonly spoil foods. The process can be used with a variety of foods, including meats, fish, vegetables, and fruits.
- *High-pressure processing* is a technique that subjects food to extremely high pressure. This inactivates most bacteria while retaining the food's quality and freshness.

Addition of Preservatives

Food preservatives are substances added to foods to prevent or slow spoilage. There are many natural and synthetically derived preservatives used in our food supply. One of the most commonly used natural preservatives is vitamin C. This powerful antioxidant helps protect foods from damage due to oxygen exposure. EDTA (ethylenediaminetetraacetic acid) is a commonly used synthetic preservative. It is used to trap trace amounts of metal impurities that can get into foods from containers and processing machinery.

Most processed foods contain preservatives, unless the package touts that it is "preservative free." All preservatives must be listed in the ingredients, but to recognize them, you need to know their chemical names. **Table 13.3** identifies some common preservatives and the types of foods in which they are typically found. A few of these are discussed in more detail here.

Aseptic packaging allows foods to be stored unrefrigerated for several months without spoilage.

Antioxidants In addition to certain vitamins, two antioxidants commonly used in foods are BHT (butylated hydroxytoluene) and BHA (butylated hydroxyanisole). They keep oils and fats in packaged foods from going rancid. BHT is frequently added to breakfast cereals to decrease spoilage. BHA is stable at high temperatures and is used in soup bases, ice cream, potato flakes, gelatine desserts, dry mixes for desserts, unsmoked dry sausage, and chewing gum.

Propyl gallate, another antioxidant, works synergistically with both BHA and BHT to enhance their effectiveness. Propyl gallate is used in mayonnaise, ice cream, potato flakes, gelatine desserts, fruits, baked goods, and chewing gum.

pasteurization A form of sterilization using high temperatures for short periods of time.

food preservatives Chemicals that help prevent microbial spoilage and enzymatic deterioration.

TABLE 13.3 Common Food Preservatives

Preservative	Foods Found In
Alpha-tocopheral (vitamin E)	Vegetable oils
Ascorbic acid (vitamin C)	Breakfast cereal, cured meat, fruit drinks
BHA	Breakfast cereal, chewing gum, oil, potato chips
BHT	Breakfast cereal, chewing gum, oil, potato chips
Calcium proprionate/sodium proprionate	Breads, cakes, pies, rolls
EDTA	Canned shellfish, margarine, mayonnaise, processed fruits and vegetables, salad dressings, sandwich spreads, soft drinks
Propyl gallate	Mayonnaise, chewing gum, chicken soup base, vegetable oil, meat products, potato sticks, mashed potato flakes, fruits, ice cream
Sodium benzoate	Carbonated drinks, fruit juice, pickles, preserves
Sodium chloride (salt)	Most processed foods
Sodium nitrate/sodium nitrite	Bacon, corned beef, ham, lunch meat, hot dogs, smoked fish
Sorbic acid/potassium sorbate	Cakes, cheese, dried fruit, jelly, syrup, wine
Sulphites (sodium bisulphite, sulphur dioxide)	Dried fruit, processed potatoes, wine

Mould Inhibitors   The bread you bought, left on the counter, and finally got around to eating a week later would have become mouldy if it had not been treated with mould inhibitors. *Propionic acid* occurs naturally in apples, strawberries, and tea and is used to prevent mould growth in baked goods and processed cheese. *Sodium propionate* and *calcium propionate* are salts synthesized from propionic acid and are used as mould inhibitors in a variety of foods.

Sulphites   Sodium bisulphite and sulphur dioxide are *sulphites*, sulphur-containing compounds used as preservatives, antioxidants, bleaching agents, and antibrowning agents. Sulphites also have antibacterial and antifungal properties. They are widely used in the beer and wine industry as well as in dehydrated foods, Maraschino cherries, and processed potatoes. Sulphites are not used in enriched grain products because of their capacity to bind with thiamine (vitamin B_1), making it unavailable for absorption.

Sulphur dioxide is used to control mould growth on fresh fruits and vegetables. For example, it has become standard commercial practice to fumigate stored grapes every 10 days with this chemical. Because of such procedures, it is important to remember to wash all fresh fruit and vegetables before eating.

All foods that contain added sulphites must be labelled to warn people who have adverse reactions or sensitivities to sulphites (Health Canada, 2009b).

Nitrates and Nitrites   The processed meat industry has long relied on *nitrates* and *nitrites* as antibacterial agents and colour enhancers. They give ham, hot dogs, and bologna their familiar pink colour. They also inhibit microbial growth and rancidity. However, nitrites can easily be converted to *nitrosamines* during the cooking process. The concentration of nitrates in cured meat products has been decreasing as a result of regulation for these food additives (Health Canada, 2009a).

Irradiation

Irradiation is an effective process for eliminating harmful bacteria often found in foods, such as *Trichinella spiralis* and *Salmonella* in meats and poultry, and inhibits spoilage by fungus. It involves the use of x-rays, beams of high-energy electrons produced by electron accelerators, or gamma rays from cobalt 60 or cesium 137. Most of this energy simply passes through the food, leaving no residue.

In contrast to the many foods authorized for irradiation in the United States, Canada has a limited selection of foods that can be irradiated. Although amendments have been proposed to add fresh and frozen ground beef, poultry, fish, mangoes, and dried shrimp, currently only onions, potatoes, wheat, flour, whole wheat flour, dehydrated seasonings, and whole or ground spices can be irradiated.

irradiation A sterilization process utilizing gamma rays or other forms of radiation, which does not impart any radiation to the food being treated.

Polluted Packaging?

In December 2009, *Consumer Reports* magazine published the results of a study that shocked food-safety experts nationwide. It had found a chemical called bisphenol A, or BPA, in nearly all of the canned foods it had tested, from soups to infant formula. BPA is an industrial chemical used to make a hard plastic called polycarbonate and to make epoxy resins. Polycarbonate is used in a number of household items, including baby bottles, reusable water bottles, pitchers, water carboys, tableware, and storage containers. Epoxy resins are used as a protective coating in metal-based food and beverage cans.

The epoxy resins serve an important safety function in the composition of the thin coating applied on the interior surface of the can. The coating prevents corrosion of the can and contamination of food and beverages with dissolved metals. It also plays an important role in preserving the quality and safety of the canned food.

Why the concern about BPA? Although the effects of this chemical on humans are unknown, it is a form of synthetic estrogen, a female reproductive hormone, and scientists have linked it to genital abnormalities and breast cancer in both males and females, prostate cancer, miscarriage, reduced sperm count, and even heart disease and diabetes.

In early 2008, Health Canada committed to addressing BPA levels in infant formula and other canned foods (Health Canada, 2008a). But the problem involves more than cans. BPA is in beverage containers (including baby bottles), plastic dinnerware, auto parts, toys, dental sealants, and other products. So it is no wonder that scientists at the CDC have found measurable levels of BPA in the urine of nearly all the people it has tested (CDC, 2010; FDA, 2010; Kristof, 2009).

What to do? Although you cannot control the level of BPA in canned foods you eat, you can control your use of plastics. Polycarbonate is a clear, hard plastic, which can be coloured. It typically has the number 7 in the centre of the recycling symbol, which is found on the bottom of the bottle (Government of Canada, 2010). The #7 recycling symbol on the bottom of these plastic containers stands for "other" plastics and is a catch-all description for plastics or combinations of plastics that are not covered by the recycling symbols #1 to #6. The #7 symbol does not always mean the bottle contains bisphenol A. For example, soft squeezable bottles used for ketchup and salad dressings are not made from polycarbonate and do not contain bisphenol A. You can only be sure a bottle is polycarbonate if it is made from a hard and clear plastic, and it has the letters "PC" shown near the recycling symbol. If the container does not have a recycling symbol, you should contact the manufacturer to ask if the product contains BPA. For an excellent set of Questions and Answers on BPA, see www.chemicalsubstanceschimiques.gc.ca/fact-fait/bisphenol-a_qa-qr-eng.php#q.

A product must display the international symbol for irradiated food, the radura, if it has been wholly irradiated, and any irradiated ingredient that makes up more than 10% of a product must be stated as irradiated on the list of ingredients **(Figure 13.11)**. Irradiation has been approved for use by 50 countries and endorsed by the World Health Organization (WHO), the Food and Agriculture Organization of the United Nations (FAO), and the International Atomic Energy Agency (IAEA).

▲ **Figure 13.11** Radura—the international symbol of irradiated food—is found on products that have been wholly irradiated.

RECAP Traditional food-preservation techniques include salting, sugaring, drying, and smoking, as well as storage in cellars and other cold areas. The canning process was developed in the late eighteenth century and pasteurization in the nineteenth century. Aseptic packaging, modified atmosphere packaging, and high-pressure processing are relatively new techniques that increase shelf life. Preservatives are often added to keep foods fresher longer. Irradiation typically involves the use of gamma rays to destroy microbes in foods.

What Are Food Additives, and Are They Safe?

Have you ever picked up a loaf of bread and started reading its ingredients? You would expect to see flour, yeast, water, and some sugar, but what are all those other items? And why does it feel as if you have to have a degree in chemistry to understand what they are? They are collectively called **food additives**, and they are in almost every processed food. Without additives, that loaf of bread would go stale within a day or two.

Although their use is regulated by health authorities, food additives have been a source of controversy for the past 50 years. Nevertheless, their use has steadily increased, allowing food producers to offer consumers a greater variety of foods at lower costs.

Additives Can Enhance a Food's Taste, Appearance, Safety, or Nutrition

It is estimated that more than 3000 different additives are currently used in North America. This section discusses some of the most common.

Many of the additives used by the food industry come from natural sources. Beet juice (a natural food colouring), salt, and citric acid are common, naturally derived food additives. Often, supply or cost prohibits using naturally derived additives. In such cases, additives are synthesized. For instance, vanillin, the main flavouring substance in vanilla beans, is synthesized at a cost considerably lower than the cost of extracting it from the natural beans. Even if the costs were comparable, it is doubtful that natural sources of vanillin could meet consumer demands.

Flavourings

Flavouring agents can be obtained from natural or synthetic sources. Essential oils, extracts, and spices supply most of the naturally derived flavourings.

Flavour enhancers are also widely used. These additives have little or no flavour of their own but accentuate the natural flavour of foods. They are often added when very little of a natural ingredient is used (CSPI, 2006). The most common flavour enhancers are maltol and MSG (monosodium glutamate). MSG is the sodium salt of glutamic acid, one of the non-essential amino acids, which also serves as a neurotransmitter. It is found in many processed foods; however, the glutamate portion of MSG can cross the blood–brain barrier and, in susceptible people, can cause symptoms such as headaches, difficulty breathing, and heart palpitations. A review of the research conducted in this area indicates that most individuals who report sensitivity to MSG do not show adverse reactions when they are fed MSG in controlled studies, particularly when MSG is given with food (Geha et al., 2000).

food additives Substances intentionally put into food to enhance appearance, palatability, and quality.

Colourings

Food colourings, derived from both natural and synthetic sources, are used extensively in processed foods. Natural colourings such as beet juice (which gives a red colour), beta-carotene (which gives a yellow colour), and caramel (which adds brown colour) are commonly used and do not need to be tested for safety. The colouring tartrazine (FD&C yellow #5) causes an allergic reaction in some people, and its use must be indicated on the product packaging. Sudan I is a red dye that has caused cancer in lab animals and is not allowed in Canada (CFIA, 2003).

Vitamins and Other Nutrients

Vitamin E is usually added to fat-based products to keep them from going rancid, and vitamin C is commonly added to foods such as

Many foods, such as ice cream, contain colourings.

frozen fruit, dry milk, apple juice, soft drinks, candy, and meat products containing sodium nitrates. Sodium ascorbate, a form of vitamin C with sodium added to produce a salt, is used as an antioxidant in foods such as concentrated milk products, cereals, and cured meats.

Iodine, calcium, vitamin D, and folate are examples of purely nutritive additives. Iodine is added to table salt to help decrease the incidence of goitre, a condition that causes the thyroid gland to enlarge. Calcium and vitamin D are added to foods to promote bone health. Folate is added to many breads and ready-to-eat cereals to decrease the incidence of neural tube defects during fetal development.

Additives That Improve Texture or Moisture Content

Certain chemicals are added to foods to improve their texture. **Texturizers**, such as calcium chloride, are added to foods to improve their texture. For instance, they are added to canned tomatoes and potatoes so they do not fall apart. **Stabilizers** are added to products to give them body and help them maintain a desired texture or colour. **Thickening agents** are used to absorb water and keep the complex mixtures of oils, water, acids, and solids in foods balanced (CSPI, 2012). Natural thickeners include pectin, alginate, and carrageenan. **Emulsifiers**, like thickening agents and stabilizers, help to keep fats evenly dispersed within foods. Texturizers, stabilizers, thickening agents, and emulsifiers have no known adverse effect on humans when used according to regulations.

Humectants and Desiccants

Moisture content is a critical component to food, and humectants and desiccants are added to maintain the correct moisture levels. **Humectants** keep such foods as marshmallows, chewing gum, and shredded coconut soft and stretchy. Common humectants are glycerine, sorbitol, and propylene glycol. Food-grade waxes used on produce also help maintain moisture content. The best way to remove wax from produce is to peel the outer layer off or scrub it with hot, soapy water and rinse well. **Desiccants** prevent moisture absorption from the air; for example, they are used to prevent table salt from forming clumps.

Bleaching Agents

Bleaching agents are used primarily in baked goods. Fresh ground flour is pale yellow, and when stored it slowly becomes white. Processors have added bleaching agents to flour to speed this process and decrease the possibility of spoilage or insect infestation. Benzoyl peroxide is commonly used to bleach flour, as well as blue and Gorgonzola cheeses.

Some Substances Get into Our Food Unintentionally

Trace amounts of substances (such as insects, fragments of packaging materials, pesticides, and hormones or antibiotics given to livestock) can get into our food during harvesting, processing, storage, or packaging. These are unintentional or incidental additions and do not have to be included on the label. This small amount of incidental substances present in food has not been shown to cause any problems with quality or safety.

Are Food Additives Considered Safe?

Although there is often controversy over food additives, they have been tested and approved for use in the food industry, and they are strictly regulated according to Canada's Food and Drugs Act. These additives have allowed our food supply to increase and diversify, providing consumers more variety at lower costs. Without additives, such as flavourings, strawberry ice cream would only be available for a short time and only in limited quantities during the early summer. If you are interested in reducing the amount of food additives in your diet, you should start by comparing food labels of different brands of the same foods. Some brands use fewer additives than others, and some brands are additive-free.

Mayonnaise contains emulsifiers to prevent the separation of fats.

texturizers Chemicals used to improve the texture of various foods.

stabilizers Chemicals used to help maintain smooth texture and uniform colour and flavour in some foods.

thickening agents Natural or chemically modified carbohydrates that absorb some of the water present in food, making the food thicker while keeping food components balanced.

emulsifiers Chemicals that improve texture and smoothness in foods; stabilise oil-water mixtures.

humectants Chemicals that help retain moisture in foods, keeping them soft and pliable.

desiccants Chemicals that prevent foods from absorbing moisture from the air.

bleaching agents Chemicals used to speed the natural process of ground flour changing from pale yellow to white.

RECAP Food additives are chemicals intentionally added to foods to enhance their colour, flavour, texture, nutrient density, moisture level, or shelf life. Although there is continuing controversy over food additives, they are considered safe based on testing and use in the food industry or as a result of consensus among experts qualified by scientific training and experience.

How Is Genetic Modification Used in Food Production?

⬥ Corn is one of the most widely cultivated genetically modified crops.

genetic modification The process of changing an organism by manipulating its genetic material.

recombinant DNA technology A type of genetic modification in which scientists combine DNA from different sources to produce a transgenic organism that expresses a desired trait.

In **genetic modification**, also referred to as *genetic engineering*, the genetic material, or DNA, of an organism is altered to bring about specific changes in its seeds or offspring. Selective breeding is one example of genetic modification; for instance, Brahman cattle that have poor-quality meat but high resistance to heat and humidity are bred with English shorthorn cattle that have good meat but low resistance to heat and humidity. The outcome of this selective breeding process is Santa Gertrudis cattle, which have the desired characteristics of higher-quality meat and resistance to heat and humidity. Although selective breeding is effective and has helped increase crop yields and improve the quality and quantity of our food supply, it is a relatively slow and imprecise process, as a great deal of trial and error typically occurs before the desired characteristics are achieved.

Recently, advances in biotechnology have moved genetic modification beyond selective breeding. These advances include the manipulation of the DNA of living cells of one organism to produce the desired characteristics of a different organism. Called **recombinant DNA technology**, the process commonly begins when scientists isolate from the cell of an animal, a plant, or a microbe a particular segment of DNA that codes for a protein conferring a desirable trait, such as salt tolerance in tomato plants. Scientists extract and copy the DNA, then identify, isolate, and cultivate the precise genes that code for the desired functions. The next step is to splice the genes into strands of DNA in a "host cell," usually a microorganism. The cell is cultured to produce many copies—a *gene library*—of the beneficial gene. Now many scientists can readily obtain these genes to modify other organisms that lack the desired trait—for example, traditional tomato plants. The modified DNA causes the plant's cells to build the protein of interest, and the plant expresses the desired trait (**Figure 13.12**). Not only plants but also animals and even microorganisms (including bacteria and

▶ **Figure 13.12** Recombinant DNA technology involves producing plants and other organisms that contain modified DNA that enables them to express desirable traits that are not present in the original organism.

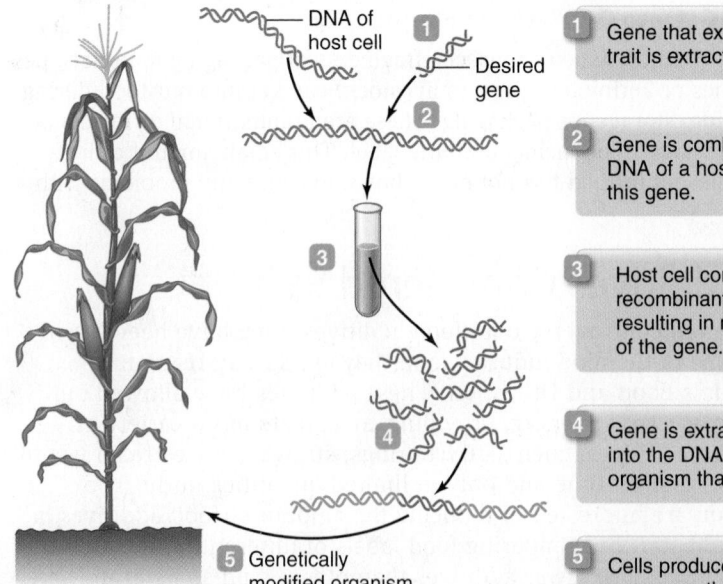

DNA of host cell — ① — Desired gene — ②

③

④

⑤ Genetically modified organism

① Gene that expresses a desired trait is extracted from cell.

② Gene is combined with the DNA of a host cell that lacks this gene.

③ Host cell containing recombinant DNA is cultured, resulting in many copies of the gene.

④ Gene is extracted and inserted into the DNA of cells of an organism that lacks this gene.

⑤ Cells produce an organism that expresses the desired trait.

fungi) can be genetically engineered. The term *genetically modified organism* (*GMO*) refers to any organism in which the DNA has been altered using recombinant DNA technology.

In agriculture, the initial objective for developing GMOs was to improve crop protection (WHO, 2010). A common protective measure is to induce resistance to herbicides and pesticides. For example, genetically modified soybean, corn, and cotton crops can be sprayed with chemicals that kill weeds without harming the plants. Genetic modification can also increase resistance to insects or viruses that cause disease in plants. Scientists can also insert genes to protect crops from environmental conditions, such as drought or soils high in salt. Another use is to increase the nutritional value of a crop. For instance, researchers have modified soybeans and canola to increase their content of monounsaturated fatty acids.

Since 1994, hundreds of plants and animals have been genetically modified and incorporated into our current food market. In the United States, soy, corn, canola, and cotton crops make up the majority of the genetically modified crop acreage. In Canada, genetically modified corn, wheat, potatoes, soybeans, tomatoes, are all approved for cultivation (Health Canada, 2011). However, the commercial success of GM foods is not guaranteed: in 1994, the FlavrSavr tomato became the first commercially sold GMO. Developing this tomato involved identifying the gene that codes for an enzyme called polygalacturonase, which causes ripening in the tomato. This gene was removed and inserted back in reverse orientation. As a result, polygalacturonase was not synthesized, and ripening slowed dramatically—making the tomato appear "fresh" longer and enabling it to maintain a longer shelf life (McHughen, 2000). Unfortunately, consumers felt the FlavrSavr tomato had poor flavour, and it was taken off the market in 1997.

The relative benefits and harm of genetic modification have been debated worldwide. For instance, some environmentalists have raised the concern that seeds from genetically modified crops disrupt other crops through cross-pollination, even those many miles from where the altered ones are growing. Another concern is the long-term effect of genetically modified crops on the plants, insects, and animals that consume them or use them for their habitat. For more information about the debate surrounding genetic modification, see the Nutrition Debate on page 478.

RECAP In genetic modification, the genetic material, or DNA, of an organism is altered to enhance certain qualities. In agriculture, genetic modification is often used to improve crop protection or to increase nutrients in the resulting food. Genetic modification is also used in animals and microorganisms.

Do Residues Harm Our Food Supply?

Food **residues** are chemicals that remain in foods despite cleaning and processing. Three types of residues of global concern are persistent organic pollutants, pesticides, and hormones and antibiotics used in animals.

Persistent Organic Pollutants Can Cause Illness

Many different organic chemicals are released into the atmosphere as a result of industry, agriculture, automobile emissions, and improper waste disposal. These chemicals, collectively referred to as **persistent organic pollutants (POPs)**, eventually enter the food supply through the soil or water. If a pollutant gets into the soil, a plant can absorb the chemical into its structure and pass it on as part of the food chain. Fish and land animals can also absorb the pollutants into their tissues or consume them when feeding on plants in the polluted water or soil. Fat-soluble pollutants are especially problematic, as they tend to accumulate in the animal's body tissues and are then absorbed by humans when the animal is used as a food source. *Bioaccumulation*, the process by which increasing concentrations of pollutants are seen in species higher up the food chain, is illustrated in **Figure 13.13**.

residues Chemicals that remain in foods despite cleaning and processing.

persistent organic pollutants (POPs) Chemicals released into the environment as a result of industry, agriculture, or improper waste disposal; automobile emissions also are considered POPs.

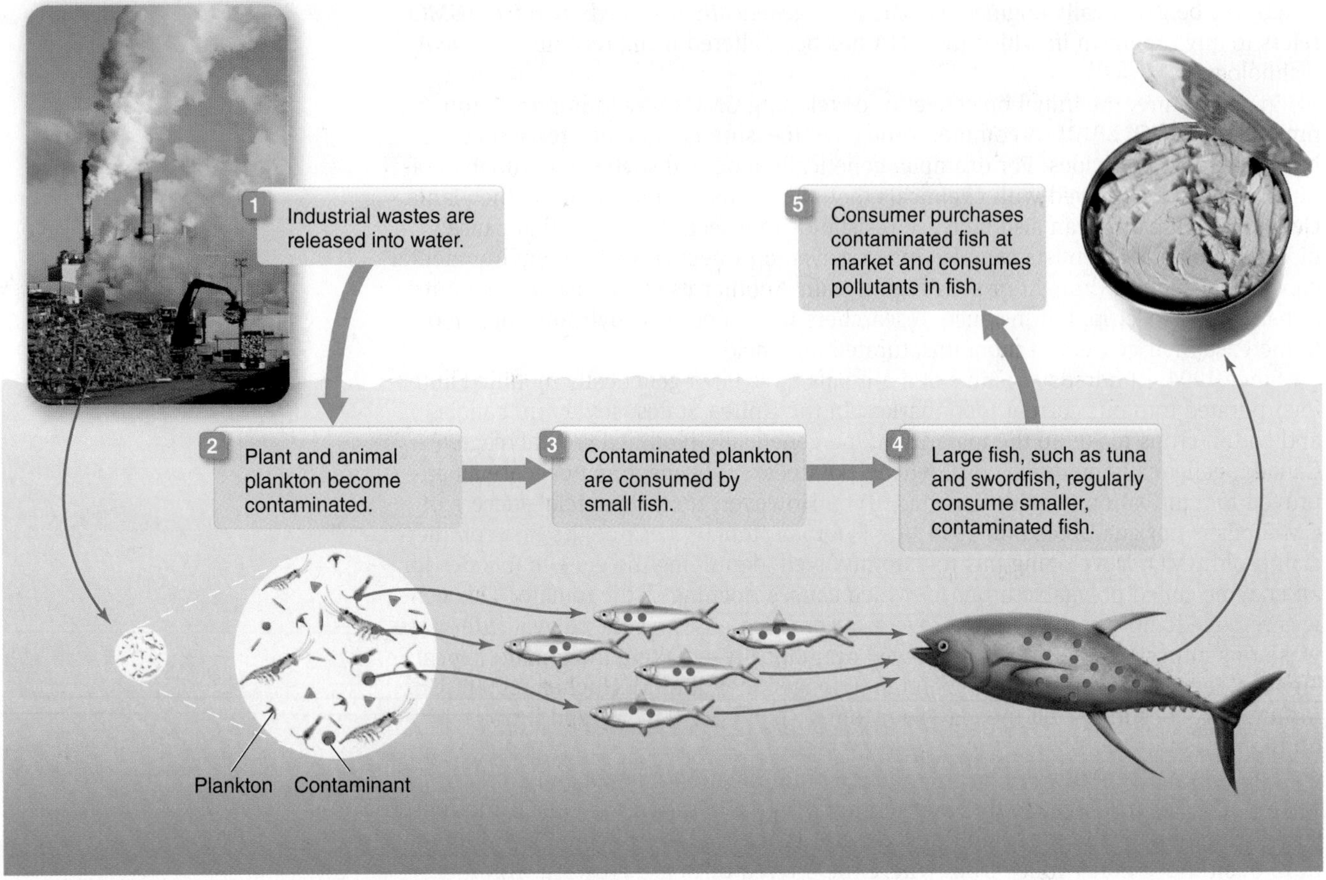

1 Industrial wastes are released into water.

5 Consumer purchases contaminated fish at market and consumes pollutants in fish.

2 Plant and animal plankton become contaminated.

3 Contaminated plankton are consumed by small fish.

4 Large fish, such as tuna and swordfish, regularly consume smaller, contaminated fish.

Plankton   Contaminant

Figure 13.13 Bioaccumulation of persistent organic pollutants in the food supply.

POP residues have been found in virtually all categories of foods, including baked goods, fruits, vegetables, meat, poultry, and dairy products. The chemicals can travel long distances in trade winds and water currents, moving from tropical and temperate regions to concentrate in the northern latitudes. It is believed that all living organisms on Earth carry a measurable level of POPs in their tissues (Schafer and Kegley, 2002).

Mercury and Lead Are Nerve Toxins

Mercury, a naturally occurring element, is found in soil and rocks, lakes, streams, and oceans. It is also released into the environment by pulp and paper processing and the burning of garbage and fossil fuels. As mercury is released into the environment, it falls from the air, eventually finding its way to streams, lakes, and the ocean, where it accumulates. Fish absorb mercury as they feed on aquatic organisms. This mercury is passed on to humans when they consume the fish. As mercury accumulates in the body, it has a toxic effect on the nervous system.

Predatory fish tend to accumulate higher levels of methyl mercury and therefore should be eaten less often by young children and women who are or may become pregnant or are breastfeeding. These fish species include fresh and frozen tuna, shark, swordfish, marlin, orange roughy, and escolar (sometimes called snake mackerel or oilfish). See Chapter 5 for the specific amounts recommended. Anchovy, capelin, char, hake, herring, Atlantic mackerel, mullet, pollock, salmon, smelt, rainbow trout, lake whitefish, shrimp, clam, mussel, oysters, and canned light tuna are safe to consume (Health Canada, 2008b). Freshwater fish caught in local lakes and rivers have variable levels of mercury; thus, provincial and territorial governments routinely monitor mercury levels.

One of the ways mercury is released into the environment is by burning fossil fuels.

Lead, another naturally occurring element, can be found in the soil, the water, and even the air. It also occurs as industrial waste from leaded gasolines, lead-based paints, and lead-soldered cans, now outlawed but decomposing in landfills. Some ceramic mugs and other dishes are fired with lead-based glaze. Thus, residues can build up in foods. Excessive lead exposure can cause learning and behavioural impediments in children and cardiovascular and kidney disease in adults. It is impossible to avoid lead residues completely, but because of its health implications, everyone should try to limit his or her exposure.

Industrial Pollutants also Create Residues   Polychlorinated biphenyls (PCBs) and dioxins are two industrial pollutants that have been found in food worldwide. Dioxins (by-products of waste incineration) and PCBs (from discarded transformers) enter the soil and can persist in the environment for years, easily accumulating in fatty tissues. PCBs and dioxins, along with other POPs, have been linked to cancer, learning disorders, impaired immune function, and infertility (Schafer and Kegley, 2002). Dioxin levels have been declining quite steadily in the environment over the last 30 years as a result of increased regulation, especially over the burning of municipal and medical wastes (Health Canada, 2005). For most Canadians, about 90% of our exposure to dioxins comes from our diets.

⬆ Antique porcelain is often coated with lead-based glaze.

Pesticides Protect Against Crop Losses

Pesticides are a family of chemicals used in both the field and storage areas to help protect crops from weeds, insects, fungi, and other organisms, including birds and mammals. Rodents, for example, in addition to consuming food, also contaminate large quantities of food with their excreta. Pesticides also help reduce the number of microorganisms on crops and increase overall crop yield and crop diversity. The three most common types of pesticides used in food production are insecticides, herbicides, and fungicides. Insecticides are used to control insects that can infest crops; herbicides are used to control weeds and other unwanted plant growth; and fungicides are used to control plant-destroying fungal growth.

Pesticides Can Be Natural or Synthetic

Many pesticides used today are **biopesticides**, species-specific chemicals or microorganisms that work to suppress a pest's population, not eliminate it. Biopesticides do not leave residues on crops—most degrade rapidly and are easily washed away with water. Synthetic pheromones are a type of chemical biopesticide. In nature, insects use pheromones, chemicals that act as signals, to attract mates. Synthetic pheromones are used to disrupt insect mating by attracting males into traps. Microbial biopesticides are derived from naturally occurring or genetically altered bacteria, viruses, or fungi. One genetically engineered microbial biopesticide is *Bacillus thuringiensis,* or *Bt.* This is a common soil bacterium that is genetically altered to be toxic to several species of insects.

Aside from biopesticides, many natural products, such as salt, boric acid, dried blood, crushed egg shells, and diatomaceous earth (soil made up of a type of algae called *diatoms*), are used as pesticides. Ladybugs are bred and sold commercially to reduce aphids, and marigolds, mint, sage, garlic, chives, onion, and other strong-smelling plants can be placed among crops to deter slugs and insect pests.

Many synthetic pesticides are made from petroleum-based products. Examples of commonly used synthetic pesticides are thiabendazole (a fungicide used on potatoes) and fungicides commonly used to prevent apple diseases (such as dithane, manzate, and polyram).

Synthetic Pesticides Are Potential Toxins

Years of studies show that synthetic pesticides can remain on food and pose a risk to human health. The liver is responsible for detoxifying chemicals that enter the body; however, if diseases (such as cancer or AIDS) or toxins (such as alcohol) already

pesticides Chemicals used either in the field or in storage to destroy plant, fungal, and animal pests.

biopesticides Chemicals—primarily insecticides—that are derived naturally to kill insects and reduce crop damage.

stress the liver, it may be unable to effectively remove pesticide residues. When pesticide residues are not effectively removed, they can build up and damage body tissues. The health effects depend on the type of pesticide. Some affect the nervous system, others the endocrine system; still others are potential carcinogens (EPA, 2005a). These effects depend on how toxic the pesticide is and how much of it is consumed (EPA, 2005b).

Children may be especially sensitive to pesticides for several reasons. First, their internal organs are still developing and maturing (EPA, 2005c). Second, they consume more food and water per unit of body weight than adults, possibly increasing their exposure. If a child's excretory system is not fully developed, the child may have a limited ability to remove pesticide residues. Also, pesticides may harm a developing fetus or child by blocking the absorption of important food nutrients necessary for normal healthy growth. Because of the potential risks from pesticides to a developing child, pregnant and breastfeeding women should peel fruit and vegetable rinds to decrease their exposure to residues. This is also a sensible precaution when preparing fruits or vegetables for small children.

To protect people from any possible harm arising from pesticide residues, Maximum Residue Limits (MRLs) have been set for each pesticide–crop combination. The Canadian Food Inspection Agency monitors all commercially available fruits and vegetables for pesticide residues and issues recalls of products that may not be safe. Special consideration is given to products like fruit juice that children may consume in higher than average amounts. No groups of the population are exposed to residues in food at levels that threaten their health.

Government Regulations Control the Use of Pesticides

Through the Pest Control Products Act, Health Canada's Pest Management Regulatory Agency is the government agency responsible for the registration of pesticides and assessment of the human health and safety aspects and environmental impacts of pesticides in Canada. Regulations concerning the transportation, sale, storage, use, and disposal of pesticides are at the provincial or territorial levels. Bylaws for the use of pesticides in residential and commercial areas are put in place and enforced at the municipal level.

What Are Organic Foods?

Organic food is produced by farmers who emphasize the use of renewable resources and the conservation of soil and water to protect the environment for future generations. Organic meat, poultry, eggs, and dairy products come from animals that are given no antibiotics or growth hormones and that are treated humanely. Organic food is produced without using most conventional pesticides, fertilizers made with synthetic ingredients or sewage sludge, bioengineering, or ionizing radiation (Canadian General Standards Board, 2006).

The General Principles and Management Standards set out by the Canadian General Standards Board Canadian General Standards Board, 2006 for organic production state the following principles:

1. Protect the environment, minimize soil degradation and erosion, decrease pollution, optimize biological productivity, and promote a sound state of health.
2. Maintain long-term soil fertility by optimizing conditions for biological activity within the soil.
3. Maintain biological diversity within the system.
4. Recycle materials and resources to the greatest extent possible within the enterprise.
5. Provide attentive care that promotes the health and meets the behavioural needs of livestock.
6. Prepare organic products, emphasizing careful processing and handling methods in order to maintain the organic integrity and vital qualities of the products at all stages of production.
7. Rely on renewable resources in locally organized agricultural systems.

How Are Organic Foods in Canada Regulated?

In the 1990s, when organic foods first began appearing in major grocery chains, the organic food industry was small and there was no pressing reason for it to be regulated by government. Now there are an estimated 3900 producers working on 695 000 hectares of land who produce certified organic products in Canada (Agriculture and Agri-Food Canada, 2011). Approximately 1.7% of all farms in Canada are certified organic farms, and organic livestock is one of the fastest growing sectors. Canada exports organic products, mostly grains, worth an estimated $2 billion annually, with the largest amounts sold to the United States, the European Union, and Japan (Agriculture and Agri-Food Canada, 2011). CODEX organic standards regulate international trade, and Canada complies with these standards.

In Canada, the Organic Products Regulations were put in place in 2009. These regulations are intended for all organic agricultural products, whether they are imported, exported, or traded among provinces and territories. Labels are allowed to carry the terms *organic, organically produced, organically grown,* and *organically raised* if 95% of the ingredients in the product are organic. If the product contains 70% to 95% organic ingredients, the label may specify the percentage of organic material—for example, "contains 75% Organic"—and must state which ingredients are organic in the ingredient list.

Studies Comparing Organic and Conventionally Grown Foods Are Limited

Over the past decade, several promising studies at the University of California, Davis, and other institutions indicated that some organically grown fruits and vegetables are higher in vitamins E and C and in certain antioxidant phytochemicals than their non-organic counterparts (Asami et al., 2003; Carbonaro et al., 2002; Grinder-Pedersen et al., 2003). However, a 2009 systematic review of 162 studies published from 1958 through 2008 found no nutritional superiority of organically produced foods over foods conventionally produced. The study's lead author concluded that there is currently no evidence to support the selection of organic foods for nutritional superiority (Dangour et al., 2009). What is more, an organic seal does not guarantee food safety: the peanut company responsible for the *Salmonella* outbreak described at the beginning of this chapter had federal organic certification (Severson and Martin, 2009). Still, as discussed earlier in the chapter, you might decide to choose organic produce if you are concerned about reducing your exposure to pesticides.

RECAP Pesticides are used to protect our food from damage by weeds, bacteria, fungi, and other organisms, including birds and mammals. Biopesticides are species-specific and less toxic to humans and to the environment. Organic food is produced without using most conventional pesticides, fertilizers made with synthetic ingredients or sewage sludge, bioengineering, or ionizing radiation.

Nutrition DEBATE

Genetically Modified Organisms: A Blessing or a Curse?

As we noted earlier in this chapter, genetic modification is a process in which entirely new (*transgenic*) organisms are created by splicing genes from one species into another. Supporters of this process envision an ever-expanding role for genetic modification in food production. The following are a few of the potential benefits seen as resulting from the application of this technology:

- Enhanced taste and nutritional quality of food
- Crops that grow faster, have higher yields, and can be grown in inhospitable soils with increased resistance
- Increased production of high-quality meat, eggs, and milk
- Improved animal health
- Environmentally responsible outcomes—such as the use of less harmful herbicides and insecticides; the conservation of soil, water, and energy; and more efficient food processing

Despite these potential benefits, there has been significant opposition to genetic engineering including the following:

- Gene transfer from GM foods to cells of the body or to bacteria in the gastrointestinal tract (WHO, 2010).
- Unintentional crossing of genes through cross-pollination. This can result in undesirable plants—such as "superweeds" that can tolerate conventional herbicides—or in foods tainted with non-food-grade ingredients. The risks of such unintended gene crossing (called "outcrossing") were revealed when traces of a type of maize (corn) that was approved for use only in animal feed appeared in maize products for human consumption in the United States (WHO, 2010).

- Loss of biodiversity of plants and animals.
- Development of new diseases that can attack plants, animals, and humans.
- Production of bacteria that are resistant to all antibiotics.
- Potential for only a few food companies and countries to control the majority of world food production, such as in the seed industry (Neuman, 2010).
- Creation of biological weapons and increased risk of bioterrorism.

Some people who oppose genetic engineering believe it is unnatural and unethical to alter the genes of any organism. Most opponents base their concerns on the fact that potential long-term risks and dangers are still unknown and may far outweigh the potential short-term benefits.

GMOs are welcomed in some countries but outlawed in others. Six countries grow almost 100% of the world's genetically modified crops: the United States (59%), Argentina (20%), Canada (6%), Brazil (6%), China (5%), and Paraguay (2%) (James, 2004). Although the United

States and Canada are among the top three, regions within these countries have succeeded in banning the production of GMOs, including Prince Edward Island and several counties in California.

The European Union (EU) has strict regulations regarding GMOs, including mechanisms for tracking GMO products through production and distribution chains and monitoring of the environmental effects of GMOs. All foods produced for human consumption and all animal feed products that contain GMOs must be clearly labelled. Companies desiring to market GMOs and genetically modified foods in the EU must include a full environmental risk assessment and a safety assessment in their application.

What do you think about the cultivation and distribution of genetically modified foods? Do you have any reservations about buying and consuming genetically modified foods? Because GMOs and modified foods have been available for only a few years, it will take more time to fully understand their impact.

Many people oppose the genetic engineering of foods for environmental, health, or economic reasons.

Chapter Review

Test Yourself ANSWERS

1. False. Freezing inhibits the ability of most microscopic organisms to reproduce, but when the food is thawed, reproduction can resume.

2. False. Some ground hamburger meat will still look slightly pink even when thoroughly cooked. It is important to use a meat thermometer to check doneness, even with hamburger patties.

3. False. Bacteria cause the vast majority of cases of food-borne illness.

Find the Quack

You visit your cousin Lori, who has three school-age children. You take out a pack of chewing gum and offer a piece to each of the kids. "No way!" Lori says. "You need to check with me before offering food to the kids. Most foods sold in North America are full of harmful additives, including chewing gum!" Lori takes out a leaflet advertising a new book on food additives. It's called *Stealth Ingredients: The Dangerous Additives in Your Food*. You read the front of the leaflet. It states:

- "Additives in your food destroy your health and may even cause cancer!"
- "Many of the most harmful ingredients in packaged foods are not listed on the label."
- "Powerful food manufacturers' lobbies influence government to pass laws allowing food companies to add cancer-causing ingredients to your food."
- "Health authorities do not protect you against dangerous ingredients in your food."

The leaflet then offers a solution: a new book identifying and describing every ingredient added to foods. It suggests purchasing the book and taking it to the grocery store, so that you can check the ingredients panels of foods to make sure the foods you buy are safe.

The leaflet closes with three testimonials from individuals who state that, prior to reading the book, they were very ill and now that they avoid all harmful food additives their health has returned.

"See what I mean?" Lori asks you. "I bet you wish you knew what was *really* in that chewing gum!"

1. Evaluate the leaflet's statement "Additives in your food destroy your health and may even cause cancer."

2. Comment on the statement that health authorities "do not protect you against dangerous ingredients in your food."

3. Look again at the leaflet's argument "Many of the most harmful ingredients in packaged foods are not listed on the label." Identify the flaw in the argument that purchasing the book will protect you.

4. Discuss the value of the three testimonials at the end of the leaflet.

Answers can be found in the study area of MasteringNutrition.

Review Questions

1. The factors that promote bacterial growth can be summarized as
   a. food, acid, oxygen, heat, and light.
   b. food, acid, time, temperature, moisture, and light.
   c. food, acid, time, moisture, heat, and cold.
   d. food, acid, time, temperature, oxygen, and moisture.

2. Yeasts are a type of
   a. mould used to make bread rise.
   b. bacteria that can cause food intoxication.
   c. fungus used to ferment foods.
   d. mould inhibitor used as a food preservative.

3. Monosodium glutamate (MSG) is
   a. a thickening agent used in baby foods.
   b. a flavour enhancer used in a variety of foods.
   c. a mould inhibitor used on grapes and other foods.
   d. an amino acid added as a nutrient to some foods.

4. You should store uncooked meat, poultry, and seafood in the refrigerator and use it within
   a. 24 hours.
   b. 48 hours.
   c. three days.
   d. a week.

5. Beginning with the most ancient method, what is the correct chronological order for the following techniques for food preservation?
   a. Freezing, drying, pasteurization, aseptic packaging
   b. Freeze-drying, smoking, irradiation, pasteurization
   c. Freezing, pasteurization, canning, aseptic packaging
   d. Cooling, canning, pasteurization, irradiation

6. Hemolytic uremic syndrome (HUS) is a complication of
   a. *E. coli* O157:H7 poisoning.
   b. salmonellosis.
   c. *Clostridium botulinum* poisoning.
   d. avian influenza.

7. Which one of the following microbes secretes a toxin that causes food intoxication?
   a. *Campylobacter jejuni*
   b. *E. coli* O157:H7
   c. *Clostridium botulinum*
   d. Hepatitis A

8. Steven and Dante go to a convenience store after a tennis match looking for something to quench their thirst. Steven chooses a national brand of orange juice, and Dante chooses a bottle of locally produced, organic, unpasteurized apple juice. Steven points out to Dante that his juice is not pasteurized, but he shrugs and says, "I'm more afraid of the pesticides they used on the oranges in your juice than I am about microorganisms in mine!" Which juice would *you* choose, and why?

9. Pickling is a food-preservation technique that involves soaking such foods as cucumbers in a solution containing vinegar (acetic acid). Why would pickling be effective in preventing food spoilage?

10. In the 1950s and 1960s in Minamata, Japan, more than 100 cases of a similar illness were recorded: patients, many of whom were infants or young children, suffered irreversible damage to the nervous system. A total of 46 people died. Adults with the disease and mothers of afflicted young children had one thing in common: they had frequently eaten fish caught in Minamata Bay. What do you think might have been the cause of this disease? Using key words from this description, research the event on the internet and identify the culprit(s).

11. Your sister Joy, who attends a culinary arts school, is visiting you for dinner. You want to impress her, so you've decided to make chicken marsala. You begin that afternoon by removing two chicken breasts from the freezer and putting them in a bowl in the refrigerator to thaw. Then you go shopping for fresh salad ingredients. When you get home from the market, you wash your hands in cold water, then take the chicken breasts from the refrigerator and wash them thoroughly. You set them aside on a clean cutting board. You then take the lettuce, red pepper, and scallions you just bought, put them in a colander, and rinse them. Next, you slice them with a clean knife on your marble counter top and toss them together in a salad. You put the chicken breasts in a frying pan and cook them until they lose their pink colour. In a separate pan, you prepare the sauce, using a new carton of cream and the marsala. Finally, using a clean knife, you slice some freshly baked bread on the countertop. You then wash the knives and the cutting board you used for the chicken. Joy arrives and admires your skill in cooking. Later that night, you both wake up vomiting. Identify *at least two* aspects of your food preparation that might have contributed to your illness.

12. A couple of hours after a family potluck picnic where Vakeesh ate some turkey casserole and potato salad and drank a soft drink, he starts to feel terribly sick. He spends the whole evening in the bathroom and can barely move without feeling ill. The next morning he feels a bit better, but is still very weak and exhausted. When he calls his relatives to find out if anybody else got sick, he is surprised to hear that nobody else fell ill—but he is still convinced that it was a dish at the picnic that made him sick. Do you think that the illness was food-borne? If so, what food(s) do you most suspect? What precautions might you advise Vakeesh to take in the future to prevent food-borne illness?

13. Louis's family owns a farm in Saskatchewan that has been passed from generation to generation since his family immigrated to Canada. Louis is refusing to take it over, however, because he feels very strongly that pesticides are ruining the environment and poisoning people. Louis's father argues that pesticides are necessary to prevent disease-causing microorganisms, but Louis will not agree. Who do you think is correct in this case: Louis, who says pesticides are dangerous, or his father, who argues that they prevent disease? How do you think this situation could be resolved?

Answers to Review Questions can be found at the back of this text.

Web Resources

www.phac-aspc.gc.ca/id-mi/index-eng.php
Public Health Agency of Canada—Infectious Diseases

This website provides information on infectious diseases—everything from avian flu, cholera, and *E. coli* to SARS, *Salmonella*, and West Nile virus.

www.canfightbac.org
The Canadian Partnership for Consumer Food Safety Education

This is a national association of public and private organizations dedicated to helping consumers understand the importance of safe food handling practices at home. Click on "Food

Safety Tips" for practical information and tips on keeping food safe to eat.

www.kidney.ca
The Kidney Foundation of Canada

A great site for anyone interested in learning more about hemolytic uremic syndrome (HUS), other kidney diseases, and research in progress.

www.foodsafety.gov
Foodsafety.gov

Use this website as a gateway to government food-safety information; it contains news and safety alerts, an area to report illnesses and product complaints, information on food-borne pathogens, and much more.

www.cspinet.org/foodsafety/index.html
Center for Science in the Public Interest: Food Safety

Visit this website for summaries of food additives and their safety, alerts and other information, and interactive quizzes.

www.inspection.gc.ca
Canadian Food Inspection Agency

This site contains information about food-safety standards in Canada.

www.cdc.gov/travel/foodwater
Centers for Disease Control and Prevention

Before your next trip, check out this webpage for information on food safety when travelling.

www.fsis.usda.gov
The USDA Food Safety and Inspection Service

This site provides information on all aspects of food safety. Click on "Fact Sheets" for links to additional information.

http://www.hc-sc.gc.ca/hl-vs/iyh-vsv/prod/micro-f-a-eng .php
Health Canada: Microwave Ovens and Food Safety

This fact sheet provides information on the safe cooking and reheating of foods in a microwave oven.

www.healthfinder.gov/orgs/HR2504.htm
healthfinder.gov: FDA Center for Food Safety and Applied Nutrition

This site contains thorough information on topics such as national food-safety programs, recent news, and food labelling.

www.extension.iastate.edu/foodsafety
Food Safety Project

The Food Safety Project compiles educational materials about food safety for consumer use. Provided on the site are links for food safety from farm to table.

www.epa.gov/pesticides
The U.S. Environmental Protection Agency: Pesticides

This site provides information about agricultural and home-use pesticides, pesticide health and safety issues, environmental effects, and government regulation.

www.organicagcentre.ca
Organic Agriculture Centre of Canada

This partnership of federal and provincial governments, industry groups, commodity boards, and universities calls itself "Canada's national website for organic research and education." You can look at student job postings, take a virtual tour of a farm, and see consumer resources on a variety of topics.

www.ams.usda.gov
The USDA Agricultural Marketing Service

Click on "National Organic Program" to find the website describing the NOP's standards and labelling program, consumer information, and publications.

www.slowfoodusa.org
Slow Food USA

The Slow Food movement sponsors training and activities to promote a good, clean, and fair food system. Check out Slow Food on Campus, its network of chapters at colleges and universities throughout the United States.

MasteringNutrition®

Study Area
Practice Tests • Diet Analysis • eText

Global Nutrition

WANT TO FIND OUT...

- **how many people worldwide are under-nourished?**

- **why so many people are starving in a world with surplus food?**

- **what you can do to combat malnutrition?**

READ ON. In Malawi, a small land-locked country in southern Africa, a widowed mother of three risks death to pull the stems of water lilies from crocodile-infested waters. They are bitter and give her children diarrhea, but they are the only food she can find. She is not alone: in many African nations, mismanagement, corruption, drought, lack of irrigation, and disease—especially infection with HIV—combine to cause recurring cycles of hunger for millions of people. And hunger contributes to early death: in Malawi, one in ten mothers dies in childbirth, and nearly one in five children dies before reaching age five (Associated Press, 2005).

The Food and Agriculture Organization of the United Nations (FAO) estimates that, in 2009, more than 1 billion of the world's people—nearly one in six—were undernourished (FAO, 2009). Why is this so? Does malnutrition occur only in developing nations? And is there anything you can do to help? We explore these questions *In Depth* here.

Malnutrition in the Developing World

Malnutrition is a fiend with two faces. In developing nations, it typically appears in the form of undernutrition—people simply do not have enough to eat. Undernutrition results in **wasting**, a condition of very low body weight for height. Children who are chronically undernourished also suffer from **stunting**; that is, they are shorter than expected for their age. People who are undernourished

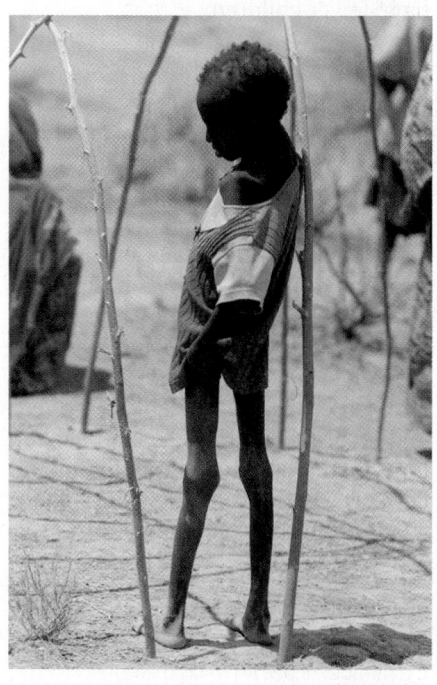

⬆ Wasting (extreme thinness) and stunting (short stature for age) are commonly seen in undernourished children.

are also highly susceptible to infectious diseases, such as pneumonia, infectious diarrhea, measles, and HIV. Worldwide, undernutrition is estimated to contribute to more than one-third of the 10 million childhood deaths each year—more than 1000 every hour—largely because of this decreased resistance to infection (WHO, 2010).

For about the past 20 years, all over the world, another form of malnutrition has been emerging: overnutrition, or the consumption of more energy than the body expends. Overnutrition causes overweight and obesity and threatens its victims with chronic diseases, such as heart disease and diabetes. It is increasingly seen not only in developed areas, such as North America and Western Europe, but also in nations transitioning from the poorest to the middle range of median income, including Brazil, India, and China. It is also emerging in many developing nations, sometimes in the very same communities where others are starving.

Despite the increasing prevalence of overnutrition and its accompanying chronic diseases, the greater threat to developing nations remains undernutrition—both nutrient deficiencies and true hunger. So we begin our discussion there.

What Causes Undernutrition in the Developing World?

Undernutrition exists in every nation of the world; however, it is most severe in sub-Saharan Africa and Southeast Asia, in developing countries ranging from Ethiopia to Uzbekistan (**Figure 1**). In wealthy nations it is usually caused by unequal distribution of abundant food to people who are poor, while in developing countries the most common causes are natural disasters, war, overpopulation, poor farming practices, lack of infrastructure, and disease.

Natural Disasters

In the summer of 2004, a drought in western Africa brought life-threatening undernutrition to about

⬆ An Indian farmer inspects what is left of his crop during a drought.

20% of the population of Niger and Mali (NASA, 2005). Such natural disasters often result in widespread hunger because they destroy substantial amounts of local crops in a short time. Drought and other natural disasters—including floods, earthquakes, tsunamis, high winds, hurricanes, frosts, and infestations by insects, worms, or microbes—can even result in **famine**, a severe food shortage affecting a large percentage of the population in a limited geographic area at a particular time.

War

Unfortunately, famine is often a human-made disaster. In 2003, a rebellion against the Sudanese government led to violent repression in the Darfur region of Sudan. An estimated 200 000 to 400 00 people either were killed outright or died of starvation when crops and food supplies were burned. Nearly 2 million more were displaced from their homes; many relocated to camps where, because of governmental obstacles

wasting Very low weight for height.

stunting Low height for age.

famine A widespread severe food shortage that causes starvation and death in a large portion of a population in a region.

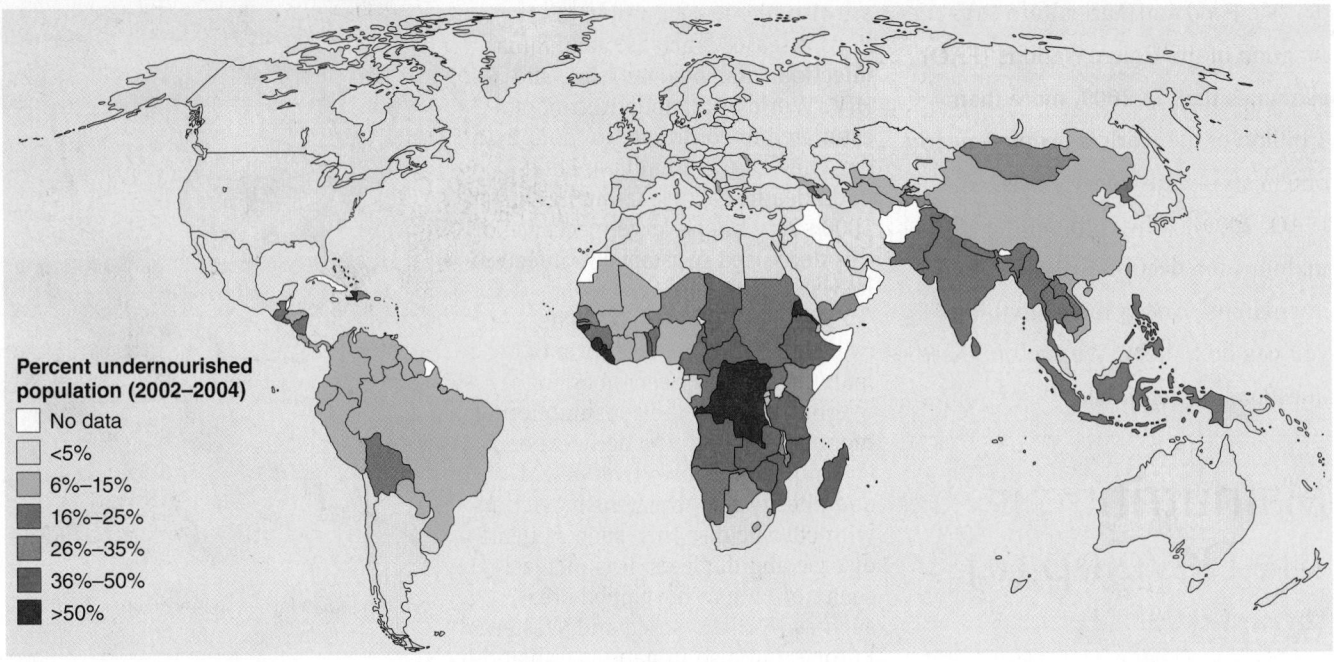

Figure 1 Undernutrition is most prevalent in parts of sub-Saharan Africa and Southeast Asia.
Data from © Food and Agriculture Organization of the United Nations 2008. Undernourished Population (2006–2008). http://www.fao.org/economic/ess/food-security-statistics/ fao-hunger-map/en/. Used with permission.

Percent undernourished population (2002–2004)
- No data
- <5%
- 6%–15%
- 16%–25%
- 26%–35%
- 36%–50%
- >50%

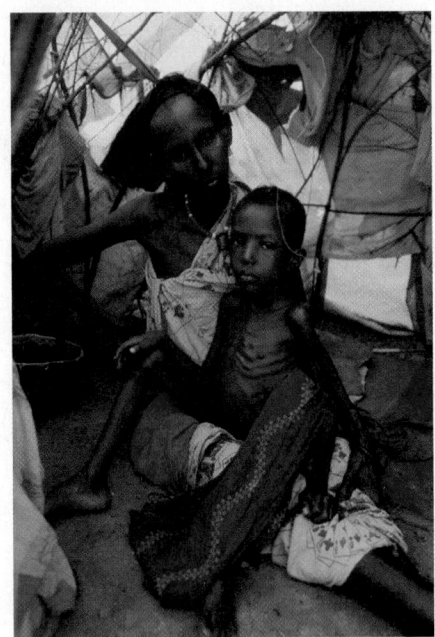

Hunger is common among people displaced by conflict into refugee camps.

to international aid, they, too, faced starvation (CIA, 2010). In 2010, the United Nations reported that problems in Sudan were ongoing: a combination of armed conflict and drought left over 4 million in need of food aid (Friends of the World Food Program, 2010).

Wars also induce famine when they interfere with planting or harvest times, or when farmlands are taken over by military forces. Explosives may destroy roads, bridges, or rail lines needed for the distribution of food, and fear of military activity may keep markets closed.

Overpopulation

An area is said to be **overpopulated** when its resources are insufficient to support the number of people living there. In parts of the world with fertile land and adequate rainfall or irrigation systems to support abundant harvests, food shortages are rare. In more arid climates, especially in areas with high fertility rates and poor access to imported foods, food shortages are common.

One way of improving the food:population ratio is to increase food production and importation. Another strategy is to focus on slowing population growth. One of the most effective ways to do this is to improve the education of women and girls (UNICEF, 2008). Their increased earning potential, access to information about contraception, and better health practices lead to smaller, healthier, more economically stable families.

Yet another way of slowing population growth is through improved public health measures, such as immunization programs that reduce the spread of infectious disease. When parents feel confident that their children will survive to adulthood, they have fewer children.

Poor Farming Practices

Some traditional farming practices have the potential to destroy useable land. Deforestation and the overgrazing of pastures and croplands destroy the trees and grass roots that preserve soils from wind and water erosion. Growing the same crop year after year on the same plot of ground can deplete the soil of nutrients and reduce crop yield. The use of agricultural land for **cash crops**, such as cotton, coffee, and tobacco, may replace land use for local food crops, such as sorghum and corn. The end result may be less food available for local consumption.

---

overpopulated A term used to describe a region that has insufficient resources to support the number of people living there.

cash crops Crops grown to be sold rather than eaten, such as cotton, tobacco, jute, and sugarcane.

⬆ Cotton is a cash crop that farmers often grow instead of local food crops.

Lack of Infrastructure

Many developing countries lack roads and transportation into rural areas. This limits available food to whatever can be produced locally. Lack of electricity and refrigeration can limit storage and allow the spoilage of even local foods before they can be used. Other crucial aspects of infrastructure are irrigation systems, sanitation services, communication systems, an adequate healthcare delivery system, and adequate public education.

Impact of Disease

Disease reduces the work capacity of individuals, and this in turn reduces their ability to ward off poverty and malnutrition. This vicious cycle is demonstrated by the AIDS epidemic. In sub-Saharan Africa, more than 5% of adults are infected with HIV, and 2 million died from AIDS in 2008 (UNAIDS/ WHO, 2009). Because AIDS most commonly strikes young adults who are the primary wage earners in their families, their illness or death orphans their children, impoverishes their elderly parents, and devastates their communities. By creating populations in which children and the elderly predominate, the AIDS epidemic has exacerbated the risk for undernutrition in many developing countries.

Unequal Distribution

The world produces a surplus of food. In 2009, the number of hungry people worldwide increased to unprecedented levels, despite the fact that the world food harvests in 2008 and 2009 were the largest on record (Squires, 2009). The major cause of unequal distribution of food within a community is, of course, poverty. At greatest risk are people who do not own enough land to grow their own food and must work to buy food in areas where employment opportunities are scarce.

Unequal distribution also occurs because of cultural biases. In some communities, limited food is distributed first to men and boys and only secondarily to women and girls. Food distribution to the elderly is also sometimes limited. Access to food also can differ by ethnicity and religion. For example, higher mortality was documented in some ethnic and religious groups during the drought-induced famine in northern Ethiopia in the 1980s (Ezra and Kiros, 2000).

What Health Problems Result from Undernutrition?

Undernutrition can cause a wide variety of health problems. The most common are discussed here.

Increased Infant and Child Mortality

Undernutrition increases by close to 50% the likelihood that a child will die between birth and age five (Black, Morris, and Bryce, 2003). In 2009, in industrialized countries, the infant mortality rate was only 5 per 1000, and the childhood mortality rate (the rate of deaths for all children under five) was 6 per 1000. In contrast, in the least developed countries of the world, the infant mortality rate was 84 per 1000 and the child mortality rate was 103 per 1000 (UNICEF, 2009).

Increased Vulnerability to Infection

We noted earlier that the most common way that undernutrition kills infants and children is by making them more vulnerable to infectious diseases, such as pneumonia and infectious diarrhea. By decreasing a child's general health, malnutrition increases the likelihood that the child will not survive infection. Moreover, infection exacerbates malnutrition by decreasing appetite, causing vomiting and diarrhea, and generally weakening the immune system. A vicious cycle of malnutrition, infection, worsening malnutrition, and increased vulnerability to infection develops.

Macronutrient Deficiencies

Marasmus is a disease of children that results from grossly inadequate intakes of energy. As we explained in Chapter 6, it commonly occurs when chronic food shortages reduce children's total energy intake. As a result, the children slowly starve to death. Typically, their weakened immune system makes them highly vulnerable to infection; thus, they often die from pneumonia or from dehydration caused by diarrhea. Alternatively, they suffer heart failure from a weakened heart muscle.

Kwashiorkor is a disease of toddlers who have recently been weaned from breast milk, which is replaced with a watery porridge that has inadequate and poor-quality protein. The lack of dietary protein causes edema, because the level of

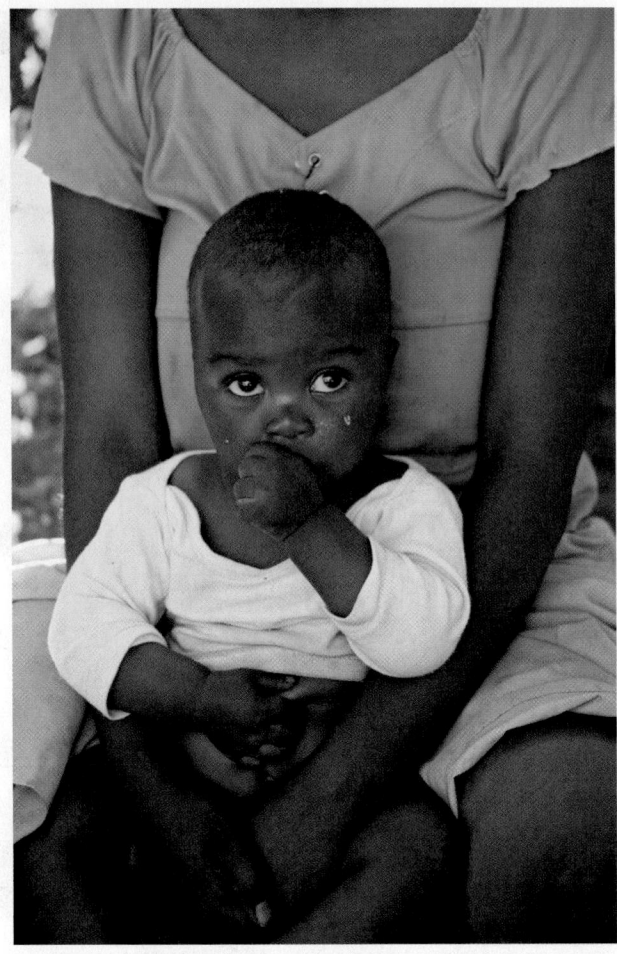

In developing nations, providing vitamin A supplements to children under age five has significantly reduced mortality.

protein in the blood is inadequate to keep fluids from seeping into the tissue spaces. Edema swells the child's belly and makes the face and limbs appear adequately nourished. The child experiences severe wasting of muscle tissue and easily succumbs to infection.

Micronutrient Deficiencies

Undernourished people are at risk for a variety of micronutrient deficiencies. Iron deficiency is the world's most common nutrient deficiency. It increases the risk for infection, premature birth, low birth weight, and maternal death during or immediately following childbirth. It also impairs children's ability to learn and adults' ability to work. Iodine deficiency is responsible for mental impairment in children and goitre in adults. Zinc deficiency

reduces growth and immune function. Deficiency of vitamin B_{12} can result in severe cognitive impairment. Lack of sufficient vitamin A in the diet is a preventable cause of night blindness in children. Adding iron, iodine, zinc, B-vitamins, and vitamin A to common foods, such as salt and flour, costs only about 30 cents per person reached per year and is a major initiative of several international aid organizations (Kristof, 2010). See the Highlight on Sprinkles for one initiative that has been successful.

Poor Work Capacity in Adults

The debilitating weakness caused by undernutrition affects the productivity of adults in many developing nations. It is especially detrimental when manual labour involved in subsistence farming is the main source

HIGHLIGHT
Dr. Stanley Zlotkin: Preventing and Treating Iron Deficiency Anemia

"Every penny counts!" We have all heard this age-old adage, but nowhere does it ring truer than in the case of providing nutritional supplements to impoverished children in developing countries. It may seem hard to believe, but just 3 cents a day can supply a child with a dose of micronutrients capable of preventing a host of debilitating diseases.

While warding off these illnesses is no small task, these precious micronutrients are in fact delivered in tiny packages—no bigger than a sugar packet! This landmark creation is the brainchild of Dr. Stanley Zlotkin of the Hospital for Sick Children and University of Toronto. It is known as *Supplefer Sprinkles*, and it has the potential to purge developing countries of preventable diseases that severely diminish countless children's quality of life every day.

Anemia is a global public health problem, with 1.6 billion people affected (WHO, 2008). Anemia increases the risk of maternal and child mortality, and negatively affects the development of children and the work capacity of adults. Iron deficiency is the most common cause of anemia, and in many cases supplementation could have a significant impact on prevention and treatment. But how can this be done effectively?

Providing micronutrient supplements to children in developing countries is not a new venture, but product design and unclear instructions have hindered past efforts. Before the introduction of Sprinkles, anemia was primarily prevented by giving an iron-fortified syrup to young children, who cannot swallow pills. This concoction, however, stained teeth, tasted bad, often caused diarrhea, and lacked understandable instructions, sometimes leading to inadequate or dangerously high amounts being ingested (Bell, 2004).

In developing Sprinkles, Zlotkin and his team had to address these issues to produce a product that could realistically be used by all families. To eliminate the tooth discolouration and bad taste, the iron in Sprinkles is encapsulated, a concept that has long been used to disguise the unpleasant taste of many medications (Zlotkin et al., 2001).

Encapsulation, in this case with soy lipid, prevents the oxidation process that is the culprit in altering the taste and colour of food (Zlotkin et al., 2001). To reduce the likelihood of insufficient quantities or accidental overdose, the brilliant idea of distributing micronutrients in a single-serving sachet was put into action. Another matter that had to be attended to was the addition of some type of filler to bring the micronutrient mixture up to the 0.5 g minimum weight required to be packaged. Maltodextrin was decided to be the best candidate for this job. Ensuring that Sprinkles met the religious dietary requirements of Muslims (halal) and Jews (kosher), as well as developing a three-layer packaging system that could withstand the humidity of tropical environments, were other considerations while developing this product.

In 2000, Zlotkin and the H. J. Heinz Company of Pittsburgh, Pennsylvania, established a private–public partnership to help overcome obstacles associated with production of the tiny sachets of micronutrients. The actual cost per packet of Sprinkles varies according to how much is ordered, where it is produced, and the composition of the packet—it can range from US$0.015 to US$0.035.

The result of this long and careful development process is a convenient sachet filled with a fine powder that parents and guardians can easily sprinkle into their children's food without confusion or disagreeable side effects.

Sprinkles was pilot tested in three projects in Pakistan (Sharieff et al., 2006), Mongolia (Nyamsuren et al., 2004), and Bangladesh (Haseen, 2007) and shown to be effective in treating and preventing anemia in children. Sprinkles have since been used in many different countries, including Northern Canada, China, Bangladesh, India, and Pakistan, Ghana, Bolivia, and Haiti. The Sprinkles Global Health Initiative conducts community based research when it implements a new project and reports on the results. Overall the cure rate for anemia ranges from 49%–91%, depending on other confounding factors such as malaria.

Sprinkles have two main formulations, the *nutritional anemia formulation* that contains iron, zinc, folic acid, vitamin C, and vitamin A, and the *multi-micronutrient formulation*, which contains vitamins A, C, D, E, B_1, B_2, B_6, B_{12}, folic acid, niacin, iron, zinc, copper, and iodine. This allows the application of Sprinkles to potentially have an impact on nutritional and health status beyond iron-deficiency anemia.

The remarkable success of Sprinkles so far is only the beginning. According to Zlotkin, "The long-term goal is to make Sprinkles available to populations in need throughout the world to help control the significant public health problem of anemia. Sprinkles for pregnant women and lactating mothers are currently being developed, and it is hoped that these formulations will contribute to reducing the prevalence of anemia in this population group (Hartman-Craven et al., 2007). The other long-term goal is to ensure sustainable methods of distribution in a country and to ensure that the most vulnerable people have access to them."

Over four million sachets of Sprinkles were distributed in 2009, and this number will likely climb in the years to come as Zlotkin's vision is realized. Production of Sprinkles has been made available by placing the specifications in the public domain. This means that companies outside of North America can produce Sprinkles for local use. Another exciting area of research that Zlotkin is pursuing is the effect of double-fortified table salt. It is clear that Stanley Zlotkin has had, and will continue to make, a huge impact on nutrition around the world.

Zlotkin is a professor in the departments of paediatrics, nutritional sciences, and public health sciences at the University of Toronto, senior scientist in the Research Institute of the Hospital for Sick Children, and staff physician in the Division of Gastroenterology, Hepatology, and Nutrition in the Department of Paediatrics at the Hospital for Sick Children, and Vice President, Medical and Academic Affairs, at the Hospital for Sick Children in Toronto.

Sprinkles Global Health Initiative, http://www.sghi.org/about_sprinkles/index.html.

---

of food and income. Nutrient deficiency also contributes to poor work capacity. Iron-deficiency anemia is particularly debilitating because of iron's role in oxygen transport.

Figure 2 illustrates the varied and cruel effects of chronic undernutrition throughout the life span. As you can see, the cycle is perpetuated across generations when undernourished women give birth to undernourished infants.

Why Is Obesity a Growing Problem in Developing Nations?

People living in countries with growing economies, such as Egypt, Brazil, and China, enjoy increased food availability and variety. Unfortunately, their new diet usually includes more processed foods with high energy density due to added fat and sugar, including snack foods and fast foods. These foods are usually less expensive than traditional foods, such as fish, milk, and fresh fruits and vegetables (Drewnowski, 2004). This shift in dietary pattern as poverty is relieved is called the **nutrition transition**. And while

the population is consuming more energy, greater access to motorized transportation and a decrease in manual labour are reducing their energy expenditure. The result of this equation is overnutrition.

In addition, there is now significant evidence linking undernutrition during fetal life to overnutrition in adulthood. The hypothesis known as "fetal origins of adult disease" states that fetal adaptations to poor maternal nutrition help the child during times of food shortages but also make the child susceptible to obesity and chronic disease when food is plentiful (Adair and Prentice, 2004). For example, when a mother is malnourished during pregnancy, her newborn will tend to have a low birth weight but be relatively fat. This may occur because the fetal body has favoured growth of the brain, which is more than 50% fat, at the expense of muscle tissue. Researchers theorize that this

nutrition transition A shift in dietary pattern toward greater food security, greater variety of foods, and more foods with high energy density; associated with increased incidence of obesity and chronic disease.

◆ Overnutrition is becoming a global concern now that low-cost, energy-dense foods are becoming widely available.

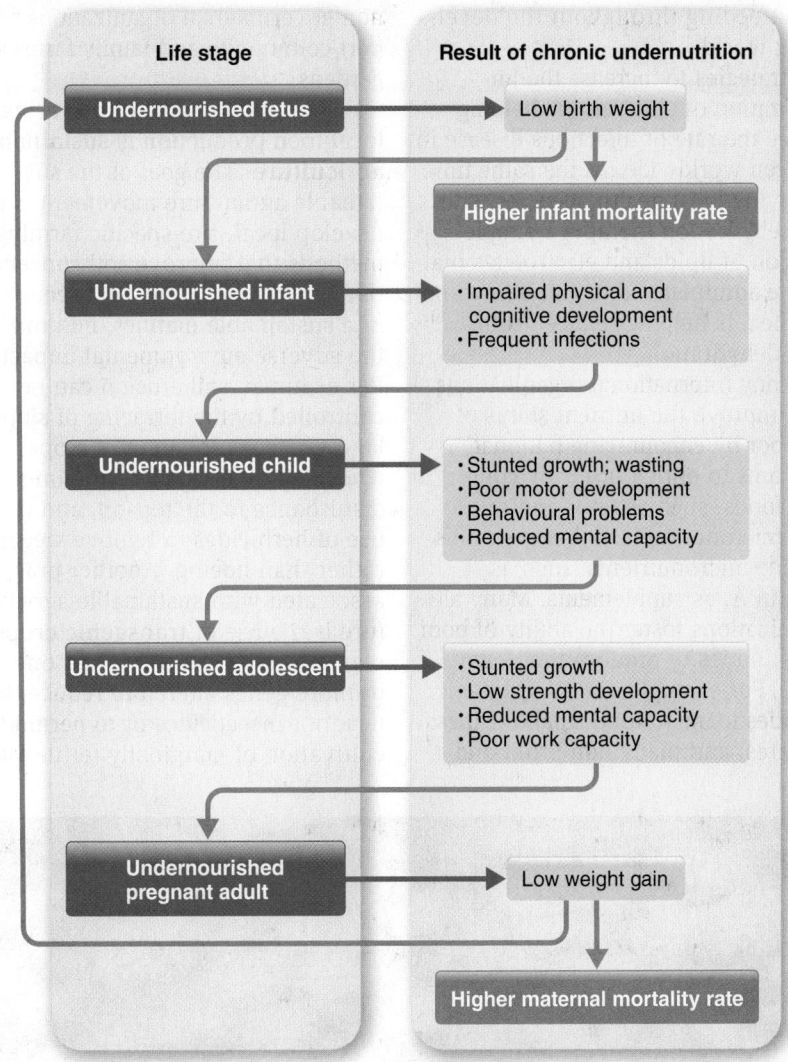

Life stage | **Result of chronic undernutrition**

Undernourished fetus → Low birth weight

Higher infant mortality rate

Undernourished infant →
• Impaired physical and cognitive development
• Frequent infections

Undernourished child →
• Stunted growth; wasting
• Poor motor development
• Behavioural problems
• Reduced mental capacity

Undernourished adolescent →
• Stunted growth
• Low strength development
• Reduced mental capacity
• Poor work capacity

Undernourished pregnant adult → Low weight gain

Higher maternal mortality rate

⬆ **Figure 2** Acute and long-term effects of malnutrition throughout the life cycle.

adaptation may prompt a permanent physiologic tendency to gain fat tissue when food is plentiful (Yajnik, 2004).

Given these factors, it is not surprising that countries throughout the world have been experiencing an alarming increase in the prevalence of obesity. The World Health Organization (WHO) estimates that, since 1980, obesity rates have increased threefold or more. In 2010, 300 million adults worldwide were clinically obese, and the WHO predicts that, by 2015, more than 700 million will be obese (WHO, 2006). As we have pointed out throughout this text, overweight and obesity increase the risk for cardiovascular disease, type 2 diabetes, and some cancers. Of these,

type 2 diabetes is fast becoming an especially significant burden in the developing world. The WHO predicts that, by 2020, deaths due to diabetes will increase worldwide by more than 50% (WHO, 2006).

Malnutrition in Canada

As we discussed in Chapter 11, overnutrition is becoming a national health crisis. Approximately 60% of Canadians are now overweight or obese, and the prevalence of type 2 diabetes and other chronic diseases associated with obesity is increasing. Paradoxically, obesity is increasingly

a problem of the poor. That is in part because, for many poor families, the priority is to maximize caloric intake for each dollar spent. This can lead to an overconsumption of Calories and a less healthful diet. Energy-dense foods with longer shelf lives, such as cookies, chips, and soft drinks, are less expensive than perishable foods, such as fresh produce. They also tend to have a higher satiety value, keeping hunger at bay for longer. For example, $1.50 will buy a couple of sweet peppers, or an entire package of store-brand cookies. If you were hungry and had just a few dollars to spend for groceries, which would you purchase? Moreover, research suggests that, during periods of insufficient income, poor mothers restrict their food intake in favour of their children. Such chronic ups and downs of food intake can contribute to obesity (Food Research and Action Center, 2006).

How many people in Canada are affected by this inability to reliably purchase healthful food? Data from 2007–08 show that an estimated 7.7% of Canadians aged 12 years and older experienced some degree of food insecurity (Health Canada, 2011). An estimated 2.7% of households, comprising 60 000 children between the ages of 12 and 17 and 546 100 adults, experienced severe **food insecurity**. This means that they are unable to obtain enough food to meet their physical needs every day.

What Can Be Done to Relieve Malnutrition?

To combat malnutrition and achieve global food security, long-term solutions are critical. We discuss some of the most effective here.

food insecurity Circumstances in which households are uncertain of having, or unable to acquire, enough food to meet the needs of all their members because they have insufficient money or other resources for food.

Global Solutions

Among the most important long-term solutions for improving the health and nutrition of children worldwide are programs that encourage breastfeeding. This is because breast milk provides optimal nutrition for the healthy growth of the newborn and contains antibodies that protect against infections. In contrast, feeding infants with formula increases the infant's risk for diarrhea if the powder is mixed with unsanitary water. The WHO sponsors programs to encourage breastfeeding throughout the developing world.

Strategies to increase the immunization of children are helping reduce the rate of infectious disease in children worldwide. At the same time, supplying local health agencies with oral rehydration therapy, a simple solution of fluids and electrolytes that can be administered to children with diarrhea, is helping reduce deaths from dehydration.

Many international organizations help improve the nutrient status of the poor by encouraging national programs to enrich or fortify common foods, such as flour and salt, with micronutrients. Other programs provide micronutrients, such as vitamin A, as supplements. Many aid organizations foster the ability of poor communities to produce their own foods. For example, the World Bank provides loans to fund small business ventures, and many non-profit and non-governmental organizations support community and family farms and gardens.

Another method for increasing local food production is **sustainable agriculture**. The goal of the sustainable agriculture movement is to develop local, site-specific farming methods that improve soil conservation, crop yields, and food security in a sustainable manner, minimizing the adverse environmental impact. For example, soil erosion can be controlled by the terracing of sloped land for the cultivation of crops **(Figure 3)**, by tillage that minimizes disturbance to the topsoil, and by the use of herbicides to remove weeds rather than hoeing. Another practice associated with sustainable agriculture is the use of **transgenic crops**, plant varieties that have had one or more genes altered to reduce the need for insecticides or to permit the cultivation of marginally fertile land.

---

sustainable agriculture Techniques of food production that preserve the environment indefinitely.

transgenic crops Plant varieties that have had one or more genes altered through the use of genetic technologies; also called genetically modified organisms, or GMOs.

Figure 3 Terracing sloped land to avoid soil erosion is one practice of sustainable agriculture.

Local Solutions

Unlike the United States, Canada does not have a national school lunch program. However, many communities and non-profit organizations have taken steps to develop school breakfast, snack, and lunch programs with their local school boards or individual schools. In some communities, local neighbourhood associations work with schools to develop and maintain school food gardens that benefit both the students and neighbourhood residents.

Many other local initiatives are underway in different communities. These include food banks, where qualifying clients can choose a variety of foods for their families; free meals, often distributed by churches or community centres; and gleaning, a practice in which volunteers comb fields and orchards after harvesting and gather any remaining edible produce, then clean it and distribute it to the poor. Some community groups are fostering home gardens for poor inner-city residents, including raised beds, seeds, a drip irrigation system, and gardening classes, to give the residents immediate access to organic produce in neighbourhoods.

Are any of these initiatives in your neighbourhood? They can be great opportunities to volunteer your time and learn new skills.

Web Resources

www.actionagainsthunger.org/about/ acf-international
Action Against Hunger/ACF International

This site explains the mission of an international organization that aids in food crises and promotes long-term food security. The site also explains how you can help.

feedingamerica.org
Feeding America

Check out this site for information on programs for fighting hunger in the United States.

www.bread.org
Bread for the World

Visit this site to learn about a faith-based effort to advocate local and global policies that help the poor obtain food.

www.care.ca
CARE Canada

This site links to CARE organizations working in many countries to improve economic conditions in over seventy developing nations.

www.doctorswithoutborders.org
Doctors Without Borders/Médecins Sans Frontières

This organization works in nearly 70 countries providing independent, impartial medical aid to those most in need.

www.feedingminds.org
Feeding Minds, Fighting Hunger

Visit this international electronic classroom to explore the problems of hunger, malnutrition, and food insecurity.

www.oxfam.ca
Oxfam Canada

Oxfam Canada works with partner organizations in developing countries, tackling the root causes of poverty and inequity and helping people to create self-reliant and sustainable communities.

www.sghi.org
The Sprinkles Global Health Initiative

Visit this site to learn more about the use of this micronutrient powder to combat nutrient deficiencies in Northern Canada and around the world.

www.unicef.org
The United Nations Children's Fund

Visit this site to learn about international concerns affecting the world's children, including nutrient deficiencies and hunger.

www.who.int/nutrition/en
The World Health Organization Nutrition Site

Visit this site to learn about global malnutrition, micronutrient deficiencies, nutrition transition, and other issues of world hunger.

14

Nutrition Through the Life Cycle: Pregnancy and the First Year of Life

CHAPTER OBJECTIVES

After reading this chapter you will be able to:

1. Explain why maintaining a nutritious diet is important for prospective parents even before conception, p. 494.

2. Describe the relationship between fetal development, physiologic changes in the mother, and increasing nutrient requirements during the course of a pregnancy, pp. 494–504.

3. Identify the range of optimal weight gain for a pregnant woman in the first, second, and third trimesters, pp. 498–499.

4. Describe the physiologic events that lead to lactation, pp. 511–512.

5. Compare and contrast the nutrient requirements of pregnant and lactating women, pp. 499–505 and 513–514.

6. Identify the primary advantages and most common challenges of breastfeeding, pp. 514–518.

7. Relate the growth and activity patterns of infants to their nutrient needs, pp. 518–520.

8. Discuss some common nutrition-related concerns for infants, pp. 520–523.

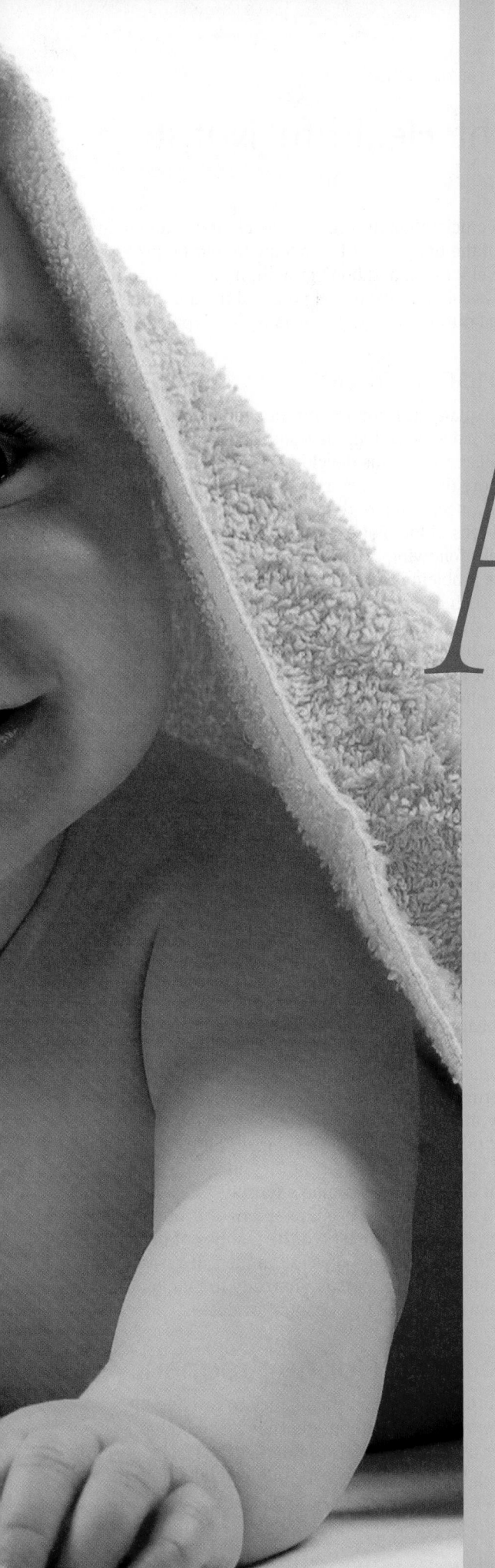

An active, curious two-year-old, Tomas brings joy and laughter to his parents and family. That was not always the case, however. Tomas weighed just over 1.5 kg (3 lb. 5 oz.) at birth—about half of what an average full-term newborn weighs. Even today, Tomas is still small for his age and continues to struggle with his coordination and speech. Although Canada has an excellent health-care system, the numbers of low-, very-low-, and extremely low-birth-weight infants, such as Tomas, continue to increase, to 6% in 2008 (Statistics Canada, 2011b). Moreover, our infant mortality rate—the number of deaths of infants before their first birthday—is higher than the rate in 23 other countries: in 2008, Canada recorded 5.0 infant deaths for every 1000 live births (Statistics Canada, 2011a), as compared to just 2.75 for Sweden and 2.31 for Singapore, the best-ranked (United Nations Statistics, 2012).

What contributes to these troubling statistics? What are the short- and long-term effects of low and extremely low birth weights on children? On a broader scale, what role does prenatal diet play in determining the future health and well-being of the child? Why is inadequate iron or folate intake especially dangerous to a pregnant woman and her fetus? What roles do other nutrients play in maternal, fetal, and infant health? In this chapter, we'll discuss how adequate nutrition supports fetal development, maintains the pregnant woman's health, and contributes to lactation. We'll then explore the nutrient needs of breastfeeding and formula-feeding infants.

Starting Out Right: Healthful Nutrition in Pregnancy

At no stage of life is nutrition more crucial than during fetal development and infancy. From conception through the end of the first year of life, adequate nutrition is essential for tissue formation, neurologic development, and bone growth, modeling, and remodelling. The ability to reach peak physical and intellectual potential in adult life is in part determined by the nutrition received during the earliest years of development.

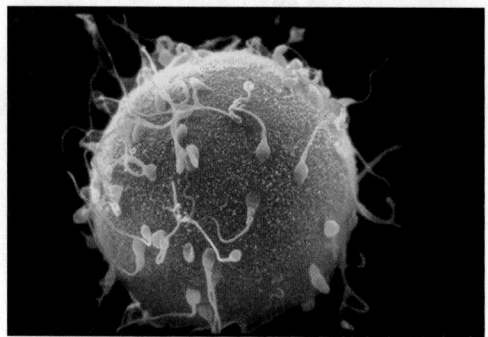

⬆ During conception, a sperm fertilizes an egg, creating a zygote.

Is Nutrition Important Before Conception?

Several factors make adequate nutrition important even before **conception**, the point at which a woman's ovum (egg) is fertilized with a man's sperm. First, some deficiency-related problems develop extremely early in the pregnancy, typically before the mother even realizes she is pregnant. An adequate and varied preconception diet reduces the risk for such problems during those first few weeks of life. For example, inadequate levels of folate during the first few weeks following conception can result in brain and spinal cord defects. This problem is discussed in more detail shortly. To reduce the incidence of such defects, federal guidelines advise all women capable of becoming pregnant to consume 400 μg of folic acid daily, whether or not they plan to become pregnant.

Second, adopting a healthful diet prior to conception includes the avoidance of alcohol, illegal drugs, and other known teratogens (substances that cause birth defects). Women should also consult their health-care provider about their consumption of caffeine, medications, herbs, and supplements, and if they smoke they should attempt to quit.

Third, a healthful diet and an appropriate level of physical activity can help women achieve and maintain an optimal body weight prior to pregnancy. Women with a pre-pregnancy body mass index (BMI) between 19.8 and 26.0 kg/m² have the best chance of a successful pregnancy (CDC, 2009a). As we will discuss shortly, women with a BMI above or below this range are at greater risk for pregnancy-related complications.

Finally, maintaining a balanced and nourishing diet before conception reduces a woman's risk of developing a nutrition-related disorder during her pregnancy. These disorders, which we discuss later in the chapter, include gestational diabetes and hypertensive disorders. Although genetic and metabolic abnormalities are beyond the woman's control, following a healthful diet prior to conception is something a woman can do to help her fetus develop into a healthy baby.

The man's nutrition prior to pregnancy is important as well, since malnutrition contributes to abnormalities in sperm (Davidson, London and Ladewig, 2008). Both sperm number and motility (ability to move) are reduced by alcohol consumption, as well as by the use of certain prescription and illegal drugs. Finally, infections accompanied by a high fever can destroy sperm, so to the extent that adequate nutrition keeps the immune system strong, it also promotes a man's fertility.

Are you ready to have a child? The decision to become pregnant is often complex, and it is best to plan ahead. It is important to understand the realities of becoming a parent before making the decision to start a family. Several online self-assessments are available that can help you decide if you are personally ready to take on the role of parenthood. See Web Resources at the end of this chapter for details.

Why Is Nutrition Important During Pregnancy?

A balanced, nourishing diet is important throughout pregnancy to provide the nutrients needed to support fetal development without depriving the mother of the nutrients she needs to maintain her own health. It also minimizes the risk of excess energy intake. A full-term pregnancy lasts 38 to 42 weeks and is divided into three **trimesters**, with each trimester lasting about 13 to 14 weeks.

conception (also called **fertilization**) The uniting of an ovum (egg) and sperm to create a fertilized egg, or zygote.

trimester Any one of three stages of pregnancy, each lasting 13 to 14 weeks.

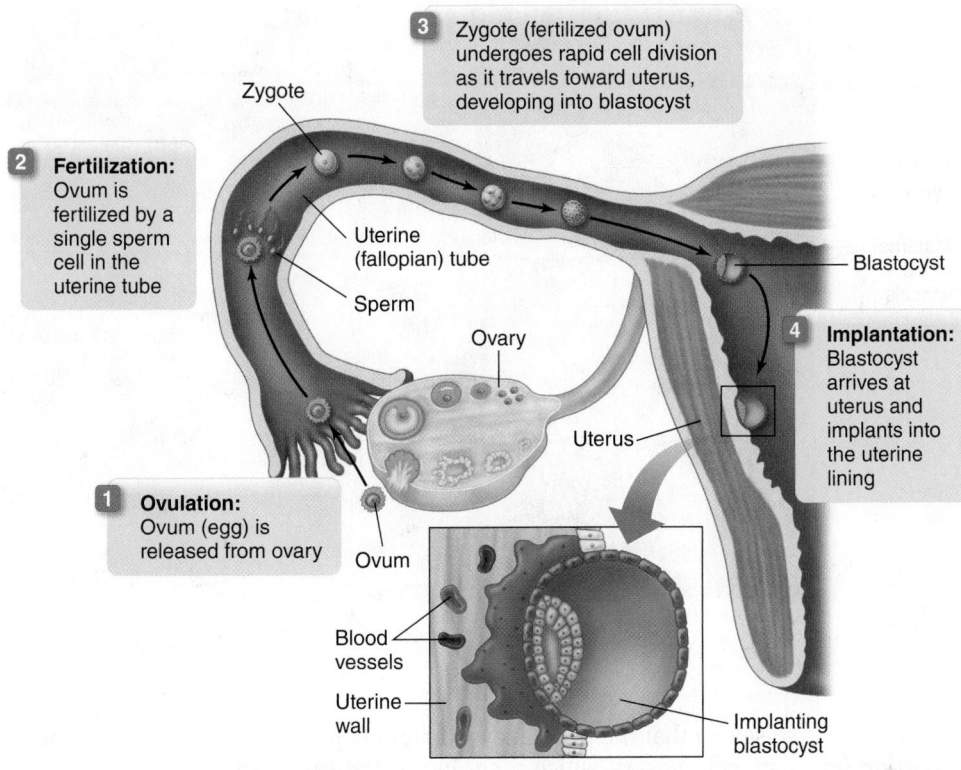

Figure 14.1 Ovulation, conception, and implantation.

3 Zygote (fertilized ovum) undergoes rapid cell division as it travels toward uterus, developing into blastocyst

Zygote

2 **Fertilization:** Ovum is fertilized by a single sperm cell in the uterine tube

Uterine (fallopian) tube

Sperm

Ovary

Blastocyst

4 **Implantation:** Blastocyst arrives at uterus and implants into the uterine lining

Uterus

1 **Ovulation:** Ovum (egg) is released from ovary

Ovum

Blood vessels

Uterine wall

Implanting blastocyst

The First Trimester

About once each month, a non-pregnant woman of childbearing age experiences **ovulation**, the release of an ovum (egg cell) from an ovary. The ovum is then drawn into the uterine tube. The first trimester of pregnancy begins when the ovum and sperm unite to form a single, fertilized cell called a **zygote**. As the zygote travels through the uterine tube, it divides into a ball of 12 to 16 cells, which, at about day four, arrives in the uterus **(Figure 14.1)**. By day 10, the inner portion of the zygote, called the *blastocyst,* has implanted into the uterine lining. The outer portion becomes part of the placenta, which is discussed shortly.

Further cell growth, multiplication, and differentiation occur, resulting in the formation of an **embryo**. Over the next six weeks, embryonic tissues continue to differentiate and fold into a primitive, tubelike structure with limb buds, organs, and facial features recognizable as human **(Figure 14.2)**. It is not surprising, then, that the embryo is most vulnerable to teratogens during this time. Not only alcohol and illegal drugs, but also some prescription and over-the-counter medications, megadoses of certain supplements, several herbs, some viruses, cigarette smoking, and radiation can interfere with embryonic development and cause birth defects. In some cases,

ovulation The release of an ovum (egg) from a woman's ovary.

zygote A fertilized egg (ovum) consisting of a single cell.

embryo The human growth and developmental stage lasting from the third week to the end of the eighth week after fertilization.

Figure 14.2 Human embryonic development during the first 10 weeks. Organ systems are most vulnerable to teratogens during this time, when cells are dividing and differentiating.

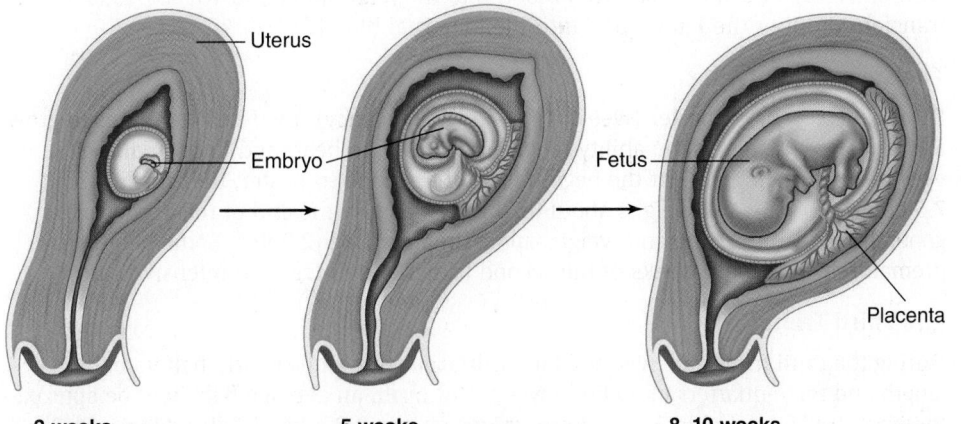

Uterus

Embryo

Fetus

Placenta

3 weeks　　　　**5 weeks**　　　　**8–10 weeks**

▶ **Figure 14.3** Placental development. The placenta is formed from both embryonic and maternal tissues. When the placenta is fully functional, fetal blood vessels and maternal blood vessels are intimately intertwined, allowing the exchange of nutrients and wastes between the two. The mother transfers nutrients and oxygen to the fetus, and the fetus transfers wastes to the mother for disposal.

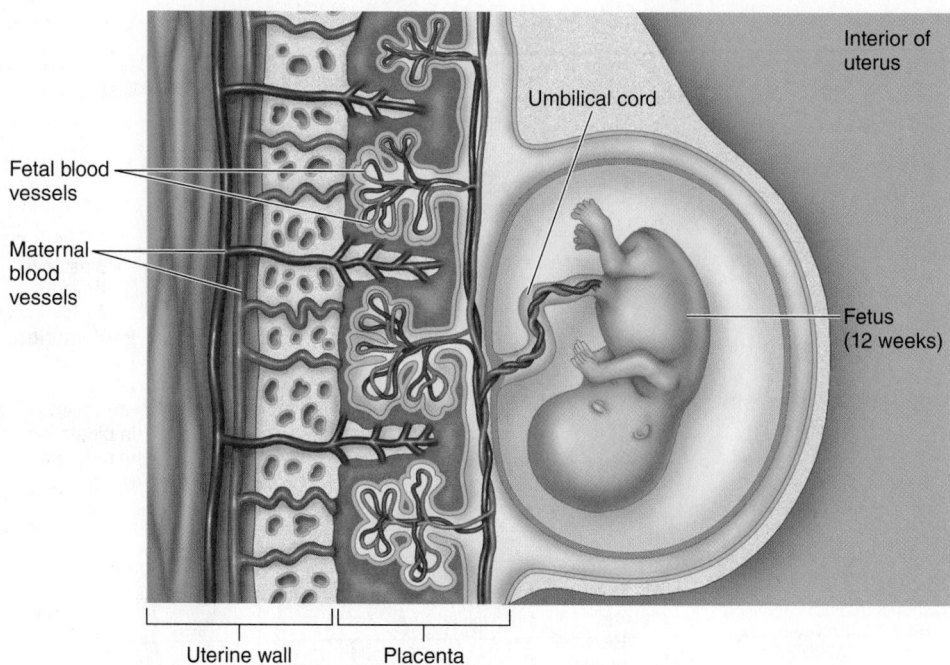

Interior of uterus

Umbilical cord

Fetal blood vessels

Maternal blood vessels

Fetus (12 weeks)

Uterine wall   Placenta

spontaneous abortion (also called **miscarriage**) The natural termination of a pregnancy and expulsion of pregnancy tissues because of a genetic, developmental, or physiologic abnormality that is so severe that the pregnancy cannot be maintained.

placenta A pregnancy-specific organ formed from both maternal and embryonic tissues. It is responsible for oxygen, nutrient, and waste exchange between mother and fetus.

fetus The human growth and developmental stage lasting from the beginning of the ninth week after conception to birth.

umbilical cord The cord containing the arteries and veins that connect the baby (from the navel) to the mother via the placenta.

the damage is so severe that the pregnancy is naturally terminated in a **spontaneous abortion** (*miscarriage*), most of which occur in the first trimester.

During the first weeks of pregnancy, the embryo obtains its nutrients from cells lining the uterus. But by the fourth week, a primitive **placenta** has formed in the uterus from both embryonic and maternal tissue. Within a few more weeks, the placenta will be a fully functioning organ, through which the mother will provide nutrients and remove fetal wastes **(Figure 14.3)**.

By the end of the embryonic stage, about eight weeks postconception, the embryo's tissues and organs have differentiated dramatically. A primitive skeleton, including fingers and toes, has formed. Muscles have begun to develop in the trunk and limbs, and some movement is possible. A primitive heart has begun to beat, and the digestive organs are becoming distinct. The brain has differentiated, and the head has a mouth, eyespots with eyelids, and primitive ears.

The third month of pregnancy marks the transition from embryo to **fetus**. To support its dramatic growth, the fetus requires abundant nutrients from the placenta. It is connected to the fetal circulatory system via the **umbilical cord**, an extension of fetal blood vessels emerging from the fetus's navel (called the *umbilicus*). Blood rich in oxygen and nutrients flows through the placenta and into the umbilical vein (Figure 14.3). Wastes are excreted in blood returning from the fetus to the placenta via the umbilical arteries. Although many people think there is a mixing of blood from the fetus and the mother, the two blood supplies remain separate. Nutrients move from the maternal blood into the fetal blood and waste products are transferred out of the fetal blood into the maternal blood.

The Second Trimester

During the second trimester (weeks 14 to 27 of pregnancy), the fetus continues to grow and mature. It develops the ability to suck its thumb, to hear, and to open and close its eyes in response to light. At the beginning of the second trimester, the fetus is about 7.5 cm (3 in.) long and weighs about 0.7 kg (1.5 lb.). By the end of this trimester, it is generally over a foot long and weighs approximately 1 kg (2.2 lb.). Some babies born prematurely in the last weeks of the second trimester survive with intensive care.

The Third Trimester

During the third trimester (weeks 28 to birth), the fetus gains nearly half its body length and three-quarters of its body weight! At birth, an average baby will be approximately 45 to 55 cm (18 to 22 in.) long and weigh about 3.4 kg (7.5 lb.) **(Figure 14.4)**.

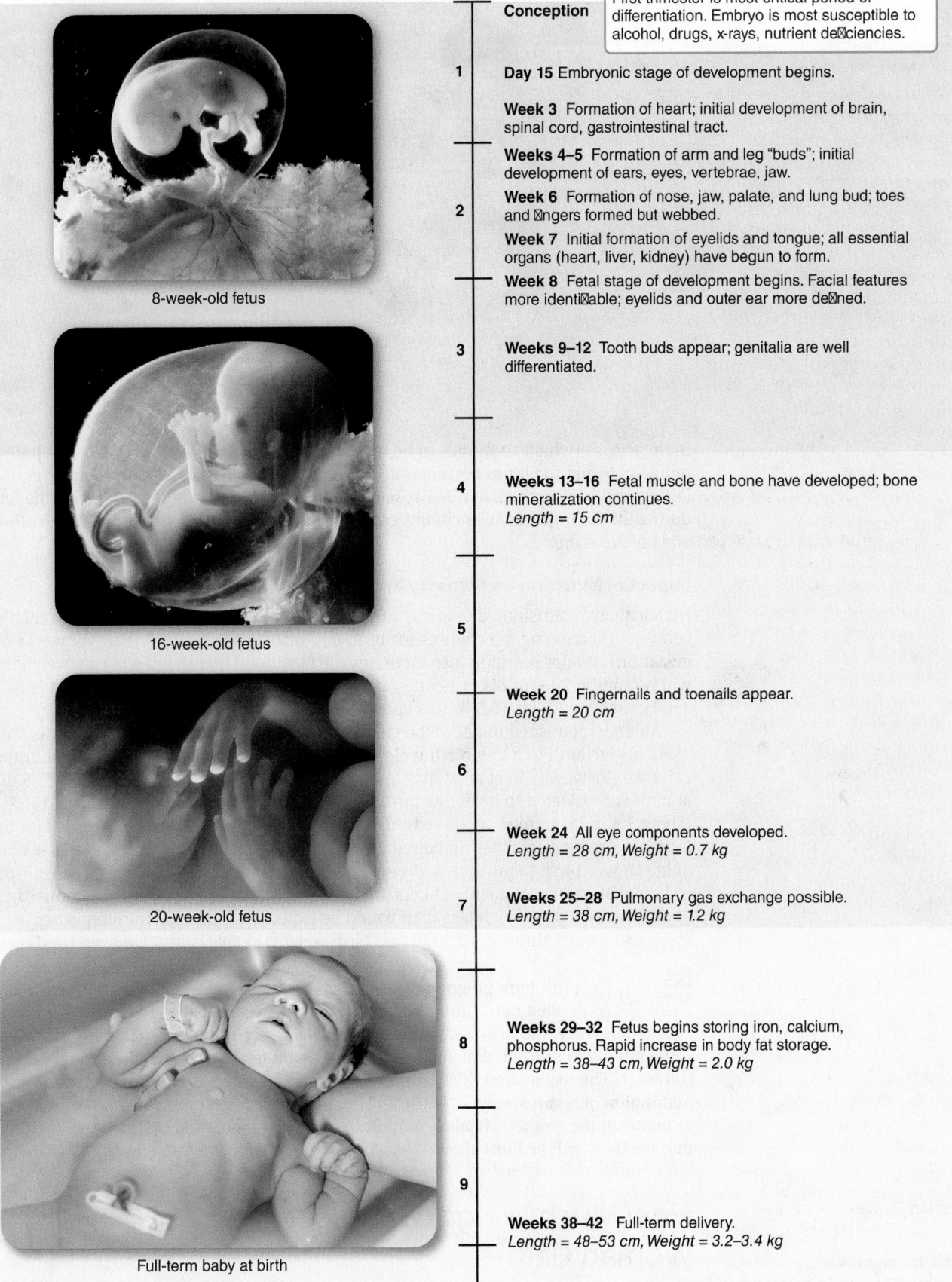

MONTH

Conception

First trimester is most critical period of differentiation. Embryo is most susceptible to alcohol, drugs, x-rays, nutrient deficiencies.

1

Day 15 Embryonic stage of development begins.

Week 3 Formation of heart; initial development of brain, spinal cord, gastrointestinal tract.

Weeks 4–5 Formation of arm and leg "buds"; initial development of ears, eyes, vertebrae, jaw.

2

Week 6 Formation of nose, jaw, palate, and lung bud; toes and fingers formed but webbed.

Week 7 Initial formation of eyelids and tongue; all essential organs (heart, liver, kidney) have begun to form.

Week 8 Fetal stage of development begins. Facial features more identifiable; eyelids and outer ear more defined.

8-week-old fetus

3

Weeks 9–12 Tooth buds appear; genitalia are well differentiated.

4

Weeks 13–16 Fetal muscle and bone have developed; bone mineralization continues.
Length = 15 cm

16-week-old fetus

5

Week 20 Fingernails and toenails appear.
Length = 20 cm

6

Week 24 All eye components developed.
Length = 28 cm, Weight = 0.7 kg

20-week-old fetus

7

Weeks 25–28 Pulmonary gas exchange possible.
Length = 38 cm, Weight = 1.2 kg

8

Weeks 29–32 Fetus begins storing iron, calcium, phosphorus. Rapid increase in body fat storage.
Length = 38–43 cm, Weight = 2.0 kg

Full-term baby at birth

9

Weeks 38–42 Full-term delivery.
Length = 48–53 cm, Weight = 3.2–3.4 kg

Figure 14.4 A timeline of embryonic and fetal development.

Figure 14.5 A healthy two-day-old infant (right) compared to two low-birth-weight infants.

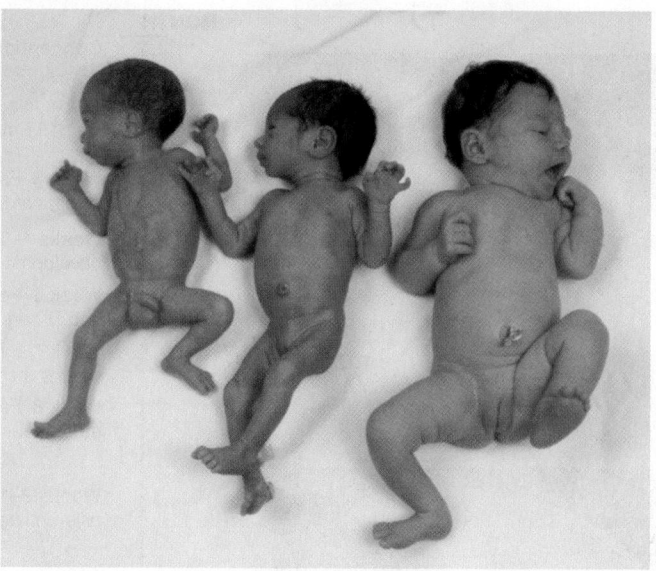

Brain growth (which continues to be rapid for the first two years of life) is also quite remarkable and the lungs become fully mature. The fetus acquires eyebrows, eyelashes, and hair on the head. Because of the intense growth and maturation of the fetus during the third trimester, it continues to be critical that the mother eat an adequate and balanced diet.

Impact of Nutrition on Maturity and Birth Weight

An adequate, nourishing diet is one of the most important variables under a woman's control for increasing the chances for birth of a mature newborn (at 38 to 42 weeks of **gestation**). Proper nutrition also increases the likelihood that the newborn's weight will be appropriate for his or her gestational age. Generally, a birth weight of at least 2500 grams, or 2.5 kg. (5.5 lb.), is considered a marker of a successful pregnancy.

An undernourished mother who gains too little weight during her pregnancy is more likely to give birth to a **low birth weight** baby than a woman with appropriate nutritional intake (Viswanathan et al., 2008). An infant weighing less than 2500 g (about 5.5 lb.) at birth is considered to be of low birth weight and an infant weighing less than 1500 g (about 3.3 lb.) is termed very low birth weight. Both groups are at increased risk for infection, learning disabilities, impaired physical development, and death in the first year of life (Figure 14.5). Many low- and very low birth weight babies are born **preterm**—that is, before 38 weeks' gestation. Others are born at term but are small for gestational age; in other words, they weigh less than would be expected. Although nutrition is not the only factor contributing to maturity and birth weight, its role cannot be overstated.

RECAP A full-term pregnancy lasts from 38 to 42 weeks and is traditionally divided into trimesters lasting 13 to 14 weeks. During the first trimester, cells differentiate and divide rapidly to form the various tissues of the human body. Vulnerability to nutrient deficiencies, toxicities, and teratogens is highest during this trimester. The second and third trimesters are characterized by continued growth and maturation of organ systems. Nutrition is important before and throughout pregnancy to maintain the mother's health, support fetal development, and increase the likelihood that the baby will be born after 37 weeks and will weigh at least 2500 grams (5.5 lb.).

gestation The period of intrauterine development from conception to birth.

low birth weight Having a weight of less than 2500 grams (5.5 lb.) at birth.

preterm The birth of a baby prior to 38 weeks' gestation.

How Much Weight Should a Pregnant Woman Gain?

Recommendations for weight gain vary according to a woman's weight *before* she became pregnant and whether she is expecting a single or multiple birth (Table 14.1). The average recommended weight gain for women of normal pre-pregnancy weight

TABLE 14.1 Recommended Weight Gain for Women During Pregnancy		
Pre-Pregnancy Weight Status	Body Mass Index (kg/m²)	Recommended Weight Gain kg (lb.)
Normal	18.5–24.9	11.5–16.0 kg (25–35 lb.)
Underweight	18.5	12.5–18.0 kg (28–40 lb.)
Overweight	25.0–29.9	7.0–11.5 kg (15–25 lb.)
Obese	30+	5–9 kg (11–20 lb.)

Source: The Sensible Guide to a Healthy Pregnancy. Health Canada, 2011. Reproduced with the permission from the Minister of Health, 2012.

is 11.5 to 16 kg or 25 to 35 pounds; underweight women should gain a little more than this amount, and overweight and obese women should gain less. The Institute of Medicine suggests that adolescents should follow the same recommendations as those for adult women (Rasmussen and Yaktine, 2009). Women of normal pre-pregnancy weight who are pregnant with twins are advised to gain 37 to 54 pounds (Rasmussen and Yaktine, 2009).

Women who have a low pre-pregnancy BMI (18.5 kg/m²) or gain too little weight during their pregnancy increase their risk of having a preterm or low-birth-weight baby and of dangerously depleting their own nutrient reserves. Gaining *too* much weight or being overweight (BMI $\geq$ 25 kg/m²) or obese (BMI $\geq$ 30 kg/m²) prior to conception is also risky. Excessive pre-pregnancy weight or prenatal weight gain increases the risk that the fetus will be large for gestational age, increasing the likelihood of trauma during vaginal delivery and of Cesarean birth. Also, children born to overweight or obese mothers have higher rates of childhood obesity (Wrotniak et al., 2008) and adolescent obesity (IOM, 2006). In addition, the more weight a woman gains during pregnancy, the more difficult it will be for her to return to pre-pregnancy weight and the more likely it is that her weight gain will be permanent.

In addition to amount of weight, the *pattern* of weight gain is important. During the first trimester, a woman of normal weight should gain no more than 1.4 to 2.3 kg (3 to 5 lb.). During the second and third trimesters, about 0.5 kg or 1 pound a week is considered healthful. Overweight women should gain only 300 grams (0.6 lb.) a week and, for obese women, a gain of 250 grams (0.5 lb.) a week is appropriate (Rasmussen and Yaktine, 2009). If weight gain is excessive in a single week, month, or trimester, the woman should not attempt to lose weight. Instead, the woman should merely attempt to slow the rate of weight gain. In short, weight gain throughout pregnancy should be slow and steady.

In a society obsessed with thinness, it is easy for pregnant women to worry about weight gain. Focusing on the quality of food consumed, rather than the quantity, can help women feel more in control. In addition, following a physician-approved exercise program helps women maintain a positive body image and prevent excessive weight gain.

A pregnant woman may also feel less anxious about her weight gain if she understands how that weight is distributed. Of the total weight gained in pregnancy, 4.5 to 5.5 kg (10 to 12 lb.) are accounted for by the fetus itself, the amniotic fluid, and the placenta **(Figure 14.6)**. In addition, the woman's blood volume increases 40%–50%, accounting for another 1.4 to 1.8 kg (3 to 4 lb.). A woman can expect to be about 4.5 to 5.5 kg (10 to 12 lb.) lighter immediately after the birth and, within about two weeks, another 2.3 to 3.6 kg (5 to 8 lb.) lighter because of fluid loss. After that, losing the remainder of pregnancy weight depends on more energy being expended than is taken in. Although the production of breast milk requires significant energy, the effect of breastfeeding on postpartum weight loss varies (USDHHS, 2007). We discuss breastfeeding on pages 511–518.

What Are a Pregnant Woman's Nutrient Needs?

The requirement for nearly all nutrients increases during pregnancy to accommodate the growth and development of the fetus without depriving the mother of the nutrients she needs to maintain her own health. With the exception of iron, most of these increased needs can be met by carefully selecting foods high in nutrient density.

Following a physician-approved exercise program helps pregnant women maintain a positive body image and prevent excess weight gain.

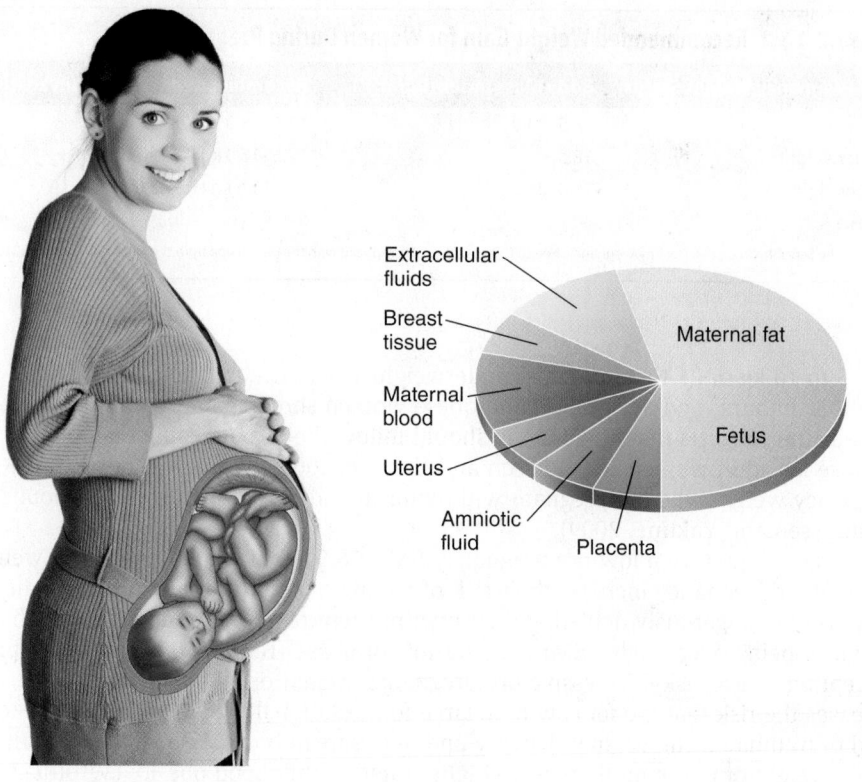

Figure 14.6 The weight gained during pregnancy is distributed between the mother's own tissues and the pregnancy-specific tissues.

Macronutrient Needs of Pregnant Women

During pregnancy, macronutrients provide necessary energy for building tissue. They are also the building blocks for the physical form and structure of the fetus, as well as for other pregnancy-associated tissues.

Energy Energy requirements increase only modestly during pregnancy. In fact, during the first trimester, a woman should consume approximately the same amount of energy (number of calories) daily as during her non-pregnant days. Instead of eating more, she should attempt to maximize the nutrient density of what she eats. For example, drinking low-fat milk is preferable to drinking soft drinks. Low-fat milk provides valuable protein, vitamins, and minerals to feed the fetus's rapidly dividing cells, while soft drinks provide nutritionally empty calories.

During the last two trimesters of pregnancy, energy needs increase by about 1470 to 1890 kJ (350 to 450 kcal) a day. For a woman consuming 8400 kJ or 2000 kcal/day, an extra 1680 kJ or 400 kcal represents only a 20% increase in calorie intake. For example, 250 mL (1 cup) of low-fat yogurt and a graham cracker with jam is about 1680 kJ (400 kcal). At the same time, some vitamin and mineral needs increase by as much as 50%, so again, the key for getting adequate micronutrients while not consuming too many extra calories is choosing nutrient-dense foods.

Protein and Carbohydrate During pregnancy, protein needs increase to 1.1 g/day/kg body weight (an additional 25 g or so of protein per day). Many women already eat this much protein each day. Dairy products, meats, eggs, and soy products are all rich sources of protein, as are legumes, nuts, and seeds.

Carbohydrate intake should be at least 175 g/day. The majority of carbohydrate intake should come from whole-grain breads and cereals, brown rice, fruits, vegetables, and legumes. Not only are these carbohydrate-rich foods good sources of the B-vitamins and other nutrients, but they also contain a lot of fibre. Fibre-rich foods contribute to one's sense of fullness, helping to avoid excess weight gain, and may lower risk of constipation.

Fat The guideline for the percentage of daily calories that come from fat does not change during pregnancy. Pregnant women should be aware that because new tissues and cells are being built some fat in the diet is essential. In addition, the fetus stores most of its own body fat during the third trimester; these fat stores serve as a critical source of fuel in the newborn period and allow newborns to effectively regulate their body temperature.

Moderation in the amount of dietary fat and consumption of the right kinds of fats are important. Like anyone else, pregnant women should limit their intakes of saturated and *trans* fats because of their negative impact on cardiovascular health (as discussed in Chapter 5). An omega-3 polyunsaturated fatty acid known as *docosahexaenoic acid (DHA)* has been found to be uniquely critical for both brain growth and eye development. Because the fetal brain grows dramatically during the third trimester, DHA is especially important in the maternal diet. Women who breastfeed also need to choose good dietary sources of DHA because of the rapid brain growth that occurs during the first three months of life. Good sources of DHA are oily fish, such as salmon, sardines, anchovies, and mackerel. It is also found in smaller amounts in tuna, shrimp, and lean fish such as cod and haddock. Another source is eggs that are DHA-enhanced by feeding hens a DHA-rich diet.

Pregnant women who eat fish should be aware of the potential for mercury contamination, as even a limited intake of mercury during pregnancy can impair a fetus's developing nervous system. For this reason, pregnant and breastfeeding women should limit their consumption of fresh and frozen tuna, shark, swordfish, marlin, orange roughy, and escolar (sometimes called snake mackerel or oilfish) to 150 grams per month. Canned tuna that is "light" (such as Skipjack or Yellowfin) is safe, but canned tuna from the large Albacore or Bluefin species (often labelled as "white") should be limited to 300 grams (4 *Canada's Food Guide* servings) a month (Health Canada, 2007a).

Micronutrient Needs of Pregnant Women

During pregnancy, expansion of the mother's blood supply and growth of the uterus, placenta, breasts, body fat levels, and the fetus itself all contribute to an increased need for micronutrients. In addition, the increased need for energy during pregnancy correlates with an increased need for the micronutrients involved in energy metabolism. Discussions of the micronutrients that are most critical during pregnancy follow. See **Table 14.2** for an overview of the changes in micronutrient needs with pregnancy.

Folate   Folate is the form of the vitamin that occurs naturally in food; folic acid is the synthetic form used in fortified foods (such as wheat) and supplements (Health Canada, 2008). Since folate is necessary for cell division, it follows that, during a time when both maternal and fetal cells are dividing rapidly, the requirement for this vitamin increases. Adequate folate is especially critical during the first 28 days after conception, when it is required for the formation and closure of the **neural tube**, an embryonic structure that eventually becomes the brain and spinal cord. Folate deficiency is associated with neural tube defects, such as **anencephaly**, a fatal defect in which brain tissue is partially or fully absent, and **spina bifida**, in which a portion

TABLE 14.2 Changes in Nutrient Recommendations with Pregnancy for Adult Women

Micronutrient	Pre-Pregnancy	Pregnancy	% Increase
Folate	400 μg/day	600 μg/day	50
Vitamin B$_{12}$	2.4 μg/day	2.6 μg/day	8
Vitamin C	75 mg/day	85 mg/day	13
Vitamin A	700 μg/day	770 μg/day	10
Vitamin D	15 μg/day	15 μg/day	0
Calcium	1000 mg/day	1000 mg/day	0
Iron	18 mg/day	27 mg/day	50
Zinc	8 mg/day	11 mg/day	38
Sodium	1500 mg/day	1500 mg/day	0
Iodine	150 μg/day	220 μg/day	47

neural tube Embryonic tissue that forms a tube, which eventually becomes the brain and spinal cord.

anencephaly A fatal neural tube defect in which there is partial absence of brain tissue, most likely caused by failure of the neural tube to close.

spina bifida The embryonic neural tube defect that occurs when the spinal vertebrae fail to completely enclose the spinal cord, allowing it to protrude.

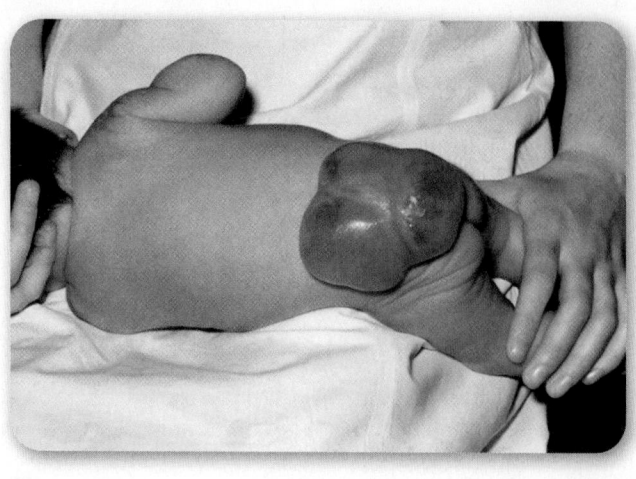

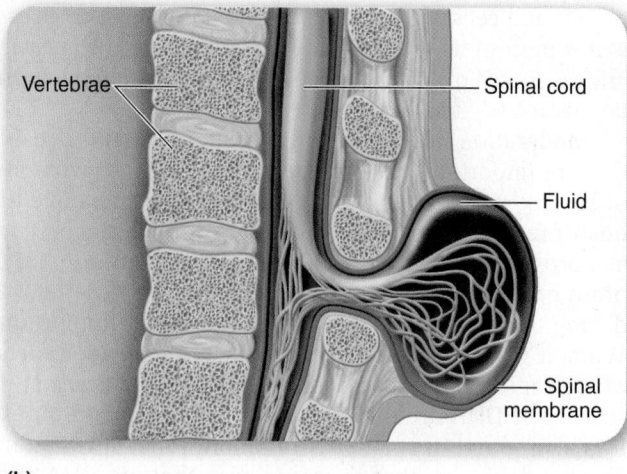

(a)

(b)

Vertebrae

Spinal cord

Fluid

Spinal membrane

◆ **Figure 14.7** Spina bifida, a common neural tube defect. **(a)** An external view of an infant with spina bifida. **(b)** An internal view of the protruding spinal membrane and fluid-filled sac.

◆ Spinach is an excellent source of folate.

of the spinal cord protrudes through the spinal vertebrae **(Figure 14.7)**. In the mildest form, occulta, there is a break between spinal vertebrae that is covered by skin but can be seen on x-rays. In meningocele, the spinal cord develops normally, but the meninges (the protective covering) protrudes through an opening in the lower back. In myelomeningocele, which is the most severe form, both the spinal nerves and their protective covering protrude through the opening (see Figure 14.7). Sometimes surgery can help to repair the spinal opening; however, there is usually some permanent nerve damage and many children with spina bifida suffer some paralysis of their lower bodies and need braces, crutches, or wheelchairs.

Adequate folate intake does not guarantee normal neural tube development, as the precise cause of neural tube defects is unknown, and there is a genetic component in some cases. In 2007, Dr. Philippe Gros, a biochemist at McGill University, and his team of researchers identified folate-responsive genes and non–folate-responsive genes associated with spina bifida, moving scientists one step closer to one day eradicating this debilitating birth defect (Bourguignon, 2007). Still, it is estimated that 70% of all neural tube defects could be prevented if all women of childbearing age consumed enough folate or folic acid (CDC, 2009b).

To reduce the risk for a neural tube defect, all women capable of becoming pregnant are encouraged to consume 400 µg of folate per day. Of course, folate remains very important even after the neural tube has closed. The RDA for folate for pregnant women is therefore 600 µg/day, a full 50% increase over the RDA for a non-pregnant female (IOM, 1998). A deficiency of folate during pregnancy can result in macrocytic anemia (a condition in which blood cells do not mature properly) and has been associated with low birth weight, preterm delivery, and failure of the fetus to grow properly. Sources of folate include fortified cereals and grains, spinach, and lentils.

An interesting fact about this vitamin is that the synthetic form, folic acid, is 1.7 times more bioavailable than the folate naturally found in food. All wheat flour in Canada is fortified with folic acid; 85% of the folic acid in a fortified product like bread is available for absorption, whereas only 50% of the folate naturally found in orange juice is available for absorption. Taking folic acid supplements on an empty stomach further increases the bioavailability (Health Canada, 2008).

Vitamin B$_{12}$ Vitamin B$_{12}$ (cobalamin) is vital during pregnancy because it regenerates the active form of folate. Not surprisingly, deficiencies of vitamin B$_{12}$ can also result in macrocytic anemia. Yet the RDA for vitamin B$_{12}$ for pregnant women is only 2.6 µg/day, a mere 8% increase over the RDA of 2.4 µg/day for non-pregnant women. How can this be? One reason is that, during pregnancy, absorption of vitamin B$_{12}$ is more efficient. The required amount of vitamin B$_{12}$ can easily be obtained from animal food sources. However, deficiencies have been observed in

HIGHLIGHT

Do Current Folate Recommendations Meet the Needs of Pregnant Women?

"Prior to folic acid fortification of the food supply in Canada, it was clear that most women did not consume the recommended intakes for folate. Unless their diet was meticulously planned, it was highly unlikely that women met their requirement for folate during pregnancy and lactation from dietary sources alone," explains Dr. Deborah O'Connor, director of Clinical Dietetics at the Hospital for Sick Children in Toronto. O'Connor's research career has been dedicated to increasing awareness of folate requirements before and during pregnancy and breastfeeding. She has been motivated by the growing body of evidence linking poor folate status during pregnancy and neural tube defects (NTD) in infants. Although she believes that Canada has made great improvements through the mandatory fortification of wheat flour with folic acid, her current research suggests that more needs to be done.

In her 2006 study published in the *Journal of Nutrition*, O'Connor demonstrates that almost one-third of the pregnant and breastfeeding women participating in her research did not meet current folate recommendations from diet alone (Sherwood et al., 2006). She states that "this is of obvious concern as it looks like, at mandated fortification levels, even well-off women with higher education are at risk." Therefore she recommends that "women still consume a multivitamin containing 400 µg folic acid at least three months before and three months after conception to prevent neural tube defects, regardless of the quality of their diet."

What other strategies might help women increase their folate intakes? O'Connor believes that "education is the cornerstone of this issue," particularly education on *Eating Well with Canada's Food Guide* with a focus on healthy foods, such as leafy green vegetables. These foods are naturally high in folate, whereas foods "fortified with folic acid are mostly made with white flour and are low in fibre." We need to encourage healthy eating, rather than giving the impression that folic acid supplements are the answer to a healthy pregnancy.

Should Canada increase folic acid fortification in foods to improve the status of pregnant and lactating women? O'Connor's 2006 study also touches on the risk of folic acid supplementation masking vitamin B_{12} deficiencies (Sherwood et al., 2006). She explains that "B_{12} deficiency is becoming more common in pregnant and lactating women. It is a deficiency not just seen in the elderly and those who follow a vegan diet. And unlike most nutrients, B_{12} deficiency is often reflected in breast milk, which is why all prenatal multivitamins now have B_{12} in them." She notes that "more is not always better" and we need to be mindful that increasing the levels of supplemental folic acid could have negative health effects. So what does O'Connor see for the future of folate? She hopes that "more research is done on how much folate is actually in our food supply. We have to understand what we are eating now before we move ahead with changes in fortification policies."

women who follow a vegan diet. Fortified foods or supplementation provides these women with the needed B_{12}.

Vitamin C Vitamin C is necessary for the synthesis of collagen, a component of connective tissue (including skin, blood vessels, and tendons) and part of the organic matrix of bones. The RDA for vitamin C during pregnancy is increased by a little more than 10% over the RDA for non-pregnant women (from 75 to 85 mg/day). A deficiency of vitamin C during pregnancy increases the risk for preterm birth and other complications. Abundant amounts of vitamin C are found in many food sources, such as citrus fruits and juices and numerous other fruits and vegetables.

Vitamin A Vitamin A needs increase during pregnancy by about 10%, to 770 µg/day. However, excess preformed vitamin A can cause fetal abnormalities, particularly heart defects and facial malformations. A well-balanced diet supplies sufficient vitamin A, so supplementation during pregnancy is not recommended. Beta-carotene (which is converted to vitamin A in the body) has not been associated with birth defects.

Vitamin D Despite the role of vitamin D in calcium absorption, the RDA for this nutrient does not increase during pregnancy. Pregnant women who receive adequate exposure to sunlight do not need vitamin D supplements. However, pregnant women with darkly pigmented skin and/or limited sun exposure who do not regularly drink milk will benefit from vitamin D supplementation. Most prenatal vitamin supplements contain 10 µg/day of vitamin D, which is considered safe and acceptable (IOM, 1997). Pregnant women should be cautious and avoid consuming excessive vitamin D from supplements, as toxicity can cause developmental disability in the newborn.

Calcium Growth of the fetal skeleton requires a significant amount of calcium. However, the AI for adult pregnant women is the same as that for non-pregnant women, 1000 mg/day, for two reasons. First, pregnant women absorb calcium from the diet more efficiently than do non-pregnant women. Second, the extra demand for calcium has not been found to cause demineralization of the mother's bones or to increase fracture risk; thus, there is no justification for higher intakes (IOM, 1997). Sources of calcium include milk, yogurt, and cheese; vegetables, such as kale, collard greens, and broccoli; and calcium-fortified soy milk, juices, and cereals.

Iron Recall from Chapter 10 the importance of iron in the formation of red blood cells, which transport oxygen throughout the body. During pregnancy, the demand for red blood cells increases to accommodate the needs of the mother's expanded blood volume, the growing uterus, the placenta, and the fetus itself. Thus, more iron is needed. Fetal demand for iron increases even further during the last trimester, when the fetus stores iron in the liver for use during the first few months of life.

Meats provide protein, vitamin B₁₂, heme iron, and zinc.

Severely inadequate iron intake has the potential to harm the fetus, resulting in an increased risk for low birth weight, preterm birth, and death of the newborn in the first weeks after birth. However, in most cases, the fetus builds adequate stores by "robbing" maternal iron, prompting iron-deficiency anemia in the mother. During pregnancy, maternal iron deficiency causes paleness and exhaustion, but at birth it endangers her life: anemic women are more likely to die during or shortly following childbirth because they are less able to tolerate blood loss and fight infection.

The RDA for iron for pregnant women is 27 mg/day, compared to 18 mg/day for non-pregnant women. This represents a 50% increase, despite the fact that iron loss is minimized during pregnancy because menstruation ceases. Typically, women of childbearing age have poor iron stores, and the demands of pregnancy are likely to produce a deficiency. To ensure adequate iron stores during pregnancy, an iron supplement (as part of, or distinct from, a total prenatal supplement) is routinely prescribed during the last two trimesters. Vitamin C enhances iron absorption, as do dietary sources of heme iron, whereas substances in coffee, tea, milk, bran, and oxalates decrease iron absorption. Therefore, many health-care providers recommend taking iron supplements with foods high in vitamin C and/or heme iron. Sources of iron include clams, fortified cereals, legumes, spinach, and meats.

Zinc The RDA for zinc for adult pregnant women increases by about 38% over the RDA for non-pregnant women, from 8 mg/day to 11 mg/day. Zinc is critical in DNA, RNA, and protein synthesis, and inadequate intake can lead to malformations in the fetus, premature labour, and extended labour. It should be noted that the absorption of zinc is inhibited by high intakes of non-heme iron, such as high-potency iron supplements, when these two minerals are taken with water (ODS NIH, 2007). However, when food sources of iron and zinc are consumed together in a meal, absorption of zinc is not affected. In addition, the heme form of iron does not appear to inhibit zinc absorption.

Sodium and Iodine During pregnancy, the AI for sodium is the same as for a non-pregnant adult woman, or 1500 mg (1.5 g) per day (IOM, 2004). Although too much sodium is associated with fluid retention, bloating, and high blood pressure, an increase in body fluids is a normal and necessary part of pregnancy, so some sodium is necessary to maintain fluid balance.

Iodine needs increase significantly during pregnancy, but the RDA of 220 µg/day is easy to achieve by using a modest amount of iodized salt (sodium chloride) during cooking.

Do Pregnant Women Need Supplements?

Prenatal multivitamin and mineral supplements are not strictly necessary during pregnancy, but most health-care providers recommend them. Meeting all the nutrient needs would otherwise take careful and somewhat complex dietary planning. Prenatal supplements are especially good insurance for special populations, such as vegans, adolescents, and others whose diet might normally be low in one or more micronutrients. It is important that pregnant women understand, however, that supplements are to be taken *in addition to*, not as a substitute for, a nutrient-rich diet.

Fluid Needs of Pregnant Women

Fluid allows for the necessary increase in the mother's blood volume, aids in regulating body temperature, and helps maintain the **amniotic fluid** that surrounds, cushions, and protects the fetus in the uterus. The AI for total fluid intake, which includes drinking water, beverages, and food, is 3 litres/day (or about 12.7 cups). This recommendation includes approximately 2.3 litres (10 cups) of fluid as total beverages, including drinking water (IOM, 2004).

Drinking adequate fluid also helps combat two common discomforts of pregnancy: fluid retention and, possibly, constipation. Drinking lots of fluids may also lower the risk for **urinary tract infections**, which are common in pregnancy. Fluids also combat dehydration, which can develop if a woman has frequent bouts of vomiting. For these women, fluids such as soups, juices, and sports beverages are usually well tolerated.

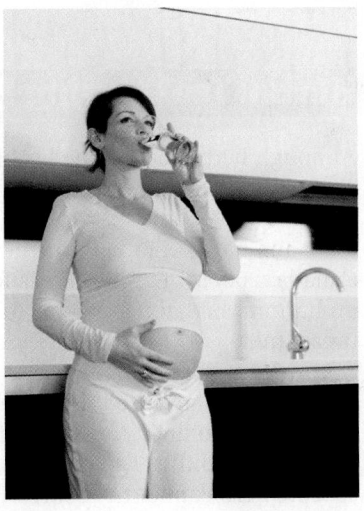

It is important that pregnant women drink about 2.3 litres or 10 cups of fluid a day.

RECAP Sufficient calories should be consumed so that a pregnant woman gains an appropriate amount of weight, typically 11.5 to 16.0 kg (25 to 35 lb.), to ensure adequate growth of the fetus. The calories consumed during pregnancy should be nutrient-dense. Protein, carbohydrates, and fats provide the building blocks for fetal growth. Folate deficiency has been associated with neural tube defects. Most health-care providers recommend prenatal supplements for pregnant women. Fluid provides for increased maternal blood volume and amniotic fluid.

Nutrition-Related Concerns for Pregnant Women

Pregnancy-related conditions involving a particular nutrient, such as iron-deficiency anemia, have already been discussed. The following sections describe some of the most common discomforts and disorders of pregnant women that are related to their general nutrition.

Morning Sickness

Morning sickness, or *nausea and vomiting of pregnancy (NVP)*, is a potentially serious medical condition (Lacasse et al., 2009). The symptoms vary in severity, from occasional mild queasiness to constant nausea with bouts of vomiting. In truth, "morning sickness" is not an appropriate name because the nausea and vomiting can begin at any time of the day and may last all day. NVP usually peaks between weeks 8 and 12, then resolves by weeks 12 to 16, but some women experience it throughout the pregnancy. Usually, the mother and fetus do not suffer lasting harm. However, some women experience such frequent vomiting that they are unable to nourish or hydrate themselves or their fetus adequately and may require hospitalization or in-home intravenous (IV) therapy.

There is no cure for morning sickness. However, some women find the following strategies helpful for reducing its severity:

- Eating small, frequent meals and snacks throughout the day. An empty stomach can trigger nausea.
- Consuming the majority of fluids between meals. Frozen ice pops, watermelon, gelatine desserts, and mild broths are some well-tolerated sources of fluid.
- Keeping snacks such as dry cereal or crackers at the bedside to ease nighttime queasiness or to eat before rising.

amniotic fluid The watery fluid contained within the innermost membrane of the sac containing the fetus. It cushions and protects the growing fetus.

urinary tract infection A bacterial infection of the urethra, the tube leading from the bladder to the body exterior.

morning sickness Varying degrees of nausea and vomiting associated with pregnancy, most commonly in the first trimester.

HIGHLIGHT
Herbal Teas During Pregnancy and Breastfeeding

Although herbs seem to be healthy and all natural, there are some herbs that can have dangerous drug-like effects (Ernst, 2002). Some may contain ingredients that can be toxic and harmful to both the mother and fetus (Health Canada, 2007b). Further, breastfeeding mothers may pass on harmful herbal ingredients to their baby through their breast milk.

In many cultures, the use of herbs is common and many benefits are cited. However, the current research on herbs is still limited; thus the potential benefits of herbal products are difficult to evaluate and the safety of any specific herb cannot be assured (Ernst, 2002).

According to Health Canada, there are certain herbal teas that are generally considered to be safe if taken in moderation. Drinking tea in moderation refers to having two to three cups of weak tea infusions a day. These teas

are ginger, linden flower, rose hip, lemon balm, orange peel, and citrus peel (PHAC, 2008). Drink a variety of these teas, rather than the same tea repeatedly, and make sure that tea is not replacing other nutrient-dense beverages, such as milk and juice.

Chamomile tea and teas with aloe, coltsfoot, juniper berry, pennyroyal, buckthorn bark, comfrey, sassafras, duck root, lobelia, and senna leaves are not recommended during pregnancy and breastfeeding (Health Canada, 2008). Some herbal teas contain caffeine, which should be limited to a total of 300 mg from all sources (coffee, colas, etc.) a day. Overall, pregnant and breastfeeding mothers need to be cautious with herbal products and read ingredient lists on labels. When in doubt about a product's safety, consult a health-care provider for advice.

⬆ Deep-fried foods are often unappealing to pregnant women.

- Taking prenatal supplements at a time of day when vomiting is least likely.
- Avoiding sights, sounds, smells, and tastes that bring on or worsen queasiness. Cold or room-temperature foods are often easier to tolerate than hot foods.
- Decreasing stress and getting some rest and relaxation time, if possible.

Raspberry tea soothes nausea in some women. Ginger tea may also be helpful but should be consumed in moderation. Women should always check with their health-care provider that the therapy they are using is safe and does not interact with other treatments, medications, or supplements. See the Highlight on herbal teas for further information.

Cravings and Aversions

It seems like nothing is more stereotypical about pregnancy than the image of a frazzled husband getting up in the middle of the night to run to the convenience store to get his pregnant wife some pickles and ice cream. This image, although humorous, is far from reality for most women. Although some women have specific cravings, most crave a general type of food ("something sweet" or "something salty") rather than a particular food.

Why do pregnant women crave certain tastes? Does a desire for salty foods mean that the woman is experiencing a sodium deficit? While some people believe that we crave what we need, scientific evidence is lacking. It is more likely that cravings during pregnancy are due to hormonal fluctuations or physiologic changes or have familial or cultural roots. Most cravings are, of course, for edible substances. But a surprising number of pregnant women crave non-foods, such as laundry starch and clay. This craving, called **pica**, can result in nutritional or health problems for the mother and fetus (Francis, 2010).

Food aversions are also common during pregnancy and may originate from social, cultural, or religious beliefs. In some cultures, for example, pregnant women avoid shellfish ("causes allergies") or citrus fruits ("may increase risk for a miscarriage"). These types of aversions may not be scientifically valid, but they are often strongly woven into the family's belief system.

Gastroesophageal Reflux

pica An abnormal craving to eat non-food substances such as clay, paint, or chalk.

Gastroesophageal reflux (GER), which was described in Chapter 3, is common during pregnancy because pregnancy-related hormones relax the smooth muscle of the lower esophagus. During the last two trimesters, the enlarging uterus pushes up on the stomach, worsening the problem. Practical tips for minimizing GER during pregnancy include the following:

- Avoid excessive weight gain, tight clothing, overeating, and foods that seem to trigger the problem.
- Chew food slowly.
- Wait for at least one hour after eating before lying down.
- Sleep with the head of the bed elevated.

In addition, the woman's health-care provider may be able to suggest an antacid that is safe for use during pregnancy.

Constipation

Hormone production during pregnancy causes the smooth muscles to relax, including the muscles of the large intestine, slowing the movement of food residue through the large intestine or colon. In addition, pressure exerted by the growing uterus on the colon can slow movement even further, making elimination difficult. Practical hints that may help a pregnant woman avoid constipation include the following:

- Eat 25 to 35 g of fibre each day, concentrating on fresh fruits and vegetables, legumes, and whole grains.
- Keep fluid intake high as fibre intake increases. Drink plenty of water and eat water-rich fruits and vegetables, such as melons, citrus, and lettuce.
- Keep physically active, as exercise is one of many factors that help increase motility of the large intestine.

Gestational Diabetes

Gestational diabetes, diagnosed in approximately 3.7% of non-Aboriginal women and up to 8%–18% in Aboriginal women (Canadian Diabetes Association, 2012), is generally a temporary condition in which a pregnant woman is unable to produce sufficient insulin or becomes insulin resistant, resulting in elevated levels of blood glucose. Fortunately, gestational diabetes has no ill effects on either the mother or the fetus if blood glucose levels are strictly controlled through diet, exercise, and/ or medication. Screening for gestational diabetes is routine for almost all healthcare practitioners and is necessary because the symptoms, which include frequent urination, fatigue, and an increase in thirst and appetite, appear to be the same as normal pregnancy symptoms.

If not controlled, gestational diabetes can result in a baby who is too large as a result of receiving too much glucose across the placenta during fetal life. Inappropriately large infants are at risk for early delivery and trauma during vaginal birth, and they may need to be born by Cesarean section. There is also evidence that exposing a fetus to maternal diabetes significantly increases the risk for overweight, type 2 diabetes, and metabolic syndrome during later life (Clausen et al., 2009; Reece, 2010).

Women who are obese, women who are age 35 years or older, and women of Aboriginal, African American, or Hispanic origin have a greater risk of developing gestational diabetes. Any woman who develops gestational diabetes has a 40%–60% risk of developing type 2 diabetes within the next 5 to 10 years—particularly if she is obese to begin with or fails to maintain normal body weight after pregnancy. As with any form of diabetes, attention to diet, weight control, and physical activity reduces the risk for gestational diabetes.

Hypertensive Disorders of Pregnancy

About 1% of pregnancies are complicated by pre-existing hypertension, or high blood pressure, and 5%–6% develop gestational hypertension (Magee et al., 2008). The term *hypertensive disorders of pregnancy* encompasses several different conditions (JOGC, 2008). A woman who develops high blood pressure, with no other symptoms, during her pregnancy is said to have *gestational hypertension*. **Preeclampsia** is characterized by a sudden increase in maternal blood pressure with swelling, excessive and rapid weight gain unrelated to food intake, and protein in the urine; 1%–2% of pregnant women will

Foods high in fibre, such as dried fruits, reduce the chances of constipation.

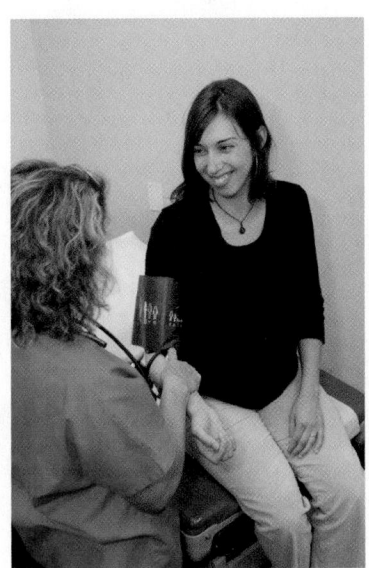

Pregnant women have their blood pressures taken to test for gestational hypertension.

gestational diabetes Insufficient insulin production or insulin resistance that results in consistently high blood glucose levels, specifically during pregnancy; the condition typically resolves after birth occurs.

preeclampsia High blood pressure that is pregnancy-specific and accompanied by protein in the urine, edema, and unexpected weight gain.

develop preeclampsia (JOGC, 2008). If left untreated, it can progress to *eclampsia*, characterized by seizures, kidney failure, and, potentially, fetal and/or maternal death.

No one knows exactly what causes the various hypertensive disorders of pregnancy, but deficiencies in dietary protein, vitamin C, vitamin E, calcium, and magnesium seem to increase the risk. Women who are pregnant for the first time, adolescents, over the age of 35 to 40 years, African American, or diabetic and those with a family history of eclampsia are at greater risk. Management focuses mainly on blood pressure control. Typical treatments include medication and close monitoring, with hospitalization if necessary. Ultimately, the only thing that will cure the condition is childbirth. Today, with good prenatal care, gestational hypertension is nearly always detected early and can be appropriately managed, and outcomes for both mother and fetus are usually very good. In nearly all women without prior chronic high blood pressure, maternal blood pressure returns to normal within about a day after the birth.

Adolescent Pregnancy

Throughout the adolescent years, a woman's body continues to change and grow. Peak bone mass has not yet been reached. Full physical stature may not have been attained, and teens are more likely to be underweight than are young adult women. Thus, pregnant adolescents have higher needs for calories and bone-related nutrients, such as calcium. In addition, many adolescents have not established healthful nutritional patterns. Adolescent mothers are more likely than more mature women to have preterm births, low-birth-weight babies, and other complications related to nutritional deficiencies (Stewart, Walsh, and Van Eyk, 2008). With adequate and thorough prenatal care and close attention to proper nutrition and other healthful behaviours, the likelihood of a positive outcome for both the adolescent mother and the infant is greatly increased.

Vegetarianism

Dietetics professionals recognize that well-planned vegetarian diets are appropriate for pregnant women (Craig, Mangels, and the American Dietetic Association, 2009). With the possible exception of iron and zinc, vegetarian women who consume dairy products and/or eggs (lacto-ovo-vegetarians) have no nutritional concerns beyond those encountered by every pregnant woman. In contrast, women who are totally vegetarian (vegan) need to be more vigilant than usual about their intake of nutrients that are derived primarily or wholly from animal products. These include vitamin D (unless regularly exposed to adequate sunlight throughout pregnancy), vitamin B_6, vitamin B_{12}, calcium, iron, and zinc. Supplements containing these nutrients are usually necessary. A regular prenatal supplement will fully meet the vitamin and iron needs of a vegan woman but does not fulfill calcium needs, so a separate calcium supplement, or consumption of calcium-fortified soy milk or orange juice, is usually required.

Consumption of Caffeine

Caffeine is a stimulant found in several foods, including coffee, tea, soft drinks, and chocolate. Caffeine crosses the placenta and thus reaches the fetus. Current thinking holds that women should avoid caffeine intakes above 300 mg per day (the equivalent of 250 to 500 mL or 1 to 2 cups of coffee) (ADA, 2008). Evidence suggests that consuming higher daily doses of caffeine (the higher the dose, the more compelling the evidence) may increase the risk for miscarriage and low birth weight. Coffee and colas have no nutritional value and can make one feel full and provide considerable calories (if sweetened). Low- or non-fat decaf lattes offer a more healthful nutrient profile than coffee alone.

Consumption of Alcohol

Frequent drinking (more than seven drinks per week) or occasional binge drinking (more than four to five drinks on one occasion) during pregnancy increases the risk for miscarriage, complications during delivery, preterm birth, and sudden infant death syndrome. In addition, as we discuss *In Depth* on pages 530–533, alcohol is a known teratogen, and its consumption during pregnancy increases the risk that the baby will be born with any of a variety of birth defects **(Figure 14.8)**. The more the mother drinks, the greater the potential harm to the fetus. The term fetal alcohol spectrum disorders (FASD) refers to a range of conditions that result from maternal intake of alcohol (National Organization on Fetal Alcohol Syndrome, 2001–2004).

Heavy drinking (more than three to four drinks per day) throughout pregnancy can result in a condition called **fetal alcohol syndrome (FAS)**, the most severe form of FASD. Babies born with FAS have characteristic malformations, particularly of the face, limbs, heart, and nervous system. They have a high mortality rate, and those who survive typically have emotional, behavioural, social, learning, and developmental problems throughout life.

Other birth defects associated with maternal alcohol consumption are *alcohol-related birth defects* (*ARBD*), *alcohol-related neurodevelopmental disorder* (*ARND*), and *fetal alcohol effects* (*FAE*). Children with ARBD are born with heart, skeletal, kidney, ear, and eye malformations, while those with ARND demonstrate a range of lifelong developmental, behavioural, and mental problems (for example, hyperactivity and attention deficit disorder). The diagnosis of FAE is used when a child does not meet all the traits of FAS. Although some women do have the occasional alcoholic drink with no apparent ill effects, there is no amount of alcohol that is known to be safe. The best advice regarding alcohol during pregnancy is to abstain, if not from before conception then as soon as pregnancy is suspected.

Figure 14.8 A child with fetal alcohol spectrum disorder (FASD). The facial features characteristic of children with FASD include a short nose with a low, wide bridge, drooping eyes with an extra skinfold, and a flat, thin upper lip. Behavioural problems and learning disorders are also characteristic. The effects of FASD are irreversible.

Smoking

Although the dangers of smoking are well known, approximately 20%–30% of pregnant women in Canada use tobacco during some or all of their pregnancy (Health Canada, 2007c). Maternal smoking exposes the fetus to toxins such as lead, cadmium, cyanide, nicotine, and carbon monoxide. Fetal blood flow is reduced, which limits the delivery of oxygen and nutrients, resulting in impaired fetal growth and development. Maternal smoking greatly increases the risk for miscarriage, stillbirth, placental abnormalities, preterm delivery, and low birth weight. Rates of sudden infant death syndrome, respiratory illness, and allergies are higher in the infants and children of smokers compared to those of non-smokers.

Illegal Drugs

Despite the fact that the use of illegal drugs is unquestionably harmful to the fetus, more than 5% of U.S. pregnant women report using illicit drugs (Substance Abuse and Mental Health Services Administration, 2008). Unfortunately, Canadian data on the prevalence of illicit drug use during pregnancy is lacking. Most drugs pass through the placenta into fetal blood, where they accumulate in fetal tissues and organs, including the liver and brain. Prenatal use of illegal drugs also impairs placental blood flow (thereby reducing the transfer of nutrients to the fetus) and increases the risk for low birth weight, premature delivery, miscarriage, and placental defects. Newborns suffer signs of withdrawal, including tremors, excessive crying, sleeplessness, and poor feeding. Even after several years, children are at greater risk for developmental delays, impaired learning, and behavioural problems. All women are strongly advised to stop taking drugs before becoming pregnant. There is no safe level of use for illegal drugs during pregnancy.

Food Safety

As mentioned earlier, women who are or could become pregnant, as well as breast-feeding mothers, are advised to avoid eating large fish, particularly fresh or frozen tuna, shark, swordfish, marlin, orange roughy, and escolar, and to limit their intake of canned albacore tuna, because of their high mercury content. In addition, other foods should be avoided because pregnant women are at higher risk of developing food-borne illnesses that are dangerous for them and their unborn babies. These

fetal alcohol syndrome (FAS) The most serious form of FASD, characterized by irreversible birth defects and mental abnormalities.

TABLE 14.3 Foods to Avoid and Safer Alternatives During Pregnancy

Type of Food	Food to Avoid	Safer Alternative
Hot Dogs	Hot dogs straight from the package without further heating	Hot dogs thoroughly cooked to a safe internal temperature. The middle of the hot dog should be steaming hot or 74°C (165°F) Wash your hands after handling hot dogs.
Deli meats	Non-dried deli meats, such as bologna, roast beef and turkey breast.	Dried and salted deli meats such as salami and pepperoni. Non-dried deli meats heated throughout to steaming hot.
Egg and egg products	Raw or lightly cooked egg or egg products, including salad dressings, cookie dough or cake batter, sauces, and drinks such as homemade eggnog.	Egg dishes thoroughly cooked to a safe internal temperature. Eggs should be cooked until the yolk is firm. Homemade eggnog must be heated to 71°C (160°F). Pasteurized egg products can be used when making uncooked food that calls for raw eggs.
Meat and poultry	Raw or undercooked meat or poultry, such as steak tartare.	Meat and poultry cooked to a safe internal temperature (check using a digital food thermometer).
Seafood	Raw seafood, such as sushi. Raw oysters, clams, and mussels. Refrigerated, smoked seafood.	Seafood cooked to a safe internal temperature of 74°C (165°F). Cook until the shell has opened. Smoked seafood in cans that do not require refrigeration until after opening. Refrigerated smoked seafood can be eaten safely when fully cooked to a safe internal temperature.
Dairy products	Raw or unpasteurized dairy products, including soft and semi-soft cheese, such as Brie, Camembert, and blue-veined cheese.	Pasteurized dairy products, hard cheeses such as Colby, Cheddar, Swiss, and Parmesan.
Sprouts	Raw sprouts such as alfalfa, clover, radish, and mung beans.	Thoroughly cooked sprouts.
Pâtés and meat spreads	Refrigerated pâtés and meat spreads.	Pâtés and meat spreads sold in cans or those that do not require refrigeration until after opening.
Fruit juice and cider	Unpasteurized fruit juice and cider.	Unpasteurized fruit juice and cider brought to a rolling boil and cooled. Pasteurized fruit juice and cider.

Source: It's Your Health: Food Safety for Pregnant Women. Health Canada, 2010. Reproduced with the permission from the Minister of Health, 2012.

⬥ During pregnancy, women should adjust their physical activity to comfortable low-impact exercises.

include infections from *Listeria*, **E. coli** O157:H7, vibrio (found in raw and undercooked shellfish), and salmonella (Health Canada, 2010). See **Table 14.3** for foods to avoid and safer alternatives during pregnancy.

Soft cheeses, such as Brie, feta, Camembert, and Mexican-style cheeses, also called *queso blanco* or *queso fresco*, should be avoided unless the label specifically states the product is made with pasteurized milk. Unpasteurized milk and cheeses may be contaminated with the bacterium *Listeria monocytogenes*, which triggers miscarriage, premature birth, or fetal infection when consumed during pregnancy. Pregnant women should follow all the safe food-handling practices discussed in Chapter 13 to ensure a healthy pregnancy outcome.

Exercise

Physical activity during pregnancy is beneficial and recommended for healthy women experiencing normal pregnancies (Gavard and Artal, 2008). Exercise can help keep a woman physically fit during pregnancy, enhance mood, and, by moderating weight gain, help women feel more in control of their changing bodies. Moreover, regular moderate exercise will improve cardiovascular fitness and help keep blood pressure low.

If a woman was not active prior to pregnancy, she should begin an exercise program slowly and progress gradually under the guidance of her health-care provider. If a woman was physically active before pregnancy, she can continue to be physically active during pregnancy, within reason and comfort. Walking, the most common activity among pregnant women, is an excellent low-impact choice. Women who were avid runners before pregnancy can often continue to run, although they may need to limit the distance and intensity of their runs.

RECAP About half of all pregnant women experience morning sickness. Heartburn and constipation in pregnancy are related to hormonal relaxation of smooth muscle. Gestational diabetes and hypertensive disorders can seriously affect maternal and fetal well-being. The nutrient needs of pregnant adolescents are so high that adequate nourishment becomes difficult. Women who follow a vegan diet usually need to consume supplements during pregnancy. Caffeine intake should be limited, and the use of alcohol, cigarettes, and illegal drugs should be completely avoided during pregnancy. Safe food choices and handling practices are especially important during pregnancy. Exercise (provided the mother has no contraindications) can enhance the health of a pregnant woman.

Lactation: Nutrition for Breastfeeding Mothers

Throughout most of human history, infants have thrived on only one food: breast milk. But during the first half of the twentieth century, commercially prepared infant formulas slowly began to replace breast milk as the mother's preferred feeding method. Aggressive marketing campaigns convinced many families, even in developing nations, to switch. Soon formula-feeding had become a status symbol, proof of the family's wealth and modern thinking. In the 1970s, this trend began to reverse with a renewed appreciation for the natural simplicity of breastfeeding. At the same time, several international organizations, including the World Health Organization, UNICEF, and La Leche League, began to promote the nutritional, immunologic, financial, and emotional advantages of breastfeeding and developed programs to encourage and support breastfeeding worldwide. These efforts have paid off: data from the Canadian Health Survey 2009–10 showed that 87% of mothers breastfed or attempted breastfeeding with their last child. The rates range from 93% in British Columbia and gradually decline across Canada to 75% in the Atlantic provinces (Health Canada, 2012). Worldwide, more than half of all women breastfeed exclusively for at least six months, but rates of initiation and continuation of breastfeeding vary greatly between countries. For example, rates of initiation of breastfeeding are extremely low in Eastern Europe and Central Asia, whereas the highest rates are in Latin America, the Caribbean, and Eastern and Northern Africa (Jana, 2009).

How, exactly, does breastfeeding occur? What nutrients are important for breastfeeding mothers? And what exactly are the advantages that everyone is talking about? The answers to these questions are presented in the following sections.

How Does Lactation Occur?

Lactation, the production of breast milk, is a process that is set in motion during pregnancy in response to several hormones. Once established, lactation can be sustained as long as the mammary glands continue to receive the proper stimuli.

The Body Prepares During Pregnancy

Throughout pregnancy, the placenta produces estrogen and progesterone. In addition to performing various functions to maintain the pregnancy, these hormones prepare the breasts physically for lactation. The breasts increase in size, and milk-producing glands (alveoli) and milk ducts are formed **(Figure 14.9)**. Toward the end of pregnancy, the hormone *prolactin* increases. Prolactin is released by the anterior pituitary gland and is responsible for milk synthesis. However, estrogen and progesterone suppress the effects of prolactin during pregnancy.

What Happens After Childbirth

By the time a pregnancy has come to full term, the level of prolactin is about ten times higher than it was at the beginning of pregnancy. At birth, the suppressive effect of estrogen and progesterone ends, and prolactin is free to stimulate milk production. The first substance to be released is **colostrum**, sometimes called pre-milk or first milk. It is thick, yellowish in colour, and rich in protein and micronutrients, and it includes

lactation The production of breast milk.

colostrum The first fluid made and secreted by the breasts from late in pregnancy to about a week after birth. It is rich in immune factors and protein.

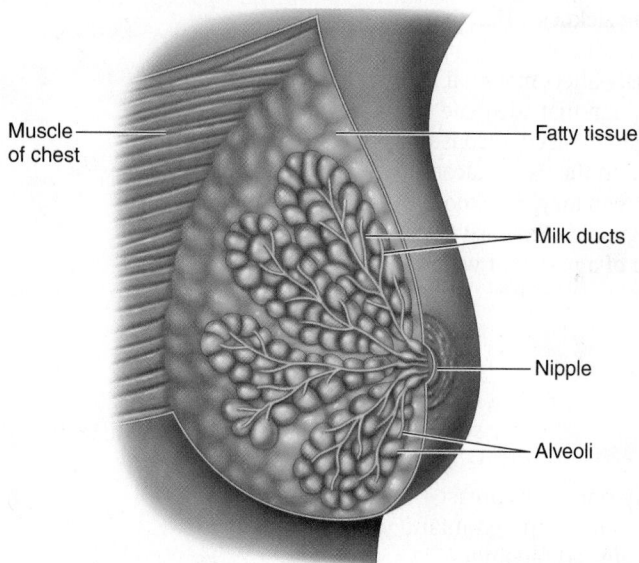

⬆ Figure 14.9 Anatomy of the breast. During pregnancy, estrogen and progesterone secreted by the placenta foster the preparation of breast tissue for lactation. This process includes breast enlargement and development of the milk-producing glands, or alveoli.

antibodies that help protect the newborn from infection. Colostrum also contains a factor that fosters the growth of a particular species of "friendly" bacteria in the infant gastro-intestinal tract. These bacteria in turn prevent the growth of other, potentially harmful bacteria. Finally, colostrum has a laxative effect in infants, helping the infant expel *meconium,* the sticky "first stool."

Within two to four days in most women, colostrum is fully replaced by mature milk. Mature breast milk contains protein, fat, and carbohydrate (in the form of the sugar lactose). Much of the protein and fat is synthesized in the breast, while the rest enters the milk from the mother's bloodstream.

Mother–Infant Interaction Maintains Milk Production

Continued, sustained breast milk production depends entirely on infant suckling (or a similar stimulus, such as a mechanical breast pump). Infant suckling stimulates the continued production of prolactin, which in turn stimulates more milk production. The longer and more vigorous the feeding, the more milk will be produced. Thus, even multiples (twins, triplets) can be successfully breastfed.

Prolactin allows for milk to be produced, but that milk has to move through the milk ducts to the nipple to reach the baby's mouth. The hormone responsible for this "let down" of milk is *oxytocin.* Like prolactin, oxytocin is produced by the pituitary gland, and its production is dependent on the suckling stimulus at the beginning of a feeding **(Figure 14.10)**. This response usually occurs within 10 to 30 seconds but can be significantly inhibited by stress. Finding a relaxed environment in which to breastfeed is therefore important.

▶ Figure 14.10 Sustained milk production depends on the mother–child interaction during breastfeeding, specifically the suckling of the infant. Suckling stimulates the continued production of prolactin, which is responsible for milk production, and oxytocin, which is responsible for the "let down" response.

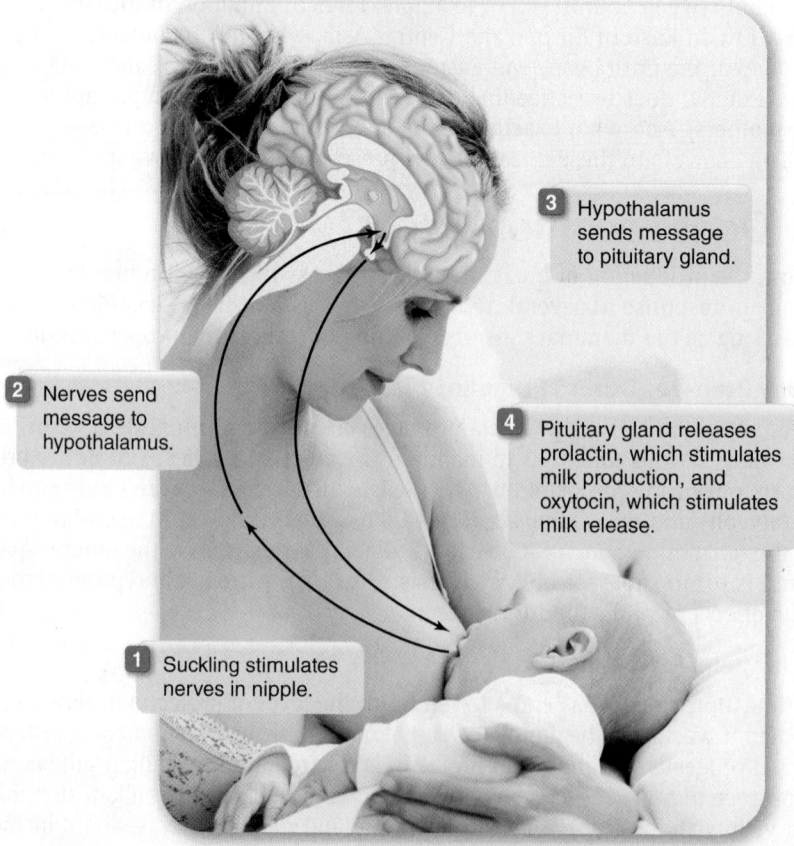

3 Hypothalamus sends message to pituitary gland.

2 Nerves send message to hypothalamus.

4 Pituitary gland releases prolactin, which stimulates milk production, and oxytocin, which stimulates milk release.

1 Suckling stimulates nerves in nipple.

What Are a Breastfeeding Woman's Nutrient Needs?

You might be surprised to learn that breastfeeding requires even more energy than pregnancy! This is because breast milk has to supply an adequate amount of all the nutrients an infant needs to grow and develop.

Nutrient Recommendations for Breastfeeding Women

It is estimated that milk production requires about 2930 to 3350 kJ (700 to 800 kcal) per day. It is generally recommended that lactating women 19 and older consume 1390 kJ (330 kcal) per day above their pre-pregnancy energy needs during the first six months of lactation and 1680 kJ (400 kcal) per day during the second six months. This additional energy is sufficient to support adequate milk production. The remaining energy deficit will assist in the gradual loss of excess fat and body weight gained during pregnancy. It is critical that lactating women avoid severe energy restriction, as this practice can result in decreased milk production.

The weight loss that occurs during breastfeeding should be gradual, approximately 0.5 to 2.0 kg (1 to 4 lb.) per month. Both breastfeeding and participation in regular physical activity can assist with weight loss. Some active women, however, may lose too much weight during breastfeeding and must either increase their energy intake or reduce their activity level to maintain health.

Of the macronutrients, protein and carbohydrate needs are different from pregnancy requirements. Increases of 15 to 20 g of protein per day and 80 g of carbohydrate per day above pre-pregnancy requirements are recommended during lactation.

Can a Mother Breastfeed Her Adopted Baby?

It might sound impossible, but it's not! Some women who wish to breastfeed their adopted baby have induced lactation by stimulating production of the hormones that naturally cause milk production and "let down." How? The most common method is to pump both breasts using a hospital-grade breast pump three times a day, beginning about two months before the expected adoption date. The woman's physician can also prescribe pharmaceutical estrogen, progesterone, or other medications that mimic the effects of pregnancy. If used, these are discontinued before breastfeeding begins, at which point the infant's suckling should stimulate and maintain milk production (Mayo Clinic, 2008).

Women who breastfeed also need good dietary sources of the omega-3 fatty acid DHA to support the rapid brain growth of the newborn.

The needs for several vitamins and minerals increase over the requirements of pregnancy. These include vitamins A, C, and E; riboflavin; vitamin B_{12}; biotin; and choline and the minerals copper, chromium, manganese, iodine, selenium, and zinc. The requirement for folate during lactation is 500 μg/day, which is decreased from the 600 μg/day required during pregnancy, but it is still higher than pre-pregnancy needs (400 μg/day).

Requirements for iron decrease significantly during lactation, to a mere 9 mg/day. This is because iron is not a significant component of breast milk, and breastfeeding usually suppresses menstruation for at least a few months, minimizing iron losses.

Calcium is a significant component of breast milk; however, as in pregnancy, calcium absorption is enhanced during lactation, and urinary loss of calcium is decreased. In addition, some calcium appears to come from the demineralization of the mother's bones, and increased dietary calcium does not prevent this. Thus, the recommended intake for calcium for a lactating woman is unchanged from pregnancy and non-pregnant guidelines—that is, 1000 mg/day. Because of their own continuing growth, however, teen mothers who are breastfeeding should continue to consume 1300 mg/day. Typically, if calcium intake is adequate, a woman's bone density returns to normal shortly after lactation ends.

Do Breastfeeding Women Need Supplements?

If a breastfeeding woman appropriately increases her energy intake, and does so with nutrient-dense foods, her nutrient needs can usually be met without supplements. However, there is nothing wrong with taking a basic multivitamin for insurance, as long as it is not considered a substitute for proper nutrition. Lactating women should consume omega-3 fatty acids in either fish or supplements to increase the levels of DHA in their breast milk to support the infant's developing nervous system. Women who do not consume dairy products should monitor their calcium intake carefully.

Fluid Recommendations for Breastfeeding Women

Because extra fluid is expended with every feeding, lactating women need to consume about an extra 1 litre (about 1 quart) of fluid per day. This extra fluid facilitates milk production and reduces risk for dehydration. Many women report that, within a minute or two of beginning to nurse their baby, they become intensely thirsty. To prevent this thirst and achieve the recommended fluid intake, women are encouraged to drink a nutritious beverage, such as water, juice, or milk, each time they nurse their baby. However, it is not good practice to drink hot beverages while nursing because accidental spills could burn the infant.

RECAP Lactation is the result of the coordinated effort of several hormones, including estrogen, progesterone, prolactin, and oxytocin. Breasts are prepared for lactation during pregnancy, and infant suckling provides the stimulus that sustains the production of the prolactin and oxytocin needed to maintain the milk supply. It is recommended that lactating women consume an extra 1260 to 1680 kJ (300–400 kcal) per day above pre-pregnancy energy intake, including increased protein, DHA, certain vitamins and minerals, and fluids. The requirements for folate and iron decrease from pregnancy levels, while the requirement for calcium remains the same.

Getting Real About Breastfeeding: Advantages and Challenges

Breastfeeding is the perfect way to nourish a baby for its first six months of life. However, the technique does require patience and practice, and teaching by an experienced mother or a certified lactation consultant is important. La Leche League International (see Web Resources at the end of this chapter) and "Baby Friendly" hospitals can provide ongoing support and advice. For some women, illness, medication use, or other factors may make breastfeeding a difficult choice. The decision to breastfeed or use formula must be made by each family after careful consideration of all the factors that apply to their situation.

Advantages of Breastfeeding

As adept as formula manufacturers have been at simulating the components of breast milk, an exact replica has never been produced. In addition, there are benefits that mother and baby can access only through breastfeeding (ESPGHAN Committee on Nutrition, 2009).

Nutritional Quality of Breast Milk The amount and types of protein in breast milk are ideally suited to the human infant. The main protein in breast milk, lactalbumin, is easily digested in infants' immature gastrointestinal tracts, reducing the risk for gastric distress. Other proteins in breast milk bind iron and prevent the growth of harmful bacteria that require iron. Antibodies from the mother are additional proteins that help prevent infection while the infant's immune system is still immature. Certain proteins in human milk improve the absorption of iron; this is important, since breast milk is low in iron. Cow's milk contains too much protein for infants, and the types of protein in cow's milk are harder for the infant to digest.

The primary carbohydrate in milk is lactose, a disaccharide composed of glucose and galactose. The galactose component is important in nervous system development. Lactose provides energy and prevents ketosis in the infant, promotes the growth of beneficial bacteria, and increases the absorption of calcium. Breast milk has more lactose than cow's milk does, reinforcing the advantages of the breast-feeding process.

The amounts and types of fats in breast milk are ideally suited to the human infant. DHA and arachidonic acid (ARA) have been shown to be essential for growth and development of the infant's nervous system and for development of the retina of the eyes. In 2003, Health Canada approved their addition to commercial infant formulas (Health Canada, 2003). Interestingly, the concentration of DHA in breast milk varies considerably, reflecting the amount of DHA in the mother's diet, and is highest in women who regularly consume fish.

The fat content of breast milk, which is higher than that of whole cow's milk, changes according to the gestational age of the infant and during the course of every feeding: The milk that is initially released (called *foremilk*) is watery and low in fat, somewhat like skim milk. This milk is thought to satisfy the infant's initial thirst. As the feeding progresses, the milk acquires more fat and becomes more like whole milk. Finally, the very last 5% or so of the milk produced during a feeding (called the *hind milk*) is very high in fat, similar to cream. This milk is thought to satiate the infant. It is important to let infants suckle for at least 20 minutes at each feeding, so that they get this hind milk. Breast milk is also relatively high in cholesterol, which supports the rapid growth and development of the brain.

Another important aspect of breastfeeding (or any type of feeding) is the fluid it provides the infant. Because of their small size, infants are at risk for dehydration, which is one reason feedings must be consistent and frequent. This topic will be discussed at greater length in the section on infant nutrition.

In terms of micronutrients, breast milk is a good source of readily absorbed calcium and magnesium. It is low in iron, but the iron it does contain is easily absorbed. Since healthy full-term infants store iron in preparation for the first few months of life, most experts agree that their iron needs can be met by breast milk alone for the first six months, after which iron-rich foods are needed. Health Canada (2007) recommends that breastfed infants receive 10 µg (400 IU) per day of a vitamin D supplement for the first 12 months of life.

Breast milk composition continues to change as the infant grows and develops. Because of this ability to change as the baby changes, breast milk alone is entirely sufficient to sustain infant growth for the first six months of life (Health Canada, 2007b). In addition, exclusively breast-fed infants maintain total control over their food intake, allowing them to self-regulate energy intake during a critical period of growth and development. Some researchers believe this self-regulation accounts for the finding that breast-fed babies grow in length and weight at a slower rate than formula-fed infants. The relationship between breastfeeding and lifelong patterns of weight gain are explored in more detail in the Nutrition Debate at the end of this chapter.

Throughout the next six months of infancy, as solid foods are gradually introduced, breast milk remains the baby's primary source of superior-quality nutrition. Health Canada's recommendation (2007) is to: "Encourage exclusive breastfeeding for the first 6 months of life, as breast milk is the best food for optimal growth. Breastfeeding may continue for up to 2 years and beyond."

Protection from Infections, Allergies, and Residues   Immune factors from the mother, including antibodies and immune cells, are passed directly from the mother to the newborn through breast milk. These factors provide important disease protection for the infant while its immune system is still immature. It has been shown that breast-fed infants have a lower incidence of respiratory tract, gastrointestinal tract, and urinary tract infections than formula-fed infants. Even a few weeks of breastfeeding is beneficial, but the longer a child is breastfed, the greater the level of passive immunity from the mother. In the United States, infant mortality rates are reduced by 21% in breast-fed infants (American Academy of Pediatrics, 2005).

In addition, breast milk is nonallergenic, and breastfeeding is associated with a reduced risk for allergies during childhood and adulthood. Breast-fed babies also have fewer ear infections, die less frequently from **sudden infant death syndrome (SIDS)**,

Breastfeeding has benefits for both the mother and her infant.

Some breastfed babies refuse to take a bottle.

sudden infant death syndrome (SIDS) The sudden death of a previously healthy infant; the most common cause of death in infants over one month of age.

and have a decreased chance of developing diabetes, overweight and obesity, and chronic digestive disorders.

Exclusively breast-fed infants are also protected from exposure to known and unknown contaminants and residues that may be found in baby bottles and cans of infant formulas. Recent concerns have centred on bisphenol A (BPA), a toxic chemical that has been found in some brands of reusable bottles and formula cans. See the Hot Topic in Chapter 13, page 469.

Physiologic Benefits for Mother   Breastfeeding causes uterine contractions, which quicken the return of the uterus to pre-pregnancy size and reduce bleeding. Many women also find that breastfeeding helps them lose the weight they gained during pregnancy, particularly if it continues for more than six months. In addition, breastfeeding appears to be associated with a decreased risk for breast cancer (Collaborative Group on Hormonal Factors in Breast Cancer, 2003). The relationship between breastfeeding and osteoporosis is still unclear, and more research on this topic is needed (Agency for Healthcare Research and Quality, 2007).

Breastfeeding also suppresses ovulation, lengthening the time between pregnancies and giving a mother's body the chance to recover before she conceives again. This benefit can be life-saving for malnourished women living in countries that discourage or outlaw the use of contraceptives. Ovulation may not cease completely, however, so it is still possible to become pregnant while breastfeeding. Health-care providers typically recommend the use of additional birth control methods while breastfeeding to avoid another conception occurring too soon to allow a mother's body to recover from the earlier pregnancy.

Mother–Infant Bonding   Breastfeeding is among the most intimate of human interactions. Ideally, it is a quiet time away from distractions when mother and baby begin to develop an enduring bond of affection known as *attachment*. Breastfeeding enhances attachment by providing the opportunity for frequent, direct skin-to-skin contact, which stimulates the baby's sense of touch and is a primary means of communication. Most hospitals now permit round-the-clock rooming-in of breast-fed infants to optimize the initiation and continuation of breastfeeding. The cuddling and intense watching that occur during breastfeeding begin to teach the mother and baby about the other's behavioural cues. Breastfeeding also reassures the mother that she is providing the best possible nutrition for her baby.

Undoubtedly, bottle-feeding does not preclude parent–infant attachment! As long as attention is paid to closeness, cuddling, and skin and eye contact, bottle-feeding can foster bonding as well.

Convenience and Cost   Breast milk is always ready, clean, at the right temperature, and available on demand, whenever and wherever it is needed. In the middle of the night, when the baby wakes up hungry, a breastfeeding mother can respond almost instantaneously, and both are soon back to sleep. In contrast, formula-feeding is a time-consuming process: parents have to continually wash and sterilize bottles, and each batch of formula must be mixed and heated to the proper temperature.

In addition, breastfeeding costs nothing other than the price of a modest amount of additional food for the mother. In contrast, formula can be relatively expensive, and there are the additional costs of bottles and other supplies, as well as the cost of energy used for washing and sterilization. A hidden cost of formula-feeding is its effect on the environment: the energy used and waste produced during formula manufacturing, marketing, shipping and distribution, preparation, and disposal of used packaging. In contrast, breastfeeding is environmentally responsible, using no external energy and producing no external wastes.

Challenges Associated with Breastfeeding

For some women and infants, breastfeeding is easy from the very first day. Others experience some initial difficulty, but with support from an experienced nurse, lactation consultant, or volunteer mother from La Leche League, the experience becomes successful and pleasurable. In contrast, some families encounter difficulties that make formula-feeding their best choice. This section discusses some challenges that may impede the success of breastfeeding.

Effects of Drugs and Other Substances on Breast Milk   Many substances, including illegal, prescription, and over-the-counter drugs, pass into breast milk. Breastfeeding mothers should inform their physician that they are breastfeeding. If a safe and effective form of a necessary medication cannot be found, the mother will have to avoid breastfeeding while she is taking the drug. During this time, she can pump and discard her breast milk, so that her milk supply will be adequate when she resumes breastfeeding.

Caffeine, alcohol, and nicotine also enter breast milk. Caffeine can make the baby agitated and fussy, whereas alcohol can make the baby sleepy, depress the central nervous system, and slow motor development, in addition to inhibiting the mother's milk supply. Women who are breastfeeding should abstain from alcohol, since it easily passes into the breast milk at levels equal to blood alcohol concentrations. Nicotine also passes into breast milk; therefore, it is best for the woman to quit smoking altogether.

Environmental contaminants, including pesticides, industrial solvents, dioxins, and heavy metals (such as lead and mercury), can pass into breast milk when breastfeeding mothers are exposed to these chemicals. Mothers can limit their infants' exposure to these harmful substances by controlling their own environments. Fresh fruits and vegetables should be thoroughly washed and peeled to minimize exposure to pesticides and fertilizer residues. Exposure to paint fumes, gasoline, solvents, and similar products should be greatly limited. Even with some exposure to these environmental contaminants, U.S. and international health agencies all agree that the benefits of breastfeeding almost always outweigh potential concerns (Nickerson, 2006).

Food components that pass into the breast milk may seem innocuous; however, some substances, such as those found in garlic, onions, peppers, broccoli, and cabbage, are distasteful enough to the infant to prevent proper feeding. Some babies have allergic reactions to foods the mother has eaten, such as wheat, cow's milk, eggs, or citrus, and suffer gastrointestinal upset, diaper rash, or another reaction. The offending foods must then be identified and avoided.

Maternal HIV Infection   HIV, which causes AIDS, can be transmitted from mother to baby through breast milk. Thus, HIV-positive women in the United States and Canada are encouraged to feed their infants formula. This recommendation does not apply to all women worldwide, however, since the low cost and sanitary nature of breast milk, as compared to the potential for water-borne diseases with formula-feeding, often make breastfeeding the best choice for women in developing countries, even among populations with high rates of HIV infection and exposure (Kline, 2009).

▲ Working moms can be discouraged from—or supported in— breastfeeding in a variety of ways.

Conflict Between Breastfeeding and the Mother's Employment   Breast milk is absorbed more readily than formula, making more frequent feedings necessary. Newborns commonly require breastfeedings every one to three hours versus every two to four hours for formula feedings. In Canada, full-time working women are entitled to 12 months of maternity leave, although not all new mothers use their full maternity leave. Mothers who are exclusively breastfeeding and return to work within the first six months after the baby's birth must leave several bottles of pumped breast milk for others to feed the baby in their absence each day. This means that working women have to pump their breasts to express the breast milk during the workday. This can be a challenge in companies that do not provide the time, space, and privacy required.

Work-related travel is also a concern: if the mother needs to be away from home for longer than 24 to 48 hours, she can typically pump and freeze enough breast milk for others to give the baby in her absence. When longer business trips are required, some mothers take the baby with them and arrange for childcare at their destination. Others resort to pumping, freezing, and shipping breast milk home via overnight mail. Understandably, many women cite returning to work as the reason they switch to formula-feeding (Adams et al., 2001).

Some working women successfully combine breastfeeding with commercial formula-feeding. For example, a woman might breastfeed in the morning before she leaves for work, as soon as she returns home, and once again before retiring at night. The remainder of the feedings are formula given by the infant's father or a childcare

☞ Although a much more common practice today than in the past, breastfeeding in public can still meet with disapproval.

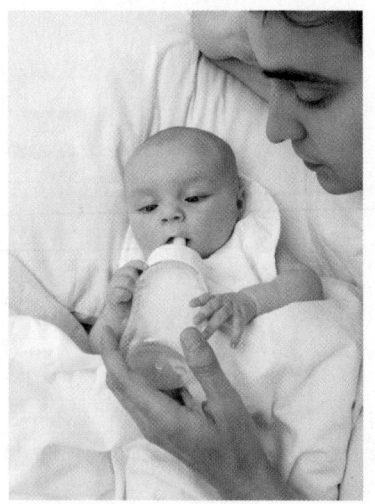

☞ Fathers and siblings can bond with infants through bottle-feeding and other forms of close contact.

provider. Women who choose supplemental formula-feedings usually find that their bodies adapt quickly to the change and produce ample milk for the remaining breastfeedings.

Social Concerns In North America, women have been conditioned to keep their breasts covered in public, even when feeding an infant. However, public places are beginning to be more accommodating for nursing mothers. For example, separate nursing rooms can often be found adjacent to, but not within, public restrooms. Special nursing clothing or judicious placement of a scarf or shawl allows women to breastfeed discreetly. When women feel free to breastfeed in public, the baby's feeding schedule becomes much less confining. According to the human rights legislation under Canadian law, women have the right to breastfeed in the workplace and in public. However, only British Columbia (www.ag.gov.bc.ca/human-rights-protection/pdfs/SexDiscrimination&Harassment.pdf) and Ontario (www.ohrc.on.ca/en/pregnancy-and-breastfeeding) have provincial human rights laws that specifically address breastfeeding. Despite this legal protection, many women find it extremely challenging to breastfeed in a public place or at work.

What About Bonding for Fathers and Siblings?

With all the attention given to attachment between a breastfeeding mother and her infant, it is easy for fathers and siblings to feel left out. One option that allows other family members to participate in infant feeding is to supplement breastfeedings with bottle-feedings of stored breast milk or formula. If a family decides to share infant feeding in this manner, bottle-feedings can begin as soon as breastfeeding has become well established. That way, the infant will not become confused by the artificial nipple. Fathers and other family members can also bond with the infant when bathing and/or clothing the infant, as well as through everyday cuddling and play.

RECAP Breastfeeding provides many benefits to both mother and newborn, including superior nutrition, heightened immunity, mother–infant bonding, convenience, and cost. However, breastfeeding may not be the best option for every family. The mother may need to use a medication that enters the breast milk and makes it unsafe for consumption. A mother's job may interfere with the baby's requirement for frequent feedings. The infant's father and siblings can participate in feedings using a bottle filled with either pumped breast milk or formula.

Infant Nutrition: From Birth to One Year

Most first-time parents are amazed at how rapidly their infant grows. Optimal nutrition is extremely important during the first year, as the baby's organs and nervous system continue to develop and the baby grows physically. In fact, physicians use length and weight measurements as the main tools for assessing an infant's nutritional status. These measurements are plotted on growth charts (there are separate charts for boys and girls), which track an infant's growth over time (**Figure 14.11** and appendices for additional growth charts). Although every infant is unique, in general, physicians look for a correlation between length and weight. In other words, an infant who is in the 60th percentile for length is usually in about the 50th to 70th percentile for weight. An infant who is in the 90th percentile for weight but is in the 20th percentile for length might be overfed. Consistency over time is also a consideration: for example, an infant who suddenly drops well below her established profile for weight might be underfed or ill.

Typical Infant Growth and Activity Patterns

Babies' basal metabolic rates are high, in part because their body surface area is large compared to their body size. Still, their limited physical activity keeps total energy expenditure relatively low. For the first few months of life, an infant's activities

WHO GROWTH CHARTS FOR CANADA

GIRLS

BIRTH TO 24 MONTHS: GIRLS

Length-for-age and Weight-for-age percentiles

NAME: _____

DOB: _____ RECORD # _____

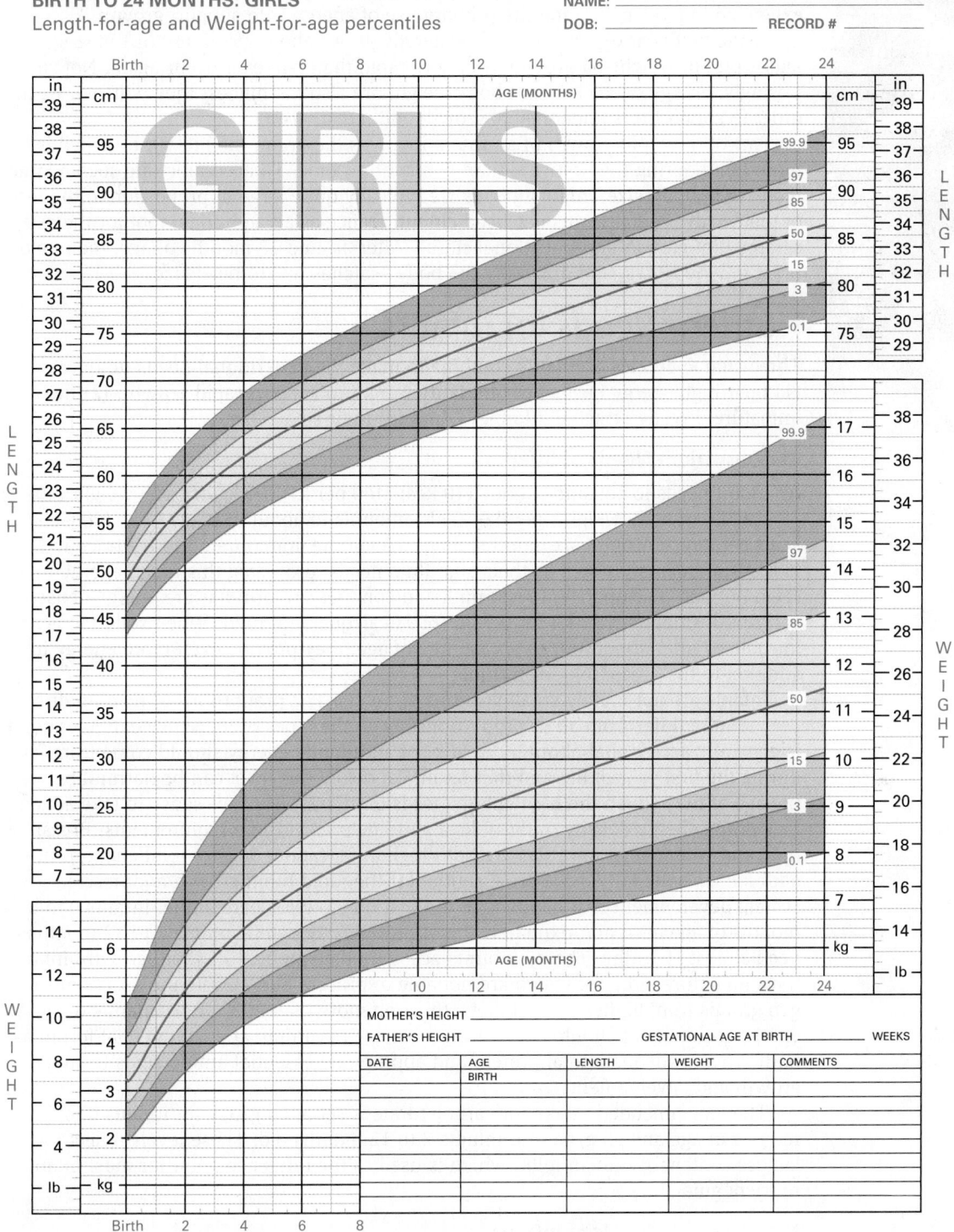

Figure 14.11 The 2006 World Health Organization (WHO) Child Growth Standards have been adapted for Canada by Dietitians of Canada, Canadian Paediatric Society, the College of Family Physicians of Canada, and Community Health Nurses of Canada. This growth chart is for girls from birth to 24 months, and has both length-for-age and weight-for-age percentiles.

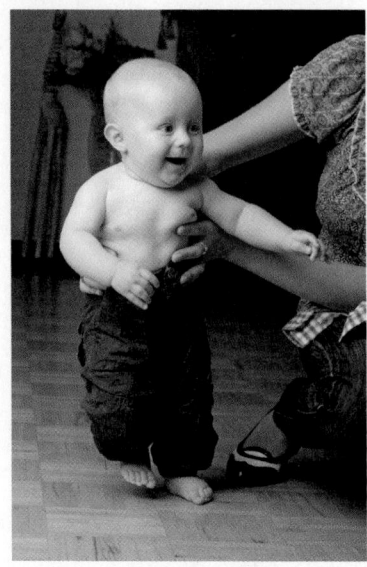

⬆ An infant's physical activity will progress beyond crawling before the first year of life is over.

consist mainly of eating and sleeping. As the first year progresses, the repertoire of activity gradually expands to include rolling over, sitting up, crawling, standing, and finally taking the first few wobbly steps. Nevertheless, relatively few calories are expended in movement, and the primary use of energy is to support growth.

In the first year of life, an infant generally grows about 25 cm (10 in.) in length and triples in weight—a growth rate more rapid than will ever occur again. Not surprisingly, energy needs per unit body weight are also the highest they will ever be in order to support this phenomenal growth and metabolism.

Part of the rapid growth of an infant involves the brain, the growth of which is more rapid during the first year than at any other time. To accommodate such a large increase in brain size, infants' heads are typically quite large in proportion to the rest of their body. Pediatricians use head circumference as an additional tool for the assessment of growth and nutritional status. After around 18 months of age, the rate of brain growth slows, and gradually the body "catches up" to head size.

Nutrient Needs for Infants

Three characteristics of infants combine to make their nutritional needs unique: (1) their high energy needs per unit body weight to support rapid growth, (2) their immature digestive tract and kidneys, and (3) their small size.

Macronutrient Needs of Infants

An infant needs to consume about 110 kcal (460 per kJ) per kg of body weight (40–50 kcal/lb. of body weight) per day. This amounts to about 2520–2730 kJ (600–650 kcal) per day at around six months of age. Given the immature digestive tract and kidneys of infants, as well as their high fluid needs, providing this much energy may seem difficult. Fortunately, breast milk and commercial formulas are energy dense, contributing about 2730 kJ per 0.95 L (650 kcal/quart) of fluid. When solid foods are introduced after about four to six months of age, they provide even more energy in addition to the breast milk or formula.

Infants are not merely small versions of adults. The proportions of macronutrients they require differ from adult proportions, as do the types of food they can tolerate. It is generally agreed that about 40%–50% of an infant's energy should come from fat during the first year of life and that fat intake below this level can be harmful before the age of two. Given the high energy needs of infants, it makes sense to take advantage of the energy density of fat (9 kcal/g) to help meet these requirements. Breast milk and commercial formulas are both high in fat (about 50% of total energy). In addition, specific fatty acids are essential for the rapid brain growth and nervous system development that happens in the first one to two years of life. Infants 0 to 6 months of age need approximately 9 g of protein/day, while infants 7 to 12 months need almost 10 g/day. These amounts accommodate an infant's rapid growth. Infants have immature kidneys, which are not able to process and excrete the excess nitrogen groups from higher-protein diets; thus, no more than 20% of an infant's daily energy requirement should come from protein. Breast milk and commercial formulas both provide adequate total protein and appropriate essential amino acids to support growth and development.

The recommended intake for carbohydrate is set at 60 g/day for infants 0 to 6 months of age and 95 g/day for infants 7 to 12 months old. These levels reflect the lactose content of human milk, which is used as the reference point for most infant nutrient guidelines.

Micronutrient Needs of Infants

Infants need micronutrients to accommodate their rapid growth and development. The micronutrients of particular concern are iron, vitamin D, zinc, fluoride, and iodide. Fortunately, breast milk and commercial formulas provide most of the micronutrients needed for infant growth and development, with some special considerations, discussed shortly.

In addition, all infants are routinely given an injection of vitamin K shortly after birth. This provides vitamin K until the infant's intestine can develop its own healthful bacteria, which then contribute to the infant's supply of vitamin K.

Do Infants Need Supplements?

Breast milk and commercial formulas provide most of the vitamins and minerals infants need. However, several micronutrients may warrant supplementation. For breastfed infants, a supplement containing vitamin D is commonly prescribed from birth to 12 months of age, even in sunny climates, because exposure of a young infant's skin to adequate direct sunlight for vitamin D synthesis is not advised (American Academy of Pediatrics, 2005). Breastfed infants also require additional iron beginning no later than six months of age because the infant's iron stores become depleted and breast milk is a poor source of iron. Iron is extremely important for cognitive development and prevention of iron-deficiency anemia. Starting solid foods (infant rice cereal) fortified with iron at four to six months of age can serve as an additional iron source. In addition, if the mother is a vegan, her breast milk may be low in vitamin B_{12}, and a supplement of this vitamin should be given to the baby. Fluoride is important for strong tooth development, but fluoride supplementation is not recommended during the first six months of life.

For formula-fed infants, supplementation depends on the formula composition and the water supply used to make the formula. Many formulas are already fortified with iron, for example, and some municipal water supplies contain fluoride. If the municipal water supply has fluoride at 0.3 parts per million or greater, then no fluoride supplements should be given for the first two years of life (Health Canada, 2007b). If the water supply has less than 0.3 ppm, babies between the ages of six months and two years may receive 0.25 mg/day of fluoride supplements.

If a supplement is given, the dose should be considered carefully. The supplement should be formulated specifically for infants, and the daily dose should not be exceeded. High doses of micronutrients can be dangerous. Too much iron can be fatal, too much fluoride can cause discoloration and pitting of the teeth, and too much vitamin D can lead to calcification of soft tissue, such as the kidneys.

Fluid Recommendations for Infants

Fluid is critical for everyone, but for infants the balance is more delicate for two reasons. First, because infants are so small, they proportionally lose more water through evaporation than adults. Second, their kidneys are immature and unable to concentrate urine. Hence, they are at even greater risk for dehydration. An infant needs about 65 mL (2 fl. oz.) of fluid per 0.5 kg (1 lb.) of body weight, and either breast milk or formula is almost always enough to provide this amount. Experts agree that "infants exclusively fed human milk do not require supplemental water" (IOM, 2004). However, certain conditions, such as diarrhea, vomiting, fever, or hot weather, can greatly increase fluid loss. In these instances, supplemental fluid, ideally water, may be necessary. Since too much fluid can be particularly dangerous for an infant, supplemental fluids (whether water or an infant electrolyte formula) should be given only under the advice of a physician. Generally, it is advised that supplemental fluids not exceed 125 mL (4 fl. oz.) per day, and parents should avoid giving sugar water, fruit juices, or any sweetened beverage in a bottle. Parents can be sure that their infant's fluid intake is appropriate if the infant produces six to eight wet diapers per day.

What Types of Formula Are Available?

We discussed the advantages of breastfeeding earlier in this chapter, and indeed both national and international health-care organizations consider breastfeeding the best choice for infant nutrition, when possible. However, if breastfeeding is not feasible, several types of commercial formulas provide nutritious alternatives. The composition, processing, packaging and labelling of all infant formulas are regulated under the Canadian Food and Drug Regulations (Health Canada, 2007b). In Canada, iron-fortified infant formulas are designed to meet the nutritional needs of healthy term infants until 9 to 12 months of age (Health Canada, 2007b).

Most formulas are based on cow's milk proteins, casein and whey, that have been modified to make them more appropriate for human infants. The sugars lactose and sucrose, alone or in combination, provide carbohydrates, and vegetable oils and/or

NUTRITION LABEL ACTIVITY
Reading Infant Food Labels

Imagine that you are a new parent shopping for infant formula. **Figure 14.12** shows the label from a typical can of formula. As you can see, the ingredients list is long and has many technical terms. Even well-informed parents would probably be stumped by many of them. Fortunately, with the information you learned in previous chapters, you can probably answer the following questions.

- The first ingredient listed is water, followed by *modified milk ingredients*. What do you think this provides: protein, fat, or carbohydrate?
- The fourth ingredient listed is *lactose*. Is lactose a form of protein, fat, or carbohydrate? Why is it important for infants?
- The front label states that the formula has a blend of *docosahexaenoic acid (DHA)* and *arachidonic acid (ARA)*. Are DHA and ARA forms of protein, fat, or carbohydrate? Why are these two nutrients thought to be important for infants?

The label also claims that this formula is "Our Closest Formula to Breast Milk." Can you think of some differences between breast milk and this formula that still exist?

Look at the list of nutrients on the label. You will notice that there is no "% Daily Value" column, which you see on most food labels. The next time you are at the grocery store, look at other baby food items, such as baby cereal or pureed fruits. Do their labels simply list the nutrient content or is the "% Daily Value" column used? Why do you think infant formula has a different label format?

Let's say you are feeding a six-month-old infant who needs about 2100 kJ or 500 kcal/day. Using the information from the nutrition section of the label, you

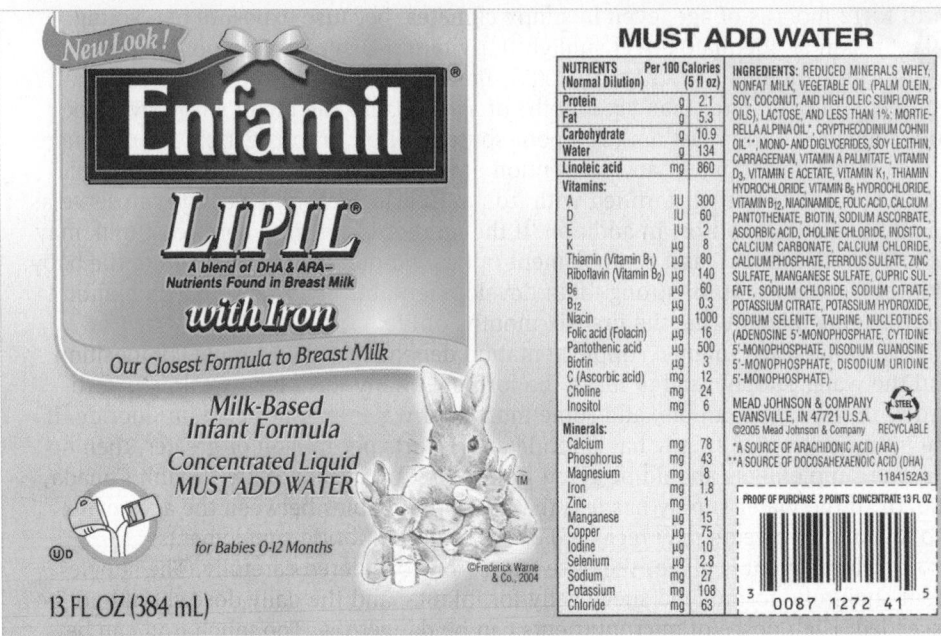

Figure 14.12 An infant formula label. Notice that there is a long list of ingredients and no % Daily Value.

can calculate the number of millilitres of formula the baby needs (this assumes that no cereal or other foods are eaten):

There are 280 kJ or 68 kcal per 100 mL or 2.8 kJ per mL
2100 kJ ÷ 2.8 kJ per mL = 750 mL of formula per day to meet the baby's energy needs

A six-month-old infant needs about 210 mg calcium per day. Based on an intake of 750 mL (approx. 25 fl. oz.) of formula per day, as just calculated, you can use the label nutrition information to calculate the amount of calcium that is provided:

There are 53 mg calcium per 100 mL serving of formula.

53 mg ÷ 100 mL = 0.53 mg calcium per mL
0.53 mg calcium per mL × 750 mL = approx.
400 mg calcium per day

You can see that the infant's need for calcium is easily met by the formula alone.

microbiologically produced fatty acids provide the fat component. Recently, some manufacturers have added other nutrients, such as the fatty acids AA and DHA, to more closely mimic the nutrient profile of human milk. This chapter's Nutrition Label Activity gives you the opportunity to review some of these ingredients.

Soy-based formulas are a viable alternative for infants who are lactose intolerant (although this is rare in infants) or cannot tolerate the proteins in cow's milk–based formulas. Soy formulas may also satisfy the requirements of families who are strict vegans. However, soy-based formulas are not without controversy. Because soy contains isoflavones, or plant forms of estrogens, there is some concern over the effects these compounds have on growing infants. Babies can also have allergic reactions to soy-based formulas (ESPGHAN Committee on Nutrition, 2006). Soy-based formulas are not the same as soy milk, which is not suitable for infant feeding.

There are specialized formula preparations for specific medical conditions. Some contain proteins that have been predigested, for example, or have compositions designed to accommodate certain diseases. Some have been specially formulated for preterm infants, older infants, and toddlers. The final choice of formula should depend on infant tolerance, stage of infant development, cost, and the advice of the infant's pediatrician. It is important to note that the use of cow's milk (fresh, dried, evaporated, or condensed) is inappropriate for infants under the age of one year, as is the use of goat's milk.

When Do Infants Begin to Need Solid Foods?

Infants begin to need solid, or complementary, foods at around six months of age. Before this age, several factors make most infants unable to consume solid food.

One factor is the *extrusion reflex*. During infant feeding, the suckling response depends on a particular movement of the tongue that draws liquid out of the breast or bottle. But when solid foods are introduced with a spoon, this tongue movement (the extrusion reflex) causes the baby to push most of the food back out of the mouth. The extrusion reflex begins to lessen around four to five months of age.

Another factor is muscle development. To minimize the risk for choking, the infant must have gained muscular control of the head and neck and be able to sit up (with or without support).

Still another part of being ready for solid foods is sufficient maturity of the digestive and kidney systems. While infants can digest and absorb lactose from birth, the ability to digest starch does not fully develop until the age of three to four months. If an infant is fed cereal, for example, before he can digest the starch, diarrhea and discomfort may develop. In addition, early introduction of solid foods can lead to improper absorption of intact, undigested proteins, setting the stage for allergies. Finally, the kidneys must have matured so that they are better able to process nitrogen wastes from proteins and concentrate urine.

The need for solid foods is also related to nutrient needs. At about six months of age, infant iron stores become depleted; thus, iron-fortified infant cereals are often the first foods introduced. Rice cereal rarely provokes an allergic response and is easy to digest. Once a child reaches six months of age, other single-grain cereals, strained vegetables, fruits, and protein sources can gradually be incorporated into the diet.

Infant foods should be introduced one at a time, with no other new foods for about one week, so that parents can watch for signs of allergies, such as a rash, gastrointestinal problems, a runny nose, or wheezing. Gradually, a variety of foods should be introduced by the end of the first year. Commercial baby foods are convenient, nutritious, and typically made without added salt or sugar; however, home-prepared baby foods are usually cheaper and reflect the cultural food patterns of the family. Throughout the first year, solid foods should only be a supplement to, not a substitute for, breast milk or iron-fortified formula. Infants still need the nutrient density and energy that breast milk and formula provide.

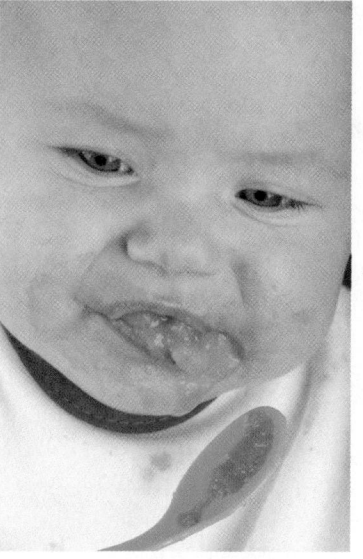

The extrusion reflex will push solid food out of an infant's mouth.

What Not to Feed an Infant

The following foods should never be offered to an infant:

- Foods that can cause choking. Infants cannot adequately chew foods such as grapes, hot dogs, nuts, popcorn, raw carrots, raisins, and hard candies. These can cause choking.
- Corn syrup and honey. These may contain spores of the bacterium *Clostridium botulinum.* These spores can germinate and grow into viable bacteria in the immature digestive tract of infants, whereupon they produce a potent toxin, which can be fatal. Children older than one year can safely consume these substances because their digestive tract is mature enough to kill any *C. botulinum* bacteria.

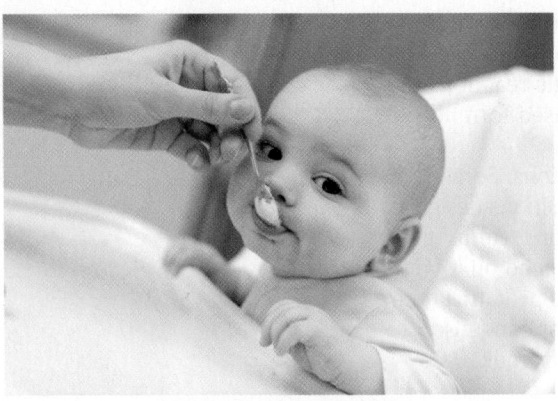

▲ Early introduction of solid foods may play a role in the development of food allergies, especially if infants are introduced to highly allergenic foods early on.

- Goat's milk. Goat's milk is notoriously low in many nutrients that infants need, such as folate, vitamin C, vitamin D, and iron.
- Cow's milk. For children under one year, cow's milk is too concentrated in minerals and protein and contains too few carbohydrates to meet infant energy needs. Infants can begin to consume whole cow's milk after the age of one year. Infants and toddlers should not be given reduced-fat cow's milk before the age of two, as it does not contain enough fat and is too high in mineral content for the kidneys to handle effectively. Infants should not be given evaporated milk or sweetened condensed milk.
- Too much salt and sugar. Infant foods should not be seasoned with salt or other seasonings. Naturally occurring sugars, such as those found in fruits, can provide needed energy. Cookies, cakes, and other excessively sweet, processed foods should be avoided.
- Too much breast milk or formula. As nutritious as breast milk and formula are, once infants reach the age of six months, solid foods should be introduced gradually. Six months of age is a critical time; it is when a baby's iron stores begin to be depleted. Over-reliance on breast milk or formula can limit the infant's intake of iron-rich foods, resulting in a condition known as *milk anemia*. In addition, infants are physically and psychologically ready to eat solid foods at this time, and solid foods can help appease their increasing appetites. Between six months and the time of weaning (from breast or bottle), solid foods should gradually make up an increasing proportion of the infant's diet.

Nutrition-Related Concerns for Infants

Nutrition is one of the biggest concerns of new parents. Infants cannot speak, and their cries are sometimes indecipherable. Feeding time can be very frustrating for parents, especially if the child is not eating, is not growing appropriately, or has problems such as diarrhea, vomiting, or persistent skin rashes. The following are some nutrition-related concerns for infants.

Allergies

Many foods have the potential to stimulate an allergic reaction. Breastfeeding helps deter allergy development, as does delaying the introduction of solid foods until the age of six months. One of the most common allergies in infants is to the proteins in cow's milk–based formulas. Egg whites, peanuts, and wheat are other common triggers of food allergies. Symptoms vary but may include gastrointestinal distress, such as diarrhea, constipation, bloating, blood in the stool, and vomiting. As stated earlier, every food should be introduced in isolation, so that any allergic reaction can be identified and the offending food avoided.

colic A condition of inconsolable infant crying that lasts for hours at a time.

Dehydration

Whether the cause is diarrhea, vomiting, or inadequate fluid intake, dehydration is extremely dangerous to infants and, if left untreated, can quickly result in death. The factors behind infants' increased risk for dehydration were discussed on page 521. Treatment includes providing fluids, a task that is difficult if vomiting is occurring. In some cases, the physician may recommend that a pediatric electrolyte solution be administered on a temporary basis. In more severe cases, hospitalization may be necessary. If possible, breastfeeding should continue throughout an illness. A physician should be consulted concerning formula-feeding and solid foods.

Colic

Perhaps nothing is more frustrating to new parents than the relentless crying spells of some infants, typically referred to as **colic**. In

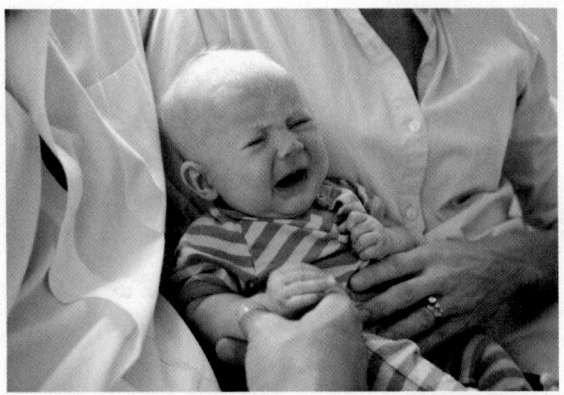

▲ Colicky babies will begin crying for no apparent reason, even if they otherwise appear well nourished and happy.

this condition, newborns and young infants who appear happy, healthy, and well nourished suddenly begin to cry or even shriek, continuing for several minutes to three hours or more, no matter what their caregiver does to console them. The spells tend to occur at the same time of day, typically late in the afternoon or early in the evening, and often occur daily for a period of several weeks. Overstimulation of the nervous system, feeding too rapidly, swallowing of air, and intestinal gas pain are considered possible culprits, but the precise cause is unknown.

As with allergies, if a colicky infant is breastfed, breastfeeding should be continued, but the mother should try to determine whether eating certain foods seems to prompt crying and, if so, eliminate the offending food(s) from her diet. Formula-fed infants may benefit from a change in type of formula. In the worst cases of colic, a physician may prescribe medication. Fortunately, most cases disappear spontaneously, possibly because of the maturity of the gastrointestinal tract, around three months of age.

Anemia

As stated earlier, full-term infants are born with sufficient iron stores to last for approximately the first six months of life. In older infants and toddlers, however, iron is the mineral most likely to be deficient. Iron-deficiency anemia causes pallor (pale skin), lethargy, and impaired growth. Iron-fortified formula is a good source for formula-fed infants. Some pediatricians prescribe a supplement containing iron especially formulated for infants. Iron for older infants is typically supplied by iron-fortified rice cereal.

Nursing Bottle Syndrome

Infants should not be left alone with a bottle, whether lying down or sitting up. As infants manipulate the nipple of the bottle in their mouths, the high-carbohydrate fluid (whether breast milk, formula, or fruit juice) drips out, coming into prolonged contact with the developing teeth. This high-carbohydrate fluid provides an optimal food source for the bacteria that are the underlying cause of **dental caries** (cavities). Severe tooth decay can result **(Figure 14.13)**. Encouraging the use of a cup around the age of eight months helps prevent nursing bottle syndrome, along with weaning the baby from a bottle entirely by the age of 15 to 18 months.

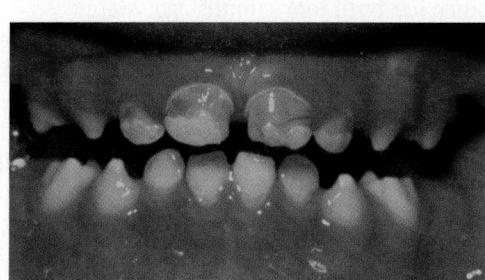

Figure 14.13 Leaving a baby alone with a bottle can result in the tooth decay of nursing bottle syndrome.

Lead Poisoning

Lead is especially toxic to infants and children because their brain and central nervous system are still developing. Lead poisoning can result in decreased mental capacity, behavioural problems, impaired growth, impaired hearing, and other problems. Unfortunately, leaded pipes and lead paint can still be found in older homes and buildings. The following measures can reduce lead exposure:

* Allowing tap water to run for a minute or so before use, to clear the pipes of any lead-contaminated water
* Using only cold tap water for drinking and cooking, as hot tap water is more likely to leach lead
* Professionally removing lead-based paint or painting over it with latex paint

RECAP Infancy is characterized by the most rapid growth a human being will ever experience, and appropriate growth is the most reliable long-term indicator of adequate infant nutrition. Infants need large amounts of energy per unit body weight to keep up with growth. Breast milk or iron-fortified formula provides all necessary nutrients for the first six months of life. After that, solid foods can gradually be introduced into an infant's diet. Micronutrient supplements should be given only if prescribed. Infants must be monitored for allergies, dehydration, and other signs of distress.

dental caries Dental erosion and decay caused by acid-secreting bacteria in the mouth and on the teeth. The acid produced is a by-product of bacterial metabolism of carbohydrates deposited on the teeth.

Nutrition DEBATE

Should Formula-Feeding be Penalized with High Taxes?

The year is 2021. Obesity rates have remained unacceptably high, especially among children, many of whom are experiencing high blood glucose, high blood pressure, and other signs of metabolic syndrome. In this climate, Marcy goes shopping for infant formula. Although her daughter Sidney has been exclusively breastfed since her birth four months ago, Marcy needs to go back to work full-time and has decided to switch to formula. At the checkout, Marcy is horrified at the price of the can of powdered formula she has selected. "It's not our fault," the clerk replies. "There's a new provincial surcharge to discourage families from using formula!"

If this scenario sounds preposterous, you might be interested to learn that some health-care providers in the United States are actually proposing that states implement a system of rewards for breastfeeding and penalties for formula-feeding—and a surcharge like the one just described is among the various proposals. Why? What is behind these recommendations, and could they ever become law? Let's have a look.

As obesity rates have climbed, some researchers have posed the question "Do adults and children who were breastfed as infants have lower rates of obesity than adults and children who were formula-fed?" (Gillman et al., 2001; Grummer-Strawn and Zuguo, 2004; Koletzko et al., 2009; O'Tierney et al., 2009; Owen et al., 2005; Weyerman, Rothenbacher, and Brenner, 2006). These researchers point to the theory of *metabolic programming*, which states that

⬥ Formula-feeding has been associated with an increased risk for obesity in childhood and adulthood.

infant-feeding practices and other factors in early postnatal life greatly influence an infant's physiology and subsequent risk for obesity and chronic diseases. Supporting this theory is the established fact that breastfed infants grow in length and weight at a slower rate than formula-fed infants. But does this lower weight persist into childhood and adulthood?

While some studies show no protective effect, most have concluded that breastfeeding for longer than three to six months does, in fact, lower rates of child and adult overweight and obesity (Gillman et al., 2001; Grummer-Strawn and Zuguo, 2004; Koletzko et al., 2009; Weyerman, Rothenbacher, and Brenner, 2006). Some researchers have found that exclusive breastfeeding provides greater protection than partial breastfeeding and that, the longer breastfeeding persists, the greater the protection against obesity (Grummer-Strawn and Zuguo, 2004; Owen et al., 2005).

The obesity risk reduction may stem from the lower protein and energy intakes of breastfed infants, alterations in insulin secretion, and/or differences in metabolism (Owen et al., 2005). In contrast, rapid weight gain during infancy, which is more common among formula-fed infants, is associated with a higher risk for obesity later in life (Grummer-Strawn and Zuguo, 2004). Some scientists have suggested that differences in feeding patterns influence the risk for obesity: formula-fed infants suck at a faster and more powerful rate, consume a larger volume at each feeding, and have fewer feedings per day with longer intervals between feedings compared to breasted infants (O'Tierney et al., 2009). It is possible that these differences translate into different eating habits as the infant transitions to child and adult diets.

The data from these studies prompt a complex question: does this difference in weight gain suggest that our society should do more to encourage or even require prolonged breastfeeding? Before you answer, consider the costs of obesity: as you have learned in previous chapters of this book, obesity is a well-established risk factor for heart disease, stroke, type 2 diabetes, and some forms of cancer. What is more, obesity-related costs account for 5%–7% of annual U.S. health-care expenditures, an estimated $100 billion annually, with additional costs related to lost productivity, reduced longevity, and impaired quality of life (Ludwig and Pollack, 2009). (Canadian data are not available.) Given this staggering financial burden of obesity, and the fact that much of it is borne by the public in the form of higher health-care costs and insurance premiums, not to mention reduced tax revenues (from lost productivity) and increased disability payments, should we legislate actions that could reduce obesity rates? After all, we have laws restricting sales of alcohol and tobacco to adults, and most provinces and territories tax these products heavily. These laws were enacted not only to improve public health but also to reduce the financial burden of disease on the public. Although some would argue that such laws take away our "personal freedoms," others point out that they protect primarily children and adolescents, either from the poor choices of their parents or from the harmful consequences of their own choices, which they are too young to fully understand.

If breastfeeding were conclusively shown to lower obesity rates, should it be encouraged via incentives and surcharges, or even required by law? Or do you believe the decision to breast- or formula-feed an infant should rest only with the family? At what point does "the public good" override personal freedoms, especially in an area as individualized as infant feeding?

Chapter Review

Test Yourself ANSWERS

1. False. Pregnant women need only 350–450 additional calories per day, and only during the second and third trimesters of pregnancy. This is an increase of only 20% or less, not a doubling of calories.

2. True. Breast milk contains various immune factors (antibodies and immune system cells) from the mother that protect the infant against infection. The nutrients in breast milk are structured to be easily digested by an infant, resulting in fewer symptoms of gastrointestinal distress and fewer allergies.

3. False. Most infants do not have a physiologic need for solid food until about six months of age.

Find the Quack

Three weeks ago, Kaitlyn gave birth to her first child, Sean, whom she has been breastfeeding successfully. Or at least she thinks so. But sometimes she finds herself wondering whether her breast milk is providing everything her son needs to grow up healthy and strong. This afternoon, while Sean naps, she leafs through a magazine and notices an ad for infant formula; it looks so thick and creamy in comparison to her breast milk, which looks thin and watery. On the next page, she sees another ad. "Are you breastfeeding?" it asks. "If so, congratulations on making this healthy choice. But how can you be sure you're meeting all of your infant's nutrient needs?" Attracted by the healthy-looking newborn in the photo, Kaitlyn reads the full-page ad, which promotes an infant vitamin supplement called First Days "ID" Drops. She reads:

- "Mother's milk provides almost all the nutrition a growing baby needs. But two vital nutrients are low in breast milk. These are iron and vitamin D."
- "Both iron and vitamin D are low in breast milk. Both are critical to your baby's growth and health."
- "Available without a prescription, First Days 'ID' Drops will provide your baby with the level of iron and vitamin D he or she needs."
- "For pennies a day, First Days 'ID' Drops will safeguard your baby's growth and health."

1. Kaitlyn is consuming a diet rich in iron and vitamin D. Is it possible that her breast milk is low in these two nutrients? Why or why not?

2. Kaitlyn's newborn, Sean, is three weeks old. Does Sean need to consume iron in either breast milk or a supplement? Why or why not? Does Sean need supplemental vitamin D? Why or why not?

3. The ad states that First Days "ID" Drops are "available without a prescription." Should Kaitlyn consult her health-care provider before giving her baby these drops? Why or why not?

4. Does the ad for First Days "ID" Drops suggest that this is a legitimate product, or would you characterize it as an example of quackery? Defend your position.

Answers can be found in the study area of MasteringNutrition.

Review Questions

1. Folate deficiency in the first weeks after conception has been linked with which of the following problems in the newborn?
   a. Anemia
   b. Neural tube defects
   c. Low birth weight
   d. Preterm delivery

2. Which of the following hormones is responsible for the milk "let down" response?
   a. Progesterone
   b. Estrogen
   c. Oxytocin
   d. Prolactin

3. Which of the following nutrients is not essential in a newborn's diet?
   a. Fibre
   b. Fat
   c. Iron
   d. Vitamin D

4. A pregnancy weight gain of 11.5–16.0 kg (25–35 lb.) is recommended for
   a. all women.
   b. women who begin their pregnancy underweight.
   c. women who begin their pregnancy overweight.
   d. women who begin their pregnancy at a normal weight.

5. The best solid food to introduce first to infants is
   a. Cream of Wheat cereal.
   b. applesauce.
   c. teething biscuits.
   d. iron-fortified rice cereal.

6. All women of childbearing age are encouraged to consume which of the following daily?
   a. 400 micrograms of folic acid
   b. 40 grams of folic acid
   c. 4 grams of folate
   d. 400 milligrams of folic acid

7. A woman weighs 78 kg (172 lbs.) and is 1.67 metres (5'7") tall. How much weight would you recommend she gain during pregnancy?
   a. 11.5–16.0 kg (25–35 lb.)
   b. 12.7–18.2 kg (28–40 lb.)
   c. 7.0–11.5 kg (15–25 lb.)
   d. 5–9 kg (11–20 lb.)

8. If an infant weighs 5 kg, how many calories would it need to consume in a day?
   a. 550 kcal
   b. 100 kcal
   c. 110 kcal
   d. 5010 kcal

9. A family friend has just recently become pregnant; she comes to you and says, "Now I can start eating twice as much food, because I'm eating for two." What advice would you give her?

10. Explain the relationship between the increased need for iron and the increased need for fluid in a pregnant woman.

11. Your cousin, who is pregnant with her first child, tells you that her physician prescribed supplemental iron tablets for her but that she decided not to take them. "You know me," she says, "I'm a natural-food nut! I'm absolutely certain that my careful diet is providing all the nutrients my baby needs." Is it possible that your cousin is partly right and partly wrong? Explain.

12. You visit your neighbours one afternoon to congratulate them on the birth of their new daughter, Katie. While you are there, two-week-old Katie suddenly starts crying as if she is in terrible pain. "Oh, no," Katie's dad says to his wife. "Here we go again!" He turns to you and explains, "She's been like this every afternoon for the past week, and it goes on until sunset. I just wish we could figure out what we're doing wrong." What would you say?

13. You are on a picnic at a park with your sister, who drapes a shawl over her shoulders and breastfeeds her 14-month-old son. A woman walking by stops and says, "Isn't that child getting too old for that?" What information could you share with her in response to her question?

14. Mary's doctor has just informed her that she has gestational diabetes. At this point, she does not need to give herself insulin shots as long as she watches what she eats. After hearing the list of foods she should avoid, Mary is worried that she will not be able to follow her doctor's orders. All the foods she is supposed to stay away from are the foods she has found she craves most during pregnancy. On top of this, Mary is also scared about the long-term effects of gestational diabetes. After learning about diabetes in Chapter 4, what foods do you think her doctor advised Mary to stay away from? What strategies might you suggest to help her control her cravings for carbohydrates? Besides diet, what other measures can Mary take to control her gestational diabetes? Assuming that her condition is under control, does she need to be afraid for her baby's health? Will she need to maintain her strict diet for the rest of her life?

15. Tera has a decision to make. She knows that breast milk is the best thing for her newborn but she is having trouble with the techniques involved. Her delivery was a smooth one and she was discharged early from the hospital before she could ask about how to breastfeed. Moreover, Tera wants to return to work within the next four months and is concerned with being able to continue breastfeeding her baby at that time. Explain to Tera the advantages of breastfeeding. Whom can Tera ask about correct breastfeeding techniques? What accommodations in Tera's workplace would help her to continue breastfeeding after she returns to work?

Case Study

Daniel is 19 years old and his mother keeps hinting that he and his girlfriend, Samantha, should really settle down and start a family. In Nigeria, where Daniel's family is from, people marry young and usually have kids right away. Both Daniel and Samantha agree that they want to graduate from university before they consider marriage. This is a constant source of conflict between Daniel and his mother.

Considering what you have learned so far in this chapter, do you think there is any ideal age to have children? If so,

what would that age be and why? What are the pros and cons of starting a family at a young age? What practical information could Daniel offer his mom to justify his decision to wait a few years before starting a family?

Answers to Review Questions can be found at the back of this text.

Web Resources

www.healthycanadians.gc.ca/hp-gs/index_e.html
Public Health Agency of Canada: A Healthy Pregnancy is in Your Hands

This is a great site for anyone wanting easy-to-understand information about pregnancy.

www.womenshealthmatters.ca
Women's Health Matters: The New Women's College Hospital

This site is devoted to providing information on a range of current women's health topics.

www.caringforkids.cps.ca
Caring for Kids, Canadian Paediatric Association

This is a great site for parents who want credible and accurate information. It lists product recalls and has information about immunizations, pregnancy, healthy eating, and much more.

www.motherisk.org/women/index.jsp
The Motherisk Program at the Hospital for Sick Children

This is a clinical, research, and teaching program that provides information and guidance about the effects of drugs, chemicals, diseases, radiation, and environmental substances on the developing fetus.

www.aap.org
American Academy of Pediatrics

Visit this website for information on infants' and children's health. Searches can be performed on such topics as "neural tube defects" or "infant formulas."

fnic.nal.usda.gov
Food Nutrition Information Center

Click on Topics A–Z and then Child Nutrition and Health for a list of infant nutrition topics and a listing of child nutrition programs, links, and resources.

www.marchofdimes.com/pregnancy/pregnancy.html
March of Dimes

Here you can find links on nutrition during pregnancy, breast-feeding, and baby care.

www.diabetes.ca
Canadian Diabetes Association

Search for "gestational diabetes" to find information about diabetes that develops during pregnancy.

www.llli.org
La Leche League

Search this site to find multiple articles on the health effects of breastfeeding for mother and infant.

www.nofas.org
National Organization on Fetal Alcohol Syndrome

This site provides news and information relating to fetal alcohol syndrome.

MasteringNutrition®

Study Area
Practice Tests • Diet Analysis • eText

The Fetal Environment: A Lasting Impression

WANT TO FIND OUT...

- **why an undernourished fetus is more likely to become an obese adult?**

- **about the consequences of excessive nutrient availability during fetal development?**

- **what the link is between maternal smoking and adult-onset diabetes?**

READ ON. Would you be surprised to learn that your risk of developing obesity and certain chronic diseases as an adult can be influenced by what happened even before your birth? It's true. Over the last several decades, a growing body of evidence has revealed that the fetal environment, including the mother's nutritional status, influences the risks for obesity and chronic diseases later in life. To describe this relationship, researchers have coined the phrases "fetal origins theory" and "developmental origins of adult health and disease."

This *In Depth* explores this relationship and describes the lifelong effects of a variety of factors in the fetal environment.

Exposure to Famine

Some of the earliest research into the fetal origins theory investigated the health of adults born during or shortly after a famine in the Netherlands in 1944 and 1945 that resulted from an extended German embargo during World War II. Because the Dutch maintained an excellent system of health-care records, scientists were able to learn important information about not only pregnancy outcomes but also the health of the offspring of the Dutch famine victims over the next 60 years. Not surprisingly, maternal weight gain and infant birth weight were much lower than normal. What was surprising, however, was the long-term impact of the famine on babies born there during this period as they progressed through adulthood (Lumey et al., 2009; Lussana et al., 2008).

In any circumstances, exposure to famine during the first trimester of pregnancy results in a much higher risk among the offspring for obesity, abdominal obesity, coronary heart disease, abnormal serum lipid profile, and metabolic syndrome during adulthood. If a pregnancy progresses to the third trimester by the time a famine begins, there is a higher rate of glucose intolerance and type 2 diabetes in adulthood **(Figure 1)** (Lussana et al., 2008).

Why, you might wonder, would low pregnancy weight gain and low birth weight lead to an increased risk for overweight, obesity, heart disease, high blood pressure, abnormal blood lipids, stroke, diabetes, premature death, and even schizophrenia, some 50 years later? While there are many theories, most relate to a process known as **fetal adaptation** (Jaddoe, 2008; Kaijser et al., 2009). In this process, a fetus exposed to a harmful environment, such as maternal starvation or malnutrition, goes into

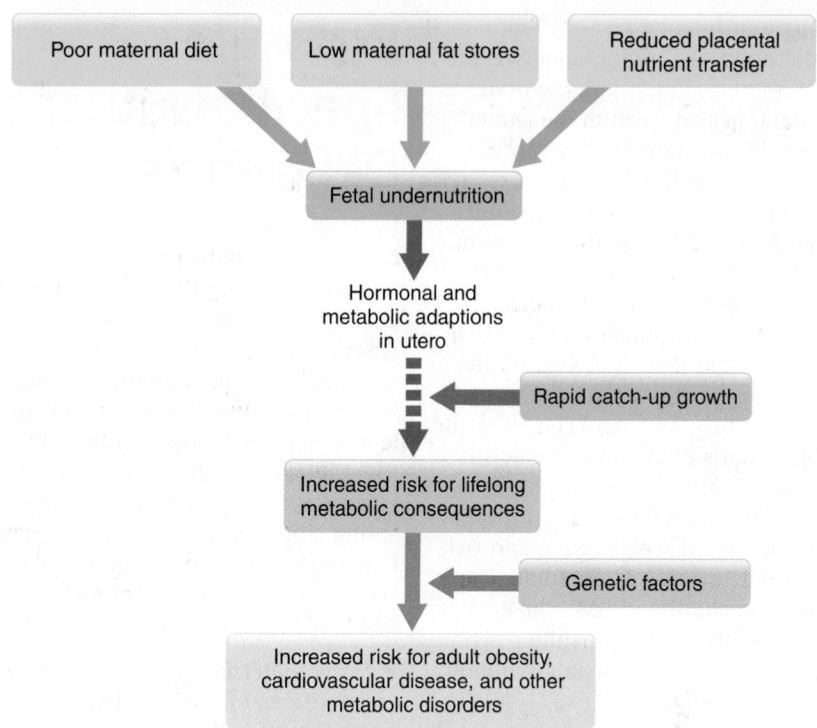

Figure 1 Fetal origins of adult diseases are complex and interrelated.
Source: Stanner, S. A., K. Bulmer, C. Andres, O. E. Lantseva, V. Borodina, V. V. Poteen, and J. S. Yudkin, 1997. Does malnutrition in utero determine diabetes and coronary heart disease in adulthood? Results from the Leningrad siege study, a cross sectional study. *Brit. Med. J.* 315:1342–1348.

survival mode. The body's production of various hormones may shift in favour of those that promote energy storage, the activity of certain enzymes may increase or decrease, and the size and functioning of body organs such as the liver, kidneys, and pancreas may change. There may even be changes in the activation—and thus the expression—of certain genes. Although these adaptations are beneficial to the fetus, allowing it to survive the harmful prenatal environment, the same hormonal, enzymatic, organ, and genetic changes may contribute to the development of chronic diseases over the life span (see Figure 1).

The Dutch Famine Study provided some of the earliest evidence supporting the fetal origins theory, but the results of many other "natural experiments" suggest that the effects of the prenatal environment on adult health depend quite heavily on the precise circumstances in each situation. For example, the Russian city of Leningrad was under siege during World War II for over 2 1/2 years; as a result, the population experienced starvation—over a million people died. However, adults who were born

during this period did not have the same increased disease risks as those found in the adults exposed, *in utero*, to the Dutch famine (Stanner and Yudkin, 2001; Stanner et al., 1997). How can this be, since the Leningrad babies were exposed to conditions far worse than those experienced by the Dutch babies? Researchers theorize that the impact of fetal exposure to malnutrition is actually worsened if followed by high nutrient intakes shortly after birth (Barker et al., 2005). This was a key difference between the Netherlands and Leningrad famines: once the Dutch embargo was lifted, the population returned to a normal, adequate diet. This allowed the underweight infants to experience rapid weight gain and catch-up growth during their first year of life. In contrast, the Leningrad infants who survived into adulthood may have continued to suffer from malnutrition

fetal adaptation The process by which a fetus's metabolism, hormone production, and other physiologic processes shift in response to factors, such as inadequate energy intake, in the maternal environment.

throughout infancy and even into toddlerhood, remaining underweight and underfed. Catch-up growth in the postnatal period, seen in the Dutch babies, is associated with a more severe increase in blood pressure and other chronic diseases during adulthood. As you can see, the long-term effect of fetal exposure to malnutrition is, in part, shaped by dietary and other environmental factors that infants face in their first year of life.

Studies of the medical records of Finnish adults born between 1934 and 1944, periods of great economic stress for that country, have also confirmed the link between fetal malnutrition, early childhood weight gain, and risk for chronic disease as an adult. The higher the childhood BMI, the greater the risk of developing insulin resistance and heart disease in adulthood (Miranda et al., 2008).

More recently, people born during weather- and war-related famines in Africa and other parts of the world have provided researchers with additional information on the impact of the fetal environment on adult health/disease outcomes. These more recent studies, including ones from South Africa and the Democratic Republic of Congo, confirm that low birth weight is associated with higher blood pressure in childhood and adolescence (Oken et al., 2008). Cardiovascular disease is now the second most common cause of adult death in sub-Saharan Africa, in stark contrast to previous decades, when infectious diseases accounted for the majority of deaths. In addition, half of the cardiovascular deaths in the sub-Saharan population were among adults 30 to 69 years of age, a far younger age than is seen in the United States and other developed nations (Miranda et al., 2008) **(Figure 2)**.

⬆ Figure 2 The consequences of childhood starvation are often lifelong.

Exposure to Specific Nutrient Deficiencies

By definition, a famine is a widespread lack or severe reduction in all food. Thus, research on the long-term health effects of famines cannot identify or describe the impact of *in utero* deficiencies of specific nutrients. Other studies, however, have been able to look at specific food patterns and nutrient intakes to determine the possible effects on the future health of the offspring. For example, evidence suggests long-term consequences of the following maternal deficiencies (Jaddoe, 2008; Maret and Sandstead, 2008):

- Low maternal intake of calcium increases the risk for hypertension in the offspring.
- Poor maternal folate status has been linked not only to neural tube defects in the newborn but also to early signs of atherosclerosis in adult offspring.
- Low maternal intake of fish, possibly a marker for DHA or omega-3 fatty acid intake, has been associated with developmental delays in childhood.
- Maternal zinc deficiency may account for some of the metabolic abnormalities and disease risks seen in adult offspring.

Thus, fetal stressors that influence adult health include not only starvation and inadequate energy but also specific nutrient deficiencies.

Exposure to Dietary Excesses

While our discussion so far has focused on maternal deficiencies, very strong evidence also links maternal dietary excesses to poor health outcomes in adult offspring. Maternal obesity has been linked not only to an increased risk for childhood and adult obesity (Catalano et al., 2009; Stuebe, Forman and Michels, 2009), but also to changes in the "programming" of the fetal brain, resulting in altered feeding behaviours (Bouret, 2010). Maternal obesity is also linked to a higher risk for birth defects, many of which have lifelong implications for health (Stothard et al., 2009). Infants born to overweight or obese women have higher rates of spina bifida and other neural tube defects, heart defects, cleft lip and palate, and abnormalities of their arms and/or legs. These birth defects are more likely to occur in the babies of women who are obese prior to their pregnancies or who gain an excessive amount of weight during their pregnancies. Population studies have also reported an association between high birth weight, common in infants born to obese women, and in increased risk for breast cancer in adulthood.

Maternal diabetes and its high-glucose environment has been shown to greatly increase the risk for type 2 diabetes (Clausen et al., 2008), overweight, and metabolic syndrome (Clausen et al., 2009) in adult offspring. The children of these diabetic women are up to eight times more likely to develop type 2 diabetes or pre-diabetes as adults compared to the general population. High blood levels of triglycerides, an increased waist circumference, and increased blood pressure are other measures of adult-onset diseases associated with maternal diabetes.

While research on prenatal exposure to excessive levels of individual nutrients typically is done with animal models, some human research results are available. It is known, for example, that a high maternal intake of vitamin A as retinol (but not as its precursor, beta-carotene) is associated with an increased risk for congenital heart defects (Jenkins et al., 2007), skull abnormalities, and other defects (Cetin, Berti, and Calabrese, 2009). Scientists continue to investigate the possible lifelong effects of other nutrient excesses, including the impact of high maternal intake of sodium on the risk for hypertension in adult offspring and the effect of high maternal saturated fat intake on the risk for congenital defects.

In short, research suggests that there are lifelong consequences to any type of nutrient imbalance during pregnancy, whether the imbalance is a total energy deficit, a single nutrient deficiency, or an energy or nutrient excess.

Exposure to Alcohol, Tobacco, and Other Toxic Agents

You have already learned of the lifelong impact of fetal alcohol syndrome, resulting from exposure to high maternal blood alcohol levels in the *In Depth* following Chapter 1. In addition, maternal smoking has been shown to negatively impact the long-term health of the offspring. Not only are the offspring of women who smoked during pregnancy at high risk for preterm delivery and low birth weight, but they are also at higher risk for childhood allergies and respiratory diseases, adult-onset high blood pressure, childhood behavioural problems (Jaddoe, 2008), and cleft lip and palate (Lie et al., 2008).

New evidence also confirms a link between maternal smoking and increased risk for adult-onset diabetes among offspring, as well as a lifelong higher risk for obesity (Zucker, 2002).

Not surprisingly, maternal exposure to lead and other environmental pollutants also has lifelong implications for offspring (March of Dimes, 2007). Maternal lead exposure increases the offspring's risk for developmental delays, behavioural and learning problems, and hearing loss, whereas exposure to mercury can result in irreversible damage to the nervous system and subsequent learning disabilities. In each of these examples, the mother's dietary intake and her immediate environment can lead to harmful effects that persist into and throughout adulthood.

◆ Regular physical activity is one of the most significant factors in maintaining wellness.

Implications for Your Health

What does this research on fetal origins of adult disease mean to you? If your mother experienced some type of nutritional, metabolic, or environmental stress during pregnancy, are you doomed to suffer from one or more of the health problems mentioned earlier? Although there is not yet a definitive answer, it is important to remember that this research is looking at "risk" and "susceptibility" in terms of populations. In other words, all of this research reported on large groups of people, not individuals. Moreover, it calculated increases in risk for—or susceptibility to—certain conditions, but it did not and cannot condemn anyone to any particular disease.

Any type of fetal programming or genetic influence that develops as a result of the fetal environment is just one factor in your wellness. A much more significant influence is your own lifestyle,

especially your personal food choices, dietary patterns, activity habits, alcohol intake, and smoking. In fact, the Centers for Disease Control and Prevention (2009) cite these as the primary factors influencing your risk of actually experiencing any of the most common chronic diseases. In short, you have the power to optimize your health by making smart lifestyle choices every day.

Web Resources

www.healthycanadians.gc.ca/hp-gs /index_e.html
Public Health Agency of Canada: A Healthy Pregnancy is in Your Hands

This is a great site for anyone wanting easy-to-understand information about pregnancy.

www.motherisk.org/women/index.jsp
The Motherisk Program at the Hospital for Sick Children

This is a clinical, research, and teaching program that provides information and guidance about the effects of drugs, chemicals, diseases, radiation, and environmental substances on the developing fetus.

◆ Maternal smoking is extremely harmful to the fetus and increases the risk for a variety of health problems in childhood and adulthood.

15

Nutrition Through the Life Cycle: Childhood to Late Adulthood

CHAPTER OBJECTIVES

After reading this chapter you will be able to:

1. Compare and contrast the nutrient needs of toddlers and children, pp. 536–537, and 541–544.

2. List at least three nutrients of concern when feeding a vegan diet to young children, pp. 540–541.

3. Define puberty and describe how it influences changes in body composition, pp. 547.

4. Explain why adequate intakes of calcium and vitamin D are particularly important during the adolescent years, p. 548.

5. List at least two factors that can increase the risk for obesity during childhood and adolescence, pp. 551–552.

6. Identify at least three physiologic changes that occur with aging and describe how they affect the nutrient needs of older adults, pp. 553–554.

7. Describe two reasons why older adults may not be able to drink adequate amounts of fluid, p. 557.

8. Discuss several changes in health that can contribute to inadequate nutrient intake in older adults, pp. 557–559.

W

hat would you think if you saw a young teenager quickly downing three espresso shots and then gulping down two handfuls of jelly beans? Would you be alarmed? Well, some children are doing just that, with the rapid influx of energy drinks available on the market today. The two big culprits in energy drinks are caffeine and sugar, with some energy drinks offering up to 70 mL or 14 teaspoons of sugar and the equivalent of two or three espresso shots' worth of caffeine. According to Health Canada, children between 10 and 12 should not consume more than 85 mg of caffeine per day, while some energy drinks have between 100 and 200 mg of caffeine, and the government does not regulate the amount of caffeine in these natural health products. Energy drinks are also heavily marketed to children and young teenagers, and although many of the cans include warnings that the product should not be consumed by children or by pregnant or breastfeeding women, it is of no surprise that some estimate at least 40% of children and adolescents report that they consume the drinks. Furthermore, there is growing concern about young adults in university mixing energy drinks with alcohol at parties and that the dangerous combination could prove fatal due to its effects on the heart.

What effect do you think consuming energy drinks has on the rising rates of childhood obesity? Do you wonder what nutrients are being displaced in their diet by these energy drinks? What do you think can be done to promote weight management across the lifespan? How do our nutrient needs change as we grow and age, and what other nutrient-related concerns develop in each life stage? This chapter will help you answer these questions.

⬥ Canadian children of all ethnicities experience overweight and obesity.

Nutrition for Toddlers

As babies begin to walk and explore, they transition out of infancy and into the active world of toddlers. From their first to their third birthday, a toddler will grow a total of about 14 to 19 cm (5.5 to 7.5 in.) and gain an average of 4 to 5 kg (9 to 11 lb.). Toddlers need to consume a lot of energy to fuel their increasing levels of activity as they explore their ever-expanding world and develop new skills. But feeding a toddler raises new challenges for parents and caregivers.

What Are a Toddler's Nutrient Needs?

Nutrient needs increase as a child progresses from infancy to toddlerhood. Although toddlers' rate of growth has slowed, their increased nutrient needs reflect their larger body size and increased activity. Refer to **Table 15.1** for a review of specific nutrient recommendations.

Energy and Macronutrient Recommendations for Toddlers

Although the energy requirement per kilogram of body weight for toddlers is slightly less than for infants, *total* energy requirements are higher because toddlers are larger and much more active than infants. The estimated energy requirements (EERs) vary according to the toddler's age, body weight, and level of activity (IOM, 2002). In general, toddlers should consume a diet that provides enough energy to sustain a healthy and appropriate rate of growth.

Although there is currently insufficient evidence to set a DRI for fat for toddlers, healthy toddlers of appropriate body weight should consume 30%–40% of their total daily energy intake as fat (IOM, 2002). We know that fat provides a concentrated source of energy in a relatively small amount of food, and this is important for toddlers, especially those who are fussy eaters or have little appetite. Fat is also necessary to support the toddler's continuously developing nervous system.

Toddlers' protein needs increase modestly because they weigh more than infants and are still growing rapidly. The RDA for protein for toddlers is 1.10 g/kg body weight per day, or approximately 13 g of protein daily (IOM, 2002). Remember that 500 mL or 2 cups of milk alone provide 16 g of protein; thus, most toddlers have little trouble meeting their protein needs.

⬥ Toddlers expend significant amounts of energy actively exploring their world.

TABLE 15.1 Nutrient Recommendations for Children and Adolescents

Nutrient	Toddlers (1–3 years)	Children (4–8 years)	Children (9–13 years)	Adolescents (14–18 years)
Fat	No DRI	No DRI	No DRI	No DRI
Protein	1.10 g/kg body weight per day	0.95 g/kg body weight per day	0.95 g/kg body weight per day	0.85 g/kg body weight per day
Carbohydrate	130 g/day	130 g/day	130 g/day	130 g/day
Vitamin A	300 µg/day	400 µg/day	600 µg/day	Boys = 900 µg/day Girls = 700 µg/day
Vitamin C	15 mg/day	25 mg/day	45 mg/day	Boys = 75 mg/day Girls = 65 mg/day
Vitamin E	6 mg/day	7 mg/day	11 mg/day	15 mg/day
Calcium	500 mg/day	800 mg/day	1300 mg/day	1300 mg/day
Iron	7 mg/day	10 mg/day	8 mg/day	Boys = 11 mg/day Girls = 15 mg/day
Zinc	3 mg/day	5 mg/day	8 mg/day	Boys = 11 mg/day Girls = 9 mg/day
Fluid	1.3 litres/day	1.7 litres/day	Boys = 2.4 litres/day Girls = 2.1 litres/day	Boys = 3.3 litres/day Girls = 2.3 litres/day

The RDA for carbohydrate for toddlers is 130 g/day, and carbohydrate intake should be about 45%–65% of total energy intake (IOM, 2002). As is the case for older children and adults, most of the carbohydrates eaten should be complex, and refined carbohydrates from high-fat/high-sugar items, such as desserts and snack foods, should be kept to a minimum. Fruits and fruit juices are nutritious sources of simple carbohydrates; however, too much fruit juice can displace other foods and can cause diarrhea. The American Academy of Pediatrics recommends that the intake of fruit juice be limited to 125 mL to 175 mL (4–6 fl. oz.) per day for children one to six years of age (Kleiman, 2009).

Adequate fibre is important for toddlers to maintain regularity. The AI is 14 g of fibre per 1000 kcal of energy, or, on average, 19 g/day (IOM, 2002). Whole-grain breads and cereals and fresh fruits and vegetables are healthful choices for toddlers. Too much fibre, however, can inhibit the absorption of iron, zinc, and other essential nutrients, harm the toddler's small digestive tract, and cause satiation before the toddler has consumed adequate nutrients.

Determining the macronutrient requirements of toddlers can be challenging. See the You Do the Math box on page 538 for an analysis of the macronutrient levels in one toddler's daily diet.

Micronutrient Recommendations for Toddlers

As toddlers grow, their micronutrient needs increase (Table 15.1). Of particular concern with toddlers is an adequate intake of the minerals calcium and iron.

Calcium is necessary for children to promote optimal bone mass, which continues to accumulate until early adulthood. For toddlers, the AI for calcium is 500 mg/day (IOM, 1997). Dairy products are excellent sources of calcium. When a child reaches the age of one year, whole cow's milk can be given; however, reduced-fat milk (2% or less) should *not* be given until age two due to the relatively high need for total energy. If dairy products are not feasible, calcium-fortified orange juice or soy milk can supply calcium, or children's calcium supplements can be given. Toddlers generally cannot consume enough food to depend on alternate calcium sources, such as dark-green vegetables.

Iron-deficiency anemia is the most common nutrient deficiency in young children around the world. Iron-deficiency anemia can affect a child's energy level, attention span, and mood. The RDA for iron for toddlers is 7 mg/day (IOM, 2001). Good sources of well-absorbed heme iron include lean meats, fish, and poultry; non-heme iron is provided by eggs, legumes, greens, and fortified foods, such as breakfast cereals. When toddlers consume non-heme sources of iron, eating vitamin C at the same meal will enhance the absorption of iron from these sources.

Given toddlers' typically erratic eating habits, pediatricians often recommend a multivitamin and mineral supplement as a precaution against deficiencies. The toddler's physician or dentist may also prescribe a fluoride supplement, if the community water supply is not fluoridated. Any supplement given should be formulated especially for toddlers, and the recommended dose should not be exceeded. A supplement should not contain more than 100% of the daily value of any nutrient per dose. Toddlers are at particularly high risk of overdosing on iron supplements, so parents must be careful to keep such products out of reach of their children.

Fluid Recommendations for Toddlers

Toddlers lose less fluid from evaporation than infants, and their more mature kidneys are able to concentrate urine, thereby sparing fluid. However, as toddlers become active, they start to lose significant fluid through sweat, especially in hot weather. Parents need to make sure an active toddler is drinking adequately. The recommended fluid intake for toddlers—about 1 litre (or 4 cups) as total beverages, including drinking water—is listed in Table 15.1 (IOM, 2004). Suggested beverages are plain water, milk and soy milk, diluted fruit juice, and foods high in water content, such as vegetables and fruits.

YOU DO THE MATH
Is This Menu Good for a Toddler?

A dedicated mother and father want to provide the best nutrition for their son, Ethan, who is now 1 1/2 years old and has just been completely weaned from breast milk. Ethan weighs about 11.8 kg (26 lb.). In the accompanying table is a typical day's menu for Ethan. Grams of protein, fat, and carbohydrate are given for each food. The day's total energy intake is 4900 kJ or 1168 kcal. Calculate the percentage of Ethan's calories that come from protein, fat, and carbohydrate (the numbers may not add up to exactly 100% because of rounding). In what areas are Ethan's parents doing well, and where can they improve?

Note: This activity focuses on the macronutrients. It does not ask you to consider Ethan's intake of micronutrients or fluids.

Calculations:

There is a total of 47.5 g protein in Ethan's menu.

47.5 g × 4 kcal (17 kJ) per gram = 190 kcal (800 kJ)
190 kcal protein ÷ 1168 total kcal × 100 = 16% protein

There is a total of 25.75 g fat in Ethan's menu.

25.75 g × 9 kcal (37 kJ) per gram = 232 kcal (970 kJ)
232 kcal fat ÷ 1168 total kcal × 100 = 20% fat

There is a total of 186.5 g carbohydrate in Ethan's menu.

186.5 g × 4 kcal (17 kJ) per gram = 746 kcal (3130 kJ)
746 kcal carbohydrate ÷ 1168 total kcal × 100
= 64% carbohydrate

Analysis:

Ethan's parents are doing very well at offering a wide variety of foods from various food groups; they are especially doing well with fruits and vegetables. Also, according to his estimated energy requirement, Ethan requires about 970 kcal (4070 kJ) per day, and he is consuming 1168 kcal (4900 kJ) per day, thus meeting his energy needs.

Ethan's total carbohydrate intake for the day is 186.5 g, which is higher than the RDA of 130 g/day; however, this value falls within the recommended 45%–65% of total energy intake that should come from the carbohydrates. Thus, high carbohydrate intake is adequate to meet his energy needs.

However, Ethan is being offered far more than enough protein. The DRI for protein for toddlers is about 13 g/day, and Ethan is eating more than three times that much!

It is also readily apparent that Ethan is being offered too little fat for his age. Toddlers need at least 30%–40% of their total energy intake from fat, and Ethan is consuming only about 20% of his calories from fat. He should be drinking whole milk, not 1% milk. He should occasionally be offered higher-fat foods, such as cheese for his snacks or macaroni and cheese for a meal. Yogurt is fine, but it should not be non-fat at Ethan's age. In conclusion, Ethan's parents should continue to offer a variety of nutritious foods but should shift some of the energy Ethan currently consumes as protein and carbohydrate to fat.

Meal	Foods	Protein (g)	Fat (g)	Carbohydrate (g)
Breakfast	Oatmeal (125 mL/1/2 cup, cooked)	2.5	1.5	13.5
	Brown sugar (5 mL/1 tsp.)	0	0	4
	Milk (1%, 125 mL/4 fl. oz.)	4	1.25	5.5
	Grape juice (125 mL/4 fl. oz.)	0	0	20
Mid-morning snack	Banana slices (1 small banana)	0	0	16
	Yogurt (non-fat, fruit-flavoured (90 mL/6 Tbsp)	5.5	0	15.5
	Orange juice (125 mL/4 fl. oz.)	1	0	13
Lunch	Whole-wheat bread (1 slice)	1.5	0.5	10
	Peanut butter (15 mL/1 Tbsp)	4	8	3.5
	Strawberry jam (15 mL/1 Tbsp)	0	0	13
	Carrots (cooked, 30 mL/2 Tbsp)	0	0	2
	Applesauce (sweetened, 65 mL/1/4 cup)	0	0	12
	Milk (1%, 125 mL/4 fl. oz.)	4	1.25	5.5
Afternoon snack	Bagel (1/2)	3	1	20
	Processed cheese, (1 slice)	3	5	1
	Water	0	0	0
Dinner	Scrambled egg (1)	11	5	1
	Baby food spinach (90 mL/3 fl. oz.)	2	0.5	5.5
	Whole-wheat toast (1 slice)	1.5	0.5	10
	Mandarin orange slices (65 mL/1/4 cup)	0.5	0	10
	Milk (1%, 125 mL/4 fl. oz.)	4	1.25	5.5

RECAP Growth during toddlerhood is slower than during infancy; however, toddlers are highly active, and total energy, fat, and protein requirements are higher for toddlers than for infants. While all forms of milk can be used to meet calcium requirements, until age two, toddlers should drink energy-rich whole milk rather than reduced-fat milk. Iron deficiency can be avoided by feeding toddlers lean meats/fish/poultry, eggs, and iron-fortified foods. Toddlers need to drink about 1 litre or 4 cups of water or other beverages per day.

Encouraging Nutritious Food Choices with Toddlers

Parents and pediatricians have long known that toddlers tend to be choosy about what they eat. Some avoid entire food groups, such as all meats or vegetables. Others will refuse all but one or two favourite foods (such as peanut butter on crackers) for several days or longer. Still others eat extremely small amounts, seemingly satisfied by a single slice of apple or two bites of toast. These behaviours frustrate and worry many parents, but in fact, as long as a variety of healthful food is available, most toddlers have the ability to match their intake with their needs. A toddler will most likely make up for one day's deficiency later on in the week. Parents who offer only nutritious foods can feel confident that their children are being well fed, even if a child's choices seem odd or erratic on any particular day. Food should never be "forced" on a child, as doing so sets the stage for eating and control issues later in life.

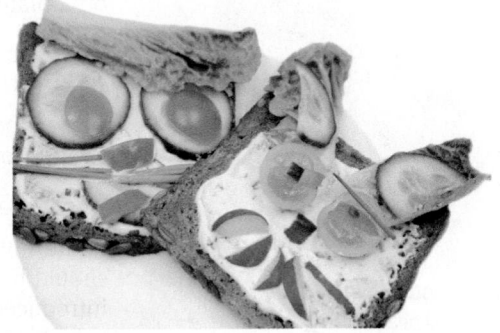

▲ **Figure 15.1** Most toddlers are delighted by food prepared in a fun way.

It is also important to recognize that toddlers' stomachs are still very small, and they cannot consume all of the calories they need in three meals. Toddlers need small meals, alternated with nutritious snacks, every two to three hours. A successful technique is to create a snack tray filled with small portions of nutritious food choices, such as one-third of a banana, two pieces of cheese, and two whole-grain crackers, and leave it within reach of the child's play area. The child can then "graze" on these healthful foods while he or she plays. A snack tray plus a spill-proof cup of milk or water is particularly useful on car trips.

Foods prepared for toddlers should be developmentally appropriate. Nuts, carrots, grapes, raisins, and cherry tomatoes are difficult for a toddler to chew and pose a choking hazard. Foods should be soft and sliced into strips or wedges that are easy for children to grasp. As the child develops more teeth and becomes more coordinated, the range of food can expand.

Foods prepared for toddlers can also be fun **(Figure 15.1)**. Parents can use cookie cutters to turn a peanut butter sandwich into a pumpkin face, or arrange cooked peas or carrot slices to look like a smiling face on top of mashed potatoes. Juice and yogurt can be frozen into "popsicles" or blended into "milkshakes."

Even at mealtime, portion sizes should be small. One tablespoon (15 mL) of a food for each year of age constitutes a serving throughout the toddler and preschool years **(Figure 15.2)**. Realistic portion sizes can give toddlers a sense of accomplishment when they "eat it all up" and minimize parents' fears that their child is not eating enough.

New foods should be introduced gradually. Most toddlers are leery of new foods, spicy foods, hot (temperature) foods, mixed foods (such as casseroles), and foods with strange textures. A helpful rule is to encourage the child to eat at least one bite of a new food: if the child does not want the rest, nothing negative should be said and the child should be praised just for the willingness to try. The food should be reintroduced a few weeks later. Eventually,

▲ **Figure 15.2** Portion sizes for preschoolers are much smaller than those for older children. Use the following guideline: 15 mL (1 Tbsp) of the food for each year of age equals 1 serving. For example, 30 mL (2 Tbsp) of rice, 30 mL (2 Tbsp) of black beans, and 30 mL (2 Tbsp) of chopped tomatoes is appropriate for a two-year-old.

Foods that may cause allergies, such as peanuts and citrus fruits, should be introduced to toddlers one at a time.

after several tries, the child might accept it. Parents should never bribe with food—for example, promising dessert if the child finishes her squash. Bribing teaches children that food can be used to reward and manipulate. Instead, parents can try to positively reinforce good behaviours—for example, "Wow! You ate every bite of your squash! That's going to help you grow big and strong!"

Role modelling is important, since toddlers mimic older children and adults: if they see their parents eating a variety of healthful foods, they are likely to do so as well. Providing limited healthful alternatives will also help toddlers make nutritious food choices. For example, parents might say, "It's snack time! Would you like apples and cheese or bananas and yogurt?" Finally, toddlers are more likely to eat food they help prepare: encourage them to assist in the preparation of simple foods, such as helping pour a bowl of cereal or helping arrange the raw vegetables on a plate.

Nutrition-Related Concerns for Toddlers

Just as toddlers have their own specific nutrient needs, they also have toddler-specific nutrition concerns, while others continue from infancy.

Continued Allergy Watch

As during infancy, new foods should be presented one at a time, and the toddler should be monitored for allergic reactions for a week before additional new foods are introduced. To prevent the development of food allergies, even foods that are established in the diet should be rotated, rather than served every day.

Overweight: A Concern Now?

Believe it or not, the signs of a tendency toward overweight can occur as early as the toddler years. Toddlers should *not* be denied nutritious food; however, they should not be forced or encouraged to eat when they are full. In the toddler years, a child who is above the 80th percentile for weight (one who weighs more than 80% of children of the same age and height) should be monitored. These children should be encouraged and supported in increasing their physical activity, and, as for all children, their intake of foods with low nutritional value should be limited. See the discussion on pages 551–553 for more information on obesity in children.

Vegetarian Families

For toddlers, a lacto-ovo-vegetarian diet, in which dairy foods and eggs are included, can be as wholesome as a diet including meats and fish. However, because red meat is an important source of zinc and heme iron, families who do not serve red meat must be careful to include enough zinc and iron from other sources in their child's diet. A fast-growing young child needs specific nutrients in their early years for normal functioning and healthy development.

In contrast, a vegan diet, in which no foods of animal origin are consumed, poses several potential nutritional risks for toddlers:

- Protein—Vegan diets can be too low in total protein or protein quality for toddlers, who need adequate amounts of high-quality protein for growth and increasing activity. Few toddlers can consume enough legumes and whole grains to provide sufficient protein. The high fibre content of legumes and whole grains results in a rapid sense of fullness for toddlers, decreasing their total food intake. Soy-based products are excellent sources of dietary protein.
- Calcium—Children who consume no milk, yogurt, or cheese are at risk for calcium deficiency. As with protein, few children can consume enough calcium from plant sources to meet their daily requirement. Although some brands of soy milk and rice milk, and certain fruit juices and cereals, are now fortified with calcium, supplementation is advised.
- Zinc and iron—These minerals are also commonly low in vegan diets due to the absence of meat, poultry, and seafood. While both of these minerals are found in legumes, young children simply cannot eat enough legumes to meet their iron and zinc needs.

- Vitamins D and B$_{12}$—Children consuming strict vegan diets are at risk for deficiencies of both of these vitamins. Some cereals and soy milks are fortified with vitamin D; however, many toddlers may still need a vitamin D–containing supplement. Vitamin B$_{12}$ is not available in any amount from plant foods and must be supplemented.
- Fibre—Vegan diets often contain a higher amount of fibre than is recommended for toddlers, resulting in lowered absorption of iron and zinc, as well as the early onset of fullness or satiety.

Although adults following a vegan diet have the ability to choose alternative foods and/or supplements to meet the demands for these nutrients, toddlers depend on their parents to make appropriate food choices for them. If parents are determined to maintain a vegan diet for their toddler, choosing to include fortified juices, soy milk, and other soy products, along with an appropriate pediatric supplement and ongoing consultation with a pediatrician, can ensure adequate nutrition in the toddler's diet.

The practice of feeding a vegan diet to infants and young children is highly controversial. See the Nutrition Myth or Fact? box on page 542 for more information about this controversy.

RECAP Toddlers require small, frequent, nutritious meals and snacks, and food should be cut in small pieces, so that it is easy to handle, mash, and swallow. Because toddlers are becoming more independent and can self-feed, parents need to be alert for choking and should watch for allergies and monitor weight gain. Role modelling by parents and access to ample healthful foods can help toddlers make nutritious choices. Feeding vegan diets to toddlers poses the potential for deficiencies in protein, calcium, zinc, iron, vitamin D, and vitamin B$_{12}$.

⬆ Enriched foods, such as fortified soy milk, should be given to toddlers consuming vegan diets.

Nutrition for Preschool and School-Age Children

During the preschool and school-age years, children become even more active, but their growth rate slows. Children grow an average of 5 to 10 cm (2 to 4 inches) per year at a slow and steady pace, the "calm before the storm" of adolescence, when growth rates again become very rapid. The nutrient requirements and nutrition issues of importance to preschool and school-age children are discussed in this section.

What Are a Child's Nutrient Needs?

Until the age of eight or nine years, the nutrient needs of young boys and girls do not differ; because of this, the DRI values for the macronutrients, fibre, and

◀ Children grow an average of 5 to 10 cm (2 to 4 inches) per year.

NUTRITION MYTH OR FACT?
Are Vegan Diets Appropriate for Young Children?

A glance at the headlines reveals that feeding a vegan diet to young children is a controversial issue. Supporters of veganism state that any consumption of animal products is wrong and that feeding animal products to children is forcing them into a life of obesity and chronic diet-related diseases. Some feel that the consumption of animal products wastes natural resources and contributes to environmental damage and is therefore morally wrong. Those who oppose veganism for young children assert that feeding a vegan diet to toddlers and developing children deprives them of the essential nutrients for both body and brain functioning that can be found only in animal products. Some people even suggest that veganism for young children is, in essence, a form of child abuse.

As with many controversies, there is some truth on both sides. For example, there have been documented cases of children failing to thrive, and even dying, on extreme vegan diets (King, 2010; Stern, 2007). Cases of protein deficiency as well as vitamin B_{12} and other micronutrient deficiencies have been cited in vegan children. The nutrients of concern are found primarily or almost exclusively in animal products, and deficiencies can have serious and lifelong consequences. For example, not all of the neurologic impairments caused by vitamin B_{12} deficiency can be reversed by timely B_{12} supplement intervention. In addition, inadequate zinc, calcium, vitamin D, and omega-3 fatty acids can result in impaired bone growth and strength, failure to reach peak bone mass, and impaired development.

However, a close inspection of the cases of nutrition-related illness in children due to veganism reveals that lack of education, fanaticism, and/or extremism is usually at the root of the problem. Informed parents following a responsible vegan diet, in conjunction with pediatric monitoring, are rarely involved. Such cases point to the vital importance of education in the challenges of administering this diet to young children. Specifically, parents need to know *which nutrients are not available in plant products and therefore must be supplemented*. They also need to understand that typical vegan diets are high in fibre and low in fat, a combination that can be dangerous for very young children (Anon, 2009). Moreover, certain staples of the vegan diet, such as wheat, soy, and nuts, commonly provoke allergic reactions in children; when this happens, finding a plant-based substitute that contains adequate nutrients can be very challenging.

⬆ Most nutrition experts recommend a more moderate diet—one that includes fish, dairy products, and eggs—rather than a vegan diet for young children. This snack of a peanut butter sandwich and milk is a healthful choice.

Both the American Dietetic Association (Craig and Mangels, 2009) and the American Academy of Pediatrics have stated that a vegan diet can promote normal growth and development in childhood. Well-planned vegan diets in infancy and childhood do not impair childhood growth, although vegetarian children tend to be slightly smaller and leaner (Craig and Mangels, 2009; Sanders and Manning, 2008). It has also been shown that well-planned vegan diets can have no negative effect on final adult height or weight. Parents should ensure that adequate supplements and/or fortified foods are consumed to account for the nutrients that are normally found in animal products. Many health organizations, however, continue to advocate a more moderate approach during the early childhood years. There are several reasons for this level of caution:

- Some vegan parents are not adequately educated on the planning of meals, the balancing of foods, and the inclusion of supplements to ensure adequate intake of all nutrients.
- Most young children are picky eaters and are hesitant to eat certain food groups, particularly vegetables, a staple in the vegan diet.
- The high fibre content of vegan diets may not be appropriate for very young children.
- Children on vegan diets may require slightly higher amounts of dietary protein due to the lower digestibility and quality of plant proteins.
- Young children have small stomachs, and they are not able to consume enough plant-based foods to ensure adequate intakes of all nutrients and energy.

Because of these concerns, most nutrition experts advise parents to take a more moderate dietary approach, one that emphasizes plant foods but also includes some animal-based foods, such as fish, dairy, and/or eggs.

Once children reach school age, the low fat, abundant fibre, antioxidants, and many micronutrients in a vegan diet will promote their health as they progress into adulthood. However, those who consume animal products can also live a healthful life and reduce their risk for chronic diseases by choosing low-fat, nutrient-dense foods, such as lean meats, non-fat dairy products, whole grains, and fruits and vegetables. When a varied diet is consumed, there are fewer worries about consuming adequate amounts of all nutrients.

micronutrients are grouped together for children age four to eight years. The beginning of sexual maturation, however, has a dramatic impact on the nutrient needs of children. Boys' and girls' bodies develop differently in response to gender-specific hormones. These changes in sexual maturation can begin subtly between the ages of 8 and 9 years; thus, the DRI values are separately defined for boys and girls age 9 to 13 years (IOM, 2002). Table 15.1 (page 536) identifies the nutrient needs of children and adolescents.

Energy and Macronutrient Recommendations for Children

Total energy requirements continue to increase throughout childhood because of increasing body size and, for some children, higher levels of physical activity. The estimated energy requirement (EER) varies according to the child's age, body weight, and level of activity. Parents should provide diets that allow for normal growth and support physical activity while minimizing the risk for excess weight gain.

Fat Although dietary fat remains a key macronutrient in the preschool years, total fat intake should gradually be reduced to a level closer to that of an adult, 25%–35% of total energy (IOM, 2002). One easy way to start reducing dietary fat is to gradually introduce lower-fat dairy products, such as 2% or 1% milk, and to minimize the intake of fried foods. A diet providing fewer than 25% of calories from fat is not recommended for children, as they are still growing, developing, and maturing. Foods such as meats and dairy products should not be withheld solely because of their fat content, since they have important nutrient value. In fact, parents should avoid putting too much emphasis on fat at this age. Impressionable and peer-influenced children can easily be led to categorize foods as "good" or "bad," leading to skewed views of food and inappropriate eating habits.

Carbohydrate The RDA for carbohydrate for children is 130 g/day, which is about 45%–65% of total daily energy intake (IOM, 2002). Complex carbohydrates from whole grains, fruits, vegetables, and legumes should be emphasized. Simple sugars should come from fruits and fruit juices, with foods high in refined sugars, such as cakes, cookies, and candies, saved for occasional indulgences. The AI for fibre for children is 14 g/1000 kcal of energy consumed (IOM, 2002). As is the case with toddlers, too much fibre can be harmful because it can make a child feel prematurely full and interfere with adequate food intake and nutrient absorption.

Protein As you can see in Table 15.1, the protein recommendation for boys and girls is 0.95 g/kg body weight per day (IOM, 2002). Although the recommended protein intake per kg body weight for children age 4 to 13 years is lower than that of toddlers, the total protein intake of school-age children is higher due to their higher body weight. Lean meats/fish/poultry, lower-fat dairy products, soy-based foods, and legumes are nutritious sources of protein that can be provided to children of all ages.

Micronutrient Recommendations for Children

The need for most micronutrients increases slightly for children up to age eight because of their increasing size. A sharper increase in micronutrient needs occurs during the transition into full adolescence; this increase is due to the beginning of sexual maturation and in preparation for the impending adolescent growth spurt. Children who fail to consume the USDA-recommended 4 cups of fruits and vegetables each day may become deficient in vitamins A, C, and E. Minerals of concern continue to be calcium, iron, and zinc, which come primarily from animal-based foods (IOM, 1997, 2001). Notice that the RDA for iron is based on the assumption that most girls do not begin menstruation until after age 13 (IOM, 2001). Refer to Table 15.1 for a review of the nutrient needs of children.

If there is any concern that a child's nutrient needs are not being met for any reason (for instance, breakfasts are skipped, lunches are traded, or parents lack money for nourishing food), a pediatric vitamin/mineral supplement that provides

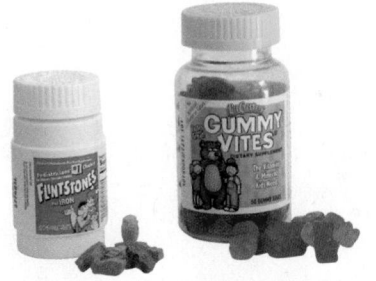

Children's multivitamins often appear in shapes or bright colours.

◄ Fluid intake is important for children, who may become so involved in their play that they ignore the sensation of thirst.

no more than 100% of the daily value for the micronutrients may help correct any existing deficit.

Fluid Recommendations for Children

The fluid recommendations for children are about 1.2 to 2 litres (approximately 5–8 cups) as beverages, including drinking water (Table 15.1). The exact amount of fluid needed varies according to a child's level of physical activity and the weather conditions. At this point in life, children are mostly in control of their own fluid intake. However, as they engage in physical activity at school and in sports and play, young children in particular may need reminders to drink to stay properly hydrated, especially if the weather is hot.

RECAP Total protein and energy needs are higher for children due to their larger size and higher activity levels. Dietary fat should be gradually reduced to the level of 25%–35% of total energy. Calcium, iron, and zinc requirements are higher for children than toddlers. Children need to drink from 1.2 to 2 litres (approximately 5 to 8 cups) of water and other beverages throughout the day.

Encouraging Nutritious Food Choices with Children

Peer pressure can be extremely difficult for both parents and their children to deal with during this life stage. Most children want to feel as if they "belong," and they admire and like to emulate children they believe to be popular. If the popular children at school are eating chips and drinking sugared soft drinks, it may be hard for a child to eat a peanut butter on whole-wheat sandwich, apple, and low-fat milk without embarrassment.

One strategy for combating peer pressure is to introduce kids to "cool" role models, such as star athletes and popular entertainers who follow nutritious diets. Involving children in growing their own food, shopping, and preparing meals is also a good idea. If they have input into what is going into their bodies, children may be more likely to take an active role in their health. In addition, adults should consistently model healthful eating and physical activity patterns.

What Is the Effect of School Attendance on Nutrition?

Children's school attendance can affect their nutrition in several ways. First, in the hectic time between waking and getting out the door, many children minimize or skip breakfast completely. Many nutrition and education experts believe that children who skip breakfast are at increased risk for behavioural and learning problems associated with hunger in the classroom. Some schools in Canada have organized volunteer-led breakfast programs to help children optimize their nutrient intake and avoid these problems, but not all children take advantage of them. You have probably heard people say that breakfast is the most important meal of the day. Is that so? Read the Nutrition Myth or Fact? box on page 545 to find out.

Another consequence of attending school is that, with little or no supervision of what they eat, children do not always consume appropriate types or amounts of food. They may spend their lunchtime talking or playing with friends rather than eating. If they purchase a school lunch, they might not like all the foods being served, or their friends might influence them to skip certain foods with comments such as "This broccoli's nasty!" Even homemade lunches that contain nutritious foods may be left uneaten or traded for less nutritious fare.

RECAP Peer pressure has a strong influence on children's nutritional choices. Involving children in growing, purchasing, and preparing foods can help them make more healthful food choices. Skipping breakfast can reduce a child's school performance.

NUTRITION MYTH OR FACT?

Is Breakfast the Most Important Meal of the Day?

What did you eat for breakfast this morning? Whole-grain cereal with low-fat milk? A strawberry Pop-Tart? Or nothing at all? What does it matter, anyway? Sure, you've heard the saying that breakfast is the most important meal of the day, but that's just a myth—isn't it? As long as you eat a nutritious lunch and dinner, why should breakfast matter?

Over the past 20 years, dozens of published research studies have confirmed the importance of a healthful breakfast. Many of these studies highlight the ability of breakfast to support our physical and mental functioning. Let's examine the evidence for this claim.

The word *breakfast* was first used as a verb meaning "to break the fast"—that is, to end the hours of fasting that naturally occur while we sleep. When we fast, our body breaks down stored nutrients to provide fuel for

➤ Breakfast doesn't have to be boring! A breakfast burrito with scrambled eggs, low-fat cheese, and vegetables wrapped in a whole-grain tortilla provides energy and nutrients to start your day off right.

the resting body. First, cells break down glycogen stores in the liver and muscle tissues, using the newly released glucose for energy. These stores last about 12 hours.

But people who skip breakfast typically go without food for much longer than that: if they finish dinner about 7:00 p.m. and do not eat again until noon the next day, they are fasting (going without fuel) for 17 hours! Long before that point, essentially all stored glycogen is used up, and the body has turned to fatty acids and amino acids as fuel sources.

If you are like most people, when your blood glucose is low, you are not only hungry but also weak, shaky, and irritable, and you have poor concentration. So it is not surprising that children and teens who skip breakfast do not function as well as their breakfast-eating peers: their physical, academic, and behavioural performances are all negatively affected (Hoyland, Dy, and Lawton, 2009; Ingwersen et al., 2007). Recent research confirms the following conclusions:

- Missing breakfast and experiencing hunger impair students' ability to learn. Exam scores are lower, their attention span is reduced, and they have more behavioural problems than students who arrive at school in a well-nourished state.
- Eating breakfast at school helps students perform better on demanding mental tasks and improves attention and memory. Children who eat a complete breakfast make fewer mistakes and work faster in math and vocabulary.
- Breakfast improves students' behaviour, decreases their tardiness, and improves their school attendance.

What do you think? Is breakfast the most important meal of the day? And what—if anything—will you be having for breakfast tomorrow?

Nutrition-Related Concerns for Children

In addition to the potential nutrient deficiencies that have already been discussed, new concerns arise during childhood. Foremost among these are overweight and obesity, a topic we discuss in detail on pages 551–553.

Dental Caries

As discussed in Chapter 4, *dental caries*, or cavities, occur when bacteria in the mouth feed on carbohydrates deposited on teeth. As a result of metabolizing the carbohydrates, the bacteria then secrete acid, which begins to erode tooth enamel, leading to tooth decay. The occurrence of dental caries can be minimized by limiting sugary sweets, especially those that stick to teeth, such as jelly beans. Frequent brushing helps eliminate the sugars on teeth, as well as the bacteria that feed on them.

Fluoride, through a municipal water supply, through fluoridated toothpaste or mouthwash, or through supplements, also helps deter the development of dental caries. Even though the teeth of a young child will be replaced by permanent teeth in several years, it is critical to keep them healthy and strong. This is because they make room for and guide the permanent teeth into position. Children should start having regular dental visits at the age of three.

⬥ Engaging in physical play with friends is a good way for children to maintain self-confidence and a positive body image.

Inadequate Calcium Intake

Another nutrition-related concern for children is an inadequate intake of calcium. Adequate calcium is necessary to achieve peak bone mass, as well as for numerous other critical body and cell functions. As you learned in Chapter 9, peak bone mass is achieved in the late teens or early twenties, and childhood and adolescence are critical times to ensure an adequate deposition of bone tissue. Inadequate calcium intake during childhood and adolescence can set the stage for osteoporosis in later years.

Dairy products are an important source of calcium. During the infant, toddler, and preschool years, milk consumption can largely be monitored by parents or caregivers. However, once children begin to attend school, they may choose to spend the money intended for milk on soft drinks, if available. This "milk displacement" is a recognized factor in low calcium, phosphorus, magnesium, potassium, and vitamin A intakes and the subsequent risk for poor bone health (Murphy et al., 2008; Weaver, 2010).

Body Image Concerns

As children, particularly girls, approach puberty, concerns about their appearance play increasingly important roles in their food choices. These concerns are not necessarily detrimental to health, particularly if they prompt children to make more healthful food choices, such as eating more whole grains, fruits, and vegetables. However, it is important for children to understand that being thin does not guarantee health, popularity, or happiness and that we can be physically fit and healthy at a variety of weights, shapes, and sizes. Children who are physically active may be more confident and accepting of their body image; thus, it is important to encourage daily participation in organized sports or active games. Excessive concern with thinness can lead children to experiment with fad diets, food restriction, and other behaviours that can result in undernutrition and perhaps even trigger a clinical eating disorder. (Disordered eating is discussed *In Depth* following Chapter 12.)

Childhood Food Insecurity

As previously we discussed, an estimated 7.7% of Canadian households, comprising approximately 961 000 Canadians, suffer some degree of food insecurity (Health Canada, 2011). These statistics are at odds with Canada's image as a prosperous developed nation.

The effects of food insecurity and hunger can be very harmful to children. Without an adequate breakfast, children are not able to concentrate or pay attention to their parents, teachers, or other caretakers. Impaired nutrient status can blunt children's immune responses, making them more susceptible to common childhood illnesses. The options for families facing food insecurity include a number of charitable and privately funded programs, including some school breakfast and snack programs. Private and church-based food banks and soup kitchens can provide a narrow range of foods for a limited period of time but cannot be relied on to meet the long-term nutritional needs of children and their families.

RECAP Parents can communicate effectively with children to encourage healthful eating and can act as role models in regard to food choices and level of physical activity. To prevent dental caries, children should brush their teeth regularly, limit sweets, and visit the dentist frequently beginning at age three. Consuming adequate calcium to support the development of peak bone mass is also a primary concern for school-age children. Body image is increasingly important to children as they grow older, and disordered eating behaviours can result. Food insecurity is a threat to the health and well-being of Canadian children.

Nutrition for Adolescents

Although there is no consensus on the exact age range corresponding to the term *adolescence*, this life stage begins with the onset of **puberty**, the period in life in which secondary sexual characteristics develop and we become capable of reproducing. This is a physically and emotionally tumultuous time for adolescents and their families. The nutritional needs of adolescents are influenced by their rapid growth in height, increased weight, changes in body composition, and individual levels of physical activity.

Adolescent Growth and Activity Patterns

Growth during adolescence is driven primarily by hormonal changes, including increased levels of testosterone for boys and estrogen for girls. Both boys and girls experience *growth spurts,* or periods of accelerated growth, during later childhood and adolescence. The timing and length of these growth spurts vary by race, gender, nutritional status, and other factors. Growth spurts for girls can begin as early as 9 to 10 years of age, while growth spurts for boys can begin as early as 10 or 11 years (Strang and Story, 2005). On average, girls tend to grow approximately 5 to 25 cm (2 to 10 in.) and boys tend to grow about 10 to 30 cm (4 to 12 in.) during puberty (Strang and Story, 2005). While most girls reach their full adult height by about age 17, some continue to increase in height past age 19, although the rate of growth slows considerably. Most boys continue to grow up to the age of 18 to 21, although their rate of growth also slows over time. Not surprisingly, the adolescent growth spurt can be greatly limited in teens who are on severe caloric restrictions, such as those with an eating disorder.

About half of peak bone mass is deposited during the adolescent years (Strang and Story, 2005). Skeletal growth ceases once closure of the *epiphyseal plates* occurs **(Figure 15.3)**. The **epiphyseal plates** are plates of cartilage located toward the end of the long bones that provide for their growth in length. In some circumstances, the epiphyseal plates close early in adolescents and result in a failure to reach full stature. The most common causes of this failure are malnutrition during childhood and adolescence and the use of anabolic steroids during this critical growth period.

Weight and body composition also change dramatically during adolescence. Weight gain is extremely variable during this time and reflects the adolescent's energy intake, physical activity level, and genetics. The average weight gained by girls and boys during this time is approximately 18 kg (39 lb.) and 24 kg (52 lb.), respectively (Strang and Story, 2005). The weight gained by girls and boys is considerably different in terms of its composition. Girls tend to gain significantly more body fat than boys, with this fat accumulating around the buttocks, hips, breasts, thighs, and upper arms. Although many girls are uncomfortable or embarrassed by these changes, they are a natural result of maturation. Boys gain significantly more muscle mass than girls, and they experience an increase in muscle definition.

The physical activity levels of adolescents are highly variable. Many are physically active in sports or other organized physical activities, whereas others become less interested in sports and more interested in intellectual or artistic pursuits. This variability in activity levels of adolescents results in highly individual energy needs. Although the rapid growth and maturation that occur during puberty require a significant amount of energy, adolescence is often a time in which overweight begins. The following section discusses the unique nutrient needs of adolescents.

What Are an Adolescent's Nutrient Needs?

The nutrient needs of adolescents are influenced by rapid growth, weight gain, and sexual maturation, in addition to the demands of physical activity (Table 15.1).

Energy and Macronutrient Recommendations for Adolescents

Adequate energy intake is necessary to maintain adolescents' health, support their dramatic growth and maturation, and fuel their physical activity. Because of these competing demands, the energy needs of adolescents can be quite high. While it is

Epiphyseal plate

Bone growth occurs at epiphyseal plate

Long bone

▲ **Figure 15.3** Skeletal growth ceases once closure of the epiphyseal plates occurs.

puberty The period of life in which secondary sexual characteristics develop and people become biologically capable of reproducing.

epiphyseal plates Plates of cartilage located toward the end of long bones that provide for growth in the length of long bones.

possible to calculate the estimated energy requirements of an adolescent by using a published equation, it is more practical to monitor the growth pattern of the adolescent to ensure that weight remains in proportion to height (IOM, 2002).

Fat As with the younger age groups, there is no DRI for fat for adolescents (IOM, 2002). However, adolescents are at risk for the same chronic diseases as adults, including type 2 diabetes, obesity, coronary heart disease, and various cancers. Thus, it is prudent for adolescents to consume no more than 25%–35% of total energy from fat and no more than 10% of total energy from saturated fat sources.

Carbohydrate The RDA for carbohydrate for adolescents is 130 g/day (IOM, 2002). As with adults, this amount of carbohydrate covers what is needed to supply adequate glucose to the brain, but it does not cover the amount of carbohydrate needed to support daily activities. Thus, it is recommended that adolescents consume more than the RDA, or about 45%–65% of their total energy as carbohydrate, and most should come from complex carbohydrate sources. The AI for fibre for adolescents is 26 g/day, which is similar to adult values.

Protein The RDA for protein for adolescents is similar to that of adults, at 0.85 g of protein per kg body weight per day (IOM, 2002). This value was selected because data are not available to determine protein maintenance requirements for this age group, and the amount of nitrogen needed to maintain protein balance in children is similar to that of adults (Kleinman, 2009). This amount is assumed to be sufficient to support health and to cover the additional needs of growth and development during the adolescent stage.

Micronutrient Recommendations for Adolescents

The micronutrients of particular concern for adolescents are calcium, iron, and vitamins A and D.

Calcium and Vitamin D Adequate calcium and vitamin D intakes are critical to achieve peak bone density. The AI for calcium from age nine through adolescence is 1300 mg/day (IOM, 1997). This amount of calcium can be difficult for many adolescents to consume because the quality of the foods they select is often less than optimal to meet their nutrient needs. However, this level of calcium intake is easily achieved by eating at least 4 servings of dairy foods or calcium-fortified products daily.

The RDA for vitamin D for children, women and men aged 1 to 70 years is 15 µg/day (Health Canada, 2010). Most foods are naturally low in vitamin D; thus, fortified foods, such as milk, are important sources of this vitamin. If an adolescent is not consuming adequate milk and does not get enough sunlight year round, he or she may need to take a supplement providing both calcium and vitamin D.

Iron The iron requirements of adolescents are relatively high; this is because iron is needed to replace the blood lost during menstruation in girls and to support the growth of muscle mass in boys. The RDA for iron for boys is 11 mg/day, while the RDA for girls is 15 mg/day (IOM, 2001). If energy intake is adequate and adolescents consume food sources of heme iron, such as lean meat/fish/poultry, each day, they should be able to meet the RDA for iron. However, many young people adopt a vegetarian lifestyle during this life stage, or they consume foods that have limited amounts of iron. Both of these situations can prevent adolescents from meeting the RDA for iron and, particularly in females, can increase their risk for iron-deficiency anemia.

Vitamin A Vitamin A is critical to support the rapid growth and development that occur during adolescence. The RDA for vitamin A is 900 µg/day for boys and 700 µg/day for girls (IOM, 2001). The RDA can be met by consuming at least 5 servings of dark-green, yellow, and orange fruits and vegetables each day. As with iron and calcium, meeting the RDA for vitamin A can be a challenging goal if the adolescent fails to make healthful food choices. In such cases, a multivitamin and mineral supplement that provides no more than 100% of the daily value for the micronutrients can be beneficial as a safety net. As with younger children and adults, a supplement should not be considered a substitute for a balanced, healthful diet.

Fluid Recommendations for Adolescents

The fluid needs of adolescents are higher than those of children because of their higher physical activity levels and the extensive growth and development that occur during this phase of life. The AI for total fluid for adolescent girls and boys is listed in Table 15.1; it includes about 2 litres (8 cups) and 2.7 litres (11 cups), respectively, as beverages, including drinking water (IOM, 2004). Boys require a higher fluid intake because they are generally more active than girls and have more lean tissue. Highly active adolescents who are exercising in the heat may have higher fluid needs than the AI, and these individuals should be encouraged to drink often to quench their thirst and avoid dehydration.

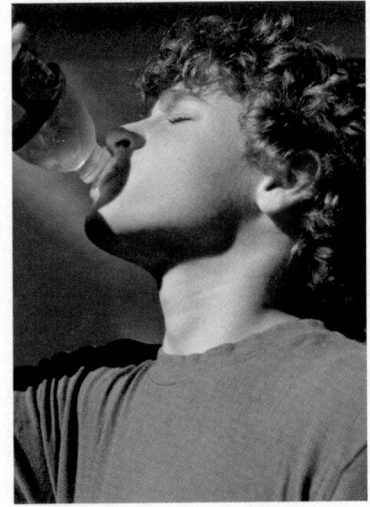

RECAP Puberty is the period in life in which secondary sexual characteristics develop and the physical ability to reproduce begins. Adolescents experience rapid increases in height, weight, and lean body mass and fat mass. Energy needs can be very high. Fat intake should be 25%–35% of total energy, and carbohydrate intake should be 45%–65%. Calcium is needed to optimize bone growth and to achieve peak bone density, and iron needs are increased due to increased muscle mass in boys and to menstruation in girls. Adolescents need to drink about 2 litres or 8 cups (girls) and 2.7 litres or 11 cups (boys) of water or other beverages daily.

◄ Adolescents have higher fluid needs than younger children.

Encouraging Nutritious Food Choices with Adolescents

At this point in their lives, adolescents are making most of their own food choices, and many are buying and preparing a significant amount of the foods they consume. Although parents can still be effective role models, adolescents are generally strongly influenced by their peers, their personal food preferences, and their own developing sense of which foods constitute a healthful and adequate diet. Adolescents are anxious to develop their own identity and establish a more self-reliant lifestyle. The decision to adopt a vegetarian diet, for example, may represent an adolescent's effort to establish some distance from the family unit.

One area of concern in most adolescents' diets is a lack of vegetables, fruits, and whole grains. Many teens eat on the run, skip meals, and select fast foods and convenience foods because they are inexpensive, are accessible, and taste good. High school students are often allowed to leave campus for lunch, increasing their opportunities to eat high-fat, low-nutrient fast foods. Parents and school food service personnel can capitalize on adolescents' preferences for pizza, burgers, spaghetti, and sandwiches by providing more healthful meat and cheese alternatives, whole-grain breads, and plenty of appealing vegetable-based sides or additions to these foods. And keeping healthful snacks accessible, such as fruits and vegetables that are cleaned and prepared in easy-to-eat pieces, may encourage adolescents to choose more of these foods as between-meal snacks. Teens should also be encouraged to consume adequate milk and other calcium-enriched beverages, while minimizing soft drinks, sports drinks, and other high-sugar beverages.

◄ By stocking healthful foods in their kitchens, parents can encourage teens to choose healthful snacks.

As adolescents "leave the nest" for college or their own apartments, it is important that they set the foundation for healthful eating. One question teens often have is how to stock their first kitchen. What basic foods—or staples—should they always have on hand, so that they can quickly and easily assemble healthful meals and snacks? The Quick Tips checklist shown here includes the foods that many Canadians consider to be staples. It can be modified to include items that are staples in non-Western cultures and to address vegetarian, vegan, low-fat, low-sodium, or other diets. By stocking healthful foods such as those listed here, they will be much more likely to make healthful food choices every day!

Nutrition-Related Concerns for Adolescents

Nutrition-related concerns for adolescents include bone density, body image issues, acne, cigarette smoking, and the use of alcohol and illegal drugs.

QUICK TIPS

Stocking Your First Kitchen

Keep your refrigerator stocked with:

- Low-fat or skim milk or soy milk
- Calcium-enriched orange juice
- Hard cheeses
- Eggs
- Lean deli meats or soy meat alternatives
- Lower-fat hummus, peanut butter, and other perishable spreads
- A 2- to 3-day supply of dark-green lettuce and other salad fixings, or ready-to-eat salads
- A 2- to 3-day supply of other fresh veggies
- A 2- to 3-day supply of fresh fruits
- Low-fat salad dressings, mustards, and salsas
- Whole-grain breads, rolls, bagels, pizza crusts, and tortillas

Stock your freezer with:

- Individual servings of chicken breast, extra-lean ground beef, pork loin chops, fish fillets, or soy meat alternatives
- Lower-sodium frozen entrées ("boost" with salad, whole-grain roll, and extra veggies)
- Frozen veggies (no sauce)

- Frozen cheese or veggie pizza ("boost" with added mushrooms, green peppers, and other nutritional toppings)
- Low-fat ice cream or frozen yogurt

Stock your pantry with:

- Staples such as potatoes, sweet potatoes, onions, and garlic
- Canned or vacuum-packed tuna, salmon, and crab (in water, not oil)
- Canned legumes, such as black beans, refried beans, pinto/kidney beans, and garbanzo beans (chick peas)
- Low-sodium, low-fat, high-fibre canned soups (read the label!)
- Dried beans and/or lentils
- Whole-grain pasta and rice
- Tomato-based pasta sauces
- Canned fruit in juice with no added sugar
- Dried fruits, such as golden raisins, cranberries, and apricots
- Nuts, such as peanuts, almonds, and walnuts
- Whole-grain ready-to-eat cereals or oatmeal
- Whole-grain, low-fat crackers
- Low-salt pretzels, low-fat tortilla/corn chips, and low-fat microwave popcorn
- Salt, pepper, balsamic vinegar, low-sodium soy sauce, and similar condiments and spices
- Olive and canola oils

Bone Density Watch

Early adolescence, 13 to 15 years of age, is a crucial time for ensuring adequate dietary calcium to maximize bone calcium uptake and bone mineral density over the next several years (IOM, 1997). Achieving and maintaining optimal bone density during adolescence and into young adulthood is critical for delaying or preventing the onset of osteoporosis.

As previously noted, meeting the adolescent DRI for calcium (1300 mg/day) is challenging. One of the most reliable sources of calcium is dairy foods, yet by age 18 average fluid milk consumption has fallen by more than 25% compared to intake at age eight years, whereas soft drink intake has tripled among U.S. adolescent girls (Striegel-Moore et al., 2006). Although not the only factor, milk consumption during adolescence is strongly linked to higher bone mineral content and lower risk for adult bone fractures.

Body Image and Eating Disorders

An initially healthful concern about body image and weight can turn into a dangerous obsession during this emotionally challenging life stage. As we discussed *In Depth* following Chapter 12, clinical eating disorders frequently begin during adolescence and can occur in boys as well as girls. Parents, teachers, and friends should be aware of the warning signs, which include rapid and excessive weight loss, a preoccupation with weight and body image, regular trips to the bathroom after meals, and signs of frequent vomiting or laxative use.

Adolescent Acne

The hormonal changes of puberty are largely responsible for the acne flare-ups that plague many adolescents. Emotional stress, genetic factors, and personal hygiene are secondary contributors. But what about foods? For decades, chocolate, fried foods, fatty foods, and other foods have been wrongfully linked to acne; it is now believed that diet has virtually no role in its development. On the other hand, a healthful diet, rich in fruits, vegetables, whole grains, and lean meats, can provide vitamin A, vitamin C, zinc, and other nutrients to optimize skin health and maintain an effective immune system.

Prescription medications, including the vitamin A derivative 13-*cis*-retinoic acid (Accutane), effectively control severe forms of acne. Prescription topical creams, applied directly to the skin, may also be used under the guidance of a physician. Neither Accutane nor any other prescription vitamin A derivative should be used by women who are pregnant, are planning a pregnancy, or may become pregnant. Accutane is a known teratogen, causing severe fetal malformations. Adolescent females who treat their acne with vitamin A–derivative prescription drugs must protect themselves against pregnancy and immediately contact their physician if they discover or believe they are pregnant. Incidentally, vitamin A taken in supplement form is not effective in acne treatment and, due to its own risk for toxicity, should not be used in amounts that exceed 100% of the daily value.

Use of Tobacco, Alcohol, and Illegal Drugs

Adolescents are naturally curious and many are open to experimenting with tobacco, alcohol, and illegal drugs. Cigarette smoking diminishes appetite and can interfere with nutrient metabolism. Indeed, it is frequently used by adolescent girls to maintain a low body weight. The following are other effects of smoking on young people (WHO, 2010):

- addiction to nicotine
- reduced rate of lung growth
- impaired athletic performance and endurance
- shortness of breath
- early signs of heart disease and stroke
- increased risk for lung cancer and other smoking-related cancers

Among adolescents, smoking is also associated with an increased incidence of participation in other risky behaviours, such as abusing alcohol and other drugs, fighting, and engaging in unprotected sex.

Alcohol and illegal drug use can start at early ages, even in school-age children. The primary cause of death among high school–age youth is a motor vehicle accident; the risk of being involved in an accident is greatly increased by using alcohol and illegal drugs. Alcohol can also interfere with proper nutrient absorption and metabolism, and it can take the place of foods in an adolescent's diet; these adverse effects of alcohol put adolescents at risk for various nutrient deficiencies. Alcohol consumption and the use of many illegal drugs are also associated with "the munchies," a feeling of food craving that usually results in the intake of large quantities of high-fat, high-sugar, nutrient-poor foods. This behaviour can result in overweight or obesity, and it increases the risk for nutrient imbalance. Teens who use illegal drugs and alcohol are typically in poor physical condition, are either underweight or overweight, have poor appetites, and perform poorly in school.

RECAP Adolescents' food choices are influenced by peer pressure, personal preferences, and their own developing sense of what foods are healthful. Adolescents are at risk of skipping meals and selecting fast foods and snack foods in place of whole grains, fruits, and vegetables. Milk is commonly replaced with regular soft drinks, reducing the calcium available for building bone density. Disordered eating behaviours, eating disorders, acne, inappropriate use of supplements, cigarette smoking, and use of alcohol and illegal drugs are also concerns for this age group.

Cigarette smoking may interfere with nutrient metabolism.

Active, healthy-weight children are less likely to become overweight adults.

Pediatric Obesity Watch: A Concern for Children and Adolescents

During the past 30 years, the rate of obesity has increased dramatically for Canadian children (PHAC, 2011). Currently, about 8.6% of children and youth aged 6 to 17 years old are classified as obese according to data collected in the Canadian Health Measures Survey 2007–09 (PHAC, 2011).

Overweight and obese children are at higher risk for numerous short- and long-term health problems. Even in early childhood, significant overweight can worsen asthma, cause sleep apnea, impair the child's mobility, and lead to intense teasing, low self-esteem, and social isolation. Among children and adolescents who are overweight, rates of type 2 diabetes have increased tenfold over the past 20 years. Fatty liver is diagnosed in one-third of obese children, and increasing numbers of obese children are experiencing unhealthful blood lipids, high blood pressure, gallstones, depression, and other medical problems (Ludwig, 2007). While there is some evidence that the prevalence rates of childhood obesity and overweight may have levelled off (Ogden, Carroll, and Flegal, 2008), a reversal of the epidemic of pediatric obesity can be accomplished only through an aggressive, comprehensive, nationwide health campaign.

The Seeds of Pediatric Obesity

As mentioned earlier, the signs of overweight can occur as early as the toddler years. The best approach in dealing with overweight at an early age is one that combines constructive support for increased physical activity with healthful, balanced eating. Young children should never be denied nutritious food, or have food forced upon them. Parents should not be offended if the child's pediatrician or other health-care provider expresses concern over the child's weight status; early intervention is often the most effective measure against lifelong obesity.

⬆ Families should try to have shared meals with their children whenever possible.

Prevention Through a Healthful Diet

Obese children are at significant risk of maintaining their higher weight as adults, so preventing childhood obesity is important for long-term health and happiness. The introduction and retention of healthful eating habits within the family unit are key interventions in the fight against pediatric obesity (Agras et al., 2004).

Rather than singling out overweight children and placing them on restrictive diets, experts encourage family-wide improvements in food choices and mealtime habits (Zeller and Daniels, 2004). Parents should strive to consistently provide nutritious food choices, encourage children to eat a healthful breakfast every morning, and sit down to a shared family meal each evening or as often as possible (Ritchie et al., 2005). The television should be off throughout mealtimes to encourage attentive eating and true enjoyment of the food.

Parents should retain control over the purchase and preparation of foods until older children and teens are responsible and knowledgeable enough to make healthful decisions. For children "on the run," parents can keep a supply of non-perishable snacks—such as granola bars, dried fruits and nuts, and kid-friendly fruits, including apples, bananas, and oranges—to grab as everyone dashes out the door. Mealtimes should offer a colourful variety of vegetables, and children should drink milk or water, not soft drinks.

Whenever possible, parents should minimize the number of meals eaten in restaurants, especially fast-food franchises. When families do eat out, large portion sizes can be shared and grilled, broiled, or baked foods substituted for fried foods.

As discussed earlier, schools play a role in shaping eating behaviours. Parents can work with local school boards to eliminate or restrict the sale of soft drinks, candy, chips, and pastries. Schools can set aside land or construct raised beds for vegetable gardens, and food service providers can use the produce in lunch menus. Consistent and repeated school-based messages on good nutrition can reinforce the efforts of parents and health-care providers.

⬆ Regular physical activity is important for adolescents.

Prevention Through an Active Lifestyle

Increased energy expenditure through increased physical activity is essential for successful weight management among children. The Institute of Medicine recommends that children participate in daily physical activity and exercise for at least an hour each day (IOM, 2002). For younger children, this can be divided into two or three shorter sessions, allowing them to regroup, recoup, and refocus between activity sessions. Overweight children are more likely to engage in physical activities that are non-competitive, fun, and structured in a way that allows them to proceed at their own pace. Children should be exposed to a variety of activities, so that they move different muscles, play at various intensities, avoid boredom, and find out what they like and do not like to do.

RECAP Obesity is an important concern for children of all ages, their families, and their communities. Parents should model healthy eating and activity behaviours. Schools play an important role in providing nutritious breakfasts and snacks (if programs are available) and varied opportunities for daily physical activity.

Nutrition for Older Adults

Canada's population is getting older each year, and this is expected to continue for several decades as the "baby-boomers" become seniors and fewer women of child-bearing age have children. It was estimated that 4.8 million Canadians were aged 65 or older in 2010, and it is predicted that in the next 25 years (i.e., by 2036), that number will more than double to 10.4 million (Human Resources and Skills Development Canada, 2012).

These statistics have important nutrition-related implications even for younger adults, since a nutritious diet and regular physical activity throughout life can help prevent or delay the onset of chronic diseases and keep adults happy and productive in their later years. Throughout this book, our exploration of nutrition and physical activity has focused mainly on young and middle-age adults. In the following section, we discuss the unique nutritional needs and concerns of older adults, and we identify ways in which diet and lifestyle affect the aging process.

What Physiologic Changes Accompany Aging?

◀ Centenarians will be more common in the future.

Older adulthood is a time in which body systems begin to slow and degenerate. If the following discussion of this degeneration seems disturbing or depressing, remember that the changes described are at least partly within an individual's control. For instance, some of the decrease in muscle mass, bone mass, and muscle strength is due to low physical activity levels. In addition, there are intriguing lines of research actively searching for a modern-day "Fountain of Youth," some of which are discussed *In Depth* following this chapter.

Age-Related Changes in Sensory Perception

For most individuals, eating is a social and pleasurable process; the sights, sounds, odours, and textures associated with food stimulate and enhance one's appetite. However, odour, taste, touch, and vision all decline with age and negatively affect the food intake and nutritional status of older adults.

It has been estimated that over half of older adults experience a significant impairment in their sense of smell. The nerve receptors for taste and smell are complementary; thus, enjoyment of food relies heavily on the sense of smell. Older adults who cannot adequately appreciate the appealing aromas of food may be unable to fully enjoy the foods offered in a meal. While often a simple consequence of aging, loss of odour perception can also be caused by a zinc deficiency or a medication. If this is the case, a zinc supplement or change of medication may be a simple solution. Taste perception declines as well, especially the ability to detect salt and bitter tastes. The ability to perceive sweetness and sourness also declines, but to a lesser extent.

Loss of visual acuity has unexpected consequences for the nutritional health of older adults. Many have difficulty reading food labels, including nutrient information and "pull dates" for perishable foods. Driving skills decline, limiting the ability of some older adults to get to a market offering healthful, affordable foods. Older adults with vision loss may not be able to see the temperature knobs on stoves or the controls on microwave ovens and may therefore choose cold meals, such as sandwiches, rather than meals that require heating. Also, the visual appeal of a colourful, attractively arranged plate of food is lost to visually impaired elderly people, further reducing their desire to eat healthful meals.

Age-Related Changes in Gastrointestinal Function

Significant changes in the mouth, stomach, intestinal tract, and related organs occur with aging. Some of these changes can increase the risk for nutrient deficiency.

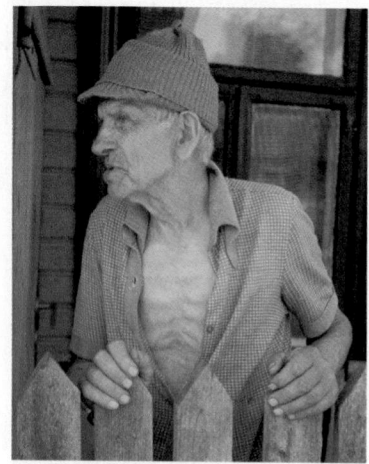

⬆ A variety of gastrointestinal and other physiologic changes can lead to weight loss in older adults.

⬆ Regular physical activity slows age-related loss of muscle mass.

⬆ Bone health can be promoted through regular weight-bearing activity.

With increasing age, salivary production declines. A dry mouth reduces taste perception, increases tooth decay, and makes chewing and swallowing more difficult. Thus, a diet rich in moist foods, including fruits and vegetables; sauces or gravies on meats; and high-fluid desserts, such as puddings, is advised. Difficulty swallowing foods can also result from a stroke or a condition such as Parkinsonism. Smooth, thick foods, such as cream soups, applesauce, milkshakes, fruit nectars, and puddings, are usually well tolerated. Older adults are also at risk for a reduced secretion of gastric acid, which limits the absorption of minerals such as calcium, iron, and zinc and food sources of folic acid and vitamin B_{12}. A lack of intrinsic factor greatly reduces the absorption of vitamin B_{12} (see Chapter 10). These elderly, therefore, benefit from vitamin B_{12} supplements and/or B_{12} shots.

Age-Related Changes in Body Composition

With aging, body fat increases and muscle mass declines (Jarosz and Bellar, 2008). It has been estimated that women and men lose 20%–25% of their lean body mass, respectively, as they age from 35 to 70 years. The decreased production of certain hormones, including testosterone and growth hormone, and chronic diseases contribute to this loss of muscle, as do poor diet and an inactive lifestyle. Along with adequate dietary intake, regular physical activity, including strength or resistance training, can help older adults maintain their muscle mass and strength, delaying or preventing the need for institutionalization.

Body fat increases from young adulthood through middle age, peaking at approximately 55–65 years of age, then declining in persons over the age of 70. With aging, body fat shifts from subcutaneous stores, just below the skin, to internal, or visceral, fat stores. Older men and women tend to deposit more fat in their abdominal region compared to younger adults. Among women, this shift in body fat stores is most dramatic after the onset of menopause and coincides with an increased risk for heart disease, diabetes, and metabolic syndrome.

Bone mineral density declines with age and may eventually drop to the critical fracture zone. Among older women, the onset of menopause leads to a sudden and dramatic loss of bone due to the lack of estrogen. Although it is less dramatic, elderly men also experience this loss of bone, due in part to decreasing levels of testosterone. In addition to the well-known benefits of calcium and vitamin D, intakes of vitamins A, C, and K, phosphorus, magnesium, fluoride, and protein are now recognized as influencing bone density. Bone health can be promoted through regular weight-bearing activity in adults well into their nineties and beyond.

RECAP The physiologic changes that can occur with aging include sensory declines; an impaired ability to chew, swallow, and absorb and metabolize various nutrients; a loss of muscle mass and lean tissue; increased fat mass; and decreased bone density. These age-related changes influence the nutritional needs of older adults and their ability to consume a healthful diet.

What Are an Older Adult's Nutrient Needs?

The requirements for many nutrients are the same for older adults as for young and middle-aged adults. A few nutrient requirements increase, and a few are actually lower. **Table 15.2** identifies the nutrient recommendations that change, as well as the physiologic reasons behind these changes.

Energy and Macronutrient Recommendations for Older Adults

The energy needs of older adults are lower than those of younger adults. This decrease is due to a loss of muscle mass and lean tissue, a reduction in thyroid hormones, and a less physically active lifestyle. It is estimated that total daily energy expenditure decreases approximately 40 kJ (10 kcal) each year for men and 30 kJ (7 kcal) each year for women ages 19 and older (IOM, 2002). This means that a woman who needs 8400 kJ (2000 kcal) at age 20 needs just 6930 kJ (1650 kcal) at age 70. Some of this decrease in energy expenditure is an inevitable response to aging, but some of the decrease can be delayed or minimized by staying physically active. To avoid weight gain, older

TABLE 15.2 Nutrient Recommendations That Change with Increased Age

Changes in Nutrient Recommendations	Rationale for Changes
Vitamin D Increased need for vitamin D from 15 µg/day for children, women and men from 9 to 70 years to 20 µg/day for adults over age 70 years	Decreased bone density Decreased ability to synthesize vitamin D in the skin
Calcium Increased need for calcium from 1000 mg/day for young adults to 1200 mg/day for adults 51 years of age and older	Decreased bone density Decreased absorption of dietary calcium
Fibre Decreased need for fibre from 38 g/day for young men to 30 g/day for men 51 years and older; decreases for women from 25 g/day for young women to 21 g/day for women 51 years and older	Decreased energy intake
B-Vitamins Increased need for vitamin B_6 and need for vitamin B_{12} as a supplement or from fortified foods Decreased absorption of food B_{12} from gastrointestinal tract	Lower levels of stomach acid Increased need to reduce homocysteine levels and to optimize immune function

adults need to consume a diet high in nutrient-dense foods but not too high in energy. Refer to the **In Depth** following this chapter to learn more about the theory of energy (caloric) restriction, which proposes that low-energy diets may significantly prolong lives.

Fat As with other age groups, there is no DRI for total fat intake for older adults (IOM, 2002). However, to reduce their risk for heart disease and other chronic diseases, it is recommended that their total fat intake remain within 20%–35% of total daily energy intake, with no more than 10% of total energy intake coming from saturated fat.

Carbohydrate The RDA for carbohydrate for older adults is 130 g/day (IOM, 2002). As with all other age groups, this level of carbohydrate is sufficient to support brain glucose utilization. Complex carbohydrates should be emphasized over simple sugars: it is recommended that older individuals consume a diet that contains no more than 30% of total energy intake as sugars (IOM, 2002). The fibre recommendations are slightly lower for older adults than for younger adults because older adults eat less energy. After age 50, 30 g of fibre per day for men and 21 g for women is assumed sufficient to reduce the risks for constipation and diverticular disease, maintain healthful blood levels of glucose and lipids, and provide good sources of nutrient-dense, low-energy foods.

Protein The DRI for protein is the same for adults of all ages: 0.80 g protein/kg body weight per day (IOM, 2002). Some researchers have argued for a protein allowance of 1.0 to 1.2 g protein/kg body weight for older adults to optimize their protein status; however, the issue remains unresolved (Campbell et al., 2008; Houston et al., 2008). Protein is important to help minimize the loss of muscle and lean tissue, optimize healing after injury or disease, maintain immunity, and help prevent excessive bone loss. Many protein-rich foods are also important sources of the vitamins and minerals that are typically low in the diets of older adults; thus, protein is an important nutrient for this age group.

▲ A less physically active lifestyle will lead to lower total energy requirements in older adults.

Micronutrient Recommendations for Older Adults

The vitamins and minerals of particular concern for older adults are identified in Table 15.2.

Calcium and Vitamin D Preventing or minimizing the consequences of osteoporosis is a top priority for older adults. The requirements for both calcium and vitamin D are higher because of a reduced absorption of calcium from the gut, along with reduced production of vitamin D in the skin. Many older adults are at risk for vitamin D deficiency because they are institutionalized and are not exposed to adequate amounts of sunlight. The widespread use of sunscreen has lowered the risk for skin cancer among older adults; however, these products also block the sunlight needed for vitamin D synthesis in the skin. It is critical that older adults consume foods that are high in calcium and vitamin D and, when needed, use supplements.

Iron   Iron needs decrease with aging. This decrease is primarily due to reduced muscle and lean tissue in both men and women and the cessation of menstruation in women. The decreased need for iron in older men is not significant enough to change the recommendations for iron intake in this group; thus, the RDA for iron is the same for older and younger men, 8 mg/day. However, the RDA for iron for older women is 8 mg/day, which is 10 mg/day lower than the RDA for younger women (IOM, 2001). Heme iron from meat, fish, and poultry represents the most available source of dietary iron; however, some older adults reduce their intake of these foods due to cost and possibly to difficulties in chewing and swallowing. Fortified grains and cereals, as well as legumes, greens, and dried fruits, can provide additional iron in the diet.

Zinc   Although zinc recommendations are the same for all adults, it is a critical nutrient for optimizing immune function and wound healing in older adults. Zinc intake can be inadequate in older adults for the same reasons that heme iron intake may be deficient: red meats, poultry, and fish are relatively expensive, and older adults may have a difficult time chewing meats due to loss of teeth and/or the use of dentures.

Vitamins C and E   Although it is speculated that older adults have increased oxidative stress, the recommendations for the antioxidant vitamins C and E are the same as for younger adults. While some research suggests that taking supplements containing vitamins C and E can lower the risk for age-related vision impairment, it is not possible to reach a conclusion regarding the benefits of supplementation.

B-Complex Vitamins   Older adults need to pay close attention to their intake of the B-complex vitamins—specifically, vitamin B_{12}, vitamin B_6, and folate (IOM, 1998). As discussed in detail in Chapter 10, inadequate intakes of these nutrients increase the levels of the amino acid homocysteine in the blood, and elevated homocysteine levels have been associated with an increased risk for cardiovascular, cerebrovascular, and peripheral vascular diseases (Hackam and Anand, 2003). These diseases are common among older adults.

The RDA for both folate and vitamin B_{12} is the same for younger and older adults, but up to 30% of older adults cannot absorb enough vitamin B_{12} from foods due to low stomach acid production. It is recommended that older adults consume supplements or foods that are fortified with vitamin B_{12} because the vitamin B_{12} in these sources is absorbed more readily. Vitamin B_{12} is also available via injection. Vitamin B_6 recommendations are slightly higher for older adults, as these higher levels appear necessary to reduce homocysteine levels and optimize immune function in this population (IOM, 1998).

Vitamin A   Vitamin A requirements are the same for adults of all ages; however, older adults should be careful not to consume more than the RDA, as the absorption of vitamin A is actually greater in older adults. Thus, this group is at greater risk for vitamin A toxicity, which can cause liver damage and neurologic problems. In addition, high intakes of vitamin A by older adults have been linked to increased risk for hip fractures (IOM, 2001). While older adults should avoid high dietary vitamin A and high-potency vitamin A supplements, consuming fruits and vegetables high in beta-carotene or other carotenoids is safe and does not lead to vitamin A toxicity.

A variety of factors may limit an older adult's ability to eat healthfully. These include limited financial resources that prevent some older people from buying nutrient-dense foods on a regular basis, reduced appetite, social isolation, an inability to prepare foods, and illnesses and physiologic changes that limit the absorption and metabolism of many nutrients. Thus, some older adults may benefit from taking a multivitamin and mineral supplement that contains no more than the RDA for all the nutrients contained in the supplement. Additional supplementation may be necessary for nutrients such as calcium, vitamin D, and vitamin B_{12}. However, supplementation with individual nutrients should be done only under the supervision of the individual's primary health-care provider, as the risk of nutrient toxicity is high in this population.

Fluid Recommendations for Older Adults

The AI for fluid is the same for older and younger adults (IOM, 2004). Men should consume 3.7 litres of total water per day, which includes 3.0 litres (about 13 cups) as beverages, including drinking water. Women should consume 2.7 litres of total water

⬧ Older adults have unique nutritional needs.

Senior Supplements: A Marketing Ploy?

Are the so-called "silver" supplements really better for seniors than ordinary formulations? Only minor differences exist between most standard and silver products. Let's take a look.

Iron and tin are omitted from the silver supplement, and vitamin K is reduced. Why? Eliminating iron lowers a senior's increased risk for iron overload. Since tin has no daily value or DRI, there is no justification for including it. Also, many seniors take prescription anti-clotting medications, so less vitamin K reduces the risk for a negative drug–nutrient interaction.

Silver supplements provide 40 mg more calcium, which helps supply the additional 200 mg of calcium that older adults need. Vitamins E and B$_6$ are also increased. The DRI for vitamin E does not change with age; however, increased oxidative stress and age-associated eye disorders explain the modest increase in the silver version. The increase in vitamin B$_6$ may help lower serum homocysteine, and the silver supplement provides four times more vitamin B$_{12}$. Why? Many adults over age 50 malabsorb vitamin B$_{12}$ from foods, so it is better absorbed in a supplement. Seniors should evaluate the potential benefits of silver supplements; their differences can be small but appropriate.

per day, which includes 2.2 litres (about 9 cups) as beverages. Kidney function changes with age, and the thirst mechanism of older people can be impaired. These changes can result in chronic dehydration and hypernatremia (elevated blood sodium levels) in this population. Some older adults intentionally limit their beverage intake because they have urinary incontinence or do not want to be awakened for night-time urination. This practice can endanger their health, so it is important for them to seek treatment for the incontinence and continue to drink plenty of fluids.

RECAP Older adults have lower energy needs due to their loss of lean tissue and lower physical activity levels. Older adults should consume 20%–35% of total energy as fat and 45%–65% of their energy as carbohydrate. Protein recommendations are the same as for younger adults. The micronutrients of concern are calcium, vitamin D, iron, zinc, vitamin B$_{12}$, vitamin B$_6$, and folate. Older adults need to carefully select nutrient-dense foods to meet their micronutrient needs, and supplementation may be necessary. Older adults are at risk for chronic dehydration. Men need to drink about 3.0 litres (13 cups) of water and other beverages per day, and women need about 2.2 litres (9 cups).

⬆ Many supplements are targeted at the elderly.

Nutrition-Related Concerns for Older Adults

Older adults have a number of unique nutritional concerns. In addition to overweight and underweight, they commonly face dental problems, eye disorders, and potential interactions between nutrients and medications. Also, some older adults face financial difficulties that affect their nutritional choices. Each of these concerns is discussed briefly in the following sections.

Overweight and Underweight: A Delicate Balancing Act

Not surprisingly, overweight and obesity are of concern to older adults. The elderly population as a whole has a high risk for heart disease, hypertension, type 2 diabetes, and cancer, and these diseases are more prevalent in older adults who are overweight or obese. Obesity increases the severity and consequences of osteoarthritis, limits mobility, and is associated with

⬆ Older adults need the same amount of fluids as other adults.

functional declines in daily activities (Zoico et al., 2004). In contrast, overweight can be protective against osteoporosis and fall-related fractures in older adults.

Underweight is also risky for older adults; mortality rates are actually higher in the underweight elderly than in the overweight elderly (Dolan et al., 2007). Significantly underweight older adults have fewer protein reserves to call upon during periods of catabolic stress, such as post-surgery or trauma, and are more susceptible to infection. Inappropriate weight loss suggests inadequate energy intake, which also

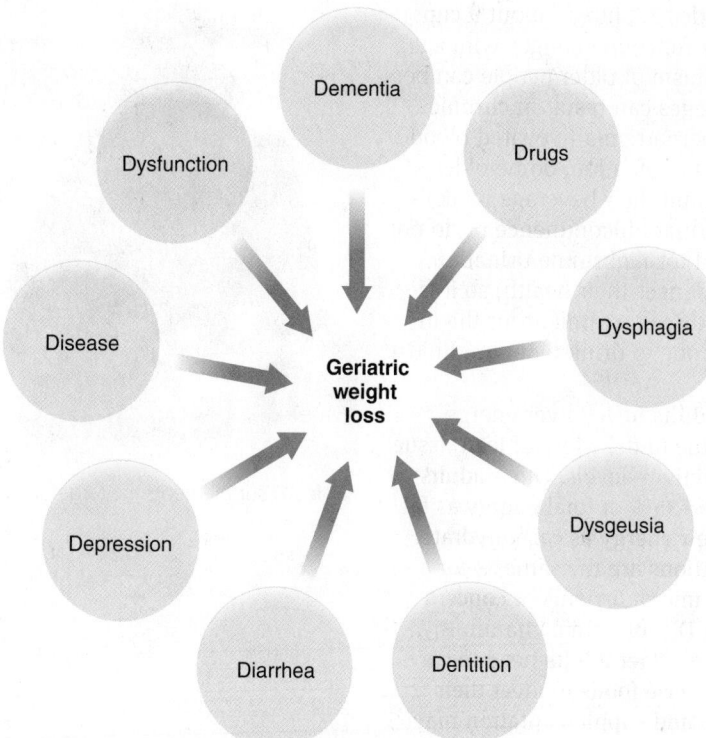

↞ **Figure 15.4** The nine Ds of geriatric weight loss. Many factors contribute to inappropriate weight loss in the elderly.

implies inadequate nutrient intake. Chronic deficiencies of protein, vitamins, and minerals leave older adults at risk for poor wound healing and a depressed immune response.

Gerontologists have identified "nine Ds" that account for most cases of geriatric weight loss (**Figure 15.4**). Several of these factors promote weight loss by reducing energy intake, others by increasing energy expenditure or loss of nutrients.

Dental Health Issues

Diet plays an important role in the maintenance of dental health in the elderly. Vitamin B-complex deficiencies contribute to irritation, inflammation, and cracking of the lips and tongue, whereas vitamin C deficiency increases the risk for periodontal (gum) disease. A lack of adequate calcium, vitamin D, and protein contributes to bone loss in the oral cavity, which increases risk for tooth loss. Saliva helps neutralize the decay-promoting acids produced by oral bacteria; however, with aging, saliva production decreases.

Despite great advances in dental health, older adults remain at high risk of losing some or all of their teeth, suffering from gum disease, or having poorly fitting dentures. These conditions cause considerable mouth pain and make chewing difficult and sometimes embarrassing. Thus, older adults may avoid eating foods such as meats and firm fruits and vegetables, leading to nutrient deficiencies. Older adults can compensate for a loss of chewing ability by selecting soft, protein-rich foods, such as eggs, peanut butter, cheese, yogurt, ground meat, fish, and well-cooked legumes. Red meats and poultry can be stewed or cooked in liquid for a long period of time. Oatmeal and other whole-grain cooked cereals can provide needed fibre, as do mashed berries and bananas, ripened melons, and canned vegetables. Shredded and minced raw vegetables can be added to dishes. With planning, older adults with oral health problems can maintain a varied, healthful diet.

Age-Related Eye Diseases

Two age-related eye disorders are responsible for vision impairment and blindness in older adults. *Macular degeneration* is damage to the macula, a portion of the retina of the eye (**Figure 15.5a**). It is the most common cause of blindness in the elderly. A *cataract* is a cloudiness in the lens of the eye (Figure 15.5b). This condition affects 20% of adults in their sixties and almost 70% of those in their eighties. Although

▶ **Figure 15.5** These photos simulate two forms of vision loss common in older adults. **(a)** Macular degeneration results in a loss of central vision. **(b)** Cataracts impair vision across the visual field.

National Eye Institute, National Institutes of Health. November 2003. Photos, Images, and Videos. Ref. no. EDS05. www.nei.nih.gov/photo/search/keyword.asp?keyword5macular; and National Eye Institute, National Institutes of Health. November 2003. Photos, Images, and Videos. Ref. no. EDS03. www.nei.nih.gov/photo/search/keyword.asp?keyword cataract.

(a)

(b)

TABLE 15.3 Examples of Common Drug–Nutrient Interactions

Category of Drug	Interactions
Antacids	May decrease the absorption of iron, calcium, folate, vitamin B_{12}
Antibiotics	May reduce the absorption of calcium, fat-soluble vitamins; reduces the production of vitamin K by gut bacteria
Anticonvulsants	Interfere with activation of vitamin D
Anticoagulants ("blood thinners")	Reduce the activity of vitamin K
Antidepressants	May cause weight gain as a result of increased appetite
Antiretroviral agents (used in treatment of HIV/AIDS)	Reduce absorption of most nutrients
Aspirin	Lowers blood folate levels; increases iron loss due to gastrointestinal bleeding
Diuretics	May increase urinary excretion of potassium, sodium, calcium, magnesium; may cause retention of potassium, other electrolytes
Laxatives	Increase fecal excretion of dietary fat, fat-soluble vitamins, calcium and other minerals

these are different conditions, sunlight exposure and smoking are lifestyle practices that increase the risk for both.

Recent research suggests, but does not prove, that dietary choices may slow the progress of these two degenerative eye diseases, saving millions of dollars and preventing or delaying the functional losses associated with impaired vision. Several studies have shown the beneficial effects of antioxidants, including vitamins C and E, on cataract formation, whereas others have reported no significant benefit. Two phytochemicals, lutein and zeaxanthin, have also been identified as protective by some, but not all, studies. These four antioxidants, as well as zinc, may also provide protection against macular degeneration. Although the research is not yet conclusive, older adults can benefit by consuming foods rich in these nutrients, primarily colourful fruits and vegetables, nuts, and whole grains. Vision-enhancing nutrient supplements remain an unproved therapy.

▲ For homebound, disabled, and older adults, community programs such as Meals on Wheels provide nourishing, balanced meals as well as vital social contact.

Interactions Between Medications and Nutrition

Although persons 65 years of age and above account for only approximately 14% of the Canadian population, they are the largest consumers of prescription medications (Ramage-Morin, 2009). Of the seniors living in institutional care, 53% receive five or more medications, and among those living in the community, 13% take five or more prescribed drugs (Ramage-Morin, 2009). Little Canadian data are currently available on the prevalence of adverse drug effects because of *polypharmacy*, or the use of multiple drugs. The use of over-the-counter drugs adds to the potential for harmful interactions: more than half of all older adults use five or more products (prescription medications, over-the-counter drugs, and/or dietary supplements) at the same time. It should come as no surprise, then, that older adults make many emergency room visits annually for medication-related problems.

Medications interact not only with each other but also with nutrients and other food components. Some medications increase or decrease food intake, while others alter nutrient digestion, absorption, or excretion. Several drugs negatively affect the metabolism of nutrients such as vitamin D, folate, and vitamin B_6. **Table 15.3** summarizes some of the more common drug–nutrient interactions.

RECAP Overweight and obesity are important concerns for older adults, as they increase the risk for chronic diseases. Underweight is also a concern, as it can lead to increased illness and injury. Older adults may lose their sense of smell and taste, and dental and vision problems can limit their intake of meats, fruits, and vegetables, leading to nutrient deficiencies. Medications and certain nutrients can have adverse interactions.

Nutrition DEBATE

Should the Sale of Energy Drinks to Children Be Restricted?

Your 10-year-old son likes to buy Rock Star and Monster, two popular energy drinks sold in supermarkets and convenience stores. Tyler says they give him a jolt of energy when he's feeling tired, and all his friends drink them. You haven't given it much thought—they are just like caffeinated pop, right?

Then you read the headline in your July 26, 2010, issue of *The Globe and Mail*, "Energy drinks pose serious health risks to kids: Canadian Medical Journal."

Energy drinks that contain high amounts of caffeine—some more than five times the amount in a can of cola, or nearly double the amount in a cup of brewed coffee—can pose serious health risks to children and adolescents and require stronger warning labels, according to the *Canadian Medical Association Journal*'s editorial.

"It is time for the federal minister of health to be awakened and alerted to concerns about energy drinks sold to children," states the editorial, written by Noni MacDonald, section editor of population and public health at *CMAJ*, Matthew Stanbrook, *CMAJ*'s deputy editor, scientific, and editor-in-chief Paul Hébert.

"Strict regulations are required if business practices and consumer trends are not curbed."

The editorial comes as an increasing number of health experts and consumer advocates are urging action.

The Medical Society of Prince Edward Island has been pushing for the province to restrict the sale of caffeinated energy drinks to young people.

The House of Commons health committee has also been investigating the use of caffeine in energy drinks and other carbonated beverages. In June, it heard from a man named

James Shepherd who said his 15-year-old son died from an unexplained arrhythmia (irregular heartbeat) in 2008 after he had consumed a Red Bull energy drink. He said he believes the drink contributed to his son's death.

Chris Turner, Health Canada's director-general of the marketed health

⬆ The federal government will start regulating energy drinks as foods instead of natural health products and require new labels with warning and nutrition information. (Paul Chiasson)

Source: www.cbc.ca/news/canada/story/2011/10/06/pol-energy-drink-rules.html.

products directorate, said the department has received several dozen reports of adverse reactions linked to energy drinks, and that 15 of them were cardiac events.

Red Bull is one well-known example of a caffeinated energy drink. But as the market has exploded in recent years, a growing number of products

that deliver high levels of caffeine are available.

Unlike cola drinks or similar carbonated beverages, energy drinks usually contain much higher levels of caffeine.

For instance, a 250 mL bottle of Coca-Cola contains 26 milligrams of caffeine, according to the company's website. But a 75 mL bottle of Rockstar "energy shot" contains 200 mg of caffeine. A 355 mL can of Red Bull contains 113.6 mg of caffeine.

Health Canada says children between 10 and 12 should not consume more than 85 mg of caffeine a day (children 4 to 6 should not exceed 45 mg, while those 7 to 9 should not exceed 62.5 mg). Healthy adults should not consume more than 400 mg a day, the department says.

It does not have specific limits for teens because it says there is "insufficient data," but recommends caffeine consumption for that group not exceed 2.5 mg per kilogram of body weight.

Excessive caffeine consumption can lead to irritability, loss of sleep, or nervousness. But there is also concern that its stimulating effects can cause rapid heat rate, an abnormal rhythm, or other problems that could have serious health consequences.

One of the major reasons for concern, according to the editorial, is that makers of energy drinks regularly target young consumers through event sponsorships and promotional materials.

For instance, Rockstar sponsors off-road racing and extreme sports events.

Health experts are also concerned by the fact many young people may mix energy drinks with alcohol, a potentially dangerous combination because the stimulating effects of caffeine can allow an individual to drink more over a longer period of time, which could lead to alcohol poisoning or risky behaviour.

Caffeinated energy drinks are sold as natural health products in Canada. They must undergo a review to determine they are safe and effective, and those that are approved have a licence number printed on their label, according to Health Canada spokesman Gary Holub.

But since there is a major backlog of products to be reviewed and approved by Health Canada's Natural Health Products Directorate, the government has allowed many to go on sale while waiting for approval. That could mean some energy drinks and other natural health products on the market have never been reviewed for efficacy or safety.

But Holub suggested some energy drinks could represent a section of the market that may soon see increased scrutiny. He wrote in an email that Health Canada is "reviewing the latest information and safety data on energy drinks and reassessing the labelling requirements for these products."

To date, Health Canada has approved 18 energy drinks as natural health products, including eight varieties of Red Bull and six types of Full Throttle energy drinks.

Red Bull and other companies that sell caffeinated energy drinks did not respond to requests for comment.

Refreshments Canada, an industry association representing beverage makers, issued a statement saying companies that sell caffeinated energy drinks are responsible and do not engage in marketing campaigns aimed at children. It states that energy drink labels clearly indicate the products should not be consumed by children and that the products have been approved for sale in more than 100 countries.

What do you think? Should energy drinks be regulated like drugs, sold by pharmacists, and kept behind pharmacy counters? Will warning labels on cans discourage children and teens from consuming them? Do you think they are harmful enough that their sale should not be permitted to children? What is the role of parents in this issue?

Chapter Review

Test Yourself ANSWERS

1. True. Experts agree that food choices, including the consumption of fried foods, chocolate, and sodas, have virtually no impact on the development of acne.

2. True. Although a reduction in muscle mass and lean tissue is inevitable with aging, some of this loss can be attenuated with regular physical activity.

3. False. It is unlikely that the human life span will exceed 125 years.

Find the Quack

Sal is having lunch at the golf club with his friend Donald. Normally they spend most of their time discussing their game, which Sal usually wins and Donald often complains that he's lost because of his painful joints. But today is different. Donald shows Sal something he's just received free in the mail: *Longevity Today* magazine. He says there are articles in it that prove that most of the problems of aging can be cured by a remedy containing a substance called procaine. Sal shakes his head. "Sounds like a scam to me!"

"But these articles are written by doctors," his friend insists. "And scientists. And one is even written by a former nutrition consultant for the Olympics! For instance," he continues, stabbing his finger at a particular page, "here's an article written by an MD that says that this procaine stuff 'reverses the physical and cognitive effects of aging, including hypertension, enlarged prostate, joint pain, constipation, and even depression!' That's a quote!"

Sal laughs. "One pill is supposed to do all that?"

"They cite studies!" Donald exclaims. "Listen: 'Clinical trials in Europe, Asia, and the United States have consistently demon-

strated the benefits of procaine as an anti-aging wonder drug.' It's only 20 bucks for a month's supply. I say it's worth a try."

Sal shrugs. "Listen, Donald, if you want to throw away your money, go ahead. But I'd rather save my 20 bucks and take Doris out for a walk on the beach at sunset. That's my anti-aging remedy!"

1. Look up procaine in a reputable online encyclopedia or another source. What is it, and what is behind the claims for its anti-aging properties?

2. Donald is impressed by the authorship of the articles he read in *Longevity Today* magazine—physicians, scientists, and a nutrition consultant—and by the fact that the articles "cite studies." Are you? Why or why not?

3. Comment on the fact that Donald received *Longevity Today* magazine free in the mail.

4. What do you think of Sal's "anti-aging remedy"?

Answers can be found in the study area of MasteringNutrition.

Review Questions

1. Which of the following nutrients is needed in increased amounts in older adulthood?
   a. Fibre
   b. Vitamin D
   c. Protein
   d. Vitamin A

2. Carbohydrate should make up what percentage of total energy for school-age children?
   a. 25% to 40%
   b. 35% to 50%
   c. 45% to 65%
   d. 45% to 70%

3. Which of the following is a major nutrition-related concern for preschoolers?
   a. Choking
   b. Skipping breakfast
   c. Botulism
   d. Dental caries

4. Which of the following breakfasts would be most appropriate to serve a 20-month-old child?
   a. 125 mL (1/2 cup) of iron-fortified cooked oat cereal, 30 mL (2 Tbsp) mashed pineapple, and 250 mL (8 fl. oz.) whole milk
   b. 30 mL (2 Tbsp) of non-fat yogurt, 30 mL (2 Tbsp) applesauce, 1 slice of melba toast spread with strawberry jam, and 250 mL (8 fl. oz.) calcium-fortified orange juice
   c. 125 mL (1/2 cup) of iron-fortified cooked oat cereal, 65 mL (1/4 cup) pineapple tidbits, and 250 mL (8 fl. oz.) 1% milk
   d. 2 small link sausages, cut into small pieces, 30 mL (2 Tbsp) scrambled egg, 1 slice whole-wheat toast, 4 cherry tomatoes, cut in pieces, 30 mL (2 Tbsp) applesauce, and 250 mL (8 fl. oz.) whole milk

5. Which of the following statements about cigarette smoking is true?
   a. Cigarette smoking can interfere with the absorption of nutrients
   b. Cigarette smoking commonly causes food cravings, such as "getting the munchies"
   c. Cigarette smoking is the number-one cause of death in adolescents
   d. All of the above statements are true

6. Tom was raised by his parents to always finish all of his dinner; he was often told, "No dessert until you finish your plate." Since this is how he was raised, he feels it is the best strategy to use at meal time with his own two-year-old son. Do you have any concerns about this approach?

7. Joe is a 65-year-old man who has a BMI of 28 and feels that he should lose some weight. He knows that you just recently took a nutrition course and asks for your advice. What would you recommend he do?

8. Identify some advantages and disadvantages of modern technology (such as television and computers) in terms of their impact on lifestyle and nutrition.

9. Explain why a toddler in a vegan family might be at risk for protein deficiency.

10. Imagine that you are taking care of four, five-year-old children for an afternoon. Design a menu for the children's lunch that is nutritious and that will be fun for them to eat.

11. Imagine that you manage a college cafeteria. Design a menu with three lunch choices that are nutritious and that are likely to be popular with 18- to 21-year-old students.

12. You and your parents live in Edmonton, where you attend university and your parents are employed as teachers. A year ago, your maternal grandmother, who lives in Halifax, stayed with you for several weeks following the death of your grandfather. She seemed fit at the time, going for walks with you and your dog, and cooking large meals for your family and special treats for you throughout her stay. Last night your mother received a phone call from a Halifax hospital saying that her mother had been admitted following a hip fracture suffered in a fall at home and was battling significant dehydration and moderate dementia as well. Identify several factors that might have contributed to your grandmother's condition.

13. Lillian is trying to no avail to convince her elderly parents to start taking vitamin-mineral supplements. Her mother has agreed, but her father refuses to even have them in his house. Even when her mother's doctor advised calcium and vitamin D supplements, her father decided it was just a hoax to make money. Lillian doesn't know what to do and is becoming increasingly worried about her parents' health. Do you agree with Lillian that her parents should be taking vitamin-mineral supplements? If you learned that her parents have never eaten dairy products regularly but enjoy a wide array of vegetables and whole grains, would this change your view? If you side with Lillian, which vitamin-mineral supplements would you recommend and why?

Case Study

Elizabeth has always been a heavy-set child, but recently her weight has become a health concern. Elizabeth's mother is advised by their doctor to help her daughter lose weight, so they sit down and make a list of everything Elizabeth eats and all her physical activity. They realize that Elizabeth rarely eats a full breakfast and ends up eating hamburgers and french fries every day at lunch. Usually Elizabeth's mom is too tired to cook dinner, so they order in from the local Thai restaurant or the pizza place. Because Elizabeth is heavier than her classmates, she hates joining in their games at recess and will not even consider joining a sports team. She walks home from school every day and then watches her favourite television shows until dinnertime.

Given what you know about Elizabeth's lifestyle and the nutrients needed for school-age children, what would you say about the quality of her diet? What about her activity level? What could Elizabeth and her parents do to help her achieve a healthier body weight?

Answers to Review Questions can be found at the back of this text.

Web Resources

www.dietitians.ca
Dietitians of Canada (DC)

Ask nutrition and diet questions or get the names of qualified dietitians in your community from this national professional organization.

www.hc-sc.gc.ca
Health Canada

Search this site for food and nutrition guidelines and policies, and for reports and statistics on the health of Canadians.

www.bcm.edu/cnrc/?PMID = 0
USDA/ARS Children's Nutrition Research Center, Baylor College of Medicine

This site provides information about current research projects, nutrition weblinks, and consumer and nutrition news.

www.keepkidshealthy.com
Keep Kids Healthy.com

Find information about nutrition and health for toddlers, children, and adolescents on this website.

www.cdc.gov
The Centers for Disease Control and Prevention

Click on Life Stages & Populations; then you can select topics such as Adolescents & Teens or Older Adults & Seniors.

www.vrg.org
The Vegetarian Resource Group

Learn more about vegetarianism for all ages. Included on the site are sections for teens and kids, as well as recipes and eating guides.

MasteringNutrition®

Study Area
Practice Tests • Diet Analysis • eText

Searching for the Fountain of Youth

READ ON.

How old do you want to live to be—80 years, 90, 100? Worldwide, throughout human history, legends have told of a "fountain of youth" that reverses decades of aging in anyone who drinks its waters. Of course, no one believes such tales any longer, but pick up a fashion or fitness magazine and you are likely to find modern equivalents: anti-aging diets, supplements, cosmetics, spa treatments, and other therapies. For instance, if you were to read that you could live to celebrate your 100th birthday in good health by eating about a quarter less than your current energy intake, would you do it? If there

We may no longer believe in an actual "fountain of youth," but our search for health and longevity continues today.

were a supplement ad that claimed the product could give you an extra decade of healthful living, would you buy it? Or would you assume that these are just fairy tales, too?

Believe it or not, a growing number of people are trying such approaches in an effort to extend both their youthfulness and their longevity. Are these measures effective? What other actions can you take right now to live longer in good health? Let's find out.

Does Calorie Restriction Increase Life Span?

The practice known as *calorie restriction (CR)* has been getting a lot of media attention lately. Although researchers have not defined a precise number of calories, or level of nutrients, that qualifies as a calorie-restricted diet, the practice typically involves eating fewer calories than your body needs to maintain your normal weight—while getting enough vitamins and other nutrients to keep your body functioning in good health. In general—allowing for differences in how many calories people are consuming prior to CR, as well as their gender, age, body composition, level of activity, and so forth—CR may call for a person to consume 20%–30% fewer calories than usual (Mayo Clinic, 2009a).

Effects of Calorie Restriction

Research over many years has consistently shown that CR can significantly extend the life span of small animals, such as rats, mice, fish, flies, and yeast cells (Fontana, Partridge, and Longo, 2010). Research with monkeys has followed more recently, with similar results. But only in the past few years have researchers begun to design and conduct studies of CR in humans. The results of these preliminary studies suggest that CR can also improve the metabolic measures of health in humans and thus may be able to extend the human life span (Speakman, 2010).

How might CR prolong life span? The answer to this question is not fully understood, but it is thought that the reduction in metabolic rate that occurs with restricting energy intake results in a much lower production of free radicals, which in turn reduces oxidative damage to DNA, cell membranes, and other cell structures, possibly lowering chronic disease risk and prolonging life. Calorie restriction also causes marked improvements in insulin sensitivity and other hormonal changes that can lower the risk for chronic diseases, such as heart disease, stroke, and diabetes. There is also evidence that CR can alter gene expression in ways that reduce the effects of aging and lower the risk for cancer and other diseases. The following are some of the metabolic effects of CR reported in several, but not all, human studies (Fontana and Klein, 2007; Fontana, Partridge, and Longo, 2010; Speakman, 2010):

- Decreased fat mass and lean body mass
- Decreased insulin levels and improved insulin sensitivity, decreased fasting blood glucose levels

⬆ On a calorie-restricted diet, all food must be highly nutritious, and both nutrients and energy must be calculated precisely.

- Decreased core body temperature and blood pressure
- Decreased serum LDL- and total cholesterol, increased serum HDL-cholesterol
- Decreased energy expenditure, beyond that expected for the weight loss that occurred, which suggests a generalized slowing of metabolic rate
- Decreased oxidative stress (i.e., reduced cell degeneration from free radicals)
- Reduced levels of DNA damage
- Lower levels of chronic inflammation
- Protective changes in various hormone levels

It is important to emphasize that the species known to live longer with CR are fed highly nutritious diets. Conditions such as starvation, anorexia nervosa, and wasting diseases, such as cancer, in which energy and nutrient intakes are severely restricted, do *not* result in prolonged life. In fact, these conditions are associated with increased risks for illness and premature death.

It is also essential to understand that the benefits of CR are seen as correlating to the age at which a person begins the program. In other words, the later in life the CR protocol

is started, the less the expected benefit. For example, if a person did not start CR until the age of 55 years, he or she would be expected to gain only about four months of extended life (Speakman, 2010)!

Challenges of Calorie Restriction

Although the benefits of CR appear promising, the research data supporting them in humans is still preliminary. Research that could precisely study and measure the results of CR in humans may never be conducted because of logistical and ethical concerns. For instance, finding enough people to participate in any research study over the course of their lifetime would be extremely difficult. In addition, most people find it very challenging to follow a calorie-restricted diet for even a few months; compliance with this type of diet for 80 years or more may be almost impossible. There are also ethical concerns about potential malnutrition in study participants.

In the absence of high-quality human studies, several CR groups, including the Caloric Restriction Society (Helibron and Ravussin, 2003; Kostoff, 2001; Masoro, 2005) and the "CRONies" (people in the group Caloric Restriction with Optimal Nutrition), have provided researchers with some data. Most of the members of the Caloric Restriction Society are men with an average age of 50 years, and 75% of CRONies are men in their late thirties or mid-fifties. One report indicated that most CRONies had followed the CR diet for about 10 years, although some had restricted their caloric intake for longer (Speakman, 2010). CRONies also reportedly reduce their caloric intake by about 30%. Overall, the members of CR groups report improved blood lipids and the other health benefits listed earlier. Still, researchers lack specific data on how well free-living adults actually follow the rigid and extensive demands of CR protocols (Mayo Clinic, 2009a).

You may be wondering how much less energy *you* would have to consume to meet the definition of calorie

restriction—and when you would have to begin. It has been estimated that humans would need to restrict their typical caloric intake by at least 20% for 40 years or more to gain an additional four to five years of healthy living. If you normally eat about 8400 kJ (2000 kcal) per day, a 20% reduction would require an energy intake of about 6720 kJ (1600 kcal) per day. Although this amount of energy reduction does not seem excessive, it would be very difficult to achieve every day for a lifetime—particularly if you lived to be over 100 years of age!

Also keep in mind that this diet must be of very high nutritional quality. This requirement presents a huge number of challenges, including the meticulous planning of meals; the preparation of most, if not all, of your own foods; limited options for eating meals outside of your home; and the challenge of working the demands of your special diet around the eating behaviours of family members and friends.

Also, those who follow the CR program report several side effects. The top three complaints are constant hunger, frequently feeling cold, and a loss of libido (sex drive) (Speakman, 2010). Finally, the long-term effects of the diet are not known. There is concern that, if initiated in early adulthood, CR would reduce bone density, increasing the risk for osteoporosis. It could also lead to inappropriate loss of muscle mass. And because the production of female reproductive hormones is linked to a certain level of body fat, CR could impair a woman's fertility. Interestingly, as noted earlier, most of the members of the Caloric Restriction Society and the CRONies are men.

Alternatives to Calorie Restriction

An interesting alternative to CR is the practice of *intermittent fasting* (*IF*), also known as every-other-day-feeding (EODF) or alternate-day fasting (ADF) (Heilbron et al., 2005). This approach, which does *not* reduce average caloric intake but simply alters the pattern of food consumption, has also been shown in animals to prolong life span and improve a range of metabolic measures of health. Although not as well studied as calorie restriction, IF has produced beneficial changes in insulin and glucose status, blood lipid levels, and blood pressure in humans in at least some studies.

Additionally, some researchers have proposed that limiting total protein intake, which is much easier to implement than extreme calorie restriction, may limit the onset of cancer and aging. As noted in Chapter 6, surveys indicate that many of us eat 15%–17% of our total daily energy intake as protein, so limiting total protein might mean consuming a diet with 10% of energy intake from protein, which is still within the AMDR. While this reduction may be challenging for those who follow a "meat and potatoes" diet, others would find this dietary modification very easy to follow over the long term.

Finally, research suggests that exercise-induced leanness may slow the aging process without the need for CR (Fontana, Partridge, and Longo, 2010). That is, it may not be the energy intake per se that extends life span but the overall energy balance a person maintains. For example, a person would not have to strictly limit energy or calorie intake as long as his or her activity (energy expenditure) were high enough to maintain a lean body profile (low percent body fat, high muscle mass).

Maintaining an energy-restricted diet that is also highly nutritious requires significant planning and preparation of most of your own meals.

Can Supplements Slow Aging?

Recently, some researchers have speculated that consuming the optimum level of nutrients can maximize a person's healthy life span (Ames, 2005). Can supplements take the place of whole foods in providing this "optimum level of nutrients"? And can other ingredients, besides vitamins and minerals, also slow aging?

The anti-aging market is said to generate about $50 billion in total revenues, with individual patients spending as much as $4000 to $20 000 annually on a variety of treatments. Primary among these are "anti-aging" or "age-management" supplements. Some of these supplements provide specific vitamins and minerals, while others provide exotic "metabolites," "glandular extracts," or "food concentrates." Many of these products are heavily marketed and, as just noted, can be very expensive. Are they worth the investment? Let's take a look at some of the research into supplements promoted for longevity.

Many well-designed, carefully conducted research studies have looked at the effect of vitamin and/or mineral supplements on chronic disease risk and rates of death, or mortality. Antioxidants such as vitamins A, E, and C and beta-carotene have gotten the most attention (Thomas, 2006). Unfortunately, not even one trial of these nutrients (alone or in combination) has shown them to lower rates of death from heart disease or other causes. In fact, several of the studies actually reported a *higher* rate of death with high doses of vitamins A or E and of beta-carotene supplements (Bjelakovic et al., 2007). However, a quick search on your computer will open up a world of promises, all guaranteeing better health and longer life spans, if you use these supplements!

Other supplements that claim to enhance longevity include products based on

- food extracts, such as resveratrol from red wines, and other foods
- herbals, including Siberian ginseng, ginkgo biloba, and various combinations of Eastern botanicals
- animal extracts, such as royal jelly and dried glandulars
- hormone-based preparations, such as DHEA (dehydroepiandrosterone), human growth hormone, and melatonin
- metabolites, such as alpha lipoic acid

Manufacturers promote these products with claims such as "used since prehistoric times," "revered in Eastern cultures," and "nature's own therapeutic powers." However, no well-designed research studies support the claims of life-extending effectiveness for any of products in humans. Moreover, researchers have been unable to identify any plausible scientific explanations for why or how these supplements might increase longevity in humans.

More disturbingly, like antioxidant supplements, many of these non-nutrient supplements have serious side effects. For example, ginkgo can cause gastrointestinal upset, nausea, diarrhea, headache, dizziness, or an allergic reaction (National Center for Complementary and Alternative Medicine, 2008). Human growth hormone can contribute to heart disease and diabetes and cause joint pain, muscle pain, and

Anyone can benefit from the antioxidant nutrients in fresh fruits and vegetables. Antioxidant supplements are not necessary, and they may be harmful.

What About You?

How Long Are You Likely to Live?

First, let's get one thing straight: no "longevity calculator," game, or quiz, no matter how complex or high-tech, can predict how long you'll live. That is not only because death from traumatic injury is unpredictable, but also because chronic diseases, as we have discussed throughout this text, are multifactorial, and we have a long way to go before we understand fully how all the factors interact to produce or prevent disease. That said, studies of large populations have demonstrably linked certain behaviours with an increased life span. These include regular physical activity, a nourishing diet, no tobacco use, and no excessive alcohol consumption. These factors are included in all longevity tools. In addition, most tools ask about other factors, such as drug abuse, stress, sleep quality and duration, seat belt use, and social support. Want to learn more? If so, you'll find longevity games and quizzes on many websites. Here is one popular option:

Living to 100 Life Expectancy Calculator

www.livingto100.com
This quiz, developed by Dr. Thomas Perls, has 40 questions related to your family and health. It provides some brief feedback and a list of suggested lifestyle changes to improve your health.

---

other symptoms (Mayo Clinic, 2009b). DHEA may decrease HDL-cholesterol and increase the risk for certain types of cancer. However, despite these concerns, the sales of such supplements continue to grow (Mayo Clinic, 2009c).

Are Your Actions Today Promoting a Longer, Healthier Life?

The debate over the effectiveness and safety of CR, IF, and the variety of anti-aging supplements will continue as more research is conducted. In the meantime, what can you do to increase your chances of living a long and healthful life? The U.S. Centers for Disease Control and Prevention (CDC) reminds us that chronic disease is responsible for seven out of every ten U.S. deaths. Moreover, just four behaviours, all within our control, are responsible for much of the illness, suffering, and early death associated with chronic disease (CDC, 2009; CDC, 2010). They are:

- Lack of physical activity
- Poor nutrition
- Tobacco use
- Excessive alcohol consumption

QUICK TIPS

Promoting Your Longevity

▶ Engage in at least 30 minutes of moderate physical activity most days of the week.
▶ Eat a diet based on *Eating Well with Canada's Food Guide.*
▶ Use only the nutrient supplements that have been recommended to you by your health-care provider and within the recommended amounts.

▶ Maintain a healthful weight and body composition. Both underweight and overweight are associated with increased mortality. (See Chapter 11.)
▶ If you smoke or use any other form of tobacco, stop. If you don't smoke, don't start. On average, smokers die 13 to 14 years earlier than non-smokers.
▶ If you drink alcohol, do so only in moderation, meaning no more than two drinks per day for men and one drink per day for women. The health risks of alcohol were discussed **In Depth** following Chapter 1.

So if you want to live a longer, healthier life, the CDC advises that you adopt the health habits highlighted in the Quick Tips box.

Maybe you are already engaging in these healthful behaviours but still wonder how long you are likely to live. If so, check out the What About You? feature box for a fun longevity quiz: your results might make you laugh, or put you on track to more healthful choices starting today!

Web Resources

www.hc-sc.gc.ca/hl-vs/seniors-aines/ index-eng.php
Health Canada, Healthy Living—Seniors

Visit this website for information on healthy eating, injury prevention, oral health, physical activity, and smoking cessation.

www.nia.nih.gov
The National Institute on Aging

The National Institute on Aging provides information about how older adults can benefit from physical activity and a good diet.

www.nihseniorhealth.gov
National Institutes of Health, Senior Health

This website, written in large print, offers up-to-date information on popular health topics for older Americans.

REFERENCES

Chapter 1

Grierson, B. 2003. What your genes want you to eat. *New York Times*, May 4.

IOM (Institute of Medicine, Food and Nutrition Board). 2002. *Dietary Reference Intakes for Energy, Carbohydrates, Fiber, Fat, Protein and Amino Acids (Macronutrients)*. Washington, DC: National Academies Press.

IOM (Institute of Medicine, Food and Nutrition Board). 2003. *Dietary Reference Intakes: Applications in Dietary Planning*. Washington, DC: National Academies Press.

Johnson, N., and J. Kaput. 2003. Nutrigenomics: an emerging scientific discipline. *Food Technology* 57(4):60–67.

Kaput, J., and R. Rodriguez. 2004. Nutritional genomics: the next frontier in the postgenomic era. *Physiological Genomics* 16:166–177.

NCMHD Center of Excellence for Nutritional Genomics. Retrieved April 2007, from http://nutrigenomics.ucdavis.edu.

Raine, K. 2004. *Overweight and Obesity in Canada: A Population Health Perspective*. Toronto: Canadian Institute for Health Information.

Statistics Canada. 2011a. Body mass index, overweight or obese, self-reported, youth, by sex. CANSIM. Table 105-0501, catalogue 82-221-X. Accessed June 2012. www.statcan.gc.ca/tables-tableaux/sum-som/l01/cst01/health83b-eng.htm.

Statistics Canada. 2011b. Body mass index, overweight or obese, self-reported, adult, by age group and sex. CANSIM. Table 105-0501, catalogue 82-221-X. Accessed June 2012 from www.statcan.gc.ca/tables-tableaux/sum-som/l01/cst01/health81b-eng.htm.

Wallace, K. 2007. Diet, exercise may lower colon cancer risk [television broadcast]. CBS News, March 15.

Watters, E. 2006. DNA is not destiny. *Discover* 27(11):32–75.

In Depth: Alcohol

Brown, S. A., S. F. Tapert, E. Granholm, and D. C. Delis. 2000. Neurocognitive functioning of adolescents: effects of protracted alcohol use. *Alc. Clin. Exp. Res.* 24:164–171.

Butt, P., D. Beirness, F. Cesa, L. Gliksman, C. Paradis, and T. Stockwell. 2011. Alcohol and Health in Canada: A summary of Evidence and Guidelines for Low Risk Drinking. Ottawa, ON: Canadian Centre on Substance Abluse.

Caton, S. J., M. Ball, A. Ahern, et al. 2004. Dose-dependent effects of alcohol on appetite and food intake. *Physiol. Behav.* 81:51–58.

Chudley, A. E., J. Conry, J. L. Cook, C. Loock, T. Rosales and N. LeBlanc. 2005. Fetal alcohol spectrum disorder: Canadian guidelines for diagnosis. *CMAJ* 172:S1–S21.

Dufour, M. C., L. Archer, and E. Gordis. 1992. Alcohol and the elderly. *Clin. Geriatr. Med.* 8:127–141.

Gunzerath, L., V. Faden, S. Zakhari, and K. Warren. 2004. National Institute on Alcohol Abuse and Alcoholism Report on moderate drinking. *Alcohol. Clin. Exp. Res.* 28L:829–847.

Meister, K. A., E. M. Whelan, and R. Kava. 2000. The health effects of moderate alcohol intake in humans: an epidemiologic review. *Crit. Rev. Clin. Lab. Sci.* 37:261–296.

Naimi, T. S., R. D. Brewer, A. Mokdad, C. Denny, and M. K. Serdula. 2003. Binge drinking among US adults. 289:70–79.

NIAAA (National Institute of Alcohol Abuser and Alcoholism). 2004. NIAAA Council approves definition of binge drinking. http://pubs.niaaa.nih.gov/publications/Newsletter/winter2004/Newsletter_Number3.pdf. NIAA Newsletter 2004: 3:3.

NIAAA (National Institute on Alcohol Abuse and Alcoholism). 2007. A Snapshot of High-Risk College Drinking Consequences. www.collegedrinkingprevention.gov/facts/snapshot.aspx.

Oscar-Berman, M., and K. Marinkovic. 2003. Alcoholism and the brain: an overview. *Alc. Res. Health* 27:161–173.

PHAC (Public Health Agency of Canada). 2008. What is Fetal Alcohol Spectrum Disorder (FASD)? Accessed June 2012 from www.phac-aspc.gc.ca/hp-ps/dca-dea/prog-ini/fasd-etcaf/publications/fs-fi_01-eng.php.

Stranges, S., T. Wu, J. M. Born., et al. 2004. Relationship of alcohol drinking pattern to risk of hypertension. *Hypertension* 44:813–819.

Chapter 2

CFIA (Canadian Food Inspection Agency). 2011. Health Claims. www.inspection.gc.ca/english/fssa/labeti/insthse.shtml. Accessed June 2012.

CTV.ca. 2008. Dannon sued over probiotic yogurt claims. www.ctvnews.ca/dannon-sued-over-probiotic-yogurt-claims-1.272735.

Doron, S., and S. L. Gorbach. 2006. Probiotics: Their role in the treatment and prevention of diseases. *Expert Rev. Anti-Infect. Ther.* 4(2):261–275.

Ezendam, J., and H. van Loveren. 2006. Probiotics: Immunomodulation and evaluation of safety and efficacy. *Nutr. Rev.* 64(1):1–14.

FAO. 2001. Health and Nutritional Properties of Probiotics in Food including Powder Milk with Live Lactic Acid Bacteria. Report of a Joint FAO/WHO Expert Consultation. Available at: www.who.int/foodsafety/publications/fs_management/en/probiotics.pdf.

Health Canada. 2003. Frequently Asked Questions About Nutrition Labelling. http://hc-sc.gc.ca/fn-an/label-etiquet/nutrition/educat/te_quest-eng.php#18. Accessed September 2008.

Health Canada. 2007. *Eating Well with Canada's Food Guide*, www.hc-sc.gc.ca/fn-an/food-guide-aliment/index-eng.php. © Her Majesty the Queen in Right of Canada, represented by the Minister of Health Canada, 2007. HC Pub.:4651, Cat.:H164-38/1-2007E, ISBN:0-662-44467-1.

Health Canada. 2011. Health Claim Assessments. Reproduced from www.hc-sc.gc.ca/fn-an/label-etiquet/claims-reclam/assess-evalu/index-eng.php.

Health Check. March 2008. Nutrient criteria. www.healthcheck.org/en/nutritional-information/nutrient-criteria-grocery.html. Accessed April 2008.

Reid, G., K. Anukam, and T. Koyama. 2008. Probiotic products in Canada with clinical evidence: what can gastroenterologists recommend? *Can. J. Gastroentero* 22:169–175.

Saier, M. H., Jr., and N. M. Mansour. 2005. Probiotics and prebiotics in human health. *J. Mol. Microbiol. Biotechnol.* 10(1):22–25.

Sanders, M. E., D. C. Walker, K. M. Walker, K. Aoyama, and T. R. Klaenhammer. 1996. Performance of commercial cultures in fluid milk applications. *J. Dairy Sci.* 79:943–955.

Statistics Canada 2011. Body mass index, overweight or obese, self-reported, adult, by age group and sex. CANSIM. Table 105-0501, catalogue 82-221-X. Accessed June 2012 from www.statcan.gc.ca/tables-tableaux/sum-som/l01/cst01/health81b-eng.htm.

Statistics Canada. 2012. Survey of Household Spending, 2010. *The Daily*. April 25, 2012. www.statcan.gc.ca/daily-quotidien/120425/dq120425a-eng.htm.

In Depth: Phytochemicals

Baur, J. A., et al. 2006. Resveratrol improves health and survival of mice on a high calorie diet. *Nature* 444:337–342.

Beauchamp, G. K., R. S. Keast, D. Morel, J. Lin, J. Pika, Q. Han, C. H. Lee, A. B. Smith, and P. A. Breslin. 2005. Ibuprofen-like activity in extra virgin olive oil. *Nature* 437:45–46.

Boileau, T. W. -M., et al. 2003. Prostate carcinogenesis in N-methyl-N-nitrosurea (NMU)-testosterone-treated rats fed tomato powder, lycopene, and energy-restricted diets. *J. Natl. Cancer Inst.* 95: 1578–1586.

Chun, O. K., et al. 2007. Estimated dietary flavonoid intake and major food sources of US adults. *J. Nutr.* 137:1244–1252.

Food and Nutrition Board, IOM (Institute of Medicine) Panel on Dietary Antioxidants and Related Compounds. Subcommittee on Upper Reference Levels of Nutrients and Interpretation and Uses of Dietary Reference Intakes. Standing Committee on the Scientific Evaluation of Dietary Reference Intakes. 2000. Dietary Reference Intakes for Vitamin C, Vitamin E, Selenium, and Carotenoids. Washington, DC: National Academies Press.

Lagouge, M., et al. 2006. Resveratrol improves mitochondrial function and protects against metabolic disease by activating SIRT1 and PGC-1alpha. *Cell* 27(6):1109–1122.

Linus Pauling Institute, Oregon State University. 2005. Micronutrient information center: Flavonoids. Available at http://lpi.oregonstate.edu/infocenter/phytochemicals/flavonoids.

Liu, R. H. 2003. Health benefits of fruit and vegetables are from additive and synergistic combinations of phytochemicals. *Am. J. Clin. Nutr.* 78(suppl.):517S–520S.

Liu, R. H. 2004. Potential synergy of phytochemicals in cancer prevention: Mechanism of action. *J. Nutr.* 134:3479S–3485S.

Melton, L. 2006. The antioxidant myth: A medical fairy tale. *New Sci.* 2563:40–43.

Meyskens, F. L., and E. Szabo. 2005. Diet and cancer: The disconnect between epidemiology and randomized clinical trials. *Cancer Epidemiol. Biomarkers Prev.* 14(6):1366–1369.

Milner, J. A. 2001. A historical perspective on garlic and cancer. *J. Nutr.* 131:1027S–1031S.

Omenn, G. S., et al. 1996. Risk factors for lung cancer and for intervention effects in CARET, the Beta-Carotene and Retinol Efficacy Trial. *J. Natl. Cancer Inst.* 88(21):1550–1559.

Rice S., and S. A. Whitehead. 2006. Phytoestrogens and breast cancer—promoters or protectors? *Endocr. Relat. Cancer* 13(4):995–1015.

The Alpha-Tocopherol, Beta-Carotene Cancer Prevention Study Group. 1994. The effect of vitamin E and beta carotene on the incidence of lung cancer and other cancers in male smokers. *N. Engl. J. Med.* 330(15):1029–1035.

U. S. Preventive Services Task Force. 2003. Routine vitamin supplementation to prevent cancer and cardiovascular disease: Recommendations and rationale. *Ann. Intern. Med.* 139(1):51–55.

Chapter 3

Batterham, R. L., M. A. Cowley, C. J. Small, H. Herzog, M. A. Cohen, C. L. Dakin, A. M. Wren, A. E. Brynes, J. M. Low, M. A. Ghatei, R. D. Cone, and S. R. Bloom. 2002. Gut hormone PYY3-36 physiologically inhibits food intake. *Nature* 418:650–654.

Bauman, R. 2011. *Microbiology*, 3rd ed. San Francisco: Benjamin Cummings.

Bell, E. A., and B. J. Rolls. 2001. Regulation of Energy Intake: Factors Contributing to Obesity. In *Present Knowledge in Nutrition*, 8th ed., edited by B. A. Bowman and R. M. Russell. Washington, DC: ILSI Press.

Blom, W. A. M., A. Stafleu, C. de Graaf, F. J. Kok, G. Schaafsma, G. Hendriks, and H. F. J. Hendriks. 2005. Ghrelin response to carbohydrate-enriched breakfast is related to insulin. *Am. J. Clin. Nutr.* 81:367–375.

Canadian Digestive Health Foundation. 2011. www.cdhf.ca/digestive-disorders/statistics.shtml.

Davidson, N. O. 2003. Intestinal lipid absorption. In *Textbook of Gastroenterology*, Volume 1, 4th ed., edited by T. Yamada, D. H. Alpers, N. Kaplowitz, L. Laine, C. Owyang, and D. W. Powell. Philadelphia: Lippincott Williams & Wilkins.

DuPont, H. L. 2006. New insights and directions in traveler's diarrhea. Gastroenterol. *Clin. N. Am.* 35(2):337–353, viii–ix.

Gancz, H., K. R. Jones, and D. S. Merrell. 2008. Sodium chloride affects *Helicobacter pylori* growth and gene expression. *J Bacteriol* 190:4100–4105.

Garrett, W. S., C. A. Gallini, Y. Yatsunenko, M. Michaud, A. DuBois, M. L. Delaney, S. Punit, M. Karlsson, L. Bry, J. N. Glickman, J. I. Gordon, A. B. Onderdonk, and L. Glimcher. 2010. Enterobacteriaceae Act in Concert with the Gut Microbiota to Induce Spontaneous and Maternally Transmitted Colitis. *Cell Host & Microbe* 8: 292–300.

Lewis S. J., and K. W. Heaton. 1997. Stool form scale as a useful guide to intestinal transit time. *Scand. J. Gastroenterol.* 32(9): 920–4.

Loh, J. T., V. J. Torres, and T. L. Cover. 2007. Regulation of *Helicobacter pylori cagA* expression in response to salt. *Cancer Res.* 67: 4709–4715.

Mayo Clinic. 2009. Colon cleansing: Is it helpful or harmful? Mayo Foundation for Medical Education and Research. Available at: www.mayoclinic.com/health/colon-cleansing/AN00065.

NIDDK (National Institute of Diabetes and Digestive and Kidney Diseases). 2007b. Heartburn, Gastroesophageal Reflux (GER), and Gastroesophageal Reflux Disease (GERD). NIH Publication No. 07-0882. http://digestive.niddk.nih.gov/ddiseases/pubs/gerd/index.htm.

NIDDK (National Institute of Diabetes and Digestive and Kidney Diseases). 2007a. Diarrhea. NIH Publication No. 07–2749. http://digestive.niddk.nih.gov/ddiseases/pubs/diarrhea/index.htm.

NIDDK (National Institute of Diabetes and Digestive and Kidney Diseases). 2007c. Irritable Bowel Syndrome. NIH Publication No. 07-693. http://digestive.niddk.nih.gov/ddiseases/pubs/ibs/.

NIDDK (National Institute of Diabetes and Digestive and Kidney Diseases). 2004. H. pylori and Peptic Ulcer. NIH Publication No. 05-4225. http://digestive.niddk.nih.gov/ddiseases/pubs/hpylori/.

NIH (National Institutes of Health). 2004, NIH Consensus Development Conference on Celiac Disease. http://consensus.nih.gov/2004/2004Celiac Disease118html.htm.

NIH (National Institutes of Health). 2009. Allergy Testing. Medline Plus. Available at www.nlm.nih.gov/medlineplus/ency/article/003519.htm.

Orr, J., and B. Davy. 2005. Dietary influences on peripheral hormones regulating energy intake: potential applications for weight management. *J. Am. Diet. Assoc.* 105:1115–1124; Astrup, A. 2005. The satiating power of protein—a key to obesity prevention? *Am. J. Cl. Nutr.* Vol. 82 No. 1, 1–2, July 2005. Available at www.ajcn.org/cgi/content/full/82/1/1.

Picco, M. 2008. Detox diets: Do they offer any health benefits? Mayo Foundation for Medical Education and Research. Available at: www.mayoclinic.com/health/detox-diets/AN015334.

Tobin, M. C., B. Moparty, A. Farhadi, M. T. DeMel, P. J. Bansal, and A. Keshavarzian. 2008. Atopic irritable bowel syndrome: A novel subgroup of irritable bowel syndrome with allergic manifestations. *Ann. Allergy Asthma Immunol.* 100:49–53.

WebMD. 2009. Natural Colon Cleansing: Is It Necessary? WebMD Medical Reference. Available at www.webmd.com/balance/natural-colon-cleansing-is-it-necessary.

Wroblewski, L. E., R. M. Peek, and K. T Wilson. 2010. *Helicobacter pylori* and gastric cancer: Factors that modulate disease risk. *Clin. Microbiol. Rev.* 23:713–739.

In Depth: Specific Disorders Related to Food

Canadian Society for Intestinal Research. 2012. Celiac disease. www.badgut.org/information-centre/celiac-disease.html. Accessed June 2012.

CFIA (Canadian Food Inspection Agency). 2010. General Information About Food Allergies. Available at: www.inspection.gc.ca/food/consumer-centre/food-safety-tips/labelling-food-packaging-and-storage/information/eng/1332281644550/1332282437601.

Health Canada 2010. Health Canada's Modifications to Regulatory Project 1220—Enhanced Labelling for Food Allergens, Gluten Sources and Added Sulphites. Available at: www.hc-sc.gc.ca/fn-an/label-etiquet/allergen/proj1220-modifications-eng.php.

Health Canada. 2011. Regulations Amending the Food and Drug Regulations (1220—Enhanced Labelling for Food Allergen and Gluten Sources and Added Sulphites). Available at: www.hc-sc.gc.ca/fn-an/securit/allerg/fa-aa/index-eng.php.

NIDDK (National Institute of Diabetes and Digestive and Kidney Diseases. 2009. Lactose Intolerance. NIH Publication No. 09-2751. http://digestive. niddk.nih.gov/ddiseases/pubs/lactoseintolerance/.

Chapter 4

Atkins, R. C. 1992. *Dr. Atkins' New Diet Revolution*. New York: M. Evans & Company, Inc.

Augustin, L. S. A., C. Galeone, L. Dal Maso, C. Pelucchi, V. Ramazzotti, D. J. A. Jenkins, M. Montella, R. Talamini, E. Negri, S. Franceschi, and C. La Vecchia. 2004. Glycemic index, glycemic load and risk of prostate cancer. Int. J. Cancer 112: 446–450.

Aune, D., D. S. Chan, R. Lau, R. Vieira, D. C. Greenwood, E. Kampman, and T. Norat. 2011. Dietary fibre, whole grains, and risk of colorectal cancer: systematic review and dose-response meta-analysis of prospective studies. *BMJ 2011;343:d6617*.

Buyken, A. E., M. Toeller, G. Heitkamp, G. Karamanos, B. Rottiers, R. Muggeo, and M. Fuller. 2001. Glycemic index in the diet of European outpatients with type 1 diabetes: relations to glycated hemoglobin and serum lipids. *Am. J. Clin. Nutr.* 73:574–581.

Canadian Sugar Institute. 2006. Estimates of added sugars consumption in Canada. Nutrition Information Service. Toronto.

Canadian Sugar Institute. n.d. Types of sugars. www.sugar.ca/english/consumers/typessugar.cfm#s22. Accessed August 8, 2012.

Colditz, G. A., J. E. Manson, M. J. Stampfer, B. Rosner, W. C. Willett, and F. E. Speizer. 1992. Diet and risk of clinical diabetes in women. *Am. J. Clin. Nutr.* 55:1018–1023.

Dietitians of Canada. 2010. Safety of artificial sweeteners for pregnant wormen. www.dietitians.ca/Nutrition-Resources-A-Z/Factsheets/Food-Safety/Artificial-Sweeteners.aspx. Accessed May 2012.

Elliott, S. S., N. L. Keim, J. S. Stern, K. Teff, and P. J. Havel. 2002. Fructose, weight gain, and the insulin resistance syndrome. *Am. J. Clin. Nutr.* 76:911–922.

Foster-Powell, K., S. H. A. Holt, and J. C. Brand-Miller. 2002. International table of glycemic index and glycemic load values: 2002. *Am. J. Clin. Nutr.* 76:5–56.

Garriguet, D. 2006. Canadians' Eating Habits 2004. Statistics Canada, 2006, Cat. No. 82–620-MIE. www.statcan.ca/bsolc/english/bsolc?catno=82–620-MIE2006002. Accessed January 2008.

Health Canada. 2007. Canadian Community Health Survey, Cycle 2. 2, Nutrition (2004) Nutrient Intakes from Food. Provincial, Regional and National Summary Data Tables, Volume 1. Cat. : H164–45/1–2007E-PDF. www.hc-sc.gc.ca/ fn-an/pubs/cchs-nutri-escc/index_e.html. Accessed May 2008.

Health Canada. 2010a. Frequently Asked Questions on Stevia. Retrieved April 13, 2012 from www.hc-sc.gc.ca/fn-an/securit/addit/sweeten-edulcor/stevia-faq-eng.php.

Health Canada. 2010b. Health Canada is considering reinstating saccharin as a sweetner. www.hc-sc.gc.ca/fn-an/securit/addit/sweeten-edulcor/index-eng.php. Accessed May 2012.

Howard, B. V., and J. Wylie-Rosett. 2002. Sugar and cardiovascular disease. A statement for healthcare professionals from the Committee on Nutrition of the Council on Nutrition, Physical Activity, and Metabolism of the American Heart Association. *Circulation* 106:523–527.

IFICF (International Food Information Council Foundation). 2009. Facts About Low-Calorie Sweeteners. www.foodinsight.org/Content/6/LCS%20Fact%20Sheet_11-09.pdf.

Institute of Medicine, Food and Nutritition Board. 2002. *Dietary Reference Intakes for Energy, Carbohydrates, Fibre, Fat, Protein and Amino Acids (Macronutrients)*. Washington, DC: The National Academy of Sciences.

Jacobson, M. F. 2004. Letter to the editor. High-fructose corn syrup and the obesity epidemic. *Am. J. Clin. Nutr.* 80:1081–1090.

Lê, K. -A., D. Faeh, R. Stettler, M. Ith, R. Kreis, P. Vermathen, C. Boesch, E. Ravussin, and L. Tappy. 2006. A 4-wk high-fructose diet alters lipid metabolism without affecting insulin sensitivity or ectopic lipids in healthy humans. *Am. J. Clin. Nutr.* 84:1374–1379.

Liu, S., J. E. Manson, M. J. Stampfer, M. D. Holmes, F. B. Hu, S. E. Hankinson, and W. C. Willett. 2001. Dietary glycemic load assessed by food-frequency questionnaire in relation to plasma high-density-lipoprotein cholesterol and fasting plasma triacylglycerols in postmenopausal women. *Am. J. Clin. Nutr.* 73:560–566.

Meyer, K. A., L. H. Kushi, D. R. Jacobs, J. Slavin, T. A. Sellers, and A. R. Folsom. 2000. Carbohydrates, dietary fibre, and incident type 2 diabetes in older women. *Am. J. Clin. Nutr.* 71:921–930.

Pan, J. W., D. L. Rothman, K. L. Behar, D. T. Stein, and H. P. Hetherington. 2000. Human brain β-hydroxybutyrate and lactate increase in fasting-induced ketosis. *J. Cerebral Blood Flow Metabol.* 20:1502–1507.

Park, Y., Hunter, D. J., Spiegelman, D., Bergkvist, L., Berrino, F., van den Brandt, P. A., Buring, J. E., Colditz, G. A., Freudenheim, J. L., Fuchs, C. S., Giovannucci, E., Goldbohm, R. A., Graham, S., Harnack, L., Hartman, A. M., Jacobs, D. R. Jr., Kato, I., Krogh, V., Leitzmann, M. F., McCullough, M. L., Miller, A. B., Pietinen, P., Rohan, T. E., Schatzkin, A., Willett, W. C., Wolk, A., Zeleniuch-Jacquotte, A., Zhang, S. M., & Smith-Warner, S. A. (2005). Dietary fiber intake and risk of colorectal cancer: a pooled analysis of prospective cohort studies. *JAMA294(22)*, 2849–57.

Schultze, M. B., J. E. Manson, D. S. Ludwig, G. A. Colditz, M. J. Stampfer, W. C. Willett, and F. B. Hu. 2004. Sugar-sweetened beverages, weight gain, and incidence of type 2 diabetes in young and middle-aged women. *JAMA.* 292:927–934.

Sears, B. 1995. *The Zone. A Dietary Road Map.* New York: HarperCollins Publishers.

Sloth, B., I. Krog-Mikkelsen, A. Flint, I. Tetens, I. Björck, S. Vinoy, H. Elmståhl, A. Astrup, V. Lang, and A. Raben. 2004. No difference in body weight decrease between a low-glycemic-index and a high-glycemic-index diet but reduced LDL cholesterol after 10-wk ad libitum intake of the low-glycemic-index diet. *Am. J. Clin. Nutr.* 80:337–347.

Statistics Canada. 2003. Food consumption in Canada 2003—Part II. www.statcan.ca/english/ads/23F0001XCB/1. Accessed February 2005.

Statistics Canada. 2008. Beverage consumption of children and teens. Available at: www.statcan.gc.ca/pub/82-003-x/2008004/article/6500820-eng.pdf.

Statistics Canada. 2009. Soft drinks available for consumption adjusted for losses, in 2009. www.statcan.gc.ca/pub/21-020-x/2009001/t040-eng.htm. Accessed May 2012.

Steward, H. L., M. C. Bethea, S. S. Andrews, and L. A. Balart. 1995. *Sugar Busters Cut Sugar to Trim Fat.* New York: Ballantine Books.

Topping, D. L., and P. M. Clifton. 2001. Short-chain fatty acids and human colonic function: Roles of resistant starch and nonstarch polysaccharides. *Physiol. Rev.* 81:1031–1064.

USDHHS and USDA (U. S. Department of Health and Human Services and U. S. Department of Agriculture. 2006. Eating healthier and feeling better using the Nutrition Facts Label. www.cfsan.fda.gov/~acrobat/nutfacts.pdf.

In Depth: Diabetes

American College of Sports Medicine (ACSM). 2000. Position stand: Exercise and type 2 diabetes. *Med. Sci. Sports Exerc.* 32:1345–1360.

American Diabetes Association. 2010. Genetics of diabetes. Available online at www.diabetes.org/diabetes-basics/genetics-of-diabetes.html.

Canadian Diabetes Association. 2012. Prevalence of diabetes. www.diabetes.ca/diabetes-and-you/what/prevalence/. Accessed May 2012.

CDC (Centers for Disease Control). 2000. Non-polio enterovirus infections. www.cdc.gov/ncidod/dvrd/entrvirs.htm. Accessed February 2005.

Grundy, S. M., J. I. Cleeman, S. R. Daniels, K. A. Donato, R. H. Exkel, B. A. Franklin, D. J. Gordon, R. M. Krauss, P. J. Savage, S. C. Smith, J. A. Spertus, and F. Costa. 2005. Diagnosis and management of the metabolic syndrome: An American Heart Association/National

Heart, Lung, and Blood Institute scientific statement. *Circulation* 112(17):2735–2752.

Kleinfield, N. R. 2006. Diabetes and its awful toll quietly emerge as a crisis. *The New York Times*. January 9, 2006. www.nytimes.com/2006/01/09/nyregion/nyregionspecial5/09diabetes.html.

Pan, X. P., G. W. Li, Y. H. Hu, J. X. Wang, W. Y. Yang, Z. X. An, Z. X. Hu, J. Lin, J. Z. Xiao, H. B. Cao, P. A. Liu, X. G. Jiang, Y. Y. Jiang, J. P. Wang, H. Zheng, H. Zhang, P. H. Bennett, and B. V. Howard. 1997. Effects of diet and exercise in preventing NIDDM in people with impaired glucose tolerance. *Diabetes Care* 20:537–544.

Statistics Canada. 2011. Body mass index, overweight or obese, self-reported, youth, by sex. CANSIM. Table 105-0501, catalogue 82-221-X. Accessed June 2012. www.statcan.gc.ca/tables-tableaux/sum-som/l01/cst01/health83b-eng.htm.

Chapter 5

Champe, P. C., R. A. Harvey, and D. R. Ferrier. 2008. Lippincott's Illustrated Reviews: Biochemistry. 4th ed. Philadelphia: Lippincott Williams & Wilkins.

Chanoine, J. P., S. Hampl, C. Jensen, M. Boldrin, and J. Hauptman. 2005. Effect of orlistat on weight and body composition in obese adolescents: A randomized controlled trial. *JAMA* 293:2873–2883.

Cialdella-Kam L. C., Manore M. M. 2009. Macronutrient requirements of active individuals: An Update. *Nutrition Today*. 44(3):104–111.

Din, J. N., D. E. Newby, and A. D. Flapan. 2004. Omega 3 fatty acids and cardiovascular disease—fishing for a natural treatment. *British Med. J.* 328(3):30–35.

Health Canada 2007a. Canadian Community Health Survey, Cycle 2. 2, Nutrition (2004) Nutrient Intakes from Food. Provincial, Regional and National Summary Data Tables, Volume 1. Cat. : H164–45/1–2007E-PDF. www.hc-sc.gc.ca/ fn-an/pubs/cchs-nutri-escc/index_e.html. Accessed May 2008.

Health Canada. 2007b. *Eating Well with Canada's Food Guide*, www.hc-sc.gc.ca/fn-an/food-guide-aliment/index-eng.php. © Her Majesty the Queen in Right of Canada, represented by the Minister of Health Canada, 2007. HC Pub.:4651, Cat.:H164-38/1-2007E, ISBN:0-662-44467-1.

Health Canada. 2007c. It's Your Health: Trans Fat. www.hc-sc.gc.ca/hl-vs/iyh-vsv/food-aliment/trans-eng.php. Accessed December 2007.

Hutton, B. and D. Fergusson. 2004. Changes in body weight and serum lipid profile in obese patients treated with orlistat in addition to a hypocaloric diet: A systematic review of randomized clinical trials. *Am. J. Clin. Nutr.* 80:1461–1468.

Institute of Medicine, Food and Nutrition Board. 2002. Dietary Reference Intakes for Energy, Carbohydrate, Fiber, Fat, Fatty Acids, Cholesterol, Protein, and Amino Acids (Macronutrients). Washington, DC: National Academies Press.

Jebb, S. A, A. M. Prentice, G. R. Goldberg, P. R. Murgatroyd, A. E. Black, and W. A. Coward. 1996. Changes in macronutrient balance during over- and underfeeding assessed by 12-d continuous whole-body calorimetry. *Am. J. Clin. Nutr.* 64:259–266.

Klingberg, S., L. Ellegard, I. Johansson, G. Hallmans, L. Weinehall, H. Andersson, and A. Winkvist. 2008. Inverse relation between dietary intake of naturally occurring plant sterols and serum cholesterol in northern Sweden. *Am. J. Clin. Nutr.* 87:993–1001.

Lau, V. W. Y., M. Journoud, and P. J. H. Jones. 2005. Plant sterols are efficacious in lowering plasma LDL and non-HDL cholesterol in hypercholesterolemic type 2 diabetic and nondiabetic persons. *Am J Clin Nutr.* 81(6):1351–8.

Lichtenstein, A. H., and L. Van Horn. 1998. Very low fat diets. *Circulation* 98:935–939.

Marangoni, A. G., S. H. J. Idziak, C. Vega, H. Batte, M. Ollivon, P. S. Jantzi, and J. W. E. Rush. 2007. Encapsulation-structuring of edible oil attenuates acute elevation of blood lipids and insulin in humans. *Soft Matter* 3:183–187.

Micha, R. and D. Mozaffarian. 2010. Saturated fat and cardiometabolic risk factors, coronary heart disease, stroke, and diabetes: A fresh look at the evidence. *Lipids* 45:893–905.

Micha, R., S. K. Wallace, and D. Mozaffarian. 2010. Red and processed meat consumption and risk of incident coronary heart disease, stroke, and diabetes mellitus: A systematic review and meta-analysis. *Circulation* 121:2271–2283.

Rodriguez N. R., DiMarco N. M., Langley S. 2009. Position of the American Dietetic Association, Dietitians of Canada, and the American College of Sports Medicine: Nutrition and Athletic Performance. *J. Am. Diet. Assoc.* 109:509–527.

Smith, C., A. D. Marks, and M. Lieberman. 2005. Mark's Basic Medical Biochemistry: A Clinical Approach. 2nd ed. Philadelphia: Lippincott Williams & Wilkins.

Teegala S. M., W. C. Willett, and D. Mozaffarian. 2009. Consumption and health effects of Trans fatty acids: a review. *J. AOAC International.* 92(5):1250–1257.

US FDA. 2010. Questions and Answers: Orlistat and Severe Liver Injury. Accessed at: www.fda.gov/Drugs/DrugSafety/PostmarketDrugSafetyInformationforPatientsandProviders/ucm213040.htm.

Wang, Y., M. Jacome-Sosa, D. F. Vine, and S. D. Proctor. 2010. Beneficial effects of vaccenic acid on postprandial lipid metabolism and dyslipidemia: Impact of natural trans-fats to improve CVD risk. *Lipid Tech* 22:103–106.

Wijendran, V., and K. C. Hayes. 2004. Dietary n-6 and n-3 fatty acid balance and cardiovascular health. *Annu. Rev. Nutr.* 24:597–615.

In Depth: Cardiovascular Disease

CHEP (Canadian Hypertension Education Program). 2011. CHEP 2011 Recommendations Summary. Accessed Dec. 2011 from www.hypertension.ca/chep-2011-recommendations-summaries.

DHHS (Dept of Health and Human Services, Centers for Disease Control and Prevention (CDC)). 2010. Smoking and Tobacco Use, Frequently Asked questions. Accessed, Feb. 2010. http://apps.nccd.cdc.gov/osh_faq/topic.aspx?TopicID=8#11.

Hahn, R. A., and G. W. Heath. 1998. Cardiovascular disease risk factors and preventive practices among adults—United States, 1994: a behavioral risk factor atlas. *Morbid. Mortal. Wkly. Rep.* 47(SS-5):35–69.

Harris, W. S. 1997. n-3 Fatty acids and serum lipoproteins: human studies. *Am. J. Clin. Nutr.* 65(suppl.):1645S–1654S.

Health Canada. 2006. It's Your Health: Strokes. Accessed Dec. 2011 from www.hc-sc.gc.ca/hl-vs/iyh-vsv/diseases-maladies/stroke-vasculaire-eng.php.

Heart and Stroke Foundation of Canada. 2005. Cholesterol Article Updates, Nov. 7, 2005. www.heartandstroke.ca.

Heart and Stroke Foundation of Canada. 2008. Statistics. www.heartandstroke.com/site/c.ikIQLcMWJtE/b.3483991/k.34A8/Statistics.htm#heartdisease. Accessed May 2008.

Hypertension Canada. 2011. Frequently asked questions. Accessed Dec. 2011 from www.hypertension.ca/faq.

Kris-Etherton, P. M., W. S. Harris, L. J. Appel, and the Nutrition Committee of the American Heart Association. 2002. Fish consumption, fish oil, omega-3 fatty acids and cardiovascular disease. *Circulation* 106:2747–2757.

Libby P., P. M. Ridker, and A. Maseri. 2002. Inflammation and atherosclerosis. *Circulation* 105:1135–1143.

Lloyd-Jones D., R. J. Adams, T. M. Brown, M. Carnethon, S. Dai, G. DeSimone, et al. 2010. Heart Disease and Stroke Statistics 2010 Update. A Report from the American Heart Association. *Circulation* 121:e1–e170.

Marwick T. H., M. D. Hordern, T. Miller, D. A. Chyun, A. G. Bertoni, R. S. Blumenthal, G. Philippides, and A. Rocchini. 2009. Exercise training for type 2 diabetes Mellitus: Impact on cardiovascular risk: A Scientific Statement from the American Heart Association. *Circulation.* 119:3244–3262.

McPherson, R., J. Frohlich, G. Fodor, and J. Genest. 2006. Canadian Cardiovascular Society position statement—Recommendations for the diagnosis and treatment of dyslipidemia and prevention of cardiovascular disease. *Can J Cardiol* 22:913–927.

Wilson, P. W. F. 2004. CDC/AHA workshop on markers of inflammation and cardiovascular disease. Application to clinical and public health practice. Ability of inflammatory markers to predict disease in asymptomatic patients. A background paper. Circulation 110:e568–e571.

Zoeller, R. F. 2007. Physical activity and fitness in the prevention of coronary heart disease and associated risk factors. *Am. J. Lifestyle Med.* 1(1):29–33.

Chapter 6

Canadian Diabetes Association. 2009. Diet for Diabetes and Chronic Kidney Disease Tips for Health Professionals. Accessed from: www.diabetes.ca/files/for-professionals/diet-kidney-disease.pdf.

CSPI (Centre for Science in the Public Interest). 2011. CSPI Quorn Complaints. Accessed Dec. 2011 at www.cspinet.org/quorn/.

Dietitians of Canada. 2003. Position of the American Dietetic Association and Dietitains of Canada: Vegetarian diets. *Can. J. Diet. Prac. Res.* 2003;64;62–81.

Eshel, G., and P. Martin. 2006. Diet, energy and global warming. Earth Interactions (March)10:1–17. http://geosci.uchicago.edu/~gidon/papers/nutri/nutri.html.

FAO (Food and Agriculture Organization). 2006. Livestock a major threat to environment: Remedies urgently needed. FAO Newsroom. 29 November.

Health Canada. 2007. Canadian Community Health Survey, Cycle 2. 2, Nutrition (2004) Nutrient Intakes from Food. Provincial, Regional and National Summary Data Tables, Volume 1. Cat. : H164–45/1–2007E-PDF. www.hc-sc.gc.ca/fn-an/pubs/cchs-nutri-escc/index-eng.php.

IOM (Institute of Medicine, Food and Nutrition Board). 2002. Dietary Reference Intakes for Energy, Carbohydrate, Fiber, Fat, Fatty Acids, Cholesterol, Protein, and Amino Acids (Macronutrients). Washington, DC: National Academies Press.

Jowit, J. 2008. UN says eat less meat to curb global warming. *The Observer* (September 7). www.guardian.co.uk/environment/2008/sep/07/food.foodanddrink.

Klopp, S. A., C. J. Heiss, and H. S. Smith. 2003. Self-reported vegetarianism may be a marker for college women at risk for disordered eating. *J. Am. Diet. Assoc.* 103(6):745–747.

Manore, M. M, N. L. Meyer, and J. Thompson. 2009. Sport Nutrition for Health and Performance. 2nd Edition. Champaign, IL: Human Kinetics.

National Cattlemen's Beef Association. 2010. Beef Industry Myths and Facts. www.beefusa.org/beefFactoidFighter.aspx.

Owusu-Apenten, R, K. 2002. *Food Protein Analysis: Quantitative Effects on Processing*. The Pennsylvania State University. New York: Marcel Dekker, Inc.

Schaafsma, G. 2000. The protein digestibility–corrected amino acid score. *J Nutr* 130: 1865S–1867S.

Schaafsma, G. 2005. The protein digestibility-corrected amino acid score (PDCAAS)—A concept for describing protein quality in foods and food ingredients: A critical review. *J. AOAC Int.* 88:988–994.

In Depth: Vitamins and Minerals: Micronutrients with Macro Powers

Bjelakovic, G., D. Nikolova, L. L. Gluud, R. G. Simonetti, and C. Gluud. 2007. Mortality in randomized trials of antioxidant supplements for primary and secondary prevention. *J. Am. Med. Assoc.* 297:842–857.

IOM (Institute of Medicine, Food and Nutrition Board). 2001. Dietary Reference Intakes for Vitamin A, Vitamin K, Arsenic, Boron, Chromium, Copper, Iodine, Iron, Manganese, Molybdenum, Nickel, Silicon, Vanadium, and Zinc. Washington, DC: National Academy Press.

Penniston, K. L., and S. A. Tanumihardjo. 2006. The acute and chronic toxic effects of vitamin A. *Am. J. Clin. Nutr.* 83:191–201.

Stover, P. J. 2006. Influence of human genetic variation on nutritional requirements. *Am. J. Clin. Nutr.* 83:436S–443S.

Chapter 7

Canadian Bottled Water Association. n. d. www.cbwa.ca/en/faq.htm#1. Accessed Feb. 2012.

Frassetto, L. A., R. C. Morris, D. E. Sellmeyer, and A. Sebastian. 2008. Adverse effects of sodium chloride on bone in the aging human population resulting from habitual consumption of typical American diets. *J. Nutr.* 138:419S–422S.

Godek, S. F., A. R. Bartolozzi, R. Burkholder, E. Sugarman, and C. Peduzzi. 2008. Sweat rates and fluid turnover in professional football players: a comparison of national football league linemen and backs. *J. Athletic Training* 43:184–189.

Health Canada. 2006. Water quality. www.hc-sc.gc.ca/fn-an/securit/facts-faits/faqs_bottle_water-eau_embouteillee_e.html. Accessed April 2008.

Health Canada. May 2011. Drinking Water. Accessed from: www.hc-sc.gc.ca/ewh-semt/water-eau/drink-potab/index-eng.php.

Health Canada. Nov. 2010. It's Your Health. The Safety of Bottled Water. www.hc-sc.gc.ca/hl-vs/iyh-vsv/food-aliment/bottled-embouteillee-eng.php.

Hew-Butler, T., J. C. Ayus, C. Kipps, R. J. Maughan, S. Mettler, W. H. Meeuwisse, A. J. Page, S. A. Reid, N. J. Rehrer, W. O. Roberts, I. R. Rogers, M. H. Rosner, A. J. Siegel, D. B. Speedy, K. J. Stuempfle, J. G. Verbalis, L. B. Weschler, and P. Wharam. 2008. Statement of the second international exercise-associated hyponatremia consensus development conference, New Zealand, 2007. *Clin. J. Sport Med.* 18:111–121.

IFICF (International Food Information Council Foundation). 2005. Sodium in food and health. www.ific.org. Accessed March 2005.

Institute of Medicine. 2004. *Dietary Reference Intakes for Water, Potassium, Sodium, Chloride, and Sulfate*. Washington, DC: The National Academies Press.

International Council of Bottled Water Associations. n.d. Global bottled water statistics 2000–2003. www.icbwa.org/2000-2003_Zenith_and_Beverage_Marketing_Stats.pdf. Accessed August 2008.

Manore, M., N. L. Meyer, and J. Thompson. 2009. *Sport Nutrition for Health and Performance*, 2nd ed. Champaign, IL: Human Kinetics (117).

Natural Resources Canada. 2009. The Atlas of Canada: Groundwater. atlas.nrcan.gc.ca/site/english/maps/freshwater/distribution/groundwater/1. Accessed August 2008.

Sawka, M. N., L. M. Burke, E. R. Eichner, R. J. Maughan, S. J. Montain, and N. S. Stachenfeld. 2007. American College of Sports Medicine Position Stand: Exercise and fluid replacement. *Med. Sci. Sports Exer.* 39:377–390.

Speedy, D. B., T. D. Noakes, I. R. Rogers, J. M. Thompson, R. G. Campbell, J. A. Kuttner, D. R. Boswell, S. Wright, and M. Hamlin. 1999. Hyponatremia in ultradistance triathletes. *Med. Sci. Sports Exerc.* 31:809–815.

Tanase, C. M., K. G. Koski, P. J. Laffey, M. J. Cooper, and K. A. Cockell. 2011. Canadians continue to consume too much sodium and not enough potassium. *Can J Pub Health* 102:164–168.

Chapter 8

Albanes, D., O. P. Heinonen, J. K. Huttunen, P. R. Taylor, J. Virtamo, B. K. Edwards, J. Haapakoski, M. Rautalahti, A. M. Hartman, J. Palmgren, and P. Greenwald. 1995. Effects of a-tocopherol and b-carotene supplements on cancer incidence in the Alpha-Tocopherol Beta-Carotene Cancer Prevention Study. *Am. J. Clin. Nutr.* 62 (suppl.):1427S–1430S.

Burri, B. J. 1997. Beta-carotene and human health: A review of current research. *Nutr. Res.* 17:547–580.

El-akawi, Z., N. Abdel-Latif, and K. Abdul-Razzak. 2006. Does the plasma level of vitamins A and E affect acne condition? *Clin. Experimen. Dermatol.* 31:430–434.

Geleijnse, J. M., L. J. Launer, D. A. M. van der Kuip, A. Hofman, and J. C. M. Witteman. 2002. Inverse association of tea and flavonoid intakes with incident myocardial infarction: The Rotterdam Study. *Am. J. Clin. Nutr.* 75:880–886.

Gutteridge, J. M. C., and B. Halliwell. 1994. *Antioxidants in Nutrition, Health, and Disease.* Oxford, UK: Oxford University Press.

Hemilä, H., E. Chalker, B. Treacy, and B. Douglas. 2007. Vitamin C for preventing and treating the common cold. Cochrane Database of Systematic Reviews. Issue 3. Art. No. CD000980. DOI: 10.1002/14651858. CD000980. pub3.

Institute of Medicine. 2000. *Dietary Reference Intakes for Vitamin C, Vitamin E, Selenium, and Carotenoids.* Washington, DC: The National Academies Press.

Institute of Medicine. Food and Nutrition Board. 2001. *Dietary Reference Intakes for Vitamin A, Vitamin K, Arsenic, Boron, Chromium, Copper, Iodine, Iron, Manganese, Molybdenum, Nickel, Silicon, Vanadium, and Zinc.* Washington, DC: National Academy Press.

Joshipura, K. J., F. B. Hu, J. E. Manson, M. J. Stampfer, E. B. Rimm, F. E. Speizer, G. Colditz, A. Ascherio, B. Rosner, D. Spiegelman, and W. C. Willett. 2001. The effect of fruit and vegetable intake on risk for coronary heart disease. *Ann. Intern. Med.* 134:1106–1114.

Larsson, S., L. Bergkvist, I. Näslund, J. Rutegård, and A. Wolk. 2007. Vitamin A, retinol, and carotenoids and the risk of gastric cancer: a prospective cohort study. *Am. J. Clin. Nutr.* 85:497–503.

Lee, I. M., N. R. Cook, J. M. Gaziano, D. Gordon, P. M. Ridker, J. E. Manson, C. H. Hennekens, and J. E. Buring. 2005. Vitamin E in the primary prevention of cardiovascular disease and cancer: The Women's Health Study: A randomized controlled trial. *JAMA* 294(1):56–65.

Liu, S., I. -M. Lee, U. Ajani, S. R. Cole, J. E. Buring, and J. E. Manson. 2001. Intake of vegetables rich in carotenoids and risk of coronary heart disease in men: The Physicians' Health Study. *Intl. J. Epidemiol.* 30:130–135.

Livrea, M. A., L. Tesoriere, A. Bongiorno, A. M. Pintaudi, C. Ciaccio, and A. Riccio. 1995. Contribution of vitamin A to the oxidation resistance of human low-density lipoproteins. *Free Radic. Biol. Med.* 18:401–409.

Omenn, G. S., G. E. Goodman, M. D. Thornquist, J. Balmes, M. R. Cullen, A. Glass, J. P. Keogh, F. L. Meyskens, B. Valanis, J. H. Williams, S. Barnhart, and S. Hammar. 1996. Effects of a combination of beta carotene and vitamin A on lung cancer and cardiovascular disease. *New Engl. J. Med.* 334:1150–1155.

Sesso, H. D., J. E. Buring, W. G. Christen, T. Kurth, C. Belanger, J. MacFadyn, V. Bubes, J. E. Manson, R. J. Glynn, and J. M. Gaziano. 2008. Vitamins E and C in the prevention of cardiovascular disease in men: The Physicians' Health Study II randomized controlled trial. *JAMA* 300(18):2123–2133.

The ATBC Study Group (The Alpha-Tocopherol, Beta-Carotene Cancer Prevention Study Group). 1994. The effect of vitamin E and beta carotene on the incidence of lung cancer and other cancers in male smokers. *N. Engl. J. Med.* 330:1029–1035.

The HOPE and HOPE-TOO Trial Investigators. 2005. Effects of long-term vitamin E supplementation on cardiovascular events and cancer. A randomized controlled trial. *JAMA* 293:1338–1347.

USDA (U. S. Department of Agriculture, Agricultural Research Service). 2009. USDA National Nutrient Database for Standard Reference, Release 22. Available at www.ars.usda.gov/ba/bhnrc/ndl.

World Health Organization (WHO). 2009. Micronutrient deficiencies. Vitamin A deficiency. Available at www.who.int/nutrition/topics/vad/en/.

Yeomans, V. C., J. Linseisen, and G. Wolfram. 2005. Interactive effects of polyphenols, tocopherol, and ascorbic acid on the Cu2+-mediated oxidative modification of human low density lipoproteins. *Eur. J. Nutr.* 44(7): 422–428.

In Depth: Cancer

American Cancer Society. 2009. Cancer Facts & Figures 2009. Available at www.cancer.org/downloads/STT/500809web.pdf.

Canadian Cancer Society. 2011. Statistics 2011 Publication number: 113-303. www.cancer.ca/Canada-wide/Publications/.

Canadian Cancer Society. 2012a. Canadian cancer statistics. Report retrieved from www.cancer.ca on Feb 27, 2012.

Canadian Cancer Society. 2012b. General cancer statistics. www.cancer.ca/Canada-wide/About%20cancer/Cancer%20statistics/Stats%20at%20a%20glance/General%20cancer%20stats.aspx?sc_lang=en#ixzz246l7id4w.

Greenwald P., C. K. Clifford, and J. A. Milner. 2001. Diet and cancer prevention. *Eur. J. Cancer* 37:948–965.

Heinonen, O. P., D. Albanes, J. Virtamo, P. R. Taylor, J. K. Huttunen, A. M. Hartman, J. Haapakoski, N. Malila, M. Rautalahti, S. Ripatti, H. Maepaa, and International Agency for Research on Cancer (IARC). 2007. The association of use of sunbeds with cutaneous malignant melanoma and other skin cancers: A systematic review. *Int. J. Cancer* 120:1116–1122.

McConnell, T. H. 2007. *The Nature of Disease: Pathology for the Health Professions.* Baltimore: Lippincott Williams & Wilkins. p. 96.

Pfahlberg, A., K. F. Kolmel, and O. Gefeller. 2002. Adult vs. childhood susceptibility to melanoma. Is there a difference? *Arch. Dermatol.* 138:1234–1235.

Thune, I., and A. S. Furberg. 2001. Physical activity and cancer risk: Dose-response and cancer, all sites and site-specific. *Med. Sci. Sports Exerc.* 33(suppl.):S530–S550.

USDHHS (U. S. Department of Health and Human Services). 2004. *The Health Consequences of Smoking: A Report of the Surgeon General.* Washington, DC: U. S. Department of Health and Human Services, Centers for Disease Control and Prevention, National Center for Chronic Disease Prevention and Health Promotion, Office on Smoking and Health.

Chapter 9

American Dietetic Association. 2005. Position of the American Dietetic Association: the impact of fluoride on health. *J. Am. Diet. Assoc.* 105:1620–1628.

Barrett, S. 2004. Be wary of coral calcium and Robert Barefoot. *Quackwatch,* www.quackwatch.org/01QuackeryRelatedTopics/DSH/coral.html. Accessed April 2008.

CaMos (Canadian Multicentre Osteoporosis Study). 2012. Camoscope Issue February 2012. www.camos.org/pdf/English%20Camoscope%20February%202012.pdf. Accessed May 2012.

CBC News. Nov. 4, 2010. Vitamin D testing limit a mistake: MD. www.cbc.ca/health/story/2010/10/04/vitamin-d-testing.html.

Chevalley, T., R. Rizzoli, D. Hans, S. Ferrari, and J. P. Bonjour. 2005. Interaction between calcium intake and menarcheal age on bone mass gain: an eight-year follow-up study from prepuberty to postmenarche. *J. Clin. Endocrinol. Metab.* 90:44–51.

Dietitians of Canada. May 2008. Current Issues: Vitamin D Current Dilemas. Retrieved October 15, 2010 from www.dietitians.ca/members_only/backgrounders.asp?fn=view&id=11965&idstring=13964|12210|11965. Accessed May 2012.

Florez, H., R. Martinez, W. Chacra, N. Strickman-Stein, and S. Levis. 2007. Outdoor exercise reduces the risk of hypovitaminosis D in the obese. *J. Steroid Biochem. Mol. Biol.* 103:679–681.

Health Canada. 2008a. Findings and recommendations of the Fluoride Expert Panel (January 2007). www.hc-sc.gc.ca/ewh-semt/pubs/water-eau/2008-fluoride-fluorure/index-eng.php. Accessed August 2008.

Health Canada. 2008b. Fluoride and human health. www.hc-sc.gc.ca/hl-vs/iyh-vsv/environ/fluor-eng.php. Accessed August 2008.

Ho, A. Y. Y., and A. W. C. Kung. 2005. Determinants of peak bone mineral density and bone area in young women. *J. Bone Miner. Metab.* 23:470–475.

Holick, M. F. 2004. Sunlight and vitamin D for bone health and prevention of autoimmune diseases, cancers, and cardiovascular disease. *Am. J. Clin. Nutr.* 80:1678S–1688S.

Holick, M. F. 2005. The vitamin D epidemic and its health consequences. *J. Nutr.* 135:2739S–2748S.

Holick, M. F. 2006. Resurrection of vitamin D deficiency and rickets. *J. Clin. Invest.* 116:2062–2072.

Holick, M. F., L. Y. Matsuoka, and J. Wortsman. 1989. Age, vitamin D, and solar ultraviolet. *Lancet* 2:1104–1105.

IFIC Foundation. 2007. *Food Insight*. Vitamin D in the spotlight: An expanded role emerges for promoting health. Washington, DC: International Food Information Council (IFIC) Foundation.

Institute of Medicine (Food and Nutrition Board). 1997. *Dietary Reference Intakes for Calcium, Phosphorus, Magnesium, Vitamin D, and Fluoride*. Washington, DC: National Academies Press.

Institute of Medicine (Food and Nutrition Board). 2002. *Dietary Reference Intakes for Vitamin A, Vitamin K, Arsenic, Boron, Chromium, Copper, Iodine, Iron, Manganese, Molybdenum, Nickel, Silicon, Vanadium, and Zinc*. Washington, DC: National Academies Press.

Institute of Medicine (Food and Nutrition Board). 2010. *Dietary Reference Intakes for Calcium, Phosphorus, Magnesium, Vitamin D, and Fluoride*. www.iom.edu/Reports/2010/Dietary-Reference-Intakes-for-Calcium-and-Vitamin-D. aspx. Accessed May 2012.

Iuliano-Burns, S., S. J. Whiting, R. A. Faulkner, and D. A. Bailey. 1999. Levels, sources, and seasonality of dietary calcium intake in children and adolescents enrolled in the University of Saskatchewan Pediatric Bone Mineral Accrual Study. *Nutr. Res.* 19:1471–1483.

Keller, J. L., A. J. Lanou, and N. D. Barnard. 2002. The consumer cost of calcium from food and supplements. *J. Am. Diet. Assoc.* 102:1669–1671.

Langlois, K., L. Greene-Finestone, J. Little, N. Hidiroglou, and S. Whiting. 2010. Vitamin D status of Canadians as measured in the 2007 to 2009 Canadian Health Measures Survey. *Health Rep* 21(1) www.statcan.gc.ca/healthreports. Accessed May 2012.

Lappe, J. M., D. Travers-Gustafson, K. M. Davies, R. R. Recker, and R. P. Heaney. 2007. Vitamin D and calcium supplementation reduces cancer risk: Results of a randomized trail. *Am. J. Clin. Nutr.* 85:1586–1591.

Larsson, S. C., L. Bergkvist, and A. Wolk. 2005. Magnesium intake in relation to risk of colorectal cancer in women. *JAMA* 293:86–89.

McGartland, C., P. J. Robson, G. Cran, M. J. Savage, D. Watkins, M. Rooney, and C. Boreham. 2003. Carbonated soft drink consumption and bone mineral density in adolescence: The Northern Ireland Young Hearts Project. *J. Bone Min. Res.* 18:1563–1569.

Need, A. G., H. A. Morris, M. Horowitz, and C. Nordin. 1993. Effects of skin thickness, age, body fat, and sunlight on serum 25-hydroxyvitamin D. *Am. J. Clin. Nutr.* 58:882–885.

Nelms M., K. Sucher, and S. Long. 2007. *Nutrition Therapy and Pathophysiology*. Tomson Brooks/Cole Canada, Chapter 27.

Nusser, S. M., A. L. Carriquiry, K. W. Dodd, and W. A. Fuller. 1996. A semiparametric transformation approach to estimating usual daily intake distributions. *J. Am. Stat. Assoc.* 91:1440–1449.

Pak, C. Y., K. Sakhaee, B. Adams-Huet, V. Piziak, R. D. Peterson, and J. R. Poindexter. 1995. Treatment of postmenopausal osteoporosis with slow-release sodium fluoride. Final report of a randomized controlled trial. *Ann. Int. Med.* 123:401–408.

Paolisso G., S. Sgambato, A. Gambardella, G. Pizza, P. Tesauro, M. Varricchio, and F. D'Onofrio. 1992. Daily magnesium supplements improve glucose handling in elderly subjects. *Am. J. Clin. Nutr.* 55:1161–1167.

PHAC (Public Health Agency of Canada). 2009. Report on Seniors' Falls. www.phac-aspc.gc.ca/seniors-aines/publications/pro/injury-blessure/falls-chutes/foreword-dedicace-eng.php. Accessed May 2012.

Raiten, D. J., and M. F. Picciano. 2004. Vitamin D and health in the 21st century: Bone and beyond. Executive Summary. *Am. J. Clin. Nutr.* 80(suppl): 1673S–1677S.

Reginster, J. Y., D. Felsenberg, I. Pavo, J. Stepan, J. Payer, H. Resch, C. C. Glüer, D. Mühlenbacher, D. Quail, H. Schmitt, and T. Nickelsen. 2003. Effect of raloxifene combined with monofluorophosphate as compared with monofluorophosphate alone in postmenopausal women with low bone mass: a randomized, controlled trial. *Osteoporosis Int.* 14:741–749.

Ringe, J. D., A. Dorst, H. Faber, C. Kipshoven, L. C. Rovati, and I. Setnikar. 2005. Efficacy of etidronate and sequential monofluorophosphate in severe postmenopausal osteoporosis: a pilot study. *Rheumatol. Int.* 25:296–300.

Ross, E. A., N. J. Szabo, and I. R. Tebbett. 2000. Lead content of calcium supplements. *JAMA* 284:1425–1433.

Rucker, D., J. A. Allan, G. H. Fick, and D. A. Hanley. 2002. Vitamin D insufficiency in a population of healthy Western Canadians. *Can. Med. Assoc. J.* 166: 1517–1524.

USDA (United States Department of Agriculture, Economic Research Service). 2008. Dietary assessment of major trends in U. S. food consumption, 1970-2005. Economic Information Bulletin No. EIB-33, 1-27. www.ers.usda/Publications/EIB33/. EIB33_ReportSummary .html.

USDHHS (U. S. Department of Health and Human Services. Public Health Service). 1991. Review of Fluoride: Benefits and Risks. Report of the Ad Hoc Subcommittee on Fluoride of the Committee to Coordinate Environmental Health and Related Programs. www.health.gov/environment/ReviewofFluoride/default.htm. Accessed April 2007.

Vatanparast, H., E. Lo, C. J. Henry, and S. J. Whiting. 2006. Trends of beverage intake from 1991–2003 in Grade 9 students living in Saskatoon show substitution of milk by non-carbonated soft drinks. *Nutr. Rev.* 26:325–329.

Weisberg, P., K. S. Scanlon, R. Li, and M. E. Cogswell. 2004. Nutritional rickets among children in the United States: review of cases reported between 1986 and 2003. *Am. J. Clin. Nutr.* 80(suppl.): 1697S–1705S.

Whiting, S. J., A. Healey, S. Psiuk, R. Mirwald, K. Kowalski, and D. A. Bailey. 2001. Relationship between carbonated and other low nutrient dense beverages and bone mineral content of adolescents. *Nutr. Res.* 21: 1107–1115.

Whiting, S. J., H. Vatanparast, A. Baxter-Jones, R. A. Faulkner, R. Mirwald, and D. A. Bailey. 2004. Factors that affect bone mineral accrual in the adolescent growth spurt. *J. Nutr.* 134: 696S–700S.

Wyshak, G. 2000. Teenaged girls, carbonated beverage consumption, and bone fractures. *Arch. Pediatr. Adolesc. Med.* 154:610–613.

Wyshak, G., and R. E. Frisch. 1994. Carbonated beverages, dietary calcium, the dietary calcium/ phosphorus ratio, and bone fractures in girls and boys. *J. Adolesc. Health* 15:210–215.

Wyshak, G., R. E. Frisch, T. E. Albright, N. L. Albright, I. Schiff, and J. Witschi. 1989. Nonalcoholic carbonated beverage consumption and bone fractures among women former college athletes. *J. Orthop. Res.* 7:91–99.

In Depth: Osteoporosis

Bischoff-Ferrari, H. A., W. C. Willett, J. B. Wong, A. E. Stuck, H. B. Staehelin, E. J. Orav, A. Thoma, D. P. Kiel, and J. Henschkowski. 2009. Prevention of nonvertabral fractures with oral vitamin D and dose dependency: a meta-analysis of randomized controlled trials. *Arch. Intern. Med.* 169:551–561.

CaMos (Canadian Multicentre Osteoporosis Study). 2004. *Camoscope* 8 (January). www.camos.org/Camoscope_Jan04_ENG.pdf. Accessed April 2005.

Dawson-Hughes, B., and S. S. Harris. 2002. Calcium intake influences the association of protein intake with rates of bone loss in elderly men and women. *Am. J. Clin. Nutr.* 75:773–779.

Devine A., R. A. Criddle, I. M. Dick, D. A. Kerr, and R. L. Prince. 1995. A longitudinal study of the effect of sodium and calcium intakes on regional bone density in post-menopausal women. *Am. J. Clin. Nutr.* 62:740–745.

Felson, D. T., Y. Zhang, M. T. Hannan, W. B. Kannel, and D. P. Kiel. 1995. Alcohol intake and bone mineral density in elderly men and women. The Framingham Study. *Am. J. Epidemiol.* 142:485–492.

Feskanich, D., S. A. Korrick, S. L. Greenspan, H. N. Rosen, and G. A. Colditz. 1999. Moderate alcohol consumption and bone density among post-menopausal women. *J. Women's Health* 8:65–73.

Garriguet, D. 2011. Bone health: Osteoporosis, calcium and vitamin D. Stats Canada: www.statcan.gc.ca/pub/82-003-x/2011003/article/11515-eng.htm. Accessed May 2012.

Holbrook, T. L., and E. Barrett-Connor. 1993. A prospective study of alcohol consumption and bone mineral density. *BMJ* 306:1506–1509.

Institute of Medicine (Food and Nutrition Board). 1997. *Dietary Reference Intakes for Calcium, Phosphorus, Magnesium, Vitamin D, and Fluoride.* Washington, DC: National Academies Press.

International Osteoporosis Foundation. 2007. Facts and statistics about osteoporosis and its impact. Available at www.iofbonehealth.org/facts-and-statistics.html.

Laitinen, K., M. Valimaki, and P. Keto. 1991. Bone mineral density measured by dual-energy x-ray absorptiometry in healthy Finnish women. *Calcif. Tissue Int.* 48:224–231.

Massey, L. K. 2001. Is caffeine a risk factor for bone loss in the elderly? *Am. J. Clin. Nutr.* 74:569–570.

National Institutes of Health Office of Dietary Supplements. 2009. Dietary supplement fact sheet: vitamin D. ods. od. nih.gov/factsheets/vitamind. asp.

National Osteoporosis Foundation. 2008. Osteoporosis Fast Facts. www.nof.org/osteoporosis/diseasefacts.htm.

Osteoporosis Canada. 2007a. Osteoporosis Update: A Practical Guide for Physicians. www.osteoporosis.ca/local/files/health_professionals/pdfs/Osteo1103Fall07_WebEdit.pdf. Accessed January 2008.

Osteoporosis Canada. 2007b. 25 Facts About Osteoporosis. www.osteoporosis.ca/english/Media%20Room/Background/2007_25facts/default. asp?s=1. Accessed January 2008.

Osteoporosis Canada. 2007c. Zoledronic acid (Aclasta) approved for osteoporosis. www.osteoporosis.ca/english/news/aclasta-short-nov1/default. asp?s=1. Accessed January 2008.

Osteoporosis Canada. 2007d. 10 top things you need to know about osteoporosis. www.osteoporosis.ca/english/Media%20Room/Background/Top%2010/default.asp?s=1. Accessed January 2008.

Rapuri, P. B., J. C. Gallagher, H. K. Kinyamu, and K. L. Ryschon. 2001. Caffeine intake increases the rate of bone loss in elderly women and interacts with vitamin D receptor genotypes. *Am. J. Clin. Nutr.* 74:694–700.

Rapuri, P. B., J. C. Gallagher, K. E. Balhorn, and K. L. Ryschon. 2000. Alcohol intake and bone metabolism in elderly women. *Am. J. Clin. Nutr.* 72:1206–1213.

South-Pal, J. E. 2001. Osteoporosis: Part II. Nonpharmacologic and pharmacologic treatment. *Am. Fam. Physician* 63:1121–1128.

Tucker, K. L., H. Chen, M. T. Hannan, L. A. Cupples, P. W. F. Wilson, D. Felson, and D. P. Kiel. 2002. Bone mineral density and dietary patterns in older adults: The Framingham Osteoporosis Study. *Am. J. Clin. Nutr.* 76:245–252.

Tucker, K. L., M. T. Hannan, H. Chen, L. A. Cupples, P. W. F. Wilson, and D. P. Kiel. 1999. Potassium, magnesium, and fruit and vegetable intakes are associated with greater bone mineral density in elderly men and women. *Am. J. Clin. Nutr.* 69:727–736.

Writing Group for the Women's Health Initiative Investigators. 2002. Risks and benefits of estrogen plus progestin in healthy postmenopausal women. Principal results from the Women's Health Initiative randomized control trial. *JAMA* 288:321–332.

Chapter 10

Bacon, B. R., J. K. Olynyk, E. M. Brunt, R. S. Britton, and R. K. Wolff. 1999. HFE genotype in patients with hemochromatosis and other liver diseases. *Ann. Intern. Med.* 130:953–962.

Bates, C. J. 2006. Thiamin. In: Bowman, B. A., and R. M. Russel, eds. *Present Knowledge in Nutrition,* 9th edn., pp. 242–249. Washington, DC: ILSI Press.

Beard, J. 2006. Iron. In: Bowman, B. A., and R. M. Russel, eds. *Present Knowledge in Nutrition,* 9th edn., pp. 430–444. Washington, DC: ILSI Press.

Beresford, S. A., and C. J. Boushey. 1997. Homocysteine, folic acid, and cardiovascular disease risk. In *Preventive Nutrition: The Comprehensive Guide for Health Professionals,* edited by A. Bendich and R. J. Deckelbaum. Totowa, NJ: Humana Press.

Bernstein, L. 2000, February. Dementia without a cause: Lack of vitamin B12 can cause dementia. *Discover.* www.discover.com/issues/feb-00/departments/featdementia. Accessed March 2004.

Booth, S. L., and J. W. Suttie. 1998. Dietary intake and adequacy of vitamin K. *J. Nutr.* 128: 785–788.

Boushey, C. J., S. A. Beresford, G. S. Omenn, and A. G. Motulsky. 1995. A quantitative assessment of plasma homocysteine as a risk factor for vascular disease. Probable benefits of increasing folic acid intakes. *JAMA* 274:1049–1057.

Campbell, W. W., L. J. Joseph, S. L. Davey, D. Cyr-Campbell, R. A. Anderson, and W. J. Evans. 1999. Effects of resistance training and chromium picolinate on body composition and skeletal muscle in older men. *J. Appl. Physiol.* 86:29–39.

Campbell, W. W., L. J. O. Joseph, R. A. Anderson, S. L. Davey, J. Hinton, and W. J. Evans. 2002. Effects of resistive training and chromium picolinate on body composition and skeletal muscle size in older women. *Int. J. Sports Nutr. Exerc. Metab.* 12:125–135.

Carmel, R. 2006. Folic acid. In: Shils, M. E., M. Shike, A. C. Ross, B. Caballero, and R. Cousins, eds. Modern Nutrition in Health and Disease, 10th edn., pp. 470–481. Philadelphia: Lippincott Williams & Wilkins.

Caruso, T. J., C. G. Prober, and J. M Gwaltney. 2007. Treatment of naturally acquired common colds with zinc: a structured review. *Clin. Infect Dis.* 45(5):569–574.

Chandra, R. K. 1984. Excessive intake of zinc impairs immune responses. *JAMA.* 252:1443–1446.

Combs G. F. The vitamins. 2008. Fundamental Aspects in Nutrition and Health. 3rd ed. Elsevier: San Francisco, p. 62.

Connolly, M., 2001. Premenstrual syndrome: An update on definitions, diagnosis and management. *Advances in Psychiatric Treatment* 7:469–477.

Day, E., P. Bentham, R. Callaghan, T. Kuruvilla, and S. George. 2004. Thiamine for Wernicke-Korsakoff Syndrome in people at risk from alcohol abuse (review). *Cochrane Database Syst. Rev.* 1:CD0040033.

Diaz M. L., B. A. Watkins, Y. Li, R. A. Anderson, and W. W. Campbell. 2008. Chromium picolinate and conjugated linoleic acid do not synergistically influence diet- and exercise-inudced changes in body composition and health indexes in overweight women. *J. Nutr Biochem* 19:61–68.

Evans, G. W. 1989. The effect of chromium picolinate on insulin controlled parameters in humans. Int. *J. Biosoc. Med. Res.* 11:163–180.

Feskanich, D., S. A. Korrick, S. L. Greenspan, H. N. Rosen, and G. A. Colditz. 1999. Moderate alcohol consumption and bone density among post-menopausal women. *J. Women's Health* 8:65–73.

Freake, H. C. 2006. Iodine. In: Stipanuk, M. H., ed. *Biochemical and Physiological Aspects of Human Nutrition,* 2nd Ed, pp. 1068–1090. Philadelphia, PA: W. B. Saunders Co.

Hallmark, M. A., T. H. Reynolds, C. A. DeSouza, C. O. Dotson, R. A. Anderson, and M. A. Rogers. 1996. Effects of chromium and resistive training on muscle strength and body composition. *Med. Sci. Sports Exerc.* 28:139–144.

Hasten, D. L., E. P. Rome, D. B. Franks, and M. Hegsted. 1992. Effects of chromium picolinate on beginning weight training students. *Int. J. Sports Nutr.* 2:343–350.

Institute of Medicine, Food and Nutrition Board. 1998. *Dietary Reference Intakes for Thiamin, Riboflavin, Niacin, Vitamin B6, Folate, Vitamin B12, Pantothenic Acid, Biotin, and Choline.* Washington, DC: National Academies Press.

Institute of Medicine, Food and Nutrition Board. 2001. *Dietary Reference Intakes for Vitamin A, Vitamin K, Arsenic, Boron, Chromium, Copper, Iodine, Iron, Manganese, Molybdenum, Nickel, Silicon, Vanadium, and Zinc.* Washington, DC: National Academies Press.

Jackson, J. L., E. Lesho, and C. Peterson. 2000. Zinc and the common cold: A meta-analysis revisited. *J. Nutr.* 130:1512S–1515S.

Jacob, R. A. 2006. Niacin. In: Bowman, B. A., and R. M. Russel, eds. *Present Knowledge in Nutrition,* 9th edn., pp. 260–268. Washington, DC: ILSI Press.

Jacques, P. F., A. Taylor, S. Moeller, et al. 2005. Long-term nutrient intake and 5-year change in nuclear lens opacities. *Arch. Ophthalmol.* 123:571–526.

Joubert, L. M., and M. M. Manore. 2006. Exercise, nutrition and homocysteine. Int. *J. Sport Nutr. Exer. Metab.* 16:341–361.

Jukes, T. H. 1990. Nutrition science from vitamins to molecular biology. *Annual Reviews of Nutrition,* 10:1–10.

Kim, Y. 2006. Does a high folate intake increase the risk of breast cancer? *Nutr. Rev.* 64(10):468–475.

Lukaski H. C., W. A. Siders, J. G. Penland. 2007. Chromium picolinate supplementation in women: effects on body weight, composition and iron status. *Nutr* 23:187–185.

Lukaski, H. C., W. W. Bolonchuk, W. A. Siders, and D. B. Milne. 1996. Chromium supplementation and resistance training: effects on body composition, strength, and trace element status of men. *Am. J. Clin. Nutr.* 63:954–965.

Mackey, A. D., S. R. Davis, and J. F. Gregory III. 2006. Vitamin B6. In: Shils, M. E., M. Shike, A. C. Ross, B. Caballero, and R. Cousins, eds. *Modern Nutrition in Health and Disease,* 10th edn., pp. 452–261. Philadelphia: Lippincott Williams & Wilkins.

Mayer, E. L., D. W. Jacobsen, and K. Robinson. 1996. Homocysteine and coronary atherosclerosis. *J. Am. Coll. Cardiol.* 27:517–527.

McCollum, E. V. 1957. *A History of Nutrition.* Boston: Houghton Mifflin Co.

McCormick, D. B. 2005. Riboflavin. In: Shils, M. E., M. Shike, A. C. Ross, B. Caballero, and R. Cousins, eds. *Modern Nutrition in Health and Disease,* 10th ed., pp. 434–441. Philadelphia: Lippincott Williams & Wilkins.

Miller, W. J., L. M. Rogers, and R. B. Rubker, 2006. Pantothenic acid. In: Bowman, B. A., and R. M. Russel, eds. *Present Knowledge in Nutrition,* 9th edn., pp. 327–339. Washington, DC: ILSI Press.

NIH (National Institute of Allergy and Infectious Diseases, National Institutes of Health). 2007. The Common Cold. www3.niaid. nih. gov/topics/commonCold.

Pasman, W. J., M. S. Westerterp-Plantenga, and W. H. Saris. 1997. The effectiveness of long-term supplementation of carbohydrate, chromium, fibre and caffeine on weight maintenance. *Int. J. Obes. Relat. Metab. Disord.* 21:1143–1151.

Prasad, A. 1996. Zinc: The biology and therapeutics of an ion. *Ann. Intern. Med.* 125:142–143.

Rapkin, A. 2003. The review of treatment of premenstrual syndrome & premenstrual dysphoric disorder. *Psychoneuroendocrinology* 28:39–53.

Rivlin, R. S. 2006. Riboflavin. In: Bowman, B. A., and R. M. Russel, eds. *Present Knowledge in Nutrition,* 9th edn., pp. 250–259. Washington, DC: ILSI Press.

Sabler, S. P. 2006. Vitamin B12. In: Bowman, B. A., and R. M. Russel, eds. *Present Knowledge in Nutrition,* 9th edn., pp. 302–313. Washington, DC: ILSI Press.

Schaumburg, H., J. Kaplan, A. Winderbank, N. Vick, S. Rasmus, D. Pleasure, and M. J. Brown. 1983. Sensory neuropathy from pyridoxine abuse: A new megavitamin syndrome. *N. Engl. J. Med.* 309:445–448.

Shils, M. E., J. A. Olson, M. Shike, and A. C. Ross. 1999. *Modern Nutrition in Health and Disease,* 9th ed. Philadelphia: Lippincott Williams & Wilkins.

U. S. FDA (Food and Drug Administration). 1997. Preventing Iron Poisoning in Children. FDA Backgrounder. www.fda.gov/opacom/ backgrounders/ironbg.html. Accessed January 2004.

Volpe, S. L., H. W. Huang, K. Larpadisorn, and I. I. Lesser. 2001. Effect of chromium supplementation and exercise on body composition, resting metabolic rate and selected biochemical parameters in moderately obese women following an exercise program. *J. Am. Coll. Nutr.* 20:293–306.

Walker, L. S., M. G. Bemben, D. A. Bemben, and A. W. Knehans. 1998. Chromium picolinate effects on body composition and muscular performance in wrestlers. *Med. Sci. Sports Exerc.* 30:1730–1737.

Wyatt, K. M., P. W. Dimmock, P. W. Jones, and P. M. Shaughn O'Brien. 1999. Efficacy of vitamin B-6 in the treatment of premenstrual syndrome: Systemic review. *Br. J. Med.* 318:1375–1381.

In Depth: Dietary Supplements: Necessity or Waste?

Blendon, R. J., C. M. DesRoches, J. M. Benson, M. Brodie, and D. E. Altman. 2001. Americans' views on the use and regulation of dietary supplements. *Arch. Intern. Med.* 26:805–810.

Dancho C., and M. M. Manore. 2001. Dietary supplement information on the World Wide Web. Sorting fact from fiction. *ACSM's Health and Fitness Journal* 5:7–12.

Health Canada. 2006. Safe Use of Natural Health Products. Accessed May 2012 from: www.hc-sc.gc.ca/hl-vs/iyh-vsv/med/nat-prod-eng. php.

Health Canada. 2009. Information Kit- Regulation of Natural Health Products. Accessed May 2012 from: www.hc-sc.gc.ca/dhp-mps/ prodnatur/about-apropos/info_reg-eng.php.

Health Canada. 2011a. About Natural Health Products. Accessed May 2012 from: www.hc-sc.gc.ca/dhp-mps/prodnatur/about-apropos/ cons-eng.php.

Health Canada. 2011b. About Natural Health Product Regulation in Canada. Accessed May 2012 from: www.hc-sc.gc.ca/dhp-mps/ prodnatur/about-apropos/index-eng.php.

Health Canada. 2012. Natural Health Products. Accessed August 2012 from: www.hc-sc.gc.ca/dhp-mps/prodnatur/index-eng.php.

NCCAM (National Center for Complementary and Alternative Medicine). 2004. Herbal Supplements: Consider Safety, Too. Available at http:// nccam. nih.gov/health/supplement-safety.

NIH (National Institutes of Health). 2005. Important information to know when you are taking Coumadin and Vitamin K. Available at: http:// dietary supplements.info. nih.gov/factsheets/cc/coumadin1.pdf.

Chapter 11

Alhassan, S., L. Kim, A. Bersamin, A. C. King, C. D. Gardner. 2008. Dietary adherence and weight loss success among overweight women: Results from the A TO Z weight loss study. *Int. J. Obes.* (Lond). 32:985–991.

Allison, D. B., K. R. Fontaine, S. Heshka, J. L. Mentore, and S. B. Heymsfield. 2001. Alternative treatments for weight loss: a critical review. *Crit. Rev. Food Sci. Nutr.* 41(1):1–28.

Batterham, R. L., M. A. Cohen, S. M. Ellis, C. W. Le Roux, D. J. Withers, G. S. Frost, M. A. Ghatei, and S. R. Bloom. 2003. Inhibition of food intake in obese subjects by peptide YY3-36. *N. Engl. J. Med.* 349:941–948.

Batterham, R. L., M. A. Cowley, C. J. Small, H. Herzog, M. A. Cohen, C. L. Dakin, A. M. Wren, A. E. Brynes, M. J. Low, M. A. Ghatel, R. D. Cone, and S. R. Bloom. 2002. Gut hormone PYY3-36 physiologically inhibits food intake. *Nature* 418:650–664.

Bouchard, C., A. Tremblay, J. P. Després, A. Nadeau, P. J. Lupien, G. Thériault, J. Dussault, S. Moorjani, S. Pinault, and G. Fournier. 1990. The response to long-term overfeeding in identical twins. *N. Engl. J. Med.* 322: 1477–1482.

Buchwald, H. 2005. Consensus Conference Statement Bariatric Surgery for morbid obesity. *Surgery for Obesity and Related Diseases,* 1 (2005), 371–381.

CBC. 2010. CBC news. February 5th, 2010. Obese teens offered surgery option. Retrieved May 27th, 2011 from www.cbc.ca/news/health/ story/2010/02/05/obesity-surgery-children.html.

Clifton, P. M., J. B. Keogh and M. Noakes. 2008. Long-term effects of a high-protein weight-loss diet. *Am. J. Clin. Nutr.* 87:23-29.

Cummings, D. E., D. S. Weigle, R. S. Frayo, P. A. Breen, M. K. Ma, E. P. Dellinger, and J. Q. Purnell. 2002. Plasma ghrelin levels after diet-induced weight loss or gastric bypass surgery. *N. Engl. J. Med.* 346:1623–1630.

Cypess, A. M., S. Lehman, G. Williams, I. Tal, D. Rodman, A. B. Goldfine, F. C. Kuo, E. L. Palmer, Y-H. Tseng, A. Doria, G. M. Kolodny, and C. R. Kahn. 2009. Identification and importance of brown adipose tissue in adult humans. *N. Engl. J. Med.* 360(15):1509–1517.

Deurenberg, P., M. Yap, and W. A. van Staveren. 1998. Body mass index and percent body fat: a meta analysis among different ethnic groups. *Int. J. Obes.* 22:1164–1171.

Druce, M. R., A. M. Wren, A. J. Park, J. E. Milton, M. Patterson, G. Frost, M. A. Ghatei, C. Small, and S. R. Bloom. 2005. Ghrelin increases food intake in obese as well as lean subjects. *Int. J. Obes.* 29: 1130–1136.

Ello-Martin, J. A., J. H. Ledikwe, and B. J. Rolls. 2005. The influence of food portion size and energy density on energy intake: implications for weight management. *Am. J. Clin. Nutr.* 82(suppl.): 236S–241S.

Eyler, A. E., D. Matson-Koffman, D. Rohm-Young, S. Wilcox, J. Wilbur, J. L. Thompson, B. Sanderson, and K. R. Evenson. 2003. Quantitative study of correlates of physical activity in women from diverse racial/ethnic groups: The Women's Cardiovascular Health Network Project. *Am. J. Prev. Med.* 25(3Si):93–103.

Eyler, A. E., D. Matson-Koffman, J. R. Vest, K. R. Evenson, B. Sanderson, J. L. Thompson, J. Wilbur, S. Wilcox, and D. Rohm-Young. 2002. Environmental, policy, and cultural factors related to physical activity in a diverse sample of women: The Women's Cardiovascular Health Network Project—summary and discussion. *Women and Health.* 36:123–134.

Flood, J. E., L. S. Roe, and B. J. Rolls. 2006. The effect of increased beverage portion size on energy intake at a meal. *J. Am. Diet. Assoc.* 106:1984–1990.

Foster, G. D., H. R. Wyatt, J. O. Hill, A. P. Makris, D. L. Rosenbaum, C. Brill, R. I. Stien, B. S. Mohammed, B. Miller, D. J. Rader, B. Zemel, T. A. Wadden, T. Tenhave, C. W. Newcomb, and S. Klein. 2010. Weight and metabolic outcomes after 2 years on a low-carbohydrate versus low-fat diet: A randomized trial. *Ann. Int. Med.* 1553: 147–157.

Freedman, M. R., J. King, and E. Kennedy. 2001. Popular diets: a scientific review. *Obes. Res.* 9(suppl. 1):1S–40S.

Gardner, C. D., A. Kiazand, S. Alhassan, S. Kim, R. S. Stafford, R. R. Balise, H. C. Kraemr, and A. C. King. 2007.comparison of the Atkins, Zone, Ornish, and LEARN diets for change in weight and related risk factors among overweigh premenopausal women. The a to z weight loss study: a randomized trial. *AMA.* 297: 969–977.

Inge, T. H., G. Miyano, J. Bean, M. Helmrath, A. Courcoulas, C. M. Harmon, M. K. Chen, K. Wilson, S. R. Daniels, V. F Garcia, M. L. Brandt, and L. M. Dolan. 2009. Reversal of type 2 diabetes mellitus and improvements in cardiovascular risk factors after surgical weight loss in adolescents. *Pediat* 123, 214–222.

Inge, T. H., S. A. Xanthakos, and M. H. Zeller. 2007. Bariatric surgery for pediatric extreme obesity: now or later? *Int. J. Obes. (London)* 31: 1-14.

Janssen, I., P. T. Katzmarzyk, and R. Ross. 2004. Waist circumference and not body mass index explains obesity-related health risk. *Am. J. Clin. Nutr.* 79:379–384.

Kieffer, T. J., and J. F. Habener. 2000. The adipoinsular axis: Effects of leptin on pancreatic -cells. *Am. J. Phys. Endo. Metab.* 278:E1–E14.

Koh-Banerjee, P., N. F. Chu, D. Spiegelman, B. Rosner, G. Colditz, W. Willett, and E. Rimm. 2003. Prospective study of the association of changes in dietary intake, physical activity, alcohol consumption, and smoking with 9-y gain in waist circumference among 16,587 U. S. men. *Am. J. Clin. Nutr.* 78:719–27.

Kuk, J. L., S. Lee, S. B. Heymsfield, and R. Ross. 2005. Waist circumference and abdominal adipose tissue distribution: influence of age and sex. *Am. J. Clin. Nutr.* 81:1330–1334.

Lopes da Silva, M. V. and R. de Cássia Gon,alves Alfenas. 2011. Effect of the glycemic index on lipid oxidation and body composition. *Nutr. Hosp.* 26:48–55.

Lumeng J. C., Forrest P., Appugliese D. P., Kaciroti N., Corwyn R. F., and Bradley R. H. 2010. Weight status as a predictor of being bullied in third through sixth grades. Pediatrics. e-publication ahead of print, doi:10. 1542/peds. 2009-0774. Published online May 3, 2010.

Lynn, K. H. and J. L. Miller. 2009. Bariatric surgery for obese adolescents: should surgery be used to treat the childhood obesity epidemic? *Ped Health* 3:33–40.

Manore, M. M, N. L. Meyer, and J. Thompson. 2009. *Sport Nutrition for Health and Performance.* 2nd Edition. Champaign, IL: Human Kinetics.

McCargar, L. 2007. New insights into body composition and health through imaging analysis. *Can. J. Diet. Prac. Res.* 68:160–165.

Pickett, K. E., S. Kelly, E. Brunner, T. Lobstein, and R. G. Wilkinson. 2005. Wider income gaps, wider waistbands? An ecological study of obesity and income inequality. *J. Epidemiol.community Health* 59:670–674.

Prospective Studies Collaboration. 2009. Body-mass index and cause-specific mortality in 900?000 adults: collaborative analyses of 57 prospective studies. *Lancet.* 373(9669): 1083–1096.

Puzziferri, N., P. A. Nakonezny, E. H. Livingston, T. J. Carmody, D. A. Provost, and A. J. and Rush. 2008. Variations of weight loss following gastric bypass and gastric band. *Ann. Surg.* 248: 233–243.

Saper, R. B., D. M. Eisenberg, and R. S. Phillips. 2004.common dietary supplements for weight loss. *Am. Fam. Phys.* 70(9):1731–1738.

Shai, I., D. Schwarzfuchs, Y. Henkin, D. R. Shahar, S. Witkow, I. Greenberg, et al. 2008. Weight loss with a low-carbohydrate, mediterranean, or low-fat diet. *NEJM.* 359:229–241.

Shai, I., R. Jiang, J. E. Manson, M. J. Stampfer, W. C. Willett, G. A. Colditz, and F. B. Hu. 2006. Ethnicity, obesity, and risk of type 2 diabetes in women. *Diabet. Care* 29:1585–1590.

SickKids. 2010. February 5, 2010. New SickKids program helps teens STOMP out obesity. Retrieved May 27, 2011 from www.sickkids .ca/AboutSickKids/Newsroom/Past-News/2010/STOMP.html.

Stunkard, A. J., T. I. A. Sørensen, C. Hanis, T. W. Teasdale, R. Chakraborty, W. J. Schull, and F. Schulsinger. 1986. An adoption study of human obesity. *N. Engl. J. Med.* 314:193–198.

Tsai, W. S., T. H. Inge, and R. S. Burd. 2007. Bariatric Surgery in Adolescents: Recent National Trends in Use and In-Hospital Outcome. *Arch Pediatr Adolesc Med.* 161:217–221.

Virtanen, K. A., M. E. Lidell, J. Orava, M. Heglind, R. Westergren, T. Niemi, M. Taittonen, J. Laine, N-J. Savito, S. Enerbäck, and P. Nuutila. 2009. Functional brown adipose tissue in healthy adults. *N. Engl. J. Med.* 360(15):1518–1525.

Wang, Y. 2004. Epidemiology of childhood obesity—methodological aspects and guidelines: what is new? *Int. J. Obes.* 23:S21–S28.

Weeks, C. 2010. SickKids first to offer teens surgery for obesity. *The Globe and Mail.* February 5, 2010. Retrieved May 27th, 2011 from www.theglobeandmail.com/life/health/sickkids-first-to-offer-teens-surgery-for-obesity/article1457031/.

Wing, R. R., and S. Phelan. 2005. Long-term weight loss maintenance. *Am. J. Clin. Nutr.* 82(1):222S–225S.

Zernike, K. 2004. U. S. body survey, head to toe, finds signs of expansion. *The New York Times.* March 1, 1, 12.

In Depth: Obesity

American Obesity Association. 2002. Discrimination. http://obesity1 . tempdomainname.com/discrimination/employment. shtml.

Buchwald, H. 2005. Consensus Conference Statement Bariatric Surgery for morbid obesity. Surgery for Obesity and Related Diseases, 1 (2005), 371–381.

Christakis, N. A. and J. H. Fowler. 2007. The spread of obesity in a large social network over 32 years. *N. Engl. J. Med.* 357(4):370–379.

Department of Health and Human Services (National Institutes of Health. National Heart, Lung and Blood Institute). 2010. Diseases and conditions index. Metabolic syndrome. What is metabolic syndrome? Available at www.nhlbi.nih.gov/health/dci/Diseases/ ms/ms_whatis.html.

Dietz, W. H. 1994. Critical periods in childhood for the development of obesity. *Am. J. Clin. Nutr.* 59:955–959.

Health Canada 2010. Drug Products Database Online Query. Retrieved Jan. 2012 from webprod3 hg-sc.gc.ca/dpd-bdpp/index-eng.jsp.

Health Canada. 2003. Health Canada Reminds Canadians of the Dangers of *Ephedra*/Ephedrine Products. www.hc-sc.gc.ca/ ahc-asc/media/advisories-avis/2003/2003_43_e.html. Accessed July 2005.

Health Canada. 2011. Natural Health Products Database. Retrieved Jan. 2012 from webprod3.hc-sc.gc.ca/lnhpd-bdpsnh/index-eng.jsp.

Huizinga M. M., Cooper L. A., Bleich S. N., Clark J. M., Beach M. C. 2009. Physician respect for patients with obesity. *J. Gen. Intern. Med.* 24(11):1236–1239.

Institute of Medicine (Food and Nutrition Board). 2002. Dietary Reference Intakes for Energy, Carbohydrate, Fiber, Fat, Fatty Acids, Cholesterol, Protein, and Amino Acids (Macronutrients). Washington, DC: The National Academies Press.

NIDDK (National Institute of Diabetes and Digestive and Kidney Diseases. Weight-control Information Network). 2008. Understanding Adult Obesity. NIH Publication No. 06–3680 www.win.niddk.nih.gov/publications/understanding.htm#environmental.

NIH (National Institutes of Health, National Heart, Lung, and Blood Institute). 1998. *Clinical Guidelines on the Identification, Evaluation, and Treatment of Overweight and Obesity in Adults.* Executive Summary. www.nhlbi.nih.gov/guidelines/obesity/ob_exsum.pdf. Accessed February 2004.

Sjöström, L., A-K. Lindroos, M. Peltonen, J. Torgerson, C. Bouchard, B. Carlsson, S. Dahlgren, B. Larsson, K. Narbro, C. D. Sjöström, M. Sullivan, and H. Wedel. 2004. Lifestyle, diabetes, and cardiovascular risk factors 10 years after bariatric surgery. *N. Engl. J. Med.* 351(26):2683–2693.

Statistics Canada. 2010. Health Measures Survey 2007–2009. Accessed from: www.statcan.gc.ca/daily-quotidien/100113/dq100113a-eng.htm.

Torgan, C. 2002. Childhood obesity on the rise. The NIH Word on Health. Available at www.nih.gov/news/WordonHealth/jun2002/childhoodobesity.htm.

USFDA (U. S. Food and Drug Administration). 2000. FDA Talk Paper: FDA issues public health warning on phenylpropanolamine. November 6, 2000. www.fda.gov/bbs/topics/ANSWERS/ANS01051.html. Accessed July 2005.

van den Hooven, C., J. Ploemacher, and M. Goodwin. 2006. Metabolic syndrome in a family practice population. *Can. Fam. Physician.* 52(8): 983-989.

Wing, R. R., and S. Phelan. 2005. Long-term weight loss maintenance. *Am. J. Clin. Nutr.* 82(1):222S–225S.

Chapter 12

American College of Sports Medicine, American Dietetic Association, and Dietitians of Canada. 2009. Nutrition and athletic performance. Joint position statement. *Med. Sci. Sports Exerc.* 41:709–731.

Anderson, M. E., C. R. Bruce, S. F. Fraser, N. K. Stepto, R. Klein, W. G. Hopkins, and J. A. Hawley. 2000. Improved 2000-meter rowing performance in competitive oarswomen after caffeine ingestion. *Int. J. Sport Nutr. Exerc. Metab.* 10:464–475.

Anorexia Report. 2012. Anorexia Athletica. Accessed May 2012 from: www.anorexiareport.com/anorexia-athletica/.

Ara, G., L. M. Gravelin, R. Kaddurah-Daouk, and B. A. Teicher. 1998. Antitumor activity of creatine analogs produced by alterations in pancreatic hormones and glucose metabolism. *In Vivo* 12:223–231.

Balsom, P. D., K. Söderlund, B. Sjödin, and B. Ekblom. 1995. Skeletal muscle metabolism during short duration high-intensity exercise: influence of creatine supplementation. *Acta Physiol. Scand.* 1154: 303–310.

Broeder, C. E., J. Quindry, K. Brittingham, L. Panton, J. Thomson, S. Appakondu, K. Breuel, R. Byrd, J. Douglas, C. Earnest, C. Mitchell, M. Olson, T. Roy, and C. Yarlagadda. 2000. The Andro Project: Physiological and hormonal influences of androstenedione supplementation in men 35 to 65 years old participating in a high-intensity resistance training program. *Arch. Intern. Med.* 160:3093–3104.

Brooks, G. A. 2000. Intra- and extra-cellular lactate shuttles. *Med. Sci. Sports Exerc.* 32: 790–799.

Brooks, G. A. 2009. Cell-cell and intracellular lactate shuttles. *J. Physiol.* 587(23):5591–5600.

Bucci, L. 2000. Selected herbals and human exercise performance. *Am. J. Clin. Nutr.* 72: 624S–636S.

Burke, L. 2010. Nutrition for recovery after training and competition. In: Burke, L., and Deakin, V., eds. *Clinical Sports Nutrition*, 4th ed. Sydney, Australia: McGraw-Hill, pp. 358–392.

Canadian Fitness and Lifestyle Research Institute. 2005. Physical activity among Canadians: The current situation. www.cflri.ca/eng/statistics/surveys/documents/pam2005_sec1.pdf. Accessed May 2008.

Caspersen, C. J., K. E. Powell, and G. M. Christensen. 1985. Physical activity, exercise, and physical fitness: Definitions and distinctions for heath-related research. *Public Health Reports* 100: 126–131.

Centers for Disease Control and Prevention. 2010. Physical Activity for Everyone. Target Heart Rate and Estimated Maximum Heart Rate. www.cdc.gov/physicalactivity/everyone/measuring/heartrate.html.

CIHI (Canadian Institute for Health Information). 2004. *Improving the Health of Canadians.* Ottawa: CIHI.

CSEP (Canadian Society for Exercise Physiology). 2012. Canadian Physical Activity Guidelines. Available at: www.csep.ca/english/view.asp?x=804.

Davidson, M. R., M. L. London, and P. W. Ladewig. 2008. *Olds' Maternal-Newborn Nursing and Women's Health Across the Lifespan,* 8th edn. Upper Saddle River, NJ: Prentice Hall Health.

Earnest, C. P., G. M. Morss, F. Wyatt, A. N. Jordan, S. Colson, T. S. Church, Y. Fitzgerald, L. Autrey, R. Jurca, and A. Lucia. 2004. Effects of a commercial herbal-based formula on exercise performance in cyclists. *Med. Sci. Sports Exerc.* 36(3):504–509.

FDA (Food and Drug Administration). 2004. HHS Launches Crackdown on Products Containing Andro. www.fda.gov/NewsEvents/Newsroom/PressAnnouncements/2004/ucm108262.htm.

Grindstaff, P. D., R. Kreider, R. Bishop, M. Wilson, L. Wood, C. Alexander, and A. Almada. 1997. Effects of creatine supplementation on repetitive sprint performance and body composition in competitive swimmers. *Int. J. Sport Nutr.* 7:330–346.

Hawley, J. A. 2002. Effect of increased fat availability on metabolism and exercise capacity. *Med. Sci. Sports Exerc.* 34(9):1485–1491.

Haymes, E. M. 1998. Trace minerals and exercise. In *Nutrition and Exercise and Sport,* edited by I. Wolinsky. Boca Raton, FL: CRC Press, 1997–2218.

Haymes, E. M., and P. M. Clarkson. 1998. Minerals and trace minerals. In *Nutrition and Sport and Exercise,* edited by J. R. Berning and S. N. Steen. Gaithersburg, MD: Aspen Publishers, 77–107.

Health Canada. 2011. Health Canada reminds Canadians not to use ephedra/ephedrine products. www.hc-sc.gc.ca/ahc-asc/media/advisories-avis/_2008/2008_41-eng.php. Accessed May 2008.

Heinonen, O. J. 1996. Carnitine and physical exercise. *Sports Med.* 22:109–132.

Hellsten, Y., L. Skadhauge, and J. Bangsbo. 2004. Effect of ribose supplementation on resynthesis of adenine nucleotides after intense intermittent training in humans. *Am. J. Physiol. Regul. Integr.comp. Physiol.* 286:R182–R188.

Heyward, V. H. 2006. *Advanced Fitness Assessment and Exercise Prescription,* 5th ed. Champaign, IL: Human Kinetics.

Jentjens, R. L., L. J. C. van Loon, C. H. Mann, A. J. M. Wagenmakers, and A. E. Jeukendrup. 2001. Addition of protein and amino acids to carbohydrates does not enhance postexercise muscle glycogen synthesis. *J. Appl. Physiol.* 91:839–846.

Jeong, K. S., S. J. Park, C. S. Lee, T. W. Kim, S. H. Kim, S. Y. Ryu, B. H. Williams, R. L. Veech, and Y. S. Lee. 2000. Effects of cyclocreatine in rat hepatocarcinogenesis model. *Anticancer Res.* 20(3A):1627–1633.

Kreider, R. B., C. Melton, M. Greenwood, C. Rasmussen, J. Lundberg, C. Earnest, and A. Almada. 2003. Effects of oral D-ribose supplementation on anaerobic capacity and selected metabolic markers in healthy males. *Int. J. Sport Nutr. Exerc. Metab.* 13(1):76–86.

Kreider, R. B., M. Ferreira, M. Wilson, P. Grindstaff, S. Plisk, J. Reinardy, E. Cantler, and A. L. Almada. 1998. Effects of creatine supplementation on body composition, strength, and sprint performance. *Med. Sci. Sports Exerc.* 30:73–82.

Kreider, R., M. Ferreira, M. Wilson, and A. L. Almada. 1999. Effects of calcium beta-hydroxy-beta-methylbutyrate (HMB) supplementation during resistance-training on markers of catabolism, body composition and strength. *Int. J. Sports Med.* 20(8):503–509.

Lein, S. 2012. Anoexia Athletica. Accessed on May 2012 from www .eatingdisordersonline.com/explain/anorathletica.php.

Manore, M., N. L. Meyer, and J. Thompson. 2009. *Sports Nutrition for Health and Performance.* 2nd ed. Champaign, IL: Human Kinetics (117).

PHAC (Public Health Agency of Canada). 2012. Physical activity tips for adults 18-64 years. www.phac-aspc.gc.ca/hp-ps/hl-mvs/pa-ap/ 07paap-eng.php, accessed May 15, 2012.

Pliml, W., T. von Arnim, A. Stablein, H. Hofmann, H. G. Zimmer, and E. Erdmann. 1992. Effects of ribose on exercise-induced ischaemia in stable coronary artery disease. *Lancet* 340(8818):507–510.

Reuters. 2001. Creatine use could lead to cancer, French government reports. *New York Times*, January 25.

Sears, B. 1995. *The Zone: A Dietary Road Map.* New York: HarperCollins Publishers.

Spriet, L. L., and R. A. Howlett. 2000. Caffeine. In *Nutrition in Sport*, edited by R. J. Maughan. Oxford: Blackwell Science, 379–392.

Statistics Canada. 2009. *Canada Year Book 2009.* Catalogue no. 11-402-X. Table 17.5 Leisure-time physical activity, by age group and sex, selected years from 2000/2001 to 2007. www.statcan.gc.ca/ pub/11-402-x/2009000/pdf/health-sante-eng.pdf.

Statistics Canada. 2012. Physical activity during leisure time, by age group and sex. CANSIM, table 105-0501 and Catalogue no. 82-221-X. www.statcan.gc.ca/tables-tableaux/sum-som/l01/cst01/ health77b-eng.htm.

Tarnopolsky, M. 2010. Protein and amino acid needs for training and bulking up. In: Burke, L., and Deakin, V., eds. *Clinical Sports Nutrition*, 3rd edn. Sydney, Australia: McGraw-Hill, pp. 61–95.

Tarnopolsky, M. A., and D. P. MacLennan. 2000. Creatine monohydrate supplementation enhances high-intensity exercise performance in males and females. *Int. J. Sport Nutr. Exerc.* Metab. 10:452–463.

USDHHS (U. S. Department of Health and Human Services). 1996. *Physical Activity and Health: A Report of the Surgeon General.* Atlanta, GA: U. S. Department of Health and Human Services, Centers for Disease Control and Prevention, National Centers for Chronic Disease Prevention and Health Promotion.

van Hall G., M. Stromstad, P. Rasmussen, O. Jans, M. Zaar, C. Gam, B. Quistorff, N. H. Secher, and H. B. Nielsen. 2009. Blood lactate is an important energy source for the human brain. *J. Cerebral Blood Flow & Metab.* 29(6):1121–1129.

van Loon, L. J. C., W. H. M. Saris, M. Kruijshoop, and A. J. M. Wagenmakers. 2000. Maximizing postexercise muscle glycogen synthesis: carbohydrate supplementation and the application of amino acid or protein hydrolysate mixtures. *Am. J. Clin. Nutr.* 72:106–111.

Vincent, J. B. 2003. The potential value and toxicity of chromium picolinate as a nutritional supplement, weight loss agent and muscle development agent. *Sports Med.* 33(3):213–230.

Volek, J. S., N. D. Duncan, S. A. Mazzetti, R. S. Staron, M. Putukian, A. L. Gomez, D. R. Pearson, W. J. Fink, and W. J. Kraemer. 1999. Performance and muscle fiber adaptations to creatine supplementation and heavy resistance training. *Med. Sci. Sports Exerc.* 31:1147–1156.

Weaver, C. M., and S. Rajaram. 1992. Exercise and iron status. *J. Nutr.* 122:782–787.

Westerblad, H., D. G. Allen, and J. Lännergren. 2002. Muscle fatigue: lactic acid or inorganic phosphate the major cause? *News Physiol. Sci.* 17(1):17–21.

Williams, M. H. 1998. *The Ergogenics Edge.* Champaign, IL: Human Kinetics.

In Depth: Disordered Eating

American Psychiatric Association, 2000. Diagnostic and Statistical Manual of Mental Disorders, Text Revision.

American Psychiatric Association. 1994. Diagnostic and Statistical Manual of Mental Disorders (DSM-IV). 4th ed. Washington, DC: American Psychiatric Association.

Andersen, A. E. 2001. Eating disorders in males: Gender divergence management. *Currents* 2(2). University of Iowa Health Care. Available at www.uihealthcare.com/news/currents/vol2issue2/ eatingdisordersinmen.html.

Beals, K. A. 2004. *Disordered Eating in Athletes: A Comprehensive Guide for Health Professionals.* Champaign, IL: Human Kinetics Publishers.

Garfinkel, P. E. 2002. Classification and diagnosis of eating disorders. In: Fairburn D. G., and K. D. Brownell, eds. *Eating Disorders and Obesity: A Comprehensive Handbook.* 2nd ed. New York: Guilford Press, pp. 155–161.

Grilo, C. M. 2002. Binge eating disorder. In: D. G. Fairburn and K. D. Brownell, eds. *Eating Disorders and Obesity: A Comprehensive Handbook.* 2nd ed. New York: Guilford Press, pp. 178–182.

Health Canada. 2002. *A Report on Mental Illnesses in Canada.* Chapter 6: Eating Disorders. Health Canada: Ottawa. www.phac-aspc.gc.ca. Accessed April 2005.

Nattiv A., A. B. Loucks, M. M. Manore, C. F. Sanborn, J. Sundgot-Borgen, and M. P. Warren. 2007. The female athlete triad. *Medicine and Science in Sport and Exercise.* 39(10):1867–1882.

Patrick, L. 2002. Eating disorders: A review of the literature with emphasis on medical complication and clinical nutrition. *Altern. Med. Rev.* 7(3):184–202.

Pope H. G., K. A. Phillips, and R. Olivardia. 2000. *The Adonis Complex: The Secret Crisis of Male Body Obsession.* New York: The Free Press.

Robb, A. S., and M. J. Dadson. 2002. Eating disorders in males. Child Adolesc. *Psychiatric. Clin. N. Am.* 11:399–418.

Steinberg, L. 2002. *Adolescence.* 6th ed. New York: McGraw-Hill.

Stice E. 2002. Sociocultural influences on body image and eating disturbances. In: Fairburn, D. G., and K. D. Brownell, eds. *Eating Disorders and Obesity: A Comprehensive Handbook.* 2nd ed. New York: Guilford Press, pp. 103–107.

Striegel-Moore, R. H., and L. Smolak. 2002. Gender, ethnicity, and eating disorders. In: Fairburn, D. G., and K. D. Brownell, eds. *Eating Disorders and Obesity: A Comprehensive Handbook.* 2nd ed. New York: Guilford Press, pp. 251–255.

Stunkard, A. J. 2002. Night eating syndrome. In: DG Fairburn and KD Brownell, eds. *Eating Disorders and Obesity: A Comprehensive Handbook.* 2nd ed. New York: Guilford Press, pp. 183–187.

Treasure J., Claudino A. M., Zucker N. Eating Disorders. 2010. *Lancet* 375:583–593.

Vandereycken, W. 2002. Families of patients with eating disorders. In: Fairburn, D. G., and K. D. Brownell, eds. *Eating Disorders and Obesity: A Comprehensive Handbook.* 2nd ed. New York Guilford Press, pp. 215–220.

Wonderlich, S. A. 2002. Personality and eating disorders. In: Fairburn, D. G., and K. D. Brownell, eds. *Eating Disorders and Obesity: A Comprehensive Handbook.* 2nd ed. New York: Guilford Press, pp. 204–209.

Chapter 13

Agriculture and Agri-Food Canada. 2011. Canada's Organic Industry at a Glance—2009. Available at: www4.agr.gc.ca/AAFC-AAC/ display-afficher. do?id=1276292934938&lang=eng.

Asami, D. K., Y. J. Hong, D. M. Barrett, and A. E. Mitchell. 2003. Comparison of the total phenolic and ascorbic acid content of freeze-dried and air-dried marionberry, strawberry, and corn grown using conventional, organic, and sustainable agricultural practices. *J. Agric. Food Chem.* 51(5):1237–1241.

Aseptic Packaging Council. 2005. The award-winning, Earth smart packaging for a healthy lifestyle. Available at www.aseptic.org/ main.shtml.

Bauman, R. W. 2009. *Microbiology.* San Francisco: Pearson Benjamin Cummings.

Canadian Food Inspection Agency. 2012a. 11 million Canadians affected, March 7, 2012, www.inspection.gc.ca/food/consumer-centre/food-safety-tips/causes-of-food-borne-illness/eng/ 1331151916451/1331152055552.

Canadian General Standards Board. 2006. Organic Production Systems General Principles and Management Standards. CAN/

GSB-32. 310–2006. www.organicagcentre.ca/Docs/Cdn_Stds_Principles2006_e.pdf. Accessed April 2008.

Canadian Institutes of Health Research. 2003. Canadian researchers develop *E. coli* vaccine for cattle. www.cihr-irsc.gc.ca/e/19939.html. Accessed May 2005.

Carbonaro, M., M. Mattera, S. Nicoli, P. Bergamo, and M. Cappelloni. 2002. Modulation of antioxidant compounds in organic vs conventional fruit (peach, *Prunus persica L.*, and pear, *Pyrus communis L.*). *J. Agric. Food Chem.* 50(19):5458–5462.

CDC (Centers for Disease Control and Prevention). 2005. Foodborne Illness. January 10, 2005. Available at www.cdc.gov/ncidod/dbmd/diseaseinfo/foodborneinfections_g.htm.

CDC (Centers for Disease Control and Prevention. 2010. Fact Sheet: Bisphenol A (BPA). February 11, 2010. Available at www.cdc.gov/exposurereport/BisphenolA_FactSheet.html.

CFIA (Canadian Food Inspection Agency). 2003. Consolidated Health Hazard Alert: Some Products May contain Sudan I Dye. www.inspection.gc.ca/english/corpaffr/recarapp/2003/20031107e.shtml. Accessed April 2008.

CFIA (Canadian Food Inspection Agency). 2012b. Durable life. www.inspection.gc.ca/food/consumer-centre/food-safety-tips/labelling-food-packaging-and-storage/date/eng/1332357469487/1332357545633.

CSPI (Center for Science in the Public Interest). 2006. Food safety. Chemical cuisine. CSPI's guide to food additives. Available at www.cspinet.org/reports/chemcuisine.htm.

CSPI (Center for Science in the Public Interest). 2012. Food safety. Chemical cuisine. CSPI's guide to food additives. www.cspinet.org/reports/chemcuisine.htm#safety_summary.

Dangour, A. D., S. K. Dodhia, A. Hayter, E. Allen, K. Lock, and R. Uauy. 2009. Nutritional quality of organic foods: a systematic review. *American Journal of Clinical Nutrition.* July 29, 2009. Doi:10.3945/ajcn.2009.28041.

EPA (Environmental Protection Agency). 2005a. Pesticides: Health and Safety: Human Health Issues. Available at www.epa.gov/pesticides/health/human.htm.

EPA (Environmental Protection Agency). 2005b. Pesticides: Health and Safety: Pesticides and Food: Health Problems Pesticides May Pose. Available at www.epa.gov/pesticides/food/risks.htm.

EPA (Environmental Protection Agency). 2005c. Pesticides: Health and Safety: Pesticides and Food: Why Children May Be Especially Sensitive to Pesticides. Available at www.epa.gov/pesticides/food/pest.htm.

FDA (U. S. Food and Drug Administration). 2005. Eating defensively: Food safety advice for persons with AIDS. Available at www.cfsan.fda.gov/~dms/aidseat.html.

FDA (United States Food and Drug Administration). 2010. News & Events. Bisphenol A (BPA). January 2010. Available at www.fda.gov/NewsEvents/PublicHealthFocus/ucm064437.htm.

Food Marketing Institute. 2003. A Consumer Guide to Food Quality and Safe Handling: Meat, Poultry, Seafood, Eggs [pamphlet]. Washington, DC: Food Marketing Institute, pp. 1–5.

Geha, R. S., A. Beiser, C. Ren, R. Patterson, P. A. Greenberger, L. C. Grammer, A. M. Ditto, K. E. Harris, M. A. Shaughnessy, P. R. Yarnold, et al. 2000. Review of alleged reaction to monosodium glutamate and outcome of a multicenter double-blind placebo-controlled study. *J. Nutr.* 130(4S Suppl):1058S–1062S.

Government of Canada. 2010. Questions and Answers for Action on Bisphenol A Under the *Chemicals Management Plan.* Available from: www.chemicalsubstanceschimiques.gc.ca/fact-fait/bisphenol-a_qa-qr-eng.php#q.

Grinder-Pedersen, L., S. E. Rasmussen, S. Bügel, L. O. Jørgensen, D. Vagn Gundersen, and B. Sandström. 2003. Effect of diets based on foods from conventional versus organic production on intake and excretion of flavonoids and markers of antioxidative defense in humans. *Agric. Food Chem.* 51(19):5671–5676.

Health Canada. 2005. Dioxins and Furans. Available at: www.hc-sc.gc.ca/hl-vs/iyh-vsv/environ/dioxin-eng.php.

Health Canada. 2006a. It's your health: Infant botulism. www.hc-sc.gc.ca/iyh-vsv/diseases-maladies/botu_e.html. Accessed March 2008.

Health Canada. 2006b. It's your health: Salmonella prevention. www.hc-sc.gc.ca/iyh-vsv/food-aliment/salmonella_e.html. Accessed April 2008.

Health Canada. 2008a. Bisphenol A. Available at: www.hc-sc.gc.ca/fn-an/securit/packag-emball/bpa/index-eng.php.

Health Canada. 2008b. Mercury in Fish. Available at: www.hc-sc.gc.ca/fn-an/securit/chem-chim/environ/mercur/cons-adv-etud-eng.php.

Health Canada. 2009a. Nitrate/Nitrite. Available at: www.hc-sc.gc.ca/ewh-semt/pubs/water-eau/nitrate_nitrite/index-eng.php#Food.

Health Canada. 2009b. Sulphites—One of the nine most common food products causing severe adverse reactions. Available at: www.hc-sc.gc.ca/fn-an/securit/allerg/fa-aa/allergen_sulphites-sulfites-eng.php.

Health Canada. 2010. Safety Tips for Microwave Ovens. www.hc-sc.gc.ca/fn-an/securit/kitchen-cuisine/micro-eng.php.

Health Canada. 2011. Genetically modified food in Canada. Available at: www.hc-sc.gc.ca/fn-an/gmf-agm/appro/index-eng.php.

International Society for Infectious Diseases. Prion Disease Update 2010. March 4, 2010. Available at http://promedmail.oracle.com/pls/otn/pm?an=20100304.0709.

James, C. 2004. Preview: Global Status of Commercialized Biotech/GM Crops: 2004. ISAAA Briefs No. 32. Ithaca, NY: ISAAA.

Kidney Foundation of Canada. 2002. Hemolytic uremic syndrome. www.kidney.ca/english/publications/factsheets/hemolytic.htm. Accessed February 2005.

Kristof, N. 2009. Chemicals in Our Food, and Bodies. November 8, 2009. *New York Times.* Available at www.nytimes.com/2009/11/08/opinion/08Kristof.html.

Lacroix, B. M., K. W. M. Li, and D. A. Powell. 2003. Consumer food handling recommendations: Is thawing of turkey a food safety issue? *Can. J. Diet. Prac, Res.* 64:59–61.

McHughen, A. 2000. Pandora's Picnic Basket: The potential and hazards of genetically modified foods. Oxford: Oxford University Press, pp. 17–45.

NDDIC (National Digestive Diseases Information Clearinghouse). 2007. Bacteria and foodborne illness. NIH Publication No. 07-4730. Available at http://digestive. niddk. nih.gov/ddiseases/pubs/bacteria/index.htm.

Neuman, W. 2010. Justice Dept. Tells Farmers It Will Press Agriculture Industry on Antitrust. *New York Times.* March 12. Available at www.nytimes.com/2010/03/13/business/13seed.html.

Pavlista, A. D. 2001. Green potatoes: The problem and solution. NebGuide. The University of Nebraska-Lincoln Cooperative Extension. Available at http://ianrpubs.unl.edu/horticulture/g1437.htm.

PHAC (Public Health Agency of Canada). 2005. http://dsol-smed.phac-aspc.gc.ca/dsol-smed/ndis/list-eng.php [notifiable diseases].

PHAC (Public Health Agency of Canada). 2012. www.phac-aspc.gc.ca/ep-mu/rido-iemi/index-eng.php [role of PHAC in notifying public].

Schafer, K. S., and S. E. Kegley. 2002. Persistent toxic chemicals in the US food supply. *J. Epidemiol.community Health* 56:813–817.

Severson, K. and A. Martin. 2009. It's organic, but does that mean it's safer? *New York Times.* March 4. Available at www.nytimes.com/2009/03/04/dining/04cert.html.

Shephard, S. 2000. *Pickled, Potted and Canned: The Story of Food Preserving.* London: Headline Publishing.

University of Florida. 2002. *E. coli* 0157:H7: A Potential Health Concern. http://edis.ifas.ufl.edu/BODY_SS197. Accessed May 2005.

USDA (U. S. Department of Agriculture. Partnership for Food Safety Education—PFSE). 2006. Fight Bac! Safe Food Handling. www.fightbac.org/content/view/6/11/.

USDA (United States Department of Agriculture Food Safety and Inspection Service). 2001. Parasites and Foodborne Illness. Available at http://origin-www.fsis.usda.gov/Fact_Sheets/Parasites_and_Foodborne_Illness/index.asp.

WHO (World Health organization). 2010. Twenty Questions on Genetically Modified (GM) Foods. Available at www.who.int/foodsafety/publications/biotech/20questions/en/.

In Depth: Global Nutrition

Adair, L. S., and A. M. Prentice. 2004. A critical evaluation of the fetal origins hypothesis and its implications for developing countries. *J. Nutr.* 134:191–193.

Associated Press. 2005. Malawi drought highlights food shortage. *New York Times*, October 17.

Bell, J. 2004. Good things come in small packages. *Childview* (Spring) vol. 16, no. 4: 9–13.

Black, R. E., S. S. Morris, and J. Bryce. 2003. Where and why are 10 million children dying every year? *Lancet* 361:2226–2234.

CIA (Central Intelligence Agency). 2010. The World Factbook: Sudan. February 15, 2010. Available at www.cia.gov/library/publications/the-world-factbook/geos/su.html.

Drewnowski, A. 2004. Poverty and obesity. www.niehs.nih.gov/drcpt/beoconf/postconf/overview/drewnowski2.pdf.

Ezra, M., and G. E. Kiros. 2000. Household vulnerability to food crisis and mortality in the drought-prone areas of northern Ethiopia. *J. Biosoc. Sci.* 32:395–409.

FAO (Food and Agriculture Organization). 2009. The State of Food Insecurity in the World 2009. FAO Media Centre, October 14, 2009. Available at www.fao.org/news/story/en/item/36207/icode/.

Food Research and Action Center (FRAC). 2006. Hunger in the U. S.: The Paradox of Obesity and Hunger. Available at www.frac.org.html/hunger_in_the_us/hunger&obesity.htm.

Friends of the World Food Program. 2010. Number of Hungry Quadruples in Southern Sudan Amidst Conflict and Drought. February 2. Available at www.friendsofwfp.org/site/apps/nlnet/content2.aspx?c=hrKJI.

Hartman-Craven, B., A. Christofides, D. L. O'Connor, S. Zlotkin. 2007. Bioavailability of iron and folic acid in a traditional pregnancy supplement vs. a new powdered supplement. *FASEB J* 21(5):701. 2.

Haseen F. 2007. Home fortification with sprinkles to address childhood anaemia in Bangladesh. *Nutrition Bulletin*. 10(1):4–5.

Health Canada. 2011. Household Food Insecurity In Canada in 20072008: Key Statistics and Graphics. Available at: www.hc-sc.gc.ca/fn-an/surveill/nutrition/commun/insecurit/key-stats-cles-2007-2008-eng.php.

Kristof, N. D. 2010. World's Healthiest Food. *New York Times*, January 3. Available at www.nytimes.com/2010/01/03/opinion/03kristof.html.

NASA (National Aeronautics and Space Administration). 2005. Earth observatory: Famine in Niger and Mali. http://earthobservatory.nasa.gov/NaturalHazards/natural_hazards_v2.php3?img_id=13028. Accessed August 2007.

Nyamsuren N., C. Emary, G. S. Bat, S. Gerein, S. H. Zlotkin, M. Chan. 2004. Integrated programming, including homebased fortification using Sprinkles is an effective strategy for addressing anemia in Mongolian children. [abstract]. In: *International Nutritional Anemia Consultative Group [INACG] Symposium*; 2004 November; Peru: ILSI Research Foundation. p. 47.

Sharieff, W., Z. Bhutta, C. Schauer, G. Tomlinson, and S. Zlotkin. 2006. Using Sprinkles to supplement micronutrients and probiotics to reduce diarrhea-related morbidity among Pakistani children: A triple blind community based placebo controlled trial. *Archives of diseases in childhood*. Published online first: 23 March 2006. doi:10.1136/adc.2005.086199.

Squires, N. 2009. At UN food summit, Ban Ki-Moon warns of rise in child hunger deaths. *The Christian Science Monitor*. October 16, 2009. Available at www.csmonitor.com/World/Europe/2009/1116/p06s04-woeu.html.

Stroehlein, A. 2004. Darfur starvation will be televised ... eventually. *Christian Science Monitor*, June 8. www.csmonitor.com/2004/0608/p09s02-coop.htm.

UNAIDS/WHO. 2009. AIDS Epidemic Update: Global Facts & Figures: December. http://data.unaids.org/pub/FactSheet/2009/20091124_FS_global_en.pdf.

UNICEF. 2008. Basic education and gender equity. February, 2008. Available at www.unicef.org/girlseducation/index_bigpicture.html.

UNICEF. 2009. The State of the World's Children 2009. UNICEF. Available at www.unicef.org/sowc09/press/fastfacts.php.

WHO (World Health Organization). 2006. Obesity and Overweight. Available at www.who.int/dietphysicalactivity/publications/facts/obesity/en/.

WHO (World Health Organization). 2008. Worldwide prevalence of anaemia 1993–2005 WHO Global Database on Anaemia. Available at: http://whqlibdoc.who.int/publications/2008/9789241596657_eng.pdf.

WHO (World Health Organization). 2010. What are the key health dangers for children? July 24, 2008. Geneva: World Health Organization. Available at www.who.int/features/qa/13/en/.

Yajnik, C. S. 2004. Early life origins of insulin resistance and type 2 diabetes in India and other Asian countries. *J. Nutr.* 134:205–210.

Zlotkin, S., P. Arthur, K. A. Antwi, and G. Yeung. 2001. Treatment of anemia with microencapsulated ferrous fumarate plus ascorbic acid supplied as Sprinkles. *Am. J. Clin. Nutr.* 74:791–795.

Chapter 14

ADA (American Dietetic Association). 2008. Position of the American Dietetic Association: nutrition and lifestyle for a healthy pregnancy outcome. 108:553–561.

Adams, C., R. Berger, P. Conning, L. Cruikshank, and K. Dore. 2001. Breastfeeding trends at a community breastfeeding center: an evaluative survey. *J. Obstet. Gynecol. Neonatal Nurs.* 30(4):392–400.

Agency for Healthcare Research and Quality. 2007. Breastfeeding and Maternal and Infant Health Outcomes in Developed Countries. U.S. Department of Health and Human Services. Rockville, MD. AHRQ Publication No. 07-E007.

American Academy of Pediatrics (AAP, Section on Breastfeeding). 2005. Breastfeeding and the use of human milk policy statement. *Pediatrics* 115:496–506.

Bourguignon, M. 2007. McGill-led team identifies spina bifida gene: Groundbreaking research can make diagnosis easier. www.thechildren.com/en/news/news.aspx?id=187.

Canadian Diabetes Association. 2012. Gestational Diabetes: Preventing Complications in Pregnancy. www.diabetes.ca/diabetes-and-you/what/gestational/.

CDC (Centers for Disease Control and Prevention). 2009a. Births and Natality. Available at www.cdc.gov/nchs/fastats/births.htm.

CDC (Centers for Disease Control and Prevention. 2009b. Facts about folic acid: Folic acid home page. Available at www.cdc.gov/ncbddd/folicacid/about.html. Accessed March 2010.

Clausen, T. D., E. R. Mathiesen, T. Hansen, O. Pedersen, D. M. Jensen, J. Lauenborg, L. Schmidt, and P. Bamm. 2009. Overweight and the metabolic syndrome in adult offspring of women with diet-treated gestational diabetes mellitus or type 1 diabetes. *J. Clin. Endocrinology Metab.* 94:2464–2470.

Collaborative Group on Hormonal Factors in Breast Cancer. 2003. Breast cancer and breastfeeding: collaborative reanalysis of individual data from 47 epidemiological studies in 30 countries, including 50,302 women with breast cancer and 96,973 women without the disease. *Lancet* 360:187–195.

Craig, W. J., A. R. Mangels, and the American Dietetic Association. 2009. Position of the American Dietetic Association: vegetarian diets. *J. Am. Diet. Assoc.* 109:1266–1282.

Davidson, M. R., M. L. London, and P. W. Ladewig. 2008. *Olds' Maternal-Newborn Nursing and Women's Health Across the Lifespan*, 8th ed. Upper Saddle River, NJ: Prentice Hall Health.

Ernst, E. 2002. Herbal medicinal products during pregnancy: Are they safe? *Br. J. Obstet. Gynaecol.* 109:227–235.

ESPGHAN Committee on Nutrition (C. Agostoni, C. Braegger, T. Decsi, S. Kolacek, B. Koletzko, K.F. Michaelsen, W. Mihatsch,

L.A. Moreno, J. Puntis, R. Shamir, H. Szajewska, D. Turck, and J. van Goudoever). 2009. Breast-feeding: a commentary by the ESPGHAN Committee on Nutrition. *J. Ped. Gastroentrerol Nutr.* 49:112–125.

ESPGHAN Committee on Nutrition (C. Agostoni, I. Axelsson, O. Goulet, B. Koletzko, K.F. Michaelsen, J. Puntis, D. Rieu, J. Rigo, R. Shamir, H. Szajewska, and D. Turck). 2006. Soy protein infant formulae and follow-on formulae: a commentary by the ESPGHAN committee on nutrition. *J. Ped. Gastroenterol Nutr.* 42:352–361.

Francis, J. J. Pregnancy: 2010. Preparation for the Next Generation. In: Wilson, T, G. A. Bray, N. J. Temple, and M. B. Struble. *Nutrition Guide for Physicians*. Humana Press.

Gavard, J. A. and R. Artal. 2008. Effect of exercise on pregnancy outcome. *Clin. Obstet. Gynec.* 51:467–480.

Gillman, M. W., S. L. Rifas-Shiman, C. A. Camargo Jr., C. S. Berkey, A. L. Frazier, H. R. Rockett, A. E. Field, and G. A. Colditz. 2001. Risk of overweight among adolescents who were breastfed as infants. *JAMA* 285:2461–1467.

Grummer-Strawn, L. M., and M. Zuguo. 2004. Does breastfeeding protect against pediatric overweight? Analysis of longitudinal data from the Centers for Disease Control and Prevention Pediatric Nutrition Surveillance System. *Pediatrics* 113e:e81–e86.

Health Canada. 2003. Novel Food Information - DHASCO® and ARASCO® as Sources of Docosahexaenoic Acid and Arachidonic Acid in Infant Formulas. Available from www.hc-sc.gc.ca/fn-an/gmf-agm/appro/dhasco_arasco-eng.php. Accessed May 2012.

Health Canada. 2005. *Nutrition for a Healthy Pregnancy—National Guidelines for the Childbearing Years.* www.hc-sc.gc.ca/fn-an/nutrition/prenatal/national_guidelines-lignes_directrices_nationales-06g_e.html. Accessed May 2008.

Health Canada. 2007a. Mercury in Fish. Consumption Advice: Making Informed Choices about Fish. www.hc-sc.gc.ca/fn-an/securit/chem-chim/mercur/cons-adv-etud_e.html. Accessed December 2007.

Health Canada. 2007b. *Nutrition for Healthy Term Infants—Statement of the Joint Working Group: Canadian Paediatric Society, Dietitians of Canada and Health Canada.* www.hc-sc.gc.ca/fn-an/pubs/infant. Accessed May 2008.

Health Canada. 2007c. Pregnancy. www.hc-sc.gc.ca/hc-ps/tobac-tabac/body-corps/preg-gros-eng.php. Accessed September 2012.

Health Canada. 2008. *Nutrients of Special Concern for a Healthy Pregnancy.* www.hc-sc.gc.ca/fn-an/consultation/init/prenatal/folate-cons_e.html. Accessed April 2008.

Health Canada. 2010. Food Safety for Pregnant Women. www.hc-sc.gc.ca/hl-vs/iyh-vsv/food-aliment/pregnant-enceintes-eng.php. Accessed May 2012.

Health Canada. 2012. Breastfeeding Initiation in Canada: Key Statistics and Graphics (2009-2010). www.hc-sc.gc.ca/fn-an/surveill/nutrition/commun/prenatal/initiation-eng.php#a3.

IOM (Institute of Medicine, Food and Nutrition Board). 1997. *Dietary Reference Intakes for Calcium, Phosphorus, Magnesium, Vitamin D, and Fluoride.* Washington, DC: National Academies Press.

IOM (Institute of Medicine, Food and Nutrition Board). 1998. *Dietary Reference Intakes for Thiamin, Riboflavin, Niacin, Vitamin B6, Folate, Vitamin B12, Pantothenic Acid, Biotin, and Choline.* Washington, DC: National Academies Press.

IOM (Institute of Medicine, Food and Nutrition Board). 2004. *Dietary Reference for Water, Potassium, Sodium, Chloride, and Sulfate.* Washington, DC: National Academies Press.

IOM (Institute of Medicine, Food and Nutrition Board, Board on Children, Youth, and Families). 2006. *Influence of Pregnancy Weight on Maternal and Child Health: Workshop Report Influence of Pregnancy Weight on Maternal and Child Health.* Washington, DC: National Academies Press.

Jana, A. K. Interventions for promoting the initiation of breastfeeding: RHL commentary. 2009. The WHO Reproductive Health Library; Geneva: World Health Organization. Available at http://apps.who.int/rhl/pregnancy_childbirth/care_after_childbirth/cd001688_JanaAK_com/en/.

Kline, M.W. 2009. Early exclusive breastfeeding: still the cornerstone of child survival. *Am. J. Clin. Nutr.* 89:1281–1282.

Koletzko, B., Scaglioni, R. von Kries, R. Closa Monasterolo, J. Excribano Subias, S. Scaglioni, M. Giovannini, J. Beyer, et al., for the European Childhood Obesity Trial Study Group. 2009. Can infant feeding choices modulate later obesity rates? *Am. J. Clin. Nutr.* 89 (suppl):1502S–1580S.

Lacasse, A., E. Rey, E. Ferreira, C. Morin, and A. Bérard. 2009. Epidemiology of nausea and vomiting of pregnancy: prevalence, severity, determinants, and the importance of race/ethnicity. *BMC Pregnancy and Childbirth* 9:26.

Ludwig, D. S., and H. A. Pollack. 2009. Obesity and the economy: From crisis to opportunity. *JAMA* 301:533–535.

Magee L. A., M. Helewa, J. M. Moutquin, P. van Dadelszen, for the Hypertension Guideline Committee. 2008. Diagnosis, evaluation, and management of the hypertensive disorders of pregnancy. SOGC Clinical Practice Guideline, No. 206, *J Obstet Gynaecol Can.* 30:S1–S48.

Mayo Clinic. Induced lactation: Can I breast-feed my adopted baby? October 29, 2008. Available at www.mayoclinic.com/health/induced-lactation/AN01882.

National Organization on Fetal Alcohol Syndrome (NOFAS). 2001–2004. FAQs. What are fetal alcohol spectrum disorders? Available at www.nofas.org/faqs.aspx?id=15. Accessed March 2010.

Nickerson, K. 2006. Environmental contaminants in breast milk. *J. Midwifery Women's Health* 51:26–34.

O'Tierney, P. F., D. J. P. Barker, C. Osmond, E. Kajantie, and J. G. Eriksson. 2009. Duration of breastfeeding and adiposity in adult life. *J. Nutr.* 139:422S–425S.

ODS NIH (Office of Dietary Supplements: National Institutes of Health.). 2007. Dietary supplement fact sheet: Iron. Available at http://dietary-supplements.info.nih.gov/factsheets/Iron_pf.asp. Accessed March 2010.

Owen, C. G., R. M. Martin, P. H. Whincup, D. Smith, and D. G. Cppk. 2005. Effect of infant feeding on the risk of obesity across the life course: A quantitative review of published evidence. *Pediatrics* 115:1367–1377.

PHAC (Public Health Agency of Canada). 2008. Healthy Pregnancy. Caffeine and Pregnancy. www.phac-aspc.gc.ca/hp-gs/know-savoir/caffeine-eng.php.

Rasmussen, K. M., and A. L. Yaktine, eds. 2009. *Weight Gain During Pregnancy: Reexamining the Guidelines.* Institute of Medicine; National Research Council. Washington, DC: National Academy Press.

Reece, E. A. 2010. The fetal and maternal consequences of gestational diabetes. *J. Maternal–Fetal Neonatal Med.* 23:199-203.

Sherwood K. L., L.A. Houghton, V. Tarasuk, D. L. O'Connor. 2006. One-third of pregnant and lactating women may not be meeting their folate requirements from diet alone based on mandated levels of folic acid fortification. *J Nutr* 136(11):2820-6.

Statistics Canada. 2011a. Infant deaths per 1000 live births. Table 102-0030, 2011, Accessed May 22, 2012. http://www5.statcan.gc.ca/cansim/a26?lang=eng&retrLang=eng&id=1020030&tabMode=dataTable&srchLan=-1&p1=-1&p2=9.

Statistics Canada. 2011b. Low Birth Weight. CANSIM table 102-4005. http://www5.statcan.gc.ca/cansim/pick-choisir?lang=eng&p2=33&id=1024005.

Stewart, A., J. Walsh, and N. Van Eyk. 2008. Adverse outcomes associated with adolescent pregnancy. *J. Ped. Adolesc. Gynecol.* 21:59–60.

Substance Abuse and Mental Health Services Administration. 2008. Results from the 2007 National Survey on Drug Use and Health: National Findings. NSDUH Series H-34, DHHS Publication No. SMA 08-4343. Rockville, MD.

United Nations Statistics. 2012. Live births, deaths, and infant deaths, latest available year (1996–2010) Last updated 17 May 2012. http://unstats.un.org/unsd/demographic/products/vitstats/serATab3.pdf.

USDHHS (U.S. Department of Health & Human Services). 2007. Breastfeeding, Maternal & Infant Health Outcomes in Developed Countries. www.ahrq.gov/clinic/tp/brfouttp.htm. Accessed March 2010.

Viswanathan, M., A. M. Siega-Riz, M-K. Moos, A. Deierlein, S. Mumford, J. Knaack, P. Thieda, L. J. Lux, and K. N. Lohr. 2008. Outcomes of Maternal Weight Gain, Evidence Report/Technology Assessment No. 168. AHRQ Publication No. 08-E009. Rockville, MD: Agency for Healthcare Research and Quality.

Weyerman, M., D. Rothenbacher, and H. Brenner. 2006. Duration of breastfeeding and risk of overweight in childhood: A prospective birth cohort study from Germany. *Int. J. Obesity.* (London) 30:1281–1287.

Wrotniak, B. H., J. Shults, S. Butts, and N. Stettler. 2008. Gestational weight gain and risk of overweight in the offspring at age 7 in a multicenter, multiethnic cohort study. *Am J. Clin. Nutr.* 87: 1818–1824.

In Depth The Fetal Environment: A Lasting Impression

Barker, D. J., C. Osmond, T. J. Forsen, E. Kajantie, and J. G. Eriksson. 2005. Trajectories of growth among children who have coronary events as adults. *N. Engl. J. Med.* 353:1802–1809.

Bouret, S. G. 2010. Role of early hormonal and nutritional experiences in shaping feeding behavior and hypothalamic development. *J. Nutr.* 140:653–657.

Catalano, P. M., K. Farrell, A. Thomas, L. Huston-Presley, P. Mencin, S. Hauguel de Mouson, and S. B. Amini. 2009. Perinatal risk factors for childhood obesity and metabolic dysregulation. *Am. J. Clin. Nutr.* 90:1303–1313.

CDC (Centers for Disease Control and Prevention. Chronic Disease and Health Promotion). 2009. Chronic Disease Overview. December 17. Available at www.cdc.gov/chronicdisease/overview/index.htm#2. Accessed March 2010.

Cetin, I., C. Berti, and S. Calabrese. 2009. Role of micronutrients in the periconceptual period. *Hum. Reproduction Update.* 16:80–95.

Clausen, T. D., E. R. Mathiesen, T. Hansen, O. Pedersen, D. M. Jensen, J. Lauenborg, and P. Damm. 2008. High prevalence of type 2 diabetes and pre-diabetes in adult offspring of women with gestational diabetes mellitus or type 1 diabetes. *Diab. Care* 31:340–346.

Clausen, T. D., E. R. Mathiesen, T. Hansen, O. Pedersen, D. M. Jensen, J. Lauenborg, L. Schmidt, and P. Damm. 2009. Overweight and the metabolic syndrome in adult offspring of women with diet-treated gestational diabetes mellitus or type 1 diabetes. *J. Clin. Endocrinology.* Metab. 94:2464–2470.

Jaddoe, V. W. V. 2008. Fetal nutritional origins of adult diseases: challenges for epidemiological research. *Eur. J. Epidemiol.* 23: 767–771.

Jenkins, K. J., A. Correa, J. A. Feinstein, L. Botto, A. E. Britt, S. R. Daniels, M. Elixson, C. A. Warnes, and C. L. Webb. 2007. Noninherited risk factors and congenital cardiovascular defects: current knowledge. *Circulation.* 115:2995–3014.

Kaijser, M., A. K. E. Bonamy, O. Akre, S. Cnattingius, F. Granath, M. Norman, and A. Ekbom. 2009. Perinatal risk factors for diabetes in later life. *Diabetes* 58:523–526.

Lie, R. T., A. J. Wilxoc, J. Taylor, H. K. Gjessing, L. D. Saugstad, F. Aabyholm, and H. Vindenes. 2008. Maternal smoking and oral clefts: the role of detoxification pathway genes. *Epidemiology.* 55:382–288.

Lumey, L. H., A. D. Stein, H. S. Kahn, and J. A. Romijn. 2009. Lipid profiles in middle-aged men and women after famine exposure during gestation: the Dutch Hunger Winter Families Study. *Am. J. Clin. Nutr.* 90:1737–1743.

Lussana, F., R. C. Painter, M. C. Ocke, H. R. Buller, P. M. Bossuyt, and T. J. Roseboom. 2008. Prenatal exposure to the Dutch famine is associated with a preference for fatty foods and a more atherogenic lipid profile. *Am. J. Clin. Nutr.* 88:1648–1652.

March of Dimes. 2007. Quick Reference Fact Sheets: Environmental Risks and Pregnancy. www.marchofdimes.com/professionals/14332_9146.asp. Accessed March 2010.

Maret, W., and H. H. Sandstead. 2008. Possible roles of zinc nutriture in the fetal origins of disease. *Experimental Gerontology* 43:378–381.

Miranda, J. J., S. Kinra, J. P. Casas, G. Davey Smith, and S. Ebrahim. 2008. Non-communicable diseases in low- and middleincome countries: context, determinants and health policy. *Trop. Med. Int. Health.* 13: 1225–1234.

Oken, E., J. S. Radesky, R. O. Wright, D. C. Bellinger, C. J. Amarasiriwardena, K. P. Kleinman, H. Hu, and M. W. Gillman. 2008. Associations of maternal fish intake during pregnancy and breastfeeding duration with attainment of developmental milestones in early childhood. *Am. J. Clin. Nutr.* 88:789–796.

Stanner, S. A., and J. S. Yudkin. 2001. Fetal programming and the Leningrad siege study. *Twin Research.* 4:287–292.

Stanner, S. A., K. Bulmer, C. Andres, O. E. Lantseva, V. Borodina, V. V. Poteen, and J. S. Yudkin. 1997. Does malnutrition in utero determine diabetes and coronary heart disease in adulthood? Results from the Leningrad siege study, a cross sectional study. *Brit. Med. J.* 315:1342–1348.

Stothard, K. J., P. W. G. Tennant, R. Bell, and J. Rankin. 2009. Maternal overweight and obesity and the risk of congenital anomalies: a systematic review and meta-analysis. *JAMA* 301:636–650.

Stuebe, A. M., M. R. Forman, and K. B. Michels. 2009. Maternal recalled gestational weight gain, pre-pregnancy body mass index, and obesity in the daughter. *Int.l J. Obesity.* 33:743–752.

Zucker, M. 2002. Smoking during pregnancy: even worse than you think. Pulmonary Reviews.com 7(3). Available at www.pulmonaryreviews.com/march02/smoking.html. Accessed March 2010.

Chapter 15

Agras, W. S., L. D. Hammer, F. McNicholas, and H. C. Kraemer. 2004. Risk factors for childhood overweight: A prospective study from birth to 9.5 years. *J. Pediatr.* 145:19–24.

Anon. 2009. Vegetarian Diets—Is it safe for children to be vegetarians? Available at www.webmd.com/food-recipes/tc/vegetarian-diets-is-it-safe-for-children-to-be-vegetarians. Accessed June 2010.

Campbell, W. W., C. A. Johnson, G. P. McCabe, and N. S. Carnell. 2008. Dietary protein requirements of younger and older adults. *Am. J. Clin. Nutr.* 88:1322–1329.

Craig, W. C., and A. R. Mangels. 2009. Position of the American Dietetic Association: Vegetarian Diets. *J. Am. Diet. Assoc.* 109:1266–1282.

Dolan, C. M., H. Kraemer, W. Browner, K. Ensrud, and J. L. Kelsy. 2007. Associations between body composition, anthropometry, and mortality in women aged 65 years and older. *Am. J. Public Health.* 97:913–918.

Hackam, D. G., and S. S. Anand. 2003. Emerging risk factors for atherosclerotic vascular disease: a critical review of the evidence. *J. Am. Med. Assoc.* 290:932–940.

Health Canada. 2010. Vitamin D and Calcium: Updated Dietary Reference Intakes. www.hc-sc.gc.ca/fn-an/nutrition/vitamin/vita-d-eng.php.

Health Canada. 2011. Household Food Insecurity In Canada in 2007-2008: Key Statistics and Graphics. Available at: www.hc-sc.gc.ca/fn-an/surveill/nutrition/commun/insecurit/key-stats-cles-2007-2008-eng.php.

Houston, D. K., B. J. Nicklas, J. Ding, T. B. Harris, F. A. Tylavsky, A. B. Newman, J. Sun Lee, N. R. Sahyoun, M. Visser, and S. B. Kritchevsky for the Health ABC Study. 2008. Dietary protein intake is associated with lean mass change in older, community-dwelling adults: The Health, Aging, and Body Composition (Health ABC) Study. *Am. J. Clin. Nutr.* 87:150–155.

Hoyland, A., L. Dye, and C. L. Lawton. 2009. A systematic review of the effect of breakfast on the cognitive performance of children and adolescents. *Nutr. Res. Rev.* 22:220–243.

Human Resources and Skills Development Canada. 2012. Canadians in Context–Aging Population. Available at: www4.hrsdc.gc.ca/.3ndic .1t.4r@-eng.jsp?iid=33.

Ingwersen, J., M. A. Defeyter, D. O. Kennedy, K. A.Wesnes, and A. B. Scholey. 2007. A low glycaemic index breakfast cereal preferentially prevents children's cognitive performance from declining throughout the morning. *Appetite.* 49:240–244.

IOM (Institute of Medicine, Food and Nutrition Board). 1997. *Dietary Reference Intakes for Calcium, Phosphorus, Magnesium, Vitamin D, and Fluoride.* Washington, DC: National Academies Press.

IOM (Institute of Medicine, Food and Nutrition Board). 1998. *Dietary Reference Intakes for Thiamin, Riboflavin, Niacin, Vitamin B6, Folate, Vitamin B12, Pantothenic Acid, Biotin, and Choline.* Washington, DC: National Academies Press.

IOM (Institute of Medicine, Food and Nutrition Board). 2001. *Dietary Reference Intakes for Vitamin A, Vitamin K, Arsenic, Boron, Chromium, Copper, Iodine, Iron, Manganese, Molybdenum, Nickel, Silicon, Vanadium, and Zinc.* Washington, DC: National Academies Press.

IOM (Institute of Medicine, Food and Nutrition Board). 2002. *Dietary Reference Intakes for Energy, Carbohydrates, Fiber, Fat, Protein and Amino Acids (Macronutrients).* Washington, DC: The National Academy of Sciences.

IOM (Institute of Medicine, Food and Nutrition Board). 2004. *Dietary Reference for Water, Potassium, Sodium, Chloride, and Sulfate.* Washington, DC: National Academies Press.

Jarosz, P. A., and A. Bellar. 2008. Sarcopenic obesity: An emerging cause of frailty in older adults. *Ger. Nursing.* 30:64–70.

King, L. 2010. Vegan Children Malnutrition Myths. Available at www .associatedcontent.com/article/2917766/vegan_children_ malnutrition_myths.html.

Kleinman, R. E. (ed.) 2009. *Pediatric Nutrition Handbook*, 6th edn. Elk Grove Village, IL: American Academy of Pediatrics.

Ludwig, D. S. 2007. Childhood obesity—the shape of things to come. *New Engl. J. Med.* 357:2325–2327.

Murphy, M. M., J. S. Douglass, R. K. Johnson, and L. A. Spence. 2008. Drinking flavored or plain milk is positively associated with nutrient intake and is not associated with adverse effects on weight status in U.S. children and adolescents. *J. Am. Diet. Assoc.* 108:631–639.

Ogden, C. L., M. D. Carroll, and K. M. Flegal. 2008. High body mass index for age among U.S. children and adolescents, 2003–2006. *JAMA.* 299:2401–2405.

PHAC (Public Health Agency of Canada). 2011. Obesity in Canada. www.phac-aspc.gc.ca/hp-ps/hl-mvs/oic-oac/index-eng.php.

Ramage-Morin, 2009. Medication use among senior Canadians. Statistics Canada, Catalogue no. 82-003-XPE. *Health Reports,* 20(1).

Ritchie, L. D., G. Welk, D. Styne, D. E. Gerstein, and P. B. Crawford. 2005. Family environment and pediatric overweight: What is a parent to do? *J. Am. Diet. Assoc.* 105:S70–S79.

Sanders, T. A. B., and J. Manning. 2008. The growth and development of vegan children. *J. Hum. Nutr. Diet.* 5:11–21.

Stern, R. 2007. Diet from hell. *Phoenix New Times*, May 10, 2007. www .phoenixnewtimes.com/2007-05-10/news/diet-from-hell/.

Strang, J., and M. Story. 2005. Adolescent growth and development. In: Stang, J. and M. Story (eds). *Guidelines for Adolescent Nutrition Services.* Minneapolis, MN. University of Minnesota.

Striegel-Moore, R. H., D. Thompson, S. G. Affenito, D. L. Franko, E. Obarzanek, B. A. Barton, G. B. Schreiber, S. R. Daniels, M. Schmidt, and P. B. Crawford. 2006. Correlates of beverage intake in adolescent girls: The National Heart, Lung, and Blood Institute growth and health study. *J. Pediatr.* 148:183–187.

Weaver, C. M. 2010. Consequences of excluding dairy, milk avoiders, calcium requirements in children. Lactose Intolerance and Health: NIH Consensus Development Conference Program and Abstracts. National Institutes of Health. Bethesda, MD.

WHO (World Health organization). 2010. Health effects of smoking among young people. Retrieved from www.who.int/tobacco/ research/youth/health_effects/en/index.html.

Zeller, M., and S. Daniels. 2004. The obesity epidemic: Family matters. *J. Pediatr.* 145:3–4.

Zoico, E., V. DiFrancesco, J. M. Guralmik, G. Mazzali, A. Bortolani, S. Guariento, G. Sergi, O. Bosello, and M. Zamboni. 2004. Physical disability and muscular strength in relation to obesity and different body composition indexes in a sample of healthy elderly women. *International J. Obesity.* 28:234–241.

In Depth Searching for the Fountain of Youth

Ames, B. 2005. Increasing longevity by tuning up metabolism. *EMBO Reports.* 6:S20–S23.

Bjelakovic, G., D. Nikolova, L. Lotte Gluud, R. G. Simonetti, and C. Gluud. 2007. Mortality in randomized trials of antioxidant supplements for primary and secondary prevention: Systemic review and analysis. *JAMA.* 297:842–857.

CDC (Centers for Disease Control and Prevention). 2009. Chronic disease overview. Available at: www.cdc.gov/chronicdisease/ overview/.

CDC (Centers for Disease Control and Prevention). 2010. Smoking and Tobacco Use: Fast Facts, April 30, 2010. Available at www.cdc.gov/ tobacco/data_statistics/fact_sheets/fast_facts/index.htm#toll.

Fontana, L., L. Partridge, and V. D. Longo. 2010. Extending healthy life span—from yeast to humans. *Science* 328:321–226.

Fontana, L. and S. Klein. 2007. Aging, adiposity, and calorie restriction. *J. Am. Med. Assoc.* 297:986–994.

Heilbronn, L. K., S. R. Smith, C. K. Martin, S. D. Anton, and E. Ravussin. 2005. Alternate-day fasting in nonobese subjects: effects on body weight, body composition, and energy metabolism. *Am. J. Clin. Nutr.* 81:69–73.

Helibron, L. K., and E. Ravussin. 2003. Calorie restriction and aging: review of the literature and implications for studies in humans. *Am. J. Clin. Nutr.* 78(3):361–369.

Kostoff, R. N. 2001. Energy restriction. *Am. J. Clin. Nutr.* 74(4): 556–557.

Masoro, E. J. 2005. Overview of caloric restriction and ageing. *Mech. Ageing Dev.* 126:913–922.

Mayo Clinic 2009c. DHEA: Evidence for anti-aging claims is weak. Available at: www.mayoclinic.com/health/dhea/HA00084.

Mayo Clinic. 2009a. Calorie-restriction diet for anti-aging. www .mayoclinic.com/health/calorie-restriction-diet/MY00578.

Mayo Clinic. 2009b. Human growth hormone (HGH): Does it slow aging? Available at: www.mayoclinic.com/health/growth-hormone/ HA00030. Accessed June 2010.

National Center for Complementary and Alternative Medicine. 2008. Herbs at a Glance: Ginkgo. Available at http://nccam.nih.gov/ health/ginkgo.

Speakman, J. 2010. Can calorie restriction increase the human lifespan? *Experimental Biology.* April 24 2010.

Thomas, D. R. 2006. Vitamins in aging, health, and longevity. *Clinical Interventions in Aging.* 1:81–91.

NUTRIENT VALUES OF FOODS

The following table of nutrient values is taken from the EvaluEat diet analysis software that is included with every new copy of this text. The foods in the table are just a fraction of the foods provided in the software. When using the software you can quickly find foods shown here by entering the EvaluEat code in the search field. Values are obtained from the USDA Nutrient Database for Standard Reference, Release 16. A "0" indicates that nutrient value is determined to be zero; a blank space indicates that nutrient information is not available.

Amt = serving amount; **Wt** = weight; **Ener** = energy; **Prot** = protein; **Carb** = carbohydrate; **Fiber** = dietary fiber; **Fat** = total fat; **Mono** = mono-unsaturated fat; **Poly** = poly-unsaturated fat; **Sat** = saturated fat; **Chol** = cholesterol; **Calc** = calcium; **Iron** = iron; **Mag** = magnesium; **Phos** = phosphate; **Sodi** = sodium; **Zinc** = zinc; **Vit A** = vitamin A; **Vit C** = vitamin C; **Thia** = thiamin; **Ribo** = riboflavin; **Niac** = niacin; **Vit B$_6$** = vitamin B$_6$; **Vit B$_{12}$** = vitamin B$_{12}$; **Vit E** = vitamin E; **Fol** = folate; **Alc** = alcohol.

EvaluEat Code	Food Name	Amt	Wt (g)	Energy (kcal)	Prot (g)	Carb (g)	Fiber (g)	Fat (g)	Mono (g)	Poly (g)	Sat (g)
2047	Salt, table (sodium chloride)	1 tsp	6	0	0	0	0	0	0	0	0
4609	Animal fat, bacon grease	1 tbsp	12.8	114.8	0	0	0	12.736	5.744	1.426	4.993
4542	Animal fat, chicken	1 cup	205	1845	0	0	0	204.59	91.635	42.845	61.09
43388	Apple cider-flavored drink, powder, low calorie, with vitamin C, prepared	1 fl. oz.	29.8	0.298	0	0.089	0	0	0	0	0
9357	Apricots, canned, heavy syrup, drained	1 fruit	122	101.26	0.781	25.998	3.294	0.134	0.055	0.026	0.009
7921	Bacon and beef sticks	1 oz	28	145.6	8.148	0.224	0	12.376	6.132	1.204	4.48
43212	Bacon bits, meatless	1 cup	186	885.36	59.52	53.196	18.972	48.174	11.578	25.199	7.542
16104	Bacon, vegetarian, meatless	1 strip	5	15.5	0.534	0.316	0.13	1.476	0.355	0.772	0.231
18005	Bagel, cinnamon-raisin	1 bagel (4"dia)	89	243.86	8.722	49.128	2.047	1.513	0.156	0.597	0.244
18003	Bagel, egg	1 large bagel (4-1/2"dia)	131	364.18	13.886	69.43	3.013	2.751	0.55	0.841	0.552
18504	Bagel, Lender's Bagel Shop Blueberry	1 bagel (4"dia)	102	264.18	10.71	53.377	1.734	1.53	0.408	0.51	0.306
18007	Bagel, oatbran	1 bagel (4"dia)	89	226.95	9.523	47.437	3.204	1.068	0.222	0.433	0.17
18001	Bagel, plain/onion/poppy/sesame, enriched	1 bagel (4"dia)	89	244.75	9.345	47.526	2.047	1.424	0.117	0.619	0.196
43449	Baked beans, canned, no salt added	1 fl. oz.	29.8	31.29	1.43	6.142	1.639	0.119	0.01	0.051	0.031
42182	Bean beverage	1 oz	28.34	9.636	0.794	1.644	0	0	0	0	0
16115	Bean flour, soy, fullfat, raw	1 cup, stirred	84	366.24	29.014	29.56	8.064	17.346	3.831	9.792	2.509
16119	Bean meal, soy, defatted, raw	1 cup	122	413.58	54.839	48.971		2.916	0.499	1.275	0.327
16112	Bean sauce, fermented soy product, Miso	1 cup	275	566.5	32.478	76.89	14.85	16.693	3.688	9.427	2.414
16113	Bean sauce, fermented soy product, Natto	1 cup	175	371	31.01	25.13	9.45	19.25	4.253	10.868	2.784
16114	Bean sauce, fermented soy product, Tempeh	1 cup	166	320.38	30.776	15.587		17.928	4.98	6.353	3.685
16424	Bean sauce, soy & wheat (Shoyu) low sodium	1 tbsp	18	9.54	0.931	1.532	0.144	0.014	0.002	0.006	0.002
16124	Bean sauce, soy (Tamari)	1 tsp	6	3.6	0.631	0.334	0.048	0.006	0.001	0.003	0.001
16375	Beans, baby lima, mature seed, boiled w/salt	1 cup	182	229.32	14.633	42.424	14.014	0.692	0.062	0.308	0.16
16008	Beans, baked w/franks, canned	1 cup	259	367.78	17.483	39.86	17.871	17.016	7.33	2.165	6.092
16006	Beans, baked, plain or vegetarian, canned	1 cup	254	236.22	12.167	52.121	12.7	1.143	0.099	0.493	0.295
16015	Beans, black, mature seeds, boiled w/o salt	1 cup	172	227.04	15.239	40.781	14.964	0.929	0.081	0.397	0.239
16353	Beans, broadbeans (Fava) mature seed, boiled w/salt	1 cup	170	187	12.92	33.405	9.18	0.68	0.134	0.279	0.112
43112	Beans, chili, barbeque, ranch style, cooked	1 cup	186	180.42	9.3	31.527	7.812	1.86	0.143	1.032	0.27

Chol (g)	Calc (mg)	Iron (mg)	Mag (mg)	Phos (mg)	Pota (mg)	Sodi (mg)	Zinc (mg)	Vit A (RAE)	Vit C (mg)	Thia (mg)	Ribo (mg)	Niac (mg)	Vit B6 (mg)	Vit B12 (µg)	Vit E (mg)	Fol (µg)	Alc (g)
0	1.44	0.02	0.06	0	0.48	2325.48	0.006	0	0	0	0	0	0	0	0	0	0
12.16	0	0	0	0	0	19.2	0.014	0	0	0	0	0	0	0	0.077	0	0
174.25	0	0	0	0	0	0	0	0	0	0	0	0	0	0	5.535	0	0
0	3.278	0.009	0.298	3.576	0		0.009	0		0	0	0	0	0	0	0	0
0	12.2	0.366	8.54	15.86	174.46	4.88	0.134	178.1	3.782	0.026	0.029	0.459	0.067	0	1.086	2.44	0
28.56	3.92	0.521	4.76	39.76	107.8	397.6	0.904	0	0	0.168	0.08	1.363	0.14	0.532	0.078	0.56	0
0	187.86	1.339	176.7	403.62	269.7	3292.2	3.478	0	3.534	1.116	0.13	2.976	0.149	2.232	12.834	236.2	0
0	1.15	0.121	0.95	3.5	8.5	73.25	0.021	0.2	0	0.22	0.024	0.378	0.024	0	0.345	2.1	0
0	16.91	3.382	24.92	89	131.72	286.58	1.006	18.69	0.623	0.342	0.247	2.741	0.055	0	0.276	98.79	0
31.44	17.03	5.214	32.75	110.04	89.08	661.55	1.009	43.23	0.786	0.702	0.308	4.51	0.114	0.21		115.3	0
0	57.12	1.836			158.1	427.38			0	0.265	0.204	4.08	0.061	0		75.48	
0	10.68	2.741	27.59	97.9	102.35	451.23	0.801	0.89	0.178	0.295	0.301	2.634	0.038	0	0.294	87.22	0
0	65.86	3.168	25.81	85.44	89.89	475.26	0.783	0	0	0.479	0.28	4.06	0.045	0	0.258	94.34	0
0	14.9	0.086	9.536	30.992	88.208	0.298	0.417	1.49	0.924	0.045	0.018	0.128	0.039	0	0.158	7.152	0
0	4.818	0.354	13.603	26.073	95.506	0.567	0.105	0	0	0.043	0.028	0.176	0.028	0	0.068	17	0
0	173.04	5.351	360.36	414.96	2112.6	10.92	3.293	5.04	0	0.488	0.974	3.629	0.387	0	1.638	289.8	0
0	297.68	16.714	373.32	855.22	3037.8	3.66	6.173	2.44	0	0.843	0.306	3.156	0.694	0		369.67	0
0	181.5	7.535	115.5	420.75	451	10029.23	9.13	11	0	0.267	0.688	2.365	0.591	0	0.027	90.75	0
0	379.75	15.05	201.25	304.5	1275.75	12.25	5.302	0	22.75	0.28	0.332	0	0.227	0	0.018	14	0
0	184.26	4.482	134.46	441.56	683.92	14.94	1.892	0	0	0.129	0.594	4.382	0.357	0.133		39.84	0
0	3.06	0.364	6.12	19.8	32.4	599.94	0.067	0	0	0.009	0.023	0.605	0.031	0	0	2.88	0
0	1.2	0.143	2.4	7.8	12.72	335.16	0.026	0	0	0.004	0.009	0.237	0.012	0	0	1.08	0
0	52.78	4.368	96.46	231.14	729.82	434.98	1.875	0	0	0.293	0.1	1.201	0.142	0		273	0
15.54	124.32	4.481	72.52	269.36	608.65	1113.7	4.843	10.36	5.957	0.15	0.145	2.334	0.119	0	1.191	77.7	0
0	127	0.737	81.28	264.16	751.84	1008.38	3.556	12.7	7.874	0.389	0.152	1.087	0.34	0	1.346	60.96	0
0	46.44	3.612	120.4	240.8	610.6	1.72	1.926	0	0	0.42	0.101	0.869	0.119	0		256.3	0
0	61.2	2.55	73.1	212.5	455.6	409.7	1.717	1.7	0.51	0.165	0.151	1.209	0.122	0	0.034	176.8	0
0	57.66	3.46	83.7	286.44	837	1348.5	3.72	1.86	3.162	0.074	0.279	0.67	0.502	0.019	0.391	48.36	0

EvaluEat Code	Food Name	Amt	Wt (g)	Energy (kcal)	Prot (g)	Carb (g)	Fiber (g)	Fat (g)	Mono (g)	Poly (g)	Sat (g)
16137	Beans, hummus, garbanzo or chickpea spread, homemade	1 tbsp	15	26.55	0.729	3.018	0.6	1.289	0.737	0.312	0.168
16029	Beans, kidney, mature seeds, canned	1 cup	256	207.36	13.312	38.093	8.96	0.794	0.061	0.44	0.115
16033	Beans, kidney, red, mature seeds, boiled w/o salt	1 cup	177	224.79	15.346	40.356	13.098	0.885	0.069	0.487	0.127
16072	Beans, large lima, mature seeds, boiled w/o salt	1 cup	188	216.2	14.664	39.254	13.16	0.714	0.064	0.321	0.167
16073	Beans, large lima, mature seeds, canned	1 cup	241	190.39	11.881	35.933	11.568	0.41	0.036	0.178	0.094
16070	Beans, lentils, mature seeds, boiled w/o salt	1 cup	198	229.68	17.86	39.857	15.642	0.752	0.127	0.347	0.105
16081	Beans, mung, mature seeds, boiled w/o salt	1 cup	202	212.1	14.18	38.683	15.352	0.768	0.109	0.259	0.234
16080	Beans, mung, mature seeds, raw	1 tbsp	13	45.11	3.102	8.141	2.119	0.149	0.021	0.05	0.045
16038	Beans, navy, mature seeds, boiled w/o salt	1 cup	182	258.44	15.834	47.884	11.648	1.037	0.091	0.448	0.269
16039	Beans, navy, mature seeds, canned	1 cup	262	296.06	19.729	53.579	13.362	1.127	0.1	0.487	0.293
16044	Beans, pinto, mature seeds, canned	1 cup	240	206.4	11.664	36.6	11.04	1.944	0.389	0.694	0.401
16109	Beans, soy, mature seeds, boiled w/o salt	1 cup	172	297.56	28.621	17.08	10.32	15.428	3.407	8.71	2.231
16108	Beans, soy, mature seeds, raw	1 cup	186	773.76	67.871	56.098	17.298	37.088	8.191	20.934	5.364
16110	Beans, soy, mature seeds, roasted w/salt	1 cup	172	810.12	60.578	57.706	30.444	43.688	9.649	24.663	6.319
16162	Beans, soy, tofu, Mori-Nu, silken, firm	1 slice	84	52.08	5.796	2.016	0.084	2.268	0.453	1.247	0.341
16164	Beans, soy, tofu, Mori-Nu, silken, lite firm	1 slice	84	31.08	5.292	0.924	0	0.672	0.114	0.377	0.112
16161	Beans, soy, tofu, Mori-Nu, silken, soft	1 slice	84	46.2	4.032	2.436	0.084	2.268	0.438	1.302	0.3
16129	Beans, soy, tofu, nigari, fried	1 oz	28.35	76.829	4.873	2.974	1.106	5.721	1.263	3.229	0.827
16050	Beans, white, mature seeds, boiled w/o salt	1 cup	179	248.81	17.417	44.911	11.277	0.626	0.055	0.272	0.163
16051	Beans, white, mature seeds, canned	1 cup	262	306.54	19.021	57.483	12.576	0.76	0.065	0.322	0.194
16048	Beans, yellow, mature seeds, boiled w/o salt	1 cup	177	254.88	16.213	44.728	18.408	1.912	0.166	0.825	0.494
51696	Beef & onion patty, flame broiled, Lean Magic product #9676	1 piece	74	138.38	17.094	1.939	1.036	6.727	2.857	0.276	2.633
51738	Beef & turkey, flame broiled patty w/teriyaki sauce, Lean Magic 30 product #9128	1 piece	20	28.2	3.892	1.672	0.26	0.72	0.306	0.099	0.248
51737	Beef & turkey, flame broiled rib-B-Q w/BBQ sauce, Rib-B-Q lean magic 30	1 piece	85	115.6	14.348	8.024	1.36	3.094	1.301	0.42	1.008
13168	Beef bottom round, all grades, lean (1/4" trim) braised	3 oz	85	177.65	26.852	0	0	6.97	3.052	0.264	2.355
13160	Beef bottom round, all grades, lean & fat (1/4" trim) braised	3 oz	85	233.75	24.361	0	0	14.365	6.247	0.544	5.415
13319	Beef brain, pan fried	3 oz	85	166.6	10.684	0	0	13.456	3.383	1.964	3.179
13022	Beef brisket, whole, all grades, lean & fat (1/4" trim) braised	3 oz	85	327.25	19.975	0	0	26.826	11.815	0.961	10.523
13345	Beef cured breakfast strip, cooked	3 slices	34	152.66	10.642	0.476	0	11.696	5.729	0.537	4.879
13322	Beef heart, simmered	3 oz	85	133.45	24.208	0.128	0	4.021	0.859	0.837	1.193
13324	Beef kidney, simmered	3 oz	85	128.35	23.18	0	0	3.953	0.604	0.703	0.906
13327	Beef liver, pan fried	1 slice (yield from 112 g raw liver)	81	141.75	21.481	4.18	0	3.791	0.529	0.471	1.209
22529	Beef pot pie, frozen	1 package	198	449.46	13.266	44.154	2.178	24.354	9.682	2.673	8.514
7956	Beef sausage, fresh, cooked	1 hot dog	52	172.64	9.469	0.182	0	14.55	6.572	0.345	5.671
7954	Beef sausage, pre-cooked	1 hot dog	52	210.6	8.06	0.016	0	19.536	8.521	0.457	7.851
13458	Beef short loin, porterhouse steak, all grades, lean & fat (1/4" trim) broiled	3 oz	85	279.65	19.134	0	0	21.964	9.822	0.849	8.642
13472	Beef short loin, T-bone steak, all grades, lean & fat (1/4" trim) broiled	3 oz	85	260.1	19.949	0	0	19.363	8.63	0.701	7.582
13270	Beef short loin, top loin, all grades, lean (1/4" trim) broiled	3 oz	85	175.95	24.327	0	0	7.99	3.213	0.264	3.052

Chol (g)	Calc (mg)	Iron (mg)	Mag (mg)	Phos (mg)	Pota (mg)	Sodi (mg)	Zinc (mg)	Vit A (RAE)	Vit C (mg)	Thia (mg)	Ribo (mg)	Niac (mg)	Vit B$_6$ (mg)	Vit B$_{12}$ (µg)	Vit E (mg)	Fol (µg)	Alc (g)
0	7.35	0.236	4.35	16.5	25.95	36.3	0.164	0	1.185	0.013	0.008	0.06	0.06	0	0.113	8.85	0
0	69.12	3.149	79.36	268.8	657.92	888.32	1.408	0	3.072	0.279	0.184	1.285	0.177	0		125.4	0
0	49.56	5.204	79.65	251.34	713.31	3.54	1.894	0	2.124	0.283	0.103	1.023	0.212	0	1.54	230.1	0
0	31.96	4.493	80.84	208.68	955.04	3.76	1.786	0	0	0.303	0.103	0.791	0.303	0	0.338	156	0
0	50.61	4.362	93.99	178.34	530.2	809.76	1.566	0	0	0.133	0.082	0.629	0.219	0		120.5	0
0	37.62	6.593	71.28	356.4	730.62	3.96	2.515	0	2.97	0.335	0.145	2.099	0.352	0	0.218	358.4	0
0	54.54	2.828	96.96	199.98	537.32	4.04	1.697	2.02	2.02	0.331	0.123	1.166	0.135	0	0.303	321.2	0
0	17.16	0.876	24.57	47.71	161.98	1.95	0.348	0.78	0.624	0.081	0.03	0.293	0.05	0	0.066	81.25	0
0	127.4	4.514	107.38	285.74	669.76	1.82	1.929	0	1.638	0.368	0.111	0.966	0.298	0		254.8	0
0	123.14	4.847	123.14	351.08	754.56	1173.76	2.017	0	1.834	0.369	0.144	1.276	0.27	0	2.044	162.4	0
0	103.2	3.504	64.8	220.8	583.2	705.6	1.656	0	2.16	0.242	0.151	0.701	0.178	0	1.416	144	0
0	175.44	8.841	147.92	421.4	885.8	1.72	1.978	0	2.924	0.267	0.49	0.686	0.402	0	0.602	92.88	0
0	515.22	29.202	520.8	1309.44	3342.42	3.72	9.095	0	11.16	1.626	1.618	3.019	0.701	0	1.581	697.5	0
0	237.36	6.708	249.4	624.36	2528.4	280.36	5.401	17.2	3.784	0.172	0.249	2.425	0.358	0	1.565	362.9	0
0	26.88	0.865	22.68	75.6	162.96	30.24	0.512	0	0	0.085	0.034	0.207	0.009	0	0.16		0
0	30.24	0.63	8.4	68.04	52.92	71.4	0.277	0	0	0.034	0.017	0.092	0	0	0.05		0
0	26.04	0.689	24.36	52.08	151.2	4.2	0.437	0	0	0.084	0.034	0.252	0.009	0	0.168		0
0	105.462	1.381	17.01	81.365	41.391	4.536	0.564	0.284	0	0.048	0.014	0.028	0.028	0	0.011	7.655	0
0	161.1	6.623	112.77	202.27	1004.19	10.74	2.47	0	0	0.211	0.082	0.251	0.166	0	1.736	145	0
0	191.26	7.834	133.62	238.42	1189.48	13.1	2.934	0	0	0.252	0.097	0.296	0.197	0		170.3	0
0	109.74	4.39	130.98	323.91	575.25	8.85	1.876	0	3.186	0.331	0.182	1.253	0.228	0		143.4	0
42.18	23.68	2.153	28.86	240.5	283.42	313.02	5.025		0.518	0.139	0.152	2.917	0.278	1.643	0.068	5.18	0
8.2	6.2	0.43	6.6	45.8	59.2	127.4	0.878		0	0.034	0.023	0.561	0.058	0.264	0.005	0.4	0
28.9	33.15	1.87	26.35	202.3	244.8	560.15	3.179		1.275	0.144	0.086	2.356	0.264	1.403	0.046	1.7	0
81.6	4.25	2.941	21.25	231.2	261.8	43.35	4.658	0	0	0.06	0.221	3.468	0.306	2.1	0.119	9.35	0
81.6	5.1	2.652	18.7	208.25	239.7	42.5	4.174	0	0	0.06	0.204	3.171	0.281	1.997	0.162	8.5	0
1695.75	7.65	1.887	12.75	328.1	300.9	134.3	1.148	0	2.805	0.111	0.221	3.213	0.331	12.92		5.1	0
79.9	6.8	1.904	15.3	158.95	196.35	51.85	4.335	0	0	0.051	0.153	2.55	0.204	1.938	0.204	5.1	0
40.46	3.06	1.068	9.18	80.24	140.08	766.02	2.166	0	0	0.031	0.088	2.2	0.105	1.173	0.099	2.72	0
180.2	4.25	5.423	17.85	215.9	186.15	50.15	2.439	0	0	0.086	1.029	5.678	0.208	9.18	0.247	4.25	0
608.6	16.15	4.93	10.2	258.4	114.75	79.9	2.414	0	0	0.136	2.525	3.332	0.332	21.165	0.068	70.55	0
308.61	4.86	4.998	17.82	392.85	284.31	62.37	4.236	6273	0.567	0.143	2.774	14.155	0.832	67.335	0.373	210.6	0
37.62						736.56											
42.64	5.72	0.816	7.28	73.32	134.16	339.04	2.278	6.76	0	0.025	0.078	1.872	0.163	1.045	0.125	1.56	0
43.16	7.8	0.796	6.76	96.2	121.68	473.2	1.518	13	0.364	0.015	0.061	1.669	0.1	1.056	0.255	2.6	0
61.2	6.8	2.278	17	150.45	216.75	52.7	3.511	0	0	0.077	0.178	3.272	0.284	1.793	0.187	5.95	0
55.25	5.95	2.626	18.7	157.25	239.7	56.95	3.655	0	0	0.079	0.183	3.367	0.286	1.811	0.178	5.95	0
64.6	6.8	2.1	22.95	185.3	336.6	57.8	4.437	0	0	0.077	0.17	4.539	0.357	1.7	0.119	6.8	0

EvaluEat Code	Food Name	Amt	Wt (g)	Energy (kcal)	Prot (g)	Carb (g)	Fiber (g)	Fat (g)	Mono (g)	Poly (g)	Sat (g)
13262	Beef short loin, top loin, all grades, lean & fat (1/4" trim) broiled	3 oz	85	243.95	21.726	0	0	16.796	7.064	0.604	6.647
13340	Beef tongue, simmered	3 oz	85	236.3	16.397	0	0	18.955	8.587	0.557	6.906
13341	Beef tripe, raw	1 oz	28.35	23.247	3.422	0	0	1.046	0.435	0.051	0.366
13012	Beef, all cuts, all grades, lean (1/4" trim) cooked	3 oz	85	183.6	25.143	0	0	8.424	3.545	0.289	3.222
13004	Beef, all cuts, all grades, lean & fat (1/4" trim) cooked	3 oz	85	259.25	22.049	0	0	18.309	7.837	0.663	7.259
43384	Beef, bologna, reduced sodium	1 fl. oz.	29.8	93.274	3.487	0.596	0	8.463	3.963	0.313	3.479
13870	Beef, bottom round, all grades, lean & fat (1/8" trim) roasted	1 piece, cooked, (yield from 1 lb raw meat)	338	736.84	89.266	0	0	39.343	16.778	1.518	14.933
13953	Beef, bottom sirloin, tri-tip roast, separable lean and fat, 0" trim, all grades, cooked, roasted	3 oz (1 serving)	85	176.8	22.142	0	0	9.41	4.659	0.309	3.46
13055	Beef, brisket, flat half, separable lean and fat, 1/8" trim, select, cooked, braised	3 oz	85	238	24.625	0	0	14.765	6.359	0.546	5.855
13034	Beef, chuck, arm pot roast, all grades, lean & fat (1/4" trim) braised	3 oz	85	282.2	23.316	0	0	20.239	8.679	0.774	7.973
13050	Beef, chuck, blade roast, all grades, lean & fat (1/4" trim) braised	3 oz	85	293.25	22.585	0	0	21.837	9.435	0.782	8.695
23553	Beef, chuck, clod roast, separable lean and fat, trimmed to 1/4" fat, all grades, cooked, roasted	3 oz (1 serving)	85	205.7	20.587	0	0	13.107	5.952	0.521	4.877
23555	Beef, chuck, clod steak, separable lean and fat, trimmed to 1/4" fat, all grades, cooked, braised	3 oz (1 serving)	85	231.2	22.262	0	0	15.071	6.809	0.599	5.694
23547	Beef, chuck, tender steak, separable lean and fat, trimmed to 0" fat, all grades, cooked, broiled	3 oz (1 serving)	85	136	21.99	0	0	4.692	2.256	0.329	1.59
23523	Beef, chuck, top blade, separable lean and fat, trimmed to 0" fat, USDA Choice, cooked, broiled	3 oz (1 serving)	85	192.95	21.905	0	0	10.991	5.329	0.39	3.538
22698	Beef, corned beef hash, canned entree/Hormel	1 cup	236	387.04	20.603	21.877	2.596	24.166	12.414	0.708	10.195
22908	Beef, corned beef hash, canned, with potato	100 grams	100	164	8.73	9.27	1.1	10.24	5.26	0.3	4.32
51658	Beef, country fried finger/Pierre product #3813	1 piece	26	82.16	4.334	4.009	0.364	5.486	1.704	1.897	1.372
51613	Beef, country fried nugget/Pierre product #1935	1 piece	14.2	48.706	2.424	2.256	0.185	3.385	1.113	1.078	0.9
51605	Beef, country fried patty/Pierre product #1840	1 piece	108	356.4	17.55	16.459	1.512	24.786	7.951	7.957	6.515
51602	Beef, country fried steak/Pierre product #1610	1 piece	108	356.4	16.859	14.083	0.432	25.607	9.168	6.324	7.897
13358	Beef, cured, smoked, chopped	1 slice (1 oz)	28	37.24	5.653	0.521	0	1.238	0.512	0.064	0.507
13360	Beef, cured, thin sliced	10 slices	28	42.84	8.708	0.773	0	0.543	0.235	0.02	0.266
13350	Beef, dried, cured	10 slices	28	42.84	8.708	0.773	0	0.543	0.235	0.02	0.267
13176	Beef, eye of round, all grades, lean & fat (1/4" trim) roasted	3 oz	85	194.65	22.772	0	0	10.838	4.658	0.391	4.233
13682	Beef, eye of round, Prime, lean & fat (1/2" trim) roasted	3 oz	85	212.5	22.958	0	0	12.708	5.67	0.459	5.117
13096	Beef, eye/small end ribs (10–12 ribs), Choice, lean & fat (1/4" trim) broiled	1 steak	236	625.4	62.729	0	0	39.554	16.197	1.468	15.354
51718	Beef, flame broiled fajita/Lean Magic Wonderbites Dipper product #9974	1 piece	18	32.58	3.897	1.089	0.27	1.483	0.626	0.062	0.576
51663	Beef, flame broiled meatloaf/Lean Magic product #3825	1 piece	74	148	16.643	4.151	0.814	7.2	3.092	0.362	2.793
51677	Beef, flame broiled patty/Pierre product #3871	1 piece	69	158.01	16.187	1.546	1.035	9.536	4.082	0.386	3.782

Chol (g)	Calc (mg)	Iron (mg)	Mag (mg)	Phos (mg)	Pota (mg)	Sodi (mg)	Zinc (mg)	Vit A (RAE)	Vit C (mg)	Thia (mg)	Ribo (mg)	Niac (mg)	Vit B6 (mg)	Vit B12 (µg)	Vit E (mg)	Fol (µg)	Alc (g)
67.15	7.65	1.896	19.55	164.9	296.65	53.55	3.885	0	0	0.068	0.153	3.995	0.315	1.649	0.017	5.95	0
112.2	4.25	2.218	12.75	123.25	156.4	55.25	34.77	0	1.105	0.019	0.25	2.967	0.132	2.661	0.255	5.95	0
34.587	19.562	0.167	3.686	18.144	18.995	27.5	0.403	0	0	0	0.018	0.25	0.004	0.394	0.026	1.418	0
73.1	7.65	2.542	22.1	198.05	306	56.95	5.891	0	0	0.085	0.204	3.511	0.315	2.244	0.119	6.8	0
74.8	8.5	2.227	18.7	172.55	266.05	52.7	4.972	0	0	0.068	0.178	3.094	0.281	2.074	0.17	5.95	0
16.688	3.576	0.417	2.98	24.436	46.19	203.236	0.596	0	0	0.018	0.039	0.784	0.054	0.42	0.057	1.49	0
253.5	20.28	7.301	57.46	554.32	723.32	118.3	14.97	0	0	0.206	0.477	15.602	1.173	4.969	1.386	27.04	0
71.4	16.15	1.411	18.7	170.85	274.55	45.05	3.97	0	0	0.06	0.107	5.893	0.463	1.301	0.34	6.8	0
60.35	14.45	2.04	16.15	153	201.45	41.65	5.882	0	0	0.054	0.134	3.549	0.242	1.632	0.425	7.65	0
84.15	8.5	2.644	16.15	187	209.1	51	5.814	0	0	0.06	0.204	2.703	0.238	2.508	0.187	7.65	0
88.4	11.05	2.635	16.15	170	196.35	54.4	7.072	0	0	0.06	0.204	2.057	0.221	1.938	0.17	4.25	0
63.75	6.8	2.388	17	166.6	286.45	56.95	4.854	0	0	0.069	0.192	2.726	0.217	2.405	0.119	7.65	0
79.9	7.65	2.831	16.15	175.95	220.15	48.45	5.772	0	0	0.057	0.192	2.428	0.205	2.329	0.094	6.8	0
53.55	6.8	2.491	19.55	192.95	249.05	60.35	6.647	0	0	0.094	0.196	3.087	0.273	2.882	0.136	6.8	0
49.3	5.95	2.355	20.4	182.75	255	57.8	7.446	0	0	0.094	0.195	3.076	0.272	2.873	0.153	6.8	0
75.52	44.84	2.36	30.68		405.92	1003	3.304	2.124									0
32	19	1	13	56	172	425	1.4	0	0.9	0.069	0.05	1.572	0.231	0.41	0.04	7	0
9.88	8.32	0.783	7.02	60.06	71.76	125.58	1.191		0	0.08	0.064	1.083	0.066	0.387	0.548	9.36	0
5.254	5.538	0.454	3.834	34.932	39.192	71.284	0.626		0	0.044	0.039	0.563	0.036	0.25	0.298	6.106	0
42.12	34.56	3.208	29.16	246.24	293.76	519.48	4.828		0	0.329	0.261	4.441	0.27	1.588	2.272	38.88	0
51.84	15.12	2.657	12.96	177.12	217.08	376.92	3.402		0	0.211	0.233	3.776	0.159	1.512	1.859	37.8	0
12.88	2.24	0.798	5.88	50.68	105.56	352.24	1.1	0	0	0.023	0.049	1.282	0.098	0.484		2.24	0
22.12	1.68	0.781	5.6	61.04	69.16	781.2	1.229	0	0	0.016	0.059	0.914	0.081	0.554	0.031	2.52	0
22.12	1.4	0.812	6.16	54.88	81.48	781.2	1.112	0	0	0.017	0.062	0.927	0.069	0.661	0	2.24	0
61.2	5.1	1.564	20.4	176.8	307.7	50.15	3.689	0	0	0.068	0.136	2.967	0.298	1.785	0.153	5.95	0
61.2	5.1	1.573	21.25	178.5	311.1	50.15	3.723	0	0	0.068	0.138	2.986	0.298	1.793		5.95	0
297.36	42.48	4.248	51.92	474.36	769.36	125.08	11.3	0	0	0.156	0.276	17.013	1.251	4.13	1.109	18.88	0
9.36	6.3	0.531	7.2	57.24	67.68	85.86	1.195		0.054	0.035	0.036	0.689	0.065	0.38	0.012	0.9	0
41.44	25.9	2.079	23.68	142.08	244.94	399.6	4.359		2.072	0.109	0.155	2.53	0.242	1.643	0.073	7.4	0
41.4	24.15	2.105	29.67	228.39	276	291.18	4.975		0	0.149	0.146	2.904	0.275	1.615	0.042	3.45	0

EvaluEat Code	Food Name	Amt	Wt (g)	Energy (kcal)	Prot (g)	Carb (g)	Fiber (g)	Fat (g)	Mono (g)	Poly (g)	Sat (g)
51683	Beef, flame broiled steak/Pierre product #9010	1 piece	74	248.64	17.856	0.326	0	18.944	8.161	0.712	7.586
13067	Beef, flank, choice, lean & fat (0" trim) broiled	1 steak	387	781.74	106.62	0	0	36.03	14.516	1.409	14.861
23580	Beef, ground, 75% lean meat/25% fat, crumbles, cooked, pan-browned	3 oz	85	235.45	22.338	0	0	15.478	7.131	0.386	6.027
23575	Beef, ground, 80% lean meat/20% fat, crumbles, cooked, pan-browned	3 oz	85	231.2	22.95	0	0	14.756	6.542	0.428	5.586
23570	Beef, ground, 85% lean meat/15% fat, crumbles, cooked, pan-browned	3 oz	85	217.6	23.57	0	0	13.005	5.605	0.406	4.925
23565	Beef, ground, 90% lean meat/10% fat, crumbles, cooked, pan-browned	3 oz	85	195.5	24.183	0	0	10.234	4.316	0.315	4.053
23560	Beef, ground, 95% lean meat/5% fat, crumbles, cooked, pan-browned	3 oz	85	164.05	24.795	0	0	6.443	2.825	0.328	3.022
13299	Beef, ground, extra lean, broiled, well done	3 oz	85	225.25	24.293	0	0	13.43	5.882	0.502	5.279
13306	Beef, ground, lean, broiled, well done	3 oz	85	238	23.97	0	0	14.994	6.562	0.561	5.891
13313	Beef, ground, regular, broiled, well done	3 oz	85	248.2	23.12	0	0	16.541	7.242	0.621	6.503
13113	Beef, large end ribs (6–9 ribs) all grades, lean (1/4" trim) roasted	yield from 1 lb raw meat	210	497.7	57.813	0	0	27.72	11.592	0.798	11.067
13101	Beef, large end ribs (6–9 ribs) all grades, lean & fat (1/4" trim) roasted	yield from 1 lb raw meat	293	1069.5	66.335	0	0	87.226	37.358	3.047	35.189
23545	Beef, loin, bottom sirloin butt, tri-tip steak, separable lean and fat (0" trim) all grades	3 oz	85	225.25	25.475	0	0	12.903	6.599	0.457	4.851
23540	Beef, plate, inside skirt steak, separable lean and fat, trimmed to 0" fat, all grades, broiled	3 oz	85	187	22.211	0	0	10.243	5.147	0.371	3.966
13979	Beef, plate, outside skirt steak, separable lean only, trimmed to 0" fat, all grades, broiled	3 oz	85	198.05	20.553	0	0	12.215	6.273	0.51	5.075
13952	Beef, rib eye, small end (ribs 10–12), separable lean and fat, 0" trim, all grades, cooked, broiled	3 oz	85	209.95	23.18	0	0	12.529	5.129	0.465	4.862
23626	Beef, rib, small end ribs (ribs 10–12), separable lean only, 1/8" trim, Choice, cooked, broiled	3 oz	85	171.7	24.047	0	0	7.693	3.07	0.275	2.928
22721	Beef, roast beef hash, canned entree/Hormel	3 oz	236	384.68	21.311	22.916	3.54	23.647	11.281	0.637	9.912
23592	Beef, round, top round, separable lean only, 1/8" trim, select, cooked, broiled	3 oz	85	150.45	26.869	0	0	3.953	1.652	0.16	1.362
23002	Beef, short loin, porterhouse steak, all grades, lean & fat (1/8" trim) broiled	3 oz	85	252.45	19.984	0	0	18.556	8.152	0.697	7.157
23006	Beef, short loin, T-bone steak, all grades, lean & fat (1/8" trim) broiled	3 oz	85	238	20.681	0	0	16.549	7.259	0.595	6.426
23630	Beef, short loin, top loin, separable lean only, 1/8" trim, Choice, cooked, broiled	3 oz	85	170.85	24.786	0	0	7.182	2.867	0.257	2.734
13148	Beef, short ribs, Choice, lean & fat, braised	3 oz	85	400.35	18.334	0	0	35.683	16.048	1.301	15.13
13124	Beef, small end ribs (10–12 ribs) all grades, lean & fat (1/4" trim) broiled	3 oz	85	285.6	20.137	0	0	22.083	9.486	0.765	8.942
13238	Beef, tenderloin, all grades, lean & fat (1/4" trim) broiled	3 oz	85	247.35	21.471	0	0	17.221	7.064	0.655	6.758
13192	Beef, tip round, all grades, lean & fat (1/4" trim) roasted	3 oz	85	198.9	22.874	0	0	11.254	4.684	0.433	4.267
13427	Beef, top round, all grades, lean & fat (1/4" trim) braised	3 oz	85	210.8	28.756	0	0	9.716	4.012	0.4	3.672
13278	Beef, top sirloin, all grades, lean & fat (1/4" trim) broiled	3 oz	85	219.3	23.639	0	0	13.099	5.636	0.502	5.219

Chol (g)	Calc (mg)	Iron (mg)	Mag (mg)	Phos (mg)	Pota (mg)	Sodi (mg)	Zinc (mg)	Vit A (RAE)	Vit C (mg)	Thia (mg)	Ribo (mg)	Niac (mg)	Vit B6 (mg)	Vit B12 (µg)	Vit E (mg)	Fol (µg)	Alc (g)
64.38	7.4	1.791	14.8	229.4	208.68	284.9	3.826		0	0.053	0.144	2.398	0.211	1.717	0.057	4.44	0
197.37	69.66	6.966	85.14	777.87	1261.62	205.11	18.54	0	0	0.267	0.468	28.913	2.125	7.043	1.509	34.83	0
75.65	28.9	2.236	18.7	181.9	300.9	79.05	5.245	0	0	0.039	0.159	4.543	0.365	2.499	0.408	10.2	0
75.65	23.8	2.363	19.55	192.1	323	77.35	5.44	0	0	0.038	0.161	4.956	0.364	2.431	0.408	9.35	0
76.5	18.7	2.491	21.25	202.3	345.95	75.65	5.627	0	0	0.037	0.162	5.37	0.364	2.372	0.4	8.5	0
75.65	13.6	2.618	22.95	212.5	368.05	73.95	5.814	0	0	0.037	0.164	5.783	0.364	2.304	0.374	6.8	0
75.65	7.65	2.746	23.8	223.55	390.15	72.25	6.001	0	0	0.036	0.166	6.197	0.364	2.244	0.34	5.95	0
84.15	7.65	2.355	21.25	161.5	313.65	69.7	5.465		0	0.06	0.272	4.972	0.272	2.176	0.153	9.35	0
85.85	10.2	2.082	20.4	154.7	296.65	75.65	5.27		0	0.051	0.204	5.075	0.255	2.312	0.173	9.35	0
85.85	10.2	2.329	18.7	162.35	277.95	79.05	4.938		0	0.034	0.178	5.499	0.255	2.788	0.196	8.5	0
170.1	16.8	5.922	52.5	438.9	749.7	153.3	15.67	0	0	0.189	0.462	9.345	0.546	5.481	0.294	18.9	0
249.05	29.3	6.768	55.67	498.1	843.84	187.52	16.7	0	0	0.205	0.527	10.577	0.674	6.798	0.674	20.51	0
57.8	10.2	3.094	22.1	225.25	371.45	61.2	5.993	0	0	0.109	0.243	3.591	0.377	2.405	0.145	8.5	0
51	9.35	2.355	20.4	195.5	245.65	63.75	6.146	0	0	0.077	0.162	3.183	0.273	3.162	0.085	5.95	0
49.3	8.5	2.261	21.25	187.85	334.05	79.9	4.862	0	0	0.101	0.166	3.681	0.421	3.655	0.094	6.8	0
94.35	17	1.488	19.55	180.2	289	47.6	4.19	0	0	0.063	0.111	6.168	0.485	1.36	0.382	6.8	0
72.25	13.6	1.632	20.4	186.15	299.2	49.3	4.514	0	0	0.064	0.123	7.095	0.501	1.505	0.357	7.65	0
73.16	42.48	2.36	33.04		431.88	792.96	3.304		1.888								0
51.85	5.95	2.261	18.7	175.95	229.5	36.55	4.735	0	0	0.065	0.145	4.621	0.354	1.377	0.289	9.35	0
60.35	6.8	2.329	19.55	158.95	272.85	54.4	3.893	0	0	0.085	0.187	3.46	0.298	1.828	0.17	5.95	0
52.7	6.8	2.405	20.4	164.05	285.6	56.1	3.978	0	0	0.085	0.187	3.519	0.298	1.845	0.162	5.95	0
67.15	13.6	1.675	21.25	192.1	307.7	51	4.649	0	0	0.065	0.127	7.313	0.516	1.547	0.349	8.5	0
79.9	10.2	1.964	12.75	137.7	190.4	42.5	4.148	0	0	0.043	0.128	2.084	0.187	2.227	0.247	4.25	0
71.4	11.05	1.862	18.7	148.75	276.25	52.7	4.752	0	0	0.077	0.153	3.391	0.281	2.457	0.187	5.95	0
73.1	6.8	2.678	22.1	178.5	312.8	50.15	4.148	0	0	0.094	0.221	2.992	0.331	2.049	0.162	5.1	0
69.7	5.1	2.338	21.25	191.25	305.15	53.55	5.525	0	0	0.077	0.213	2.992	0.315	2.346	0.145	5.95	0
76.5	4.25	2.652	20.4	180.2	267.75	38.25	3.638	0	0	0.06	0.204	3.069	0.23	2.21	0.145	7.65	0
76.5	9.35	2.601	24.65	188.7	311.1	53.55	4.972	0	0	0.094	0.23	3.341	0.349	2.287	0.153	7.65	0

EvaluEat Code	Food Name	Amt	Wt (g)	Energy (kcal)	Prot (g)	Carb (g)	Fiber (g)	Fat (g)	Mono (g)	Poly (g)	Sat (g)
13073	Beef, whole ribs (6–12 ribs) all grades, lean & fat (1/4" trim) roasted	3 oz	85	304.3	19.125	0	0	24.659	10.6	0.876	9.945
14169	Beverage mix, carob flavor, dry, prep w/milk	1 cup (8 fl. oz.)	256	192	8.09	22.221	1.024	7.962	1.989	0.484	4.554
14177	Beverage mix, chocolate flavor, dry mix, prep w/milk	1 cup (8 fl. oz.)	266	226.1	8.592	31.681	1.064	8.618	2.205	0.495	4.948
14318	Beverage mix, chocolate malted milk powder, no added nutrients, prep w/milk	1 cup (8 fl. oz.)	265	225.25	8.931	29.68	1.325	8.719	2.192	0.551	4.99
14312	Beverage mix, natural malt powder, no added nutrients, prep w/milk	1 cup (8 fl. oz.)	265	233.2	10.229	27.109	0.265	9.593	2.393	0.731	5.403
14351	Beverage mix, strawberry flavor, dry, prep w/milk	1 cup (8 fl. oz.)	266	234.08	7.98	32.718	0	8.246	2.357	0.303	5.081
14006	Beverage, alcoholic, beer, light	1 can or bottle (12 fl. oz.)	354	99.12	0.708	4.602	0	0	0	0	0
14003	Beverage, alcoholic, beer, regular	1 can	356	117.48	1.068	5.732	0.356	0.214	0	0	0
14534	Beverage, alcoholic, coffee liqueur 63 proof	1 jigger (1.5 fl. oz.)	52	160.16	0.052	16.744	0	0.156	0.011	0.055	0.055
14415	Beverage, alcoholic, coffee w/cream liqueur, 34 proof	1 jigger (1.5 fl. oz.)	47	153.69	1.316	9.823	0	7.379	2.095	0.314	4.542
14034	Beverage, alcoholic, creme de menthe, 72 proof	1 jigger (1.5 fl. oz.)	50	185.5	0	20.8	0	0.15	0.007	0.083	0.007
14010	Beverage, alcoholic, daiquiri, prep from recipe	1 cocktail (2 fl. oz.)	60	111.6	0.036	4.164	0.06	0.036	0.004	0.01	0.004
14049	Beverage, alcoholic, distilled spirits, gin 90 proof	1 jigger (1.5 fl. oz.)	42	110.46	0	0	0	0	0	0	0
14050	Beverage, alcoholic, distilled spirits, rum 80 proof	1 jigger (1.5 fl. oz.)	42	97.02	0	0	0	0	0	0	0
14051	Beverage, alcoholic, distilled spirits, vodka 80 proof	1 jigger (1.5 fl. oz.)	42	97.02	0	0	0	0	0	0	0
14052	Beverage, alcoholic, distilled spirits, whiskey 86 proof	1 jigger	42	105	0	0.042	0	0	0	0	0
14014	Beverage, alcoholic, martini, prepared from recipe	1 cocktail (2 fl. oz.)	60	145.8	0.024	1.224	0	0	0	0	0
14017	Beverage, alcoholic, pina colada, prep from recipe	1 cocktail (4.5 fl. oz.)	141	245.34	0.592	31.951	0.423	2.651	0.116	0.047	2.307
43479	Beverage, alcoholic, rice (sake)	1 oz	28.34	37.976	0.142	1.417	0	0	0	0	0
14084	Beverage, alcoholic, wine (all table)	1 glass (3.5 fl. oz.)	103	79.31	0.206	3.296	0	0	0	0	0
43154	Beverage, alcoholic, wine, cooking	1 cup	186	93	0.93	11.718	0	0	0	0	0
14536	Beverage, alcoholic, wine, dry dessert	1 glass (3.5 fl. oz.)	103	156.56	0.206	12.02	0	0	0	0	0
14096	Beverage, alcoholic, wine, red	1 glass (3.5 fl. oz.)	103	74.16	0.206	1.751	0	0	0	0	0
14104	Beverage, alcoholic, wine, rose	1 glass (3.5 fl. oz.)	103	73.13	0.206	1.442	0	0	0	0	0
14057	Beverage, alcoholic, wine, sweet dessert	1 glass (3.5 fl. oz.)	103	164.8	0.206	14.101	0	0	0	0	0
14106	Beverage, alcoholic, wine, white	1 glass (3.5 fl. oz.)	103	70.04	0.103	0.824	0	0	0	0	0
14182	Beverage, chocolate syrup w/o added nutrients, prep w/milk	1 cup (8 fl. oz.)	282	253.8	8.657	36.04	0.846	8.347	2.087	0.485	4.74
14390	Beverage, cocoa mix w/aspartame, dry, low kcal, prep w/H$_2$O	1 packet dry mix with 6 fl. oz. water	192	55.68	2.419	10.445	0.96	0.442	0.146	0.013	0
14194	Beverage, cocoa mix, dry, w/o added nutrients, prep w/H$_2$O	1 oz packet with 6 fl. oz. water	206	113.3	1.669	23.978	1.03	1.133	0.375	0.035	0.672
14195	Beverage, cocoa, hot cocoa mix w/marshmallows/Carnation	1 envelope	28	111.72	1.347	24.254	0.504	1.025	0.307	0.376	0.412
14418	Beverage, coffee mix w/sugar (cappuccino) dry, prep w/H$_2$O	6 fl. oz. H$_2$O & 2 rounded tsp mix	192	61.44	0.384	10.752	0	2.112	0.123	0.038	1.83
14419	Beverage, coffee mix w/sugar (French) dry, prep w/H$_2$O	6 fl. oz. H$_2$O & 2 rounded tsp mix	189	56.7	0.567	6.615	0	3.402	0.198	0.062	2.947
14420	Beverage, coffee mix w/sugar (mocha) dry, prep w/H$_2$O	6 fl. oz. & 2 round tsp mix	188	50.76	0.564	8.46	0.188	1.88	0.109	0.034	1.609
14232	Beverage, coffee mix, Kraft Intl Sugar-Free Fat-Free Low-Calorie French Vanilla	1 NLEA serving	7	25.41	0.217	5.32	0.343	0.343			0.056
14209	Beverage, coffee, brewed	1 cup (8 fl. oz.)	237	9.48	0.332	0	0	1.801	0	0	0

Chol (g)	Calc (mg)	Iron (mg)	Mag (mg)	Phos (mg)	Pota (mg)	Sodi (mg)	Zinc (mg)	Vit A (RAE)	Vit C (mg)	Thia (mg)	Ribo (mg)	Niac (mg)	Vit B$_6$ (mg)	Vit B$_{12}$ (µg)	Vit E (mg)	Fol (µg)	Alc (g)
71.4	9.35	1.989	17	148.75	255.85	53.55	4.548	0	0	0.06	0.145	2.899	0.196	2.159		5.95	0
25.6	250.88	0.64	25.6	204.8	335.36	117.76	0.947	69.12	0	0.108	0.445	0.353	0.102	1.075		12.8	0
23.94	252.7	0.798	47.88	234.08	457.52	154.28	1.277	69.16	0.266	0.114	0.479	0.378	0.09	1.064	0.16	13.3	0
26.5	259.7	0.557	39.75	241.15	455.8	159	1.087	68.9	0.265	0.143	0.488	0.686	0.122	1.113	0.159	23.85	0
31.8	310.05	0.239	45.05	280.9	484.95	209.35	1.14	87.45	0.53	0.215	0.641	1.375	0.175	1.219	0.329	21.2	0
31.92	292.6	0.213	31.92	228.76	369.74	127.68	0.931	69.16	2.394	0.093	0.42	0.221	0.104	0.878		13.3	0
0	17.7	0.142	17.7	42.48	63.72	10.62	0.106	0	0	0.032	0.106	1.388	0.12	0.035	0	14.16	11.328
0	17.8	0.071	21.36	46.28	89	14.24	0.036	0	0	0.021	0.093	1.613	0.178	0.071	0	21.36	12.816
0	0.52	0.031	1.56	3.12	15.6	4.16	0.016	0	0	0.002	0.006	0.075	0	0		0	13.52
27.26	7.52	0.061	0.94	23.5	15.04	43.24	0.075	81.31	0.094	0.005	0.027	0.037	0.005	0.038	0.211	0.94	6.486
0	0	0.035	0	0	0	2.5	0.02	0	0	0	0	0.002	0	0	0	0	14.9
0	1.8	0.054	1.2	3	12.6	3	0.024	0	0.96	0.008	0.003	0.031	0.005	0	0.018	1.2	13.86
0	0	0	0	0	0	0.84	0	0	0	0	0	0	0	0	0	0	15.918
0	0	0.05	0	2.1	0.84	0.42	0.029	0	0	0.003	0	0	0	0	0	0	14.028
0	0	0.004	0	2.1	0.42	0.42	0	0	0	0.002	0.003	0	0	0	0	0	14.028
0	0	0.008	0	1.26	0.42	0	0.008	0	0	0.003	0	0.021	0	0	0	0	15.12
0	0.6	0.024	1.2	1.2	9.6	1.8	0.006	0	0	0.002	0.002	0.022	0	0	0	0	20.34
0	11.28	0.296	11.28	9.87	100.11	8.46	0.183	0	6.909	0.041	0.024	0.166	0.063	0	0.028	16.92	13.959
0	1.417	0.028	1.7	1.7	7.085	0.567	0.006	0	0	0	0	0	0	0	0	0	4.563
0	8.24	0.36	9.27	13.39	86.52	6.18	0.062	0	0	0.004	0.016	0.076	0.025	0.01	0	1.03	9.579
0	16.74	0.744	18.6	27.9	163.68	1164.36	0.149	0	0	0	0.019	0.186	0.037	0	0	1.86	6.138
0	8.24	0.247	9.27	9.27	94.76	9.27	0.072	0	0	0.019	0.019	0.219	0	0	0	0	15.759
0	8.24	0.443	13.39	14.42	115.36	5.15	0.093	0	0	0.005	0.029	0.083	0.035	0.01		2.06	9.579
0	8.24	0.391	10.3	15.45	101.97	5.15	0.062	0	0	0.004	0.016	0.076	0.025	0.01		1.03	9.579
0	8.24	0.247	9.27	9.27	94.76	9.27	0.072	0	0	0.019	0.019	0.219	0	0	0	0	15.759
0	9.27	0.33	10.3	14.42	82.4	5.15	0.072	0	0	0.004	0.005	0.069	0.014	0	0	0	9.579
25.38	250.98	0.902	50.76	253.8	408.9	132.54	1.213	70.5	0	0.11	0.465	0.386	0.09	1.072	0.141	14.1	0
0	90.24	0.749	32.64	134.4	405.12	170.88	0.518	26.88	0.192	0.04	0.209	0.163	0.048	0.25	0.058	1.92	0
2.06	45.32	0.35	24.72	88.58	201.88	146.26	0.433	0	0.412	0.027	0.161	0.167	0.033	0.371	0.144	0	0
1.68	41.16	0.238	16.24	57.96	141.96	96.04	0.204	0	0	0.028	0.118	0.104	0.031	0.118	0.043	1.12	0
0	7.68	0.154	9.6	26.88	119.04	103.68	0.077		0	0.015	0.006	0.323	0	0		0	0
0	7.56	0.019	1.89	41.58	136.08	30.24	0.038		0	0	0.002	0.675	0	0		0	0
0	7.52	0.244	9.4	28.2	118.44	35.72	0.15		0	0.004	0.004	0.259	0	0		0	0
0	4.34	0.057		16.1	71.75	65.03			0								
0	2.37	0.024	4.74	7.11	113.76	2.37	0.024	0	0	0	0.118	0	0.002	0	0.047	4.74	0

EvaluEat Code	Food Name	Amt	Wt (g)	Energy (kcal)	Prot (g)	Carb (g)	Fiber (g)	Fat (g)	Mono (g)	Poly (g)	Sat (g)
14201	Beverage, coffee, brewed, prepared with tap water, decaffeinated	1 cup (8 fl. oz.)	237	9.48	0.332	0	0	1.801	0	0	0
14219	Beverage, coffee, instant powder, decaffeinated, prep	6 fl. oz.	179	3.58	0.215	0.77	0	0	0	0.002	0.002
14215	Beverage, coffee, instant	6 fl. oz.	179	3.58	0.179	0.609	0	0	0	0.004	0.004
14400	Beverage, cola w/caffeine	1 can (12 fl. oz.)	370	155.4	0.185	39.775	0	0	0	0	0
1057	Beverage, eggnog	1 cup	254	342.9	9.677	34.392	0	18.999	5.672	0.861	11.285
14119	Beverage, mixed vegetable and fruit juice drink	1 oz	28.34	32.024	0.071	7.935	0.17	0.014	0.001	0.006	0.002
14137	Beverage, Nestea Ice Tea, lemon flavor	1 cup (8 fl. oz.)	240	88.8	0	20.4	0	0.72			0.058
14121	Beverage, soft drink, club soda	1 can or bottle (16 fl. oz.)	474	0	0	0	0	0	0	0	0
14146	Beverage, soft drink, cola, low calorie, with aspartame, caffeine free	1 can or bottle (16 fl. oz.)	474	4.74	0.474	0.474	0	0	0	0	0
14416	Beverage, soft drink, cola, w/aspartame, low calorie	1 bottle 16 fl. oz.	474	4.74	0.474	0.474	0	0	0	0	0
14148	Beverage, soft drink, cola, with higher caffeine	1 can or bottle (16 fl. oz.)	492	206.64	0.246	52.89	0	0	0	0	0
14130	Beverage, soft drink, cream soda	1 can or bottle (16 fl. oz.)	494	251.94	0	65.702	0	0	0	0	0
14136	Beverage, soft drink, ginger ale	1 can or bottle (16 fl. oz.)	488	165.92	0	42.798	0	0	0	0	0
14142	Beverage, soft drink, grape	1 can or bottle (12 fl. oz.)	372	159.96	0	41.664	0	0	0	0	0
14145	Beverage, soft drink, lemon-lime	1 can or bottle (16 fl. oz.)	491	196.4	0	51.064	0	0	0	0	0
14150	Beverage, soft drink, orange	1 can or bottle (16 fl. oz.)	496	238.08	0	61.008	0	0	0	0	0
14153	Beverage, soft drink, pepper type	1 can or bottle (16 fl. oz.)	491	201.31	0	51.064	0	0.491	0	0	0.344
14157	Beverage, soft drink, root beer	1 can or bottle (16 fl. oz.)	493	202.13	0	52.258	0	0	0	0	0
14376	Beverage, tea mix, instant w/lemon flavor, w/saccharin, dry	1 cup (8 fl. oz.)	237	4.74	0.047	1.043	0	0	0	0.002	0
14369	Beverage, tea mix, Instant w/lemon, unsweetened, dry	1 cup (8 fl. oz.)	238	4.76	0	0.952	0	0	0	0.002	0
14355	Beverage, tea, brewed	1 cup (8 fl. oz.)	237	2.37	0	0.711	0	0	0.002	0.009	0.005
14352	Beverage, tea, brewed, prepared with tap water, decaffeinated	1 cup (8 fl. oz.)	237	2.37	0	0.711	0	0	0.002	0.009	0.005
14545	Beverage, tea, chamomile, brewed	1 cup (8 fl. oz.)	237	2.37	0	0.474	0	0	0.002	0.012	0.005
14381	Beverage, tea, herbal (not chamomile) brewed	1 cup (8 fl. oz.)	237	2.37	0	0.474	0	0	0.002	0.012	0.005
14429	Beverage, water	1 cup (8 fl. oz.)	237	0	0	0	0	0	0	0	0
14155	Beverage, water, carbonated, tonic (quinine)	1 fl. oz.	30.5	10.37	0	2.684	0	0	0	0	0
14553	Beverage, wine, non-alcoholic	1 fl. oz.	29	1.74	0.145	0.319	0	0	0	0	0
18629	Biscuit, buttermilk, refrigerated dough/Pillsbury	1 serving	64	154.24	4.992	30.4		1.408	0.605	0.312	0.285
18017	Biscuit, mixed grain, refrigerated dough	1 biscuit (2-1/2" dia)	44	115.72	2.684	20.856		2.464	1.29	0.387	0.601
18013	Biscuit, plain or buttermilk, refrigerated dough, baked, reduced fat	1 biscuit (2–1/4" dia)	21	62.79	1.638	11.634	0.399	1.092	0.587	0.164	0.272

Chol (g)	Calc (mg)	Iron (mg)	Mag (mg)	Phos (mg)	Pota (mg)	Sodi (mg)	Zinc (mg)	Vit A (RAE)	Vit C (mg)	Thia (mg)	Ribo (mg)	Niac (mg)	Vit B_6 (mg)	Vit B_{12} (µg)	Vit E (mg)	Fol (µg)	Alc (g)
0	2.37	0.024	4.74	7.11	113.76	2.37	0.024	0	0	0	0.118	0	0.002	0	0.047	4.74	0
0	5.37	0.107	8.95	7.16	82.34	3.58	0	0	0	0	0.025	0.505	0	0	0	0	0
0	7.16	0.072	5.37	5.37	53.7	3.58	0.018	0	0	0	0.002	0.422	0	0	0	0	0
0	11.1	0.074	3.7	48.1	3.7	14.8	0.037	0	0	0	0	0	0	0	0	0	0
149.86	330.2	0.508	48.26	276.86	419.1	137.16	1.168	114.3	3.81	0.086	0.483	0.267	0.127	1.143	0.508	2.54	0
0	2.834	0.065	1.417	1.984	51.012	5.668	0.026	29.47	7.085	0.003	0.004	0.044	0.01	0	0.045	1.134	0
						0											0
0	23.7	0.047	4.74	0	9.48	99.54	0.474	0	0	0	0	0	0	0	0	0	0
0	18.96	0.142	4.74	42.66	0	28.44	0.379	0	0	0.024	0.109	0	0	0	0	0	0
0	14.22	0.142	4.74	52.14	28.44	23.7	0	0	0	0.024	0.109	0	0	0	0	0	0
0	14.76	0.098	4.92	63.96	4.92	19.68	0.049	0	0	0	0	0	0	0	0	0	0
0	24.7	0.247	4.94	0	4.94	59.28	0.346	0	0	0	0	0	0	0	0	0	0
0	14.64	0.878	4.88	0	4.88	34.16	0.244	0	0	0	0	0	0	0	0	0	0
0	11.16	0.298	3.72	0	3.72	55.8	0.26	0	0	0	0	0	0	0	0	0	0
0	9.82	0.344	4.91	0	4.91	54.01	0.245	0	0	0	0	0.074	0	0	0	0	0
0	24.8	0.298	4.96	4.96	9.92	59.52	0.496	0	0	0	0	0	0	0	0	0	0
0	14.73	0.196	0	54.01	4.91	49.1	0.196	0	0	0	0	0	0	0	0	0	0
0	24.65	0.247	4.93	0	4.93	64.09	0.345	0	0	0	0	0	0	0	0	0	0
0	7.11	0.118	2.37	2.37	30.81	23.7	0.024	0	0	0	0.002	0.047	0.002	0	0	0	0
0	4.76	0.024	4.76	2.38	49.98	14.28	0.071	0	0	0	0.019	0.09	0.005	0	0	0	0
0	0	0.047	7.11	2.37	87.69	7.11	0.047	0	0	0	0.033	0	0	0	0	11.85	0
0	0	0.047	7.11	2.37	87.69	7.11	0.047	0	0	0	0.033	0	0	0	0	11.85	0
0	4.74	0.19	2.37	0	21.33	2.37	0.095	2.37	0	0.024	0.009	0	0	0	0	2.37	0
0	4.74	0.19	2.37	0	21.33	2.37	0.095	0	0	0.024	0.009	0	0	0	0	2.37	0
0	4.74	0	2.37	0	0	4.74	0	0	0	0	0	0	0	0	0	0	0
0	0.305	0.003	0	0	0	1.22	0.031	0	0	0	0	0	0	0	0	0	0
0	2.61	0.116	2.9	4.35	25.52	2.03	0.023	0	0	0	0.003	0.029	0.006	0	0	0.29	0
		1.549				547.2											0
0	7.48	1.21	13.2	103.84	200.64	294.8	0.264	0	0	0.172	0.092	1.496	0.029	0		36.52	0
0	3.99	0.649	3.57	97.65	38.85	304.71	0.097	0	0	0.088	0.049	0.724	0.006	0	0.015	17.43	0

EvaluEat Code	Food Name	Amt	Wt (g)	Energy (kcal)	Prot (g)	Carb (g)	Fiber (g)	Fat (g)	Mono (g)	Poly (g)	Sat (g)
9043	Blackberry juice, canned	1 cup	144	54.72	0.432	11.232	0.144	0.864	0.084	0.495	0.026
42129	Bologna, beef and pork, low-fat	1 oz	28.34	65.182	3.259	0.737	0	5.47	2.592	0.464	2.071
42161	Bologna, beef, low-fat	1 oz	28.34	65.182	3.599	0.879	0	5.356	2.594	0.205	2.269
20034	Bran, oat, cooked	1 cup	219	87.6	7.03	25.054	5.694	1.883	0.637	0.742	0.357
7924	Bratwurst, pork, beef and turkey, lite, smoked	1 serving (2.33 oz)	66	122.76	9.537	1.069	0	8.93	4.729	0.558	3.16
18376	Bread crumbs, dry, grated, seasoned	1 oz	28.35	104.05	4.026	19.958	1.191	0.737	0.274	0.187	0.206
18079	Bread crumbs, plain, grated, dry	1 oz	28.35	111.98	3.785	20.406	1.276	1.503	0.29	0.584	0.341
18080	Bread sticks, plain	1 stick, small (approx 4-1/4" long)	5	20.6	0.6	3.42	0.15	0.475	0.178	0.181	0.071
18085	Bread stuffing, corn, dry mix, prep	.5 cup	100	179	2.9	21.9	2.9	8.8	3.856	2.706	1.755
18082	Bread stuffing, plain, dry mix, prep	.5 cup	100	178	3.2	21.7	2.9	8.6	3.808	2.604	1.734
18019	Bread, banana, Elfin Loaves/Keebler	1 slice	60	195.6	2.58	32.76	0.66	6.3	2.688	1.878	1.342
18023	Bread, corn, dry mix, prepared	1 piece	60	188.4	4.32	28.86	1.44	6	3.084	0.734	1.643
18270	Bread, corn, hushpuppies, homemade	1 cup	152	512.24	11.704	69.92	4.256	20.52	4.96	10.973	3.204
18627	Bread, crusty Italian Bread w/garlic/PepFarm	1 serving	50	186	4.15	20.8		9.6	3.918	1.832	2.411
18027	Bread, egg	1 slice (5" x 3" x 1/2")	40	114.8	3.8	19.12	0.92	2.4	0.921	0.442	0.637
18029	Bread, french/vienna/sourdough	1 slice, medium (4" x 2-1/2" x 1-3/4")	64	175.36	5.632	33.216	1.92	1.92	0.778	0.444	0.41
18604	Bread, garlic, frozen/Campione	1 serving	28	101.36	2.38	12.404	1.316	4.704			0.756
18641	Bread, hamburger rolls/Wonder	1 serving	43	117.39	3.47	21.861	1.118	1.785	0.365	0.936	0.436
18031	Bread, indian (Navajo) Fry	1 piece (10-1/2" dia)	160	526.4	11.36	85.28	2.88	15.2	6.381	4.141	3.701
18032	Bread, Irish soda, homemade, prepared from recipe	1 oz	28.35	82.215	1.871	15.876	0.737	1.418	0.567	0.419	0.315
18033	Bread, Italian	1 slice, medium	20	54.2	1.76	10	0.54	0.7	0.162	0.278	0.171
18035	Bread, mixed grain/7-grain/whole grain	1 slice, large	32	80	3.2	14.848	2.048	1.216	0.488	0.295	0.258
18037	Bread, oatbran	1 slice	30	70.8	3.12	11.94	1.35	1.32	0.477	0.508	0.209
18049	Bread, oatbran, reduced kcal	1 slice	23	46.23	1.84	9.499	2.76	0.736	0.157	0.384	0.102
18039	Bread, oatmeal	1 slice	27	72.63	2.268	13.095	1.08	1.188	0.426	0.46	0.19
18041	Bread, pita, white, enriched	1 pita, large (6-1/2" dia)	60	165	5.46	33.42	1.32	0.72	0.063	0.321	0.1
18042	Bread, pita, whole wheat	1 pita, large (6-1/2" dia)	64	170.24	6.272	35.2	4.736	1.664	0.223	0.675	0.262
18044	Bread, pumpernickel	1 slice, regular	26	65	2.262	12.35	1.69	0.806	0.242	0.322	0.114
18047	Bread, raisin, enriched	1 slice	26	71.24	2.054	13.598	1.118	1.144	0.596	0.177	0.281
18060	Bread, rye	1 slice	32	82.88	2.72	15.456	1.856	1.056	0.42	0.256	0.2
18064	Bread, wheat (includes wheat berry)	1 slice	25	65	2.275	11.8	1.075	1.025	0.43	0.227	0.223
18066	Bread, wheat bran	1 slice	36	89.28	3.168	17.208	1.44	1.224	0.582	0.234	0.28
18068	Bread, wheat germ	1 slice	28	73.08	2.688	13.524	0.588	0.812	0.357	0.187	0.184
18055	Bread, wheat, reduced kcal	1 slice	23	45.54	2.093	10.028	2.76	0.529	0.058	0.223	0.079
18069	Bread, white, commercially prep, crumbs/cubes/slices	1 slice	25	66.5	1.91	12.653	0.6	0.822	0.17	0.339	0.179
18057	Bread, white, reduced kcal	1 slice	23	47.61	2.001	10.189	2.231	0.575	0.248	0.129	0.126
18075	Bread, whole wheat, commercially prep	1 slice	28	68.88	2.716	12.908	1.932	1.176	0.47	0.281	0.257
43100	Breakfast bars, oats, sugar, raisins, coconut (include granola bar)	1 cup	186	863.04	18.228	124.062	5.766	32.736	3.595	3.039	23.603

Chol (g)	Calc (mg)	Iron (mg)	Mag (mg)	Phos (mg)	Pota (mg)	Sodi (mg)	Zinc (mg)	Vit A (RAE)	Vit C (mg)	Thia (mg)	Ribo (mg)	Niac (mg)	Vit B₆ (mg)	Vit B₁₂ (µg)	Vit E (mg)	Fol (µg)	Alc (g)
0	17.28	0.691	30.24	17.28	194.4	1.44	0.59	11.52	16.27	0.017	0.026	0.642	0.03	0	1.296	14.4	0
11.053	3.117	0.187	3.401	51.295	44.21	314.007	0.425	0	0	0.048	0.037	0.72	0.051	0.371	0.062	1.417	0
10.486	2.551	0.283	3.401	50.445	41.66	319.675	0.519	0	0.283	0.014	0.028	0.709	0.043	0.397	0.054	1.417	0
0	21.9	1.927	87.6	260.61	201.48	2.19	1.161	0	0	0.35	0.074	0.315	0.055	0		13.14	0
36.96	9.24	0.62	9.24	87.12	162.36	648.12	1.769	0	0	0.059	0.11	1.219	0.141	1.056	0.03	3.3	0
0.284	28.067	0.902	10.773	37.706	76.545	751.275	0.258	1.134	0.113	0.045	0.048	0.774	0.042	0.011		30.9	0
0	51.881	1.369	12.191	46.778	55.566	207.522	0.411	0	0	0.274	0.114	1.881	0.034	0.099	0.023	30.34	0
0	1.1	0.214	1.6	6.05	6.2	32.85	0.044	0	0	0.029	0.028	0.264	0.004	0	0.051	8.1	0
0	26	0.94	13	34	62	455	0.23	78	0.8	0.117	0.092	1.247	0.038	0.01	0.85	97	0
0	32	1.09	12	42	74	543	0.28	118	0	0.136	0.107	1.475	0.04	0.01	1.4	39	0
25.8	12.6	0.84	8.4	34.8	80.4	181.2	0.21	63.6	1.02	0.103	0.12	0.868	0.09	0.06	1.071	19.8	0
36.6	43.8	1.14	12	225.6	76.8	466.8	0.378	26.4	0.06	0.146	0.162	1.234	0.062	0.096		33	
68.4	422.56	4.621	36.48	287.28	218.88	1015.36	1.003	62.32	0.304	0.535	0.505	4.229	0.155	0.289	1.915	135.3	
5.5		1.185				200											
20.4	37.2	1.216	7.6	42.4	46	196.8	0.316	25.2	0	0.175	0.174	1.939	0.026	0.04	0.104	42	0
0	48	1.619	17.28	67.2	72.32	389.76	0.557	0	0	0.333	0.211	3.039	0.028	0	0.192	94.72	0
		0.302				154											
	37.41	0.955				256.28											
0	372.8	5.76	25.6	251.2	118.4	1112	0.8	0	0	0.688	0.486	5.818	0.043	0	1.235	118.4	0
5.103	22.964	0.763	6.521	32.319	75.411	112.833	0.162	13.61	0.227	0.084	0.076	0.682	0.024	0.014	0.3	13.33	0
0	15.6	0.588	5.4	20.6	22	116.8	0.172	0	0	0.095	0.058	0.876	0.01	0	0.058	38.2	0
0	29.12	1.11	16.96	56.32	65.28	155.84	0.406	0	0.096	0.13	0.109	1.397	0.107	0.022	0.109	37.76	0
0	19.5	0.936	10.5	42.3	44.1	122.1	0.267	0.6	0	0.151	0.104	1.449	0.022	0	0.132	24.3	0
0	13.11	0.725	12.65	31.97	23.46	80.73	0.241	0	0	0.081	0.047	0.865	0.024	0	0.064	18.63	0
0	17.82	0.729	9.99	34.02	38.34	161.73	0.275	1.35	0	0.108	0.065	0.847	0.018	0.008	0.13	16.74	0
0	51.6	1.572	15.6	58.2	72	321.6	0.504	0	0	0.359	0.196	2.779	0.02	0	0.18	64.2	0
0	9.6	1.958	44.16	115.2	108.8	340.48	0.973	0	0	0.217	0.051	1.818	0.17	0	0.39	22.4	0
0	17.68	0.746	14.04	46.28	54.08	174.46	0.385	0	0	0.085	0.079	0.804	0.033	0	0.109	24.18	0
0	17.16	0.754	6.76	28.34	59.02	101.4	0.187	0	0.026	0.088	0.103	0.901	0.018	0	0.073	27.56	0
0	23.36	0.906	12.8	40	53.12	211.2	0.365	0	0.128	0.139	0.107	1.218	0.024	0	0.106	35.2	0
0	26.25	0.827	11.5	37.5	50.25	132.5	0.26	0	0	0.105	0.07	1.031	0.024	0	0.072	22.75	0
0	26.64	1.105	29.16	66.6	81.72	174.96	0.486	0	0	0.143	0.103	1.585	0.063	0	0.115	37.8	0
0	24.92	0.966	7.84	33.88	71.12	154.84	0.274	0	0.056	0.103	0.105	1.259	0.022	0.02	0.143	33.04	0
0	18.4	0.681	8.97	23.46	28.06	117.53	0.258	0	0.023	0.097	0.068	0.894	0.029	0	0.055	20.93	0
0	37.75	0.935	5.75	24.75	25	170.25	0.185	0	0	0.114	0.083	1.096	0.021	0	0.055	27.75	0
0	21.62	0.734	5.29	27.83	17.48	104.19	0.308	0	0.115	0.094	0.066	0.837	0.01	0.064	0.044	21.85	0
0	20.16	0.924	24.08	64.12	70.56	147.56	0.543	0	0	0.098	0.057	1.074	0.05	0.003	0.087	14	0
0	111.6	5.915	187.86	515.22	606.36	517.08	2.976	14.88	1.86	0.521	0.205	3.255	0.651	0	4.352	150.7	0

EvaluEat Code	Food Name	Amt	Wt (g)	Energy (kcal)	Prot (g)	Carb (g)	Fiber (g)	Fat (g)	Mono (g)	Poly (g)	Sat (g)
11097	Broccoli raab, cooked	.5 cup	92	30.36	3.524	2.87	2.576	0.478			
11096	Broccoli raab, raw	.5 cup	92	20.24	2.916	2.622	2.484	0.451	0.024	0.12	0.046
4601	Butter, light, stick, with salt	1 tbsp	12.8	63.872	0.422	0	0	7.053	2.039	0.262	4.393
4602	Butter, light, stick, without salt	1 tbsp	12.8	63.872	0.422	0	0	7.053	2.039	0.262	4.393
1001	Butter, regular (with salt)	1 tbsp	14.2	101.81	0.121	0.009	0	11.518	4.735	0.407	5.799
1145	Butter, unsalted	1 tbsp	14.2	101.81	0.121	0.009	0	11.518	2.985	0.432	7.294
1002	Butter, whipped (with salt)	1 tbsp	9.4	67.398	0.08	0.006	0	7.624	2.202	0.283	4.746
43143	Cabbage, japanese style, fresh, pickled	1 cup	186	55.8	2.976	10.546	5.766	0.186	0.015	0.089	0.024
43144	Cabbage, mustard, salted	1 cup	186	52.08	2.046	10.472	5.766	0.186	0.013	0.089	0.024
18086	Cake, angelfood, commercially prep	1 piece (1/12 of 12 oz cake)	28	72.24	1.652	16.184	0.42	0.224	0.02	0.103	0.034
18090	Cake, boston cream pie, commercially prep	1 piece (1/6 of pie)	92	231.84	2.208	39.468	1.288	7.82	4.18	0.928	2.249
18096	Cake, chocolate w/chocolate icing, commercially prep	1 piece (1/8 of 18 oz cake)	64	234.88	2.624	34.944	1.792	10.496	5.606	1.181	3.053
18101	Cake, chocolate, homemade, w/o icing	1 piece (1/12 of 9" dia)	95	340.1	5.035	50.73	1.52	14.345	5.737	2.623	5.158
18116	Cake, gingerbread, homemade	1 piece (1/9 of 8" square)	74	263.44	2.886	36.408		12.136	5.272	3.12	3.05
18120	Cake, pound, commercially prep w/butter	1 piece (1/12 of 12 oz cake)	28	108.64	1.54	13.664	0.14	5.572	1.652	0.299	3.237
18452	Cake, snack/cupcakes, chocolate w/frosting, low-fat	1 cupcake	43	131.15	1.849	28.896	1.849	1.591	0.795	0.209	0.466
18127	Cake, snack-type cream filled, chocolate w/icing	1 cupcake	50	188	1.7	30.15	0.4	7.25	2.845	2.618	1.429
18133	Cake, sponge, commercially prep	1 piece (1/12 of 16 oz cake)	38	109.82	2.052	23.218	0.19	1.026	0.361	0.17	0.305
18102	Cake, white w/coconut icing, homemade	1 piece (1/12 of 9" dia)	112	398.72	4.928	70.784	1.12	11.536	4.135	2.421	4.365
18139	Cake, white, homemade, w/o icing	1 piece (1/12 of 9" dia)	74	264.18	3.996	42.328	0.592	9.176	3.929	2.33	2.419
18140	Cake, yellow w/chocolate icing, commercially prep	1 piece (1/8 of 18 oz cake)	64	242.56	2.432	35.456	1.152	11.136	6.14	1.352	2.98
18146	Cake, yellow, homemade, w/o icing	1 piece (1/12 of 8" dia)	68	245.48	3.604	36.04	0.476	9.928	4.236	2.428	2.668
9426	Candied fruit	1 oz	28.34	90.971	0.099	23.449	0.453	0.02	0.002	0.006	0.003
43031	Candies, chocolate covered, caramel with nuts	1 cup	186	874.2	17.67	112.8	7.998	39.06	17.566	10.851	8.662
43058	Candies, hard, dietetic or low calorie (sorbitol)	1 cup	186	697.5	0	173.72	0	0	0	0	0
19236	Candies, Hershey's milk chocolate with almond bites	17 pieces	39	214.5	3.806	19.89	1.404	13.935	5.608	0.944	6.782
19279	Candies, milk chocolate coated coffee beans	1 NLEA serving	6	30.78	0.445	3.745	0.342	1.565	0.35	0.051	0.749
19068	Candies, Nestle, Bit-O'-Honey candy chews	18 pieces	40	160	0.84	32.4	0	3	0.781	0.25	2
43046	Candies, nougat	1 cup	186	740.28	6.194	171.85	6.138	3.106	0	0	3.101
19159	Candy bar, 3 Musketeers/M&M Mars	1 bar (.8 oz)	23	95.68	0.736	17.664	0.414	2.967	0.987	0.104	1.495
19065	Candy bar, Almond Joy/Hershey	1 package (1.76 oz)	49	234.71	2.024	29.16	2.45	13.196	2.577	0.578	8.619
19111	Candy bar, Baby Ruth/Nestle	1 bar (0.75 oz)	21	97.44	1.491	12.978	0.504	5.25	1.356	0.694	2.583
19069	Candy bar, Butterfinger Bar and Dessert Topping	1 bar fun size	21	99.96	1.218	15.223	0.357	3.99	1.025	0.517	2.151
19075	Candy bar, Caramello/Hershey	1 bar (1.25 oz)	35	161.7	2.167	22.333	0.42	7.417	1.851	0.22	4.452
19109	Candy bar, Kit Kat Wafer/Hershey	1 bar (1.5 oz)	42	217.14	2.692	26.951	0.798	11.386	2.012	0.214	7.346

Chol (g)	Calc (mg)	Iron (mg)	Mag (mg)	Phos (mg)	Pota (mg)	Sodi (mg)	Zinc (mg)	Vit A (RAE)	Vit C (mg)	Thia (mg)	Ribo (mg)	Niac (mg)	Vit B6 (mg)	Vit B12 (µg)	Vit E (mg)	Fol (µg)	Alc (g)
	108.56	1.168	24.84	75.44	315.56	51.52	0.497	208.8	34.04	0.155	0.129	1.854	0.202		2.328	65.32	
	99.36	1.969	20.24	67.16	180.32	30.36	0.708	120.5	18.58	0.149	0.119	1.123	0.157		1.49	76.36	
13.568	6.144	0.14	0.64	4.352	9.088	57.6	0.033	59.52	0	0.001	0.009	0.003	0.001	0.017	0.202	0.128	0
13.568	6.144	0.14	0.64	4.352	9.088	4.608	0.033	59.52	0	0.001	0.009	0.003	0.001	0.017	0.202	0.128	0
30.53	3.408	0.003	0.284	3.408	3.408	81.792	0.013	97.13	0	0.001	0.005	0.006	0	0.024	0.329	0.426	0
30.53	3.408	0.003	0.284	3.408	3.408	1.562	0.013	97.13	0	0.001	0.005	0.006	0	0.024	0.329	0.426	0
20.586	2.256	0.015	0.188	2.162	2.444	77.738	0.005	64.3	0	0	0.003	0.004	0	0.012	0.218	0.282	0
0	89.28	0.911	22.32	79.98	1586.58	515.22	0.372	16.74	1.302	0	0.074	0.335	0.186	0	0.223	78.12	0
0	124.62	1.302	27.9	50.22	457.56	1333.62	0.558	91.14	0	0.074	0.167	1.339	0.558	0	0.037	133.9	0
0	39.2	0.146	3.36	8.96	26.04	209.72	0.02	0	0	0.029	0.137	0.247	0.009	0.017		9.8	0
34.04	21.16	0.35	5.52	45.08	35.88	132.48	0.147	22.08	0.184	0.375	0.248	0.176	0.024	0.147	0.138	12.88	0
26.88	27.52	1.408	21.76	78.08	128	213.76	0.442	16.64	0.064	0.017	0.085	0.369	0.026	0.09		10.88	0
55.1	57	1.53	30.4	100.7	133	299.25	0.655	38	0.19	0.134	0.202	1.08	0.039	0.152	1.512	25.65	0
23.68	52.54	2.131	51.8	39.96	324.86	241.98	0.289	10.36	0.074	0.141	0.12	1.286	0.141	0.044		24.42	0
61.88	9.8	0.386	3.08	38.36	33.32	111.44	0.129	41.72	0	0.038	0.064	0.367	0.012	0.07		11.48	0
0	15.48	0.662	10.75	78.69	96.32	177.59	0.237	0	0	0.015	0.057	0.307	0.003	0		6.45	0
8.5	36.5	1.68	20.5	46.5	61	212.5	0.255	2.5	0	0.111	0.147	1.214	0.012	0.03	1.09	20	0
38.76	26.6	1.034	4.18	52.06	37.62	92.72	0.194	16.72	0	0.092	0.102	0.734	0.02	0.091	0.091	17.86	0
1.12	100.8	1.299	13.44	78.4	110.88	318.08	0.37	13.44	0.112	0.143	0.212	1.191	0.032	0.067	0.134	34.72	0
1.48	96.2	1.125	8.88	68.82	70.3	241.98	0.237	11.1	0.148	0.138	0.179	1.134	0.016	0.059	0.089	28.12	0
35.2	23.68	1.331	19.2	103.04	113.92	215.68	0.397	21.12	0	0.077	0.1	0.798	0.021	0.109	1.455	14.08	0
36.72	99.28	1.115	8.16	79.56	61.88	233.24	0.306	27.2	0.136	0.124	0.158	0.99	0.024	0.109	0.819	23.12	0
0	5.101	0.048	1.134	1.417	16.154	27.773	0.014	0.283	0	0	0	0	0	0	0.011	0	0
0	145.08	3.162	150.66	308.76	827.7	44.64	3.478	78.12	2.604	0.074	0.298	8.854	0.298	0	2.046	171.1	0
0	0	0	0	0	0	0	0	0	0	0	0	0	0	0	0	0	0
7.41	85.8	0.585	23.01	88.53	183.69	28.86	0.523		0.702	0.027	0.148	0.242	0.027		0.152	6.24	0
1.2	10.14	0.137	3.84	11.28	24.78	4.26	0.106	2.52	0	0.006	0.019	0.02	0.002	0.032	0.104	0.6	0
0	20	0.116	2.8	18	50.4	120	0.084	0	0	0	0.1	0.024	0.007	0.068	0.396	1.6	0
0	59.52	1.097	59.52	102.3	195.3	61.38	0.781	0	0.558	0.024	0.275	0.889	0.037	0.019	5.152	9.3	0
2.53	19.32	0.168	6.67	20.93	30.59	44.62	0.127	3.45	0.092	0.008	0.032	0.053	0.003	0.044	0.214	0	0
1.96	31.36	0.622		54.88	124.46	69.58			0.343						0.01		0
0.42	9.45	0.147	15.33	28.98	74.76	44.94	0.25	0	0.021	0.02	0.016	0.583	0.013	0.008	0.393	6.51	0
0	7.35	0.16	17.43	28.35	82.95	44.94	0.25	0	0	0.023	0.016	0.647	0.021	0.004	0.363	6.93	0
9.45	74.55	0.382		52.5	119.35	42.7			0.595						0.077		0
3.78	56.7	0.357	1.26	47.46	121.8	27.3	0.038	10.5	0.546	0.021	0.071	0.088	0.004	0.088	0.147	1.26	0

EvaluEat Code	Food Name	Amt	Wt (g)	Energy (kcal)	Prot (g)	Carb (g)	Fiber (g)	Fat (g)	Mono (g)	Poly (g)	Sat (g)
19110	Candy bar, Krackel/Hershey	1 bar (1.45 oz)	41	209.92	2.714	26.224	0.902	10.898	2.563	0.234	6.527
19115	Candy bar, Mars Almond/M&M Mars	1 bar (1.76 oz)	50	233.5	4.05	31.35	1	11.5	5.346	1.99	3.634
19135	Candy bar, Mars Milky Way/M&M Mars	1 bar (.8 oz)	23	97.29	1.035	16.491	0.391	3.703	1.385	0.138	1.792
19143	Candy bar, Mr. Goodbar/Hershey	1 bar (1.75 oz)	49	263.62	5.008	26.627	1.862	16.273	4.019	2.139	6.924
19118	Candy bar, Oh Henry!/Nestle	1 bar	26	120.12	2.002	17.004	0.546	6.006	1.734	0.707	1.747
19136	Candy bar, Skor Toffee Candy/Hershey	1 bar (1.4 oz)	39	208.65	1.221	24.071	0.507	12.55	3.623	0.499	7.324
19155	Candy bar, Snickers/M&M Mars	1 bar (2 oz)	57	273.03	4.56	33.75	1.425	14.011	5.958	2.803	5.127
19164	Candy bar, Special Dark Sweet Chocolate/Hershey	1 bar (1.45 oz)	41	217.71	2.271	24.358	2.665	13.284	2.107	0.18	7.868
19160	Candy bar, Twix Caramel Cookie/M&M Mars	1 package (2 oz)	57	284.43	2.622	37.381	0.627	13.902	7.638	0.485	5.072
19070	Candy, butterscotch	3 pieces	16	62.56	0.005	14.464	0	0.528	0.136	0.02	0.332
19074	Candy, caramel	1 piece	10.1	38.582	0.465	7.777	0.121	0.818	0.085	0.018	0.665
19071	Candy, carob	1 bar (3 oz)	87	469.8	7.09	48.972	3.306	27.283	0.42	0.257	25.246
19080	Candy, chocolate chips, semisweet	1 cup chips (6 oz package)	168	804.72	7.056	106.01	9.912	50.4	16.75	1.63	29.82
19078	Candy, chocolate, baking, unsweetened, square	1 square	29	145.29	3.741	8.654	4.814	15.17	4.671	0.451	9.382
19081	Candy, chocolate, sweet	1 bar (1.45 oz)	41	207.05	1.599	24.436	2.255	14.022	4.6	0.406	8.233
19011	Candy, fruit leather bar	1 bar	23	80.73	0.414	18.055	0.805	1.219	0.145	0.041	0.925
19013	Candy, fruit leather, pieces	1 package	27	94.77	0.27	22.815	0	0.27	0.141	0.052	0.062
19014	Candy, fruit leather, roll	1 large	21	77.91	0.021	17.997	0.693	0.63	0.311	0.113	0.136
19301	Candy, fudge, chocolate marshmallow nut, homemade	1 oz	28.34	133.77	0.915	19.022	0.595	5.966	1.585	1.152	2.829
19101	Candy, fudge, chocolate w/nuts, homemade	1 oz	28.34	130.65	1.241	19.26	0.709	5.365	1.052	2.099	1.71
19100	Candy, fudge, chocolate, homemade	1 piece	17	69.87	0.406	13.002	0.289	1.77	0.463	0.039	1.006
19106	Candy, gumdrops/gummy bears/fish/worm/dinosaur	10 gumdrops	36	142.56	0	35.604	0.036	0	0	0	0
19107	Candy, hard candy	1 piece	6	23.64	0	5.88	0	0.012	0	0	0
19108	Candy, jellybeans	10 large (1 oz)	28	105	0	26.194	0.056	0.014	0	0	0
19140	Candy, M&M's Peanut chocolate	1 package (1.67 oz)	47	242.52	4.451	28.416	1.598	12.333	5.17	1.974	4.856
19141	Candy, M&M's Plain chocolate	1 box (1.48 oz)	42	206.64	1.819	29.908	1.05	8.875	1.485	0.162	5.494
19116	Candy, marshmallow	1 regular	7.2	22.896	0.13	5.854	0.007	0.014	0.006	0.003	0.004
19120	Candy, milk chocolate	1 bar (1.55 oz)	44	235.4	3.366	26.136	1.496	13.05	5.819	0.358	6.271
19132	Candy, milk chocolate w/almonds	1 bar (1.45 oz)	41	215.66	3.69	21.812	2.542	14.104	5.531	0.935	6.962
19134	Candy, milk chocolate w/rice cereal	1 bar (1.4 oz)	40	198.4	2.52	25.36	1.32	10.6	3.456	0.312	6.356
19148	Candy, peanut brittle, homemade	1 oz	28.34	137.17	2.145	20.025	0.709	5.379	2.285	1.292	1.174
19151	Candy, peanut butter candy/Reese's Pieces/Hershey	10 pieces	8	39.76	0.997	4.789	0.24	1.982	0.357	0.15	1.314
19150	Candy, peanut butter cups, Reese's/Hershey	1 package (0.6 oz, 1 cup)	17	87.55	1.741	9.411	0.612	5.19	2.227	0.952	1.824
19126	Candy, peanuts, milk chocolate coated	10 pieces	40	207.6	5.24	19.76	1.88	13.4	5.168	1.732	5.84
19127	Candy, raisins, milk chocolate coated	10 pieces	10	39	0.41	6.83	0.42	1.48	0.474	0.051	0.88
19152	Candy, Rolo Caramel, milk chocolate/Hershey	1 package (1.91 oz)	54	255.96	2.743	36.693	0.486	11.302	2.03	0.211	7.787
19154	Candy, sesame crunch	1 piece	1.8	9.306	0.209	0.905	0.142	0.599	0.226	0.262	0.08
19370	Candy, Skittles, original bite size candy/M&M Mars	1 package	9979	40415	18.96	9045	0	436.08	295.38	11.975	86.618
19156	Candy, Starburst Fruit Chews/M&M Mars	1 package (2.07 oz)	59	233.64	0.236	49.855	0	4.897	2.106	1.841	0.73
19112	Candy, Twizzlers Strawberry/Hershey	4 pieces from 5 oz package	38	133	0.973	30.301	0	0.882			0
19091	Candy, York Peppermint Patty	1 patty (1.5 oz)	43	165.12	0.942	34.826	0.86	3.083	0.176	0.047	1.866
11683	Carrot, dehydrated	1 tbsp chopped	10	34.1	0.81	7.957	2.36	0.149	0.008	0.073	0.026

Chol (g)	Calc (mg)	Iron (mg)	Mag (mg)	Phos (mg)	Pota (mg)	Sodi (mg)	Zinc (mg)	Vit A (RAE)	Vit C (mg)	Thia (mg)	Ribo (mg)	Niac (mg)	Vit B_6 (mg)	Vit B_{12} (µg)	Vit E (mg)	Fol (µg)	Alc (g)
4.51	64.78	0.435	5.33	50.43	133.25	80.36	0.201		0.328	0.021	0.078	0.107	0.016		0.033	2.46	0
8.5	84	0.55	36	117	162.5	85	0.555	7.5	0.35	0.021	0.156	0.472	0.03	0.18	3.875	4.5	0
3.22	29.9	0.175	7.82	33.12	55.43	55.2	0.163	4.14	0.23	0.008	0.051	0.08	0.012	0.074	0.287	1.38	0
4.9	53.9	0.681	23.03	79.87	193.06	20.09	0.456	17.15	0.441	0.069	0.069	1.686	0.034	0.162	1.553	18.62	0
2.34	21.06	0.161	13.26	36.4	84.24	60.06	0.299	2.6	0.052	0.006	0.042	0.728	0.022	0.052	0.536	11.44	0
20.67	50.7	0.222	3.9	23.79	59.67	123.63	0.066		0.195	0.008	0.039	0.051			0.016	1.17	0
7.41	53.58	0.433	32.49	97.47	169.86	151.62	0.889	23.94	0.342	0.072	0.111	0.901	0.034	0.188	0.627	17.1	0
2.05	12.3	0.873	12.71	20.91	205.82	2.46	0.004		0	0	0.004	0	0	0	0.078	0	0
2.85	51.3	0.462	18.24	62.13	107.73	110.01	0.57	12.54	0.228	0.068	0.109	0.429	0.013	0.165	1.106	10.83	0
1.44	0.32	0.003	0.16	0.16	0.64	62.56	0.002	4.48	0	0	0.003	0.001	0	0	0.014	0	0
0.707	13.938	0.014	1.717	11.514	21.614	24.745	0.044	0.101	0.051	0.001	0.034	0.025	0.004	0	0.28	0.505	0
2.61	263.61	1.122	31.32	109.62	550.71	93.09	3.071	0	0.435	0.087	0.155	0.905	0.113	0.87	1.027	18.27	0
0	53.76	5.258	193.2	221.76	613.2	18.48	2.722	0	0	0.092	0.151	0.717	0.059	0	0.386	5.04	0
0	29.29	5.046	94.83	116	240.7	6.96	2.793	0	0	0.043	0.029	0.393	0.008	0	0.116	8.12	0
0	9.84	1.132	46.33	60.27	118.9	6.56	0.615	0	0	0.008	0.098	0.275	0.018	0	0.107	1.23	0
0	6.67	0.184	5.06	12.65	31.74	17.71	0.044	1.38	16.1	0.01	0.007	0.023	0.069	0		0.92	0
0	4.86	0.203	3.78	6.48	44.28	108.81	0.051	1.62	15.12	0.012	0.027	0.027	0.081	0	0.151	1.08	0
0	6.72	0.212	4.2	6.51	61.74	66.57	0.04	1.26	25.2	0.015	0.004	0.021	0.063	0	0.118	0.84	0.021
6.518	13.887	0.323	13.036	24.939	47.895	27.49	0.218	21.82	0.085	0.012	0.023	0.083	0.015	0.009	0.197	2.267	0
3.401	15.304	0.558	15.587	31.741	51.012	11.619	0.402	10.77	0.057	0.019	0.027	0.09	0.025	0.02	0.185	4.534	0
2.38	7.65	0.301	6.12	11.73	22.27	7.99	0.187	7.48	0	0.004	0.014	0.03	0.002	0.015	0.031	0.68	0
0	1.08	0.144	0.36	0.36	1.8	15.84	0	0	0	0.002	0.005	0.004	0.002	0	0	0	0
0	0.18	0.018	0.18	0.18	0.3	2.28	0.001	0	0	0	0	0	0	0	0	0	0
0	0.84	0.036	0.56	1.12	10.36	14	0.014	0	0	0.001	0.003	0.002	0.001	0	0	0	0
4.23	47.47	0.54	35.72	109.51	163.09	22.56	1.133	12.22	0.235	0.048	0.074	1.922	0.041	0.075	1.203	17.86	0
5.88	44.1	0.466	14.28	47.88	85.26	25.62	0.462	11.34	0.21	0.026	0.071	0.088	0.008	0.143	0.462	2.52	0
0	0.216	0.017	0.144	0.576	0.36	5.76	0.003	0	0	0	0	0.006	0	0	0	0.072	0
10.12	83.16	1.034	27.72	91.52	163.68	34.76	0.884	21.56	0	0.049	0.131	0.17	0.016	0.273	0.889	5.28	0
7.79	91.84	0.668	36.9	108.24	182.04	30.34	0.549	18.04	0.082	0.025	0.178	0.304	0.021	0.135	1.841	5.74	0
7.6	68.4	0.3	19.6	77.2	137.2	58	0.448	24.8	0.12	0.023	0.116	0.185	0.023	0.248	0.8	6	0
3.401	7.652	0.346	11.903	30.04	47.611	126.113	0.247	11.05	0	0.038	0.012	0.75	0.022	0.003	0.726	13.04	0
0	5.52	0.039	7.04	16.56	28.72	15.52	0.092	0	0	0.014	0.018	0.485	0.009	0.01	0.087	4.4	0
1.02	13.26	0.206	10.54	27.37	58.31	53.38	0.218	2.89	0.051	0.027	0.019	0.763	0.017	0.095	0.026	8.5	0
3.6	41.6	0.524	38.4	84.8	200.8	16.4	0.956	13.6	0	0.046	0.07	1.7	0.084	0.176	1.384	3.2	0
0.3	8.6	0.171	4.5	14.3	51.4	3.6	0.081	2.4	0.02	0.008	0.016	0.04	0.008	0.018	0.102	0.7	0
6.48	78.3	0.227	0	38.34	101.52	101.52	0	18.36	0.486	0.011	0.065	0.022	0	0.146	0.481	0	0
0	11.79	0.077	4.518	7.614	5.796	3.006	0.068	0	0.002	0.01	0.003	0.067	0.01	0	0.003	0.936	0
0	0	0.998	99.79	199.58	898.11	1596.64	0.998	0	6676	0.2	2.295	1.497	0.299	0	43.908	0	0
0	2.36	0.077	0.59	4.13	1.18	33.04	0	0	31.21	0.001	0.001	0.003	0	0	0.413	0	0
0	0	0.194				109.06			0								0
0.43	4.73	0.396		0	47.73	12.04		0							0.004		
0	21.2	0.393	11.8	34.6	254	27.5	0.157	541.6	1.46	0.053	0.042	0.657	0.104	0	0.697	5.5	0

EvaluEat Code	Food Name	Amt	Wt (g)	Energy (kcal)	Prot (g)	Carb (g)	Fiber (g)	Fat (g)	Mono (g)	Poly (g)	Sat (g)
44055	Celery flakes, dried	1 cubic inch	10.2	32.538	1.153	6.497	2.836	0.214	0.041	0.106	0.057
8053	Cereal, 100% bran (wheat bran & barley)	.333 cup									
		(1 NLEA serving)	29	83.23	3.683	22.678	8.294	0.609	0.092	0.319	0.087
8153	Cereal, 40% bran flakes/Ralston Purina	1 cup	49	158.76	5.635	39.102	6.909	0.686			
8001	Cereal, All-Bran/Kellogg	.5 cup									
		(1 NLEA serving)	30	78	3.75	22.2	9.6	0.996	0.222	0.612	0.162
8263	Cereal, Apple Cinnamon Cheerios/General Mills	.75 cup									
		(1 NLEA serving)	30	117.6	1.8	25.2	1.29	1.53	0.713	0.384	0.297
8254	Cereal, Apple Cinnamon Squares Mini-Wheats/Kellogg	.75 cup									
		(1 NLEA serving)	55	182.05	3.96	44.055	4.73	0.99	0.275	0.495	0.22
8003	Cereal, Apple Jacks/Kellogg	1 cup									
		(1 NLEA serving)	30	117	0.9	27.3	0.96	0.6	0.18	0.3	0.12
8262	Cereal, Basic 4/General Mills	1 cup									
		(1 NLEA serving)	55	201.85	4.4	42.35	3.19	2.805	0.99	1.1	0.44
8006	Cereal, Bran Chex (wheat & corn)	1 cup	49	156.31	5.047	39.053	7.938	1.372	0.254	0.671	0.198
8322	Cereal, Bran Flakes/Kraft, Post	.75 cup									
		(1 NLEA serving)	30	96	2.82	24.12	5.28	0.66			0.12
8010	Cereal, Cap'n Crunch/Quaker	.75 cup	27	108.27	1.174	22.901	0.675	1.569	0.289	0.2	0.405
8013	Cereal, Cheerios/General Mills	1 cup									
		(1 NLEA serving)	30	110.7	3.3	22.2	2.7	1.8	0.642	0.216	0.36
8139	Cereal, Cinnamon Grahams/General Mills	.75 cup	30	113.4	1.5	25.8	0.96	0.84	0.304	0.312	0.15
8215	Cereal, Cinnamon Oatmeal Squares/Quaker	1 cup									
		(1 NLEA serving)	60	226.8	6.066	47.898	4.56	2.568	0.864	1.044	0.504
8272	Cereal, Cinnamon Toast Crunch/General Mills	.75 cup									
		(1 NLEA serving)	30	126.6	1.5	23.7	1.2	3.3	1.539	1.015	0.54
8014	Cereal, Cocoa Krispies/Kellogg	.75 cup									
		(1 NLEA serving)	31	118.11	1.054	27.001	0.992	0.992	0.124	0.071	0.617
8271	Cereal, Cocoa Puffs/General Mills	1 cup									
		(1 NLEA serving)	30	117	1.2	26.4	0.69	0.96	0.501	0.184	0.21
8028	Cereal, Complete Wheat Bran Flakes/Kellogg	.75 cup									
		(1 NLEA serving)	29	92.22	2.9	22.91	5.075	0.58	0.145	0.319	0.116
8295	Cereal, Corn Blasts/Quaker	1 cup	33	132.66	1.416	28.034	0.726	1.904	1.033	0.343	0.508
8019	Cereal, Corn Chex	1 cup									
		(1 NLEA serving)	30	111.9	2.1	25.8	0.6	0.27	0.059	0.101	0.06
8020	Cereal, Corn Flakes/Kellogg	1 cup									
		(1 NLEA serving)	28	101.08	1.96	24.08	0.98	0.224	0.031	0.09	0.053
8093	Cereal, corn grits, instant, plain, prep/Quaker	1 cup	245	166.6	3.945	36.897	2.205	0.465	0.066	0.14	0.047
8161	Cereal, corn grits, white, regular/quick, enriched, prep w/salt	1 cup	242	142.78	3.436	31.145	0.726	0.46	0.116	0.201	0.061
8068	Cereal, Corn Pops/Kellogg	1 cup									
		(1 NLEA serving)	31	117.8	1.147	27.9	0.248	0.226	0.084	0.071	0.071
8023	Cereal, Cracklin' Oat Bran/Kellogg	.75 cup									
		(1 NLEA serving)	55	224.95	4.565	39.27	6.435	8.03	4.565	1.155	2.31
8168	Cereal, Cream of Rice, prep w/salt	1 cup	244	126.88	2.196	28.06	0.244	0.244	0.076	0.066	0.049
8171	Cereal, Cream of Wheat, instant, prep w/salt	1 cup	241	149.42	4.434	31.523	1.446	0.578	0.08	0.323	0.092
8169	Cereal, Cream of Wheat, regular, prep w/salt	1 cup	251	125.5	3.665	26.932	1.004	0.477	0.063	0.259	0.075

Chol (g)	Calc (mg)	Iron (mg)	Mag (mg)	Phos (mg)	Pota (mg)	Sodi (mg)	Zinc (mg)	Vit A (RAE)	Vit C (mg)	Thia (mg)	Ribo (mg)	Niac (mg)	Vit B$_6$ (mg)	Vit B$_{12}$ (µg)	Vit E (mg)	Fol (µg)	Alc (g)
0	59.874	0.799	19.992	41.004	447.576	146.37	0.283	9.996	8.823	0.045	0.051	0.473	0.047	0	0.566	10.91	0
0	22.04	8.1	80.62	235.77	274.63	120.93	3.75	225	0	0.374	0.426	5	0.502	0	0.673	100.1	0
0	22.54	7.791	117.6	272.93	286.16	456.19	2.038		25.97	0.637	0.735	8.624	0.882	2.597		173	0
0	99	4.8	114	339	339	77.4	1.8	157.5	6	0.36	0.42	4.8	1.8	6	0.369	393	0
0	99.9	4.5	20.1	65.1	57.6	120.3	3.75	150.3	6	0.375	0.426	5.01	0.501	1.5	0.15	200.1	0
0	20.9	16.225	48.4	154	166.1	19.8	1.485	0	0	0.385	0.44	5.005	0.495	1.485	0.303	110	0
0	7.5	4.17	16.5	37.5	36	142.5	1.5	46.8	13.8	0.51	0.39	4.62	0.45	1.38	0.048	93	0
0	196.35	3.52	40.15	231.55	154.55	315.7	2.97	117.7	0	0.297	0.336	3.905	0.391	1.155	0.594	78.65	0
0	29.4	13.994	69.09	172.97	216.09	345.45	6.483		25.97	0.637	0.265	8.624	0.882	2.597	0.563	173	0
0	16.8	8.1	64.2	152.4	184.8	219.6	1.5		0	0.375	0.426	5.001	0.501	1.5		99.9	
0	4.05	5.16	15.12	45.09	54	202.23	4.285	1.89	0	0.427	0.481	5.711	0.57	0	0.248	420.1	0
0	99.9	8.1	39.9	99.9	96.3	273	3.75	150.3	6	0.375	0.426	5.01	0.501	1.5	0.105	200.1	0
0	99.9	4.5	8.1	20.1	44.1	236.7	3.75	150.3	6	0.375	0.426	5.01	0.501	1.5	0.093	99.9	0
0	116.4	16.86	64.8	201.6	250.2	263.4	4.128	165	6.6	0.408	0.462	5.502	0.546	0	2.214	420	0
0	99.9	4.5	8.1	80.1	42.6	206.1	3.75	150.3	6	0.375	0.426	5.01	0.501	1.5	0.342	99.9	0
0	39.99	4.65	11.78	30.38	49.91	190.03	1.488	152.5	15	0.372	0.434	4.96	0.496	1.519	0.192	102	0
0	99.9	4.5	8.1	20.1	50.4	171.3	3.75	0	6	0.375	0.426	5.01	0.501	1.5	0.063	99.9	0
0	15.37	17.98	40.6	156.6	171.1	207.35	15.23	228.5	60.03	1.566	1.711	20.01	2.03	6.003	26.874	403.1	0
0	10.89	4.95	17.49	60.06	63.69	239.91	4.125		13.2	0.413	0.465	5.498	0.548	0	0.304	109.9	0
0	99.9	9	8.4	21.6	24.9	287.7	3.75	150.6	6	0.375	0.426	5.01	0.501	1.5	0.054	200.1	0
0	1.96	8.4	3.08	14	25.2	203	0.076	150.4	6.16	0.364	0.428	5.012	0.504	1.512	0.039	102.2	0
0	14.7	14.234	17.15	51.45	68.6	514.5	0.318	0	0	0.279	0.333	3.959	0.098	0	0.049	83.3	0
0	7.26	1.452	12.1	26.62	50.82	539.66	0.169	0	0	0.201	0.133	1.747	0.051	0	0.048	79.86	0
0	5.27	1.922	2.17	9.61	26.35	119.66	1.519	151	6.014	0.372	0.434	4.991	0.496	1.519	0.034	102	0
0	22.55	2.035	67.65	178.75	247.5	157.3	1.705	252.5	17.6	0.424	0.479	5.665	0.561	1.705	0.77	112.8	0
0	7.32	0.488	7.32	41.48	48.8	422.12	0.39	0	0	0	0	0.976	0.066	0	0.049	7.32	0
0	154.24	11.954	14.46	43.38	48.2	363.91	0.41	559.1	0	0.559	0.506	7.454	0.745	0	0.048	149.4	0
0	112.95	9.764	12.55	95.38	45.18	336.34	0.351	0	0	0.143	0.065	1.358	0.03		0.05	30.12	0

EvaluEat Code	Food Name	Amt	Wt (g)	Energy (kcal)	Prot (g)	Carb (g)	Fiber (g)	Fat (g)	Mono (g)	Poly (g)	Sat (g)
8259	Cereal, Crispix/Kellogg	1 cup (1 NLEA serving)	29	109.33	1.972	24.94	0.145	0.232	0.058	0.116	0.058
8173	Cereal, Farina, enriched, prep w/salt	1 cup	233	111.84	3.309	24.395	0.699	0.163	0.023	0.07	0.023
8244	Cereal, Fiber One/General Mills	.5 cup (1 NLEA serving)	30	59.1	2.4	24.3	14.4	0.81	0.132	0.41	0.12
8030	Cereal, Froot Loops/Kellogg	1 cup (1 NLEA serving)	30	117.9	1.02	26.25	0.93	1.23	0.129	0.204	0.456
8069	Cereal, Frosted Flakes/Kellogg	.75 cup (1 NLEA serving)	31	113.77	1.023	27.993	0.992	0.161	0.028	0.081	0.053
8319	Cereal, Frosted Mini-Wheats, bite size/Kellogg	1 cup, bite size	55	189.2	5.555	44.55	5.5	0.88	0.132	0.55	0.198
8327	Cereal, Fruit & Fiber Dates, Raisins & Walnuts/Kraft, Post	1 cup (1 NLEA serving)	55	211.75	3.905	41.91	5.335	3.08			0.44
8037	Cereal, granola (oats & wheat germ) homemade	1 cup	122	597.8	18.141	64.599	10.492	29.719	9.324	13.066	5.535
8329	Cereal, Grape-Nuts/Kraft, Post	.5 cup (1 NLEA serving)	58	208.22	6.264	47.154	5.046	1.102			0.232
8333	Cereal, Honey Bunches of Oats Honey Roasted/Kraft, Post	.75 cup (1 NLEA serving)	30	118.2	2.13	24.57	1.47	1.65			0.24
8242	Cereal, Just Right w/crunchy nuggets/Kellogg	1 cup (1 NLEA serving)	55	204.05	4.235	46.035	2.805	1.485	0.275	1.045	0.11
8048	Cereal, Kix/General Mills	1.333 cup (1 NLEA serving)	30	113.1	1.8	25.8	0.9	0.6	0.159	0.2	0.15
8049	Cereal, Life, plain/Quaker	.75 cup (1 NLEA serving)	32	120	3.174	24.992	2.112	1.402	0.477	0.451	0.259
8284	Cereal, Low-Fat Granola with Raisins/Kellogg	.667 cup (1 NLEA serving)	55	201.3	4.4	44	2.75	2.75	1.375	0.55	0.825
8050	Cereal, Lucky Charms/General Mills	1 cup (1 NLEA serving)	30	114	2.1	24.9	1.5	1.14	0.252	0.288	0.24
8176	Cereal, Maltex, prep w/salt	1 cup	249	189.24	5.702	39.367	2.241	1.071	0.115	0.386	0.152
8178	Cereal, Malt-O-Meal, plain & chocolate, prep w/salt	1 cup	240	122.4	3.6	25.92	0.96	0.24			0.048
8285	Cereal, Mueslix Apple & Almond Crunch/Kellogg	3/4 cup	55	210.65	5.39	40.865	4.675	4.95	2.585	1.045	1.045
8345	Cereal, Multi-Bran Chex/General Mills	1 cup	49	165.62	3.43	41.16	6.37	1.225	0.299	0.537	0.245
8265	Cereal, Multigrain Cheerios/General Mills	1 cup	30	111.9	2.556	24.45	1.92	1.089	0.297	0.15	0.249
8207	Cereal, Multi-Grain Flakes/Healthy Choice, Kellogg	1 cup	30	103.8	2.55	25.23	2.82	0.36	0.15	0.18	0.03
8291	Cereal, Nutri-Grain Almond and Raisin/Kellogg	1 oz	28.35	104.045	2.268	22	2.268	1.616	0.737	0.822	0.057
8152	Cereal, Nutri-Grain, Wheat	1 oz	28.34	102.02	2.466	23.976	1.785	0.283	0.032	0.119	0.052
8216	Cereal, Oat Bran Cereal/Quaker	1.25 cup	57	212.04	7.057	42.687	5.643	2.913	0.895	1.163	0.519
8214	Cereal, Oatmeal Squares/Quaker	1 cup (1 NLEA serving)	56	211.68	6.182	43.87	3.976	2.419	0.812	0.986	0.504
8125	Cereal, oatmeal, instant, w/apple & cinnamon, prep/Quaker	1 packet, prepared	149	129.63	2.712	26.477	2.682	1.49	0.513	0.428	0.249
8123	Cereal, oats, instant, plain, fortified, prep	1 cup, cooked	234	128.7	5.429	22.441	3.744	2.129	0.672	0.782	0.349
8180	Cereal, oats, regular/quick/instant, cooked w/salt	1 cup	234	145.08	6.084	25.272	3.978	2.34	0.749	0.866	0.421
8196	Cereal, Pop-Tarts Crunch, frosted strawberry/Kellogg	3/4 cup	30	117.9	1.35	26.76	0	0.81	0.24	0.27	0.33
8066	Cereal, Puffed Rice/Quaker	1 cup (1 NLEA serving)	14	53.62	0.98	12.288	0.196	0.126	0.025	0.048	0.045

Chol (g)	Calc (mg)	Iron (mg)	Mag (mg)	Phos (mg)	Pota (mg)	Sodi (mg)	Zinc (mg)	Vit A (RAE)	Vit C (mg)	Thia (mg)	Ribo (mg)	Niac (mg)	Vit B$_6$ (mg)	Vit B$_{12}$ (µg)	Vit E (mg)	Fol (µg)	Alc (g)
0	6.09	8.12	7.25	26.39	37.7	209.96	1.45	150.2	5.8	0.551	0.609	6.989	0.696	2.088	0.058	279.9	0
0	9.32	1.165	4.66	27.96	30.29	766.57	0.186	0	0	0.142	0.1	1.139	0.016	0	0.023	79.22	0
0	99.9	4.5	60	150	232.2	128.7	3.75	0	6	0.375	0.426	5.01	0.501	1.5	0.213	99.9	0
0	23.4	4.23	8.7	19.2	32.7	141.3	1.41	144.9	14.1	0.36	0.39	4.68	0.48	1.41	0.144	93.9	0
0	1.55	4.495	2.48	10.54	22.63	148.49	0.056	160.3	6.2	0.372	0.465	5.022	0.496	1.55	0.016	101.4	0
0	17.6	15.4	64.9	161.7	189.75	4.4	1.76	0	0	0.407	0.456	5.39	0.539	1.617	0	107.8	0
0	23.65	5.401	66	161.7	243.65	279.95	1.502		0	0.374	0.424	5	0.501	1.502		100.1	
0	95.16	5.185	213.5	557.54	655.14	26.84	5.014	1.22	1.464	0.898	0.356	2.58	0.379	0	7.174	101.3	0
0	19.72	16.199	58	138.62	178.06	353.8	1.201		0	0.377	0.423	5	0.499	1.502		99.76	
0	6.3	8.1	16.5	48.3	51.6	192.6	0.3		0	0.375	0.426	5.001	0.501	1.5		99.9	
0	14.3	16.225	34.1	106.15	121	337.7	0.88	375.7	0	0.385	0.44	5.005	0.495	1.485	2.2	102.3	0
0	150	8.1	8.1	39.9	35.1	267.3	3.75	159.6	6.3	0.375	0.426	5.01	0.501	1.5	0.066	200.1	0
0	112	8.954	30.72	132.8	91.2	164.16	4.128	0.64	0	0.403	0.467	5.504	0.55	0	0.176	416	0
0	23.1	1.65	41.25	128.7	165	135.3	3.465	206.3	3.3	0.347	0.385	4.565	1.815	5.5	4.615	369.6	0
0	99.9	4.5	15.9	60	57.3	203.4	3.75	150.3	6	0.375	0.426	5.01	0.501	1.5	0.093	200.1	0
0	22.41	1.793	57.27	176.79	266.43	189.24	1.868	0	0	0.264	0.102	2.373	0.077	0	1.12	29.88	0
0	4.8	9.6	4.8	24	31.2	324	0.168	0	0	0.48	0.24	5.76	0.019	0		4.8	0
0	33.55	4.675	62.7	175.45	209	270.05	3.135		0	0.385	0.44	5.17	0.495	1.265	5.775	110	0
0	89.18	14.455	53.41	178.36	189.63	321.93	3.332	133.8	5.39	0.333	0.377	4.459	0.446	1.323	0.152	356.2	0
0	57	8.1	29.7	114.3	97.2	254.1	3.75		15	0.375	0.426	5.001	0.501	0	0.191	99.9	0
0	8.7	6.3	29.1	86.4	100.2	174	1.5		0	0.54	0.6	6.99	0.69	2.1	3	90	0
0	86.468	0.709	6.521	96.674	101.21	100.643	1.928		0	0.198	0.227	2.58	0.255	0.765	2.835	56.7	0
0	7.935	0.799	22.105	105.992	77.085	192.712	3.741		15.02	0.368	0.425	4.988	0.51	1.502	7.482	100	0
0	108.87	17.072	95.76	295.26	249.66	207.48	3.961	165.3	6.612	0.41	0.467	5.495	0.547	0	2.103	420.1	0
0	112.56	17.069	65.52	205.52	204.96	268.8	4.239	166.9	6.384	0.386	0.476	5.628	0.549	0	1.49	439.6	0
0	110.26	3.844	28.31	93.87	108.77	165.39	0.641	321.8	0.298	0.288	0.346	4.066	0.428	0	0.134	84.93	0
0	131.04	10.156	53.82	126.36	124.02	105.3	1.076	376.7	0	0.339	0.405	4.76	0.501	0	0.234	100.6	0
0	18.72	1.591	56.16	177.84	131.04	374.4	1.147	0	0	0.257	0.047	0.304	0.047	0		9.36	0
0	2.4	4.08	9.6	17.4	27.3	113.7	3.42		13.8	0.33	0.39	4.56	0.45	0	0.083	90	0
0	1.26	0.4	4.2	16.52	16.24	0.7	0.154	0	0	0.062	0.036	0.493	0	0	0.017	21.56	0

EvaluEat Code	Food Name	Amt	Wt (g)	Energy (kcal)	Prot (g)	Carb (g)	Fiber (g)	Fat (g)	Mono (g)	Poly (g)	Sat (g)
8060	Cereal, Raisin Bran/Kellogg	1 cup									
		(1 NLEA serving)	61	194.59	5.185	46.543	7.259	1.525	0.305	0.885	0.336
8287	Cereal, Raisin Squares Mini-Wheats/Kellogg	.75 cup									
		(1 NLEA serving)	55	184.8	5.17	43.56	5.17	0.88	0.192	0.495	0.192
8194	Cereal, Reese's Peanut Butter Puffs/General Mills	.75 cup									
		(1 NLEA serving)	30	127.5	1.8	23.4	0	2.91	1.243	0.903	0.57
8064	Cereal, Rice Chex	1.25 cup									
		(1 NLEA serving)	31	116.87	1.86	26.66	0.31	0.31	0.067	0.069	0.124
8065	Cereal, Rice Krispies/Kellogg	1.25 cup									
		(1 NLEA serving)	33	118.8	2.046	29.04	0.132	0.429	0.132	0.175	0.122
8318	Cereal, Smart Start/Kellogg	1 cup	50	182	3.1	43	2.3	0.6	0.15	0.25	0.2
8264	Cereal, S'mores Grahams/General Mills	3/4 cup	30	117	1.677	25.59	0.84	1.2	0.393	0.15	0.177
8067	Cereal, Special K/Kellogg	1 cup									
		(1 NLEA serving)	31	117.49	6.975	22.01	0.744	0.48	0.124	0.248	0.108
8203	Cereal, Sun Crunchers/General Mills	1 cup	55	215.6	4.857	43.742	2.2	3.157	2.046	0.33	0.341
8059	Cereal, Sweet Crunch/Quisp	1 cup	27	109.35	1.199	22.95	0.702	1.644	0.302	0.205	0.427
8088	Cereal, Team Cheerios/General Mills	1 cup									
		(1 NLEA serving)	30	113.1	2.151	25.068	1.65	1.131	0.329	0.462	0.182
8341	Cereal, The Original Shredded Wheat'n Bran/Kraft, Post	1.25 cup									
		(1 NLEA serving)	59	197.06	7.375	47.141	7.906	0.826			0.118
8219	Cereal, Toasted Oatmeal Cereal, Honey Nut/Quaker	1 cup									
		(1 NLEA serving)	49	192.08	4.484	37.926	3.479	3.655	1.71	1.005	0.534
8350	Cereal, Toasty O's/Malt-o-Meal	1 cup									
		(1 NLEA serving)	30	111.6	3.321	22.401	2.7	1.809	0.669	0.609	0.369
8247	Cereal, Total Raisin Bran/General Mills	1 cup									
		(1 NLEA serving)	55	171.05	3.85	41.25	4.95	1.1	0.149	0.524	0.22
8077	Cereal, Total/General Mills	.75 cup									
		(1 NLEA serving)	30	97.2	2.4	22.5	2.4	0.75	0.123	0.273	0.159
8078	Cereal, Trix/General Mills	1 cup									
		(1 NLEA serving)	30	117.3	0.9	26.7	0.9	1.14	0.596	0.274	0.18
8305	Cereal, Waffle Crisp/Post	1 cup									
		(1 NLEA serving)	30	129	1.8	23.97	0.54	2.94	1.291	1.225	0.42
8082	Cereal, Wheat Chex	1 cup									
		(1 NLEA serving)	30	103.5	3	24.3	3.3	0.6	0.079	0.242	0.12
8157	Cereal, wheat, puffed, fortified	1 cup	12	43.68	1.764	9.552	0.528	0.144			0.024
8147	Cereal, wheat, shredded, large biscuit	2 biscuits									
		(1 NLEA serving)	46	156.4	5.235	36.138	5.336	1.104	0.161	0.58	0.207
8089	Cereal, Wheaties/General Mills	1 cup									
		(1 NLEA serving)	30	106.5	3	24.3	3	0.96	0.286	0.35	0.18
1163	Cheese fondue	1 cup	215	492.35	30.594	8.106	0	28.961	7.66	1.041	18.75
44048	Cheese food, imitation	1 cubic inch	10.2	14.382	2.285	0.898	0	0.133	0.039	0.005	0.083
19434	Cheese puffs and twists, corn based, low-fat	1 oz	28.35	122.47	2.41	20.511	3.033	3.43	0.992	1.627	0.595
43276	Cheese spread, cream cheese base	1 cup	186	548.7	13.206	6.51	0	53.196	15.012	1.921	33.517
1004	Cheese, blue	1 oz	28.35	100.08	6.067	0.663	0	8.148	2.205	0.227	5.293
1006	Cheese, brie	1 cubic inch	17	56.78	3.528	0.076	0	4.706	1.362	0.14	2.96

Chol (g)	Calc (mg)	Iron (mg)	Mag (mg)	Phos (mg)	Pota (mg)	Sodi (mg)	Zinc (mg)	Vit A (RAE)	Vit C (mg)	Thia (mg)	Ribo (mg)	Niac (mg)	Vit B$_6$ (mg)	Vit B$_{12}$ (µg)	Vit E (mg)	Fol (µg)	Alc (g)
0	29.28	4.636	82.96	258.64	372.1	361.73	1.549	154.9	0.427	0.39	0.439	5.185	0.519	1.549	0.476	103.7	0
0	21.45	15.4	43.45	155.65	264.55	3.3	1.54	0	0	0.391	0.44	5.17	0.517	1.595	0.286	104	0
0	99.9	4.5	15.9	20.1	41.7	166.5	3.75	150.3	6	0.375	0.426	5.01	0.501	1.5	0.36	99.9	0
0	103.23	9.3	9.3	35.34	30.38	291.71	3.875	155.3	6.2	0.387	0.44	5.177	0.518	1.55	0.016	206.8	0
0	5.28	1.815	13.2	45.87	43.89	318.78	0.462	153.1	6.369	0.376	0.462	5.049	0.495	1.485	0.036	104	0
0	17	18	32	101	102	280.5	15.1	231	15.5	1.55	1.7	20	2	6	20.135	402.5	0
0	14.4	4.5	10.8	40.5	48	212.4	3.75		15	0.375	0.426	5.001	0.501	0	0.218	99.9	0
0	9.3	8.37	19.22	67.89	60.76	223.51	0.899	230.3	20.99	0.527	0.589	7.13	1.984	6.045	7.074	399.9	0
0	85.25	4.499	43.45	171.6	129.8	380.05	0.798		15.02	0.374	0.424	5	0.501	0	0.056	99.55	0
0	2.97	4.96	14.85	45.36	51.03	200.07	4.134	10.8	2.916	0.413	0.467	5.511	0.551	0	0.184	420.1	0
	105.9	4.5	21.6	78.3	69.6	223.5	3.75		6	0.375	0.426	5.001	0.501	1.5	0.159	202.5	
0	26.55	2.466	80.83	234.82	247.8	2.95	1.929		0	0.153	0.071	3.723	0.195	0		27.14	
0	133.28	6.806	60.27	166.11	180.81	215.6	5.39	215.6	1.47	0.588	0.666	7.183	0.715	0	2.68	436.6	0
0	39.9	8.1	32.1	99.9	93.9	284.1	3.75	375.3	15	0.375	0.426	5.001	0.501	0	0.189	99.9	0
0	999.9	17.985	40.15	100.1	354.2	239.25	15.02	150.2	0	1.502	1.699	20.02	2.002	5.995	20.301	399.9	0
0	999.9	18	24	80.1	89.4	191.7	15	150.3	60	1.5	1.701	20.01	2.001	6	20.133	399.9	0
0	99.9	4.5	3.6	20.1	17.4	194.1	3.75	150.3	6	0.375	0.426	5.01	0.501	1.5	0.597	99.9	0
0	6	1.8	11.7	33.9	33.6	129.6	0.408	221.1	0	0.375	0.426	5.001	0.501	0	0.225	99.9	0
0	60	8.7	24	90	112.5	267.3	2.4	90	3.6	0.225	0.255	3	0.3	0.9	0.216	240	0
0	3.36	3.804	17.4	42.6	41.76	0.48	0.283	0	0	0.312	0.216	4.236	0.02	0		3.84	0
0	20.24	1.509	62.56	164.68	170.66	5.52	1.426	0	9.246	0.142	0.115	2.636	1.467	0	0.304	27.14	0
0	0	8.1	32.1	99.9	111	217.5	7.5	150.3	6	0.75	0.849	9.99	0.999	3	0.186	200.1	0
96.75	1023.4	0.839	49.45	657.9	225.75	283.8	4.214	234.4	0	0.058	0.421	0.409	0.118	1.785		17.2	0.645
0.612	56.304	0.093	3.57	50.898	34.272	126.378	0.336	1.02	0	0.003	0.049	0.015	0.013	0.125	0.001	0.816	0
0.284	101.21	0.363	11.624	101.21	81.081	364.298	0.607	12.47	6.067	0.153	0.173	2.024	0.201	0.607	1.205	27.5	0
167.4	132.06	2.102	11.16	169.26	208.32	1251.78	0.949	634.3	0	0.037	0.353	1.767	0.074	0.744	1.432	22.32	0
21.263	149.688	0.088	6.521	109.715	72.576	395.483	0.754	56.13	0	0.008	0.108	0.288	0.047	0.346	0.071	10.21	0
17	31.28	0.085	3.4	31.96	25.84	106.93	0.405	29.58	0	0.012	0.088	0.065	0.04	0.28	0.041	11.05	0

EvaluEat Code	Food Name	Amt	Wt (g)	Energy (kcal)	Prot (g)	Carb (g)	Fiber (g)	Fat (g)	Mono (g)	Poly (g)	Sat (g)
1007	Cheese, camembert	1 oz	28.35	85.05	5.613	0.13	0	6.878	1.991	0.205	4.326
1009	Cheese, cheddar	1 cup, shredded	113	455.39	28.137	1.446	0	37.448	10.612	1.064	23.834
1168	Cheese, cheddar or colby, low-fat	1 cup, shredded	113	195.49	27.516	2.158	0	7.91	2.353	0.251	4.906
1012	Cheese, cottage, creamed, large or small curd	4 oz	113	116.39	14.114	3.028	0	5.096	1.452	0.157	3.224
1015	Cheese, cottage, lowfat, 2% fat	4 oz	113	101.7	15.526	4.102	0	2.181	0.622	0.067	1.38
1014	Cheese, cottage, nonfat, uncreamed, dry, large or small curd	4 oz	113	96.05	19.515	2.091	0	0.475	0.124	0.017	0.308
1017	Cheese, cream	1 tbsp	14.5	50.605	1.095	0.386	0	5.056	1.427	0.183	3.185
1186	Cheese, cream, fat-free	1 oz	28.34	27.206	4.084	1.644	0	0.385	0.094	0.017	0.255
1018	Cheese, edam	1 oz	28.35	101.21	7.085	0.405	0	7.881	2.303	0.189	4.982
1019	Cheese, feta	1 oz	28.35	74.844	4.029	1.16	0	6.033	1.311	0.168	4.237
1020	Cheese, fontina	1 cup, shredded	108	420.12	27.648	1.674	0	33.631	9.382	1.786	20.732
1022	Cheese, gouda	1 oz	28.35	100.93	7.07	0.629	0	7.779	2.196	0.186	4.994
1188	Cheese, Kraft Cheez Whiz pasteurized process cheese sauce	2 tbsp	33	91.08	3.96	3.036	0.099	6.93			4.323
1190	Cheese, Kraft Free Singles American nonfat pasteurized process cheese product	1 slice	21	31.08	4.767	2.457	0.042	0.21			0.147
1165	Cheese, Mexican, queso anejo	1 oz	28.35	105.75	6.078	1.313	0	8.499	2.418	0.255	5.396
1025	Cheese, monterey	1 cup, shredded	113	421.49	27.662	0.768	0	34.216	9.889	1.016	21.545
1028	Cheese, mozzarella, part skim milk	1 oz	28.35	72.009	6.878	0.785	0	4.513	1.279	0.134	2.867
1026	Cheese, mozzarella, whole milk	1 oz	28.35	85.05	6.285	0.621	0	6.336	1.863	0.217	3.729
1030	Cheese, muenster	1 cup, shredded	113	415.84	26.453	1.266	0	33.945	9.843	0.747	21.598
1032	Cheese, parmesan, grated	1 tbsp	5	21.55	1.923	0.203	0	1.431	0.419	0.059	0.865
42205	Cheese, pasteurized process, cheddar or American, fat-free	1 cup	186	275.28	41.85	24.924	0	1.488	0.426	0.047	0.937
1035	Cheese, provolone	1 oz	28.35	99.509	7.252	0.607	0	7.547	2.096	0.218	4.842
1037	Cheese, ricotta, part skim milk	1 cup	246	339.48	28.019	12.644	0	19.459	5.692	0.64	12.12
1036	Cheese, ricotta, whole milk	1 cup	246	428.04	27.7	7.478	0	31.931	8.922	0.947	20.406
1038	Cheese, romano	1 oz	28.35	109.72	9.015	1.029	0	7.637	2.222	0.168	4.852
1039	Cheese, roquefort	1 oz	28.35	104.61	6.107	0.567	0	8.686	2.402	0.374	5.461
1040	Cheese, Swiss	1 oz	28.35	107.73	7.635	1.525	0	7.881	2.062	0.276	5.04
18147	Cheesecake, commercially prep	1 piece (1/6 of 17 oz cake)	80	256.8	4.4	20.4	0.32	18	6.907	1.282	7.937
18148	Cheesecake, no bake mix, prep	1 piece (1/12 of 9" dia)	99	271.26	5.445	35.145	1.881	12.573	4.474	0.8	6.624
9367	Cherries, sweet, canned, heavy syrup, drained	1 fruit (2-1/4" high x 2-1/2" dia)	122	101.26	0.891	25.705	3.05	0.256	0.06	0.067	0.049
5028	Chicken liver, simmered	1 container, cooked, yield from 400 g raw liver	256	427.52	62.618	2.227	0	16.666	3.625	3.249	5.274
22703	Chicken & dumplings, canned/Sweet Sue	1 serving	240	218.4	15.12	22.8	2.64	7.44	2.952	1.625	1.795
7932	Chicken breast, fat-free, mesquite flavor, sliced	1 serving 2 slices	42	33.6	7.056	0.945	0	0.164	0.067	0.025	0.055
7933	Chicken breast, oven-roasted, fat-free, sliced	1 serving 2 slices	42	33.18	7.052	0.911	0	0.164	0.051	0.031	0.055
5026	Chicken heart, simmered	1 cup, chopped or diced	145	268.25	38.295	0.145	0	11.484	2.914	3.335	3.277
22527	Chicken pie, frozen/Stouffers	1 package yields	283	571.66	23.206	36.507	3.113	37.073	12.367	10.443	10.726
5058	Chicken, broiler or fryer, breast w/skin, batter fried	1/2 breast, bone removed	140	364	34.776	12.586	0.42	18.48	7.644	4.312	4.928

Chol (g)	Calc (mg)	Iron (mg)	Mag (mg)	Phos (mg)	Pota (mg)	Sodi (mg)	Zinc (mg)	Vit A (RAE)	Vit C (mg)	Thia (mg)	Ribo (mg)	Niac (mg)	Vit B$_6$ (mg)	Vit B$_{12}$ (µg)	Vit E (mg)	Fol (µg)	Alc (g)
20.412	109.998	0.094	5.67	98.375	53.015	238.707	0.675	68.32	0	0.008	0.138	0.179	0.064	0.369	0.06	17.58	0
118.65	814.73	0.768	31.64	578.56	110.74	701.73	3.514	299.5	0	0.031	0.424	0.09	0.084	0.938	0.328	20.34	0
23.73	468.95	0.475	18.08	546.92	74.58	691.56	2.057	67.8	0	0.014	0.25	0.058	0.051	0.554	0.068	12.43	0
16.95	67.8	0.158	5.65	149.16	94.92	457.65	0.418	49.72	0	0.024	0.184	0.142	0.076	0.701	0.045	13.56	0
9.04	77.97	0.181	6.78	170.63	108.48	458.78	0.475	23.73	0	0.027	0.209	0.163	0.086	0.802	0.023	14.69	0
7.91	36.16	0.26	4.52	117.52	36.16	14.69	0.531	10.17	0	0.028	0.16	0.175	0.093	0.938	0	16.95	0
15.95	11.6	0.174	0.87	15.08	17.255	42.92	0.078	53.07	0	0.002	0.029	0.015	0.007	0.061	0.043	1.885	0
2.267	52.429	0.051	3.968	122.996	46.194	154.453	0.249	79.07	0	0.014	0.049	0.045	0.014	0.156	0.003	10.49	0
25.232	207.239	0.125	8.505	151.956	53.298	273.578	1.063	68.89	0	0.01	0.11	0.023	0.022	0.437	0.068	4.536	0
25.232	139.766	0.184	5.387	95.54	17.577	316.386	0.816	35.44	0	0.044	0.239	0.281	0.12	0.479	0.051	9.072	0
125.28	594	0.248	15.12	373.68	69.12	864	3.78	281.9	0	0.023	0.22	0.162	0.09	1.814	0.292	6.48	0
32.319	198.45	0.068	8.222	154.791	34.304	232.187	1.106	46.78	0	0.009	0.095	0.018	0.023	0.437	0.068	5.954	0
24.75	118.47	0.063		265.98	79.2	540.54	0.541		0.132		0.079						
3.36	149.52	0.01		193.83	49.56	272.58	0.525		0.042		0.059						
29.768	192.78	0.133	7.938	125.874	24.665	320.639	0.833	15.31	0	0.006	0.059	0.009	0.013	0.391	0.074	0.284	0
100.57	842.98	0.814	30.51	501.72	91.53	605.68	3.39	223.74	0	0.017	0.441	0.105	0.089	0.938	0.294	20.34	0
18.144	221.697	0.062	6.521	131.261	23.814	175.487	0.782	36.01	0	0.005	0.086	0.03	0.02	0.232	0.04	2.552	0
22.397	143.168	0.125	5.67	100.359	21.546	177.755	0.828	50.75	0	0.009	0.08	0.029	0.01	0.646	0.054	1.985	0
108.48	810.21	0.463	30.51	528.84	151.42	709.64	3.175	336.7	0	0.015	0.362	0.116	0.063	1.661	0.294	13.56	0
4.4	55.45	0.045	1.9	36.45	6.25	76.45	0.193	6	0	0.001	0.024	0.006	0.002	0.113	0.013	0.5	0
20.46	1281.54	0.521	66.96	1740.96	535.68	2842.08	6.361	818.4	0	0.112	0.893	0.391	0.167	2.083	0.502	50.22	0
19.562	214.326	0.147	7.938	140.616	39.123	248.346	0.916	66.91	0	0.005	0.091	0.044	0.021	0.414	0.065	2.835	0
76.26	669.12	1.082	36.9	450.18	307.5	307.5	3.296	263.22	0	0.052	0.455	0.192	0.049	0.713	0.172	31.98	0
125.46	509.22	0.935	27.06	388.68	258.3	206.64	2.854	295.2	0	0.032	0.48	0.256	0.106	0.836	0.271	29.52	0
29.484	301.644	0.218	11.624	215.46	24.381	340.2	0.731	27.22	0	0.01	0.105	0.022	0.024	0.318	0.065	1.985	0
25.515	187.677	0.159	8.505	111.132	25.799	512.852	0.59	83.35	0	0.011	0.166	0.208	0.035	0.181		13.892	0
26.082	224.249	0.057	10.773	160.745	21.83	54.432	1.236	62.37	0	0.018	0.084	0.026	0.024	0.947	0.108	1.701	0
44	40.8	0.504	8.8	74.4	72	165.6	0.408	113.6	0.32	0.022	0.154	0.156	0.042	0.136	1.265	14.4	0
28.71	170.28	0.465	18.81	231.66	208.89	376.2	0.455	95.04	0.495	0.12	0.26	0.488	0.051	0.307		29.7	0
0	12.2	0.427	10.98	24.4	180.56	3.66	0.122	14.64	4.392	0.027	0.052	0.483	0.038	0	0.281	6.1	0
1441.28	28.16	29.773	64	1036.8	673.28	194.56	10.19	10191	71.424	0.745	5.102	28.275	1.933	43.136	2.099	1480	0
36		2.568				945.6											0
15.12	1.68	0.126	15.12	107.52	132.72	436.8	0.252	0	0	0.006	0.01	1.152	0.05	0.029	0.022	0.42	0
15.12	2.52	0.134	3.78	25.2	28.14	456.54	0.126	0	0	0.008	0.012	1.44	0.063	0.038	0.028	0.42	0
350.9	27.55	13.094	29	288.55	191.4	69.6	10.59	11.6	2.61	0.102	1.074	4.064	0.464	10.571		116	0
76.41	101.88	3				942.39											0
119	28	1.75	33.6	259	281.4	385	1.33	28	0	0.161	0.204	14.732	0.602	0.42	1.484	21	0

EvaluEat Code	Food Name	Amt	Wt (g)	Energy (kcal)	Prot (g)	Carb (g)	Fiber (g)	Fat (g)	Mono (g)	Poly (g)	Sat (g)
5060	Chicken, broiler or fryer, breast w/skin, roasted	1 cup, chopped or diced	140	275.8	41.72	0	0	10.892	4.242	2.324	3.066
5063	Chicken, broiler or fryer, breast, no skin, fried	1/2 breast, bone and skin removed	86	160.82	28.758	0.439	0	4.051	1.479	0.92	1.109
5064	Chicken, broiler or fryer, breast, no skin, roasted	1 cup, chopped or diced	140	231	43.428	0	0	4.998	1.736	1.078	1.414
5035	Chicken, broiler or fryer, dark meat w/skin, batter fried	yield from 1 lb ready-to-cook chicken	167	497.66	36.489	15.665		31.129	12.659	7.398	8.266
5037	Chicken, broiler or fryer, dark meat w/skin, roasted	yield from 1 lb ready-to-cook chicken	101	255.53	26.23	0	0	15.938	6.252	3.525	4.414
5044	Chicken, broiler or fryer, dark meat, no skin, fried	1 cup	140	334.6	40.586	3.626	0	16.268	6.048	3.878	4.368
5045	Chicken, broiler or fryer, dark meat, no skin, roasted	1 cup, chopped or diced	140	287	38.318	0	0	13.622	4.984	3.164	3.724
5067	Chicken, broiler or fryer, drumstick w/skin, batter fried	1 drumstick, bone removed	72	192.96	15.804	5.962	0.216	11.34	4.63	2.729	2.981
5069	Chicken, broiler or fryer, drumstick w/skin, roasted	1 drumstick, bone removed	52	112.32	14.056	0	0	5.798	2.21	1.3	1.586
5072	Chicken, broiler or fryer, drumstick, no skin, fried	yield from 1 lb ready-to-cook chicken	25	48.75	7.155	0	0	2.02	0.735	0.493	0.533
5073	Chicken, broiler or fryer, drumstick, no skin, roasted	1 drumstick, bone and skin removed	44	75.68	12.448	0	0	2.49	0.823	0.603	0.651
5021	Chicken, broiler or fryer, giblets, floured, fried	1 cup, chopped or diced	145	401.65	47.183	6.307	0	19.517	6.409	4.901	5.51
5022	Chicken, broiler or fryer, giblets, simmered	1 cup, chopped or diced	145	229.1	39.368	0.624	0	6.525	1.395	1.177	1.917
5024	Chicken, broiler or fryer, gizzard, simmered	1 cup, chopped or diced	145	211.7	44.066	0	0	3.886	0.766	0.512	0.972
5076	Chicken, broiler or fryer, leg w/skin, batter fried	1 leg, bone removed	158	431.34	34.397	13.778	0.474	25.549	10.396	6.083	6.762
5078	Chicken, broiler or fryer, leg w/skin, roasted	1 leg, bone removed	114	264.48	29.594	0	0	15.344	5.974	3.42	4.241
5081	Chicken, broiler or fryer, leg, no skin, fried	1 leg, bone and skin removed	94	195.52	26.677	0.611	0	8.761	3.224	2.087	2.341
5082	Chicken, broiler or fryer, leg, no skin, roasted	1 leg, bone and skin removed	95	181.45	25.679	0	0	8.009	2.897	1.872	2.175
5030	Chicken, broiler or fryer, light meat w/skin, batter fried	1/2 chicken, bone removed	188	520.76	44.274	17.86		29.027	11.976	6.768	7.746
5032	Chicken, broiler or fryer, light meat w/skin, roasted	1/2 chicken, bone removed	132	293.04	38.306	0	0	14.322	5.623	3.049	4.026
5040	Chicken, broiler or fryer, light meat, no skin, fried	1 cup	140	268.8	45.948	0.588	0	7.756	2.758	1.764	2.128
5041	Chicken, broiler or fryer, light meat, no skin, roasted	1 cup, chopped or diced	140	242.2	43.274	0	0	6.314	2.156	1.372	1.778

Chol (g)	Calc (mg)	Iron (mg)	Mag (mg)	Phos (mg)	Pota (mg)	Sodi (mg)	Zinc (mg)	Vit A (RAE)	Vit C (mg)	Thia (mg)	Ribo (mg)	Niac (mg)	Vit B_6 (mg)	Vit B_{12} (µg)	Vit E (mg)	Fol (µg)	Alc (g)
117.6	19.6	1.498	37.8	299.6	343	99.4	1.428	37.8	0	0.092	0.167	17.794	0.784	0.448	0.378	5.6	0
78.26	13.76	0.98	26.66	211.56	237.36	67.94	0.929	6.02	0	0.068	0.108	12.713	0.55	0.318	0.361	3.44	0
119	21	1.456	40.6	319.2	358.4	103.6	1.4	8.4	0	0.098	0.16	19.197	0.84	0.476	0.378	5.6	0
148.63	35.07	2.405	33.4	242.15	308.95	492.65	3.474	51.77	0	0.195	0.364	9.364	0.417	0.451		30.06	0
91.91	15.15	1.374	22.22	169.68	222.2	87.87	2.515	60.6	0	0.067	0.209	6.423	0.313	0.293		7.07	0
134.4	25.2	2.086	35	261.8	354.2	135.8	4.074	33.6	0	0.13	0.349	9.898	0.518	0.462		12.6	0
130.2	21	1.862	32.2	250.6	336	130.2	3.92	30.8	0	0.102	0.318	9.167	0.504	0.448	0.378	11.2	0
61.92	12.24	0.972	14.4	105.84	133.92	193.68	1.678	18.72	0	0.081	0.155	3.669	0.194	0.202		12.96	0
47.32	6.24	0.692	11.96	91	119.08	46.8	1.492	15.6	0	0.036	0.112	3.117	0.177	0.166	0.14	4.16	0
23.5	3	0.33	6	46.5	62.25	24	0.805	4.5	0	0.019	0.059	1.536	0.097	0.087	0.123	2.25	0
40.92	5.28	0.572	10.56	80.96	108.24	41.8	1.399	7.92	0	0.033	0.103	2.673	0.172	0.15	0.119	3.96	0
646.7	26.1	14.964	36.25	414.7	478.5	163.85	9.092	5194	12.62	0.141	2.21	15.931	0.885	19.3		549.6	0
640.9	20.3	10.208	20.3	419.05	324.8	97.15	6.134	2542	18.13	0.207	1.525	9.606	0.576	13.688	0.667	372.7	0
536.5	24.65	4.626	4.35	274.05	259.55	81.2	6.409	0	0	0.038	0.305	4.524	0.103	1.508	0.29	7.25	0
142.2	28.44	2.212	31.6	240.16	298.62	440.82	3.429	42.66	0	0.183	0.349	8.584	0.427	0.442		28.44	0
104.88	13.68	1.516	26.22	198.36	256.5	99.18	2.964	44.46	0	0.078	0.243	7.063	0.376	0.342	0.308	7.98	0
93.06	12.22	1.316	23.5	181.42	238.76	90.24	2.801	18.8	0	0.078	0.232	6.287	0.367	0.32		8.46	0
89.3	11.4	1.244	22.8	173.85	229.9	86.45	2.717	18.05	0	0.071	0.22	6.003	0.352	0.304	0.257	7.6	0
157.92	37.6	2.369	41.36	315.84	347.8	539.56	1.993	45.12	0	0.212	0.276	17.213	0.733	0.526		30.08	0
110.88	19.8	1.505	33	264	299.64	99	1.624	43.56	0	0.079	0.156	14.697	0.686	0.422		3.96	0
126	22.4	1.596	40.6	323.4	368.2	113.4	1.778	12.6	0	0.102	0.176	18.711	0.882	0.504		5.6	0
119	21	1.484	37.8	302.4	345.8	107.8	1.722	12.6	0	0.091	0.162	17.389	0.84	0.476	0.378	5.6	0

EvaluEat Code	Food Name	Amt	Wt (g)	Energy (kcal)	Prot (g)	Carb (g)	Fiber (g)	Fat (g)	Mono (g)	Poly (g)	Sat (g)
5007	Chicken, broiler or fryer, meat & skin, batter fried	yield from 1 lb ready-to-cook chicken	280	809.2	63.112	26.376	0.84	48.58	19.852	11.48	12.908
5009	Chicken, broiler or fryer, meat & skin, roasted	1 cup, chopped or diced	140	334.6	38.22	0	0	19.04	7.476	4.158	5.306
5012	Chicken, broiler or fryer, meat only, no skin, fried	1 cup, chopped or diced	140	306.6	42.798	2.366	0.14	12.768	4.69	3.01	3.444
5013	Chicken, broiler or fryer, meat only, no skin, roasted	1 cup, chopped or diced	140	266	40.502	0	0	10.374	3.724	2.366	2.856
5092	Chicken, broiler or fryer, thigh w/skin, batter fried	1 thigh, bone removed	86	238.22	18.585	7.809	0.258	14.216	5.762	3.354	3.793
5094	Chicken, broiler or fryer, thigh w/skin, roasted	1 thigh, bone removed	62	153.14	15.537	0	0	9.604	3.813	2.12	2.685
5097	Chicken, broiler or fryer, thigh, no skin, fried	1 thigh, bone and skin removed	52	113.36	14.654	0.614	0	5.356	1.986	1.264	1.446
5098	Chicken, broiler or fryer, thigh, no skin, roasted	1 thigh, bone and skin removed	52	108.68	13.489	0	0	5.658	2.158	1.29	1.576
5002	Chicken, broiler or fryer, whole, batter fried	1 chicken	1028	2991.5	234.8	92.828		180.21	73.296	42.662	48.008
5001	Chicken, broiler or fryer, whole, raw	1 chicken	1046	2228	191.73	1.36	0	155.12	63.597	33.367	44.35
5004	Chicken, broiler or fryer, whole, roasted	1 chicken	682	1595.9	182.64	0.409	0	90.501	35.259	19.778	25.234
5101	Chicken, broiler or fryer, wing w/skin, batter fried	1 wing, bone removed	49	158.76	9.736	5.361	0.147	10.687	4.39	2.484	2.857
5103	Chicken, broiler or fryer, wing w/skin, roasted	1 wing, bone removed	34	98.6	9.132	0	0	6.616	2.598	1.408	1.853
5106	Chicken, broiler or fryer, wing, no skin, fried	1 wing, bone and skin removed	20	42.2	6.03	0	0	1.83	0.616	0.414	0.5
5107	Chicken, broiler or fryer, wing, no skin, roasted	1 wing, bone and skin removed	21	42.63	6.397	0	0	1.707	0.548	0.374	0.475
22697	Chicken, chicken salad ready to serve sandwich salad/Libby Spreadable	1 serving	118	171.1	5.782	11.918		11.092	3.457	4.224	2.301
5335	Chicken, feet, boiled	1 cup chopped or diced, cooked	174	374.1	33.756	0.348	0	25.404	9.57	5.185	6.821
5277	Chicken, meat only w/broth, canned	1 can (5 oz)	142	234.3	30.913	0	0	11.289	4.473	2.485	3.124
43128	Chicken, meatless	1 cup	186	416.64	43.97	6.77	6.696	23.678	5.072	13.528	3.385
51608	Chicken, nugget, breaded/Pierre product #1879	1 piece	14.2	46.718	2.378	1.889	0.156	3.321	0.977	1.478	0.653
22904	Chili con carne w/beans, canned entree	1 serving	222	255.3	20.18	24.487	8.214	8.147	2.153	1.443	2.109
16059	Chili w/beans, canned	1 cup	256	286.72	14.618	30.49	11.264	14.054	5.97	0.927	6.021
22705	Chili w/o beans, canned entree/Hormel	1 cup	236	193.52	16.992	17.912	3.068	6.561	2.242	0.85	2.195
22720	Chili, vegetarian chili w/beans, canned entree/Hormel	1 cup	247	205.01	11.93	38.013	9.88	0.692	0.074	0.395	0.124
18606	Chocolate cake, snack cake, chocolate creme filling, Ding Dongs/Hostess	1 serving	80	368	3.12	45.36	1.84	19.36	3.992	1.198	11.036
19124	Chocolate, baking, Mexican, squares	1 tablet	20	85.2	0.728	15.482	0.8	3.118	1.009	0.232	1.721
14198	Cocoa mix, No Sugar Added Hot Cocoa Mix/Carnation	1 serving	15	54.75	4.304	8.433	0.75	0.426	0.136	0.014	0.203
14197	Cocoa mix, Rich Chocolate Hot Cocoa Mix/Carnation	1 serving	28	112	1.296	24.237	0.672	1.109	0.348	0.265	0.291
1105	Cocoa, hot, homemade w/whole milk	1 cup	250	192.5	8.8	26.575	2.5	5.825	1.692	0.085	3.577
18103	Coffee cake, cheese	1 piece (1/6 of 16 oz cake)	76	257.64	5.32	33.668	0.76	11.552	5.418	1.25	4.097

Chol (g)	Calc (mg)	Iron (mg)	Mag (mg)	Phos (mg)	Pota (mg)	Sodi (mg)	Zinc (mg)	Vit A (RAE)	Vit C (mg)	Thia (mg)	Ribo (mg)	Niac (mg)	Vit B$_6$ (mg)	Vit B$_{12}$ (µg)	Vit E (mg)	Fol (µg)	Alc (g)
243.6	58.8	3.836	58.8	434	518	817.6	4.676	78.4	0	0.322	0.529	19.72	0.868	0.784	3.472	50.4	0
123.2	21	1.764	32.2	254.8	312.2	114.8	2.716	65.8	0	0.088	0.235	11.882	0.56	0.42	0.378	7	0
131.6	23.8	1.89	37.8	287	359.8	127.4	3.136	25.2	0	0.119	0.277	13.528	0.672	0.476	0.644	9.8	0
124.6	21	1.694	35	273	340.2	120.4	2.94	22.4	0	0.097	0.249	12.842	0.658	0.462	0.378	8.4	0
79.98	15.48	1.247	18.06	133.3	165.12	247.68	1.754	24.94	0	0.102	0.195	4.915	0.224	0.241		16.34	0
57.66	7.44	0.831	13.64	107.88	137.64	52.08	1.463	29.76	0	0.042	0.131	3.946	0.192	0.18	0.167	4.34	0
53.04	6.76	0.759	13.52	103.48	134.68	49.4	1.451	10.92	0	0.046	0.133	3.702	0.198	0.172		4.68	0
49.4	6.24	0.681	12.48	95.16	123.76	45.76	1.336	10.4	0	0.038	0.12	3.393	0.182	0.161	0.14	4.16	0
1058.84	215.88	18.401	215.88	1624.24	1953.2	2919.52	19.64	1861	4.112	1.162	2.549	72.813	3.29	8.532		329	0
941.4	115.06	13.703	209.2	1558.54	1976.94	732.2	15.48	2427	27.2	0.638	1.946	69.444	3.556	11.611	3.849	313.8	0
729.74	102.3	11.321	156.86	1241.24	1445.84	538.78	14.73	1303	3.41	0.43	1.528	53.933	2.592	6.411	2.251	197.8	0
38.71	9.8	0.632	7.84	59.29	67.62	156.8	0.676	16.66	0	0.052	0.074	2.58	0.147	0.123		8.82	0
28.56	5.1	0.432	6.46	51.34	62.56	27.88	0.619	15.98	0	0.014	0.044	2.26	0.143	0.099	0.092	1.02	0
16.8	3	0.228	4.2	32.8	41.6	18.2	0.424	3.6	0	0.009	0.026	1.448	0.118	0.068		0.8	0
17.85	3.36	0.244	4.41	34.86	44.1	19.32	0.449	3.78	0	0.01	0.027	1.536	0.124	0.071	0.057	0.84	0
30.68						552.24											0
146.16	153.12	1.583	8.7	144.42	53.94	116.58	1.201	52.2	0	0.104	0.348	0.696	0.017	0.818	0.47	149.6	0
88.04	19.88	2.244	17.04	157.62	195.96	714.26	2.002	48.28	2.84	0.021	0.183	8.987	0.497	0.412	0.369	5.68	0
0	65.1	6.082	31.62	623.1	100.44	1318.74	1.302	0	0	1.269	0.459	2.704	1.302	4.055	4.985	141.4	0
5.538	5.112	0.315	3.408	31.95	29.962	98.974	0.349		0	0.043	0.035	0.888	0.038	0.099	0.386	4.118	0
24.42	66.6	3.308	55.5	193.14	608.28	1032.3	2.42	44.4	0.888	0.153	0.149	2.073	0.186	0.577	0.284	57.72	0
43.52	120.32	8.781	115.2	394.24	934.4	1336.32	5.12	43.52	4.352	0.123	0.269	0.916	0.338	0	1.459	58.88	0
35.4	49.56	2.596	37.76		349.28	969.96	2.596		0								0
0	96.33	3.458	81.51		802.75	778.05	1.729		1.235								0
13.6	3.2	1.84			240.8												0
0	6.8	0.436	19	28.4	79.4	0.6	0.252	0	0.02	0.011	0.021	0.366	0.007	0	0.072	1	0
2.85	123.45	0.39	27	135	288.15	142.05	0.599	0	0.405	0.056	0.218	0.183	0.053	0.447	0.013	5.85	0
1.68	40.04	0.28	27.44	70.84	194.32	101.64	0.358	0	0	0.027	0.116	0.155	0.03	0.104	0.042	1.96	0
20	262.5	1.2	57.5	262.5	492.5	110	1.575	127.5	0.5	0.098	0.455	0.333	0.1	1.05	0.075	12.5	0
64.6	44.84	0.486	11.4	76.76	219.64	257.64	0.448	65.36	0.076	0.08	0.095	0.518	0.044	0.258	1.186	29.64	0

EvaluEat Code	Food Name	Amt	Wt (g)	Energy (kcal)	Prot (g)	Carb (g)	Fiber (g)	Fat (g)	Mono (g)	Poly (g)	Sat (g)
18105	Coffee cake, creme w/chocolate icing	1 piece (1/6 of 19 oz cake)	90	297.9	4.5	48.42	1.8	9.72	5.098	1.319	2.55
14210	Coffee, brewed, espresso, restaurant-prep	1 oz	28.34	2.551	0.003	0.434	0	0.051	0	0.026	0.026
14202	Coffee, brewed, espresso, restaurant-prepared, decaffeinated	1 cup (8 fl. oz.)	237	21.33	0.024	3.626	0	0.427	0	0.218	0.218
2055	Condiment, horseradish, prep	1 tbsp	15	7.2	0.177	1.694	0.495	0.104	0.02	0.051	0.014
2046	Condiment, mustard, prepared, yellow	1 tsp or 1 packet	5	3.3	0.198	0.389	0.16	0.155	0.107	0.029	0.008
11945	Condiment, pickle relish, sweet	1 tbsp	15	19.5	0.056	5.258	0.165	0.071	0.031	0.018	0.008
11935	Condiment, tomato catsup	1 tbsp	15	14.25	0.271	3.582	0.195	0.089	0.014	0.036	0.012
18150	Cookie, animal crackers/Arrowroot/Tea Biscuits	1 oz	28.35	126.44	1.956	21.007	0.312	3.912	2.173	0.531	0.982
18151	Cookie, brownies, commercially prep/Little Debbie	1 square, large (2-3/4" sq x 7/8")	56	226.8	2.688	35.784	1.176	9.128	5.02	1.265	2.372
18154	Cookie, brownies, homemade	1 brownie (2" square)	24	111.84	1.488	12.048		6.984	2.601	2.259	1.757
18159	Cookie, chocolate chip, enriched, commercially prep	1 cookie	12	57.72	0.648	8.016	0.3	2.712	1.401	0.284	0.897
18378	Cookie, chocolate chip, homemade w/butter	1 cookie, medium (2-1/4" dia)	16	78.08	0.912	9.312		4.544	1.319	0.727	2.251
18158	Cookie, chocolate chip, lower fat, commercially prep	1 cookie	10	45.3	0.58	7.33	0.36	1.54	0.609	0.465	0.381
18160	Cookie, chocolate chip, soft, commercially prep	1 cookie	15	68.7	0.525	8.865	0.48	3.645	1.955	0.525	1.112
18608	Cookie, Chocolate Graham Selects/Keebler	1 serving	31	144.15	2.201	22.258		5.146			0.958
18169	Cookie, coconut macaroons, homemade	1 cookie, medium (2" dia)	24	96.96	0.864	17.328	0.432	3.048	0.132	0.034	2.697
18170	Cookie, fig bar	1 individual package (2 oz package containing 2 3" bars)	57	198.36	2.109	40.413	2.622	4.161	1.712	1.58	0.64
18171	Cookie, fortune	1 cookie	8	30.24	0.336	6.72	0.128	0.216	0.108	0.037	0.054
18172	Cookie, ginger snaps	1 cookie	7	29.12	0.392	5.383	0.154	0.686	0.376	0.096	0.172
18609	Cookie, Golden Vanilla Wafers/Keebler	1 serving	31	147.25	1.612	21.607		6.045			1.11
18174	Cookie, graham crackers, chocolate coated	1 cracker (2-1/2" square)	14	67.76	0.812	9.31	0.434	3.248	1.076	0.145	1.873
18173	Cookie, graham crackers, plain/honey/cinnamon	1 large rectangular piece or 2 squares or 4 small rectangular pieces	14	59.22	0.966	10.752	0.392	1.414	0.572	0.536	0.213
18175	Cookie, Ladyfingers/Egg Jumbo w/lemon juice & rind	1 cookie	11	40.15	1.166	6.567	0.11	1.001	0.468	0.177	0.382
18612	Cookie, Little Debbie Nutty Bars, Chocolate Covered Wafers w/Peanut Butter	1 serving	57	312.36	4.56	31.464		18.696			3.585
18177	Cookie, molasses	1 large (3-1/2" to 4" dia)	32	137.6	1.792	23.616	0.32	4.096	2.282	0.553	1.028
18178	Cookie, oatmeal, commercially prep	1 cookie, big (3-1/2" to 4" dia)	25	112.5	1.55	17.175	0.7	4.525	2.506	0.636	1.13
18184	Cookie, oatmeal, homemade w/raisins	1 cookie (2-5/8" dia)	15	65.25	0.975	10.26		2.43	1.033	0.755	0.485
18185	Cookie, peanut butter, commercially prep	1 cookie	15	71.55	1.44	8.835	0.27	3.54	1.855	0.828	0.673
18189	Cookie, peanut butter, homemade	1 cookie (3" dia)	20	95	1.8	11.78		4.76	2.166	1.445	0.888
18186	Cookie, peanut butter, soft, commercially prep	1 cookie	15	68.55	0.795	8.655	0.255	3.66	2.077	0.477	0.922

Chol (g)	Calc (mg)	Iron (mg)	Mag (mg)	Phos (mg)	Pota (mg)	Sodi (mg)	Zinc (mg)	Vit A (RAE)	Vit C (mg)	Thia (mg)	Ribo (mg)	Niac (mg)	Vit B$_6$ (mg)	Vit B$_{12}$ (µg)	Vit E (mg)	Fol (µg)	Alc (g)
62.1	34.2	0.459	13.5	67.5	70.2	290.7	0.396	33.3	0.09	0.072	0.067	0.756	0.037	0.18		36.9	0
0	0.567	0.037	22.672	1.984	32.591	3.968	0.014	0	0.057	0	0.05	1.476	0.001	0	0.006	0.283	0
0	4.74	0.308	189.6	16.59	272.55	33.18	0.118	0	0.474	0.002	0.419	12.341	0.005	0	0.047	2.37	0
0	8.4	0.063	4.05	4.65	36.9	47.1	0.124	0	3.735	0.001	0.004	0.058	0.011	0	0.002	8.55	0
0	4	0.093	1.9	4.4	7.55	56	0.03	0.35	0.145	0.003	0.001	0.023	0.004	0	0.015	0.4	0
0	0.45	0.131	0.75	2.1	3.75	121.65	0.021	1.35	0.15	0	0.005	0.035	0.002	0	0.014	0.15	0
0	2.7	0.076	2.85	4.95	57.3	166.95	0.039	7.05	2.265	0.002	0.07	0.225	0.022	0	0.219	2.25	0
0	12.191	0.78	5.103	32.319	28.35	111.416	0.181	0	0	0.099	0.092	0.984	0.006	0.014	0.034	29.2	0
9.52	16.24	1.26	17.36	56.56	83.44	174.72	0.403	11.2	0	0.143	0.118	0.964	0.02	0.039	0.084	26.32	0
17.52	13.68	0.442	12.72	31.68	42.24	82.32	0.233	42.24	0.072	0.034	0.046	0.236	0.023	0.038		6.96	0
0	3	0.337	3.72	12.96	16.2	37.8	0.077	0	0	0.027	0.034	0.326	0.007	0.001	0.017	6.96	0
11.2	6.08	0.397	8.8	16	35.36	54.56	0.15	22.24	0.032	0.029	0.028	0.218	0.013	0.013		5.28	0
0	1.9	0.307	2.8	8.4	12.3	37.7	0.07	0	0	0.029	0.027	0.277	0.026	0		7	0
0	2.25	0.362	5.25	7.5	13.95	48.9	0.069	0	0	0.016	0.03	0.243	0.024	0		5.85	0
						110.67											0
0	1.68	0.18	5.04	10.32	37.44	59.28	0.17	0	0	0.003	0.026	0.031	0.024	0.007	0.036	0.96	0
0	36.48	1.653	15.39	35.34	117.99	199.5	0.222	5.13	0.171	0.09	0.124	1.068	0.043	0.051	0.37	19.95	0
0.16	0.96	0.115	0.56	2.8	3.28	21.92	0.014	0.08	0	0.015	0.01	0.147	0.001	0.001	0.002	5.28	0
0	5.39	0.448	3.43	5.81	24.22	45.78	0.038	0	0	0.014	0.021	0.226	0.007	0	0.068	6.09	0
						119.66											0
0	8.12	0.501	8.12	18.76	29.26	40.74	0.136	0.7	0	0.02	0.03	0.305	0.01	0	0.038	2.8	0
0	3.36	0.522	4.2	14.56	18.9	84.7	0.113	0	0	0.031	0.044	0.577	0.009	0	0.046	6.44	0
40.15	5.17	0.394	1.32	19.03	12.43	16.17	0.125	0.33	0.407	0.031	0.047	0.231	0.013	0.082	0.069	6.6	0
						127.11			1.14								0
0	23.68	2.058	16.64	30.4	110.72	146.88	0.144	0	0	0.114	0.084	0.97	0.033	0	0.035	28.48	0
0	9.25	0.645	8.25	34.5	35.5	95.75	0.198	1.25	0.125	0.067	0.058	0.557	0.016	0	0.065	14.75	0
4.95	15	0.398	6.3	24.15	35.85	80.7	0.129	21.45	0.075	0.037	0.025	0.189	0.011	0.012		4.5	0
0.15	5.25	0.377	6.75	12.9	25.05	62.25	0.079	0.45	0	0.026	0.027	0.641	0.013	0.006	0.33	10.8	0
6.2	7.8	0.446	7.8	23.2	46.2	103.6	0.164	27.4	0.02	0.044	0.042	0.703	0.017	0.018		11	0
0	1.8	0.134	4.8	13.05	16.05	50.4	0.083	0	0	0.037	0.025	0.324	0.004	0		10.05	0

EvaluEat Code	Food Name	Amt	Wt (g)	Energy (kcal)	Prot (g)	Carb (g)	Fiber (g)	Fat (g)	Mono (g)	Poly (g)	Sat (g)
18166	Cookie, sandwich, chocolate, cream filled	1 cookie	10	47.2	0.47	7.03	0.32	2.06	0.856	0.725	0.366
18190	Cookie, sandwich, peanut butter, regular	1 cookie	14	66.92	1.232	9.184	0.266	2.954	1.567	0.531	0.699
18210	Cookie, sandwich, vanilla, cream filled	1 cookie, oval (3-1/8" x 1-1/4" x 3/8")	15	72.45	0.675	10.815	0.225	3	1.266	1.133	0.447
18193	Cookie, shortbread, pecan, commercially prep	1 cookie (2" dia)	14	75.88	0.686	8.162	0.252	4.55	2.608	0.577	1.149
18192	Cookie, shortbread, plain, commercially prep	1 cookie (1-5/8" square)	8	40.16	0.488	5.16	0.144	1.928	1.074	0.259	0.488
18209	Cookie, sugar wafer, cream filled	1 wafer, large (3-1/2" x 1" x 1/2")	9	45.99	0.369	6.309	0.054	2.187	0.93	0.824	0.326
18206	Cookie, sugar, refrig dough, baked	1 cookie 1 pre-sliced cookie dough	23	111.32	1.081	15.088	0.184	5.313	2.992	0.665	1.358
18213	Cookie, vanilla wafer	1 wafer	6	28.38	0.258	4.266	0.12	1.164	0.665	0.146	0.296
18524	Cookies, Archway Home Style, Coconut Macaroon	1 serving	22	106.04	0.854	12.353	0.506	6.142	0.418	0.077	5.436
18555	Cookies, Archway Home Style, fat-free Oatmeal Raisin	1 serving	31	106.33	1.435	24.363	0.93	0.493	0.174	0.211	0.105
18557	Cookies, Archway Home Style, fat-free Sugar Cookies	1 serving	20	70.8	0.88	16.58	0.24	0.158	0.042	0.066	0.052
18535	Cookies, Archway Home Style, Molasses	1 serving	26	103.48	1.178	18.184	0.312	2.98	1.118	0.208	0.733
18541	Cookies, Archway Home Style, Peanut Butter	1 serving	21	100.8	1.89	12.281	0.588	5.099	2.144	0.888	1.132
18548	Cookies, Archway Home Style, Sugar	1 serving	24	98.4	1.231	16.555	0.264	3.084	1.145	0.202	0.761
13348	Corned beef brisket, canned	1 oz	28.35	70.875	7.683	0	0	4.233	1.69	0.179	1.752
20027	Cornstarch	1 cup	128	487.68	0.333	116.83	1.152	0.064	0.02	0.032	0.012
18214	Cracker, cheese	1 cup, bite size	62	311.86	6.262	36.084	1.488	15.686	7.505	1.533	5.81
18216	Cracker, crispbread, rye	1 cracker	10	36.6	0.79	8.22	1.65	0.13	0.017	0.056	0.014
18217	Cracker, Matzo, plain	1 matzo	28	110.6	2.8	23.436	0.84	0.392	0.036	0.169	0.063
18219	Cracker, Matzo, whole wheat	1 matzo	28	98.28	3.668	22.092	3.304	0.42	0.054	0.183	0.068
18220	Cracker, melba toast rounds, plain	1 cracker	3	11.7	0.363	2.298	0.189	0.096	0.023	0.038	0.013
18221	Cracker, melba toast, rye or pumpernickel	1 toast	5	19.45	0.58	3.865	0.4	0.17	0.045	0.067	0.023
18620	Cracker, Original Premium Saltine Crackers/Nabisco	1 serving	14	58.8	1.526	9.954	0.364	1.428	0.819	0.241	0.259
18228	Cracker, oyster/soda/soup	1 cup	45	195.3	4.14	32.175	1.35	5.31	2.89	0.756	1.319
18621	Cracker, Ritz/Nabisco	1 serving	16	78.72	1.152	10.272	0.304	3.664	2.872	0.283	0.627
18224	Cracker, rusk toast	1 rusk	10	40.7	1.35	7.23		0.72	0.276	0.231	0.138
18425	Cracker, saltine/oyster/soda/soup, low salt	1 cup	45	195.3	4.14	32.175	1.35	5.31	2.89	0.756	1.319
18230	Cracker, sandwich, cheese filled	1 cracker	7	33.39	0.651	4.319	0.133	1.477	0.788	0.18	0.429
18215	Cracker, sandwich, cheese w/peanut butter filling	1 sandwich	6.5	32.24	0.807	3.688	0.221	1.633	0.845	0.331	0.286
18231	Cracker, sandwich, peanut butter filled	1 sandwich	6.5	32.11	0.746	3.795	0.149	1.595	0.895	0.303	0.319
18652	Cracker, Snackwell Wheat Cracker/Nabisco	1 serving	15	62.25	1.191	11.55	0.585	1.5			
18624	Cracker, Wheat Thins, baked/Nabisco	1 serving	29	136.3	2.407	20.039	0.87	5.8	2.03	0.36	0.925
18235	Cracker, whole wheat	10 Triscuit Bits	10	44.3	0.88	6.86	1.05	1.72	0.588	0.66	0.339
18429	Cracker, whole wheat, low sodium	10 Triscuit Bits	10	44.3	0.88	6.86	1.05	1.72	0.588	0.66	0.339
18434	Crackers, cheese, Cheez-its/Goldfish, low sodium	1 gold fish	0.6	3.018	0.061	0.349	0.014	0.152	0.071	0.015	0.058
18457	Crackers, saltines, fat-free, low-sodium	6 saltines	30	117.9	3.15	24.69	0.81	0.48	0.043	0.206	0.073
9079	Cranberries, dried, sweetened	1 cup, whole	95	292.6	0.067	78.242	5.415	1.301	0.188	0.625	0.098
42136	Cream substitute, powdered, light	1 oz	28.34	122.15	0.538	20.802	0	4.449	3.259	0.056	1.077
1058	Cream, filled cream, nonbutterfat sour dressing, cultured	1 tbsp	12	21.36	0.39	0.562	0	1.988	0.235	0.056	1.593
1049	Cream, half and half	1 tbsp	15	19.5	0.444	0.645	0	1.725	0.498	0.064	1.074

Chol (g)	Calc (mg)	Iron (mg)	Mag (mg)	Phos (mg)	Pota (mg)	Sodi (mg)	Zinc (mg)	Vit A (RAE)	Vit C (mg)	Thia (mg)	Ribo (mg)	Niac (mg)	Vit B$_6$ (mg)	Vit B$_{12}$ (µg)	Vit E (mg)	Fol (µg)	Alc (g)
0	2.6	0.388	4.5	9.8	17.5	60.4	0.081	0	0	0.008	0.018	0.207	0.002	0.003	0.158	5.1	0
0	7.42	0.364	6.86	26.32	26.88	51.52	0.148	0.14	0.014	0.045	0.037	0.523	0.019	0.032	0.262	8.54	0
0	4.05	0.332	2.1	11.25	13.65	52.35	0.06	0	0	0.039	0.036	0.404	0.003	0	0.24	7.5	0
4.62	4.2	0.34	2.52	11.9	10.22	39.34	0.081	0.14	0	0.041	0.031	0.347	0.003	0.001		8.82	0
1.6	2.8	0.219	1.36	8.64	8	36.4	0.042	1.44	0	0.026	0.026	0.267	0.006	0.007	0.026	5.6	0
0	1.62	0.176	0.99	5.04	5.31	13.23	0.032	0	0	0.009	0.018	0.219	0.001	0	0.176	4.68	0
7.36	20.7	0.423	1.84	43.01	37.49	107.64	0.062	2.76	0	0.042	0.028	0.555	0.005	0.016	0.048	16.1	0
0	1.5	0.133	0.72	3.84	6.42	18.36	0.02	0	0	0.022	0.013	0.179	0.001	0.002		2.58	0
0	3.3	0.354			57.42	38.28			0	0.007	0.013	0.067				1.1	
0	11.47	0.983			86.8	164.92			0	0.081	0.043	0.505				14.57	
0	2.6	0.436			11.6	80.4			0	0.062	0.04	0.504				15.2	
8.06	8.58	1.136			29.12	143.78			0	0.073	0.06	0.658					
7.77	7.35	0.571			43.89	84.84			0	0.05	0.042	0.918					
5.04	7.2	0.528			19.92	162.24			0	0.074	0.055	0.588					
24.381	3.402	0.59	3.969	31.469	38.556	285.201	1.012	0	0	0.006	0.042	0.689	0.037	0.459	0.043	2.552	0
0	2.56	0.602	3.84	16.64	3.84	11.52	0.077	0	0	0	0	0	0	0	0	0	0
8.06	93.62	2.957	22.32	135.16	89.9	616.9	0.701	17.98	0	0.353	0.265	2.896	0.343	0.285	0.037	94.24	0
0	3.1	0.243	7.8	26.9	31.9	26.4	0.239	0	0	0.024	0.014	0.104	0.021	0	0.081	4.7	0
0	3.64	0.885	7	24.92	31.36	0.56	0.19	0	0	0.108	0.081	1.09	0.032	0	0.017	4.76	0
0	6.44	1.302	37.52	85.4	88.48	0.56	0.731	0	0	0.102	0.076	1.515	0.045	0	0.374	9.8	0
0	2.79	0.111	1.77	5.88	6.06	24.87	0.06	0	0	0.012	0.008	0.123	0.003	0	0.013	3.72	0
0	3.9	0.184	1.95	9.15	9.65	44.95	0.068	0	0	0.024	0.014	0.236	0.004	0	0.032	4.25	0
0	27.02	0.727	2.94	13.86	13.86	177.8			0	0.046	0.062	0.612	0.007			11.76	0
0	53.55	2.43	12.15	47.25	57.6	585.9	0.346	0	0	0.254	0.208	2.362	0.017	0	0.054	55.8	0
0	23.52	0.648	3.2	48	14.88	124.16	0.232		0	0.04	0.049	0.61	0.006	0		9.6	0
7.8	2.7	0.272	3.6	15.3	24.5	25.3	0.11	1.2	0	0.04	0.04	0.463	0.005	0.018		8.7	0
0	53.55	2.43	12.15	47.25	325.8	286.2	0.346	0	0	0.254	0.208	2.362	0.017	0	0.054	55.8	0
0.14	17.99	0.167	2.52	28.42	30.03	98.07	0.043	1.19	0.007	0.031	0.048	0.264	0.003	0.007	0.015	7	0
0	3.25	0.177	3.64	17.42	14.17	46.15	0.068	0	0	0.036	0.019	0.379	0.01	0.018	0.154	6.11	0
0	5.265	0.18	3.575	17.81	13.975	46.67	0.073	0	0	0.032	0.018	0.397	0.01	0.001	0.134	5.59	0
	22.35	0.585	6.9	49.5	28.5	150	0.323		0	0.042	0.055				0		
0	23.2	1.073	15.08	60.32	56.26	167.62			0	0.087	0.087	1.16	0.025			12.18	0
0	5	0.308	9.9	29.5	29.7	65.9	0.215	0	0	0.02	0.01	0.452	0.018	0	0.086	2.8	0
0	5	0.308	9.9	29.5	29.7	24.7	0.215	0	0	0.02	0.01	0.452	0.018	0	0.086	2.8	0
0.078	0.906	0.029	0.216	1.308	0.636	2.748	0.007	0.102	0	0.003	0.003	0.028	0.003	0.003	0.002	0.534	0
0	6.6	2.316	7.8	33.9	34.5	190.8	0.282	0	0	0.155	0.177	1.714	0.026	0	0.036	37.2	0
0	9.5	0.503	4.75	7.6	38	2.85	0.104	0	0.19	0.007	0.015	0.941	0.036	0	1.016	0	0
0	0.283	0.009	0	38.542	255.627	64.899	0.006	0.283	0	0	0	0	0	0	0.074	0.283	0
0.6	13.56	0.004	1.2	10.44	19.44	5.76	0.044	0.36	0.108	0.005	0.02	0.009	0.002	0.04	0.161	1.44	0
5.55	15.75	0.011	1.5	14.25	19.5	6.15	0.076	14.55	0.135	0.005	0.022	0.012	0.006	0.05	0.05	0.45	0

EvaluEat Code	Food Name	Amt	Wt (g)	Energy (kcal)	Prot (g)	Carb (g)	Fiber (g)	Fat (g)	Mono (g)	Poly (g)	Sat (g)
1053	Cream, heavy whipping	1 cup, whipped	120	414	2.46	3.348	0	44.4	12.823	1.649	27.638
1052	Cream, light whipping	1 cup, whipped	120	350.4	2.604	3.552	0	37.092	10.912	1.061	23.204
1056	Cream, sour, cultured	1 tbsp	12	25.68	0.379	0.512	0	2.515	0.726	0.093	1.566
1074	Cream, sour, imitation, cultured	1 oz	28.35	58.968	0.68	1.88	0	5.534	0.167	0.016	5.044
1055	Cream, sour, reduced fat (half and half) cultured	1 tbsp	15	20.25	0.441	0.639	0	1.8	0.52	0.067	1.12
1054	Cream, whipped cream topping, pressurized	1 tbsp	3	7.71	0.096	0.375	0	0.667	0.193	0.025	0.415
18242	Croutons, plain	.5 oz	14.2	57.794	1.69	10.437	0.724	0.937	0.434	0.181	0.214
18243	Croutons, seasoned	1 package, fast food	10	46.5	1.08	6.35	0.5	1.83	0.95	0.237	0.525
19205	Custard, egg, dry mix prep w/reduced fat (2%) milk	100 grams	100	111	4.08	17.42	0	2.74	0.852	0.197	1.357
19170	Custard, egg, dry mix prep w/whole milk	100 grams	100	121	4.04	17.29	0	4.01	1.201	0.244	2.122
9421	Dates, medjool	1 cup, drained	178	493.06	3.222	133.45	11.926	0.267			
18251	Donut, cake, chocolate w/sugar or glaze	1 doughnut (3-3/4" dia)	60	250.2	2.7	34.44	1.32	11.94	6.767	1.486	3.079
18249	Donut, cake, plain w/chocolate icing	1 doughnut, large (approx 3-1/2" dia)	57	270.18	2.85	27.36	1.14	17.67	9.976	2.158	4.621
18250	Donut, cake, plain w/sugar or glaze	1 doughnut, medium (approx 3" dia)	45	191.7	2.34	22.86	0.675	10.305	5.714	1.309	2.667
18248	Donut, cake, plain/old-fashioned	1 doughnut, medium (3-1/4" dia)	47	197.87	2.35	23.359	0.705	10.763	4.37	3.704	1.704
18253	Donut, French cruller, glazed	1 cruller (3" dia)	41	168.92	1.271	24.395	0.492	7.503	4.283	0.937	1.913
18254	Donut, yeast leavened, cream filled	1 doughnut oval (3-1/2" x 2-1/2")	85	306.85	5.44	25.5	0.68	20.825	10.268	2.62	4.615
18255	Donut/Honey Bun, yeast leavened, glazed	1 doughnut, large (approx 4-1/4" dia)	75	302.25	4.8	33.225	0.9	17.1	9.649	2.176	4.36
43287	Dove, cooked (includes squab)	1 cup	186	407.34	44.454	0	0	24.18	10.159	5.083	6.955
5143	Duck liver, domestic, raw	1 liver	44	59.84	8.246	1.553	0	2.042	0.312	0.277	0.634
5140	Duck, domestic, meat & skin, roasted	1 cup, chopped or diced	140	471.8	26.586	0	0	39.69	18.06	5.11	13.538
5142	Duck, domestic, meat, no skin, roasted	1 cup, chopped or diced	140	281.4	32.872	0	0	15.68	5.18	2.002	5.838
1142	Egg substitute, frozen	.25 cup	60	96	6.774	1.92	0	6.666	1.461	3.745	1.158
1143	Egg substitute, liquid	1 cup	251	210.84	30.12	1.606	0	8.308	2.249	4.024	1.654
1144	Egg substitute, powdered	.7 oz	20	88.8	11.1	4.36	0	2.6	1.068	0.337	0.753
1124	Egg, white, raw	1 large	33	17.16	3.597	0.241	0	0.056	0	0	0
1128	Egg, whole, fried	1 large	46	92.5	6.27	0.405	0		2.919	1.224	1.975
1129	Egg, whole, hard-cooked	1 large	50	77.5	6.29	0.56	0	5.305	2.039	0.707	1.633
1131	Egg, whole, poached	1 large	50	73.5	6.265	0.38	0	4.95	1.898	0.679	1.543
1132	Egg, whole, scrambled	1 large	61	101.26	6.765	1.342	0	7.448	2.908	1.31	2.244
1125	Egg, yolk, raw, fresh	1 large	17	54.74	2.696	0.61	0	4.512	1.995	0.715	1.624
43146	Eggplant, pickled	1 cup	186	91.14	1.674	18.172	4.65	1.302	0.117	0.547	0.26
18260	English muffin, mixed grain/granola	1 muffin	66	155.1	6.006	30.558	1.848	1.188	0.546	0.369	0.152
18258	English muffin, plain/sourdough, enriched	1 muffin	57	133.95	4.389	26.22	1.539	1.026	0.172	0.506	0.148
18264	English muffin, wheat	1 muffin	57	127.11	4.959	25.536	2.622	1.14	0.16	0.475	0.164

Chol (g)	Calc (mg)	Iron (mg)	Mag (mg)	Phos (mg)	Pota (mg)	Sodi (mg)	Zinc (mg)	Vit A (RAE)	Vit C (mg)	Thia (mg)	Ribo (mg)	Niac (mg)	Vit B$_6$ (mg)	Vit B$_{12}$ (µg)	Vit E (mg)	Fol (µg)	Alc (g)
164.4	78	0.036	8.4	74.4	90	45.6	0.276	493.2	0.72	0.026	0.132	0.047	0.031	0.216	1.272	4.8	0
133.2	82.8	0.036	8.4	73.2	116.4	40.8	0.3	334.8	0.72	0.029	0.15	0.05	0.034	0.24	1.056	4.8	0
5.28	13.92	0.007	1.32	10.2	17.28	6.36	0.032	21.24	0.108	0.004	0.018	0.008	0.002	0.036	0.072	1.32	0
0	0.851	0.111	1.701	12.758	45.644	28.917	0.335	0	0	0	0	0	0	0	0.21	0	0
5.85	15.6	0.011	1.5	14.25	19.35	6.15	0.075	15.3	0.135	0.005	0.022	0.01	0.002	0.045	0.051	1.65	0
2.28	3.03	0.002	0.33	2.67	4.41	3.9	0.011	5.64	0	0.001	0.002	0.002	0.001	0.009	0.019	0.09	0
0	10.792	0.579	4.402	16.33	17.608	99.116	0.126	0	0	0.088	0.039	0.772	0.004	0		18.74	0
0.7	9.6	0.282	4.2	14	18.1	123.8	0.094	0.7	0	0.051	0.042	0.465	0.008	0.014	0.04	10.5	0
48	145	0.35	19	138	224	89	0.52	61	0.8	0.054	0.213	0.128	0.069	0.45		9	0
53	143	0.35	19	136	221	88	0.51	37	0.8	0.054	0.211	0.126	0.068	0.44		9	0
	113.92	1.602	96.12	110.36	1238.88	1.78	0.783	12.46	0	0.089	0.107	2.866	0.443			26.7	
34.2	127.8	1.362	20.4	97.2	63.6	204	0.342	7.2	0.06	0.027	0.042	0.282	0.016	0.06	0.126	27	0
34.77	19.95	1.402	22.8	115.14	111.72	244.53	0.348	3.99	0.114	0.072	0.06	0.741	0.029	0.137	0.211	26.79	0
14.4	27	0.477	7.65	52.65	45.9	180.9	0.198	1.35	0.045	0.105	0.089	0.68	0.012	0.108		20.7	0
17.39	20.68	0.917	9.4	126.43	59.69	256.62	0.259	17.86	0.094	0.104	0.113	0.871	0.026	0.127	0.907	24.44	0
4.51	10.66	0.992	4.92	50.43	31.98	141.45	0.107	0.82	0	0.074	0.094	0.873	0.008	0.021	0.066	17.22	0
20.4	21.25	1.556	17	64.6	68	262.65	0.68	9.35	0	0.287	0.126	1.906	0.058	0.119	0.247	59.5	0
4.5	32.25	1.53	16.5	69.75	81	256.5	0.577	3	0.075	0.273	0.161	2.139	0.043	0.068	0.262	36.75	0
215.76	31.62	10.993	48.36	617.52	476.16	106.02	7.124	52.08	5.394	0.521	0.651	14.136	1.06	0.763	0.112	11.16	0
226.6	4.84	13.433	10.56	118.36	101.2	61.6	1.351	5273	1.98	0.247	0.392	2.86	0.334	23.76		324.7	0
117.6	15.4	3.78	22.4	218.4	285.6	82.6	2.604	88.2	0	0.244	0.377	6.755	0.252	0.42	0.98	8.4	0
124.6	16.8	3.78	28	284.2	352.8	91	3.64	32.2	0	0.364	0.658	7.14	0.35	0.56	0.98	14	0
1.2	43.8	1.188	9	43.2	127.8	119.4	0.588	6.6	0.3	0.072	0.232	0.084	0.08	0.204	0.954	9.6	0
2.51	133.03	5.271	22.59	303.71	828.3	444.27	3.263	45.18	0	0.276	0.753	0.276	0.008	0.753	0.678	37.65	0
114.4	65.2	0.632	13	95.6	148.8	160	0.364	73.8	0.16	0.045	0.352	0.115	0.029	0.704	0.252	25	0
0	2.31	0.026	3.63	4.95	53.79	54.78	0.01	0	0	0.001	0.145	0.035	0.002	0.03	0	1.32	0
210.2	27.1	0.911	5.98	95.7	67.6	93.8	0.552	91.1	0	0.035	0.238	0.035	0.071	0.639	0.561	23.5	0
212	25	0.595	5	86	63	62	0.525	84.5	0	0.033	0.257	0.032	0.06	0.555	0.515	22	0
211	26.5	0.915	6	95	66.5	147	0.55	69.5	0	0.034	0.238	0.035	0.071	0.64	0.48	23.5	0
214.72	43.31	0.732	7.32	103.7	84.18	170.8	0.61	87.23	0.122	0.032	0.267	0.048	0.072	0.47	0.519	18.3	0
209.78	21.93	0.464	0.85	66.3	18.53	8.16	0.391	64.77	0	0.03	0.09	0.004	0.06	0.332	0.439	24.82	0
0	46.5	1.432	11.16	16.74	22.32	3113.64	0.428	5.58	0	0.093	0.13	1.228	0.26	0	0.056	37.2	0
0	129.36	1.993	27.06	53.46	102.96	274.56	0.917	0	0	0.284	0.207	2.365	0.025	0	0	52.8	0
0	99.18	1.425	11.97	75.81	74.67	264.48	0.399	0	0	0.252	0.16	2.214	0.025	0.023	0.177	54.15	0
0	101.46	1.636	21.09	60.99	106.02	217.74	0.61	0	0	0.246	0.166	1.913	0.05	0	0.256	36.48	0

EvaluEat Code	Food Name	Amt	Wt (g)	Energy (kcal)	Prot (g)	Carb (g)	Fiber (g)	Fat (g)	Mono (g)	Poly (g)	Sat (g)
21069	Fast food, burrito w/apples or cherries	1 burrito, small	74	230.88	2.501	34.98		9.524	3.42	1.055	4.569
21060	Fast food, burrito w/beans	2 pieces	217	447.02	14.062	71.436		13.497	4.739	1.196	6.888
21061	Fast food, burrito w/beans & cheese	2 pieces	186	377.58	15.066	54.963		11.699	2.483	1.784	6.849
21064	Fast food, burrito w/beans, cheese & beef	2 pieces	203	330.89	14.575	39.686		13.297	4.458	1.019	7.15
21066	Fast food, burrito w/beef	2 pieces	220	523.6	26.598	58.52		20.812	7.41	0.854	10.459
21035	Fast food, chicken, breaded, fried, dark meat (drumstick or thigh)	2 pieces	148	430.68	30.074	15.703		26.699	10.93	6.323	7.049
21036	Fast food, chicken, breaded, fried, light meat (breast or wing)	2 pieces	163	493.89	35.713	19.576		29.519	12.228	6.786	7.844
21037	Fast food, chicken, breaded, fried, no bone, plain	1 piece	18	54.18	3.06	2.594	0	3.499	1.78	0.78	0.79
21038	Fast food, chicken, breaded, fried, no bone, w/BBQ sauce	6 pieces	130	330.2	17.147	25.025		17.966	8.765	2.389	5.57
21042	Fast food, chili con carne	1 cup (8 fl. oz.)	253	255.53	24.617	21.935		8.273	3.408	0.529	3.431
21071	Fast food, chimichanga w/beef & cheese	1 chimichanga	183	442.86	20.057	39.327		23.442	9.434	0.728	11.178
21043	Fast food, clams (shellfish) breaded, fried	.75 cup	115	450.8	12.822	38.813		26.404	11.44	6.773	6.603
21128	Fast food, corn on the cob w/butter	1 ear	146	154.76	4.468	31.945		3.431	1.004	0.612	1.643
21046	Fast food, crab cake (shellfish)	1 cake	60	159.6	11.25	5.112	0.24	10.35	4.308	3.078	2.244
21015	Fast food, Danish pastry, cheese	1 pastry	91	353.08	5.833	28.692		24.625	15.601	2.423	5.123
21016	Fast food, Danish pastry, cinnamon	1 pastry	88	349.36	4.805	46.851		16.72	10.593	1.646	3.479
21017	Fast food, Danish pastry, fruit	1 pastry	94	334.64	4.756	45.064		15.933	10.096	1.568	3.315
21074	Fast food, enchilada w/cheese	1 enchilada	163	319.48	9.633	28.541		18.843	6.311	0.817	10.588
21075	Fast food, enchilada w/cheese & beef	1 enchilada	192	322.56	11.923	30.47		17.645	6.146	1.388	9.047
21076	Fast food, enchirito w/cheese, beef & beans	1 enchirito	193	343.54	17.891	33.794		16.077	6.518	0.328	7.948
21019	Fast food, English muffin w/butter	1 muffin	63	189	4.87	30.36		5.758	1.532	1.348	2.43
21024	Fast food, French toast sticks	5 pieces	141	513.24	8.277	57.852	2.679	29.046	12.648	9.941	4.709
21023	Fast food, French toast w/butter	2 slices	135	356.4	10.341	36.045		18.765	7.074	2.444	7.749
21077	Fast food, frijoles (beans) w/cheese	1 cup	167	225.45	11.373	28.707		7.782	2.617	0.696	4.075
21116	Fast food, ham & cheese sandwich	1 sandwich	146	351.86	20.688	33.346		15.476	6.738	1.375	6.437
21117	Fast food, ham, egg & cheese sandwich	1 sandwich	143	347.49	19.248	30.945		16.302	5.744	1.69	7.4
21202	Fast food, hamburger, large, one meat patty w/condiments	1 sandwich	172	426.56	23.1	36.825	2.064	21.001	9.307	1.594	7.926
21119	Fast food, hot dog w/chili, plain	1 sandwich	114	296.4	13.509	31.293		13.441	6.595	1.188	4.854
21120	Fast food, hot dog w/corn flour coating, corn dog	1 sandwich	175	460.25	16.8	55.79		18.9	9.109	3.497	5.161
21118	Fast food, hot dog, plain	1 sandwich	98	242.06	10.388	18.032		14.543	6.853	1.706	5.109
21129	Fast food, hush puppies	5 pieces	78	256.62	4.875	34.897		11.591	7.819	0.388	2.686
21033	Fast food, ice cream sundae, hot fudge	1 sundae	158	284.4	5.641	47.669	0	8.627	2.331	0.807	5.023
14346	Fast food, milk beverage, chocolate shake/McDonald's	1 medium shake (16 fl. oz.)	333	422.91	11.322	68.265	6.327	12.321	3.58	0.466	7.702
21078	Fast food, nachos w/cheese	1 portion (6–8 nachos)	113	345.78	9.097	36.33		18.95	7.994	2.233	7.78
21080	Fast food, nachos w/cheese, beans, ground beef & peppers	1 portion (6–8 nachos)	255	568.65	19.788	55.819		30.702	10.98	5.689	12.487
21130	Fast food, onion rings, breaded, fried	1 portion (8–9 onion rings)	83	275.56	3.702	31.324		15.513	6.651	0.665	6.953
21048	Fast food, oysters (shellfish) battered/breaded, fried	6 pieces	139	368.35	12.538	39.879		17.931	6.921	4.638	4.579
21025	Fast food, pancakes w/butter & syrup	2 cakes	232	519.68	8.259	90.898		13.99	5.269	1.958	5.851
21049	Fast food, pizza w/cheese	1 slice	63	140.49	7.68	20.5		3.213	0.99	0.491	1.54
21050	Fast food, pizza w/cheese, meat & vegetables	1 slice	79	184.07	13.011	21.291		5.364	2.543	0.915	1.535

Chol (g)	Calc (mg)	Iron (mg)	Mag (mg)	Phos (mg)	Pota (mg)	Sodi (mg)	Zinc (mg)	Vit A (RAE)	Vit C (mg)	Thia (mg)	Ribo (mg)	Niac (mg)	Vit B$_6$ (mg)	Vit B$_{12}$ (µg)	Vit E (mg)	Fol (µg)	Alc (g)
3.7	15.54	1.073	7.4	14.8	104.34	211.64	0.4	20.72	0.74	0.17	0.178	1.857	0.074	0.511		24.42	0
4.34	112.84	4.514	86.8	97.65	653.17	985.18	1.519	17.36	1.953	0.629	0.608	4.058	0.304	1.085		86.8	0
27.9	213.9	2.269	79.98	180.42	496.62	1166.22	1.637	98.58	1.674	0.223	0.707	3.571	0.242	0.893		74.4	0
123.83	129.92	3.735	50.75	140.07	410.06	990.64	2.355	150.2	5.075	0.305	0.711	3.857	0.223	1.096		75.11	0
63.8	83.6	6.094	81.4	173.8	739.2	1491.6	4.73	13.2	1.1	0.242	0.924	6.446	0.308	1.958		129.8	0
165.76	35.52	1.598	37	239.76	445.48	754.8	3.241	66.6	0	0.133	0.429	7.208	0.326	0.829		25.16	0
148.33	60.31	1.483	37.49	306.44	565.61	974.74	1.548	57.05	0	0.147	0.293	11.981	0.571	0.668		29.34	0
10.44	2.34	0.16	4.14	49.14	51.84	87.12	0.169	0.9	0	0.02	0.027	1.269	0.052	0.052	0.221	5.22	0
61.1	20.8	1.456	24.7	214.5	318.5	829.4	1.118	16.9	0.78	0.104	0.156	7.02	0.338	0.299		29.9	0
134.09	68.31	5.186	45.54	197.34	690.69	1006.94	3.567	83.49	1.518	0.126	1.138	2.479	0.329	1.138		45.54	0
51.24	237.9	3.843	60.39	186.66	203.13	957.09	3.367	131.8	2.745	0.384	0.86	4.667	0.22	1.299		91.5	0
87.4	20.7	3.048	31.05	238.05	265.65	833.75	1.633	36.8	0	0.207	0.264	2.863	0.034	1.104		42.55	0
5.84	4.38	0.876	40.88	108.04	359.16	29.2	0.905	33.58	6.862	0.248	0.102	2.175	0.321	0		43.8	0
82.2	202.2	1.116	25.2	226.8	162	491.4	2.124	93	0.18	0.055	0.075	1.166	0.149	4.398		24.6	0
20.02	70.07	1.847	15.47	80.08	116.48	319.41	0.628	44.59	2.639	0.264	0.209	2.548	0.055	0.228		54.6	0
27.28	36.96	1.795	14.08	73.92	95.92	326.48	0.484	5.28	2.552	0.255	0.194	2.2	0.053	0.22		54.56	0
18.8	21.62	1.401	14.1	68.62	109.98	332.76	0.479	25.38	1.598	0.291	0.207	1.795	0.056	0.235		31.02	0
44.01	324.37	1.32	50.53	133.66	239.61	784.03	2.51	99.43	0.978	0.082	0.424	1.907	0.391	0.75		65.2	0
40.32	228.48	3.072	82.56	167.04	574.08	1319.04	2.688	97.92	1.344	0.096	0.403	2.515	0.269	1.018		67.2	0
50.18	218.09	2.393	71.41	223.88	559.7	1250.64	2.76	88.78	4.632	0.174	0.695	2.991	0.212	1.621		94.57	0
12.6	102.69	1.588	13.23	85.05	69.3	386.19	0.422	31.5	0.756	0.252	0.315	2.615	0.038	0.019	0.126	56.7	0
74.73	77.55	2.961	26.79	122.67	126.9	499.14	0.931	0	0	0.226	0.254	2.961	0.254	0.071	2.326	255.2	0
116.1	72.9	1.89	16.2	145.8	176.85	513	0.594	136.4	0.135	0.581	0.5	3.915	0.054	0.365		72.9	0
36.74	188.71	2.238	85.17	175.35	604.54	881.76	1.737	35.07	1.503	0.134	0.334	1.486	0.2	0.685		111.9	0
58.4	129.94	3.241	16.06	151.84	290.54	770.88	1.372	96.36	2.774	0.307	0.482	2.686	0.204	0.54	0.292	75.92	0
245.96	211.64	3.103	25.74	346.06	210.21	1005.29	1.988	165.9	2.717	0.429	0.558	4.204	0.157	1.23	0.586	75.79	0
70.52	134.16	4.145	34.4	213.28	395.6	731	4.764	5.16	2.58	0.342	0.284	6.562	0.246	2.58	0.034	61.92	0
51.3	19.38	3.283	10.26	191.52	166.44	479.94	0.775	3.42	2.736	0.217	0.399	3.739	0.046	0.296		72.96	0
78.75	101.5	6.177	17.5	166.25	262.5	973	1.313	59.5	0	0.28	0.7	4.165	0.087	0.438		103.25	0
44.1	23.52	2.313	12.74	97.02	143.08	670.32	1.98	0	0.098	0.235	0.274	3.646	0.049	0.51		48.02	0
134.94	68.64	1.427	16.38	190.32	187.98	964.86	0.429	8.58	0	0	0.023	2.028	0.101	0.172		57.72	0
20.54	206.98	0.585	33.18	227.52	395	181.7	0.948	58.46	2.37	0.063	0.3	1.074	0.126	0.648	0.664	9.48	0
43.29	376.29	1.032	56.61	339.66	666	323.01	1.365	86.58	1.332	0.193	0.816	0.536	0.167	1.132	0.366	16.65	0
18.08	272.33	1.277	55.37	275.72	171.76	815.86	1.785	149.2	1.243	0.192	0.373	1.537	0.203	0.825		10.17	0
20.4	385.05	2.78	96.9	387.6	451.35	1800.3	3.646	436.1	4.845	0.23	0.688	3.34	0.408	1.02		38.25	0
14.11	73.04	0.847	15.77	86.32	129.48	429.94	0.349	0.83	0.581	0.083	0.1	0.921	0.058	0.124	0.332	54.78	0
108.42	27.8	4.462	23.63	195.99	182.09	676.93	15.64	108.4	4.17	0.306	0.347	4.42	0.028	1.015		30.58	0
58	127.6	2.622	48.72	475.6	250.56	1104.32	1.021	81.2	3.48	0.394	0.557	3.387	0.116	0.232	1.392	51.04	0
9.45	116.55	0.58	15.75	112.77	109.62	335.79	0.813	73.71	1.26	0.183	0.164	2.482	0.044	0.334		34.65	0
20.54	101.12	1.533	18.17	131.14	178.54	382.36	1.114	58.46	1.58	0.213	0.174	1.959	0.095	0.363		32.39	0

EvaluEat Code	Food Name	Amt	Wt (g)	Energy (kcal)	Prot (g)	Carb (g)	Fiber (g)	Fat (g)	Mono (g)	Poly (g)	Sat (g)
21051	Fast food, pizza w/pepperoni	1 slice	71	181.05	10.125	19.866		6.958	3.14	1.165	2.236
21132	Fast food, potato, baked, topped w/cheese & bacon	1 piece	299	451.49	18.418	44.431		25.893	9.715	4.751	10.133
21131	Fast food, potato, baked, topped w/cheese sauce	1 piece	296	473.6	14.622	46.502		28.742	10.7	6.044	10.558
21135	Fast food, potato, baked, topped w/sour cream & chives	1 piece	302	392.6	6.674	50.011		22.318	7.873	3.316	10.011
21138	Fast food, potato, French fried w/vegetable oil	1 large	169	577.98	7.267	67.279	5.915	31.147	17.99	5.288	6.507
21139	Fast food, potato, mashed	.333 cup	80	66.4	1.848	12.896		0.968	0.281	0.234	0.383
21026	Fast food, potatoes, hash brown	.5 cup	72	151.2	1.944	16.15		9.216	3.858	0.47	4.324
21122	Fast food, roast beef sandwich w/cheese	1 sandwich	176	473.44	32.226	45.373		18.005	3.661	3.502	9.029
21121	Fast food, roast beef sandwich, plain	1 sandwich	139	346.11	21.503	33.443		13.761	6.804	1.706	3.606
4021	Fast food, salad dressing, Italian, w/salt, diet (2 kcal/tsp)	1 tbsp	15	11.25	0.071	0.686	0	0.957	0.329	0.256	0.068
4025	Fast food, salad dressing, mayonnaise, soybean oil, w/salt	1 tbsp	13.8	98.946	0.152	0.538	0	10.792	2.705	5.889	1.64
21127	Fast food, salad, cole slaw	.75 cup	99	146.52	1.455	12.751		10.969	2.42	6.394	1.606
21140	Fast food, salad, potato	.333 cup	95	108.3	1.453	12.853		5.728	1.605	2.869	0.978
21083	Fast food, salad, taco	1.5 cup	198	279.18	13.226	23.582		14.771	5.16	1.748	6.823
21084	Fast food, salad, taco w/chili con carne	1.5 cup	261	289.71	17.409	26.57		13.128	4.539	1.537	6
21002	Fast food, sandwich, biscuit w/egg	1 biscuit	136	372.64	11.601	31.906	0.816	22.073	9.073	6.4	4.729
21003	Fast food, sandwich, biscuit w/egg & bacon	1 biscuit	150	457.5	16.995	28.59	0.75	31.095	13.44	7.47	7.95
21004	Fast food, sandwich, biscuit w/egg & ham	1 biscuit	192	441.6	20.429	30.317	0.768	27.034	10.963	7.699	5.914
21005	Fast food, sandwich, biscuit w/egg & sausage	1 biscuit	180	581.4	19.152	41.148	0.9	38.7	16.398	4.446	14.976
21007	Fast food, sandwich, biscuit w/egg, cheese & bacon	1 biscuit	144	476.64	16.258	33.422		31.392	14.226	3.495	11.398
21008	Fast food, sandwich, biscuit w/ham	1 biscuit	113	386.46	13.391	43.787	0.791	18.419	4.833	1.037	11.408
21009	Fast food, sandwich, biscuit w/sausage	1 biscuit	124	484.84	12.115	40.04	1.364	31.781	12.82	3.026	14.22
21093	Fast food, sandwich, cheeseburger (2 patty) condiments & vegetables	1 sandwich	166	416.66	21.248	35.192		21.082	7.809	2.658	8.717
21092	Fast food, sandwich, cheeseburger (2 patty) plain	1 sandwich	155	457.25	27.667	22.056		28.474	11.008	1.914	12.997
21097	Fast food, sandwich, cheeseburger, large, one meat patty w/bacon & condiments	1 sandwich	195	608.4	32	37.128		36.758	14.488	2.711	16.243
21098	Fast food, sandwich, cheeseburger, large, one meat patty w/condiments & vegetables	1 sandwich	219	562.83	28.185	38.391		32.938	12.61	2.026	15.039
21103	Fast food, sandwich, chicken filet w/cheese	1 sandwich	228	631.56	29.412	41.587		38.76	13.65	9.948	12.449
21102	Fast food, sandwich, chicken filet, plain	1 sandwich	182	515.06	24.115	38.693		29.448	10.41	8.383	8.527
21011	Fast food, sandwich, croissant w/egg & cheese	1 croissant	127	368.3	12.789	24.308		24.701	7.541	1.367	14.065
21012	Fast food, sandwich, croissant w/egg, cheese & bacon	1 croissant	129	412.8	16.228	23.646		28.354	9.176	1.758	15.432
21013	Fast food, sandwich, croissant w/egg, cheese & ham	1 croissant	152	474.24	18.924	24.198		33.577	11.392	2.359	17.475
21020	Fast food, sandwich, English muffin w/cheese & sausage	1 muffin	115	393.3	15.341	29.164	1.495	24.265	10.081	2.694	9.851
21021	Fast food, sandwich, English muffin w/egg, cheese & Canadian bacon	1 sandwich	137	289.07	16.687	26.742	1.507	12.59	4.67	1.558	4.665
21105	Fast food, sandwich, fish w/tartar sauce	1 sandwich	158	431.34	16.938	41.017		22.768	7.693	8.248	5.235
21106	Fast food, sandwich, fish w/tartar sauce & cheese	1 sandwich	183	523.38	20.606	47.635		28.603	8.919	9.432	8.14
21114	Fast food, sandwich, hamburger, large (2 patty) w/condiments & vegetables	1 sandwich	226	540.14	34.284	40.273		26.555	10.328	2.796	10.518
21113	Fast food, sandwich, hamburger, large, one meat patty w/condiments & vegetables	1 sandwich	218	512.3	25.833	40.003		27.359	11.423	2.202	10.42
21109	Fast food, sandwich, hamburger, one patty w/condiments & vegetables	1 sandwich	110	279.4	12.914	27.291		13.475	5.29	2.577	4.131

Chol (g)	Calc (mg)	Iron (mg)	Mag (mg)	Phos (mg)	Pota (mg)	Sodi (mg)	Zinc (mg)	Vit A (RAE)	Vit C (mg)	Thia (mg)	Ribo (mg)	Niac (mg)	Vit B6 (mg)	Vit B12 (µg)	Vit E (mg)	Fol (µg)	Alc (g)
14.2	64.61	0.937	8.52	75.26	152.65	266.96	0.518	52.54	1.633	0.135	0.234	3.046	0.057	0.185		36.92	0
29.9	307.97	3.139	68.77	346.84	1178.06	971.75	2.153	188.4	28.7	0.269	0.239	3.977	0.748	0.329		29.9	0
17.76	310.8	3.019	65.12	319.68	1166.24	381.84	1.894	251.6	26.05	0.237	0.207	3.345	0.71	0.178		26.64	0
24.16	105.7	3.111	69.46	184.22	1383.16	181.2	0.906	265.8	33.82	0.272	0.181	3.715	0.785	0.211		33.22	0
0	23.66	1.318	65.91	218.01	1164.41	334.62	0.794	0	19.6	0.135	0.068	4.817	0.605	0	2.569	11.83	0
1.6	16.8	0.376	14.4	44	235.2	181.6	0.256	8.8	0.32	0.072	0.04	0.96	0.184	0.04		6.4	0
9.36	7.2	0.482	15.84	69.12	267.12	290.16	0.216	1.44	5.472	0.079	0.014	1.073	0.166	0.014	0.122	7.92	0
77.44	183.04	5.051	40.48	401.28	344.96	1633.28	5.368	58.08	0	0.387	0.458	5.896	0.334	2.059		63.36	0
51.43	54.21	4.226	30.58	239.08	315.53	792.3	3.392	11.12	2.085	0.375	0.306	5.866	0.264	1.223		56.99	0
0.9	1.35	0.098	0.6	1.65	12.75	204.9	0.029	0.15	0	0	0.002	0	0.011	0	0.03	0	0
5.244	2.484	0.069	0.138	3.864	4.692	78.384	0.022	11.59	0	0	0.001	0.08	0.036		0.72	1.104	0
4.95	33.66	0.723	8.91	35.64	177.21	267.3	0.198	35.64	8.316	0.04	0.03	0.079	0.109	0.178		38.61	0
57	13.3	0.693	7.6	53.2	256.5	311.6	0.19	28.5	1.045	0.067	0.104	0.257	0.142	0.114		23.75	0
43.56	192.06	2.277	51.48	142.56	415.8	762.3	2.693	71.28	3.564	0.099	0.356	2.455	0.218	0.634		83.16	0
5.22	245.34	2.662	52.2	153.99	391.5	884.79	3.289	258.4	3.393	0.157	0.496	2.532	0.522	0.731		91.35	0
244.8	81.6	2.897	19.04	387.6	238	890.8	0.993	179.5	0.136	0.303	0.487	2.153	0.112	0.626	3.264	57.12	0
352.5	189	3.735	24	238.5	250.5	999	1.635	106.5	2.7	0.135	0.225	2.4	0.135	1.035	1.965	60	0
299.52	220.8	4.55	30.72	316.8	318.72	1382.4	2.227	236.2	0	0.672	0.595	1.997	0.269	1.19	2.285	65.28	0
302.4	154.8	3.96	25.2	489.6	320.4	1141.2	2.16	160.2	0	0.504	0.45	3.6	0.198	1.368	2.844	64.8	0
260.64	164.16	2.549	20.16	459.36	230.4	1260	1.541	190.1	1.584	0.302	0.432	2.304	0.101	1.051		53.28	0
24.86	160.46	2.723	22.6	553.7	196.62	1432.84	1.65	30.51	0.113	0.508	0.316	3.48	0.136	0.034	1.661	38.42	0
34.72	127.72	2.579	19.84	446.4	198.4	1071.36	1.55	12.4	0.124	0.397	0.285	3.274	0.112	0.508	1.364	45.88	0
59.76	170.98	3.42	29.88	242.36	335.32	1050.78	3.486	71.38	1.66	0.349	0.282	8.051	0.183	1.926		61.42	0
110.05	232.5	3.41	32.55	373.55	308.45	635.5	4.96	99.2	0	0.248	0.372	6.014	0.248	2.309	1.193	68.2	0
111.15	161.85	4.739	44.85	399.75	331.5	1043.25	6.825	81.9	2.145	0.312	0.41	6.63	0.312	2.34		85.8	0
87.6	205.86	4.665	43.8	310.98	444.57	1108.14	4.599	140.2	7.884	0.394	0.46	7.38	0.285	2.562	1.183	81.03	0
77.52	257.64	3.625	43.32	405.84	332.88	1238.04	2.896	164.2	2.964	0.41	0.456	9.074	0.41	0.456		109.4	0
60.06	60.06	4.677	34.58	232.96	353.08	957.32	1.875	30.94	8.918	0.328	0.237	6.807	0.2	0.382		100.1	0
215.9	243.84	2.197	21.59	347.98	173.99	551.18	1.753	276.9	0.127	0.191	0.381	1.511	0.102	0.775		46.99	0
215.43	150.93	2.193	23.22	276.06	201.24	888.81	1.896	141.9	2.193	0.348	0.335	2.193	0.116	0.864		45.15	0
212.8	144.4	2.128	25.84	335.92	272.08	1080.72	2.174	130.7	11.4	0.517	0.304	3.192	0.228	1.003		45.6	0
58.65	167.9	2.254	24.15	186.3	215.05	1036.15	1.679	101.2	1.265	0.701	0.253	4.14	0.149	0.678	1.265	66.7	0
234.27	150.7	2.439	23.29	269.89	198.65	728.84	1.562	176.7	1.781	0.495	0.448	3.335	0.147	0.671	0.562	68.5	0
55.3	83.74	2.607	33.18	211.72	339.7	614.62	0.995	33.18	2.844	0.332	0.221	3.397	0.111	1.074	0.869	85.32	0
67.71	184.83	3.495	36.6	311.1	353.19	938.79	1.171	129.93	2.745	0.458	0.421	4.227	0.11	1.08	1.83	91.5	0
122.04	101.7	5.853	49.72	314.14	569.52	791	5.673	4.52	1.13	0.362	0.384	7.571	0.542	4.068		76.84	0
87.2	95.92	4.927	43.6	233.26	479.6	824.04	4.883	23.98	2.616	0.414	0.371	7.281	0.327	2.376		82.84	0
26.4	62.7	2.629	22	124.3	226.6	503.8	2.057	4.4	1.65	0.231	0.198	3.685	0.121	0.88		51.7	0

EvaluEat Code	Food Name	Amt	Wt (g)	Energy (kcal)	Prot (g)	Carb (g)	Fiber (g)	Fat (g)	Mono (g)	Poly (g)	Sat (g)
21107	Fast food, sandwich, hamburger, plain	1 sandwich	90	274.5	12.321	30.51		11.817	5.456	0.918	4.141
14347	Fast food, shake, vanilla/McDonald's	1 medium shake (16 fl. oz.)	333	369.63	11.655	59.607	0.333	9.99	2.87	0.37	6.187
21059	Fast food, shrimp (shellfish) breaded, fried	6–8 shrimp	164	454.28	18.876	40		24.895	17.379	0.645	5.379
21123	Fast food, steak sandwich	1 sandwich	204	459	30.335	51.959		14.076	5.345	3.346	3.815
21124	Fast food, submarine sandwich, cold cuts	1 sandwich	228	456	21.842	51.049		18.628	8.226	2.282	6.808
21126	Fast food, submarine sandwich, tuna salad	1 sandwich	256	583.68	29.696	55.373		27.981	13.402	7.296	5.33
21082	Fast food, taco	1 large	263	568.08	31.77	41.107		31.613	10.115	1.475	17.484
21085	Fast food, tostada w/beans & cheese	1 piece	144	223.2	9.605	26.525		9.864	3.054	0.749	5.367
21087	Fast food, tostada w/beef & cheese	1 piece	163	314.59	18.99	22.771		16.349	3.345	0.975	10.395
4002	Fat, animal, lard, pork	1 tbsp	12.8	115.46	0	0	0	12.8	5.773	1.434	5.018
6963	Fish broth	.5 cup	125	20	2.5	0.5	0	0.75	0.151	0.203	0.178
43129	Fish sticks, meatless	1 cup	186	539.4	42.78	16.74	11.346	33.48	8.139	17.358	5.299
15187	Fish, bass, freshwater, cooked w/dry heat	3 oz	85	124.1	20.553	0	0	4.021	1.56	1.156	0.851
15188	Fish, bass, striped, cooked w/dry heat	3 oz	85	105.4	19.32	0	0	2.542	0.719	0.854	0.553
15008	Fish, carp, raw	3 oz	85	107.95	15.156	0	0	4.76	1.979	1.216	0.921
15011	Fish, catfish, channel, breaded & fried	3 oz	85	194.65	15.377	6.834	0.595	11.331	4.769	2.826	2.795
15235	Fish, catfish, channel, farmed, cooked w/dry heat	3 oz	85	129.2	15.912	0	0	6.817	3.532	1.183	1.521
15012	Fish, caviar, black/red, granular	1 tbsp	16	40.32	3.936	0.64	0	2.864	0.741	1.185	0.65
15016	Fish, cod, Atlantic, baked/broiled (dry heat)	3 oz	85	89.25	19.406	0	0	0.731	0.105	0.248	0.143
15192	Fish, cod, Pacific, cooked w/dry heat	3 oz	85	89.25	19.508	0	0	0.689	0.089	0.266	0.088
15026	Fish, eel, baked or broiled (dry heat)	3 oz	85	200.6	20.103	0	0	12.708	7.835	1.032	2.57
15034	Fish, haddock, baked or broiled (dry heat)	3 oz	85	95.2	20.604	0	0	0.791	0.128	0.263	0.142
15035	Fish, haddock, smoked	3 oz	85	98.6	21.445	0	0	0.816	0.133	0.273	0.147
15037	Fish, halibut, Atlantic & Pacific, baked or broiled (dry heat)	3 oz	85	119	22.687	0	0	2.499	0.822	0.799	0.354
15196	Fish, halibut, Greenland, cooked w/dry heat	3 oz	85	203.15	15.657	0	0	15.079	9.131	1.49	2.637
15040	Fish, herring, Atlantic, baked or broiled (dry heat)	3 oz	85	172.55	19.576	0	0	9.852	4.072	2.325	2.223
15197	Fish, herring, Pacific, cooked w/dry heat	3 oz	85	212.5	17.859	0	0	15.122	7.486	2.64	3.548
15121	Fish, light tuna, canned in H$_2$O, drained	3 oz	85	98.6	21.684	0	0	0.697	0.135	0.286	0.199
15119	Fish, light tuna, canned in oil, drained	3 oz	85	168.3	24.76	0	0	6.979	2.507	2.452	1.304
15047	Fish, mackerel, Atlantic, baked or broiled (dry heat)	3 oz	85	222.7	20.273	0	0	15.139	5.955	3.655	3.55
15200	Fish, mackerel, king, cooked w/dry heat	3 oz	85	113.9	22.1	0	0	2.176	0.832	0.501	0.395
15058	Fish, ocean perch, Atlantic, baked or broiled (dry heat)	3 oz	85	102.85	20.298	0	0	1.776	0.681	0.465	0.266
15230	Fish, octopus, common, cooked w/moist heat	3 oz	85	139.4	25.347	3.74	0	1.768	0.275	0.405	0.385
15061	Fish, perch, baked or broiled (dry heat)	3 oz	85	99.45	21.131	0	0	1.003	0.166	0.401	0.201
15063	Fish, pike, northern, baked or broiled (dry heat)	3 oz	85	96.05	20.987	0	0	0.748	0.171	0.22	0.128
15204	Fish, pike, walleye, cooked w/dry heat	3 oz	85	101.15	20.859	0	0	1.326	0.32	0.487	0.271
15205	Fish, pollock, Atlantic, cooked w/dry heat	3 oz	85	100.3	21.182	0	0	1.071	0.122	0.529	0.145
15067	Fish, pollock, walleye, baked or broiled	3 oz	85	96.05	19.984	0	0	0.952	0.148	0.445	0.196
15069	Fish, pompano, Florida, baked or broiled (dry heat)	3 oz	85	179.35	20.137	0	0	10.319	2.818	1.239	3.824
15071	Fish, rockfish, Pacific, baked or broiled (dry heat)	3 oz	85	102.85	20.434	0	0	1.709	0.38	0.505	0.403
15207	Fish, roe, cooked w/dry heat	3 oz	85	173.4	24.327	1.632	0	6.995	1.81	2.893	1.586
15232	Fish, roughy, orange, cooked w/dry heat	3 oz	85	75.65	16.023	0	0	0.765	0.523	0.014	0.02

Chol (g)	Calc (mg)	Iron (mg)	Mag (mg)	Phos (mg)	Pota (mg)	Sodi (mg)	Zinc (mg)	Vit A (RAE)	Vit C (mg)	Thia (mg)	Ribo (mg)	Niac (mg)	Vit B6 (mg)	Vit B12 (µg)	Vit E (mg)	Fol (µg)	Alc (g)
35.1	63	2.403	18.9	102.6	144.9	387	1.998	0	0	0.333	0.27	3.717	0.063	0.891	0.495	53.1	0
36.63	406.26	0.3	39.96	339.66	579.42	273.06	1.199	123.2	2.664	0.15	0.606	0.616	0.173	1.199	0.2	16.65	0
200.08	83.64	2.952	39.36	344.4	183.68	1446.48	1.214	36.08	0	0.213	0.902	0	0.066	0.148		100	0
73.44	91.8	5.161	48.96	297.84	524.28	797.64	4.529	20.4	5.508	0.408	0.367	7.303	0.367	1.571		89.76	0
36.48	189.24	2.508	68.4	287.28	394.44	1650.72	2.576	70.68	12.31	1.003	0.798	5.495	0.137	1.094		86.64	0
48.64	74.24	2.637	79.36	220.16	335.36	1292.8	1.869	46.08	3.584	0.461	0.333	11.341	0.23	1.613		102.4	0
86.79	339.27	3.708	107.83	312.97	728.51	1233.47	6.049	165.7	3.419	0.237	0.684	4.944	0.368	1.604		105.2	0
30.24	210.24	1.886	59.04	116.64	403.2	542.88	1.901	44.64	1.296	0.101	0.331	1.325	0.158	0.691		43.2	0
40.75	216.79	2.869	63.57	179.3	572.13	896.5	3.684	50.53	2.608	0.098	0.554	3.146	0.228	1.174		74.98	0
12.16	0	0	0	0	0	0	0.014	0	0	0	0	0	0	0	0.077	0	0
0	37.5	0.262	1.25	37.5	107.5	397.5	0.125	1.25	0	0	0.037	1.712	0.012	0.125	0.188	5	0
0	176.7	3.72	42.78	837	1116	911.4	2.604	0	0	2.046	1.674	22.32	2.79	7.812	7.347	189.7	0
73.95	87.55	1.623	32.3	217.6	387.6	76.5	0.706	29.75	1.785	0.074	0.077	1.294	0.117	1.964		14.45	0
87.55	16.15	0.918	43.35	215.9	278.8	74.8	0.433	26.35	0	0.098	0.031	2.174	0.294	3.748		8.5	0
56.1	34.85	1.054	24.65	352.75	283.05	41.65	1.258	7.65	1.36	0.098	0.047	1.394	0.162	1.301	0.535	12.75	0
68.85	37.4	1.215	22.95	183.6	289	238	0.731	6.8	0	0.062	0.113	1.94	0.162	1.615		25.5	0
54.4	7.65	0.697	22.1	208.25	272.85	68	0.892	12.75	0.68	0.357	0.062	2.136	0.139	2.38		5.95	0
94.08	44	1.901	48	56.96	28.96	240	0.152	89.76	0	0.03	0.099	0.019	0.051	3.2	1.12	8	0
46.75	11.9	0.417	35.7	117.3	207.4	66.3	0.493	11.9	0.85	0.075	0.067	2.136	0.241	0.892	0.689	6.8	0
39.95	7.65	0.281	26.35	189.55	439.45	77.35	0.433	8.5	2.55	0.021	0.043	2.112	0.393	0.884		6.8	0
136.85	22.1	0.544	22.1	235.45	296.65	55.25	1.768	966.5	1.53	0.156	0.043	3.814	0.065	2.457	4.335	14.45	0
62.9	35.7	1.148	42.5	204.85	339.15	73.95	0.408	16.15	0	0.034	0.038	3.937	0.294	1.182		11.05	0
65.45	41.65	1.19	45.9	213.35	352.75	648.55	0.425	18.7	0	0.04	0.042	4.312	0.34	1.36	0.468	12.75	0
34.85	51	0.91	90.95	242.25	489.6	58.65	0.45	45.9	0	0.059	0.077	6.055	0.337	1.164	0.927	11.9	0
50.15	3.4	0.723	28.05	178.5	292.4	87.55	0.433	15.3	0	0.062	0.088	1.635	0.412	0.816		0.85	0
65.45	62.9	1.199	34.85	257.55	356.15	97.75	1.079	30.6	0.595	0.095	0.254	3.505	0.296	11.169	1.164	10.2	0
84.15	90.1	1.224	34.85	248.2	460.7	80.75	0.578	29.75	0	0.062	0.218	2.398	0.441	8.177		5.1	0
25.5	9.35	1.301	22.95	138.55	201.45	287.3	0.655	14.45	0	0.027	0.063	11.288	0.298	2.542	0.281	3.4	0
15.3	11.05	1.182	26.35	264.35	175.95	300.9	0.765	19.55	0	0.032	0.102	10.54	0.094	1.87	0.74	4.25	0
63.75	12.75	1.335	82.45	236.3	340.85	70.55	0.799	45.9	0.34	0.135	0.35	5.823	0.391	16.15		1.7	0
57.8	34	1.938	34.85	270.3	474.3	172.55	0.612	214.2	1.36	0.098	0.493	8.893	0.433	15.3		7.65	0
45.9	116.45	1.003	33.15	235.45	297.5	81.6	0.519	11.9	0.68	0.111	0.114	2.071	0.23	0.978		8.5	0
81.6	90.1	8.109	51	237.15	535.5	391	2.856	76.5	6.8	0.048	0.065	3.213	0.551	30.6	1.02	20.4	0
97.75	86.7	0.986	32.3	218.45	292.4	67.15	1.215	8.5	1.445	0.068	0.102	1.615	0.119	1.87		5.1	0
42.5	62.05	0.604	34	239.7	281.35	41.65	0.731	20.4	3.23	0.057	0.065	2.38	0.115	1.955		14.45	0
93.5	119.85	1.419	32.3	228.65	424.15	55.25	0.672	20.4	0	0.265	0.166	2.381	0.117	1.964		14.45	0
77.35	65.45	0.502	73.1	240.55	387.6	93.5	0.51	10.2	0	0.046	0.191	3.386	0.281	3.128		2.55	0
81.6	5.1	0.238	62.05	409.7	328.95	98.6	0.51	21.25	0	0.063	0.065	1.403	0.059	3.57	0.672	3.4	0
54.4	36.55	0.57	26.35	289.85	540.6	64.6	0.586	30.6	0	0.578	0.128	3.23	0.196	1.02		14.45	0
37.4	10.2	0.45	28.9	193.8	442	65.45	0.45	60.35	0	0.037	0.071	3.331	0.23	1.02	1.326	8.5	0
407.15	23.8	0.655	22.1	437.75	240.55	99.45	1.088	77.35	13.94	0.235	0.807	1.863	0.157	9.809		78.2	0
22.1	32.3	0.196	32.3	217.6	327.25	68.85	0.816	20.4	0	0.098	0.156	3.106	0.294	1.964		6.8	0

EvaluEat Code	Food Name	Amt	Wt (g)	Energy (kcal)	Prot (g)	Carb (g)	Fiber (g)	Fat (g)	Mono (g)	Poly (g)	Sat (g)
15237	Fish, salmon, Atlantic, farmed, cooked w/dry heat	3 oz	85	175.1	18.785	0	0	10.498	3.767	3.762	2.128
15209	Fish, salmon, Atlantic, wild, cooked w/dry heat	3 oz	85	154.7	21.624	0	0	6.911	2.292	2.768	1.068
15087	Fish, salmon, sockeye w/bone, canned, drained	3 oz	85	130.05	17.399	0	0	6.214	2.688	1.605	1.397
15086	Fish, salmon, sockeye, baked or broiled (dry heat)	3 oz	85	183.6	23.214	0	0	9.325	4.497	2.048	1.629
15092	Fish, sea bass, baked or broiled (dry heat)	3 oz	85	105.4	20.086	0	0	2.176	0.462	0.81	0.557
15214	Fish, sea trout, cooked w/dry heat	3 oz	85	113.05	18.241	0	0	3.936	0.963	0.79	1.099
15096	Fish, shark, battered, fried	3 oz	85	193.8	15.8	5.431	0	11.7	5.045	3.146	2.724
15100	Fish, smelt, rainbow, baked or broiled (dry heat)	3 oz	85	105.4	19.21	0	0	2.635	0.699	0.965	0.492
15102	Fish, snapper, baked or broiled (dry heat)	3 oz	85	108.8	22.355	0	0	1.462	0.274	0.5	0.31
15176	Fish, squid, fried	3 oz	85	148.75	15.249	6.622	0	6.358	2.337	1.816	1.596
15105	Fish, sturgeon, baked or broiled	3 oz	85	114.75	17.595	0	0	4.403	2.113	0.752	0.997
15106	Fish, sturgeon, smoked	3 oz	85	147.05	26.52	0	0	3.74	2.003	0.371	0.881
15111	Fish, swordfish, baked or broiled (dry heat)	3 oz	85	131.75	21.582	0	0	4.369	1.684	1.005	1.195
15241	Fish, trout, rainbow, farmed, cooked w/dry heat	3 oz	85	143.65	20.63	0	0	6.12	1.782	1.98	1.789
15116	Fish, trout, rainbow, wild, cooked w/dry heat	3 oz	85	127.5	19.482	0	0	4.947	1.484	1.556	1.376
15128	Fish, tuna salad	1 cup	205	383.35	32.882	19.29	0	18.983	5.918	8.45	3.165
15118	Fish, tuna, bluefin, baked or broiled (dry heat)	3 oz	85	156.4	25.424	0	0	5.338	1.745	1.567	1.37
15221	Fish, tuna, yellowfin, fresh, cooked w/dry heat	3 oz	85	118.2	25.5	0	0	1.037	0.167	0.309	0.256
15222	Fish, turbot, European, cooked w/dry heat	3 oz	85	103.7	17.493	0	0	3.213			
15126	Fish, white tuna, canned in H$_2$0, drained	3 oz	85	108.8	20.077	0	0	2.525	0.666	0.943	0.673
15124	Fish, white tuna, canned in oil, drained	3 oz	85	158.1	22.551	0	0	6.868	2.773	2.526	1.088
15223	Fish, whitefish, cooked w/dry heat	3 oz	85	146.2	20.799	0	0	6.384	2.175	2.342	0.988
15133	Fish, whiting, baked or broiled (dry heat)	3 oz	85	98.6	19.958	0	0	1.437	0.378	0.499	0.34
15225	Fish, yellowtail, cooked w/dry heat	3 oz	85	158.95	25.22	0	0	5.712			
2050	Flavoring, vanilla extract	1 tsp	4.2	12.096	0.003	0.531	0	0.003	0	0	0
20003	Flour, arrowroot	1 cup	128	456.96	0.384	112.83	4.352	0.128	0.003	0.058	0.024
20130	Flour, barley flour or meal	1 cup	148	510.6	15.54	110.29	14.948	2.368	0.303	1.141	0.496
20011	Flour, buckwheat, whole groat	1 cup	120	402	15.144	84.708	12	3.72	1.139	1.139	0.812
20017	Flour, corn, masa, enriched	1 cup	114	416.1	10.648	86.948	10.944	4.309	1.137	1.965	0.606
20070	Flour, triticale, whole grain	1 cup	130	439.4	17.134	95.082	18.98	2.353	0.238	1.032	0.413
20081	Flour, wheat, white, all purpose, bleached, enriched	1 cup	125	455	12.913	95.387	3.375	1.225	0.109	0.516	0.194
20082	Flour, wheat, white, all purpose, self-rise, enriched	1 cup	125	442.5	12.363	92.775	3.375	1.213	0.108	0.512	0.192
20083	Flour, wheat, white, bread, enriched	1 cup	137	494.57	16.413	99.366	3.288	2.274	0.192	0.996	0.334
20084	Flour, wheat, white, cake, enriched	1 cup unsifted, dipped	137	495.94	11.234	106.9	2.329	1.178	0.1	0.519	0.174
20080	Flour, whole wheat, whole grain	1 cup	120	406.8	16.44	87.084	14.64	2.244	0.278	0.935	0.386
7945	Frankfurter, beef, heated	1 serving	52	169.52	6.001	1.96	0	15.319	7.447	0.553	5.947
18268	French toast, frozen	1 piece	59	125.67	4.366	18.939	0.649	3.599	1.204	0.724	0.904
18269	French toast, homemade w/reduced fat (2%) milk	1 slice	65	148.85	5.005	16.25		7.02	2.941	1.686	1.77
22606	Frozen dinner, cacciatore chicken, pasta w/chicken breast pieces & vegetables in cacci	1 serving	354	265.5	21.983	35.86	4.956	3.965	2.372	0.637	0.991
22602	Frozen dinner, creamed spinach/Stouffer	1 cup	250	337.5	7	18	4.5	26.25	5.67	8.98	7.4
22603	Frozen dinner, spinach au gratin/The Budget Gourmet	1 serving	155	221.65	6.665	11.47	2.325	16.585			7.595
22601	Frozen dinner, Stir Fry 2, white rice & vegetables w/Oriental soy sauce/Hanover	1 serving	137	130.15	4.521	26.989	2.466	0.411			

Chol (g)	Calc (mg)	Iron (mg)	Mag (mg)	Phos (mg)	Pota (mg)	Sodi (mg)	Zinc (mg)	Vit A (RAE)	Vit C (mg)	Thia (mg)	Ribo (mg)	Niac (mg)	Vit B$_6$ (mg)	Vit B$_{12}$ (µg)	Vit E (mg)	Fol (µg)	Alc (g)
53.55	12.75	0.289	25.5	214.2	326.4	51.85	0.366	12.75	3.145	0.289	0.115	6.838	0.55	2.38		28.9	0
60.35	12.75	0.876	31.45	217.6	533.8	47.6	0.697	11.05	0	0.234	0.414	8.565	0.802	2.592		24.65	0
37.4	203.15	0.901	24.65	277.1	320.45	457.3	0.867	45.05	0	0.014	0.164	4.658	0.255	0.255	1.36	8.5	0
73.95	5.95	0.468	26.35	234.6	318.75	56.1	0.433	53.55	0	0.183	0.145	5.67	0.186	4.93		4.25	0
45.05	11.05	0.315	45.05	210.8	278.8	73.95	0.442	54.4	0	0.111	0.128	1.615	0.391	0.255		5.1	0
90.1	18.7	0.298	34	272.85	371.45	62.9	0.493	29.75	0	0.059	0.176	2.485	0.393	2.941		5.1	0
50.2	42.5	0.944	36.5	164.9	131.8	103.7	0.408	45.9	0	0.061	0.082	2.366	0.255	1.029	0	12.8	0
76.5	65.45	0.978	32.3	250.75	316.2	65.45	1.802	14.45	0	0.009	0.124	1.501	0.145	3.375		4.25	0
39.95	34	0.204	31.45	170.85	443.7	48.45	0.374	29.75	1.36	0.045	0.003	0.294	0.391	2.975		5.1	0
221	33.15	0.859	32.3	213.35	237.15	260.1	1.479	9.35	3.57	0.048	0.389	2.212	0.049	1.046		11.9	0
65.45	14.45	0.765	38.25	230.35	309.4	58.65	0.459	223.55	0	0.068	0.077	8.585	0.196	2.125	0.535	14.45	0
68	14.45	0.791	39.95	238.85	322.15	628.15	0.476	238	0	0.077	0.077	9.435	0.23	2.465	0.425	17	0
42.5	5.1	0.884	28.9	286.45	313.65	97.75	1.25	34.85	0.935	0.037	0.099	10.022	0.324	1.717		1.7	0
57.8	73.1	0.281	27.2	226.1	374.85	35.7	0.417	73.1	2.805	0.201	0.068	7.472	0.337	4.224		20.4	0
58.65	73.1	0.323	26.35	228.65	380.8	47.6	0.433	12.75	1.7	0.129	0.082	4.905	0.294	5.355		16.15	0
26.65	34.85	2.05	38.95	364.9	364.9	824.1	1.148	49.2	4.51	0.064	0.144	13.735	0.166	2.46		16.4	0
41.65	8.5	1.113	54.4	277.1	274.55	42.5	0.655	643.5	0	0.236	0.26	8.959	0.446	9.248		1.7	0
49.3	17.9	0.799	54.4	208.2	483.7	40	0.57	17	0.85	0.426	0.048	10.1	0.882	0.51	0	1.7	0
52.7	19.55	0.391	55.25	140.25	259.25	163.2	0.238	10.2	1.445	0.065	0.082	2.277	0.206	2.159		7.65	0
35.7	11.9	0.825	28.05	184.45	201.45	320.45	0.408	5.1	0	0.007	0.037	4.929	0.184	0.994	0.723	1.7	0
26.35	3.4	0.553	28.9	226.95	283.05	336.6	0.4	4.25	0	0.014	0.067	9.943	0.366	1.87	1.955	4.25	0
65.45	28.05	0.4	35.7	294.1	345.1	55.25	1.079	33.15	0	0.145	0.131	3.269	0.294	0.816		14.45	0
71.4	52.7	0.357	22.95	242.25	368.9	112.2	0.45	28.9	0	0.058	0.051	1.419	0.153	2.21	0.255	12.75	0
60.35	24.65	0.535	32.3	170.85	457.3	42.5	0.57	26.35	2.465	0.149	0.043	7.41	0.157	1.063		3.4	0
0	0.462	0.005	0.504	0.252	6.216	0.378	0.005	0	0	0	0.004	0.018	0.001	0		0	1.445
0	51.2	0.422	3.84	6.4	14.08	2.56	0.09	0	0	0.001	0	0	0.006	0		8.96	0
0	47.36	3.966	142.08	438.08	457.32	5.92	2.96	0	0	0.548	0.169	9.278	0.586	0	0.844	11.84	0
0	49.2	4.872	301.2	404.4	692.4	13.2	3.744	0	0	0.5	0.228	7.38	0.698	0	0.384	64.8	0
0	160.74	8.219	125.4	254.22	339.72	5.7	2.029	0	0	1.629	0.858	11.221	0.422	0	0.171	265.6	0
0	45.5	3.367	198.9	417.3	605.8	2.6	3.458	0	0	0.491	0.172	3.718	0.524	0	1.17	96.2	0
0	18.75	5.8	27.5	135	133.75	2.5	0.875	0	0	0.981	0.618	7.38	0.055	0	0.075	228.8	0
0	422.5	5.838	23.75	743.75	155	1587.5	0.775	0	0	0.843	0.517	7.29	0.063	0	0.063	245	0
0	20.55	6.042	34.25	132.89	137	2.74	1.164	0	0	1.112	0.701	10.349	0.051	0	0.548	250.71	0
0	19.18	10.028	21.92	116.45	143.85	2.74	0.849	0	0	1.222	0.589	9.302	0.045	0	0.027	254.8	0
0	40.8	4.656	165.6	415.2	486	6	3.516	0	0	0.536	0.258	7.638	0.409	0	0.984	52.8	0
29.12	6.24	0.811	7.28	88.92	76.44	600.08	1.222	0		0.02	0.075	1.224	0.048	0.858	0.104	3.64	0
48.38	63.13	1.304	10.03	82.01	79.06	292.05	0.454	31.86	0.177	0.163	0.225	1.606	0.293	0.991	0.395	30.68	0
75.4	65	1.085	11.05	76.05	87.1	311.35	0.435	80.6	0.195	0.133	0.209	1.058	0.048	0.201		27.95	0
31.86	53.1	2.23		254.88	750.48	552.24											0
32.5	282.5					670											0
41.85	243.35	1.953				654.1			27.13								0
						635.68			16.3								0

EvaluEat Code	Food Name	Amt	Wt (g)	Energy (kcal)	Prot (g)	Carb (g)	Fiber (g)	Fat (g)	Mono (g)	Poly (g)	Sat (g)
22618	Frozen meal, barbecue glazed chicken & sauce w/mixed vegetables/WW Ultimate 200	1 package	209	217.36	18.81	25.916		4.389	1.559	1.099	0.995
22613	Frozen meal, beef & bean burrito/Las Campanas	1 serving	114	296.4	8.664	38.19	0.798	12.084	5.518	0.787	4.184
22682	Frozen meal, beef & bean chimichanga/Fiesta Cafe	1 package	227	422.22	24.062	55.615	6.129	11.577	3.882	3.473	2.156
22402	Frozen meal, beef macaroni/Healthy Choice	1 serving	240	211.2	14.136	33.456	4.56	2.232	1.2	0.336	0.672
22578	Frozen meal, beef pot roast w/whipped potatoes/Stouffer Lean Cuisine Homestyle	1 package	255	206.55	17.34	22.44	3.57	5.355	2.285	0.808	1.306
22616	Frozen meal, beef sirloin salisbury steak w/red skinned potatoes & vegetables/Budget Gourmet	1 package	311	261.24	18.349	33.899	7.153	5.909	1.754	0.936	2.018
22686	Frozen meal, beef stir fry kit: white rice, oriental vegetables, beef strips, Oriental	1 package	810	866.7	51.597	141.59		9.963			
22677	Frozen meal, beef stroganoff and noodles w/carrots & peas/Marie Callender	1 package	368	599.84	30.397	58.696	4.416	27.011	11.96	3.974	11.077
22577	Frozen meal, chicken & vegetables w/vermicelli/Stouffer's Lean Cuisine	1 package	297	252.45	18.711	32.076	5.049	5.643	2.132	1.384	1.028
22581	Frozen meal, chicken a l'orange in sauce w/broccoli & rice/Stouffer's Lean Cuisine	1 package	255	267.75	24.48	38.505		1.785	0.502	0.413	0.418
22610	Frozen meal, chicken alfredo w/fettucini & vegetables/Stouffer's Lunch Express	1 package	272	372.64	19.04	32.64	3.808	18.496	6.256	2.394	6.99
22575	Frozen meal, chicken cordon bleu, filled w/cheese & ham/Barber Food	1 package	340	697	51.68	29.58		41.48	16.694	6.562	11.526
22615	Frozen meal, chicken enchilada & mexican rice w/monterey jack cheese sauce/Stouffer's	1 package	283	376.39	12.452	48.393	4.528	14.716	4.415	3.707	3.368
22687	Frozen meal, chicken fajita kit/Tyson	1 package	756	914.76	56.624	122.77		23.209	9.148	4.158	5.897
22688	Frozen meal, chicken mesquite w/BBQ sauce, corn medley & potatoes au gratin/Tyson	1 package	255	321.3	17.773	44.956	4.335	7.752	2.729	0.484	2.601
22906	Frozen meal, chicken pot pie, frozen entree	1 serving	217	483.91	13.042	42.706	1.736	29.1	12.478	4.488	9.667
22587	Frozen meal, chicken teriyaki w/rice, mixed vegetables w/butter sauce & apple cherry compote	1 package	312	268.32	17.066	37.097	2.808	5.616	2.153	0.468	2.995
22690	Frozen meal, cosmic chicken nuggets w/macaroni & cheese, corn, chocolate pudding	1 package	257	524.28	17.733	52.942	3.084	26.728	10.717	5.962	6.605
22619	Frozen meal, country roast turkey w/mushrooms in brown gravy & rice pilaf/Healthy Choice	1 package	240	223.2	18.984	27.84	3.12	3.936	1.8	0.888	1.248
22579	Frozen meal, creamed chipped beef/Stouffer's	1 package	311	435.4	24.569	17.727		29.545	8.739	2.923	12.533
22614	Frozen meal, escalloped chicken & noodles/Stouffer's	1 package	283	418.84	16.98	31.413		25.187	7.669	13.556	6.566
22617	Frozen meal, French recipe chicken breast, vegetables & potatoes in red wine sauce/Budget Gourmet	1 package	255	178.5	22.95	9.18	6.12	5.61	2.703	0.482	1.446
22710	Frozen meal, gravy & sliced beef, mashed potatoes & carrots/Freezer Queen	1 package	255	206.55	15.3	25.5	3.57	4.845	1.25	1.709	1.3
22585	Frozen meal, homestyle stuffed cabbage w/meat in tomato sauce & whipped pots/Stouffer's	1 package	269	199.06	11.567	25.824	6.456	5.649	2.375	0.748	1.681
22673	Frozen meal, Italian sausage lasagna/Budget Gourmet	1 package	298	455.94	20.562	39.932	2.98	23.84	9.774	1.997	8.165
22570	Frozen meal, lasagna w/meat & sauce/Stouffer's	1 package	595	767.55	51.765	73.185	8.925	29.75	9.639	1.547	13.03
22576	Frozen meal, macaroni & beef in tomato sauce/Stouffer's Lean Cuisine	1 package	283	249.04	13.867	36.507	3.396	5.377	2.057	0.702	1.636

Chol (g)	Calc (mg)	Iron (mg)	Mag (mg)	Phos (mg)	Pota (mg)	Sodi (mg)	Zinc (mg)	Vit A (RAE)	Vit C (mg)	Thia (mg)	Ribo (mg)	Niac (mg)	Vit B6 (mg)	Vit B12 (µg)	Vit E (mg)	Fol (µg)	Alc (g)
48.07		1.087				405.46			21.53								0
12.54		3.112				579.12											0
36.32		6.81				803.58			5.902								0
14.4	45.6	2.712	36	134.4	364.8	444	1.224	55.2	58.08	0.276	0.156	3.108	0.194	0.12	1.68	105.6	0
38.25						494.7											0
43.54		3.048				494.49			51								0
						3167.1			50.22								0
69.92	69.92	1.803				1140.8			0								0
23.76	103.95	1.336				582.12			14.55								0
45.9						359.55			18.11								0
57.12	146.88					587.52			24.21								0
163.2	292.4					1526.6											0
25.47	254.7					1001.82			15.28								0
90.72						2472.12			73.33								0
25.5						793.05			0								0
41.23	32.55	2.062	23.87	119.35	256.06	857.15	1.02	256.7	1.519	0.254	0.356	4.13	0.202	0.152	3.847	41.23	0
43.68	37.44	1.092		224.64	424.32	602.16			12.17								0
48.83	205.6	2.853				974.03											0
26.4	21.6	1.032				436.8											0
108.85	472.72	2.27				1545.67											0
76.41	116.03	1.132				1211.24											0
25.5						864.45											
30.6						647.7	530.4										0
24.21	104.91					411.57			52.99								0
47.68	315.88	2.682				902.94											0
113.05	636.65					2034.9											0
22.64		2.179				563.17			157.3								0

EvaluEat Code	Food Name	Amt	Wt (g)	Energy (kcal)	Prot (g)	Carb (g)	Fiber (g)	Fat (g)	Mono (g)	Poly (g)	Sat (g)
22675	Frozen meal, meat loaf w/tomato sauce, mashed potatoes & carrots in seasoned sauce/Budget Gourmet	1 package	453	611.55	29.083	33.567	6.342	40.045	17.305	7.248	15.493
22586	Frozen meal, Mexican w/tamales, beef enchiladas & chili sauce, beans & rice	1 package	376	507.6	13.912	68.432	8.272	19.928	7.708	2.707	6.768
22571	Frozen meal, original fried chicken meal w/mashed potatoes & corn in seasoned sauce	1 package	228	469.68	21.455	35.089	2.052	27.041	15.367	2.44	9.257
22569	Frozen meal, pepper, stuffed w/beef in tomato sauce/Stouffer's	1 package	439	377.54	15.804	41.705	10.536	16.243	7.507	1.058	5.444
22672	Frozen meal, roast turkey medallions & mushrooms in sauce w/rice & vegetables/WW Smart	1 package	240	213.6	15.12	34.56	3.12	1.68	0.43	0.451	0.446
22712	Frozen meal, roasted chicken w/garlic sauce, pasta & vegetable medley/Tyson	1 package	255	214.2	16.932	21.522	3.57	6.707	2.346	2.142	1.3
22595	Frozen meal, scrambled eggs & sausage w/hashed brown potatoes	1 package	177	361.08	12.567	17.169	1.416	26.904	12.673	3.628	7.345
22580	Frozen meal, spaghetti w/meat sauce/Stouffer's Lean Cuisine	1 package	326	312.96	14.344	50.53	5.542	5.868	2.282	1.324	1.353
22608	Frozen meal, spaghetti w/meatballs & pomodoro sauce, low-fat/Michelina's	1 package	284	312.4	13.632	48.564	6.248	7.1	2.627	1.051	2.212
22573	Frozen meal, Swedish meatballs w/pasta/Stouffer's Lean Cuisine	1 package	258	276.06	21.672	31.218	2.58	7.224	2.34	1.04	2.423
22599	Frozen meal, turkey w/gravy & dressing w/broccoli/Marie Callender	1 package	397	504.19	31.045	51.848		19.016	8.178	1.747	9.091
42185	Frozen yogurts, chocolate, nonfat milk, with low calorie sweetener	1 cup	186	199.02	8.184	36.642	3.72	1.488	0.398	0.056	0.939
42187	Frozen yogurts, flavors other than chocolate	1 cup	186	236.22	5.58	40.176	0	6.696	1.834	0.186	4.326
14127	Fruit beverage mix, Kool-Aid, sugar free w/aspartame & vit C, dry mix, cherry flavor	.125 envelope	1.2	3.48	0.073	1.019		0.004			
14275	Fruit beverage mix, Kraft Kool-Aid Sugar Sweetened Tropical Punch, powder	1 NLEA serving	17	63.75	0	16.252	0	0			0
14297	Fruit beverage mix, Lemonade Flavor Drink, dry, prep w/H₂O	8 fl. oz.	266	111.72	0	28.728	0	0	0.005	0.011	0.045
14290	Fruit beverage mix, Lemonade w/aspartame, low kcal, dry, prep	8 fl. oz.	237	4.74	0.047	1.232	0	0	0	0.002	0
14408	Fruit beverage mix, orange flavor drink, dry, prep w/H₂O	8 fl. oz.	271	132.79	0	34.281	0.271	0	0	0	0
14403	Fruit beverage mix, orange flavor, Tang, dry mix	8 fl. oz.	25	91.5	0	24.6	0.075	0	0	0	0
14263	Fruit beverage, citrus drink, frozen concentrate, prep w/H₂O	8 fl. oz.	248	124	0.446	30.231	0.248	0.124	0	0	0
14242	Fruit beverage, cranberry cocktail, bottled	8 fl. oz.	253	144.21	0	36.432	0.253	0.253	0.035	0.111	0.023
14431	Fruit beverage, cranberry juice cocktail, frozen concentrate, prep w/H₂O	8 fl. oz.	250	137.5	0	35	0.25	0	0	0	0
14241	Fruit beverage, cranberry-grape drink, bottled	8 fl. oz.	245	137.2	0.49	34.3	0.245	0.245	0.01	0.056	0.081
14267	Fruit beverage, fruit punch, canned	8 fl. oz.	248	116.56	0	29.686	0.496	0	0.005	0.007	0
14269	Fruit beverage, fruit punch, frozen concentrate, prep w/H₂O	8 fl. oz.	247	113.62	0.148	28.8	0.247	0	0.002	0.005	0.002
14277	Fruit beverage, grape drink, canned	8 fl. oz.	250	112.5	0.025	28.875	0	0	0	0.003	0.003
14406	Fruit beverage, juice drink, frozen concentrate, prep	8 fl. oz.	248	124	0.248	30.256	0.248	0.496	0.06	0.122	0.062
14543	Fruit beverage, lemonade, pink, frozen conc, prep w/H₂O	8 fl. oz.	247	98.8	0.247	25.935	0	0	0.005	0.032	0.015
14293	Fruit beverage, lemonade, white, frozen, prep w/H₂O	8 fl. oz.	248	131.44	0.223	34.05	0.248	0.149	0.005	0.042	0.02
14303	Fruit beverage, limeade, frozen concentrate, prep w/H₂O	8 fl. oz.	247	103.74	0.099	26.108	0	0.025	0	0	0

Chol (g)	Calc (mg)	Iron (mg)	Mag (mg)	Phos (mg)	Pota (mg)	Sodi (mg)	Zinc (mg)	Vit A (RAE)	Vit C (mg)	Thia (mg)	Ribo (mg)	Niac (mg)	Vit B$_6$ (mg)	Vit B$_{12}$ (µg)	Vit E (mg)	Fol (µg)	Alc (g)
113.25	77.01	3.941				1943.37			7.701								0
26.32	240.64	2.858				1812.32			4.888								0
88.92	38.76	1.368				1500.24			1.368								0
43.9						1154.57			173								0
24		1.416				504											0
28.05		1.556				466.65											0
283.2		1.664				771.72											0
13.04		2.119				609.62			34.88								0
14.2		2.925				1011.04			8.804								0
46.44		2.064				562.44											0
79.4	131.01	4.367				2036.61			23.82								0
7.44	295.74	0.074	74.4	239.94	630.54	150.66	0.911	3.72	1.302	0.074	0.335	0.372	0.074	0.911	0.149	22.32	0
24.18	186	0.856	18.6	165.54	290.16	117.18	0.521	91.14	1.302	0.074	0.335	0.13	0.074	0.13	0.167	7.44	0
						5.064			6.72								0
0	27.88	0.012		12.75	0.34	1.53			6.001								
0	29.26	0.053	2.66	2.66	2.66	18.62	0.08	0	34.05	0	0.003	0	0	0		0	0
0	52.14	0.095	2.37	23.7	0	4.74	0.024	0	5.925	0	0	0	0	0	0	0	0
0	138.21	0.027	2.71	51.49	65.04	10.84	0.027	208.7	79.95	0	0.236	2.772	0.276	0	0	0	0
0	92.25	0.018	0	42.25	47.5	2	0.01		60	0	0.17	2	0.2	0	2.013	0	0
0	12.4	0.124	9.92	9.92	121.52	4.96	0.05	2.48	36.21	0.04	0.02	0.151	0.04	0	0.05	7.44	0
0	7.59	0.38	5.06	5.06	45.54	5.06	0.177	0	89.56	0.023	0.023	0.089	0.048	0	0	0	0
0	12.5	0.225	5	2.5	35	7.5	0.1	2.5	24.75	0.018	0.022	0.03	0.035	0		0	0
0	19.6	0.024	7.35	9.8	58.8	7.35	0.098	0	78.4	0.024	0.044	0.294	0.069	0		2.45	0
0	19.84	0.223	7.44	7.44	62	94.24	0.025	4.96	73.41	0.055	0.057	0.052	0.027	0	0.05	9.92	0
0	9.88	0.222	4.94	2.47	32.11	9.88	0.049	0	108.2	0.025	0.032	0.052	0.015	0		2.47	0
0	5	0.45	2.5	0	30	15	0.3	0	85.25	0.003	0.01	0.025	0.005	0	0	0	0
0	17.36	0.57	9.92	0	190.96	12.4	0.546	0	13.89	0.002	0.161	0.146	0.032	0		0	0
0	7.41	0.395	4.94	4.94	37.05	7.41	0.099	0	9.633	0.015	0.052	0.04	0.015	0		4.94	0
0	9.92	0.521	4.96	7.44	49.6	7.44	0.074	0	12.9	0.02	0.069	0.055	0.017	0	0.025	2.48	0
0	7.41	0.025	2.47	2.47	22.23	4.94	0.025	0	5.928	0.005	0.007	0.02	0.01	0		2.47	0

EvaluEat Code	Food Name	Amt	Wt (g)	Energy (kcal)	Prot (g)	Carb (g)	Fiber (g)	Fat (g)	Mono (g)	Poly (g)	Sat (g)
14323	Fruit beverage, orange drink, canned	8 fl. oz.	248	126.48	0	31.992	0	0	0.005	0.007	0.005
14334	Fruit beverage, pineapple & grapefruit juice drink, canned	8 fl. oz.	250	117.5	0.5	29	0.25	0.25	0.025	0.07	0.015
14341	Fruit beverage, pineapple & orange juice drink, canned	8 fl. oz.	250	125	3.25	29.5	0.25	0	0	0	0
9100	Fruit cocktail (peach, pineapple, pear, grape & cherry)canned in heavy syrup	1 cup	248	181.04	0.967	46.897	2.48	0.174	0.032	0.077	0.025
9097	Fruit cocktail (peach, pineapple, pear, grape & cherry)canned in juice	1 cup	237	109.02	1.09	28.108	2.37	0.024	0.005	0.009	0.002
9016	Fruit juice, apple, canned or bottled, unsweetened w/o added vit C	1 cup	248	116.56	0.149	28.966	0.248	0.273	0.012	0.082	0.047
9018	Fruit juice, apple, frozen concentrate, unsweetened w/o added vit C, prep	1 cup	239	112.33	0.335	27.581	0.239	0.239	0.005	0.074	0.043
9036	Fruit juice, apricot nectar, canned w/o added vit C	1 cup	251	140.56	0.929	36.119	1.506	0.226	0.095	0.043	0.015
9124	Fruit juice, grapefruit, canned, sweetened	1 cup	250	115	1.45	27.825	0.25	0.225	0.03	0.052	0.03
9123	Fruit juice, grapefruit, canned, unsweetened	1 cup	247	93.86	1.284	22.131	0.247	0.247	0.032	0.057	0.032
9126	Fruit juice, grapefruit, frozen concentrate, unsweetened, prep	1 cup	247	101.27	1.359	24.033	0.247	0.321	0.044	0.079	0.047
9152	Fruit juice, lemon, fresh	1 fl. oz.	30.5	7.625	0.116	2.632	0.122	0	0	0	0
9160	Fruit juice, lime, fresh	1 fl. oz.	30.8	8.316	0.136	2.775	0.123	0.031	0.003	0.008	0.003
9207	Fruit juice, orange, canned, unsweetened	1 cup	249	104.58	1.469	24.527	0.498	0.349	0.062	0.085	0.045
9206	Fruit juice, orange, fresh	1 cup	248	111.6	1.736	25.792	0.496	0.496	0.089	0.099	0.06
9215	Fruit juice, orange, frozen concentrate, unsweetened, prep	1 cup	249	112.05	1.693	26.842	0.498	0.149	0.025	0.03	0.017
9217	Fruit juice, orange-grapefruit, canned, unsweetened	1 cup	247	106.21	1.482	25.392	0.247	0.247	0.042	0.047	0.027
9229	Fruit juice, papaya nectar, canned	1 cup	250	142.5	0.425	36.275	1.5	0.375	0.103	0.087	0.117
9232	Fruit juice, passion fruit, purple, fresh	1 cup	247	125.97	0.963	33.592	0.494	0.124	0.015	0.072	0.01
9251	Fruit juice, peach nectar, canned w/o added vit C	1 cup	249	134.46	0.672	34.661	1.494	0.05	0.02	0.027	0.005
9273	Fruit juice, pineapple, canned, unsweetened w/o added vit C	1 cup	250	140	0.8	34.45	0.5	0.2	0.022	0.07	0.012
9294	Fruit juice, prune, canned	1 cup	256	181.76	1.562	44.672	2.56	0.077	0.054	0.018	0.008
9223	Fruit juice, tangerine, canned, sweetened	1 cup	249	124.5	1.245	29.88	0.498	0.498	0.045	0.062	0.032
9105	Fruit salad (peach, pineapple, pear, apricot & cherry)canned in heavy syrup	1 cup	255	186.15	0.867	48.73	2.55	0.178	0.036	0.079	0.025
9103	Fruit salad (peach, pineapple, pear, apricot & cherry)canned in juice	1 cup	249	124.5	1.27	32.494	2.49	0.075	0.012	0.027	0.01
9003	Fruit, apple w/skin, raw	1 large (3-1/4" dia) (approx 2 per lb)	212	110.24	0.551	29.277	5.088	0.36	0.015	0.108	0.059
9004	Fruit, apple, peeled, raw, medium	1 medium (2-3/4" dia) (approx 3 per lb)	128	61.44	0.346	16.333	1.664	0.166	0.006	0.047	0.027
9007	Fruit, apple, slices, sweetened, canned, drained	1 cup slices	204	136.68	0.367	34.068	3.468	1	0.041	0.294	0.163
9402	Fruit, applesauce, canned, sweetened w/added vit C	1 cup	255	193.8	0.459	50.771	3.06	0.459	0.018	0.138	0.076
9401	Fruit, applesauce, canned, unsweetened w/added vit C	1 cup	244	104.92	0.415	27.548	2.928	0.122	0.005	0.034	0.02
9027	Fruit, apricot w/skin, canned in heavy syrup	1 cup, halves	258	214.14	1.367	55.393	4.128	0.206	0.085	0.039	0.013
9024	Fruit, apricot w/skin, canned in juice	1 cup, halves	244	117.12	1.537	30.11	3.904	0.098	0.041	0.017	0.007
9035	Fruit, apricot, frozen, sweetened	1 cup	242	237.16	1.694	60.742	5.324	0.242	0.106	0.048	0.017
9023	Fruit, apricot, peeled, canned in H$_2$O	1 cup, whole, without pits	227	49.94	1.566	12.44	2.497	0.068	0.03	0.014	0.005

Chol (g)	Calc (mg)	Iron (mg)	Mag (mg)	Phos (mg)	Pota (mg)	Sodi (mg)	Zinc (mg)	Vit A (RAE)	Vit C (mg)	Thia (mg)	Ribo (mg)	Niac (mg)	Vit B$_6$ (mg)	Vit B$_{12}$ (µg)	Vit E (mg)	Fol (µg)	Alc (g)
0	14.88	0.694	4.96	2.48	44.64	39.68	0.223	2.48	84.57	0.015	0.007	0.077	0.022	0	0.05	9.92	0
0	17.5	0.775	15	15	152.5	35	0.15	0	115	0.075	0.04	0.667	0.105	0	0.025	22.5	0
0	12.5	0.675	15	10	115	7.5	0.15	2.5	56.25	0.075	0.047	0.517	0.117	0	0.075	22.5	0
0	14.88	0.719	12.4	27.28	218.24	14.88	0.198	24.8	4.712	0.045	0.047	0.928	0.124	0	0.992	7.44	0
0	18.96	0.498	16.59	33.18	225.15	9.48	0.213	35.55	6.399	0.028	0.038	0.955	0.121	0	0.948	7.11	0
0	17.36	0.918	7.44	17.36	295.12	7.44	0.074	0	2.232	0.052	0.042	0.248	0.074	0	0.025	0	0
0	14.34	0.621	11.95	16.73	301.14	16.73	0.096	0	1.434	0.007	0.036	0.091	0.079	0	0.024	0	0
0	17.57	0.954	12.55	22.59	286.14	7.53	0.226	165.7	1.506	0.023	0.035	0.653	0.055	0	0.778	2.51	0
0	20	0.9	25	27.5	405	5	0.15	0	67.25	0.1	0.058	0.798	0.05	0	0.1	25	0
0	17.29	0.494	24.7	27.17	377.91	2.47	0.222	0	72.12	0.104	0.049	0.571	0.049	0	0.099	24.7	0
0	19.76	0.346	27.17	34.58	335.92	2.47	0.124	0	83.24	0.101	0.054	0.536	0.109	0	0.099	9.88	0
0	2.135	0.009	1.83	1.83	37.82	0.305	0.015	0.305	14.03	0.009	0.003	0.031	0.016	0	0.046	3.965	0
0	2.772	0.009	1.848	2.156	33.572	0.308	0.018	0.616	9.024	0.006	0.003	0.031	0.013	0	0.046	2.464	0
0	19.92	1.096	27.39	34.86	435.75	4.98	0.174	22.41	85.66	0.149	0.07	0.782	0.219	0	0.498	44.82	0
0	27.28	0.496	27.28	42.16	496	2.48	0.124	24.8	124	0.223	0.074	0.992	0.099	0	0.099	74.4	0
0	22.41	0.249	24.9	39.84	473.1	2.49	0.124	12.45	96.86	0.197	0.045	0.503	0.11	0	0.498	109.6	0
0	19.76	1.136	24.7	34.58	390.26	7.41	0.173	14.82	71.88	0.138	0.074	0.83	0.057	0	0.346	34.58	0
0	25	0.85	7.5	0	77.5	12.5	0.375	45	7.5	0.015	0.01	0.375	0.022	0	0.6	5	0
0	9.88	0.593	41.99	32.11	686.66	14.82	0.124	88.92	73.61	0	0.324	3.606	0.124	0	0.025	17.29	0
0	12.45	0.473	9.96	14.94	99.6	17.43	0.199	32.37	13.2	0.007	0.035	0.717	0.017	0	0.722	2.49	0
0	42.5	0.65	32.5	20	335	2.5	0.275	0	26.75	0.138	0.055	0.642	0.24	0	0.05	57.5	0
0	30.72	3.021	35.84	64	706.56	10.24	0.538	0	10.5	0.041	0.179	2.01	0.558	0	0.307	0	0
0	44.82	0.498	19.92	34.86	443.22	2.49	0.075	32.37	54.78	0.149	0.05	0.249	0.08	0	0.374	12.45	0
0	15.3	0.714	12.75	22.95	204	15.3	0.178	63.75	6.12	0.038	0.054	0.885	0.082	0	1.02	7.65	0
0	27.39	0.623	19.92	34.86	288.84	12.45	0.349	74.7	8.217	0.027	0.035	0.886	0.067	0		7.47	0
0	12.72	0.254	10.6	23.32	226.84	2.12	0.085	6.36	9.752	0.036	0.055	0.193	0.087	0	0.382	6.36	0
0	6.4	0.09	5.12	14.08	115.2	0	0.064	2.56	5.12	0.024	0.036	0.116	0.047	0	0.064	0	0
0	8.16	0.469	4.08	10.2	138.72	6.12	0.061	6.12	0.816	0.018	0.02	0.149	0.09	0	0.428	0	0
0	10.2	0.892	7.65	17.85	155.55	71.4	0.102	2.55	4.335	0.033	0.071	0.479	0.066	0		2.55	0
0	7.32	0.293	7.32	17.08	183	4.88	0.073	2.44	51.73	0.032	0.061	0.459	0.063	0		2.44	0
0	23.22	0.774	18.06	30.96	361.2	10.32	0.284	160	7.998	0.052	0.057	0.97	0.139	0	1.548	5.16	0
0	29.28	0.732	24.4	48.8	402.6	9.76	0.268	207.4	11.96	0.044	0.046	0.839	0.132	0	1.464	4.88	0
0	24.2	2.178	21.78	45.98	554.18	9.68	0.242	203.3	21.78	0.048	0.097	1.936	0.145	0	2.154	4.84	0
0	18.16	1.226	20.43	36.32	349.58	24.97	0.25	206.6	4.086	0.045	0.054	0.992	0.123	0		4.54	0

EvaluEat Code	Food Name	Amt	Wt (g)	Energy (kcal)	Prot (g)	Carb (g)	Fiber (g)	Fat (g)	Mono (g)	Poly (g)	Sat (g)
9028	Fruit, apricot, peeled, canned in heavy syrup	1 cup, whole, without pits	258	214.14	1.316	55.341	4.128	0.232	0.095	0.044	0.015
9021	Fruit, apricot, raw	1 apricot	35	16.8	0.49	3.892	0.7	0.136	0.06	0.027	0.009
9038	Fruit, avocado, California, peeled, raw	1 fruit without skin and seed	173	288.91	3.391	14.947	11.764	26.659	16.952	3.484	3.678
9040	Fruit, banana, peeled, raw, mashed/sliced	1 medium (7" to 7-7/8" long)	118	105.02	1.286	26.951	3.068	0.389	0.038	0.086	0.132
9048	Fruit, blackberries, frozen, unsweetened	1 cup, unthawed	151	96.64	1.782	23.662	7.55	0.649	0.062	0.37	0.023
9042	Fruit, blackberries, raw	1 cup	144	61.92	2.002	13.838	7.632	0.706	0.068	0.403	0.02
9054	Fruit, blueberries, frozen, unsweetened	1 cup, unthawed	155	79.05	0.651	18.863	4.185	0.992	0.141	0.432	0.082
9050	Fruit, blueberries, raw	1 cup	145	82.65	1.073	21.01	3.48	0.479	0.068	0.212	0.041
9056	Fruit, boysenberries, canned in heavy syrup	1 cup	256	225.28	2.534	57.114	6.656	0.307	0.031	0.174	0.01
9057	Fruit, boysenberries, frozen, unsweetened	1 cup, unthawed	132	66	1.452	16.091	6.996	0.343	0.033	0.195	0.012
9059	Fruit, breadfruit, peeled, raw	1 cup	220	226.6	2.354	59.664	10.78	0.506	0.075	0.145	0.106
9060	Fruit, carambola (starfruit) raw	1 cup, cubes	137	45.21	0.74	10.727	3.699	0.479	0.042	0.262	0.032
9066	Fruit, cherries, sour, red, canned in heavy syrup	1 cup	256	232.96	1.869	59.571	2.816	0.256	0.067	0.074	0.054
9068	Fruit, cherries, sour, red, frozen, unsweetened	1 cup, unthawed	155	71.3	1.426	17.081	2.48	0.682	0.186	0.205	0.155
9064	Fruit, cherries, sour/tart, red, canned in H₂O	1 cup	244	87.84	1.879	21.814	2.684	0.244	0.066	0.073	0.056
9074	Fruit, cherries, sweet, canned in heavy syrup	1 cup, pitted	253	209.99	1.518	53.813	3.795	0.38	0.104	0.114	0.086
9072	Fruit, cherries, sweet, canned in juice	1 cup, pitted	250	135	2.275	34.525	3.75	0.05	0.012	0.015	0.01
9070	Fruit, cherries, sweet, raw	1 cup, with pits	117	73.71	1.24	18.732	2.457	0.234	0.055	0.061	0.044
9078	Fruit, cranberries, raw	1 cup, chopped	110	50.6	0.429	13.42	5.06	0.143	0.02	0.06	0.012
9081	Fruit, cranberry sauce, canned, sweetened	1 slice (1/2" thick, approx 8 slices per can)	57	86.07	0.114	22.173	0.57	0.086	0.012	0.038	0.007
9082	Fruit, cranberry-orange relish, canned	1 cup	275	489.5	0.825	127.05	0	0.275			0.033
9084	Fruit, currant, red or white, raw	1 cup	112	62.72	1.568	15.456	4.816	0.224	0.031	0.099	0.019
9085	Fruit, currants, zante, dried	1 cup	144	407.52	5.875	106.68	9.792	0.389	0.068	0.259	0.04
9087	Fruit, dates, domestic, natural, dried	1 cup, pitted, chopped	178	501.96	4.361	133.55	14.24	0.694	0.064	0.034	0.057
9092	Fruit, figs, canned in heavy syrup	1 cup	259	227.92	0.984	59.311	5.698	0.259	0.057	0.124	0.052
9094	Fruit, figs, dried, raw	1 cup	149	371.01	4.917	95.166	14.602	1.386	0.237	0.514	0.215
9089	Fruit, figs, raw	1 large (2-1/2" dia)	64	47.36	0.48	12.275	1.856	0.192	0.042	0.092	0.038
9107	Fruit, gooseberries, raw	1 cup	150	66	1.32	15.27	6.45	0.87	0.076	0.475	0.057
9120	Fruit, grapefruit, canned in juice	1 cup	249	92.13	1.743	22.933	0.996	0.224	0.03	0.052	0.03
9111	Fruit, grapefruit, red, white or pink, peeled, raw	1/2 medium (approx 4" dia)	128	40.96	0.806	10.342	1.408	0.128	0.017	0.031	0.018
9131	Fruit, grapes, American type (slip skin) raw	1 cup	92	61.64	0.58	15.778	0.828	0.322	0.013	0.094	0.105
9139	Fruit, guava, common, raw	1 fruit	90	45.9	0.738	10.692	4.86	0.54	0.049	0.228	0.155
9148	Fruit, kiwifruit (Chinese gooseberry) peeled, raw	1 fruit without skin, medium	76	46.36	0.866	11.142	2.28	0.395	0.036	0.218	0.022
9149	Fruit, kumquat, raw	1 fruit without refuse	19	13.49	0.357	3.021	1.235	0.163	0.029	0.032	0.02
9165	Fruit, lychee (litchi) shelled, dried	1 fruit	2.5	6.925	0.095	1.767	0.115	0.03	0.008	0.009	0.007

Chol (g)	Calc (mg)	Iron (mg)	Mag (mg)	Phos (mg)	Pota (mg)	Sodi (mg)	Zinc (mg)	Vit A (RAE)	Vit C (mg)	Thia (mg)	Ribo (mg)	Niac (mg)	Vit B$_6$ (mg)	Vit B$_{12}$ (µg)	Vit E (mg)	Fol (µg)	Alc (g)
0	23.22	1.109	20.64	33.54	345.72	28.38	0.258	160	7.224	0.049	0.059	1.073	0.139	0		5.16	0
0	4.55	0.136	3.5	8.05	90.65	0.35	0.07	33.6	3.5	0.01	0.014	0.21	0.019	0	0.311	3.15	0
0	22.49	1.055	50.17	93.42	877.11	13.84	1.176	12.11	15.22	0.13	0.247	3.308	0.497	0	3.408	107.3	0
0	5.9	0.307	31.86	25.96	422.44	1.18	0.177	3.54	10.27	0.037	0.086	0.785	0.433	0	0.118	23.6	0
0	43.79	1.208	33.22	45.3	211.4	1.51	0.377	9.06	4.681	0.044	0.069	1.823	0.092	0	1.767	51.34	0
0	41.76	0.893	28.8	31.68	233.28	1.44	0.763	15.84	30.24	0.029	0.037	0.93	0.043	0	1.685	36	0
0	12.4	0.279	7.75	17.05	83.7	1.55	0.108	3.1	3.875	0.05	0.057	0.806	0.091	0	0.744	10.85	0
0	8.7	0.406	8.7	17.4	111.65	1.45	0.232	4.35	14.07	0.054	0.059	0.606	0.075	0	0.826	8.7	0
0	46.08	1.101	28.16	25.6	230.4	7.68	0.486	5.12	15.87	0.067	0.074	0.589	0.097	0	1.818	87.04	0
0	35.64	1.122	21.12	35.64	183.48	1.32	0.29	3.96	4.092	0.07	0.049	1.012	0.074	0	1.148	83.16	0
0	37.4	1.188	55	66	1078	4.4	0.264	0	63.8	0.242	0.066	1.98	0.22	0	0.22	30.8	0
0	5.48	0.356	12.33	21.92	223.31	2.74	0.151	4.11	29.04	0.038	0.037	0.563	0.137	0	0.206	19.18	0
0	25.6	3.328	15.36	25.6	238.08	17.92	0.154	92.16	5.12	0.041	0.1	0.43	0.113	0	0.589	20.48	0
0	20.15	0.821	13.95	24.8	192.2	1.55	0.155	68.2	2.635	0.068	0.053	0.212	0.104	0	0.078	7.75	0
0	26.84	3.343	14.64	24.4	239.12	17.08	0.171	92.72	5.124	0.041	0.1	0.432	0.107	0	0.561	19.52	0
0	22.77	0.885	22.77	45.54	366.85	7.59	0.253	20.24	9.108	0.053	0.101	1.002	0.076	0	0.582	10.12	0
0	35	1.45	30	55	327.5	7.5	0.25	15	6.25	0.045	0.06	1.015	0.075	0	0.575	10	0
0	15.21	0.421	12.87	24.57	259.74	0	0.082	3.51	8.19	0.032	0.039	0.18	0.057	0	0.082	4.68	0
0	8.8	0.275	6.6	14.3	93.5	2.2	0.11	3.3	14.63	0.013	0.022	0.111	0.063	0	1.32	1.1	0
0	2.28	0.125	1.71	3.42	14.82	16.53	0.029	1.14	1.14	0.009	0.012	0.057	0.008	0	0.473	0.57	0
0	30.25	0.55	11	22	104.5	88		11	49.5	0.082	0.055	0.275		0			0
0	36.96	1.12	14.56	49.28	308	1.12	0.258	2.24	45.92	0.045	0.056	0.112	0.078	0	0.112	8.96	0
0	123.84	4.694	59.04	180	1284.48	11.52	0.95	5.76	6.768	0.23	0.204	2.326	0.426	0	0.158	14.4	0
0	69.42	1.816	76.54	110.36	1167.68	3.56	0.516	0	0.712	0.093	0.117	2.268	0.294	0	0.089	33.82	0
0	69.93	0.725	25.9	25.9	256.41	2.59	0.285	5.18	2.59	0.057	0.096	1.109	0.181	0	0.311	5.18	0
0	241.38	3.025	101.32	99.83	1013.2	14.9	0.82	0	1.788	0.127	0.122	0.922	0.158	0	0.521	13.41	0
0	22.4	0.237	10.88	8.96	148.48	0.64	0.096	4.48	1.28	0.038	0.032	0.256	0.072	0	0.07	3.84	0
0	37.5	0.465	15	40.5	297	1.5	0.18	22.5	41.55	0.06	0.045	0.45	0.12	0	0.555	9	0
0	37.35	0.523	27.39	29.88	420.81	17.43	0.199	0	84.41	0.072	0.045	0.62	0.05	0	0.224	22.41	0
0	15.36	0.115	10.24	10.24	177.92	0	0.09	58.88	44.03	0.046	0.026	0.32	0.054	0	0.166	12.8	0
0	12.88	0.267	4.6	9.2	175.72	1.84	0.037	4.6	3.68	0.085	0.052	0.276	0.101	0	0.175	3.68	0
0	18	0.279	9	22.5	255.6	2.7	0.207	27.9	165	0.045	0.045	1.08	0.129	0	0.657	12.6	0
0	25.84	0.236	12.92	25.84	237.12	2.28	0.106	3.04	70.45	0.021	0.019	0.259	0.048	0	1.11	19	0
0	11.78	0.163	3.8	3.61	35.34	1.9	0.032	2.85	8.341	0.007	0.017	0.082	0.007	0	0.029	3.23	0
0	0.825	0.043	1.05	4.525	27.75	0.075	0.007	0	4.575	0	0.014	0.078	0.002	0	0.008	0.3	0

EvaluEat Code	Food Name	Amt	Wt (g)	Energy (kcal)	Prot (g)	Carb (g)	Fiber (g)	Fat (g)	Mono (g)	Poly (g)	Sat (g)
9164	Fruit, lychee (litchi) shelled, raw	1 fruit	9.6	6.336	0.08	1.587	0.125	0.042	0.012	0.013	0.01
9176	Fruit, mango, peeled, raw	1 cup, sliced	165	107.25	0.841	28.05	2.97	0.446	0.167	0.084	0.109
9185	Fruit, melon balls (cantaloupe & honeydew) frozen	1 cup, unthawed	173	57.09	1.453	13.736	1.211	0.433	0.01	0.17	0.111
9181	Fruit, melon, cantaloupe (musk) peeled, pieces/balls, raw	1 wedge, large (1/8 of large melon)	102	34.68	0.857	8.323	0.918	0.194	0.003	0.083	0.052
9183	Fruit, melon, casaba, peeled, raw	1 cup, cubes	170	47.6	1.887	11.186	1.53	0.17	0.003	0.066	0.043
9184	Fruit, melon, honeydew, peeled, wedges, raw	1 wedge (1/8 of 6" to 7" dia melon)	160	57.6	0.864	14.544	1.28	0.224	0.005	0.094	0.061
9188	Fruit, mixed (prune, apricot & pear) dried	1 package (11 oz)	293	711.99	7.208	187.7	22.854	1.436	0.68	0.322	0.117
9191	Fruit, nectarine, raw	1 fruit (2-1/2" dia)	136	59.84	1.442	14.348	2.312	0.435	0.12	0.154	0.034
9193	Fruit, olives, ripe, pitted, canned	1 tbsp	8.4	9.66	0.071	0.526	0.269	0.897	0.663	0.077	0.119
9200	Fruit, orange, all varieties, peeled, raw	1 fruit (2-5/8" dia)	131	61.57	1.231	15.392	3.144	0.157	0.03	0.033	0.02
9226	Fruit, papayas, peeled, cubed/mashed, raw	1 medium (5-1/8" long x 3" dia)	304	118.56	1.854	29.822	5.472	0.426	0.116	0.094	0.131
9231	Fruit, passion fruit/granadilla, purple, peeled, raw	1 fruit	18	17.46	0.396	4.208	1.872	0.126	0.015	0.074	0.011
9241	Fruit, peach, canned in heavy syrup	1 cup	262	193.88	1.179	52.243	3.406	0.262	0.092	0.123	0.026
9238	Fruit, peach, canned in juice	1 cup	250	110	1.575	28.925	3.25	0.075	0.03	0.04	0.01
9250	Fruit, peach, frozen, sweetened	1 cup, thawed	250	235	1.575	59.95	4.5	0.325	0.12	0.16	0.035
9236	Fruit, peach, peeled, raw	1 medium (2-1/2" dia) (approx 4 per lb)	98	38.22	0.892	9.349	1.47	0.245	0.066	0.084	0.019
9257	Fruit, pear, canned in heavy syrup	1 cup	266	196.84	0.532	50.992	4.256	0.346	0.072	0.08	0.019
9254	Fruit, pear, canned in juice	1 cup, halves	248	124	0.843	32.091	3.968	0.174	0.035	0.037	0.01
9252	Fruit, pear, raw	1 pear, medium (approx 2-1/2 per lb)	166	96.28	0.631	25.664	5.146	0.199	0.043	0.048	0.01
9265	Fruit, persimmon, native, raw	1 fruit	25	31.75	0.2	8.375		0.1			
9270	Fruit, pineapple, canned in heavy syrup	1 cup, crushed, sliced, or chunks	254	198.12	0.889	51.308	2.032	0.279	0.033	0.102	0.023
9268	Fruit, pineapple, canned in juice	1 cup, crushed, sliced, or chunks	249	149.4	1.046	39.093	1.992	0.199	0.025	0.072	0.015
9278	Fruit, plantain, peeled, cooked	1 cup, mashed	200	232	1.58	62.3	4.6	0.36	0.03	0.066	0.138
9284	Fruit, plum, purple, canned in heavy syrup	1 cup, pitted	258	229.62	0.929	59.959	2.322	0.258	0.17	0.057	0.021
9282	Fruit, plum, purple, canned in juice	1 cup, pitted	252	146.16	1.285	38.178	2.268	0.05	0.035	0.013	0.005
9279	Fruit, plum, raw	1 fruit (2-1/8" dia)	66	30.36	0.462	7.537	0.924	0.185	0.088	0.029	0.011
9286	Fruit, pomegranates, peeled, raw	1 fruit (3-3/8" dia)	154	104.72	1.463	26.442	0.924	0.462	0.071	0.097	0.059
9287	Fruit, prickly pear, peeled, raw	1 cup	149	61.09	1.088	14.259	5.364	0.76	0.112	0.317	0.1
9288	Fruit, prunes, canned in heavy syrup	5 fruits with liquid	86	90.3	0.748	23.908	3.268	0.172	0.112	0.037	0.014
9291	Fruit, prunes, dried	1 prune	8.4	20.16	0.183	5.366	0.596	0.032	0.004	0.005	0.007
9295	Fruit, pummelo, peeled, raw	1 fruit	609	231.42	4.628	58.586	6.09	0.244			
9296	Fruit, quinces, peeled, raw	1 fruit	92	52.44	0.368	14.076	1.748	0.092	0.033	0.046	0.009
9298	Fruit, raisins, seedless	1 cup (not packed)	145	433.55	4.451	114.81	5.365	0.667	0.074	0.054	0.084
9302	Fruit, raspberries, raw	1 cup	123	63.96	1.476	14.686	7.995	0.799	0.079	0.461	0.023
9306	Fruit, raspberries, red, frozen, sweetened	1 cup, unthawed	250	257.5	1.75	65.4	11	0.4	0.037	0.222	0.012

Chol (g)	Calc (mg)	Iron (mg)	Mag (mg)	Phos (mg)	Pota (mg)	Sodi (mg)	Zinc (mg)	Vit A (RAE)	Vit C (mg)	Thia (mg)	Ribo (mg)	Niac (mg)	Vit B_6 (mg)	Vit B_{12} (µg)	Vit E (mg)	Fol (µg)	Alc (g)
0	0.48	0.03	0.96	2.976	16.416	0.096	0.007	0	6.864	0.001	0.006	0.058	0.01	0	0.007	1.344	0
0	16.5	0.214	14.85	18.15	257.4	3.3	0.066	62.7	45.71	0.096	0.094	0.964	0.221	0	1.848	23.1	0
0	17.3	0.502	24.22	20.76	484.4	53.63	0.294	154	10.73	0.287	0.038	1.107	0.183	0	0.26	44.98	0
0	9.18	0.214	12.24	15.3	272.34	16.32	0.184	172.4	37.43	0.042	0.019	0.749	0.073	0	0.051	21.42	0
0	18.7	0.578	18.7	8.5	309.4	15.3	0.119	0	37.06	0.025	0.053	0.394	0.277	0	0.085	13.6	0
0	9.6	0.272	16	17.6	364.8	28.8	0.144	4.8	28.8	0.061	0.019	0.669	0.141	0	0.032	30.4	0
0	111.34	7.94	114.27	225.61	2332.28	52.74	1.465	357.5	11.13	0.129	0.46	5.646	0.466	0		11.72	0
0	8.16	0.381	12.24	35.36	273.36	0	0.231	23.12	7.344	0.046	0.037	1.53	0.034	0	1.047	6.8	0
0	7.392	0.277	0.336	0.252	0.672	73.248	0.018	1.68	0.076	0	0	0.003	0.001	0	0.139	0	0
0	52.4	0.131	13.1	18.34	237.11	0	0.092	14.41	69.69	0.114	0.052	0.369	0.079	0	0.236	39.3	0
0	72.96	0.304	30.4	15.2	781.28	9.12	0.213	167.2	187.9	0.082	0.097	1.028	0.058	0	2.219	115.5	0
0	2.16	0.288	5.22	12.24	62.64	5.04	0.018	11.52	5.4	0	0.023	0.27	0.018	0	0.004	2.52	0
0	7.86	0.707	13.1	28.82	241.04	15.72	0.236	44.54	7.336	0.029	0.063	1.609	0.05	0	1.284	7.86	0
0	15	0.675	17.5	42.5	320	10	0.275	47.5	9	0.02	0.043	1.455	0.047	0	1.225	7.5	0
0	7.5	0.925	12.5	27.5	325	15	0.125	35	235.5	0.032	0.087	1.632	0.045	0	1.55	7.5	0
0	5.88	0.245	8.82	19.6	186.2	0	0.167	15.68	6.468	0.024	0.03	0.79	0.025	0	0.715	3.92	0
0	13.3	0.585	10.64	18.62	172.9	13.3	0.213	0	2.926	0.027	0.059	0.644	0.037	0	0.213	2.66	0
0	22.32	0.719	17.36	29.76	238.08	9.92	0.223	0	3.968	0.027	0.027	0.496	0.035	0	0.198	2.48	0
0	14.94	0.282	11.62	18.26	197.54	1.66	0.166	1.66	6.972	0.02	0.041	0.261	0.046		0.199	11.62	0
0	6.75	0.625		6.5	77.5	0.25			16.5					0			0
0	35.56	0.965	40.64	17.78	264.16	2.54	0.305	2.54	18.8	0.229	0.064	0.729	0.188	0	0.025	12.7	0
0	34.86	0.697	34.86	14.94	303.78	2.49	0.249	4.98	23.66	0.237	0.047	0.707	0.184	0	0.025	12.45	0
0	4	1.16	64	56	930	10	0.26	90	21.8	0.092	0.104	1.512	0.48	0	0.26	52	0
0	23.22	2.167	12.9	33.54	234.78	49.02	0.181	33.54	1.032	0.041	0.098	0.751	0.07	0	0.464	7.74	0
0	25.2	0.857	20.16	37.8	388.08	2.52	0.277	126	7.056	0.058	0.149	1.192	0.068	0	0.454	7.56	0
0	3.96	0.112	4.62	10.56	103.62	0	0.066	11.22	6.27	0.018	0.017	0.275	0.019	0	0.172	3.3	0
0	4.62	0.462	4.62	12.32	398.86	4.62	0.185	7.7	9.394	0.046	0.046	0.462	0.162	0	0.924	9.24	0
0	83.44	0.447	126.65	35.76	327.8	7.45	0.179	2.98	20.86	0.021	0.089	0.685	0.089	0	0.015	8.94	0
0	14.62	0.353	12.9	22.36	194.36	2.58	0.163	34.4	2.408	0.029	0.105	0.745	0.175	0		0	0
0	3.612	0.078	3.444	5.796	61.488	0.168	0.037	3.276	0.05	0.004	0.016	0.158	0.017	0	0.036	0.336	0
0	24.36	0.67	36.54	103.53	1315.44	6.09	0.487	0	371.5	0.207	0.164	1.34	0.219	0			0
0	10.12	0.644	7.36	15.64	181.24	3.68	0.037	1.84	13.8	0.018	0.028	0.184	0.037	0	0.506	2.76	0
0	72.5	2.726	46.4	146.45	1086.05	15.95	0.319	0	3.335	0.154	0.181	1.111	0.252	0	0.174	7.25	0
0	30.75	0.849	27.06	35.67	185.73	1.23	0.517	2.46	32.23	0.039	0.047	0.736	0.068	0	1.07	25.83	0
0	37.5	1.625	32.5	42.5	285	2.5	0.45	7.5	41.25	0.047	0.113	0.575	0.085	0	1.8	65	0

EvaluEat Code	Food Name	Amt	Wt (g)	Energy (kcal)	Prot (g)	Carb (g)	Fiber (g)	Fat (g)	Mono (g)	Poly (g)	Sat (g)
9310	Fruit, rhubarb, frozen, cooked w/sugar	1 cup	240	278.4	0.936	74.88	4.8	0.12	0.024	0.06	0.034
9307	Fruit, rhubarb, raw	1 cup, diced	122	25.62	1.098	5.539	2.196	0.244	0.048	0.121	0.065
9319	Fruit, strawberries, frozen, whole, sweetened	1 cup, thawed	255	198.9	1.326	53.55	4.845	0.357	0.048	0.173	0.018
9316	Fruit, strawberries, halves/slices, raw	1 cup, halves	152	48.64	1.018	11.674	3.04	0.456	0.065	0.236	0.023
9322	Fruit, tamarind, raw	1 fruit (3"x 1")	2	4.78	0.056	1.25	0.102	0.012	0.004	0.001	0.005
9326	Fruit, watermelon, balls, raw	1 cup, balls	154	46.2	0.939	11.627	0.616	0.231	0.057	0.077	0.025
17345	Game meat, deer, loin, separable lean only, 1"steak, cooked, broiled	1 serving (3 oz)	85	127.5	25.67	0	0	2.023	0.298	0.088	0.746
17157	Game, bison, roasted	3 oz	85	121.55	24.174	0	0	2.057	0.808	0.204	0.774
5308	Game, cornish game hen w/skin, roasted	1/2 bird	129	335.4	28.728	0	0	23.491	10.32	4.644	6.515
5310	Game, cornish game hens, no skin, roasted	1/2 bird	110	147.4	25.63	0	0	4.257	1.364	1.034	1.089
5145	Game, duck, wild, breast, no skin, raw	1/2 breast, bone and skin removed	83	102.09	16.476	0	0	3.527	1.004	0.481	1.096
5144	Game, duck, wild, meat & skin, raw	1/2 duck	270	569.7	47.034	0	0	41.04	18.36	5.454	13.608
5157	Game, quail, meat & skin, raw	1 quail	109	209.28	21.397	0	0	13.135	4.556	3.248	3.684
17178	Game, rabbit, domestic, composite, roasted	3 oz	85	167.45	24.701	0	0	6.843	1.845	1.326	2.04
5160	Game, squab/pigeon, meat & skin, raw	1 squab	199	585.06	36.755	0	0	47.362	19.343	6.109	16.776
5282	Goose liver pate/pate de fois gras, smoked, canned	1 oz	28.35	130.98	3.232	1.324	0	12.429	7.26	0.238	4.097
5147	Goose, domestic, meat & skin, roasted	1 cup, chopped or diced	140	427	35.224	0	0	30.688	14.35	3.528	9.618
5149	Goose, domestic, meat only, no skin, roasted	yield from 1 lb ready-to-cook goose	143	340.34	41.427	0	0	18.118	6.206	2.202	6.521
20006	Grain, barley, pearled, cooked	1 cup	157	193.11	3.548	44.305	5.966	0.691	0.089	0.336	0.146
20013	Grain, bulgar, cooked	1 cup	182	151.06	5.606	33.816	8.19	0.437	0.056	0.178	0.076
20314	Grain, corn, white	1 cup	166	605.9	15.637	123.27		7.868	2.077	3.591	1.107
20014	Grain, corn, yellow	1 cup	166	605.9	15.637	123.27	12.118	7.868	2.077	3.591	1.107
20038	Grain, oats	1 cup	156	606.84	26.348	103.38	16.536	10.764	3.398	3.955	1.899
20037	Grain, rice, brown, long grain, cooked	1 cup	195	216.45	5.031	44.772	3.51	1.755	0.638	0.63	0.351
20041	Grain, rice, brown, medium grain, cooked	1 cup	195	218.4	4.524	45.845	3.51	1.618	0.585	0.577	0.322
20055	Grain, rice, white, glutinous, cooked	1 cup	174	168.78	3.515	36.697	1.74	0.331	0.122	0.12	0.068
20345	Grain, rice, white, long grain, enriched, cooked w/salt	1 cup	158	205.4	4.25	44.509	0.632	0.442	0.139	0.12	0.122
20049	Grain, rice, white, long grain, precooked/instant, enriched, cooked	1 cup	165	161.7	3.399	35.096	0.99	0.264	0.084	0.073	0.073
20051	Grain, rice, white, medium grain, cooked	1 cup	186	241.8	4.427	53.177	0.558	0.391	0.121	0.104	0.106
20066	Grain, semolina, enriched	1 cup	167	601.2	21.176	121.63	6.513	1.753	0.207	0.718	0.25
20067	Grain, sorghum	1 cup	192	650.88	21.696	143.29		6.336	1.907	2.63	0.877
20068	Grain, tapioca, pearl, dry	1 cup	152	544.16	0.289	134.81	1.368	0.03	0.008	0.005	0.008
20078	Grain, wheat germ, crude	1 cup	115	414	26.622	59.57	15.18	11.178	1.57	6.911	1.915
20087	Grain, wheat, sprouted	1 cup	108	213.84	8.089	45.932	1.188	1.372	0.163	0.602	0.222
6114	Gravy, au jus, canned	1 cup	238	38.08	2.856	5.95	0	0.476	0.19	0.024	0.238
6116	Gravy, beef, canned	1 cup	233	123.49	8.737	11.207	0.932	5.499	2.241	0.186	2.686
6119	Gravy, chicken, canned	1 cup	238	188.02	4.593	12.9	0.952	13.59	6.069	3.57	3.356
6579	Gravy, Home Style Savory Brown Gravy, canned/Heinz	.25 cup	60	24.6	0.9	3.414		0.78	0.276	0.037	0.324
6121	Gravy, mushroom, canned	1 cup	238	119	2.999	13.019	0.952	6.45	2.785	2.428	0.952
6125	Gravy, turkey, canned	1 cup	238	121.38	6.188	12.138	0.952	4.998	2.142	1.166	1.476

Chol (g)	Calc (mg)	Iron (mg)	Mag (mg)	Phos (mg)	Pota (mg)	Sodi (mg)	Zinc (mg)	Vit A (RAE)	Vit C (mg)	Thia (mg)	Ribo (mg)	Niac (mg)	Vit B_6 (mg)	Vit B_{12} (µg)	Vit E (mg)	Fol (µg)	Alc (g)
0	348	0.504	28.8	19.2	230.4	2.4	0.192	9.6	7.92	0.043	0.055	0.48	0.048	0	0.648	12	0
0	104.92	0.268	14.64	17.08	351.36	4.88	0.122	6.1	9.76	0.024	0.037	0.366	0.029	0	0.464	8.54	0
0	28.05	1.198	15.3	30.6	249.9	2.55	0.127	2.55	100.7	0.038	0.196	0.747	0.071	0	0.612	10.2	0
0	24.32	0.638	19.76	36.48	232.56	1.52	0.213	1.52	89.38	0.036	0.033	0.587	0.071	0	0.441	36.48	0
0	1.48	0.056	1.84	2.26	12.56	0.56	0.002	0.04	0.07	0.009	0.003	0.039	0.001	0	0.002	0.28	0
0	10.78	0.37	15.4	16.94	172.48	1.54	0.154	43.12	12.47	0.051	0.032	0.274	0.069	0	0.077	4.62	0
67.15	5.1	3.477	25.5	235.45	338.3	48.45	3.086	0	0	0.238	0.436	9.143	0.643	1.556	0.527	7.65	0
69.7	6.8	2.907	22.1	177.65	306.85	48.45	3.128	0	0	0.085	0.23	3.154	0.34	2.431	0.306	6.8	0
168.99	16.77	1.174	23.22	188.34	316.05	82.56	1.922	41.28	0.645	0.086	0.257	7.607	0.396	0.361	0.464	2.58	0
116.6	14.3	0.847	20.9	163.9	275	69.3	1.683	22	0.66	0.083	0.25	6.9	0.394	0.33	0.264	2.2	0
63.91	2.49	3.743	18.26	154.38	222.44	47.31	0.614	13.28	5.146	0.345	0.257	2.859	0.523	0.631		20.75	0
216	13.5	11.232	54	453.6	672.3	151.2	2.079	70.2	14.04	0.948	0.726	8.956	1.431	1.755	1.893	56.7	0
82.84	14.17	4.327	25.07	299.75	235.44	57.77	2.638	79.57	6.649	0.266	0.283	8.216	0.654	0.469	0.764	8.72	0
69.7	16.15	1.929	17.85	223.55	325.55	39.95	1.929	0	0	0.077	0.178	7.166	0.4	7.055		9.35	0
189.05	23.88	7.045	43.78	493.52	396.01	107.46	4.378	145.3	10.35	0.422	0.446	12.032	0.816	0.796		11.94	0
42.525	19.845	1.559	3.686	56.7	39.123	197.6	0.261	283.8	0.567	0.025	0.085	0.712	0.017	2.665		17.01	0
127.4	18.2	3.962	30.8	378	460.6	98	3.668	29.4	0	0.108	0.452	5.835	0.518	0.574	2.436	2.8	0
137.28	20.02	4.104	35.75	441.87	554.84	108.68	4.533	17.16	0	0.132	0.558	5.836	0.672	0.701		17.16	0
0	17.27	2.088	34.54	84.78	146.01	4.71	1.287	0	0	0.13	0.097	3.239	0.181	0	0.016	25.12	0
0	18.2	1.747	58.24	72.8	123.76	9.1	1.037	0	0	0.104	0.051	1.82	0.151	0	0.018	32.76	0
0	11.62	4.499	210.82	348.6	476.42	58.1	3.669	0	0	0.639	0.334	6.021	1.033	0			0
0	11.62	4.499	210.82	348.6	476.42	58.1	3.669	18.26	0	0.639	0.334	6.021	1.033	0	0.813	31.54	0
0	84.24	7.363	276.12	815.88	669.24	3.12	6.193	0	0	1.19	0.217	1.499	0.186	0	1.092	87.36	0
0	19.5	0.819	83.85	161.85	83.85	9.75	1.229	0	0	0.187	0.049	2.98	0.283	0	0.058	7.8	0
0	19.5	1.033	85.8	150.15	154.05	1.95	1.209	0	0	0.199	0.023	2.594	0.291	0		7.8	0
0	3.48	0.244	8.7	13.92	17.4	8.7	0.713	0	0	0.035	0.023	0.505	0.045	0	0.07	1.74	0
0	15.8	1.896	18.96	67.94	55.3	603.56	0.774	0	0	0.258	0.021	2.332	0.147	0	0.063	91.64	0
0	13.2	1.039	8.25	23.1	6.6	4.95	0.396	0	0	0.124	0.076	1.452	0.016	0	0.016	115.5	0
0	5.58	2.771	24.18	68.82	53.94	0	0.781	0	0	0.311	0.03	3.413	0.093	0		107.9	0
0	28.39	7.281	78.49	227.12	310.62	1.67	1.753	0	0	1.354	0.954	10.003	0.172	0	0.434	305.6	0
0	53.76	8.448		551.04	672	11.52		0	0	0.455	0.273	5.62		0			0
0	30.4	2.402	1.52	10.64	16.72	1.52	0.182	0	0	0.006	0	0	0.012	0	0	6.08	0
0	44.85	7.199	274.85	968.3	1025.8	13.8	14.13	0	0	2.164	0.574	7.835	1.495	0		323.2	0
0	30.24	2.311	88.56	216	182.52	17.28	1.782	0	2.808	0.243	0.167	3.334	0.286	0	0.054	41.04	0
0	9.52	1.428	4.76	71.4	192.78	119	2.38	0	2.38	0.048	0.143	2.142	0.024	0.238		4.76	0
6.99	13.98	1.631	4.66	69.9	188.73	1304.8	2.33	2.33	0	0.075	0.084	1.538	0.023	0.233	0.047	4.66	0
4.76	47.6	1.119	4.76	69.02	259.42	1373.26	1.904	2.38	0	0.04	0.102	1.054	0.024	0.238	0.309	4.76	0
2.4						351.6											0
0	16.66	1.571	4.76	35.7	252.28	1356.6	1.666	0	0	0.079	0.15	1.597	0.048	0		28.56	0
4.76	9.52	1.666	4.76	69.02	259.42	1373.26	1.904	0	0	0.048	0.19	3.094	0.024	0.238	0.119	4.76	0

EvaluEat Code	Food Name	Amt	Wt (g)	Energy (kcal)	Prot (g)	Carb (g)	Fiber (g)	Fat (g)	Mono (g)	Poly (g)	Sat (g)
22700	Hamburger Helper, cheeseburger macaroni, dry mix/Betty Crocker	1 serving	45	177.75	4.95	28.935		4.68			1.269
2003	Herb, basil, ground	1 tsp, leaves	0.7	1.757	0.101	0.427	0.283	0.028	0.003	0.015	0.002
2004	Herb, bay leaf, crumbled	1 tsp, crumbled	0.6	1.878	0.046	0.45	0.158	0.05	0.01	0.014	0.014
11215	Herb, garlic, raw	1 tsp	2.8	4.172	0.178	0.926	0.059	0.014	0	0.007	0.002
11216	Herb, ginger root, peeled, sliced, raw	5 slices (1" dia)	11	8.8	0.2	1.955	0.22	0.082	0.017	0.017	0.022
2029	Herb, parsley, dried	1 tsp	0.3	0.828	0.067	0.155	0.091	0.013	0.01	0.001	0
2036	Herb, rosemary, dried	1 tsp	1.2	3.972	0.059	0.769	0.511	0.183	0.036	0.028	0.088
2042	Herb, thyme, ground	1 tbsp, leaves	2.7	7.452	0.246	1.726	0.999	0.201	0.013	0.032	0.074
18271	Ice cream cone, cake or wafer	1 cone	4	16.68	0.324	3.16	0.12	0.276	0.074	0.131	0.049
18272	Ice cream cone, sugar, rolled	1 cone	10	40.2	0.79	8.41	0.17	0.38	0.147	0.145	0.057
19270	Ice cream, chocolate	.5 cup (4 fl. oz.)	66	142.56	2.508	18.612	0.792	7.26	2.119	0.271	4.488
19264	Ice cream, Eskimo Pie Vanilla Ice Cream Bar w/dark chocolate coating	1 bar	50	165.5	2.05	12.25		12.05			7.25
19262	Ice cream, Klondike Vanilla Ice Cream Bar w/chocolate coating	1 bar (5 fl. oz.)	148	488.4	6.216	35.668		35.668			19.388
19096	Ice cream, light, vanilla, soft serve	.5 cup (4 fl. oz.)	88	110.88	4.312	19.184	0	2.288	0.669	0.088	1.434
19271	Ice cream, strawberry	.5 cup (4 fl. oz.)	66	126.72	2.112	18.216	0.594	5.544			3.425
19095	Ice cream, vanilla	.5 cup	72	144.7	2.52	17	0.504	7.92	2.138	0.325	4.889
7934	Kielbasa, polish, turkey and beef, smoked	2 oz	56	126.56	7.336	2.184	0	9.856	4.631	1.305	3.489
17004	Lamb, domestic, choice, composite, lean (1/4" trim) cooked	3 oz	85	175.1	23.987	0	0	8.092	3.545	0.527	2.89
17002	Lamb, domestic, choice, composite, lean & fat (1/4" trim) cooked	3 oz	85	249.9	20.842	0	0	17.799	7.497	1.284	7.506
18369	Leavening agent, baking powder, double acting, Na Al sulfate	1 tsp	4.6	2.438	0	1.274	0.009	0	0	0	0
18372	Leavening agent, baking soda	1 tsp	4.6	0	0	0	0	0	0	0	0
18373	Leavening agent, cream of tartar	1 tsp	3	7.74	0	1.845	0.006	0	0	0	0
18375	Leavening agent, yeast, Baker's, active	1 tsp	4	11.8	1.532	1.528	0.84	0.184	0.102	0	0.024
11257	Lettuce, red leaf, raw	.5 cup	60	9.6	0.798	1.356	0.54	0.132			
7274	Lunch meat, beef pastrami, cooked, smoked, chopped, pressed/Carl Budding	2 oz	57	80.37	11.172	0.57	0	3.705		0.171	1.71
7272	Lunch meat, beef, smoked, sliced/Carl Budding	2 oz	57	79.23	11.001	0.342	0	3.705		0.171	1.482
7043	Lunch meat, beef, thin slices	1 oz	28.35	50.18	7.969	1.619	0	1.089	0.476	0.057	0.468
7202	Lunch meat, bologna (beef light)/Oscar Mayer	1 slice	28	56	3.29	1.568	0	4.06	2.005	0.132	1.63
7007	Lunch meat, bologna (beef)	1 slice	28	87.08	2.876	1.114	0	7.893	3.421	0.217	3.118
7207	Lunch meat, braunschweiger liver sausage, sliced/ Oscar Mayer	1 slice	28	92.68	3.99	0.728	0.056	8.218	4.334	1.044	3.063
7250	Lunch meat, chicken breast, oven roasted deluxe/Louis Rich	1 serving	28	28.28	5.124	0.7	0	0.56	0.23	0.089	0.151
7270	Lunch meat, corned beef, cooked, chopped, pressed/ Carl Budding	2 oz	57	80.94	11.001	0.57	0	3.876		0.171	1.596
7253	Lunch meat, franks (turkey & chicken)/Louis Rich	1 serving	45	84.6	5.04	2.385	0	6.075	2.499	1.423	1.728
7029	Lunch meat, ham, slices, regular (11% fat)	1 serving	56	91.28	9.296	2.145	0.728	4.816	2.438	0.442	1.644
7041	Lunch meat, liver sausage (liverwurst)	1 slice (2-1/2" dia x 1/4" thick)	18	58.68	2.538	0.396		5.13	2.401	0.468	1.908
7222	Lunch meat, old fashioned loaf/Oscar Mayer	1 serving	28	64.68	3.668	2.24	0	4.564	2.201	0.739	1.568
7051	Lunch meat, olive loaf (pork)	2 slices	57	133.95	6.726	5.244	0	9.405	4.486	1.1	3.334

Chol (g)	Calc (mg)	Iron (mg)	Mag (mg)	Phos (mg)	Pota (mg)	Sodi (mg)	Zinc (mg)	Vit A (RAE)	Vit C (mg)	Thia (mg)	Ribo (mg)	Niac (mg)	Vit B$_6$ (mg)	Vit B$_{12}$ (µg)	Vit E (mg)	Fol (µg)	Alc (g)
4.05						913.5											0
0	14.791	0.294	2.954	3.43	24.031	0.238	0.041	3.283	0.428	0.001	0.002	0.049	0.016	0	0.052	1.918	0
0	5.004	0.258	0.72	0.678	3.174	0.138	0.022	1.854	0.279	0	0.003	0.012	0.01	0	0.011	1.08	0
0	5.068	0.048	0.7	4.284	11.228	0.476	0.032	0	0.874	0.006	0.003	0.02	0.035	0	0	0.084	0
0	1.76	0.066	4.73	3.74	45.65	1.43	0.037	0	0.55	0.003	0.004	0.082	0.018	0	0.029	1.21	0
0	4.404	0.294	0.747	1.053	11.415	1.356	0.014	1.527	0.366	0.001	0.004	0.024	0.003	0	0.021	0.54	0
0	15.36	0.351	2.64	0.84	11.46	0.6	0.039	1.872	0.734	0.006	0.005	0.012	0.021	0	0.024	3.684	0
0	51.03	3.337	5.94	5.427	21.978	1.485	0.167	5.13	1.35	0.014	0.011	0.133	0.015	0	0.202	7.398	0
0	1	0.144	1.04	3.88	4.48	5.72	0.027	0	0	0.01	0.014	0.177	0.001	0	0.031	6.92	0
0	4.4	0.443	3.1	10.3	14.5	32	0.075	0	0	0.051	0.041	0.507	0.005	0	0.007	14	0
22.44	71.94	0.614	19.14	70.62	164.34	50.16	0.383	77.88	0.462	0.028	0.128	0.149	0.036	0.191	0.198	10.56	0
14	59.5					34											0
39.96	211.64					108.04											0
10.56	138.16	0.053	12.32	106.48	194.48	61.6	0.466	25.52	0.792	0.046	0.174	0.104	0.04	0.44	0.053	5.28	0
19.14	79.2	0.139	9.24	66	124.08	39.6	0.224	63.36	5.082	0.03	0.168	0.112	0.033	0.198		7.92	0
31.7	92.2	0.065	10.1	75.6	143.3	57.6	0.497	85	0.432	0.03	0.173	0.084	0.035	0.281	0.216	3.6	0.144
39.2		0.694				672		0	8.288								0
78.2	12.75	1.743	22.1	178.5	292.4	64.6	4.48	0	0	0.085	0.238	5.372	0.136	2.218	0.162	19.55	
82.45	14.45	1.598	19.55	159.8	263.5	61.2	3.791	0	0	0.085	0.213	5.661	0.111	2.168	0.119	15.3	0
0	270.296	0.507	1.242	100.786	0.92	487.6	0	0	0	0	0	0	0	0	0	0	0
0	0	0	0	0	0	1258.56	0	0	0	0	0	0	0	0	0	0	0
0	0.24	0.112	0.06	0.15	495	1.56	0.013	0	0	0	0	0	0	0	0	0	0
0	2.56	0.664	3.92	51.6	80	2	0.256	0	0.012	0.094	0.219	1.59	0.062	0.001		93.6	0
	19.8	0.72	7.2	16.8	112.2	15	0.12	225	2.22	0.038	0.046	0.193	0.06		0.09	21.6	
37.05	9.69	1.396			208.05	601.92				0.051	0.131	2.337					0
38.19	7.98	1.288			191.52	815.67				0.051	0.137	2.2					0
11.624	3.119	0.765	5.387	47.628	121.622	407.957	1.128	0	0	0.023	0.054	1.494	0.096	0.729	0.054	3.119	0
12.32	3.64	0.342	3.92	49.84	43.68	322.28	0.535	0	0							3.64	0
15.68	8.68	0.308	3.92	48.16	48.16	302.4	2.548	3.64	4.256	0.007	0.028	0.704	0.048	0.356	0.098	2.52	0
49.84	2.52	2.943	3.92	55.72	56.56	324.52	0.952	1322	2.52	0.064	0.448	2.573	0.092	5.258		13.16	0
13.72	1.96	0.322	6.72	74.48	74.2	332.64	0.204		0								0
37.05	9.69	1.368			200.64	764.94				0.051	0.137	2.394					0
41.4	58.95	0.981	10.35	66.15	72	511.2	0.837		0								0
31.92	13.44	0.571	12.32	85.68	160.72	730.24	0.756	0	2.24	0.351	0.1	1.626	0.184	0.235	0.045	3.92	0
28.44	4.68	1.152	2.16	41.4	30.6	154.8	0.414	1495	0	0.049	0.185	0.774	0.034	2.423		5.4	
17.08	31.64	0.37	6.44	58.24	82.32	331.52	0.524		0								0
21.66	62.13	0.308	10.83	72.39	169.29	845.88	0.787	34.2	0	0.168	0.148	1.046	0.131	0.718	0.142	1.14	0

EvaluEat Code	Food Name	Amt	Wt (g)	Energy (kcal)	Prot (g)	Carb (g)	Fiber (g)	Fat (g)	Mono (g)	Poly (g)	Sat (g)
13355	Lunch meat, pastrami (beef)	1 slice (1 oz)	28	97.72	4.827	0.854	0	8.17	4.052	0.277	2.918
7052	Lunch meat, pastrami (turkey)	2 slices	57	80.37	10.465	0.946	0	3.54	1.168	0.906	1.032
7225	Lunch meat, pork sausage links, cooked/Oscar Mayer	1 serving, 2 links	48	164.64	7.824	0.48	0	14.64	7.104	1.766	5.131
7226	Lunch meat, salami beef cotto/Oscar Mayer	1 serving, 2 slices	46	94.76	6.532	0.874	0	7.222	3.179	0.359	3.1
7232	Lunch meat, smokie links sausage/Oscar Mayer	1 serving	43	129.86	5.332	0.731	0	11.739	5.663	1.195	4.033
7276	Lunch meat, Spam, pork with ham, minced, canned/Hormel	1 serving, 2 oz	56	173.6	7.414	1.697	0	15.254	7.717	1.652	5.533
7238	Lunch meat, summer sausage thuringer cervalat/Oscar Mayer	1 serving, 2 slices	46	139.84	6.854	0.414	0	12.282	5.585	1.025	4.934
7254	Lunch meat, turkey bacon/Louis Rich	1 serving	14	35	2.114	0.231	0	2.842	1.051	0.658	0.738
7255	Lunch meat, turkey bologna/Louis Rich	1 serving	28	51.52	3.164	1.358	0	3.696	1.487	1.005	1.061
7079	Lunch meat, turkey breast meat	1 slice	28	26.88	2.044	3.822	0.56	0.378	0.151	0.092	0.118
7080	Lunch meat, turkey ham, cured	1 serving , .99 oz	28	35.28	4.9	0.571	0.056	1.355	0.533	0.369	0.427
7266	Lunch meat, turkey salami/Louis Rich	1 serving	28	41.16	4.284	0.112	0	2.632	0.881	0.656	0.779
7242	Lunch meat, wieners (beef franks) bun length/Oscar Mayer	1 serving, 1 link	57	184.68	6.327	1.511	0	17.157	8.333	0.547	7.142
7243	Lunch meat, wieners (beef franks) fat-free/Oscar Mayer	1 serving	50	39	6.6	2.55	0	0.25	0.095	0.024	0.112
7241	Lunch meat, wieners (beef franks)/Oscar Mayer	1 serving	45	147.15	5.108	1.057	0	13.617	6.633	0.612	5.607
22005	Macaroni and Cheese Dinner, Kraft Original Flavor, unprepared	1 NLEA serving (makes about 1 cup prepared)	70	259	11.34	47.53	1.47	2.59			1.26
20100	Macaroni, enriched, cooked	1 cup elbow shaped	140	197.4	6.678	39.676	1.82	0.938	0.111	0.382	0.133
9328	Maraschino cherries, canned, drained	1 cup, balls	154	254.1	0.339	64.634	4.928	0.323	0.075	0.085	0.06
4067	Margarine, hard, corn, soybean-hydrogenated & cottonseed-hydrogenated w/salt	1 tsp	4.7	33.793	0.042	0.042	0	3.783	1.73	1.18	0.705
4611	Margarine, regular, tub, composite, 80% fat, with salt	1 tbsp	12.8	91.648	0.102	0.077	0	10.291	4.616	3.565	1.66
20322	Meal, corn, white, degermed, enriched	1 cup	138	505.08	11.702	107.2	10.212	2.277	0.569	0.98	0.31
20022	Meal, corn, yellow, degermed, enriched	1 cup	138	505.08	11.702	107.2	10.212	2.277	0.569	0.98	0.31
1110	Milk shake, thick, chocolate	1 container (10.6 oz)	300	357	9.15	63.45	0.9	8.1	2.34	0.3	5.043
1111	Milk shake, thick, vanilla	1 container (11 oz)	313	350.56	12.082	55.558	0	9.484	2.739	0.354	5.903
1088	Milk, buttermilk, lowfat, cultured	1 cup	245	98	8.109	11.736	0	2.156	0.622	0.081	1.343
1107	Milk, human, mature breast	1 cup	246	172.2	2.534	16.949	0	10.775	4.079	1.223	4.942
1082	Milk, lowfat, 1% fat w/added vitamin A	1 cup	244	102.48	8.223	12.176	0	2.367	0.676	0.085	1.545
1104	Milk, lowfat, 1% fat, chocolate	1 cup	250	157.5	8.1	26.1	1.25	2.5	0.75	0.087	1.54
1154	Milk, nonfat, dry w/added vit A	.25 cup	30	108.6	10.848	15.594	0	0.231	0.06	0.009	0.15
1097	Milk, nonfat, skim, evaporated, canned	1 cup	256	199.68	19.328	29.056	0	0.512	0.159	0.015	0.31
1085	Milk, nonfat/fat-free, skim w/added vit A	1 cup	245	83.3	8.257	12.152	0	0.196	0.115	0.017	0.287
1079	Milk, reduced fat, 2% fat w/added vitamin A	1 cup	244	122	8.052	11.419	0	4.807	2.042	0.166	2.35
16120	Milk, soy, fluid	1 cup	245	120.05	9.188	11.368	3.185	5.096	0.799	2.041	0.524
1095	Milk, sweetened condensed, canned	1 cup	306	982.26	24.205	166.46	0	26.622	7.427	1.031	16.787
1077	Milk, whole, 3.25% fat	1 cup	244	146.4	7.857	11.029	0	7.93	1.981	0.476	4.551
1102	Milk, whole, chocolate	1 cup	250	207.5	7.925	25.85	2	8.475	2.475	0.31	5.26
1153	Milk, whole, evaporated, canned, w/added vit A	.5 cup	126	168.84	8.581	12.65	0	9.526	2.942	0.309	5.785
1106	Milk, whole, goat	1 cup	244	168.36	8.686	10.858	0	10.102	2.706	0.364	6.507
15250	Mollusks, conch, baked or broiled	3 oz	85	110.5	22.355	1.445	0	1.02	0.284	0.233	0.315
18274	Muffin, blueberry, commercially prep	1 medium	113	313.01	6.215	54.24	2.938	7.345	2.228	2.819	1.579

Chol (g)	Calc (mg)	Iron (mg)	Mag (mg)	Phos (mg)	Pota (mg)	Sodi (mg)	Zinc (mg)	Vit A (RAE)	Vit C (mg)	Thia (mg)	Ribo (mg)	Niac (mg)	Vit B_6 (mg)	Vit B_{12} (µg)	Vit E (mg)	Fol (µg)	Alc (g)
26.04	2.52	0.529	5.04	42	63.84	343.56	1.193	0	0	0.027	0.048	1.418	0.05	0.493	0.07	1.96	0
30.78	5.13	0.946	7.98	114	148.2	595.65	1.231	0	0	0.031	0.142	2.01	0.154	0.137	0.125	2.85	0
36.96	7.68	0.826	8.64	75.84	114.24	401.28	1.248		0								0
38.18	3.22	1.247	7.82	103.04	95.22	602.14	0.961		0								0
27.09	4.3	0.503	7.31	103.2	77.4	433.01	0.899		0								0
39.2	7.84	0.504	7.84		128.24	766.64	1.008	0	0.504							1.68	0
38.64	4.14	1.03	6.9	59.8	104.88	657.8	0.98		0	0.106	0.133	2.019	0.138	1.73		2.3	0
12.6	5.6	0.203	2.66	27.86	29.12	169.82	0.353	0	0							1.12	0
18.76	34.72	0.459	6.16	54.88	42.56	301.56	0.518	0	0							1.68	0
3.36	3.08	0.33	5.88	45.36	58.52	47.04	0.372	0	0	0.003	0.01	0.489	0.036	0.025	0.025	1.12	0
20.16	2.24	0.655	6.16	82.32	80.36	311.92	0.725	1.96	0	0.008	0.042	0.593	0.059	0.064	0.179	1.96	0
21.28	11.2	0.35	6.16	74.48	60.48	281.12	0.65		0								0
33.63	7.41	0.889	8.55	59.85	90.06	584.25	1.283	0	0							6.27	0
15	10	0.975	9.5	64.5	233.5	463.5	1.205		0								0
25.2	4.5	0.603	5.85	63	58.5	461.25	0.985	0	0	0.015	0.045	1.031	0.032	0.734		2.7	0
9.8	92.4	2.562		264.6	296.1	561.4			0.35	0.672	0.413	4.536				65.1	
0	9.8	1.96	25.2	75.6	43.4	1.4	0.742	0	0	0.286	0.137	2.341	0.049	0	0.084	107.8	0
0	83.16	0.662	6.16	4.62	32.34	6.16	0.4	3.08	0	0	0.006	0.008	0		0.077	0	0
0	1.41	0	0.141	1.081	1.974	44.321	0	38.49	0.009	0	0.002	0.001	0	0.005	0.517	0.047	0
0	3.328	0	0.256	2.56	4.864	138.112	0	104.8	0.013	0.001	0.004	0.003	0.001	0.01	0.64	0.128	0
0	6.9	5.699	55.2	115.92	223.56	4.14	0.994	0	0	0.987	0.562	6.947	0.355	0	0.207	321.5	0
0	6.9	5.699	55.2	115.92	223.56	4.14	0.994	15.18	0	0.987	0.562	6.947	0.355	0	0.207	321.5	0
33	396	0.93	48	378	672	333	1.44	54	0	0.141	0.666	0.372	0.075	0.96	0.15	15	0
37.56	456.98	0.313	37.56	359.95	572.79	297.35	1.221	78.25	0	0.094	0.61	0.457	0.131	1.628	0.157	21.91	0
9.8	284.2	0.123	26.95	218.05	369.95	257.25	1.029	17.15	2.45	0.083	0.377	0.142	0.083	0.539	0.123	12.25	0
34.44	78.72	0.074	7.38	34.44	125.46	41.82	0.418	150.1	12.3	0.034	0.089	0.435	0.027	0.123	0.197	12.3	0
12.2	263.52	0.854	26.84	217.16	290.36	122	2.123	141.5	0	0.049	0.451	0.227	0.09	1.074	0.024	12.2	0
7.5	287.5	0.6	32.5	257.5	425	152.5	1.025	145	2.25	0.095	0.415	0.317	0.103	0.85	0.05	12.5	0
6	377.1	0.096	33	290.4	538.2	160.5	1.224	195.9	2.04	0.124	0.465	0.285	0.108	1.209	0	15	0
10.24	742.4	0.742	69.12	499.2	849.92	294.4	2.304	302.1	3.072	0.115	0.791	0.445	0.141	0.614	0	23.04	0
4.9	222.95	1.225	22.05	181.3	237.65	107.8	2.082	149.5	0	0.11	0.446	0.23	0.091	1.298	0.024	12.25	0
19.52	270.84	0.244	26.84	224.48	341.6	114.68	1.171	134.2	0.488	0.095	0.451	0.224	0.093	1.122	0.073	12.2	0
0	9.8	1.421	46.55	120.05	345.45	29.4	0.564	4.9	0	0.394	0.171	0.36	0.1	0	0.024	4.9	0
104.04	869.04	0.581	79.56	774.18	1135.26	388.62	2.876	226.4	7.956	0.275	1.273	0.643	0.156	1.346	0.49	33.66	0
24.4	246.44	0.073	24.4	204.96	324.52	104.92	0.927	68.32	0	0.107	0.447	0.261	0.088	1.074	0.146	12.2	0
30	280	0.6	32.5	252.5	417.5	150	1.025	65	2.25	0.093	0.405	0.313	0.1	0.825	0.15	12.5	0
36.54	328.86	0.239	30.24	255.78	381.78	133.56	0.97	141.1	2.394	0.059	0.398	0.244	0.063	0.202		10.08	0
26.84	326.96	0.122	34.16	270.84	497.76	122	0.732	139.1	3.172	0.117	0.337	0.676	0.112	0.171	0.171	2.44	0
55.25	83.3	1.199	202.3	184.45	138.55	130.05	1.454	5.95	0	0.051	0.068	0.884	0.051	4.463	5.381	152.2	0
33.9	64.41	1.819	18.08	222.61	138.99	505.11	0.554	25.99	1.243	0.158	0.136	1.243	0.025	0.655	0.938	83.62	0

EvaluEat Code	Food Name	Amt	Wt (g)	Energy (kcal)	Prot (g)	Carb (g)	Fiber (g)	Fat (g)	Mono (g)	Poly (g)	Sat (g)
18279	Muffin, corn, commercially prep	1 medium	113	344.65	6.667	57.517	3.842	9.492	2.378	3.633	1.53
18283	Muffin, oatbran	1 medium	113	305.1	7.91	54.579	5.198	8.362	1.915	4.666	1.228
18639	Muffin, Thomas' English Muffins, plain/Best Foods	1 serving	57	131.67	4.959	25.992		0.855	1.052	1.86	0.697
20134	Noodles, rice, cooked	1 cup	176	191.84	1.602	43.824	1.76	0.352	0.046	0.04	0.04
22702	Noodles, alfredo egg noodles in a creamy sauce, dry mix/Lipton	1 cup	93	388.74	14.415	58.032		10.974	3.586	1.157	4.25
20113	Noodles, Chinese, chow mein	1 cup	45	237.15	3.771	25.893	1.755	13.842	3.46	7.799	1.973
20110	Noodles, egg, enriched, cooked w/salt	1 cup	160	212.8	7.6	39.744	1.76	2.352	0.688	0.653	0.496
20115	Noodles, Japanese, soba, cooked	1 cup	114	112.86	5.768	24.442		0.114	0.03	0.035	0.022
12062	Nuts, almonds, dried, blanched	1 tbsp	9.1	52.871	1.997	1.815	0.946	4.606	2.938	1.097	0.354
12566	Nuts, almonds, oil roast, blanched w/salt	1 oz (24 whole kernels)	28.35	173.79	5.398	5.109 ·	3.175	16.026	10.406	3.363	1.519
12077	Nuts, beechnuts, dried	1 oz	28.35	163.3	1.758	9.497		14.175	6.206	5.695	1.621
12078	Nuts, brazilnuts, dried, unblanched	1 oz (6–8 kernels)	28.35	185.98	4.06	3.479	2.126	18.833	6.959	5.834	4.291
12084	Nuts, butternuts, dried	1 oz	28.35	173.5	7.059	3.416	1.332	16.154	2.955	12.117	0.37
12087	Nuts, cashew nuts, raw	1 oz	28.35	160.46	5.165	7.691	0.936	13.302	7.218	2.379	2.361
12585	Nuts, cashews, dry roasted w/salt	1 oz	28.35	162.73	4.34	9.268	0.851	13.14	7.744	2.222	2.596
12094	Nuts, chestnuts, Chinese, dried	1 oz	28.35	102.91	1.933	22.612		0.513	0.268	0.133	0.075
12116	Nuts, coconut cream, canned (liquid expressed from grated meat)	1 cup	296	568.32	7.962	24.716	6.512	52.451	2.232	0.574	46.51
12119	Nuts, coconut water (liquid from coconuts)	1 cup	240	45.6	1.728	8.904	2.64	0.48	0.019	0.005	0.422
12109	Nuts, coconut, sweetened, flakes, dried	1 cup	74	350.76	2.427	35.217	3.182	23.791	1.012	0.26	21.097
12108	Nuts, coconut, unsweetened, dried	1 oz	28.35	187.11	1.95	6.705	4.621	18.294	0.778	0.2	16.221
12122	Nuts, filberts/hazelnuts, dry roasted, unblanched, w/o salt	1 oz	28.35	183.14	4.261	4.99	2.665	17.69	13.213	2.399	1.279
12132	Nuts, macadamia nuts, dry roasted, without salt added	1 oz (10–12 kernels)	28.35	203.55	2.208	3.793	2.268	21.569	16.804	0.425	3.387
12635	Nuts, mixed w/peanuts, dry roasted w/salt	1 oz	28.35	168.4	4.905	7.187	2.552	14.586	8.9	3.053	1.956
12142	Nuts, pecans, dried	1 oz (20 halves)	28.35	195.9	2.6	3.929	2.722	20.403	11.567	6.128	1.752
12147	Nuts, pine nut, pignolias, dried	1 oz (167 kernels)	28.35	190.8	3.881	3.708	1.049	19.383	5.32	9.674	1.389
12652	Nuts, pistachios, dry roasted w/salt	1 oz (49 kernels)	28.35	161.03	6.053	7.592	2.92	13.032	6.865	3.94	1.575
12154	Nuts, walnut, black, dried	1 oz	28.35	175.2	6.821	2.809	1.928	16.727	4.254	9.944	0.955
4589	Oil, fish, cod liver	1 tbsp	13.6	122.67	0	0	0	13.6	6.353	3.066	3.075
4582	Oil, vegetable, canola	1 tbsp	14	123.76	0	0	0	14	8.246	4.144	0.994
4047	Oil, vegetable, coconut	1 tbsp	13.6	117.23	0	0	0	13.6	0.789	0.245	11.764
4518	Oil, vegetable/salad/cooking, corn	1 tbsp	13.6	120.22	0	0	0	13.6	3.291	7.983	1.727
4053	Oil, vegetable/salad/cooking, olive	1 tbsp	13.5	119.34	0	0	0	13.5	9.977	1.35	1.816
4042	Oil, vegetable/salad/cooking, peanut	1 tbsp	13.5	119.34	0	0	0	13.5	6.237	4.32	2.282
4510	Oil, vegetable/salad/cooking, safflower, linoleic >70%	1 tbsp	13.6	120.22	0	0	0	13.6	1.952	10.149	0.844
4511	Oil, vegetable/salad/cooking, safflower, oleic >70%	1 tbsp	13.6	120.22	0	0	0	13.6	10.152	1.952	0.844
4058	Oil, vegetable/salad/cooking, sesame	1 tbsp	13.6	120.22	0	0	0	13.6	5.399	5.671	1.931
4044	Oil, vegetable/salad/cooking, soybean	1 tbsp	13.6	120.22	0	0	0	13.6	3.169	7.874	1.958
11294	Onions, sweet, raw	1 oz	28.34	9.636	0.227	2.14	0.255	0.023			
11292	Onions, young green, tops only	1 tbsp chopped	6	1.86	0.108	0.339	0.21	0.006	0.001	0.002	0.001
18499	Pancake/waffle, buttermilk, Eggo/Kellogg	1 oz	28.34	66.032	1.7	10.798	0.312	1.896	0.833	0.604	0.408

Chol (g)	Calc (mg)	Iron (mg)	Mag (mg)	Phos (mg)	Pota (mg)	Sodi (mg)	Zinc (mg)	Vit A (RAE)	Vit C (mg)	Thia (mg)	Ribo (mg)	Niac (mg)	Vit B_6 (mg)	Vit B_{12} (µg)	Vit E (mg)	Fol (µg)	Alc (g)
29.38	83.62	3.175	36.16	320.92	77.97	588.73	0.61	58.76	0	0.308	0.368	2.302	0.095	0.102	0.904	90.4	0
0	71.19	4.746	177.41	424.88	572.91	444.09	2.079	0	0	0.296	0.107	0.475	0.182	0.011	0.746	100.6	0
	76.38	1.704				210.33		0	0.057					0.205	0.994	82.65	0
0	7.04	0.246	5.28	35.2	7.04	33.44	0.44	0	0	0.032	0.007	0.127	0.011	0		5.28	0
104.16	118.11	2.809				1646.1											0
0	9	2.128	23.4	72.45	54	197.55	0.63	0	0	0.26	0.189	2.677	0.049	0	1.566	40.5	0
52.8	19.2	2.544	30.4	110.4	44.8	11.2	0.992	9.6	0	0.298	0.133	2.379	0.058	0.144	0.256	102.4	0
0	4.56	0.547	10.26	28.5	39.9	68.4	0.137	0	0	0.107	0.03	0.581	0.046	0		7.98	0
0	19.656	0.339	25.025	43.68	62.517	2.548	0.284	0	0	0.018	0.051	0.333	0.011	0	2.249	2.73	0
0	54.999	1.503	82.215	163.58	196.466	219.996	0.403		0.284	0.022	0.079	1.106	0.026	0	1.573	18	0
0	0.284	0.697	0	0	288.32	10.773	0.102	0	4.394	0.086	0.105	0.249	0.194	0		32.04	0
0	45.36	0.689	106.596	205.538	186.827	0.851	1.151	0	0.198	0.175	0.01	0.084	0.029	0	1.624	6.237	0
0	15.026	1.14	67.19	126.441	119.354	0.284	0.887	1.701	0.907	0.109	0.042	0.296	0.159	0	0.992	18.71	0
0	10.49	1.894	82.782	168.116	187.11	3.402	1.639	0	0.142	0.12	0.016	0.301	0.118	0	0.255	7.088	
0	12.758	1.701	73.71	138.915	160.178	181.44	1.588	0	0	0.057	0.057	0.397	0.073	0	0.261	19.56	0
0	8.222	0.649	38.84	43.943	205.821	1.418	0.4	4.536	16.59	0.074	0.083	0.369	0.189	0		31.19	0
0	2.96	1.51	50.32	65.12	298.96	148	1.776	0	5.328	0.065	0.118	0.112	0.086	0	0.385	41.44	0
0	57.6	0.696	60	48	600	252	0.24	0	5.76	0.072	0.137	0.192	0.077	0	0	7.2	0
0	10.36	1.332	35.52	74	233.84	189.44	1.295	0	0	0.022	0.015	0.222	0.193	0	0.281	5.92	0
0	7.371	0.941	25.515	58.401	153.941	10.49	0.57	0	0.425	0.017	0.028	0.171	0.085	0	0.125	2.552	0
0	34.871	1.242	49.046	87.885	214.043	0	0.709	0.851	1.077	0.096	0.035	0.581	0.176	0	4.332	24.95	0
0	19.845	0.751	33.453	56.133	102.911	1.134	0.366	0	0.198	0.201	0.025	0.645	0.102	0	0.162	2.835	0
0	19.845	1.049	63.788	123.323	169.25	189.662	1.077	0	0.113	0.057	0.057	1.332	0.084	0	3.101	14.18	0
0	19.845	0.717	34.304	78.53	116.235	0	1.284	0.851	0.312	0.187	0.037	0.331	0.06	0	0.397	6.237	0
0	4.536	1.568	71.159	163.013	169.25	0.567	1.829	0.284	0.227	0.103	0.064	1.244	0.027	0	2.645	19	0
0	31.185	1.191	34.02	137.498	295.407	114.818	0.652	3.686	0.652	0.238	0.045	0.404	0.361	0	0.547	14.18	0
0	17.294	0.885	56.984	145.436	148.271	0.567	0.955	0.567	0.482	0.016	0.037	0.133	0.165	0	0.51	8.789	0
77.52	0	0	0	0	0	0	0	4080	0		0	0	0	0		0	0
0	0	0	0	0	0	0	0	0	0	0	0	0	0	0	2.394	0	0
0	0	0.005	0	0	0	0	0	0	0	0	0	0	0	0	0.012	0	0
0	0	0	0	0	0	0	0	0	0	0	0	0	0	0	1.945	0	0
0	0.135	0.089	0	0	0.135	0.405	0	0	0	0	0	0	0	0	1.937	0	0
0	0	0.004	0	0	0	0	0.001	0	0	0	0	0	0	0	2.118	0	0
0	0	0	0	0	0	0	0	0	0	0	0	0	0	0	4.638	0	0
0	0	0	0	0	0	0	0	0	0	0	0	0	0	0	4.638	0	0
0	0	0	0	0	0	0	0	0	0	0	0	0	0	0	0.19	0	0
0	0	0.003	0	0	0	0	0	0	0	0	0	0	0	0	1.253	0	0
	5.668	0.074	2.551	7.652	33.725	2.267	0.037	0	1.36	0.012	0.006	0.038	0.037			6.518	0
0	3.66	0.115	1.2	1.98	15.6	0.24	0.027	12	2.736	0.004	0.008	0.012	0.004	0	0.013	0.84	0
3.117	9.919	0.879	5.101	96.639	29.19	150.202	0.17		0.397	0.074	0.082	0.978	0.099	0.292	0	14.74	0

EvaluEat Code	Food Name	Amt	Wt (g)	Energy (kcal)	Prot (g)	Carb (g)	Fiber (g)	Fat (g)	Mono (g)	Poly (g)	Sat (g)
18294	Pancakes, blueberry, homemade	1 pancake (4"dia)	38	84.36	2.318	11.02		3.496	0.88	1.582	0.755
18390	Pancakes, buttermilk, homemade	1 pancake (4"dia)	38	86.26	2.584	10.906		3.534	0.897	1.705	0.696
18293	Pancakes, plain, homemade	1 pancake (4"dia)	38	86.26	2.432	10.754		3.686	0.94	1.69	0.806
18288	Pancakes, plain/buttermilk, frozen	1 pancake (6"dia)	73	167.17	3.796	31.828	1.314	2.409	0.881	0.703	0.56
22515	Pasta, beef ravioli in tomato & meat sauce, canned entree/Chef Boyardee	1 serving	244	229.36	8.369	36.893	3.66	5.392	2.001	0.22	2.489
22516	Pasta, beefaroni, macaroni w/beef in tomato sauce, canned entree/Chef Boyardee	1 serving	212	184.44	8.247	31.143	2.968	2.947	1.272	0.254	1.187
22517	Pasta, mini beef ravioli in tomato & meat sauce, canned entree/Chef Boyardee	1 package	425	403.75	14.833	68.51	5.525	7.99	3.4	0.298	2.975
22518	Pasta, spaghetti & meatballs in tomato sauce, canned entree/Chef Boyardee	1 package	425	442	16.065	60.307	3.825	15.3	6.503	0.68	6.843
20121	Pasta, spaghetti, enriched, cooked w/o salt	1 cup	140	197.4	6.678	39.676	2.38	0.938	0.111	0.382	0.133
20125	Pasta, spaghetti, whole wheat, cooked	1 cup	140	173.6	7.462	37.156	6.3	0.756	0.105	0.298	0.139
22701	Pasta, whole wheat macaroni and cheese dinner, dry mix/Hodgson Mill	1 package	206	774.56	29.046	142.55	15.656	9.682			2.822
18635	Pastry, cinnamon rolls w/icing, refrigerated dough/Pillsbury	1 serving	44	150.04	2.376	23.892		5.016			1.25
18237	Pastry, cream puff/eclair shell, homemade	1 eclair (5"x 2" x 1-3/4")	48	173.76	4.32	10.944	0.384	12.432	5.341	3.542	2.688
18239	Pastry, croissant, butter	1 croissant, mini	28	113.68	2.296	12.824	0.728	5.88	1.547	0.306	3.265
18241	Pastry, croissant, cheese	1 croissant, small	42	173.88	3.864	19.74	1.092	8.778	2.734	1.001	4.464
18245	Pastry, Danish, cheese	1 pastry	71	265.54	5.68	26.412	0.71	15.549	8.032	1.828	4.824
18246	Pastry, Danish, fruit (apple/cinnamon/raisin/lemon/ raspberry/strawberry) enriched	1 toaster strudel	53	196.63	2.862	25.334	1.007	9.805	5.314	1.253	2.576
18247	Pastry, Danish, nut (almond/raisin nut/cinnamon nut)	1 pastry (4-1/4"dia)	65	279.5	4.615	29.705	1.3	16.38	8.895	2.783	3.784
18257	Pastry, eclair/cream puff, homemade, custard filled w/chocolate icing	1 cream puff (3-1/2"x 2")	112	293.44	7.168	27.104	0.672	17.584	7.262	4.422	4.613
18338	Pastry, phyllo dough	1 sheet dough	19	56.81	1.349	9.994	0.361	1.14	0.598	0.175	0.279
18354	Pastry, strudel, apple	1 piece	71	194.54	2.343	29.181	1.562	7.952	2.32	3.774	1.451
16097	Peanut butter, chunky w/salt	2 tbsp	32	188.48	8.022	6.749	2.112	15.904	7.539	4.532	3.066
16098	Peanut butter, smooth w/salt	2 tbsp	32	191.68	7.99	5.894	1.888	16.73	7.919	4.764	3.209
16390	Peanuts, all types, dry roasted w/o salt	1 oz	28.35	165.85	6.713	6.098	2.268	14.079	6.985	4.449	1.954
16090	Peanuts, all types, dry roasted w/salt	1 oz	28.35	165.85	6.713	6.098	2.268	14.079	6.985	4.449	1.954
16087	Peanuts, all types, raw	1 oz	28.35	160.75	7.314	4.573	2.41	13.96	6.926	4.411	1.937
16138	Peas, chickpea/garbanzo, falafel, homemade	1 patty (approx 2-1/4"dia)	17	56.61	2.263	5.413		3.026	1.729	0.707	0.405
16158	Peas, chickpea/garbanzo, hummus, commercial	1 tbsp	14	23.24	1.106	2.001	0.84	1.344	0.565	0.506	0.201
16363	Peas, cowpea, common (blackeyed, crowder, southern) mature seed, boiled w/salt	1 cup	171	198.36	13.218	35.5	11.115	0.906	0.075	0.385	0.236
16065	Peas, cowpeas, common (blackeyed, crowder, southern) mature seed, canned w/pork	1 cup	240	199.2	6.576	39.672	7.92	3.84	1.574	0.55	1.452

Chol (g)	Calc (mg)	Iron (mg)	Mag (mg)	Phos (mg)	Pota (mg)	Sodi (mg)	Zinc (mg)	Vit A (RAE)	Vit C (mg)	Thia (mg)	Ribo (mg)	Niac (mg)	Vit B6 (mg)	Vit B12 (µg)	Vit E (mg)	Fol (µg)	Alc (g)
21.28	78.28	0.654	6.08	57.38	52.44	156.56	0.205	19	0.836	0.074	0.103	0.579	0.019	0.076		13.68	0
22.04	59.66	0.646	5.7	52.82	55.1	198.36	0.236	11.4	0.152	0.078	0.111	0.599	0.017	0.068		14.44	0
22.42	83.22	0.684	6.08	60.42	50.16	166.82	0.213	20.52	0.114	0.076	0.107	0.595	0.017	0.084		14.44	0
6.57	45.26	2.54	10.22	271.56	53.29	371.57	0.482	21.17	0.219	0.277	0.342	2.927	0.058	0.131	0.204	32.85	0
14.64	19.52	2.416			353.8	1173.64			0.244								0
16.96	16.96	1.505				799.24			0.424								0
29.75	38.25	4.08				2018.75			0.425								0
38.25	29.75	3.145				1666			1.7								0
0	9.8	1.96	25.2	75.6	43.4	1.4	0.742	0	0	0.286	0.137	2.341	0.049	0	0.084	107.8	0
0	21	1.484	42	124.6	61.6	4.2	1.134	0	0	0.151	0.063	0.99	0.111	0	0.42	7	0
16.48	234.84	5.397				1258.66											0
						334.4											0
94.08	17.28	0.97	5.76	57.12	46.56	267.36	0.35	133.4	0	0.099	0.173	0.752	0.036	0.187	1.349	25.44	0
18.76	10.36	0.568	4.48	29.4	33.04	208.32	0.21	57.68	0.056	0.109	0.067	0.613	0.016	0.045	0.235	24.64	0
23.94	22.26	0.903	10.08	54.6	55.44	233.1	0.395	85.68	0.084	0.22	0.136	0.907	0.031	0.134	0.605	31.08	0
11.36	24.85	1.136	10.65	76.68	69.58	319.5	0.497	24.85	0.071	0.135	0.185	1.42	0.028	0.121	0.241	42.6	0
60.42	24.38	0.938	7.95	47.17	43.99	187.62	0.286	7.95	2.067	0.139	0.117	1.056	0.023	0.048	0.18	24.91	0
29.9	61.1	1.17	20.8	71.5	61.75	235.95	0.565	5.85	1.105	0.143	0.156	1.495	0.068	0.136	0.533	53.95	0
142.24	70.56	1.322	16.8	119.84	131.04	377.44	0.683	222.9	0.336	0.129	0.298	0.895	0.066	0.381	2.251	48.16	0
0	2.09	0.61	2.85	14.25	14.06	91.77	0.093	0	0	0.103	0.065	0.774	0.006	0	0.015	16.72	0
4.26	10.65	0.298	6.39	23.43	105.79	190.99	0.135	4.26	1.207	0.028	0.018	0.234	0.033	0.156	1.008	19.88	0
0	16.96	0.653	62.08	125.44	201.92	150.4	1.04	0	0	0.04	0.036	4.38	0.144	0	2.454	29.44	0
0	15.04	0.602	56	105.92	176.64	160	0.938	0	0	0.027	0.034	4.289	0.145	0	2.454	23.68	0
0	15.309	0.641	49.896	101.493	186.543	1.701	0.938	0	0	0.124	0.028	3.834	0.073	0	1.965	41.11	0
0	15.309	0.641	49.896	101.493	186.543	230.486	0.938	0	0	0.124	0.028	3.834	0.073	0	2.211	41.11	0
0	26.082	1.298	47.628	106.596	199.868	5.103	0.927	0	0	0.181	0.038	3.421	0.099	0	2.362	68.04	0
0	9.18	0.581	13.94	32.64	99.45	49.98	0.255	0.17	0.272	0.025	0.028	0.177	0.021	0		15.81	0
0	5.32	0.342	9.94	24.64	31.92	53.06	0.256	0.28	0	0.025	0.009	0.081	0.028	0		11.62	0
0	41.04	4.292	90.63	266.76	475.38	410.4	2.206	1.71	0.684	0.345	0.094	0.846	0.171	0	0.479	355.7	0
16.8	40.8	3.408	103.2	230.4	427.2	840	2.496	0	0.48	0.151	0.12	1.034	0.108	0		122.4	0

EvaluEat Code	Food Name	Amt	Wt (g)	Energy (kcal)	Prot (g)	Carb (g)	Fiber (g)	Fat (g)	Mono (g)	Poly (g)	Sat (g)
16386	Peas, split, mature seed, boiled w/salt	1 cup	196	231.28	16.346	41.356	16.268	0.764	0.159	0.323	0.106
6962	Peppers, hot, chili, immature green, canned, chili sauce	.5 cup	125	25	0.875	6.25	2.375	0.125	0.085	0.015	0.016
6961	Peppers, hot, chili, mature red, canned, chili sauce	.5 cup	125	26.25	1.125	4.875	0.875	0.75	0.514	0.093	0.1
11339	Peppers, sweet, green, sauteed	1 oz	28.34	35.992	0.221	1.196	0.51	3.358	0.662	1.672	0.451
11921	Peppers, sweet, red, sauteed	1 oz	28.34	41.093	0.295	1.862	0.51	3.613	0.735	1.839	0.501
11942	Pickles, cucumber, fresh, (bread and butter pickles)	1 slice	7	5.39	0.063	1.253	0.105	0.014	0	0.006	0.004
18398	Pie crust, chocolate wafer cookie type, chilled	1 piece (1/8 of 9" crust)	28	141.68	1.428	15.232	0.42	8.708	4.124	2.16	1.885
18618	Pie crust, cookie type Nilla Wafer, ready to use/Nabisco	1 serving	28	143.64	0.98	17.668	0.252	7.588	5.236	0.378	1.442
18335	Pie crust, frozen, baked	1 piece (1/8 of 9" crust)	16	82.24	0.704	7.936	0.16	5.248	2.514	0.645	1.693
18399	Pie crust, graham cracker cookie type, chilled	1 piece (1/8 of 9" crust)	30	145.2	1.23	19.17	0.45	7.32	3.343	2.031	1.528
18336	Pie crust, homemade, baked	1 piece (1/8 of 9" crust)	23	121.21	1.472	10.925	0.391	7.958	3.489	2.098	1.983
18628	Pie, apple turnover, frozen, ready to bake/Pepperidge Farm	1 serving	89	283.91	3.738	31.239	1.602	16.02			4.032
18301	Pie, apple, enriched, commercially prep	1 piece (1/8 of 9" dia)	125	296.25	2.375	42.5	2	13.75	5.485	2.747	4.746
18304	Pie, banana cream, homemade	1 piece (1/8 of 9" dia)	144	387.36	6.336	47.376	1.008	19.584	8.235	4.74	5.412
18305	Pie, blueberry, commercially prep	1 piece (1/8 of 9" dia)	125	290	2.25	43.625	1.25	12.5	5.305	4.405	2.099
18308	Pie, cherry, commercially prep	1 piece (1/8 of 9" dia)	125	325	2.5	49.75	1	13.75	7.296	2.569	3.203
18310	Pie, chocolate creme, commercially prep	1 piece (1/4 of 6" pie)	99	300.96	2.574	33.264	1.98	19.206	11.006	2.374	4.918
18312	Pie, chocolate mousse, no bake mix	1 piece (1/8 of 9" dia)	95	247	3.325	28.12		14.63	4.83	0.773	7.785
18313	Pie, coconut creme, commercially prep	1 piece (1/6 of 7" pie)	64	190.72	1.344	23.808	0.832	10.624	4.646	0.988	4.465
18317	Pie, egg custard, commercially prep	1 piece (1/6 of 8" pie)	105	220.5	5.775	21.84	1.68	12.18	5.037	3.909	2.466
18320	Pie, lemon meringue, commercially prep	1 piece (1/6 of 8" pie)	113	302.84	1.695	53.336	1.356	9.831	3.034	4.122	1.996
18322	Pie, mince, homemade	1 piece (1/8 of 9" dia)	165	476.85	4.29	79.2	4.29	17.82	7.679	4.689	4.425
18323	Pie, peach	1 piece (1/6 of 8" pie)	117	260.91	2.223	38.493	0.936	11.7	4.962	4.386	1.764
18324	Pie, pecan, commercially prep	1 piece (1/6 of 8" pie)	113	452	4.52	64.636	3.955	20.905	12.137	3.596	4.006
18326	Pie, pumpkin, commercially prep	1 piece (1/6 of 8" pie)	109	228.9	4.251	29.757	2.943	10.355	4.395	3.434	1.946
18328	Pie, vanilla creme, homemade	1 piece (1/8 of 9" dia)	126	350.28	6.048	41.076	0.756	18.144	7.614	4.332	5.078
22531	Pizza Rolls Pizza Snacks, hamburger, frozen/Totinos	1 serving	85	231.2	9.35	26.435		9.775			

Chol (g)	Calc (mg)	Iron (mg)	Mag (mg)	Phos (mg)	Pota (mg)	Sodi (mg)	Zinc (mg)	Vit A (RAE)	Vit C (mg)	Thia (mg)	Ribo (mg)	Niac (mg)	Vit B_6 (mg)	Vit B_{12} (µg)	Vit E (mg)	Fol (µg)	Alc (g)
0	27.44	2.528	70.56	194.04	709.52	466.48	1.96	0	0.784	0.372	0.11	1.744	0.094	0	0.059	127.4	0
0	6.25	0.5	15	17.5	705	31.25	0.188	36.25	85	0.037	0.037	0.875	0.175	0	0.425	15	0
0	11.25	0.625	15	20	705	31.25	0.188	28.75	37.5	0.012	0.113	0.75	0.175	0	0.45	13.75	0
0	2.267	0.085	2.267	4.251	37.976	4.818	0.017	3.968	50.16	0.012	0.014	0.165	0.056	0	0.397	0.567	
	1.984	0.133	3.401	6.518	54.696	5.951	0.043	39.11	46.14	0.016	0.031	0.27	0.103	0	0.876	0.567	0
0	2.24	0.028	0.14	1.89	14	47.11	0.003	0.49	0.63	0	0.002	0	0.001	0	0.011	0.28	0
0.28	8.4	0.84	11.2	29.4	47.04	188.16	0.23	59.08	0	0.043	0.058	0.599	0.001	0.006	0.792	14.84	0
2.8	11.48	0.496	2.24	23.24	19.32	62.72	0.078			0.046	0.054	0.696	0.006	0.031		8.4	0
0	3.36	0.362	2.88	9.44	17.6	103.52	0.054	0	0	0.045	0.061	0.39	0.011	0.003	0.421	8.8	0
0	6	0.636	5.4	19.2	25.8	168	0.138	57.3	0	0.031	0.052	0.627	0.011	0.006	0.684	10.2	0
0	2.3	0.665	3.22	15.41	15.41	124.66	0.101	0	0	0.09	0.064	0.761	0.006	0	0.071	15.41	0
		1.219				176.22											0
0	13.75	0.563	8.75	30	81.25	332.5	0.2	40	4	0.035	0.034	0.329	0.047	0.012	1.9	33.75	0
73.44	108	1.498	23.04	132.48	237.6	345.6	0.691	87.84	2.304	0.2	0.298	1.518	0.192	0.36	0.576	38.88	0
0	10	0.375	6.25	28.75	62.5	406.25	0.2	55	3.375	0.012	0.037	0.375	0.046	0.012	1.3	33.75	0
0	15	0.6	10	36.25	101.25	307.5	0.225	65	1.125	0.029	0.036	0.25	0.051	0.012	0.95	33.75	0
4.95	35.64	1.059	20.79	67.32	125.73	134.64	0.228	0	0	0.036	0.106	0.671	0.02	0.01	2.707	12.87	0
33.25	73.15	1.026	30.4	219.45	270.75	437	0.57	117.8	0.475	0.048	0.14	0.565	0.028	0.199		24.7	0
0	18.56	0.512	12.8	54.4	41.6	163.2	0.301	17.28	0	0.032	0.051	0.128	0.044	0.077	0.096	4.48	0
34.65	84	0.609	11.55	117.6	111.3	252	0.546	59.85	0.63	0.041	0.218	0.307	0.05	0.451	0.987	21	0
50.85	63.28	0.689	16.95	118.65	100.57	164.98	0.554	57.63	3.616	0.07	0.236	0.733	0.034	0.192	1.198	27.12	0
0	36.3	2.458	23.1	69.3	334.95	419.1	0.363	1.65	9.735	0.248	0.173	1.962	0.107	0	0.248	37.95	0
0	9.36	0.585	7.02	25.74	146.25	315.9	0.105	11.7	1.053	0.071	0.039	0.234	0.027	0	1.1	33.93	0
36.16	19.21	1.175	20.34	87.01	83.62	479.12	0.644	57.63	1.243	0.103	0.138	0.281	0.024	0.113	0.362	38.42	0
21.8	65.4	0.861	16.35	77.39	167.86	307.38	0.491	488.3	1.09	0.06	0.167	0.204	0.062	0.283	1.123	26.16	0
78.12	113.4	1.285	16.38	131.04	158.76	327.6	0.668	104.6	0.63	0.175	0.272	1.24	0.062	0.378	0.567	32.76	0
						417.35											0

EvaluEat Code	Food Name	Amt	Wt (g)	Energy (kcal)	Prot (g)	Carb (g)	Fiber (g)	Fat (g)	Mono (g)	Poly (g)	Sat (g)
22533	Pizza Rolls Pizza Snacks, pepperoni, frozen/Totinos	1 serving	141	384.93	14.382	39.48	2.256	18.894	9.236	2.214	4.991
22554	Pizza, deluxe French bread w/sausage, pepperoni & mushroom, frozen/Stouffer's	1 serving	175	428.75	16.1	44.45	3.5	20.65	8.715	2.52	6.37
22542	Pizza, deluxe w/sausage, green & red pepper & mushrooms, frozen/Celeste	1 serving	167	385.77	16.7	33.233		20.708	7.615	2.421	8.116
22556	Pizza, original pepperoni, frozen, 12"/Tombstone	1 serving	113	311.88	14.464	28.25		15.707	5.311	2.045	6
22557	Pizza, original sausage & mushroom, frozen/Tombstone	1 serving	132	306.24	14.388	31.152		13.728	4.435	2.086	5.069
22903	Pizza, pepperoni, frozen	1 serving	146	400.04	16.191	36.208	2.336	21.112	8.439	2.438	7.066
22902	Pizza, sausage & pepperoni, frozen	1 serving	146	385.44	15.768	36.179	2.336	19.695	7.796	2.599	6.336
22598	Pizza, supreme, sausage, mushrooms, pepperoni, frozen/Red Baron	1 serving	136	344.08	13.6	31.824		18.088	7.167	2.475	6.093
43572	Popcorn, microwave, low-fat and sodium	1 cup	148	634.92	18.648	108.62	21.016	14.06	6.046	5.287	2.094
19436	Popcorn, sugar syrup/caramel, fat-free	1 bag (6 oz)	170	647.7	3.4	153.1	4.25	2.38	0.442	1.078	0.34
10193	Pork back rib, fresh, lean & fat, roasted	1 piece, cooked (yield from 1 lb raw meat)	219	810.3	53.129	0	0	64.78	29.477	5.081	24.068
10857	Pork bacon, Canadian style / Hormel	1 serving	56	68.32	9.453	1.047		2.766	1.394	0.347	1.025
10124	Pork bacon, cured, broiled, pan-fried, or roasted	1 slice, cooked	8	43.28	2.963	0.114	0	3.342	1.482	0.364	1.099
10188	Pork composite (leg/loin/shoulder/sparerib) fresh, lean & fat, cooked	3 oz	85	232.05	23.434	0	0	14.603	6.494	1.233	5.287
10227	Pork composite (loin & shoulder blade) fresh, lean & fat, cooked	3 oz	85	214.2	23.613	0	0	12.546	5.568	1.003	4.505
10134	Pork ham, cured, boneless, extra lean (5% fat) roasted	3 oz	85	123.25	17.791	1.275	0	4.701	2.227	0.459	1.538
10136	Pork ham, cured, boneless, regular fat (11% fat) roasted	3 oz	85	151.3	19.227	0	0	7.667	3.774	1.199	2.652
7953	Pork sausage, pre-cooked	1 serving (1 hot dog)	52	196.56	7.535	0	0	18.221	7.888	2.532	6.064
10863	Pork, fresh, variety meats and by-products, stomach, cooked, simmered	1 serving	56	84.56	11.984	0.05	0	4.066	1.191	0.413	1.674
10220	Pork, ground, fresh, cooked	3 oz	85	252.45	21.837	0	0	17.655	7.863	1.59	6.562
10173	Pork, pig's feet, fresh, simmered	3 oz	85	197.2	18.649	0	0	13.642	6.804	1.309	3.692
19823	Potato chips, without salt, reduced fat	1 cup	146	711.02	10.366	98.988	8.906	30.368	7.008	15.972	6.074
11358	Potatoes, red, flesh and skin, baked	1 potato, large (3" to 4-1/4" dia)	299	266.11	6.877	58.574	5.382	0.449	0.006	0.129	0.078
11356	Potatoes, russet, flesh and skin, baked	1 potato, large	299	290.03	7.864	64.106	6.877	0.389	0.006	0.129	
43109	Pretzels, soft	1 cup	186	628.68	15.252	129.07	3.162	5.766	1.992	1.763	1.293
19311	Pudding, banana, ready-to-eat	1 can (5 oz)	142	180.34	3.408	30.104	0.142	5.112	2.173	1.889	0.795
19183	Pudding, chocolate, ready-to-eat	1 can (5 oz)	142	197.38	3.834	32.66	1.42	5.68	2.414	2.031	1.008
19187	Pudding, flan (caramel custard) dry mix	1 portion, amount to make 1/2 cup	21	73.08	0	19.236	0	0	0	0	0
19289	Pudding, Kraft, JELL-O fat-free Pudding Snacks, vanilla, ready-to-eat	1 NLEA serving	113	103.96	2.373	23.165	0.113	0.226			0.226
19276	Pudding, Kraft, JELL-O fat-free Sugar Free Instant, vanilla, asp & ace, powder	1 NLEA serving	8	26.48	0.064	6.232	0.104	0.072			0.008
19277	Pudding, Kraft, JELL-O Sugar Free Cook & Serve, chocolate, asp & ace, powder	1 NLEA serving	10	31	0.61	7.45	0.93	0.3			0.16
19193	Pudding, rice, ready-to-eat	1 can (5 oz)	142	231.46	2.84	31.24	0.142	10.65	4.558	3.962	1.661

Chol (g)	Calc (mg)	Iron (mg)	Mag (mg)	Phos (mg)	Pota (mg)	Sodi (mg)	Zinc (mg)	Vit A (RAE)	Vit C (mg)	Thia (mg)	Ribo (mg)	Niac (mg)	Vit B₆ (mg)	Vit B₁₂ (µg)	Vit E (mg)	Fol (µg)	Alc (g)
31.02	102.93					865.74											0
33.25	231	2.712				840			29.93								0
36.74	280.56					764.86											0
31.64	202.27					551.44											0
26.4	200.64					718.08											0
33.58	0	2.613	24.82	221.92	221.92	878.92	1.781	45.26	1.752	0.371	0.352	3.616	0.105	0.058	1.644	54.02	0
30.66	191.26	2.774	26.28	207.32	255.5	854.1	1.606	64.24	3.212	0.372	0.329	3.631	0.098	0.35	1.407	51.1	0
23.12	223.04	2.285				738.48											0
0	16.28	3.374	223.48	390.72	356.68	725.2	5.668	10.36	0	0.518	0.163	3.064	0.252	0	7.415	25.16	0
0	30.6	1.36	45.9	93.5	187	486.2	1.054	3.4	0	0.065	0.099	0.581	0.08	0	0.221	6.8	0
258.42	98.55	3.022	45.99	427.05	689.85	221.19	7.38	6.57	0.657	0.935	0.438	7.774	0.672	1.402		6.57	0
27.44	3.36	0.504	10.64		156.24	568.96	1.008		0.784								0
8.8	0.88	0.115	2.64	42.64	45.2	184.8	0.28	0.88	0	0.032	0.021	0.888	0.028	0.098	0.025	0.16	0
77.35	21.25	0.935	20.4	197.2	300.9	52.7	2.465	1.7	0.255	0.655	0.279	4.187	0.335	0.655	0.17	5.1	0
73.1	20.4	0.842	20.4	192.95	307.7	48.45	2.227	1.7	0.255	0.722	0.275	4.216	0.343	0.629	0.204	5.1	0
45.05	6.8	1.258	11.9	166.6	243.95	1022.55	2.448	0	0	0.641	0.172	3.42	0.34	0.553	0.213	2.55	0
50.15	6.8	1.139	18.7	238.85	347.65	1275	2.1	0	0	0.621	0.281	5.228	0.264	0.595	0.264	2.55	0
38.48	71.24	0.478	6.76	143	159.64	391.04	0.78	9.88	0.364	0.108	0.081	2.106	0.077	0.369	0.276	0.52	0
176.96	8.4	0.689	8.4	72.24	47.6	22.4	1.635	0	0	0.022	0.105	0.773	0.012	0.269	0.05	1.68	0
79.9	18.7	1.097	20.4	192.1	307.7	62.05	2.729	1.7	0.595	0.6	0.187	3.575	0.332	0.459	0.178	5.1	0
90.95	0	0.833	4.25	69.7	28.05	62.05	0.892	0	0	0.014	0.048	0.497	0.032	0.349	0.077	1.7	0
0	30.66	1.971	129.94	281.78	2546.24	11.68	1.475	0	37.52	0.307	0.394	10.22	0.978	0	7.986	14.6	0
0	26.91	2.093	83.72	215.28	1629.55	23.92	1.196	2.99	37.67	0.215	0.149	4.769	0.634	0	0.12	80.73	0
0	53.82	3.199	89.7	212.29	1644.5	23.92	1.046	2.99	38.57	0.2	0.144	4.031	1.058	0	0.12	32.89	0
5.58	42.78	7.291	39.06	146.94	163.68	2611.44	1.748	0	0	0.763	0.539	7.942	0.037	0	1.004	44.64	0
0	120.7	0.185	11.36	97.98	156.2	278.32	0.398	8.52	0.71	0.028	0.209	0.231	0.03	0.256		2.84	0
4.26	127.8	0.724	29.82	113.6	255.6	183.18	0.596	14.2	2.556	0.037	0.22	0.493	0.04	0	0.412	4.26	0
0	5.04	0.017	0	0.21	32.13	90.72	0.008	0	0	0	0	0	0	0	0	0	0
2.26	85.88	0.045		115.26	123.17	240.69			0.339								0
0	11.76	0.006		189.44	2.48	332.32			0								0
0	6.9	1.183		21.2	139	108.5			0								
1.42	73.84	0.426	11.36	96.56	85.2	120.7	0.696	35.5	0.71	0.026	0.102	0.229	0.041	0.298	1.954	4.26	0

EvaluEat Code	Food Name	Amt	Wt (g)	Energy (kcal)	Prot (g)	Carb (g)	Fiber (g)	Fat (g)	Mono (g)	Poly (g)	Sat (g)
19218	Pudding, tapioca, ready-to-eat	1 can (5 oz)	142	168.98	2.84	27.548	0.142	5.254	2.244	1.931	0.852
19201	Pudding, vanilla, ready-to-eat	4 oz	113	145.77	2.599	24.747	0	4.068	1.74	1.514	0.644
43282	Quail, cooked, total edible	1 cup	186	435.24	46.686	0	0	26.226	9.097	6.486	7.356
14342	Rice beverage, Rice Dream, canned/Imagine Foods	1 cup	245	120.05	0.417	24.843	0	1.985	1.345	0.309	0.167
18344	Roll, dinner, egg	1 roll (2-1/2" dia)	35	107.45	3.325	18.2	1.295	2.24	1.026	0.395	0.552
18396	Roll, dinner, plain, homemade w/reduced fat (2%) milk	1 roll (2-1/2" dia)	35	110.6	2.975	18.69	0.665	2.555	1.008	0.702	0.628
18347	Roll, dinner, wheat	1 roll (1 oz)	28	76.44	2.408	12.88	1.064	1.764	0.871	0.31	0.419
18349	Roll, french	1 roll	38	105.26	3.268	19.076	1.216	1.634	0.745	0.317	0.366
18350	Roll, hamburger/hot dog, plain	1 roll	43	119.97	4.085	21.264	0.903	1.862	0.478	0.846	0.47
18348	Roll, hamburger/hot dog, whole wheat	1 medium (2-1/2" dia)	36	95.76	3.132	18.396	2.7	1.692	0.432	0.778	0.301
18353	Roll, hard/kaiser	1 roll (3-1/2" dia)	57	167.01	5.643	30.039	1.311	2.451	0.646	0.98	0.345
4017	Salad dressing, 1000 Island, regular, w/salt	1 tbsp	16	59.2	0.174	2.342	0.128	5.61	1.261	2.915	0.815
4635	Salad dressing, 1000 Island dressing, fat-free	1 tbsp	14.6	19.272	0.08	4.273	0.482	0.212	0.05	0.092	0.029
4539	Salad dressing, blue/roquefort cheese, regular w/salt	1 tbsp	15	75.6	0.72	1.11	0	7.845	1.845	4.17	1.485
4367	Salad dressing, French dressing, fat-free	1 tbsp	14	18.48	0.028	4.5	0.308	0.038	0.02	0.009	0.005
4142	Salad dressing, French, low-fat, no salt, diet (5 kcal/tsp)	1 tbsp	16	37.28	0.093	4.685	0.176	2.154	0.944	0.805	0.176
4120	Salad dressing, French, regular w/salt	1 tbsp	16	73.12	0.123	2.493	0	7.17	1.349	3.365	0.904
4636	Salad dressing, Italian dressing, fat-free	1 tbsp	14.6	6.862	0.142	1.278	0.088	0.127	0.034	0.028	0.043
4114	Salad dressing, Italian, regular w/salt	1 tbsp	14.7	42.777	0.056	1.533	0	4.17	0.928	1.902	0.658
4641	Salad dressing, mayonnaise, light	1 tbsp	14.6	47.304	0.128	1.197	0	4.831	1.178	2.621	0.761
4026	Salad dressing, mayonnaise, regular, safflower/soybean oil, w/salt	1 tbsp	13.8	98.946	0.152	0.373	0	10.957	1.794	7.59	1.187
4012	Salad dressing, Miracle Whip Light Dressing / Kraft	1 tbsp	16	36.96	0.096	2.304	0.016	2.976			0.464
4638	Salad dressing, ranch dressing, fat-free	1 tbsp	14.6	17.374	0.036	3.87	0.015	0.28	0.065	0.117	0.075
4640	Salad dressing, ranch dressing, reduced fat	1 tbsp	14.6	32.85	0.15	2.365	0.131	2.526	0.792	0.633	0.194
4015	Salad dressing, Russian w/salt	1 tbsp	15	74.1	0.24	1.56	0	7.62	1.77	4.41	1.095
4016	Salad dressing, sesame seed	1 tbsp	15	66.45	0.465	1.29	0.15	6.78	1.785	3.765	0.93
4135	Salad dressing, vinegar & oil, homemade	1 tbsp	16	71.84	0	0.4	0	8.016	2.368	3.856	1.456
22534	Sandwich, Hot Pockets, beef & cheddar stuffed, frozen	1 serving	142	403.28	16.33	39.192		20.164	6.658	1.221	8.804
22535	Sandwich, Hot Pockets, Croissant Pocket w/chicken, broccoli, & cheddar, frozen	1 serving	128	300.8	11.392	38.912	1.408	11.008	4.378	1.664	3.354
22538	Sandwich, Lean Pockets, glazed chicken supreme stuffed, frozen	1 serving	128	232.96	9.856	34.176		6.272	2.483	0.952	1.92
22364	Sandwich, Sausage Biscuits, breakfast sandwich, frozen/Jimmy Dean	1	48	192.48	4.752	11.568	0.72	14.112			4.306
6140	Sauce, Bulls Eye Original Barbecue/Ridgs	2 tbsp	36	63	0.432	15.156		0.072			
6930	Sauce, cheese, ready-to-eat	.25 cup	63	109.62	4.227	4.303	0.315	8.373	2.408	1.637	3.786
6139	Sauce, Chunky Chili Dip, Salsa, canned/LaVictoria	2 tbsp	30	9.3	0.237	1.962	0.15	0.048			
6901	Sauce, Deluxe Marinara Sauce/Contadina	1 cup	250	145	3.05	17.375	3	7.05	3.428	2.06	1.1
6275	Sauce, Enchilada Sauce/LaVictoria	.25 cup	60	19.8	0.192	2.772	0.42	0.87			
6179	Sauce, fish, ready-to-eat	1 tbsp	18	6.3	0.911	0.655	0	0.002	0	0.001	0.001
6269	Sauce, Green Chile Salsa, mild/LaVictoria	2 tbsp	30	7.5	0.39	1.29	0.12	0.075			
6273	Sauce, Green Salsa Jalapena/LaVictoria	2 tbsp	30	9.6	0.276	1.41	0.27	0.327			
6260	Sauce, Green Taco Sauce, medium/LaVictoria	1 tbsp	15	4.5	0.119	0.873	0.09	0.054			

Chol (g)	Calc (mg)	Iron (mg)	Mag (mg)	Phos (mg)	Pota (mg)	Sodi (mg)	Zinc (mg)	Vit A (RAE)	Vit C (mg)	Thia (mg)	Ribo (mg)	Niac (mg)	Vit B$_6$ (mg)	Vit B$_{12}$ (µg)	Vit E (mg)	Fol (µg)	Alc (g)
1.42	119.28	0.327	11.36	112.18	136.32	225.78	0.383	0	0.568	0.031	0.139	0.443	0.027	0.298	0.426	4.26	0
7.91	99.44	0.147	9.04	76.84	127.69	152.55	0.282	6.78	0	0.025	0.157	0.285	0.012	0.113	0	0	0
159.96	27.9	8.24	40.92	518.94	401.76	96.72	5.766	130.2	4.278	0.409	0.558	14.731	1.153	0.67	1.302	11.16	0
0	19.6	0.196	9.8	34.3	68.6	85.75	0.245	0	1.225	0.076	0.012	1.909	0.044	0	1.764	90.65	0
17.5	20.65	1.232	8.75	35.35	36.4	190.75	0.392	1.75	0	0.184	0.181	1.15	0.019	0.084	0.126	64.4	0
12.25	21	1.036	6.65	44.1	53.2	145.25	0.245	30.45	0.07	0.138	0.143	1.207	0.021	0.049	0.339	31.5	0
0	49.28	0.994	10.08	29.12	32.2	95.2	0.252	0	0	0.121	0.076	1.14	0.021	0	0.101	16.8	0
0	34.58	1.03	7.6	31.92	43.32	231.42	0.342	0	0	0.199	0.114	1.654	0.015	0	0.114	42.94	0
0	59.34	1.428	9.03	26.66	40.42	205.97	0.284	0	0	0.172	0.137	1.786	0.031	0.086	0.03	47.73	0
0	38.16	0.871	30.6	80.64	97.92	172.08	0.724	0	0	0.089	0.055	1.324	0.07		0.324	10.8	0
0	54.15	1.87	15.39	57	61.56	310.08	0.536	0	0	0.272	0.192	2.416	0.02		0.239	54.15	0
4.16	2.72	0.189	1.28	4.32	17.12	138.08	0.042	1.76	0	0.231	0.009	0.067	0		0.182	0	0
0.73	1.606	0.041	0.584	0.146	17.812	106.434	0.013	0.146	0	0.034	0.007	0.038	0		0.109	1.752	0
2.55	12.15	0.03	0	11.1	5.55	164.1	0.041	10.05	0.3	0.002	0.015	0.015	0.006	0.041	0.9	4.2	0
0	0.7	0.081	0.42	0	11.76	111.86	0.014	0.56	0	0.002	0.004	0.016	0	0	0.003	1.96	0
0	1.76	0.139	1.28	2.56	17.12	4.8	0.032	4.32	0	0.004	0.008	0.075	0.009		0.458	0.32	0
0	3.84	0.128	0.8	3.04	10.72	133.76	0.046	3.68	0	0.003	0.008	0.03	0	0.022	0.8	0	0
0.292	4.38	0.058	0.73	15.914	14.892	164.834	0.053	0.584	0.058	0.005	0.008	0.02	0	0.045	0.111	1.752	0
0	1.029	0.093	0.441	1.323	7.056	243.138	0.019	0.294	0	0.002	0.003	0	0.009	0	0.735	0	0
5.11	1.168	0.047	0.292	5.11	5.84	98.258	0.026	3.066	0	0.003	0	0	0	0	0.448	0.584	0
8.142	2.484	0.069	0.138	3.864	4.692	78.384	0.017	11.59	0	0	0	0.001	0.08	0.036	3.036	1.104	0
4.16	0.8	0.027		2.08	3.68	131.36			0						0.14		0
1.022	7.3	0.153	1.168	16.498	16.206	110.23	0.058	0.146	0	0.004	0.004	0.001	0.004	0	0.026	0.876	0
3.066	18.25	0.127	0.876	28.178	19.272	136.072	0.091	2.628	0.102	0.003	0.004	0.001	0.004	0	0.234	0.584	0
2.7	2.85	0.09	0.3	5.55	23.55	130.2	0.065	2.25	0.9	0.008	0.008	0.09	0.005	0.045	0.603	1.5	0
0	2.85	0.09	0	5.55	23.55	150	0.015	0.3	0	0	0	0	0	0	0.75	0	0
0	0	0	0	0	1.28	0.16	0	0	0	0	0	0	0	0	0.738	0	0
52.54	336.54	2.925				905.96											0
37.12		3.802				651.52			6.272								0
23.04	121.6					561.92											0
15.84	37.92	0.792				440.64											0
						301.68											0
18.27	115.92	0.132	5.67	98.91	18.9	521.64	0.617	50.4	0.252	0.004	0.072	0.015	0.011	0.088	0.2	2.52	0
	4.2	0.012				147.9			3.15								0
0	47.5	1.5	30	65	517.5	937.5	0.325		17.5	0.108	0.08	1.43	0.21	0	0	22.5	0
0	7.2	0.072				394.8			2.64								0
0	7.74	0.14	31.5	1.26	51.84	1389.6	0.036	0.72	0.09	0.002	0.01	0.416	0.071	0.086	0	9.18	0
	4.5	0.273				172.2			4.02								0
0	4.8	0.12				180			3.6								0
0	1.2	0.008				95.1			0.72								0

EvaluEat Code	Food Name	Amt	Wt (g)	Energy (kcal)	Prot (g)	Carb (g)	Fiber (g)	Fat (g)	Mono (g)	Poly (g)	Sat (g)
6175	Sauce, hoisin	1 tbsp	16	35.2	0.53	7.053	0.448	0.542	0.154	0.272	0.091
6555	Sauce, hollandaise, with butterfat, dehydrated, prepared with water	1 cup (8 fl. oz.)	244	224.48	4.441	12.956	0.732	18.593	5.588	0.878	10.931
6308	Sauce, Kraft Barbecue Sauce Hickory Smoke	2 tbsp	34	39.44	0.17	8.908	0.306	0.102			0
6307	Sauce, Kraft Barbecue Sauce Original	2 tbsp	34	39.44	0.17	8.874	0.306	0.102			0
6136	Sauce, mole poblano, homemade	1 cup, sauce	242	396.88	8.567	31.315	10.164	26.499			
6278	Sauce, Nacho Cheese Sauce with Jalapeno Pepper, medium/LaVictoria	.25 cup	72	122.4	1.31	7.387	0.216	9.713	4.553	1.788	2.692
6933	Sauce, Old World Style Smooth Pasta Sauce, Traditional, jar/Ragu	.5 cup	125	80	1.875	12.112	2.625	2.625	0.546	1.29	0.362
6176	Sauce, oyster	1 tbsp	18	9.18	0.243	1.966	0.054	0.045	0.013	0.012	0.008
6931	Sauce, pasta, spaghetti/marinara	1 cup	250	142.5	3.55	20.55	4	5.15	2.175	1.805	0.737
6168	Sauce, pepper or hot	1 tsp	4.7	0.517	0.024	0.082	0.014	0.017	0.001	0.009	0.002
6151	Sauce, plum	1 tbsp	19	34.96	0.169	8.134	0.133	0.198	0.046	0.112	0.029
6274	Sauce, Red Salsa Jalapena/LaVictoria	2 tbsp	30	12	0.435	2.172	0.39	0.177			
6257	Sauce, Red Taco Sauce, mild/LaVictoria	1 tbsp	16	6.72	0.214	1.314	0.08	0.067			
6265	Sauce, Salsa Picante, mild/LaVictoria	2 tbsp	30	8.1	0.357	1.446	0.09	0.087			
6164	Sauce, salsa	1 cup	259	72.52	3.289	16.162	4.144	0.622	0.065	0.298	0.078
6132	Sauce, Sweet N' Sour, ready-to-eat/Nestle Chef-Mate	1 serving	33	40.26	0.158	8.181	0.264	0.785	0.229	0.377	0.122
6133	Sauce, Szechuan, ready-to-eat/Nestle Chef-Mate	1 tbsp	16	20.8	0.23	2.922	0.048	0.912	0.264	0.439	0.119
6112	Sauce, teriyaki	1 tbsp	18	15.12	1.067	2.871	0.018	0	0	0	0
6166	Sauce, white, medium, homemade	1 cup	250	367.5	9.6	22.925	0.5	26.575	11.05	7.155	7.135
6971	Sauce, worcestershire	.5 cup	125	83.75	0	24.325	0	0	0	0	0
7002	Sausage, beerwurst, beer salami (beef)	2 oz (1 slice)	56	154.56	7.84	2.106	0.504	12.617	5.659	1.165	4.725
7005	Sausage, blood	1 slice	25	94.5	3.65	0.322	0	8.625	3.975	0.865	3.35
7013	Sausage, bratwurst (pork) cooked	1 link cooked	85	281.35	11.662	2.074	0	24.803	12.495	2.244	8.6
7019	Sausage, chorizo (pork & beef)	1 link (4"long)	60	273	14.46	1.116	0	22.962	11.04	2.076	8.628
7023	Sausage, frankfurter (wiener) (beef & pork)	1 frankfurter (5 in long x 3/4 in dia, 10 per lb)	45	137.25	5.188	0.774	1.08	12.438	6.151	1.229	4.846
7022	Sausage, frankfurter (wiener) (beef)	1 frankfurter	45	148.5	5.058	1.827	0	13.306	6.437	0.532	5.26
7024	Sausage, frankfurter (wiener) (chicken)	1 frankfurter	45	115.65	5.819	3.055	0	8.766	3.816	1.818	2.493
7025	Sausage, frankfurter (wiener) (turkey)	1 frankfurter	45	101.7	6.426	0.67	0	7.965	2.511	2.25	2.65
7089	Sausage, Italian, (pork) cooked	1 link, 4/lb	83	268.09	16.625	1.245	0	21.331	9.918	2.731	7.528
7037	Sausage, kielbasa (kolbassy) (pork, beef & NFD Milk)	1 oz	28.35	87.885	3.759	0.607	0	7.697	3.668	0.873	2.809
7038	Sausage, knockwurst (knackwurst) (pork & beef)	1 link	72	221.04	7.992	2.304	0	19.944	9.223	2.102	7.351
7057	Sausage, pepperoni (pork & beef)	1 serving, 15 slices	29	135.14	5.901	1.172	0.435	11.681	5.523	0.764	4.667
7059	Sausage, Polish (pork)	1 sausage (10" long x 1-1/4"dia)	227	740.02	32.007	3.7	0	65.194	30.69	6.992	23.449
7919	Sausage, turkey, breakfast links, mild	1 serving	56	131.6	8.635	0.874	0	10.13	2.801	1.85	4.002
16107	Sausage, vegetarian, meatless	1 link	25	64.25	4.633	2.46	0.7	4.54	1.125	2.32	0.732
12220	Seeds, flax seed	1 tbsp	12	59.04	2.34	4.11	3.348	4.08	0.824	2.693	0.384
12016	Seeds, pumpkin/squash kernels, roasted w/o salt	1 oz	28.35	147.99	9.347	3.807	1.106	11.944	3.714	5.445	2.259
12166	Seeds, sesame, tahini made w/roasted & toasted kernels	1 tbsp	15	89.25	2.55	3.179	1.395	8.064	3.045	3.535	1.129

Chol (g)	Calc (mg)	Iron (mg)	Mag (mg)	Phos (mg)	Pota (mg)	Sodi (mg)	Zinc (mg)	Vit A (RAE)	Vit C (mg)	Thia (mg)	Ribo (mg)	Niac (mg)	Vit B$_6$ (mg)	Vit B$_{12}$ (µg)	Vit E (mg)	Fol (µg)	Alc (g)
0.48	5.12	0.162	3.84	6.08	19.04	258.4	0.051	0	0.064	0.001	0.035	0.187	0.01	0	0.045	3.68	0
48.8	117.12	0.854	7.32	119.56	117.12	1473.76	0.732	144	0.244	0.049	0.171	0.054	0.488	0.732	0.683	12.2	0
0	5.1	0.211		3.06	27.54	417.52			0.068								0
0	5.1	0.211		3.06	27.54	424.32			0.068								0
	58.08	4.477	77.44	198.44	788.92	324.28	1.113	363	0	0.053	0	3.969	0.607			67.76	0
3.6	64.08	0.864				550.8			1.152								0
		1.025				756.25											0
0	5.76	0.032	0.72	3.96	9.72	491.94	0.016	0	0.018	0.002	0.022	0.265	0.003	0.074	0	2.7	0
0	55	1.8	42.5	80	737.5	1030	0.425	92.5	20	0.135	0.1	2.655	0.285	0	5.1	27.5	0
0	0.376	0.023	0.235	0.517	6.768	124.221	0.005	0.376	3.516	0.002	0.004	0.012	0.007	0	0.006	0.282	0
0	2.28	0.272	2.28	4.18	49.21	102.22	0.036	0.38	0.095	0.003	0.016	0.193	0.015	0	0.037	1.14	0
0	6.3	0.051				146.1			9.63								0
0	3.36	0.029				104.8			2.864								0
0	4.5	0.033				178.8			1.83								0
0	77.7	2.512	33.67	67.34	551.67	1124.06	0.647	88.06	36	0.104	0.083	2.15	0.311	0	3.056	41.44	0
0	5.94	0.281	2.31	2.97	21.78	116.49	0.026		0	0.009	0.005	0.066	0.015	0	0.066	0.66	0
0	1.76	0.12	1.6	5.92	12.8	218.08	0.019		0.256	0.002	0.005	0.096	0.008	0.118	0.069	0.64	0
0	4.5	0.306	10.98	27.72	40.5	689.94	0.018	0	0	0.005	0.013	0.229	0.018	0	0	3.6	0
17.5	295	0.825	35	245	390	885	1.025	225	2	0.172	0.463	1.005	0.1	0.7	0.7	20	0
0	133.75	6.625	16.25	75	1000	1225	0.237	6.25	16.25	0.087	0.162	0.875	0	0	0.1	10	0
34.72	15.12	0.969	10.64	75.6	136.64	409.92	1.238	0	0.336	0.138	0.097	1.666	0.129	0.65	0.106	2.8	0
30	1.5	1.6	2	5.5	9.5	170	0.325	0	0	0.018	0.032	0.3	0.01	0.25	0.032	1.25	0
62.9	23.8	0.45	17.85	191.25	220.15	719.1	2.117	0	0	0.531	0.221	3.94	0.348	0.68	0.017	2.55	0
52.8	4.8	0.954	10.8	90	238.8	741	2.046	0	0	0.378	0.18	3.079	0.318	1.2	0.132	1.2	0
22.5	4.95	0.517	4.5	38.7	75.15	504	0.828	8.1	0	0.09	0.054	1.185	0.058	0.585	0.112	1.8	0
23.85	6.3	0.679	6.3	72	70.2	513	1.107	0	0	0.018	0.066	1.067	0.04	0.774	0.09	2.25	0
45.45	42.75	0.9	4.5	48.15	37.8	616.5	0.468	17.55	0	0.03	0.052	1.39	0.144	0.108	0.099	1.8	0
48.15	47.7	0.828	6.3	60.3	80.55	641.7	1.399	0	0	0.018	0.081	1.859	0.104	0.126	0.279	3.6	0
64.74	19.92	1.245	14.94	141.1	252.32	765.26	1.984	0	1.66	0.517	0.193	3.457	0.274	1.079	0.207	4.15	0
18.995	12.474	0.411	4.536	41.958	76.829	305.046	0.573	0	0	0.065	0.061	0.816	0.051	0.456	0.062	1.418	0
43.2	7.92	0.475	7.92	70.56	143.28	669.6	1.195	0	0	0.246	0.101	1.968	0.122	0.85	0.41	1.44	0
34.22	6.09	0.418	5.22	51.04	91.35	518.52	0.792	0	0.203	0.154	0.067	1.571	0.113	0.455	0.084	1.74	0
158.9	27.24	3.269	31.78	308.72	537.99	1988.52	4.381	0	2.27	1.14	0.336	7.816	0.431	2.225		4.54	0
33.6	17.92	0.599	14	103.6	110.32	327.6	1.193	0	17.02	0.04	0.097	2.058	0.213	0.241	0.186	4.48	0
0	15.75	0.93	9	56.25	57.75	222	0.365	0	0	0.586	0.101	2.799	0.207	0	0.525	6.5	0
0	23.88	0.746	43.44	59.76	81.72	4.08	0.5	0	0.156	0.02	0.019	0.168	0.111	0	0.038	33.36	0
0	12.191	4.235	151.389	332.262	228.501	5.103	2.109	5.387	0.51	0.06	0.09	0.494	0.026	0	0	16.16	0
0	63.9	1.342	14.25	109.8	62.1	17.25	0.693	0.45	0	0.183	0.071	0.817	0.022	0	0.038	14.7	0

EvaluEat Code	Food Name	Amt	Wt (g)	Energy (kcal)	Prot (g)	Carb (g)	Fiber (g)	Fat (g)	Mono (g)	Poly (g)	Sat (g)
12023	Seeds, sesame, whole, dried	1 tbsp	9	51.57	1.596	2.111	1.062	4.47	1.688	1.96	0.626
12037	Seeds, sunflower kernels, dry roast w/o salt	1 oz	28.35	165	5.48	6.824	3.147	14.118	2.695	9.323	1.48
15156	Shellfish, abalone, fried	3 oz	85	160.65	16.685	9.393	0	5.763	2.33	1.425	1.399
15159	Shellfish, clams, boiled/steamed (moist heat)	20 small	190	281.2	48.545	9.747	0	3.705	0.327	1.049	0.357
15158	Shellfish, clams, breaded & fried	3 oz	85	171.7	12.104	8.781		9.477	3.863	2.439	2.281
15160	Shellfish, clams, canned, drained	3 oz	85	125.8	21.718	4.361	0	1.658	0.146	0.469	0.16
15157	Shellfish, clams, raw	1 cup (with liquid and clams)	227	167.98	28.988	5.834	0	2.202	0.182	0.64	0.213
15137	Shellfish, crab, Alaskan king, boiled/steamed	1 leg	134	129.98	25.929	0	0	2.064	0.248	0.718	0.178
15138	Shellfish, crab, Alaskan king, imitation surimi	3 oz	85	86.7	10.217	8.687	0	1.113	0.17	0.57	0.221
15243	Shellfish, crayfish, farmed, cooked w/moist heat	3 oz	85	73.95	14.892	0	0	1.105	0.213	0.351	0.184
15229	Shellfish, cuttlefish, cooked w/moist heat	3 oz	85	134.3	27.608	1.394	0	1.19	0.138	0.228	0.201
15148	Shellfish, lobster, northern, boiled/steamed (moist heat)	3 oz	85	83.3	17.425	1.088	0	0.502	0.136	0.077	0.091
15165	Shellfish, mussel, blue, boiled/steamed	3 oz	85	146.2	20.23	6.281	0	3.808	0.862	1.03	0.723
15170	Shellfish, oyster, east, canned	1 oyster	8	5.52	0.565	0.313	0	0.198	0.02	0.059	0.05
15168	Shellfish, oyster, eastern, breaded & fried	6 medium	88	173.36	7.718	10.226		11.07	4.138	2.915	2.813
15245	Shellfish, oyster, eastern, farmed, raw	6 medium	84	49.56	4.385	4.645	0	1.302	0.128	0.496	0.372
15171	Shellfish, oyster, Pacific, raw	1 medium	50	40.5	4.725	2.475	0	1.15	0.179	0.447	0.255
15173	Shellfish, scallops, breaded, fried	2 large	31	66.65	5.602	3.14		3.391	1.394	0.885	0.827
15151	Shellfish, shrimp, boiled/steamed (moist heat)	4 large	22	21.78	4.6	0	0	0.238	0.043	0.097	0.064
15150	Shellfish, shrimp, breaded & fried	4 large	30	72.6	6.417	3.441	0.12	3.684	1.144	1.526	0.626
19097	Sherbet, orange	.5 cup (4 fl. oz.)	74	106.56	0.814	22.496	2.442	1.48	0.392	0.059	0.858
4615	Shortening, household, composite	1 tbsp	12.8	113.15	0	0	0	12.8	5.711	3.952	2.568
4031	Shortening, vegetable fat, soy hydrogenated & cottonseed hydrogenated	1 tbsp	12.8	113.15	0	0	0	12.8	5.696	3.341	3.2
19400	Snack, banana chips	1 oz	28.35	147.14	0.652	16.556	2.183	9.526	0.553	0.179	8.213
19002	Snack, beef jerky	1 piece, large	20	82	6.64	2.2	0.36	5.12	2.261	0.202	2.17
18501	Snack, cereal bar, mixed berry/Kellogg	1 oz	28.34	104.86	1.219	20.632	0.538	2.154	1.417	0.312	0.425
19033	Snack, Chex Snack Mix	1 oz (approx 2/3 cup)	28.35	120.49	3.119	18.456	1.588	4.905			1.568
19004	Snack, corn chips, BBQ flavor	1 oz	28.35	148.27	1.985	15.933	1.474	9.27	2.688	4.584	1.264
19003	Snack, corn chips, plain	1 oz	28.35	152.81	1.871	16.131	1.389	9.469	2.739	4.672	1.29
19401	Snack, Corn Nuts, BBQ flavor	1 oz	28.35	123.61	2.552	20.327	2.381	4.054	2.087	0.913	0.731
19009	Snack, Corn Nuts, plain	1 oz	28.35	126.44	2.41	20.372	1.956	4.434	2.682	0.865	0.689
19008	Snack, corn puffs or twists, cheese flavor	1 oz	28.35	157.06	2.155	15.252	0.312	9.752	5.749	1.349	1.868
19420	Snack, granola bar, hard, peanut butter	1 bar	24	115.92	2.352	14.952	0.696	5.712	1.68	2.899	0.768
19015	Snack, granola bar, hard, plain	1 bar (1 oz)	28	131.88	2.828	18.032	1.484	5.544	1.226	3.374	0.664
19017	Snack, granola bar, hard, w/chocolate chips	1 bar	24	105.12	1.752	17.304	1.056	3.912	0.631	0.305	2.738
19024	Snack, granola bar, soft, chocolate chip, milk chocolate cover	1 bar (1.25 oz)	35	163.1	2.03	22.33	1.19	8.715	2.72	0.637	4.977
19406	Snack, granola bar, soft, nut & raisin	1 bar (1 oz)	28	127.12	2.24	17.808	1.568	5.712	1.182	1.546	2.671
19020	Snack, granola bar, soft, plain	1 bar (1 oz)	28	124.04	2.072	18.844	1.288	4.816	1.067	1.49	2.027
19407	Snack, meat-based sticks, smoked	1 stick	20	110	4.3	1.08		9.92	4.094	0.884	4.16
19031	Snack, Oriental mix, rice-based	1 oz	28.35	143.45	4.907	14.634	3.742	7.252	2.795	3.017	1.073

Chol (g)	Calc (mg)	Iron (mg)	Mag (mg)	Phos (mg)	Pota (mg)	Sodi (mg)	Zinc (mg)	Vit A (RAE)	Vit C (mg)	Thia (mg)	Ribo (mg)	Niac (mg)	Vit B6 (mg)	Vit B12 (µg)	Vit E (mg)	Fol (µg)	Alc (g)
0	87.75	1.31	31.59	56.61	42.12	0.99	0.698	0	0	0.071	0.022	0.406	0.071	0	0.023	8.73	0
0	19.845	1.077	36.572	327.443	240.975	0.851	1.5	0.284	0.397	0.03	0.07	1.996	0.228	0	6.03	67.19	0
79.9	31.45	3.23	47.6	184.45	241.4	502.35	0.808	1.7	1.53	0.187	0.111	1.615	0.128	0.586		11.9	0
127.3	174.8	53.124	34.2	642.2	1193.2	212.8	5.187	324.9	41.99	0.285	0.809	6.373	0.209	187.891		55.1	0
51.85	53.55	11.824	11.9	159.8	277.1	309.4	1.241	77.35	8.5	0.085	0.207	1.754	0.051	34.229		30.6	0
56.95	78.2	23.766	15.3	287.3	533.8	95.2	2.321	153.9	18.79	0.128	0.362	2.851	0.094	84.057	0.527	24.65	0
77.18	104.42	31.735	20.43	383.63	712.78	127.12	3.11	204.3	29.51	0.182	0.484	4.007	0.136	112.229	0.704	36.32	0
71.02	79.06	1.018	84.42	375.2	351.08	1436.48	10.21	12.06	10.18	0.071	0.074	1.796	0.241	15.41		68.34	0
17	11.05	0.331	36.55	239.7	76.5	714.85	0.281	17	0	0.027	0.023	0.153	0.025	1.36	0.085	1.7	0
116.45	43.35	0.944	28.05	204.85	202.3	82.45	1.258	12.75	0.425	0.04	0.068	1.417	0.114	2.635		9.35	0
190.4	153	9.214	51	493	541.45	632.4	2.941	172.6	7.225	0.014	1.47	1.861	0.23	4.59		20.4	0
61.2	51.85	0.331	29.75	157.25	299.2	323	2.482	22.1	0	0.006	0.056	0.91	0.065	2.644	0.85	9.35	0
47.6	28.05	5.712	31.45	242.25	227.8	313.65	2.27	77.35	11.56	0.255	0.357	2.55	0.085	20.4		64.6	0
4.4	3.6	0.536	4.32	11.12	18.32	8.96	7.276	7.2	0.4	0.012	0.013	0.1	0.008	1.53	0.068	0.72	0
71.28	54.56	6.116	51.04	139.92	214.72	366.96	76.67	80.08	3.344	0.132	0.178	1.452	0.056	13.754		27.28	0
21	36.96	4.855	27.72	78.12	104.16	149.52	31.85	6.72	3.948	0.088	0.055	1.064	0.05	13.608		15.12	0
25	4	2.555	11	81	84	53	8.31	40.5	4	0.034	0.116	1.005	0.025	8	0.425	5	0
18.91	13.02	0.254	18.29	73.16	103.23	143.84	0.329	7.13	0.713	0.013	0.034	0.467	0.043	0.409		11.47	0
42.9	8.58	0.68	7.48	30.14	40.04	49.28	0.343	14.96	0.484	0.007	0.007	0.57	0.028	0.328	0.304	0.88	0
53.1	20.1	0.378	12	65.4	67.5	103.2	0.414	17.1	0.45	0.039	0.041	0.921	0.029	0.561		5.4	0
0	39.96	0.104	5.92	29.6	71.04	34.04	0.355	7.4	4.292	0.023	0.066	0.056	0.02	0.089	0.022	5.18	0
0	0	0	0	0	0	0	0	0	0	0	0	0	0	0	0.102	0	0
0	0	0	0	0	0	0	0	0	0	0	0	0	0	0	0.102	0	0
0	5.103	0.354	21.546	15.876	151.956	1.701	0.213	1.134	1.786	0.024	0.005	0.201	0.074	0	0.068	3.969	0
9.6	4	1.084	10.2	81.4	119.4	442.6	1.622	0	0	0.031	0.028	0.346	0.036	0.198	0.098	26.8	0
0	11.053	1.389	7.368	27.773	53.279	84.17	1.162		0	0.283	0.312	3.826	0.397	0	0	30.61	0
0	9.923	7.002	17.861	53.015	76.262	288.32	0.593	1.985	13.47	0.441	0.141	4.774	0.441	3.515		14.18	0
0	37.139	0.437	21.83	58.685	66.906	216.311	0.301	8.789	0.482	0.021	0.06	0.466	0.065	0		11.06	0
0	36.005	0.374	21.546	52.448	40.257	178.605	0.357	1.418	0	0.008	0.041	0.335	0.069	0	0.386	5.67	0
0	4.82	0.482	30.902	80.231	81.081	276.696	0.533	4.82	0.113	0.099	0.04	0.427	0.053			0	0
0	2.552	0.473	32.036	77.963	78.813	155.642	0.505	0	0	0.012	0.037	0.48	0.065		0.561	0	0
1.134	16.443	0.666	5.103	30.618	47.061	297.675	0.108	1.701	0.057	0.075	0.1	0.916	0.038	0.04	1.205	34.02	0
0	9.84	0.576	13.2	33.36	69.84	67.92	0.3	0.24	0.048	0.05	0.022	0.473	0.023	0		4.32	0
0	17.08	0.826	27.16	77.56	94.08	82.32	0.568	2.24	0.252	0.074	0.033	0.443	0.024	0		6.44	0
0	18.48	0.732	17.28	48.96	60.24	82.56	0.463	0.48	0.024	0.043	0.024	0.133	0.014	0.002		3.12	0
1.75	36.05	0.815	23.1	69.65	109.55	70	0.455	2.45	0	0.032	0.087	0.252	0.035	0.199		9.1	0
0.28	23.52	0.61	25.48	67.48	109.76	71.12	0.448	0.56	0	0.053	0.053	0.731	0.034	0.067		8.4	0
0.28	29.4	0.717	20.72	64.4	91	77.84	0.42	0	0	0.083	0.046	0.144	0.028	0.109		6.72	0
26.6	13.6	0.68	4.2	36	51.4	296	0.484	2.6	1.36	0.028	0.087	0.908	0.041	0.2		0	0
0	15.309	0.692	33.453	74.277	92.988	117.086	0.754	0	0.085	0.088	0.04	0.873	0.02	0	1.588	10.77	0

EvaluEat Code	Food Name	Amt	Wt (g)	Energy (kcal)	Prot (g)	Carb (g)	Fiber (g)	Fat (g)	Mono (g)	Poly (g)	Sat (g)
19036	Snack, popcorn cakes	1 cake	10	38.4	0.97	8.01	0.29	0.31	0.092	0.135	0.048
19034	Snack, popcorn, air-popped	1 cup	8	30.56	0.96	6.232	1.208	0.336	0.088	0.152	0.046
19039	Snack, popcorn, caramel coated, no peanuts	1 oz	28.35	122.19	1.077	22.425	1.474	3.629	0.816	1.27	1.023
19040	Snack, popcorn, cheese flavor	1 cup	11	57.86	1.023	5.676	1.089	3.652	1.067	1.691	0.705
19035	Snack, popcorn, oil-popped, yellow corn	1 cup	11	55	0.99	6.292	1.1	3.091	0.899	1.476	0.538
19041	Snack, pork skins, plain	1 oz	28.35	154.51	17.379	0	0	8.874	4.19	1.032	3.223
19042	Snack, potato chips, BBQ flavor	1 oz	28.35	139.2	2.183	14.969	1.247	9.185	1.854	4.641	2.282
19422	Snack, potato chips, light	1 oz	28.35	133.53	2.013	18.966	1.673	5.897	1.361	3.101	1.179
19811	Snack, potato chips, plain, no salt	1 oz	28.35	151.96	1.985	14.997	1.361	9.809	2.79	3.45	3.107
19411	Snack, potato chips, plain, salted	1 oz	28.35	151.96	1.985	14.997	1.276	9.809	2.79	3.45	3.107
19043	Snack, potato chips, sour cream & onion	1 oz	28.35	150.54	2.296	14.6	1.474	9.611	1.735	4.939	2.52
19814	Snack, pretzel, hard, plain, no salt	10 twists	60	228.6	5.46	47.52	1.68	2.1	0.816	0.732	0.45
19047	Snack, pretzel, hard, plain, salted	10 twists	60	228.6	5.46	47.52	1.92	2.1	0.816	0.732	0.45
19053	Snack, rice cake, brown rice & sesame seed	2 cakes	18	70.56	1.368	14.67	0.972	0.684	0.198	0.207	0.097
19051	Snack, rice cake, brown rice, plain	2 cakes	18	69.66	1.476	14.67	0.756	0.504	0.185	0.178	0.103
19524	Snack, taco chips	1 oz	28.35	141.18	0.652	19.306	2.041	7.059	1.256	3.651	1.823
19057	Snack, tortilla chips, nacho flavor	1 oz	28.35	141.18	2.211	17.69	1.503	7.258	4.278	1.004	1.389
19056	Snack, tortilla chips, plain	1 oz	28.35	142.03	1.985	17.832	1.843	7.428	4.38	1.029	1.423
19058	Snack, tortilla chips, ranch flavor	1 oz	28.35	138.92	2.155	18.314	1.106	6.747	3.983	0.936	1.293
19059	Snack, trail mix, regular	1 cup	150	693	20.7	67.35		44.1	18.795	14.475	8.325
19062	Snack, trail mix, regular, chocolate chip, salted nuts & seeds	1 cup	146	706.64	20.732	65.554		46.574	19.768	16.483	8.906
19269	Snacks, Fruit Roll Ups, berry flavored w/vit C/ General Mills-Betty Crocker	2 rolls	28	104.44	0.028	23.856		0.98	0.483	0.026	0.277
19423	Snacks, potato chips, fat-free, made with olestra	1 oz	28.35	75.128	1.88	16.783	1.106	0.198	0.071	0.081	0.045
19438	Snacks, Rice Krispies Treat Squares/Kellogg	1 oz	28.34	117.33	0.964	22.814	0.17	2.551	0.709	1.445	0.397
6190	Soup, bean & ham, canned, reduced sodium, prepared with water or ready-to-serve	1 cup	128	94.72	5.363	17.485	5.12	1.318	0.531	0.344	0.323
6474	Soup, bean w/bacon, dry, made w/H$_2$O	1 cup	265	106	5.485	16.377	9.01	2.147	0.928	0.159	0.954
6978	Soup, beef and mushroom, low sodium, chunk style	.5 cup	125	86.25	5.375	11.975	0.25	2.875	0.493	0.085	2.026
6199	Soup, beef barley, canned/Progresso Healthy Classics	1 cup	241	142.19	11.327	20.003	3.133	1.928	0.689	0.251	0.747
6008	Soup, beef broth or bouillon, canned	1 cup	240	16.8	2.736	0.096	0	0.528	0.216	0.024	0.264
6547	Soup, beef mushroom, canned, made w/H$_2$O	1 cup	244	73.2	5.783	6.344	0.244	3.001	1.244	0.122	1.488
6070	Soup, beef, chunky, canned	1 cup	240	170.4	11.736	19.56	1.44	5.136	2.136	0.216	2.544
6478	Soup, cauliflower, dry, made w/H$_2$O	1 cup	256	69.12	2.893	10.726		1.715	0.742	0.64	0.256
6411	Soup, cheese, canned, made w/H$_2$O	1 cup	247	155.61	5.409	10.522	0.988	10.473	2.964	0.296	6.669
6413	Soup, chicken broth, canned, made w/H$_2$O	1 cup	240	38.4	4.848	0.912	0	1.368	0.576	0.264	0.384
6417	Soup, chicken gumbo, canned, made w/H$_2$O	1 cup	244	56.12	2.635	8.369	1.952	1.44	0.659	0.342	0.317
6549	Soup, chicken mushroom, canned, made w/H$_2$O	1 cup	244	131.76	4.392	9.272	0.244	9.15	4.026	2.318	2.391
6018	Soup, chicken noodle, chunky, canned	1 cup	240	175.2	12.72	17.04	3.84	6	2.664	1.512	1.392
6022	Soup, chicken rice, chunky, ready-to-eat, canned	1 cup	240	127.2	12.264	12.984	0.96	3.192	1.44	0.672	0.96
6024	Soup, chicken vegetable, chunky, canned	1 cup	240	165.6	12.312	18.888		4.824	2.16	1.008	1.44
6015	Soup, chicken, chunky, canned	1 cup	240	170.4	12.144	16.512	1.44	6.336	2.832	1.32	1.896
6203	Soup, cream of broccoli, canned, ready-to-eat/Progresso Healthy Classics	1 cup	244	87.84	2.367	13.322	2.44	2.806	0.92	0.573	0.659
6410	Soup, cream of celery, canned, made w/H$_2$O	1 cup	244	90.28	1.659	8.833	0.732	5.588	1.293	2.513	1.415

Chol (g)	Calc (mg)	Iron (mg)	Mag (mg)	Phos (mg)	Pota (mg)	Sodi (mg)	Zinc (mg)	Vit A (RAE)	Vit C (mg)	Thia (mg)	Ribo (mg)	Niac (mg)	Vit B$_6$ (mg)	Vit B$_{12}$ (µg)	Vit E (mg)	Fol (µg)	Alc (g)
0	0.9	0.187	15.9	27.7	32.7	28.8	0.399	0.4	0	0.008	0.018	0.601	0.018	0	0.029	1.8	0
0	0.8	0.213	10.48	24	24.08	0.32	0.275	0.8	0	0.016	0.023	0.156	0.02	0	0.023	1.84	0
1.418	12.191	0.493	9.923	23.531	30.902	58.401	0.164	0.567	0	0.018	0.02	0.624	0.008	0.003	0.34	1.418	0
1.21	12.43	0.246	10.01	39.71	28.71	97.79	0.221	4.18	0.055	0.014	0.027	0.16	0.026	0.058	0.013	1.21	0
0	1.1	0.306	11.88	27.5	24.75	97.24	0.29	0.88	0.033	0.015	0.015	0.17	0.023	0	0.551	1.87	0
26.933	8.505	0.249	3.119	24.098	36.005	521.073	0.159	3.402	0.142	0.028	0.08	0.439	0.007	0.181	0.15	0	0
0	14.175	0.55	21.263	52.731	357.494	212.625	0.266	3.119	9.611	0.061	0.061	1.33	0.176	0	1.418	23.53	0
0	5.954	0.383	25.232	54.716	494.424	139.482	0.02	0	7.286	0.059	0.076	1.985	0.19	0	1.551	7.655	0
0	6.804	0.462	18.995	46.778	361.463	2.268	0.309	0	8.817	0.047	0.056	1.085	0.187	0	2.583	12.76	0
0	6.804	0.462	18.995	46.778	361.463	168.399	0.309	0	8.817	0.047	0.056	1.085	0.187	0	2.583	12.76	0
1.985	20.412	0.454	20.979	49.896	377.339	177.188	0.278	3.969	10.58	0.054	0.057	1.142	0.189	0.284		17.58	0
0	21.6	2.592	21	67.8	87.6	173.4	0.51	0	0	0.277	0.374	3.151	0.07	0	0.21	102.6	0
0	21.6	2.592	21	67.8	87.6	1029	0.51	0	0	0.277	0.374	3.151	0.07	0	0.21	102.6	0
0	2.16	0.284	24.48	67.5	52.2	40.86	0.54	0	0.54	0.009	0.015	1.297	0.028	0		3.24	0
0	1.98	0.268	23.58	64.8	52.2	58.68	0.54	0	0	0.011	0.03	1.405	0.027	0	0.223	3.78	0
0	17.01	0.34	23.814	37.139	214.043	96.957	0.108	1.985	1.418	0.049	0.008	0.146	0.124	0	3.215	5.67	0
0.851	41.675	0.405	23.247	69.174	61.236	200.718	0.34	6.804	0.51	0.036	0.054	0.406	0.081	0.014		3.969	0
0	43.659	0.431	24.948	58.118	55.85	149.688	0.434	1.134	0	0.021	0.052	0.363	0.081	0	1.001	2.835	0
0.284	39.974	0.414	25.232	67.757	69.174	173.502	0.352	4.253	0.255	0.03	0.067	0.412	0.057	0		4.82	0
0	117	4.575	237	517.5	1027.5	343.5	4.83	1.5	2.1	0.693	0.297	7.068	0.447	0		106.5	0
5.84	159.14	4.949	235.06	565.02	946.08	176.66	4.584	2.92	1.898	0.603	0.327	6.431	0.378	0		94.9	0
						88.76			33.6								0
0	9.639	0.422	23.247	46.778	365.715	184.842	0.272	0	8.363	0.098	0.02	1.304	0.519	0	0	8.505	0
0	0.85	0.36	3.684	11.903	11.053	99.473	0.142	91.82	0	0.359	0.387	4.615	0.255	0	0	30.89	0
2.56	48.64	1.306	24.32	16.64	202.24	239.36	0.678	44.8	1.408	0.072	0.037	0.415	0.059	0.038	0.499	37.12	0
2.65	55.65	1.325	29.15	90.1	325.95	927.5	0.689	2.65	1.06	0.053	0.265	0.398	0.026	0.026	0.557	7.95	0
7.5	16.25	1.213	2.5	62.5	175	31.25	1.375	122.5	3.75	0.05	0.138	1.413	0.075	0.325	0.275	6.25	0
19.28	28.92	1.856	31.33	118.09	366.32	469.95	1.542		3.615	0.128	0.125	2.919	0.186	0.362	0.268	24.1	0
0	14.4	0.408	4.8	31.2	129.6	782.4	0	0	0	0.005	0.05	1.872	0.024	0.168	0	4.8	0
7.32	4.88	0.878	9.76	34.16	153.72	941.84	1.464	0	4.636	0.039	0.056	0.954	0.049	0.195		9.76	0
14.4	31.2	2.328	4.8	120	336	866.4	2.64	129.6	6.96	0.058	0.151	2.705	0.132	0.624	0.672	14.4	0
0	10.24	0.512	2.56	51.2	104.96	842.24	0.256	0	2.56	0.077	0.077	0.512	0.026	0.179		2.56	0
29.64	140.79	0.741	4.94	135.85	153.14	958.36	0.642	296.4	0	0.017	0.136	0.398	0.025	0		4.94	0
0	9.6	0.504	2.4	72	206.4	763.2	0.24	0	0	0.01	0.07	3.293	0.024	0.24	0.048	4.8	0
4.88	24.4	0.903	4.88	24.4	75.64	954.04	0.366	7.32	4.88	0.024	0.049	0.664	0.063	0.024	0.366	4.88	0
9.76	29.28	0.878	9.76	26.84	153.72	941.84	0.976	56.12	0	0.024	0.112	1.63	0.049	0.049		0	0
19.2	24	1.44	9.6	72	108	849.6	0.96	67.2	0	0.072	0.168	4.32	0.048	0.312	0.336	38.4	0
12	33.6	1.872	9.6	72	108	888	0.96	292.8	3.84	0.024	0.098	4.104	0.048	0.312	0.576	4.8	0
16.8	26.4	1.464	9.6	105.6	367.2	1068	2.16	300	5.52	0.041	0.166	3.29	0.096	0.24		12	0
28.8	24	1.656	7.2	108	168	849.6	0.96	64.8	1.2	0.082	0.166	4.224	0.048	0.24	0.312	4.8	0
4.88	41.48	1.22	14.64	39.04	161.04	578.28	0.268		5.856	0.029	0.059	0.317	0.073	0	0.383	29.28	0
14.64	39.04	0.634	7.32	36.6	122	949.16	0.146	56.12	0.244	0.029	0.049	0.332	0.012	0.244	0.903	2.44	0

EvaluEat Code	Food Name	Amt	Wt (g)	Energy (kcal)	Prot (g)	Carb (g)	Fiber (g)	Fat (g)	Mono (g)	Poly (g)	Sat (g)
6443	Soup, cream of mushroom, canned, made w/H$_2$O	1 cup	244	129.32	2.318	9.296	0.488	8.979	1.708	4.221	2.44
6453	Soup, cream of potato, canned, made w/H$_2$O	1 cup	244	73.2	1.757	11.468	0.488	2.367	0.561	0.415	1.22
6582	Soup, Cup Noodles, ramen, chicken flavor, dry/Nissin	1 container, individual	64	296.32	5.568	36.8		14.08			6.253
6036	Soup, gazpacho, canned	1 cup	244	46.36	7.076	4.392	0.488	0.244	0.024	0.073	0.024
6449	Soup, green pea, canned, made w/H$_2$O	1 cup	250	165	8.6	26.5	2.75	2.925	1	0.375	1.4
6490	Soup, leek, dry, made w/H$_2$O	1 cup	254	71.12	2.108	11.43	3.048	2.057	0.864	0.076	1.016
6428	Soup, Manhattan clam chowder, canned, made w/H$_2$O	1 cup	244	78.08	2.196	12.224	1.464	2.22	0.383	1.291	0.383
6440	Soup, minestrone, canned, made w/H$_2$O	1 cup	241	81.94	4.266	11.231	0.964	2.506	0.699	1.109	0.554
6445	Soup, onion, canned, made w/H$_2$O	1 cup	241	57.84	3.76	8.17	0.964	1.735	0.747	0.651	0.265
6583	Soup, ramen noodle, any flavor, dehydrated, dry	1 container, individual	64	289.92	5.952	41.92	1.536	10.944	4.096	1.667	4.883
6180	Soup, shark fin, restaurant-prep	1 cup	216	99.36	6.912	8.208	0	4.32	1.259	0.737	1.082
6451	Soup, split pea w/ham, canned, made w/H$_2$O	1 cup	253	189.75	10.322	27.957	2.277	4.402	1.796	0.632	1.771
6174	Soup, stock, fish, homemade	1 cup	233	39.61	5.266	0	0	1.887	0.55	0.322	0.473
6499	Soup, tomato vegetable, dry, made w/H$_2$O	1 cup	241	53.02	1.904	9.736	0.482	0.819	0.289	0.072	0.362
6559	Soup, tomato, canned, made w/H$_2$O	1 cup	244	85.4	2.05	16.592	0.488	1.928	0.439	0.952	0.366
6466	Soup, turkey vegetable, canned, made w/H$_2$O	1 cup	241	72.3	3.085	8.628	0.482	3.037	1.326	0.675	0.892
6471	Soup, vegetable beef, canned, made w/H$_2$O	1 cup	244	78.08	5.588	10.175	0.488	1.903	0.805	0.122	0.854
6974	Soup, vegetable chicken, low sodium	.5 cup	125	86.25	6.375	10.95	0.5	2.5	1.119	0.523	0.746
6468	Soup, vegetarian vegetable, canned, made w/H$_2$O	1 cup	241	72.3	2.097	11.978	0.482	1.928	0.819	0.723	0.289
1180	Sour cream, fat-free	1 oz	28.34	20.972	0.879	4.421	0	0	0	0	0
1179	Sour cream, light	1 oz	28.34	38.542	0.992	2.012	0	3.004	0.879	0.113	1.87
43133	Soyburger	1 cup	186	332.94	33.313	24.924	8.556	11.104	2.055	4.382	1.337
2001	Spice, allspice, ground	1 tsp	1.9	4.997	0.116	1.37	0.41	0.165	0.013	0.045	0.048
2002	Spice, anise seed	1 tsp	2.1	7.077	0.37	1.05	0.307	0.334	0.205	0.066	0.012
2007	Spice, celery seed	1 tsp	2	7.84	0.361	0.827	0.236	0.505	0.319	0.074	0.044
2009	Spice, chili powder	1 tsp	2.6	8.164	0.319	1.421	0.889	0.436	0.093	0.194	0.077
2010	Spice, cinnamon, ground	1 tsp	2.3	6.003	0.089	1.837	1.249	0.073	0.011	0.012	0.015
2011	Spice, cloves, ground	1 tsp	2.1	6.783	0.126	1.285	0.718	0.421	0.031	0.149	0.114
2013	Spice, coriander seed	1 tsp	1.8	5.364	0.223	0.99	0.754	0.32	0.244	0.031	0.018
2014	Spice, cumin seed	1 tsp	2.1	7.875	0.374	0.929	0.22	0.468	0.295	0.069	0.032
2015	Spice, curry powder	1 tsp	2	6.5	0.253	1.163	0.664	0.276	0.111	0.051	0.045
2016	Spice, dill seed	1 tsp	2.1	6.405	0.336	1.159	0.443	0.305	0.198	0.021	0.015
2018	Spice, fennel seed	1 tsp	2	6.9	0.316	1.046	0.796	0.297	0.198	0.034	0.01
2020	Spice, garlic powder	1 tsp	2.8	9.296	0.47	2.036	0.277	0.021	0	0.011	0.004
2021	Spice, ginger, ground	1 tsp	1.8	6.246	0.164	1.274	0.225	0.107	0.018	0.024	0.035
2024	Spice, mustard seed, yellow	1 tsp	3.3	15.477	0.823	1.153	0.485	0.949	0.654	0.178	0.048
2025	Spice, nutmeg, ground	1 tsp	2.2	11.55	0.128	1.084	0.458	0.799	0.071	0.008	0.571
2026	Spice, onion powder	1 tsp	2.4	8.328	0.243	1.936	0.137	0.025	0.004	0.011	0.004
2028	Spice, paprika	1 tsp	2.1	6.069	0.31	1.171	0.785	0.272	0.026	0.175	0.044
2030	Spice, pepper, black	1 tsp	2.1	5.355	0.23	1.361	0.557	0.068	0.021	0.024	0.021

Chol (g)	Calc (mg)	Iron (mg)	Mag (mg)	Phos (mg)	Pota (mg)	Sodi (mg)	Zinc (mg)	Vit A (RAE)	Vit C (mg)	Thia (mg)	Ribo (mg)	Niac (mg)	Vit B$_6$ (mg)	Vit B$_{12}$ (µg)	Vit E (mg)	Fol (µg)	Alc (g)
2.44	46.36	0.512	4.88	48.8	100.04	880.84	0.586	14.64	0.976	0.046	0.09	0.725	0.015	0.049	0.952	4.88	0
4.88	19.52	0.488	2.44	46.36	136.64	1000.4	0.634	70.76	0	0.034	0.037	0.539	0.037	0.049	0.024	2.44	0
		2.182				1433.6											0
0	24.4	0.976	7.32	36.6	224.48	739.32	0.244	14.64	7.076	0.049	0.024	0.927	0.146	0	0.439	19.52	0
0	27.5	1.95	40	125	190	917.5	1.7	10	1.75	0.108	0.068	1.24	0.052	0	0.375	2.5	0
2.54	30.48	0.508	10.16	30.48	88.9	965.2	0.229	2.54	2.54	0.051	0.025	0.254	0.025	0.025	0.178	7.62	0
2.44	26.84	1.635	12.2	41.48	187.88	578.28	0.976	56.12	3.904	0.029	0.039	0.817	0.1	4.05	0.342	9.76	0
2.41	33.74	0.916	7.23	55.43	313.3	910.98	0.747	118.1	1.205	0.053	0.043	0.942	0.099	0	0.072	36.15	0
0	26.51	0.675	2.41	12.05	67.48	1053.17	0.603	0	1.205	0.034	0.024	0.6	0.048	0	0.193	14.46	0
0	10.24	2.733	15.36	69.12	76.8	742.4	0.403	0.64	0	0.422	0.282	3.456	0.039	0.006	1.299	94.08	0
4.32	21.6	2.03	15.12	45.36	114.48	1082.16	1.771	0	0.216	0.058	0.084	1.065	0.056	0.41	6.86	19.44	0
7.59	22.77	2.277	48.07	212.52	399.74	1006.94	1.316	22.77	1.518	0.147	0.076	1.475	0.068	0.253		2.53	0
2.33	6.99	0.023	16.31	130.48	335.52	363.48	0.14	4.66	0.233	0.077	0.177	2.763	0.086	1.608	0.396	4.66	0
0	7.23	0.603	19.28	28.92	98.81	1091.73	0.169	9.64	5.784	0.055	0.043	0.752	0.048	0	0.337	9.64	0
0	12.2	1.757	7.32	34.16	263.52	695.4	0.244	29.28	66.37	0.088	0.051	1.418	0.112	0	2.318	14.64	0
2.41	16.87	0.771	4.82	40.97	175.93	906.16	0.603	122.9	0	0.029	0.039	1.005	0.048	0.169	0.142	4.82	0
4.88	17.08	1.122	4.88	41.48	173.24	790.56	1.537	95.16	2.44	0.037	0.049	1.032	0.076	0.317	0.366	9.76	0
8.75	13.75	0.763	5	55	191.25	43.75	1.125	172.5	2.875	0.025	0.087	1.712	0.05	0.125	0.375	22.5	0
0	21.69	1.084	7.23	33.74	209.67	821.81	0.458	115.7	1.446	0.053	0.046	0.916	0.055	0	0.41	9.64	0
2.551	35.425	0	2.834	26.923	36.559	39.959	0.142	20.69	0	0.011	0.043	0.02	0.006	0.085	0	3.117	0
9.919	39.959	0.02	2.834	20.121	60.081	20.121	0.142	25.51	0.255	0.011	0.034	0.02	0.006	0.119	0.085	3.117	0
0	53.94	3.906	33.48	639.84	334.8	1023	3.348	0	0	1.674	1.116	18.6	2.232	4.464	3.218	145.1	0
0	12.559	0.134	2.565	2.147	19.836	1.463	0.019	0.513	0.745	0.002	0.001	0.054	0.004	0	0.02	0.684	0
0	13.566	0.776	3.57	9.24	30.261	0.336	0.111	0.336	0.441	0.007	0.006	0.064	0.014	0	0.022	0.21	0
0	35.34	0.898	8.8	10.94	28	3.2	0.139	0.06	0.342	0.007	0.006	0.061	0.018	0	0.021	0.2	0
0	7.228	0.37	4.42	7.878	49.816	26.26	0.07	38.56	1.667	0.009	0.021	0.205	0.095	0	0.755	2.6	0
0	28.244	0.876	1.288	1.403	11.5	0.598	0.045	0.322	0.655	0.002	0.003	0.03	0.007	0	0.022	0.667	0
0	13.566	0.182	5.544	2.205	23.142	5.103	0.023	0.567	1.697	0.002	0.006	0.031	0.012	0	0.179	1.953	0
0	12.762	0.294	5.94	7.362	22.806	0.63	0.085	0	0.378	0.004	0.005	0.038		0		0	0
0	19.551	1.394	7.686	10.479	37.548	3.528	0.101	1.344	0.162	0.013	0.007	0.096	0.009	0	0.07	0.21	0
0	9.56	0.592	5.08	6.98	30.86	1.04	0.081	0.98	0.228	0.005	0.006	0.069	0.023	0	0.44	3.08	0
0	31.836	0.343	5.376	5.817	24.906	0.42	0.109	0.063	0.441	0.009	0.006	0.059	0.005	0	0.022	0.21	0
0	23.92	0.371	7.7	9.74	33.88	1.76	0.074	0.14	0.42	0.008	0.007	0.121	0.009	0			0
0	2.24	0.077	1.624	11.676	30.828	0.728	0.074	0	0.504	0.013	0.004	0.019	0.082	0	0.018	0.056	0
0	2.088	0.207	3.312	2.664	24.174	0.576	0.085	0.126	0.126	0.001	0.003	0.093	0.015	0	0.324	0.702	0
0	17.193	0.329	9.834	27.753	22.506	0.165	0.188	0.099	0.099	0.018	0.013	0.26	0.014	0	0.095	2.508	0
0	4.048	0.067	4.026	4.686	7.7	0.352	0.047	0.11	0.066	0.008	0.001	0.029	0.004	0	0	1.672	0
0	8.712	0.061	2.928	8.16	22.632	1.296	0.056	0	0.353	0.01	0.001	0.016	0.029	0	0.006	3.984	0
0	3.717	0.495	3.885	7.245	49.224	0.714	0.085	55.38	1.493	0.014	0.037	0.322	0.084	0	0.626	2.226	0
0	9.177	0.606	4.074	3.633	26.439	0.924	0.03	0.315	0.441	0.002	0.005	0.024	0.007	0	0.015	0.21	0

EvaluEat Code	Food Name	Amt	Wt (g)	Energy (kcal)	Prot (g)	Carb (g)	Fiber (g)	Fat (g)	Mono (g)	Poly (g)	Sat (g)
2033	Spice, poppy seed	1 tsp	2.8	14.924	0.505	0.663	0.28	1.252	0.178	0.863	0.136
2037	Spice, saffron	1 tsp	0.7	2.17	0.08	0.458	0.027	0.041	0.003	0.014	0.011
2043	Spice, turmeric, ground	1 tsp	2.2	7.788	0.172	1.428	0.464	0.217	0.037	0.048	0.069
22905	Stew, beef stew, canned entree	1 serving	232	218.08	11.461	15.706	3.48	12.482	5.522	0.51	5.15
18355	Sweet roll, cheese	1 roll	66	237.6	4.686	28.842	0.792	12.078	5.978	1.341	3.999
18358	Sweet roll, cinnamon w/icing, refrigerated dough, baked	1 roll	30	108.6	1.62	16.83		3.96	2.226	0.518	1.004
18356	Sweet roll, cinnamon-raisin, commercially prep	1 large	83	308.76	5.146	42.247	1.992	13.612	3.982	6.203	2.556
19163	Sweet, chewing gum	1 stick	3	7.41	0	1.982	0.072	0.009	0.002	0.004	0.001
19711	Sweet, frosting, chocolate creamy	1/12 package	38	150.86	0.418	24.016	0.228	6.688	3.428	0.809	2.101
19228	Sweet, frosting, cream cheese flavor	2 tbsp	33	136.95	0.033	22.216	0	5.709	1.239	2.03	1.5
19715	Sweet, frosting, vanilla, creamy	1/12 package	38	159.22	0.038	26.372	0.038	6.384	3.333	0.866	1.858
19294	Sweet, fruit butter, apple	1 tbsp	17	29.41	0.066	7.271	0.255	0	0	0	0
19173	Sweet, gelatin, dry, prep w/H₂O	.5 cup	135	83.7	1.647	19.156	0	0	0	0	0
19290	Sweet, gelatin, Kraft, JELL-O Sugar Free Dessert, strawberry, powder	1 NLEA serving	2.5	8.325	1.42	0.123	0	0.003			0
19296	Sweet, honey, strained/extracted	1 tbsp	21	63.84	0.063	17.304	0.042	0	0	0	0
19283	Sweet, ice popsicle	1 bar (1.75 fl. oz.)	52	37.44	0	9.828	0	0	0	0	0
19297	Sweet, jams & preserves	1 tbsp	20	55.6	0.074	13.772	0.22	0.014	0.008	0	0.002
19300	Sweet, jellies	1 packet (0.5 oz)	14	37.24	0.021	9.793	0.14	0.003	0	0.001	0.001
19303	Sweet, marmalade, orange	1 tbsp	20	49.2	0.06	13.26	0.14	0	0	0	0
19304	Sweet, molasses	1 tbsp	20	58	0	14.946	0	0.02	0.006	0.01	0.004
19334	Sweet, sugar, brown	1 tsp packed	4.6	17.342	0	4.477	0	0	0	0	0
19335	Sweet, sugar, granulated, white	1 tsp	4.2	16.254	0	4.199	0	0	0	0	0
19340	Sweet, sugar, maple	1 tsp	3	10.62	0.003	2.727	0	0.006	0.002	0.003	0.001
19336	Sweet, sugar, powdered/confectioner's, white	1 tsp	2.5	9.725	0	2.49	0	0.003	0.001	0.001	0
19113	Sweet, syrup w/butter, pancake	1 tbsp	20	59.2	0	14.82	0	0.32	0.094	0.012	0.202
19348	Sweet, syrup, chocolate, fudge-type	2 tbsp	38	133	1.748	23.902	1.064	3.382	1.466	0.106	1.512
19351	Sweet, syrup, corn, hi-fructose	1 tbsp	19	53.39	0	14.44	0	0	0	0	0
19350	Sweet, syrup, corn, light	1 tbsp	20	58.6	0	15.926	0	0.02	0	0	0
19353	Sweet, syrup, maple	1 tbsp	20	52.2	0	13.418	0	0.04	0.013	0.02	0.007
19129	Sweet, syrup, pancake	1 tbsp	20	46.8	0	12.294	0.14	0	0	0	0
19128	Sweet, syrup, pancake, reduced-kcal	1 tbsp	15	24.6	0	6.645	0	0	0	0	0
19355	Sweet, syrup, sorghum	1 tbsp	21	60.9	0	15.729	0	0	0	0	0
19364	Sweet, topping, butterscotch or caramel	2 tbsp	41	103.32	0.615	27.019	0.369	0.041	0.008	0	0.045
19137	Sweet, topping, strawberry	2 tbsp	42	106.68	0.084	27.846	0.294	0.042	0.006	0.021	0.002
43026	Syrups, dietetic	1 cup	186	74.4	1.488	91.512	5.58	0	0	0	0
18277	Toaster muffin, blueberry	1 muffin	33	103.29	1.518	17.589	0.594	3.135	0.713	1.766	0.461
18281	Toaster muffin, corn	1 muffin	33	114.18	1.749	19.107	0.528	3.729	0.866	2.087	0.555
18361	Toaster pastry, brown sugar—cinnamon	1 pastry	50	206	2.55	34.05	0.5	7.1	4.016	0.901	1.819
18475	Toaster pastry, Pop Tart, Apple Cinnamon/Kellogg	1 pastry	52	205.4	2.288	37.45	0.572	5.304	3.052	1.352	0.879
18491	Toaster pastry, Pop Tart, Frosted Apple Cinnamon, low-fat/Kellogg	1 pastry	52	191.36	2.184	39.988	0.572	2.86	1.456	0.832	0.572

Chol (g)	Calc (mg)	Iron (mg)	Mag (mg)	Phos (mg)	Pota (mg)	Sodi (mg)	Zinc (mg)	Vit A (RAE)	Vit C (mg)	Thia (mg)	Ribo (mg)	Niac (mg)	Vit B$_6$ (mg)	Vit B$_{12}$ (µg)	Vit E (mg)	Fol (µg)	Alc (g)
0	40.544	0.263	9.268	23.772	19.6	0.588	0.286	0	0.084	0.024	0.005	0.027	0.012	0	0.031	1.624	0
0	0.777	0.078	1.848	1.764	12.068	1.036	0.008	0.189	0.566	0.001	0.002	0.01	0.007	0	0.012	0.651	0
0	4.026	0.911	4.246	5.896	55.55	0.836	0.096	0	0.57	0.003	0.005	0.113	0.04	0	0.068	0.858	0
37.12	27.84	1.647	32.48	127.6	403.68	946.56	1.902	192.6	10.21	0.167	0.142	2.856	0.299	0.858	0.172	25.52	0
50.16	77.88	0.502	12.54	64.68	90.42	235.62	0.416		0.132	0.099	0.086	0.548	0.046	0.198		28.38	0
0	10.2	0.795	3.6	104.4	18.9	249.6	0.102	0	0.06	0.123	0.073	1.087	0.01	0.015		16.5	
54.78	59.76	1.328	14.11	63.08	92.13	317.89	0.49	51.46	1.66	0.269	0.22	1.979	0.089	0.116	1.652	59.76	0
0	0	0	0	0	0.06	0.03	0	0	0	0	0	0	0	0	0	0	0
0	3.04	0.54	7.98	22.42	74.48	69.54	0.11		0	0.005	0.006	0.045	0.002	0		0	0
0	0.99	0.053	0.66	0.99	11.55	63.03	0.007	0	0	0	0.002	0.004	0	0	1.401	0	0
0	1.14	0.042	0.38	1.14	14.06	34.2	0		0	0	0.002	0.004	0			0	0
0	2.38	0.053	0.85	1.19	15.47	2.55	0.01	0.17	0.17	0.001	0.004	0.011	0.006	0	0.003	0.17	0
0	4.05	0.027	1.35	29.7	1.35	101.25	0.014	0	0	0	0.008	0.001	0	0	0	1.35	0
0.025	0.525	0.029		34.025	0.45	57.05			0								
0	1.26	0.088	0.42	0.84	10.92	0.84	0.046	0	0.105	0	0.008	0.025	0.005	0	0	0.42	0
0	0	0	0.52	0	2.08	6.24	0.01	0	0	0	0	0	0	0	0	0	0
0	4	0.098	0.8	3.8	15.4	6.4	0.012	0.2	1.76	0.003	0.015	0.007	0.004	0	0.024	2.2	0
0	0.98	0.027	0.84	0.84	7.56	4.2	0.004	0	0.126	0	0.004	0.005	0.003	0	0	0.28	0
0	7.6	0.03	0.4	0.8	7.4	11.2	0.008	0.6	0.96	0.001	0.005	0.01	0.004	0	0.012	1.8	0
0	41	0.944	48.4	6.2	292.8	7.4	0.058	0	0	0.008	0	0.186	0.134	0	0	0	0
0	3.91	0.088	1.334	1.012	15.916	1.794	0.008	0	0	0	0	0.004	0.001	0	0	0.046	0
0	0.042	0	0	0	0.084	0	0	0	0	0	0.001	0	0	0	0	0	0
0	2.7	0.048	0.57	0.09	8.22	0.33	0.182	0	0	0	0	0.001	0	0	0	0	0
0	0.025	0.001	0	0	0.05	0.025	0	0	0	0	0	0	0	0	0	0	0
0.8	0.4	0.018	0.4	2	0.6	19.6	0.008	2.8	0	0.002	0.002	0.004	0	0	0.006	0	0
0.76	38	0.597	24.32	63.84	171.38	131.48	0.319	1.9	0.038	0.027	0.107	0.139	0.029	0.106	0.946	1.9	0
0	0	0.006	0	0	0	0.38	0.004	0	0	0	0.004	0	0	0	0	0	0
0	0.6	0.01	0.4	0.4	0.8	24.2	0.004	0	0	0.002	0.002	0.004	0.002	0	0	0	0
0	13.4	0.24	2.8	0.4	40.8	1.8	0.832	0	0	0.001	0.002	0.006	0	0	0	0	0
0	0.6	0.006	0.4	1.8	3	16.4	0.016	0	0	0.001	0.002	0.002	0.001	0	0	0	0
0	0.15	0.003	0	6.45	0.45	30	0.003	0	0	0.002	0.001	0.003	0	0	0	0	0
0	31.5	0.798	21	11.76	210	1.68	0.086	0	0	0.021	0.033	0.021	0.141	0	0	0	0
0.41	21.73	0.082	2.87	19.27	34.44	143.09	0.078	11.07	0.123	0.005	0.039	0.016	0.006	0.037		0.82	0
0	2.52	0.118	1.68	2.1	21.42	8.82	0.025	0.42	5.754	0.005	0.01	0.068	0.005	0	0.042	2.52	0
0	0	0	0	0	0	39.06	0	0	0	0	0	0	0	0	0	0	0
1.98	4.29	0.168	3.96	19.47	27.39	157.74	0.129	31.02	0	0.079	0.096	0.667	0.009	0.007	0.3	21.45	0
4.29	6.27	0.485	4.62	49.83	30.36	141.9	0.129	5.94	0	0.102	0.122	0.762	0.016	0.01		18.81	0
0	17	2.015	12	66.5	57	212	0.315	148	0.05	0.186	0.288	2.287	0.213	0.11		14.5	0
0	11.96	1.82	5.72	27.56	47.32	173.68	0.338		0	0.151	0.172	1.976	0.198	0	0	41.6	0
0	5.72	1.82	4.68	21.32	28.08	205.92	0.156		0	0.156	0.156	1.976	0.208	0	0	52	0

EvaluEat Code	Food Name	Amt	Wt (g)	Energy (kcal)	Prot (g)	Carb (g)	Fiber (g)	Fat (g)	Mono (g)	Poly (g)	Sat (g)
18495	Toaster pastry, Pop Tart, Frosted Chocolate Fudge, low fat/Kellogg	1 pastry	52	190.32	2.652	39.52	0.572	3.016	1.248	0.884	0.52
18482	Toaster pastry, Pop Tart, Frosted Chocolate Fudge/Kellogg	1 pastry	52	201.24	2.652	37.336	0.572	4.836	2.704	1.144	0.988
3930	Toddler formula, Mead Johnson Next Step Soy, prepared from powder	1 fl. oz.	30.5	20.13	0.641	2.159	0	0.885	0.339	0.169	0.381
43476	Tofu yogurt	1 oz	28.34	26.64	0.992	4.523	0.057	0.51	0.113	0.288	0.073
19125	Topping, chocolate-flavored hazelnut spread	1 oz	28.34	153.32	1.533	17.616	1.53	8.425	4.614	1.919	1.528
22901	Tortellini, pasta with cheese filling	1 cup	236	724.52	31.86	110.92	4.484	17.063	4.876	1.088	8.496
18449	Tortilla, corn, w/o salt, ready to cook	1 tortilla, medium (approx 6" dia)	26	57.72	1.482	12.116	1.352	0.65	0.169	0.292	0.087
18364	Tortilla, flour, ready-to-cook	1 tortilla, medium (approx 6" dia)	46	149.5	4.002	25.576	1.518	3.266	1.733	0.489	0.803
18360	Tortilla, taco shell, baked	1 large (6-1/2" dia)	21	98.28	1.512	13.104	1.575	4.746	1.876	1.784	0.681
42130	Turkey bacon, cooked	1 oz	28.34	108.26	8.389	0.879	0	7.907	3.089	1.929	2.351
22706	Turkey chili w/beans, canned entree/Hormel	1 cup	247	202.54	18.723	25.565	6.422	2.766	0.42	1.21	0.667
5172	Turkey giblets, simmered	1 cup, chopped or diced	145	288.55	30.291	1.16	0	17.197	7.183	1.827	5.688
5174	Turkey gizzard, simmered	1	84	103.32	18.245	0.319	0	3.251	1.016	0.423	0.977
42128	Turkey ham, sliced, extra lean, prepackaged or deli-sliced	1 oz	28.34	33.441	5.555	0.425	0	1.077	0.245	0.322	0.361
5176	Turkey heart, simmered	1 heart	21	27.3	4.509	0.143	0	0.974	0.239	0.25	0.271
5178	Turkey liver, simmered	1 liver	83	226.59	16.617	1.004	0	17.048	7.56	1.678	5.766
5292	Turkey patty, breaded, fried	1 medium slice (approx 3" x 2" x 1/4")	28	79.24	3.92	4.396	0.14	5.04	2.092	1.319	1.313
22528	Turkey pot pie, frozen	1 serving	397	698.72	25.805	70.269	4.367	34.936	13.736	5.479	11.434
5296	Turkey roast, light & dark meat, no bone, frozen, seasoned, cooked	1 cup, chopped or diced	135	209.25	28.782	4.144	0	7.803	1.62	2.241	2.565
5286	Turkey w/gravy, frozen	1 cup	240	160.8	14.112	11.064	0	6.312	2.328	1.128	2.04
5218	Turkey, fryer/roaster, breast w/skin, roasted	1 unit (yield from 1 lb ready-to-cook turkey)	98	149.94	28.489	0	0	3.136	1.176	0.745	0.853
5220	Turkey, fryer/roaster, breast, no skin, roasted	1 unit (yield from 1 lb ready-to-cook turkey)	87	117.45	26.152	0	0	0.644	0.113	0.174	0.209
5208	Turkey, fryer/roaster, dark meat w/skin, roasted	1 unit (yield from 1 lb ready-to-cook turkey)	106	192.92	29.351	0	0	7.484	2.406	1.993	2.247
5206	Turkey, fryer/roaster, light meat w/skin, roasted	1 unit (yield from 1 lb ready-to-cook turkey)	123	201.72	35.387	0	0	5.633	2.091	1.341	1.538
5306	Turkey, ground, cooked	1 patty (4 oz, raw)	82	192.7	22.435	0	0	10.783	4.01	2.649	2.78
7900	Turkey, pork, and beef sausage, low-fat, smoked	1 frankfurter	56	56.56	4.48	6.44	0.336	1.4	0.577	0.185	0.476
17203	Veal liver, braised	1 slice (yield from 116 g raw liver)	80	153.6	22.736	3.016	0	5.008	0.917	0.831	1.589
17204	Veal liver, pan fried	1 slice (yield from 99 g raw liver)	67	129.31	18.338	2.995	0	4.362	0.8	0.745	1.413

Chol (g)	Calc (mg)	Iron (mg)	Mag (mg)	Phos (mg)	Pota (mg)	Sodi (mg)	Zinc (mg)	Vit A (RAE)	Vit C (mg)	Thia (mg)	Ribo (mg)	Niac (mg)	Vit B6 (mg)	Vit B12 (µg)	Vit E (mg)	Fol (µg)	Alc (g)
0	13.52	1.82	14.56	39.52	61.88	248.56	0.26		0	0.156	0.156	1.976	0.208	0	0	52	0
0	19.76	1.82	15.08	43.68	82.16	202.8	0.26		0	0.156	0.156	1.976	0.208	0	0	52	0
0	23.18	0.36	1.525	17.995	29.89	8.845	0.241	17.69	2.41	0.016	0.018	0.201	0.018	0.058	0.4	3.05	0
0	33.441	0.3	11.336	10.769	13.32	9.919	0.088	0.567	0.709	0.017	0.006	0.068	0.006	0	0.088	1.7	0
0	30.607	1.241	18.138	43.077	115.344	11.619	0.3	0.283	0	0.034	0.048	0.121	0.024	0.079	1.406	3.968	0
99.12	358.72	3.54	49.56	500.32	210.04	811.84	2.407	89.68	0	0.739	0.732	6.363	0.101	0.378	0.378	174.6	0
0	45.5	0.364	16.9	81.64	40.04	2.86	0.244	0	0	0.029	0.019	0.389	0.057	0	0.04	29.64	0
0	57.5	1.518	11.96	57.04	60.26	219.88	0.327	0	0	0.244	0.135	1.643	0.023	0	0.258	47.84	0
0	33.6	0.525	22.05	52.08	37.59	77.07	0.294	0	0	0.048	0.011	0.283	0.062	0	0.349	27.51	0
27.773	2.551	0.598	8.219	130.364	111.943	647.569	0.859	0	0	0.017	0.068	1	0.091	0.102	0.292	2.551	0
34.58	116.09	3.458	69.16		681.72	1197.95	2.717		1.482								0
419.05	8.7	11.18	26.1	334.95	391.5	92.8	4.524	15569	19.87	0.039	2.179	10.147	0.842	48.213	0.116	485.8	0
170.52	5.88	4.158	14.28	129.36	278.88	56.28	2.831	0	5.292	0.011	0.174	3.587	0.089	6.787	0.042	10.92	0
18.988	1.417	0.383	5.668	86.154	84.737	294.169	0.669	0	0	0.014	0.071	1	0.065	0.074	0.111	1.7	0
38.64	1.47	1.092	5.46	54.39	61.11	18.9	0.934	3.99	0.588	0.007	0.218	0.71	0.089	4.557	0.01	1.68	0
322.04	4.15	8.881	14.11	244.02	175.13	46.48	2.175	18758	18.76	0.032	2.291	8.466	0.863	48.306	0.091	573.5	0
17.36	3.92	0.616	4.2	75.6	77	224	0.403	3.08	0	0.028	0.053	0.644	0.056	0.062	0.353	7.84	0
63.52		3.97				1389.5											0
71.55	6.75	2.201	29.7	329.4	402.3	918	3.429	0	0	0.063	0.22	8.466	0.365	2.052	0.513	6.75	0
43.2	33.6	2.232	19.2	194.4	146.4	1329.6	1.68	31.2	0	0.058	0.305	4.318	0.24	0.576		9.6	0
88.2	14.7	1.539	27.44	211.68	273.42	51.94	1.735	0	0	0.04	0.132	6.823	0.5	0.363		5.88	0
72.21	10.44	1.331	25.23	194.88	254.04	45.24	1.514	0	0	0.037	0.114	6.519	0.487	0.339	0.078	5.22	0
124.02	28.62	2.47	24.38	201.4	251.22	80.56	4.06	0	0	0.051	0.249	3.551	0.35	0.392		9.54	0
116.85	22.14	1.98	31.98	252.15	322.26	70.11	2.558	0	0	0.047	0.171	7.718	0.603	0.443		7.38	0
83.64	20.5	1.583	19.68	160.72	221.4	87.74	2.345	0	0	0.044	0.138	3.952	0.32	0.271	0.279	5.74	0
11.76	5.6	1.232	8.96	41.44	136.08	445.76	0.672	0	1.064	0.073	0.045	0.868	0.056	0.157	0.05	3.36	0
408.8	4.8	4.088	16	368	263.2	62.4	8.984	16916	0.88	0.146	2.288	10.52	0.734	67.68	0.544	264.8	0
324.95	4.69	4.007	15.41	323.61	236.51	56.95	7.973	13450	0.469	0.119	2.05	9.615	0.597	48.575	0.402	234.5	0

EvaluEat Code	Food Name	Amt	Wt (g)	Energy (kcal)	Prot (g)	Carb (g)	Fiber (g)	Fat (g)	Mono (g)	Poly (g)	Sat (g)
17223	Veal tongue, braised	3 oz	85	171.7	21.973	0	0	8.585	3.919	0.323	3.697
17089	Veal, composite, lean & fat, cooked	3 oz	85	196.35	25.585	0	0	9.682	3.74	0.68	3.638
17143	Veal, ground, broiled	3 oz	85	146.2	20.723	0	0	6.426	2.414	0.468	2.584
11655	Vegetable juice, carrot, canned	1 cup	236	94.4	2.242	21.924	1.888	0.354	0.017	0.168	0.064
11886	Vegetable juice, tomato, canned w/o salt	1 cup	243	41.31	1.847	10.303	0.972	0.122	0.022	0.058	0.019
11001	Vege, alfalfa seeds, sprouted, raw	1 tbsp	3	0.87	0.12	0.113	0.075	0.021	0.002	0.012	0.002
11697	Vege, arrowroot, raw	1 cup, sliced	120	78	5.088	16.068	1.56	0.24	0.005	0.11	0.047
11702	Vege, artichokes (globe or French) boiled w/salt, drained	1 artichoke, medium	120	60	4.176	13.416	6.48	0.192	0.006	0.082	0.044
11009	Vege, artichokes (globe or French) frozen	1 package (9 oz)	255	96.9	6.707	19.788	9.945	1.097	0.031	0.456	0.252
11959	Vege, arugula/roquette, raw	1 leaf	2	0.5	0.052	0.073	0.032	0.013	0.001	0.006	0.002
11705	Vege, asparagus, boiled w/salt, drained	4 spears (1/2" base)	60	13.2	1.44	2.466	1.2	0.132	0.006	0.082	0.043
11015	Vege, asparagus, canned, drained	1 spear (about 5" long)	18	3.42	0.385	0.443	0.288	0.117	0.004	0.051	0.026
11011	Vege, asparagus, raw	1 spear, large (7-1/4" to 8-1/2")	20	4	0.44	0.776	0.42	0.024	0.001	0.018	0.009
11712	Vege, bamboo shoots, boiled w/salt, drained	1 cup (1/2" slices)	120	14.4	1.836	2.304	1.2	0.264	0.006	0.118	0.061
11028	Vege, bamboo shoots, canned, drained	1 cup (1/8" slices)	131	24.89	2.253	4.218	1.834	0.524	0.012	0.233	0.121
11026	Vege, bamboo shoots, raw	1 cup (1/2" slices)	151	40.77	3.926	7.852	3.322	0.453	0.011	0.202	0.104
11626	Vege, bean sprouts, mung, mature seeds, sprouted, canned, drained	1 cup	125	15	1.75	2.675	1	0.075	0.01	0.025	0.02
11973	Vege, beans, fava, in pod, raw	1 cup	126	110.88	9.979	22.214		0.92	0.131	0.431	0.149
11716	Vege, beans, lima, baby, immature seeds, frozen, boiled w/salt, drained	.5 cup	90	94.5	5.985	17.505	5.4	0.27	0.015	0.13	0.061
11033	Vege, beans, lima, immature seeds, canned, solids & liquid	.5 cup	124	88.04	5.047	16.529	4.464	0.36	0.02	0.172	0.082
11720	Vege, beans, pinto, immature seeds, boiled w/salt, drained	1 package (10 oz)	284	460.08	26.44	87.699	24.424	1.363	0.099	0.784	0.165
11723	Vege, beans, snap, green, boiled w/salt, drained	1 cup	125	43.75	2.362	9.863	4	0.35	0.014	0.181	0.08
11056	Vege, beans, snap, green, canned, drained	1 cup	135	27	1.553	6.075	2.565	0.135	0.005	0.069	0.03
11052	Vege, beans, snap, green, raw	1 cup	110	34.1	2.002	7.854	3.74	0.132	0.005	0.065	0.029
11725	Vege, beans, snap, yellow, boiled w/salt, drained	1 cup	125	43.75	2.362	9.85	4.125	0.35	0.014	0.181	0.08
11932	Vege, beans, snap, yellow, canned, regular pack, drained	1 cup	135	27	1.553	6.075	1.755	0.135	0.005	0.069	0.03
11722	Vege, beans, snap, yellow, raw	1 cup	110	34.1	2.002	7.854	3.74	0.132	0.005	0.065	0.029
11736	Vege, beet greens, boiled w/salt, drained	1 cup (1" pieces)	144	38.88	3.701	7.862	4.176	0.288	0.055	0.101	0.045
11086	Vege, beet greens, raw	1 cup	38	8.36	0.836	1.645	1.406	0.049	0.01	0.017	0.008
11734	Vege, beets, boiled w/salt, drained	.5 cup slices	85	37.4	1.428	8.466	1.7	0.153	0.03	0.054	0.024
11084	Vege, beets, canned, drained	1 cup, diced	157	48.67	1.429	11.32	2.669	0.22	0.044	0.08	0.036
11080	Vege, beets, peeled, raw	1 cup	136	58.48	2.19	13.002	3.808	0.231	0.045	0.083	0.037
11609	Vege, beets, pickled, canned, solids & liquid	1 cup slices	227	147.55	1.816	36.956	5.902	0.182	0.036	0.066	0.03
11088	Vege, broadbeans, immature seeds, raw	1 cup	109	78.48	6.104	12.753	4.578	0.654	0.019	0.338	0.15
22600	Vege, broccoli in cheese flavored sauce, frozen/Green Giant	1 cup	168	112.56	3.864	14.952		4.2	1.695	0.425	0.806
11741	Vege, broccoli stalks, raw	1 stalk	114	31.92	3.397	5.974		0.399	0.027	0.19	0.062
11742	Vege, broccoli, boiled w/salt, chopped, drained	.5 cup, chopped	78	21.84	2.324	3.947	2.574	0.273	0.019	0.13	0.042
11969	Vege, broccoli, Chinese, cooked	1 cup	88	19.36	1.003	3.353	2.2	0.634	0.044	0.29	0.097
11745	Vege, Brussels sprouts, boiled w/salt, drained	.5 cup	78	31.98	1.989	6.763	2.028	0.398	0.03	0.203	0.082
11098	Vege, Brussels sprouts, raw	1 cup	88	37.84	2.974	7.876	3.344	0.264	0.02	0.135	0.055

Chol (g)	Calc (mg)	Iron (mg)	Mag (mg)	Phos (mg)	Pota (mg)	Sodi (mg)	Zinc (mg)	Vit A (RAE)	Vit C (mg)	Thia (mg)	Ribo (mg)	Niac (mg)	Vit B$_6$ (mg)	Vit B$_{12}$ (µg)	Vit E (mg)	Fol (µg)	Alc (g)
202.3	7.65	1.776	15.3	141.1	137.7	54.4	3.834	0	5.1	0.06	0.298	1.25	0.128	4.505		7.65	0
96.9	18.7	0.978	22.1	203.15	276.25	73.95	4.046	0	0	0.051	0.272	6.774	0.264	1.335	0.34	12.75	0
87.55	14.45	0.842	20.4	184.45	286.45	70.55	3.289	0	0	0.06	0.23	6.826	0.331	1.079	0.128	9.35	0
0	56.64	1.086	33.04	99.12	689.12	68.44	0.425	2256	20.06	0.217	0.13	0.911	0.512	0	2.738	9.44	0
0	24.3	1.045	26.73	43.74	556.47	24.3	0.365	55.89	44.47	0.114	0.075	1.635	0.27	0	0.778	48.6	0
0	0.96	0.029	0.81	2.1	2.37	0.18	0.028	0.24	0.246	0.002	0.004	0.014	0.001	0	0.001	1.08	0
0	7.2	2.664	30	117.6	544.8	31.2	0.756	1.2	2.28	0.172	0.071	2.032	0.319	0		405.6	0
0	54	1.548	72	103.2	424.8	397.2	0.588	10.8	12	0.078	0.079	1.201	0.133	0	0.228	61.2	0
0	48.45	1.275	68.85	147.9	632.4	119.85	0.816	20.4	13.52	0.148	0.357	2.193	0.209	0		321.3	0
0	3.2	0.029	0.94	1.04	7.38	0.54	0.009	2.38	0.3	0.001	0.002	0.006	0.001	0	0.009	1.94	0
0	13.8	0.546	8.4	32.4	134.4	144	0.36	30	4.62	0.097	0.083	0.65	0.047	0		89.4	0
0	2.88	0.329	1.8	7.74	30.96	51.66	0.072	7.38	3.312	0.011	0.018	0.172	0.02	0	0.056	17.28	0
0	4.8	0.428	2.8	10.4	40.4	0.4	0.108	7.6	1.12	0.029	0.028	0.196	0.018	0	0.226	10.4	0
0	14.4	0.288	3.6	24	639.6	288	0.564	0	0	0.024	0.06	0.36	0.118	0		2.4	0
0	10.48	0.419	5.24	32.75	104.8	9.17	0.851	1.31	1.441	0.034	0.034	0.183	0.178	0	0.825	3.93	0
0	19.63	0.755	4.53	89.09	804.83	6.04	1.661	1.51	6.04	0.227	0.106	0.906	0.362	0	1.51	10.57	0
0	17.5	0.538	11.25	40	33.75	175	0.35	0	0.375	0.037	0.087	0.275	0.04	0	0.05	12.5	0
0	46.62	1.953	41.58	162.54	418.32	31.5	1.26	21.42	4.662	0.168	0.365	2.834	0.131	0		186.5	0
0	25.2	1.764	50.4	100.8	369.9	238.5	0.495	7.2	5.22	0.063	0.049	0.693	0.104	0	0.576	14.4	0
0	34.72	1.996	42.16	88.04	353.4	312.48	0.794	9.92	9.052	0.036	0.053	0.66	0.077	0	0.36	19.84	0
0	147.68	7.696	153.36	284	1834.64	905.96	1.96	0	1.988	0.778	0.307	1.795	0.551	0		96.56	0
0	57.5	1.6	31.25	48.75	373.75	298.75	0.45	43.75	12.13	0.093	0.121	0.768	0.07	0	0.563	41.25	0
0	35.1	1.215	17.55	25.65	147.15	353.7	0.391	29.7	6.48	0.02	0.076	0.271	0.05	0	0.378	43.2	0
0	40.7	1.144	27.5	41.8	229.9	6.6	0.264	38.5	17.93	0.092	0.115	0.827	0.081	0	0.451	40.7	0
0	57.5	1.6	31.25	48.75	373.75	298.75	0.45	5	12.13	0.093	0.121	0.768	0.07	0	0.563	41.25	0
0	35.1	1.215	17.55	25.65	147.15	338.85	0.391	6.75	6.48	0.02	0.076	0.271	0.05	0	0.391	43.2	0
0	40.7	1.144	27.5	41.8	229.9	6.6	0.264	5.5	17.93	0.092	0.115	0.827	0.081	0		40.7	0
0	164.16	2.736	97.92	59.04	1308.96	686.88	0.72	367.2	35.86	0.168	0.416	0.719	0.19	0		20.16	0
0	44.46	0.977	26.6	15.58	289.56	85.88	0.144	120.1	11.4	0.038	0.084	0.152	0.04	0	0.57	5.7	0
0	13.6	0.672	19.55	32.3	259.25	242.25	0.298	387.6	3.06	0.023	0.034	0.281	0.057	0	1.836	68	0
0	23.55	2.857	26.69	26.69	232.36	304.58	0.33	1.57	6.437	0.016	0.063	0.246	0.089	0	0.047	47.1	0
0	21.76	1.088	31.28	54.4	442	106.08	0.476	2.72	6.664	0.042	0.054	0.454	0.091	0	0.054	148.2	0
0	24.97	0.931	34.05	38.59	335.96	599.28	0.59	2.27	5.221	0.023	0.109	0.57	0.113	0		61.29	0
0	23.98	2.071	41.42	103.55	272.5	54.5	0.632	19.62	35.97	0.185	0.12	1.635	0.041	0		104.6	0
						806.4			59.47								0
0	54.72	1.003	28.5	75.24	370.5	30.78	0.456	22.8	106.2	0.074	0.136	0.727	0.181	0	1.892	80.94	0
0	31.2	0.523	16.38	52.26	228.54	204.36	0.351	76.44	32.76	0.049	0.096	0.431	0.156	0	1.131	84.24	0
0	88	0.493	15.84	36.08	229.68	6.16	0.343	72.16	24.82	0.084	0.128	0.385	0.062	0	0.422	87.12	0
0	28.08	0.936	15.6	43.68	247.26	200.46	0.257	28.08	48.36	0.083	0.062	0.473	0.139	0		46.8	0
0	36.96	1.232	20.24	60.72	342.32	22	0.37	33.44	74.8	0.122	0.079	0.656	0.193	0	0.774	53.68	0

EvaluEat Code	Food Name	Amt	Wt (g)	Energy (kcal)	Prot (g)	Carb (g)	Fiber (g)	Fat (g)	Mono (g)	Poly (g)	Sat (g)
11109	Vege, cabbage heads, raw	1 cup, chopped	89	21.36	1.282	4.966	2.047	0.107	0.008	0.053	0.014
11112	Vege, cabbage heads, red, raw	1 cup, chopped	89	27.59	1.273	6.559	1.869	0.142	0.017	0.111	0.03
11752	Vege, cabbage, red, boiled w/salt, drained	.5 cup, shredded	75	15.75	0.787	3.48	1.5	0.15	0.011	0.071	0.02
11751	Vege, cabbage, boiled w/salt, drained	.5 cup, shredded	75	16.5	0.765	3.345	1.425	0.322	0.022	0.147	0.04
11754	Vege, cabbage, pak-choi (Chinese) boiled w/salt, drained	1 cup, shredded	170	20.4	2.652	3.026	1.7	0.272	0.02	0.131	0.036
11119	Vege, cabbage, pe-tsai (Chinese) raw	1 cup, shredded	76	12.16	0.912	2.455	0.912	0.152	0.017	0.055	0.033
11960	Vege, carrots, baby, raw	1 medium	10	3.5	0.064	0.824	0.18	0.013	0.001	0.006	0.002
11757	Vege, carrots, boiled w/salt, drained	.5 cup slices	78	27.3	0.593	6.412	2.34	0.14	0.005	0.069	0.023
11128	Vege, carrots, canned, drained	1 cup, sliced	146	36.5	0.934	8.088	2.19	0.277	0.013	0.134	0.053
11124	Vege, carrots, chopped/grated, raw	1 cup, chopped	128	52.48	1.19	12.262	3.84	0.307	0.015	0.131	0.041
11134	Vege, cassava (manioc) raw	1 cup	206	329.6	2.802	78.404	3.708	0.577	0.155	0.099	0.152
11135	Vege, cauliflower head, raw	1 cup	100	25	1.98	5.3	2.5	0.1	0.014	0.099	0.032
11761	Vege, cauliflower, boiled w/salt, drained	.5 cup (1" pieces)	62	14.26	1.141	2.548	1.674	0.279	0.02	0.135	0.043
11764	Vege, celery, boiled w/salt, drained	1 cup, diced	150	27	1.245	6.015	2.4	0.24	0.045	0.113	0.06
11143	Vege, celery, raw	1 cup, diced	120	16.8	0.828	3.564	1.92	0.204	0.038	0.097	0.052
11765	Vege, chard, Swiss, boiled w/salt, drained	1 cup, chopped	175	35	3.29	7.227	3.675	0.14			
11151	Vege, chicory, witloof (Belgian endive) raw	1 head	53	9.01	0.477	2.12	1.643	0.053	0.001	0.023	0.013
11768	Vege, collards, boiled w/salt, drained	1 cup, chopped	190	49.4	4.009	9.329	5.32	0.684	0.049	0.329	0.089
11161	Vege, collards, raw	1 cup, chopped	36	10.8	0.882	2.048	1.296	0.151	0.011	0.072	0.02
11167	Vege, corn ears, yellow, sweet, raw	1 ear, medium	90	77.4	2.898	17.118	2.43	1.062	0.312	0.503	0.164
11908	Vege, corn, white, sweet, canned, vacuum/regular pack	.5 cup	105	82.95	2.53	20.412	2.1	0.525	0.154	0.249	0.081
11900	Vege, corn, white, sweet, ears, raw	1 ear, large	143	122.98	4.605	27.199	3.861	1.687	0.496	0.799	0.26
11770	Vege, corn, yellow, sweet, boiled w/salt, drained	1 cup	164	177.12	5.445	41.18	4.592	2.099	0.613	0.989	0.323
11176	Vege, corn, yellow, sweet, canned, vacuum/regular pack	.5 cup	105	82.95	2.53	20.412	2.1	0.525	0.154	0.249	0.081
11174	Vege, corn, yellow, sweet, cream style, regular pack, canned	1 cup	256	184.32	4.454	46.413	3.072	1.075	0.315	0.507	0.166
11777	Vege, cowpeas (blackeyes), immature seeds, boiled w/salt, drained	1 cup	165	160.05	5.231	33.528	8.25	0.627	0.056	0.266	0.158
11203	Vege, cress, garden, raw	1 cup	50	16	1.3	2.75	0.55	0.35	0.119	0.114	0.012
11205	Vege, cucumber, raw	.5 cup slices	52	7.8	0.338	1.888	0.26	0.057	0.002	0.028	0.018
11207	Vege, dandelion greens, raw	1 cup, chopped	55	24.75	1.485	5.06	1.925	0.385	0.008	0.168	0.094
11783	Vege, eggplant (brinjal) boiled w/salt, drained	1 cup (1" cubes)	99	34.65	0.822	8.643	2.475	0.228	0.02	0.092	0.044
11213	Vege, endive (escarole) raw	.5 cup, chopped	25	4.25	0.313	0.837	0.775	0.05	0.001	0.022	0.012
11957	Vege, fennel bulb, raw	1 cup, sliced	87	26.97	1.079	6.342	2.697	0.174			
11987	Vege, fungi, mushroom, oyster, raw	1 large	148	54.76	6.127	9.206	3.552	0.755			
11798	Vege, fungi, mushroom, shiitake, boiled w/salt, drained	4 mushrooms	72	39.6	1.123	10.282	1.512	0.158	0.049	0.022	0.04
11266	Vege, fungi, mushrooms, brown, Italian, or crimini, raw	1 piece	14	3.08	0.35	0.577	0.084	0.014	0	0.006	0.002
11264	Vege, fungi, mushrooms, canned, caps/slices, drained	1 can	132	33	2.468	6.719	3.168	0.383	0.007	0.149	0.05
11265	Vege, fungi, mushrooms, portabella, raw	1 oz	28.34	7.368	0.709	1.437	0.425	0.057	0.001	0.022	0.007
11260	Vege, fungi, mushrooms, slices, raw	1 medium	18	3.96	0.56	0.583	0.216	0.061	0.001	0.025	0.008
11961	Vege, hearts of palm, canned	1 cup	146	40.88	3.679	6.745	3.504	0.905	0.15	0.295	0.19
11790	Vege, kale, boiled w/salt, drained	1 cup, chopped	130	36.4	2.47	7.319	2.6	0.52	0.039	0.251	0.068
11233	Vege, kale, raw	1 cup, chopped	67	33.5	2.211	6.707	1.34	0.469	0.035	0.226	0.061
11793	Vege, kohlrabi, boiled w/salt, drained	1 cup slices	165	47.85	2.97	11.038	1.815	0.182	0.013	0.087	0.023
11241	Vege, kohlrabi, peeled, raw	1 cup	135	36.45	2.295	8.37	4.86	0.135	0.009	0.065	0.018

Chol (g)	Calc (mg)	Iron (mg)	Mag (mg)	Phos (mg)	Pota (mg)	Sodi (mg)	Zinc (mg)	Vit A (RAE)	Vit C (mg)	Thia (mg)	Ribo (mg)	Niac (mg)	Vit B_6 (mg)	Vit B_{12} (µg)	Vit E (mg)	Fol (µg)	Alc (g)
0	41.83	0.525	13.35	20.47	218.94	16.02	0.16	8.01	28.66	0.045	0.036	0.267	0.085	0	0.134	38.27	0
0	40.05	0.712	14.24	26.7	216.27	24.03	0.196	49.84	50.73	0.057	0.061	0.372	0.186	0	0.098	16.02	0
0	27.75	0.262	8.25	21.75	105	183	0.113	0.75	25.8	0.026	0.015	0.15	0.105	0		9.75	0
0	23.25	0.127	6	11.25	72.75	191.25	0.068	5.25	15.08	0.043	0.041	0.212	0.085	0	0.09	15	0
0	158.1	1.768	18.7	49.3	630.7	459	0.289	360.4	44.2	0.054	0.107	0.728	0.282	0	0.153	69.7	0
0	58.52	0.236	9.88	22.04	180.88	6.84	0.175	12.16	20.52	0.03	0.038	0.304	0.176	0	0.091	60.04	0
0	3.2	0.089	1	2.8	23.7	7.8	0.017	69	0.84	0.003	0.004	0.056	0.01	0		3.3	0
0	23.4	0.265	7.8	23.4	183.3	235.56	0.156	659.1	2.808	0.051	0.034	0.503	0.119	0	0.803	1.56	0
0	36.5	0.934	11.68	35.04	261.34	353.32	0.38	814.7	3.942	0.026	0.044	0.806	0.164	0	1.08	13.14	0
0	42.24	0.384	15.36	44.8	409.6	88.32	0.307	770.6	7.552	0.084	0.074	1.258	0.177	0	0.845	24.32	0
0	32.96	0.556	43.26	55.62	558.26	28.84	0.7	2.06	42.44	0.179	0.099	1.759	0.181	0	0.391	55.62	0
0	22	0.44	15	44	303	30	0.28	1	46.4	0.057	0.063	0.526	0.222	0	0.08	57	0
0	9.92	0.205	5.58	19.84	88.04	150.04	0.112	0.62	27.47	0.026	0.032	0.254	0.107	0	0.043	27.28	0
0	63	0.63	18	37.5	426	490.5	0.21	43.5	9.15	0.065	0.071	0.479	0.129	0	0.525	33	0
0	48	0.24	13.2	28.8	312	96	0.156	26.4	3.72	0.025	0.068	0.384	0.089	0	0.324	43.2	0
0	101.5	3.955	150.5	57.75	960.75	726.25	0.578	535.5	31.5	0.06	0.15	0.63	0.149	0	3.307	15.75	0
0	10.07	0.127	5.3	13.78	111.83	1.06	0.085	0.53	1.484	0.033	0.014	0.085	0.022	0		19.61	0
0	266	2.204	38	57	220.4	478.8	0.437	771.4	34.58	0.076	0.201	1.092	0.243	0	1.672	176.7	0
0	52.2	0.068	3.24	3.6	60.84	7.2	0.047	119.9	12.71	0.019	0.047	0.267	0.059	0	0.814	59.76	0
0	1.8	0.468	33.3	80.1	243	13.5	0.405	9	6.12	0.18	0.054	1.53	0.049	0	0.063	41.4	0
0	5.25	0.441	24.15	67.2	195.3	285.6	0.483	0	8.505	0.043	0.077	1.225	0.058	0		51.45	0
0	2.86	0.744	52.91	127.27	386.1	21.45	0.643	0	9.724	0.286	0.086	2.431	0.079	0	0.1	65.78	0
0	3.28	1	52.48	168.92	408.36	414.92	0.787	21.32	10.17	0.353	0.118	2.647	0.098	0	0.148	75.44	0
0	5.25	0.441	24.15	67.2	195.3	285.6	0.483	4.2	8.505	0.043	0.077	1.225	0.058	0	0.042	51.45	0
0	7.68	0.973	43.52	130.56	343.04	729.6	1.357	10.24	11.78	0.064	0.136	2.458	0.161	0	0.179	115.2	0
0	211.2	1.848	85.8	84.15	689.7	396	1.699	66	3.63	0.167	0.244	2.315	0.107	0	0.363	209.6	0
0	40.5	0.65	19	38	303	7	0.115	173	34.5	0.04	0.13	0.5	0.123	0	0.35	40	0
0	8.32	0.146	6.76	12.48	76.44	1.04	0.104	2.6	1.456	0.014	0.017	0.051	0.021	0	0.016	3.64	0
0	102.85	1.705	19.8	36.3	218.35	41.8	0.226	135.9	19.25	0.105	0.143	0.443	0.138	0	2.635	14.85	0
0	5.94	0.248	10.89	14.85	121.77	236.61	0.119	1.98	1.287	0.075	0.02	0.594	0.085	0	0.406	13.86	0
0	13	0.207	3.75	7	78.5	5.5	0.198	27	1.625	0.02	0.019	0.1	0.005	0	0.11	35.5	0
0	42.63	0.635	14.79	43.5	360.18	45.24	0.174	6.09	10.44	0.009	0.028	0.557	0.041	0		23.49	0
0	8.88	2.575	29.6	208.68	763.68	45.88	1.154	2.96	0	0.081	0.533	5.297	0.181	0		69.56	0
0	2.16	0.317	10.08	20.88	84.24	172.8	0.958	0	0.216	0.027	0.122	1.08	0.114	0		15.12	0
0	2.52	0.056	1.26	16.8	62.72	0.84	0.154	0	0	0.013	0.069	0.532	0.015	0.014	0.016	1.96	
0	14.52	1.043	19.8	87.12	170.28	561	0.95	0	0	0.112	0.028	2.103	0.081	0	0.013	15.84	0
0	2.267	0.17	3.117	36.842	137.166	1.7	0.17	0	0	0.022	0.136	1.275	0.028	0.014	0.037	6.235	
0	0.54	0.094	1.62	15.3	56.52	0.72	0.094	0	0.432	0.016	0.075	0.694	0.021	0.007	0.002	2.88	0
0	84.68	4.57	55.48	94.9	258.42	621.96	1.679	0	11.53	0.016	0.083	0.638	0.032	0		56.94	0
0	93.6	1.17	23.4	36.4	296.4	336.7	0.312	885.3	53.3	0.069	0.091	0.65	0.179	0	1.105	16.9	0
0	90.45	1.139	22.78	37.52	299.49	28.81	0.295	515.2	80.4	0.074	0.087	0.67	0.182	0	0.536	19.43	0
0	41.25	0.66	31.35	74.25	561	424.05	0.512	3.3	89.1	0.066	0.033	0.643	0.254	0	0.858	19.8	0
0	32.4	0.54	25.65	62.1	472.5	27	0.041	2.7	83.7	0.068	0.027	0.54	0.203	0	0.648	21.6	0

EvaluEat Code	Food Name	Amt	Wt (g)	Energy (kcal)	Prot (g)	Carb (g)	Fiber (g)	Fat (g)	Mono (g)	Poly (g)	Sat (g)
11246	Vege, leeks (bulb & lower leaf-portion) raw	1 leek	89	54.29	1.335	12.593	1.602	0.267	0.004	0.148	0.036
11795	Vege, leeks (bulbs & lower leaves) boiled w/salt, drained	1 leek	124	38.44	1.004	9.449	1.24	0.248	0.004	0.138	0.033
11250	Vege, lettuce, butterhead (Boston/bibb) leaves, raw	1 leaf, medium	7.5	0.975	0.101	0.167	0.083	0.016	0.001	0.009	0.002
11251	Vege, lettuce, cos/romaine, raw	1 inner leaf	10	1.7	0.123	0.329	0.21	0.03	0.001	0.016	0.004
11252	Vege, lettuce, iceberg, head, raw	1 head, medium	539	53.9	4.366	11.265	5.39	0.593	0.022	0.296	0.075
11253	Vege, lettuce, looseleaf, raw	1 leaf	10	1.5	0.136	0.279	0.13	0.015	0.001	0.008	0.002
11799	Vege, mustard greens, boiled w/salt, drained	1 cup, chopped	140	21	3.164	2.94	2.8	0.336	0.154	0.064	0.017
11270	Vege, mustard greens, raw	1 cup, chopped	56	14.56	1.512	2.744	1.848	0.112	0.052	0.021	0.006
11803	Vege, okra, boiled w/salt, drained	.5 cup slices	80	17.6	1.496	3.608	2	0.168	0.022	0.037	0.036
11278	Vege, okra, raw	1 cup	100	31	2	7.03	3.2	0.1	0.017	0.027	0.026
11296	Vege, onion rings, breaded, par fried, frozen, oven heated	10 rings, large	71	288.97	3.791	27.094	0.923	18.957	7.715	3.63	6.095
11805	Vege, onions, boiled w/salt, chopped, drained	1 cup	210	92.4	2.856	21.315	2.94	0.399	0.057	0.153	0.065
11282	Vege, onions, chopped, raw	1 cup, chopped	160	67.2	1.472	16.176	2.24	0.128	0.037	0.099	0.042
11291	Vege, onions, spring (tops & bulb) chopped, raw	1 cup, chopped	100	32	1.83	7.34	2.6	0.19	0.027	0.074	0.032
11808	Vege, parsnip, boiled w/salt, drained	.5 cup, sliced	78	63.18	1.03	15.233	3.12	0.234	0.087	0.037	0.039
11298	Vege, parsnip, peeled, raw	1 cup, sliced	133	99.75	1.596	23.927	6.517	0.399	0.149	0.063	0.067
11318	Vege, peas & carrots, canned, regular pack, solids & liquid	1 cup	255	96.9	5.534	21.624	5.1	0.688	0.059	0.329	0.125
11809	Vege, peas w/edible pod-snow/sugar, boiled w/salt, drained	1 cup	160	67.2	5.232	11.28	4.48	0.368	0.037	0.16	0.07
11300	Vege, peas w/edible pod-snow/sugar, raw	1 cup, chopped	98	41.16	2.744	7.399	2.548	0.196	0.021	0.087	0.038
11811	Vege, peas, green, boiled w/salt, drained	1 cup	160	134.4	8.576	25.024	8.8	0.352	0.03	0.163	0.062
11308	Vege, peas, green, canned, regular pack, drained	1 cup	170	117.3	7.514	21.386	6.97	0.595	0.053	0.277	0.105
11304	Vege, peas, green, raw	1 cup	145	117.45	7.859	20.967	7.395	0.58	0.051	0.271	0.103
11980	Vege, pepper, chili, green, canned	1 cup	139	29.19	1.001	6.394	2.363	0.375	0.024	0.213	0.039
11979	Vege, pepper, jalapeno, raw	1 cup, sliced	90	27	1.215	5.319	2.52	0.558	0.03	0.287	0.056
11977	Vege, pepper, serrano, raw	1 pepper	6.1	1.952	0.106	0.409	0.226	0.027	0.001	0.014	0.004
11333	Vege, pepper, sweet, green, chopped/sliced, raw	1 medium	119	23.8	1.023	5.522	2.023	0.202	0.01	0.074	0.069
11821	Vege, pepper, sweet, red, raw	1 medium	119	30.94	1.178	7.176	2.38	0.357	0.008	0.186	0.07
11951	Vege, pepper, sweet, yellow, raw	1 medium	186	50.22	1.86	11.755	1.674	0.391			0.058
11937	Vege, pickles, cucumber, dill	1 medium	65	11.7	0.403	2.678	0.78	0.123	0.002	0.05	0.031
11940	Vege, pickles, cucumber, sweet, gherkins	1 gherkin (2-3/4" long)	25	29.25	0.093	7.952	0.275	0.065	0.001	0.026	0.017
11943	Vege, pimiento, canned	1 tbsp	12	2.76	0.132	0.612	0.228	0.036	0.002	0.019	0.005
11383	Vege, potato mashed, granules w/milk, prep w/water & margarine	1 cup	210	243.6	4.599	33.768	2.73	10.059	4.105	2.824	2.541
11672	Vege, potato pancakes, homemade	1 pancake	76	206.72	4.682	21.766	1.52	11.582	3.526	4.971	2.313
11414	Vege, potato salad, homemade	1 cup	250	357.5	6.7	27.925	3.25	20.5	6.2	9.342	3.572
11373	Vege, potato, au gratin, homemade w/butter	1 cup	245	323.4	12.397	27.612	4.41	18.596	5.265	0.676	11.596
11833	Vege, potato, boiled w/o skin & w/salt	1 medium	167	143.62	2.856	33.417	3.34	0.167	0.003	0.072	0.043
11376	Vege, potato, canned, drained	1 cup	180	108	2.538	24.498	4.14	0.378	0.009	0.16	0.097
11838	Vege, potato, french fries, frozen, oven heated, w/salt	10 strips	50	100	1.585	15.595	1.6	3.78	2.381	0.389	0.631
11391	Vege, potato, hashed brown, plain, frozen, cooked	1 patty, (approx 3" x 1-1/2" x 1/2")	29	63.22	0.916	8.149	0.58	3.335	1.49	0.384	1.303
11387	Vege, potato, scalloped, mix, prep w/H₂O, whole milk & butter	1 cup (unprepared)	245	227.85	5.194	31.287	2.695	10.535	2.972	0.475	6.451

Chol (g)	Calc (mg)	Iron (mg)	Mag (mg)	Phos (mg)	Pota (mg)	Sodi (mg)	Zinc (mg)	Vit A (RAE)	Vit C (mg)	Thia (mg)	Ribo (mg)	Niac (mg)	Vit B$_6$ (mg)	Vit B$_{12}$ (µg)	Vit E (mg)	Fol (µg)	Alc (g)
0	52.51	1.869	24.92	31.15	160.2	17.8	0.107	73.87	10.68	0.053	0.027	0.356	0.207	0	0.819	56.96	0
0	37.2	1.364	17.36	21.08	107.88	305.04	0.074	2.48	5.208	0.032	0.025	0.248	0.14	0		29.76	0
0	2.625	0.093	0.975	2.475	17.85	0.375	0.015	12.45	0.278	0.004	0.005	0.027	0.006	0	0.014	5.475	0
0	3.3	0.097	1.4	3	24.7	0.8	0.023	29	2.4	0.007	0.007	0.031	0.007	0	0.013	13.6	0
0	107.8	1.886	43.12	118.58	819.28	48.51	0.862	86.24	21.02	0.199	0.113	0.668	0.248	0	0.162	301.8	0
0	3.6	0.086	1.3	2.9	19.4	2.8	0.018	37	1.8	0.007	0.008	0.038	0.009	0	0.029	3.8	0
0	103.6	0.98	21	57.4	282.8	352.8	0.154	442.4	35.42	0.057	0.088	0.606	0.137	0	1.694	102.2	0
0	57.68	0.818	17.92	24.08	198.24	14	0.112	294	39.2	0.045	0.062	0.448	0.101	0	1.126	104.7	0
0	61.6	0.224	28.8	25.6	108	4.8	0.344	11.2	13.04	0.106	0.044	0.697	0.15	0	0.216	36.8	0
0	81	0.8	57	63	303	8	0.6	19	21.1	0.2	0.06	1	0.215	0	0.36	88	0
0	22.01	1.2	13.49	57.51	91.59	266.25	0.298	7.81	0.994	0.199	0.099	2.563	0.055	0		46.86	0
0	46.2	0.504	23.1	73.5	348.6	501.9	0.441	0	10.92	0.088	0.048	0.347	0.271	0	0.042	31.5	0
0	35.2	0.304	16	43.2	230.4	4.8	0.256	0	10.24	0.077	0.04	0.133	0.235	0	0.032	30.4	0
0	72	1.48	20	37	276	16	0.39	50	18.8	0.055	0.08	0.525	0.061	0	0.55	64	0
0	28.86	0.452	22.62	53.82	286.26	191.88	0.203	0	10.14	0.065	0.04	0.565	0.073	0		45.24	0
0	47.88	0.785	38.57	94.43	498.75	13.3	0.785	0	22.61	0.12	0.067	0.931	0.12	0	1.982	89.11	0
0	58.65	1.912	35.7	117.3	255	663	1.479	737	16.83	0.189	0.135	1.482	0.224	0		45.9	0
0	67.2	3.152	41.6	88	384	384	0.592	86.4	76.64	0.205	0.122	0.862	0.23	0	0.624	46.4	0
0	42.14	2.038	23.52	51.94	196	3.92	0.265	52.92	58.8	0.147	0.078	0.588	0.157	0	0.382	41.16	0
0	43.2	2.464	62.4	187.2	433.6	382.4	1.904	64	22.72	0.414	0.238	3.234	0.346	0	0.224	100.8	0
0	34	1.615	28.9	113.9	294.1	428.4	1.207	45.9	16.32	0.206	0.133	1.244	0.109	0	0.051	74.8	0
0	36.25	2.132	47.85	156.6	353.8	7.25	1.798	55.1	58	0.386	0.191	3.03	0.245	0	0.189	94.25	0
0	50.04	1.849	5.56	15.29	157.07	551.83	0.125	8.34	47.54	0.014	0.042	0.872	0.167	0		75.06	0
0	9	0.63	17.1	27.9	193.5	0.9	0.207	36	39.87	0.13	0.051	1.005	0.457	0	0.423	42.3	0
0	0.671	0.052	1.342	2.44	18.605	0.61	0.016	2.867	2.739	0.003	0.005	0.094	0.031	0	0.042	1.403	0
0	11.9	0.405	11.9	23.8	208.25	3.57	0.155	21.42	95.68	0.068	0.033	0.571	0.267	0	0.44	13.09	0
0	8.33	0.512	14.28	30.94	251.09	2.38	0.298	186.8	226.1	0.064	0.101	1.165	0.346	0	1.88	21.42	0
0	20.46	0.856	22.32	44.64	394.32	3.72	0.316	18.6	341.3	0.052	0.047	1.655	0.312	0		48.36	0
0	5.85	0.344	7.15	13.65	75.4	833.3	0.091	5.85	1.235	0.009	0.019	0.039	0.008	0	0.058	0.65	0
0	1	0.147	1	3	8	234.75	0.02	2.25	0.3	0.002	0.008	0.043	0.004	0	0.023	0.25	0
0	0.72	0.202	0.72	2.04	18.96	1.68	0.023	15.96	10.19	0.002	0.007	0.074	0.026	0	0.083	0.72	0
4.2	67.2	0.441	42	130.2	325.5	361.2	0.504	98.7	13.65	0.189	0.181	1.814	0.336	0.21	1.071	16.8	0
72.96	18.24	1.186	25.08	84.36	597.36	386.08	0.631	5.32	16.72	0.103	0.131	1.629	0.288	0.144		17.48	0
170	47.5	1.625	37.5	130	635	1322.5	0.775	80	25	0.192	0.15	2.225	0.353	0		17.5	0
56.35	291.55	1.568	49	276.85	970.2	1060.85	1.691	156.8	24.26	0.157	0.284	2.433	0.426	0		26.95	0
0	13.36	0.518	33.4	66.8	547.76	402.47	0.451	0	12.36	0.164	0.032	2.191	0.449	0	0.017	15.03	0
0	9	2.268	25.2	50.4	412.2	394.2	0.504	0	9.18	0.122	0.023	1.647	0.338	0	0.09	10.8	0
0	4	0.62	11	41	209	133	0.2	0	5.05	0.056	0.014	1.044	0.154	0		6	0
0	4.35	0.438	4.93	20.88	126.44	9.86	0.093	0	1.827	0.032	0.006	0.702	0.037	0	0.055	2.03	0
26.95	88.2	0.931	34.3	137.2	497.35	835.45	0.613	85.75	8.085	0.047	0.137	2.521	0.103	0	0.368	24.5	0

EvaluEat Code	Food Name	Amt	Wt (g)	Energy (kcal)	Prot (g)	Carb (g)	Fiber (g)	Fat (g)	Mono (g)	Poly (g)	Sat (g)
11830	Vege, potato, skin only, baked w/salt	1 skin	58	114.84	2.488	26.715	4.582	0.058	0.001	0.025	0.015
11426	Vege, pumpkin pie mix, canned	1 cup	270	280.8	2.943	71.253	22.41	0.351	0.043	0.019	0.175
11846	Vege, pumpkin, canned w/salt	1 cup	245	83.3	2.695	19.796	7.105	0.686	0.091	0.037	0.358
11952	Vege, radicchio, raw	1 cup, shredded	40	9.2	0.572	1.792	0.36	0.1	0.004	0.044	0.024
11430	Vege, radish, oriental (daikon) raw	1 radish (7" long)	338	60.84	2.028	13.858	5.408	0.338	0.057	0.152	0.101
11429	Vege, radish, slices, raw	1 large (1" to 1-1/4" dia)	9	1.44	0.061	0.306	0.144	0.009	0.002	0.004	0.003
11851	Vege, rutabaga, boiled w/salt, drained	.5 cup, mashed	120	46.8	1.548	10.488		0.264	0.032	0.114	0.035
11439	Vege, sauerkraut, canned, solids & liquid	1 cup	142	26.98	1.292	6.078	3.55	0.199	0.018	0.087	0.05
11445	Vege, seaweed, kelp, raw	2 tbsp (1/8 cup)	10	4.3	0.168	0.957	0.13	0.056	0.01	0.005	0.025
11667	Vege, seaweed, spirulina, dried	1 cup	15	43.5	8.621	3.585	0.54	1.158	0.101	0.312	0.398
11677	Vege, shallots, peeled, raw	1 tbsp, chopped	10	7.2	0.25	1.68		0.01	0.001	0.004	0.002
11658	Vege, spinach egg souffle, homemade	1 cup	136	218.96	10.989	2.829		18.36	6.835	3.082	7.148
11854	Vege, spinach, boiled w/salt, drained	1 cup	180	41.4	5.346	6.75	4.32	0.468	0.013	0.194	0.076
11461	Vege, spinach, canned, drained	1 cup	214	49.22	6.013	7.276	5.136	1.07	0.03	0.447	0.173
11457	Vege, spinach, raw	1 cup	30	6.9	0.858	1.089	0.66	0.117	0.003	0.05	0.019
11864	Vege, squash, acorn, peeled, baked w/salt	1 cup, cubes	205	114.8	2.296	29.889	9.02	0.287	0.02	0.121	0.059
11866	Vege, squash, butternut, baked w/salt	1 cup, cubes	205	82	1.845	21.504		0.185	0.014	0.078	0.039
11870	Vege, squash, spaghetti, baked or boiled w/salt, drained	1 cup	155	41.85	1.023	10.013	2.17	0.403	0.034	0.195	0.096
11857	Vege, squash, summer, all varieties, boiled w/salt, drained	1 cup, sliced	180	36	1.638	7.758	2.52	0.558	0.041	0.236	0.115
11863	Vege, squash, winter, all varieties, baked w/salt	1 cup, cubes	205	79.95	1.824	17.938	5.74	1.291	0.096	0.543	0.266
11477	Vege, squash, zucchini w/skin, slices, raw	1 cup, chopped	124	19.84	1.5	4.154	1.364	0.223	0.017	0.094	0.046
11861	Vege, squash, zucchini w/skin, boiled w/salt, drained	.5 cup, sliced	90	14.4	0.576	3.537	1.26	0.045	0.004	0.019	0.009
11871	Vege, succotash (corn & lima beans) boiled w/salt, drained	1 cup	192	220.8	9.734	46.81		1.536	0.298	0.732	0.284
11875	Vege, sweet potato, baked in skin w/salt	1 medium (2" dia, 5" long, raw)	114	102.6	2.291	23.609	3.762	0.171	0.001	0.073	0.039
11647	Vege, sweet potato, canned w/syrup, drained	1 cup	196	211.68	2.509	49.706	5.88	0.627	0.024	0.276	0.135
11878	Vege, taro, cooked w/salt	1 cup, sliced	132	187.44	0.686	45.672	6.732	0.145	0.012	0.061	0.03
11954	Vege, tomatillos, raw	1 medium	34	10.88	0.326	1.986	0.646	0.347	0.053	0.142	0.047
11887	Vege, tomato paste, canned w/salt	1 can (6 oz)	170	139.4	7.344	32.147	7.65	0.799	0.141	0.381	0.182
11888	Vege, tomato puree, canned w/salt	1 cup	250	95	4.125	22.45	4.75	0.525	0.078	0.215	0.072
11549	Vege, tomato sauce, canned	1 cup	245	78.4	3.234	18.056	3.675	0.588	0.091	0.24	0.083
11533	Vege, tomato, red, canned, stewed	1 cup	255	66.3	2.321	15.785	2.55	0.484	0.074	0.196	0.066
11531	Vege, tomato, red, canned, whole	1 cup	240	40.8	1.92	9.384	2.16	0.312	0.05	0.13	0.043
11883	Vege, tomato, red, cherry, ripe, raw, June–October	1 cup	149	31.29	1.266	6.914	1.639	0.492	0.075	0.201	0.067
11529	Vege, tomato, red, ripe, whole, raw	1 cup, chopped or sliced	180	32.4	1.584	7.056	2.16	0.36	0.09	0.243	0.081
11955	Vege, tomato, sun-dried	1 cup	54	139.32	7.619	30.11	6.642	1.604	0.263	0.602	0.23
11696	Vege, tomato, yellow, raw	1 tomato	212	31.8	2.078	6.318	1.484	0.551	0.085	0.229	0.076
11891	Vege, turnip greens, boiled w/salt, drained	1 cup, chopped	144	28.8	1.642	6.278	5.04	0.331	0.022	0.131	0.076
11889	Vege, turnip, boiled w/salt, drained	1 cup, cubes	156	32.76	1.108	7.644	3.12	0.125	0.008	0.066	0.012
11990	Vege, wasabi, root, raw	1 cup, sliced	130	141.7	6.24	30.602	10.14	0.819			
11590	Vege, waterchestnut, Chinese, canned, solids & liquid	.5 cup, sliced	70	35	0.616	8.61	1.75	0.042	0.001	0.018	0.011
11591	Vege, watercress, raw	1 cup, chopped	34	3.74	0.782	0.439	0.17	0.034	0.003	0.012	0.009
11897	Vege, yam, boiled or baked w/salt	1 cup, cubes	136	157.76	2.026	37.509	5.304	0.19	0.007	0.082	0.039

Chol (g)	Calc (mg)	Iron (mg)	Mag (mg)	Phos (mg)	Pota (mg)	Sodi (mg)	Zinc (mg)	Vit A (RAE)	Vit C (mg)	Thia (mg)	Ribo (mg)	Niac (mg)	Vit B6 (mg)	Vit B12 (µg)	Vit E (mg)	Fol (µg)	Alc (g)
0	19.72	4.083	24.94	58.58	332.34	149.06	0.284	0.58	7.83	0.071	0.061	1.778	0.356	0	0.023	12.76	0
0	99.9	2.862	43.2	121.5	372.6	561.6	0.729	1121	9.45	0.043	0.319	1.01	0.429	0		94.5	0
0	63.7	3.405	56.35	85.75	504.7	590.45	0.417	2702	10.29	0.059	0.132	0.899	0.137	0		29.4	0
0	7.6	0.228	5.2	16	120.8	8.8	0.248	0.4	3.2	0.006	0.011	0.102	0.023	0	0.904	24	0
0	91.26	1.352	54.08	77.74	767.26	70.98	0.507	0	74.36	0.068	0.068	0.676	0.155	0	0	94.64	0
0	2.25	0.031	0.9	1.8	20.97	3.51	0.025	0	1.332	0.001	0.004	0.023	0.006	0	0	2.25	0
0	57.6	0.636	27.6	67.2	391.2	304.8	0.42	0	22.56	0.098	0.049	0.858	0.122	0	0.384	18	0
0	42.6	2.087	18.46	28.4	241.4	938.62	0.27	1.42	20.87	0.03	0.031	0.203	0.185	0	0.142	34.08	0
0	16.8	0.285	12.1	4.2	8.9	23.3	0.123	0.6	0.3	0.005	0.015	0.047	0	0	0.087	18	0
0	18	4.275	29.25	17.7	204.45	157.2	0.3	4.35	1.515	0.357	0.551	1.923	0.055	0	0.75	14.1	0
0	3.7	0.12	2.1	6	33.4	1.2	0.04	6	0.8	0.006	0.002	0.02	0.034	0		3.4	0
183.6	229.84	1.346	38.08	231.2	201.28	762.96	1.292	266.6	2.992	0.091	0.305	0.477	0.12	1.36		80.24	0
0	244.8	6.426	156.6	100.8	838.8	550.8	1.368	943.2	17.64	0.171	0.425	0.882	0.436	0	3.744	262.8	0
0	271.78	4.922	162.64	94.16	740.44	57.78	0.984	1049	30.6	0.034	0.295	0.83	0.214	0	4.152	209.7	0
0	29.7	0.813	23.7	14.7	167.4	23.7	0.159	140.7	8.43	0.023	0.057	0.217	0.058	0	0.609	58.2	0
0	90.2	1.906	88.15	92.25	895.85	492	0.348	43.05	22.14	0.342	0.027	1.806	0.398	0		38.95	0
0	84.05	1.23	59.45	55.35	582.2	492	0.266	717.5	30.96	0.148	0.035	1.986	0.254	0		38.95	0
0	32.55	0.527	17.05		181.35	393.7	0.31	9.3	5.425	0.059	0.034	1.255	0.153	0		12.4	0
0	48.6	0.648	43.2	70.2	345.6	426.6	0.702	246.6	9.9	0.079	0.074	0.923	0.117	0	0.126	36	0
0	28.7	0.677	16.4	41	895.85	485.85	0.533	364.9	19.68	0.174	0.049	1.437	0.148	0		57.4	0
0	18.6	0.434	21.08	47.12	324.88	12.4	0.36	12.4	21.08	0.06	0.176	0.604	0.27	0	0.149	35.96	0
0	11.7	0.315	19.8	36	227.7	215.1	0.162	50.4	4.14	0.037	0.037	0.385	0.07	0	0.108	15.3	0
0	32.64	2.918	101.76	224.64	787.2	485.76	1.21	28.8	15.74	0.323	0.184	2.548	0.223	0		63.36	0
0	43.32	0.787	30.78	61.56	541.5	280.44	0.365	1096	22.34	1.65	0.121	1.695	0.326	0	0.809	6.84	0
0	33.32	1.862	23.52	49	378.28	76.44	0.314	701.7	21.17	0.049	0.074	0.666	0.122	0	0.549	15.68	0
0	23.76	0.95	39.6	100.32	638.88	331.32	0.356	0	6.6	0.141	0.037	0.673	0.437	0		25.08	0
0	2.38	0.211	6.8	13.26	91.12	0.34	0.075	2.04	3.978	0.015	0.012	0.629	0.019	0	0.129	2.38	0
0	61.2	5.066	71.4	141.1	1723.8	1343	1.071	129.2	37.23	0.102	0.26	5.229	0.367	0	7.31	20.4	0
0	45	4.45	57.5	100	1097.5	997.5	0.9	65	26.5	0.063	0.2	3.665	0.315	0	4.925	27.5	0
0	31.85	2.499	39.2	63.7	810.95	1283.8	0.49	41.65	17.15	0.059	0.162	2.389	0.238	0	5.096	22.05	0
0	86.7	3.391	30.6	51	527.85	563.55	0.433	22.95	20.15	0.117	0.089	1.821	0.043	0	2.116	12.75	0
0	74.4	2.328	26.4	45.6	451.2	307.2	0.336	14.4	21.6	0.108	0.113	1.764	0.216	0	1.704	19.2	0
0	7.45	0.67	16.39	35.76	330.78	13.41	0.134	46.19	38.74	0.088	0.072	0.936	0.119	0	0.507	22.35	0
0	18	0.486	19.8	43.2	426.6	9	0.306	75.6	22.86	0.067	0.034	1.069	0.144	0	0.972	27	0
0	59.4	4.909	104.76	192.24	1850.58	1131.3	1.075	23.76	21.17	0.285	0.264	4.887	0.179	0	0.005	36.72	0
0	23.32	1.039	25.44	76.32	546.96	48.76	0.594	0	19.08	0.087	0.1	2.499	0.119	0		63.6	0
0	197.28	1.152	31.68	41.76	292.32	381.6	0.202	548.6	39.46	0.065	0.104	0.592	0.259	0	2.707	169.9	0
0	34.32	0.343	12.48	29.64	210.6	446.16	0.312	0	18.1	0.042	0.036	0.466	0.105	0		14.04	0
0	166.4	1.339	89.7	104	738.4	22.1	2.106	2.6	54.47	0.17	0.148	0.966	0.356	0		23.4	0
0	2.8	0.609	3.5	13.3	82.6	5.6	0.266	0	0.91	0.008	0.017	0.252	0.111	0	0.35	4.2	0
0	40.8	0.068	7.14	20.4	112.2	13.94	0.037	79.9	14.62	0.031	0.041	0.068	0.044	0	0.34	3.06	0
0	19.04	0.707	24.48	66.64	911.2	331.84	0.272	8.16	16.46	0.129	0.038	0.751	0.31	0	0.517	21.76	0

EvaluEat Code	Food Name	Amt	Wt (g)	Energy (kcal)	Prot (g)	Carb (g)	Fiber (g)	Fat (g)	Mono (g)	Poly (g)	Sat (g)
11601	Vege, yam, peeled, raw	1 cup, cubes	150	177	2.295	41.82	6.15	0.255	0.009	0.114	0.056
11603	Vege, yambean (jicama) peeled, slices, raw	1 cup, sliced	120	45.6	0.864	10.584	5.88	0.108	0.006	0.052	0.025
14187	Vegetable beverage, clam & tomato juice, canned	1 can (5.5 oz)	166	79.68	0.996	18.177	0.332	0.332	0.013	0.033	0.08
11578	Vegetable juice cocktail, canned	1 cup	242	45.98	1.525	11.011	1.936	0.218	0.034	0.092	0.031
11159	Vegetable salad, coleslaw, homemade	.5 cup	60	41.4	0.774	7.446	0.9	1.566	0.425	0.811	0.231
11894	Vegetables, mixed, frozen, boiled w/salt, drained	.5 cup	91	53.69	2.603	11.912	4.004	0.137	0.009	0.066	0.028
43134	Vegetarian fillets	1 cup	186	539.4	42.78	16.74	11.346	33.48	8.139	17.358	5.299
43137	Vegetarian meatloaf or patties	1 cup	186	366.42	39.06	14.88	8.556	16.74	4.07	8.679	2.65
43136	Vegetarian stew	1 cup	186	228.78	31.62	13.02	2.046	5.58	1.356	2.892	0.883
22121	Vegetarian, Better'n Burgers/vegan burgers, frozen/Worthington, Morningstar	1 patty	85	90.95	13.906	7.531	4.25	0.535	0.318	0.173	0.107
22122	Vegetarian, breakfast patties/Worthington, Morningstar	1 patty	38	79.42	9.918	3.716	1.976	2.77	0.688	1.319	0.509
22120	Vegetarian, burger crumbles/Worthington, Morningstar	1 cup	110	231	22.154	6.622	5.06	12.925	4.628	4.925	3.257
22215	Vegetarian, chili w/beans, canned entree/Nestle Chef-Mate	1 cup	253	412.39	17.735	29.044	11.132	25.022	10.747	1.397	10.93
22119	Vegetarian, deli franks/Worthington, Morningstar	1 serving	45	111.6	10.386	3.699	2.745	6.16	1.953	3.314	0.893
22118	Vegetarian, garden patties, frozen/Worthington, Morningstar	1 patty	67	119.26	11.209	10.204	4.02	3.765	1.065	2.161	0.539
22125	Vegetarian, Harvest Burger, original flavor, vegetable protein patty	1 patty	90	137.7	18	7.02	5.67	4.14	2.135	0.265	1.017
22223	Vegetarian, macaroni and cheese, canned entree/Nestle Chef-Mate	1 cup	253	283.36	10.803	35.42	3.289	11.005	3.026	0.524	6.199
22128	Vegetarian, Natural Touch Vegan Burgers, frozen/Worthington	1 patty	85	90.95	13.906	7.531	4.25	0.535	0.318	0.173	0.107
22123	Vegetarian, Spicy Black Bean Burger/Worthington, Morningstar	1 patty	78	114.66	11.786	15.202	4.758	0.78	0.25	0.351	0.179
2048	Vinegar, cider	1 tbsp	15	2.1	0	0.885	0	0	0	0	0
2053	Vinegar, distilled	1 tbsp	13	1.56	0	0.65	0	0	0	0	0
48052	Vital wheat gluten	1 cup	148	547.6	111.24	20.409	0.888	2.738	0.231	1.199	0.403
18505	Waffle, Eggo Lowfat Homestyle/Kellogg	1 waffle, round (4" dia)	35	82.6	2.471	15.453	0.35	1.246	0.35	0.375	0.315
18367	Waffle, plain, homemade	1 waffle, round (7" dia)	75	218.25	5.925	24.675		10.575	2.641	5.089	2.149
18365	Waffle, plain/buttermilk, frozen, ready-to-heat	1 waffle square	39	97.89	2.301	15.054	0.858	3.042	1.23	1.081	0.505
1072	Whipped dessert topping, nondairy, pressurized can	1 tbsp	4	10.56	0.039	0.643	0	0.892	0.077	0.01	0.756
1073	Whipped dessert topping, nondairy, semi-solid, frozen	1 tbsp	4	12.72	0.05	0.922	0	1.012	0.065	0.021	0.871
42135	Whipped topping, frozen, low-fat	1 oz	28.34	62.348	0.85	6.688	0	3.713	0.237	0.076	3.195
43406	Yeast extract spread	1 fl. oz.	29.8	47.084	8.284	3.516	0.894	0	0	0	0
19393	Yogurt, frozen, chocolate, soft serve	.5 cup (4 fl. oz.)	72	115.2	2.88	17.928	1.584	4.32	1.26	0.158	2.614
43261	Yogurt, fruit variety, nonfat	1 cup	186	174.84	8.184	35.34	0	0.372	0.093	0.03	0.221
1121	Yogurt, lowfat w/fruit, 10 g protein/8 oz	1 cup (8 fl. oz.)	245	249.9	10.707	46.673	0	2.646	0.728	0.076	1.708
1117	Yogurt, lowfat, plain, 12 g protein/8 oz	1 cup (8 fl. oz.)	245	154.35	12.863	17.248	0	3.797	1.044	0.108	2.45
1116	Yogurt, whole milk, plain, 8 g protein/8 oz	1 cup (8 fl. oz.)	245	149.45	8.502	11.417	0	7.963	2.188	0.225	5.135

Chol (g)	Calc (mg)	Iron (mg)	Mag (mg)	Phos (mg)	Pota (mg)	Sodi (mg)	Zinc (mg)	Vit A (RAE)	Vit C (mg)	Thia (mg)	Ribo (mg)	Niac (mg)	Vit B_6 (mg)	Vit B_{12} (µg)	Vit E (mg)	Fol (µg)	Alc (g)
0	25.5	0.81	31.5	82.5	1224	13.5	0.36	10.5	25.65	0.168	0.048	0.828	0.44	0	0.585	34.5	0
0	14.4	0.72	14.4	21.6	180	4.8	0.192	1.2	24.24	0.024	0.035	0.24	0.05	0	0.552	14.4	0
0	19.92	0.996	36.52	129.48	149.4	600.92	1.793	18.26	6.806	0.066	0.05	0.315	0.139	50.796		26.56	0
0	26.62	1.016	26.62	41.14	467.06	653.4	0.484	188.8	67.03	0.104	0.068	1.757	0.339	0	12.1	50.82	0
4.8	27	0.354	6	19.2	108.6	13.8	0.12	31.8	19.62	0.04	0.037	0.163	0.076	0		16.2	0
0	22.75	0.746	20.02	46.41	153.79	246.61	0.446	194.7	2.912	0.065	0.109	0.774	0.067	0		17.29	0
0	176.7	3.72	42.78	837	1116	911.4	2.604	0	0	2.046	1.674	22.32	2.79	7.812	6.417	189.7	0
0	53.94	3.906	33.48	639.84	334.8	1023	3.348	0	0	1.674	1.116	18.6	2.232	4.464	3.218	145.1	0
0	57.66	2.418	236.22	409.2	223.2	744	2.046	87.42	0	1.302	1.116	22.32	2.046	4.092	0.911	191.6	0
0	86.7	2.899	16.15	181.05	433.5	382.5	0.748		0	0.256	0.553	4.113	0.198	0	0.009	245.7	0
0.76	18.24	1.919	1.14	106.4	101.84	259.16	0.369		0	5.385	0.133	1.835	0.19	1.497	0.298		0
0	79.2	6.402	2.2	173.8	178.2	476.3	1.639		0	9.922	0.352	2.981	0.539	4.367	0.689		0
55.66	88.55	4.832	45.54	166.98	511.06	1171.39	3.871		0.759	0.106	0.202	3.476	0.228	1.442	1.209		0
0.45	17.1	0.608	3.6	42.3	49.95	430.65	0.378		0	0.144	0.022	0	0.012	0.009	1.256		0
0.67	48.24	1.213	29.48	123.95	179.56	381.9	0.576	134	0	6.465	0.101	0	0	0	0.549	58.96	0
0	101.7	3.852	70.2	225	432	411.3	8.073		0	0.315	0.198	6.3	0.387	0	1.557	21.6	0
27.83	202.4	1.923	32.89	250.47	151.8	1343.43	1.569		0	0.319	0.331	2.505	0.071	0.202	0.159		0
0	86.7	2.899	16.15	181.05	433.5	382.5	0.748		0	0.256	0.553	4.113	0.198	0	0.009	245.7	0
0.78	56.16	1.841	43.68	149.76	269.1	499.2	0.928		0	8.057	0.14	0	0.211	0.07	0.359		0
0	0.9	0.09	3.3	1.35	15	0.15	0	0	0	0	0	0	0	0	0	0	0
0	0	0	2.86	0	1.95	0.13	0	0	0	0	0	0	0	0	0	0	0
0	210.16	7.696	37	384.8	148	42.92	1.258	0	0	0	0	0	0	0	0	0	0
8.75	20.3	1.946	23.8	28.35	50.05	154.7			0	0.308	0.259	2.593	0.164	0.549		26.95	
51.75	191.25	1.732	14.25	142.5	119.25	383.25	0.51	48.75	0.3	0.197	0.26	1.555	0.042	0.188		34.5	0
12.48	86.19	1.657	8.19	155.61	47.58	291.72	0.214	149	0	0.178	0.196	1.826	0.369	0.928	0.246	23.79	0
0	0.2	0.001	0.04	0.72	0.76	2.48	0	0.16	0	0	0	0	0	0	0.034	0	0
0	0.24	0.005	0.08	0.32	0.72	1	0.001	0.28	0	0	0	0	0	0	0.038	0	0
0.567	20.121	0.028	1.984	20.972	28.623	20.405	0.028	1.134	0	0.006	0.026	0.028	0.006	0.057	0.142	0.85	0
0	25.628	1.103	53.64	30.992	774.8	1072.8	0.626	0	0	2.891	4.261	28.906	0.387	0.149	0	301	0
3.6	105.84	0.9	19.44	100.08	187.92	70.56	0.353	31.68	0.216	0.026	0.152	0.22	0.053	0.209	0.097	7.92	0
3.72	282.72	0.13	27.9	221.34	360.84	107.88	1.376	3.72	1.302	0.074	0.335	0.186	0.074	0.874	0.112	16.74	0
9.8	372.4	0.171	36.75	291.55	477.75	142.1	1.813	24.5	1.715	0.091	0.436	0.233	0.098	1.151	0.049	22.05	0
14.7	448.35	0.196	41.65	352.8	573.3	171.5	2.181	34.3	1.96	0.108	0.524	0.279	0.12	1.372	0.073	26.95	0
31.85	296.45	0.123	29.4	232.75	379.75	112.7	1.446	66.15	1.225	0.071	0.348	0.184	0.078	0.907	0.147	17.15	0

CALCULATIONS AND CONVERSIONS

Calculation and Conversion Aids

Commonly Used Metric Units

millimetre (mm): one-thousandth of a metre (0.001)
centimetre (cm): one-hundredth of a metre (0.01)
kilometre (km): one-thousand times a metre (1000)
kilogram (kg): one-thousand times a gram (1000)
milligram (mg): one-thousandth of a gram (0.001)
microgram (µg): one-millionth of a gram (0.000001)
millilitre (mL): one-thousandth of a litre (0.001)

International Units

Some vitamin supplements may report vitamin content as International Units (IU).

To convert IU to:

- Micrograms of vitamin D (cholecalciferol), divide the IU value by 40 or multiply by 0.025.
- Milligrams of vitamin E (alpha-tocopherol), divide the IU value by 1.5 if vitamin E is from natural sources. Divide the IU value by 2.22 if vitamin E is from synthetic sources.
- Vitamin A: 1 IU = 0.3 µg retinol or 3.6 µg beta-carotene

Retinol Activity Equivalents

Retinol activity equivalents (RAE) are a standardized unit of measure for vitamin A. RAE account for the various differences in bioavailability from sources of vitamin A. Many supplements will report vitamin A content in IU, as shown above, or retinol equivalents (RE).

1 RAE = 1 µg retinol
12 µg beta-carotene
24 µg other vitamin A carotenoids

To calculate RAE from the RE value of vitamin carotenoids in foods, divide RE by 2.

For vitamin A supplements and foods fortified with vitamin A, 1 RE = 1 RAE.

Folate

Folate is measured as dietary folate equivalents (DFE). DFE account for the different factors affecting bioavailability of folate sources.

1 DFE = 1 µg food folate
0.6 µg folate from fortified foods
0.5 µg folate supplement taken on an empty stomach
0.6 µg folate as a supplement consumed with a meal

To convert micrograms of synthetic folate, such as that found in supplements or fortified foods, to DFE:

$$\text{µg synthetic folate} \times 1.7 = \text{µg DFE}$$

For naturally occurring food folate, such as spinach, each microgram of folate equals 1 microgram DFE:

$$\text{µg folate} = \text{µg DFE}$$

Conversion Factors

Original	Unit Multiply by	To Get
grams	28.3495	ounces avdp
pounds	0.0625	ounces
kilograms	0.4536	pounds
ounces	16	pounds
ounces	0.0353	grams
pounds	0.002205	grams
pounds	2.2046	kilograms
pints (dry)	1.8162	litres
pints (liquid)	2.1134	litres
quarts (dry)	0.9081	litres
quarts (liquid)	1.0567	litres
gallons (imperial)	0.2642	litres
litres	0.5506	pints (dry)
litres	0.4732	pints (liquid)
litres	1.1012	quarts (dry)
litres	0.9463	quarts (liquid)
litres	3.7853	gallons (Imperial)
inches	0.0394	millimetres
inches	0.3937	centimetres
feet	0.03281	centimetres
millimetres	25.4000	inches
centimetres	2.5400	inches
metres	0.0254	inches
metres	0.3048	feet
feet	3.2808	metres
yards	1.0936	metres
cubic metres	0.0283	cubic feet
cubic feet	35.03145	cubic metres
cubic yards	1.3079	cubic metres
cubic metres	0.7646	cubic yards

Length: Imperial and Metric Equivalents

¼ inch = 0.6 centimetres
1 inch = 2.5 centimetres
1 foot = 0.3048 metre
= 30.48 centimetres
1 yard = 0.91144 metre
1 millimetre = 0.03937 inch
1 centimetre = 0.3937 inch
1 decimetre = 3.937 inches
1 metre = 39.37 inches
= 1.094 yards
1 micron = 0.00003937 inch

Weights and Measures

Food Measurement Equivalencies from U.S. to Metric

Capacity

¼ teaspoon =	1.25 millilitres
½ teaspoon =	2.5 millilitres
1 teaspoon =	5 millilitres
1 tablespoon =	15 millilitres
1 fluid ounce =	28.4 millilitres
¼ cup =	65 millilitres
⅓ cup =	80 millilitres
½ cup =	125 millilitres
1 cup =	250 millilitres
1 U.S. pint (2 cups) =	473 millilitres
1 quart (4 cups) =	0.95 litre
1 litre (1.06 quarts) =	1000 millilitres
1 gallon (4 quarts) =	3.84 litres

Weight

0.035 ounce =	1 gram
1 ounce =	28 grams
¼ pound (4 ounces) =	114 grams
1 pound (16 ounces) =	454 grams
2.2 pounds (35 ounces) =	1 kilogram

Food Measurement Equivalents

3 teaspoons =	1 tablespoon
½ tablespoon =	1½ teaspoons
2 tablespoons =	⅛ cup
4 tablespoons =	¼ cup
5 tablespoons + 1 teaspoon =	⅓ cup
8 tablespoons =	½ cup
10 tablespoons + 2 teaspoons =	⅔ cup
12 tablespoons =	¾ cup

16 tablespoons =	1 cup
2 cups =	1 pint
4 cups =	1 quart
2 pints =	1 quart
4 quarts =	1 gallon

Volumes and Capacities

1 cup =	8 fluid ounces
	½ liquid pint
1 millilitre =	0.061 cubic inches
1 litre =	1.057 liquid quarts
	0.908 dry quart
	61.024 cubic inches
1 U.S. gallon =	231 cubic inches
	3.785 litres
	0.833 British gallon
	128 U.S fluid ounces
1 British Imperial gallon =	277.42 cubic inches
	1.201 U.S gallons
	4.546 litres
	160 British fluid ounces
1 U.S. ounce, liquid or fluid =	1.805 cubic inches
	29.574 millilitres
	1.041 British fluid ounces
1 pint, dry =	33.600 cubic inches
	0.551 litre
1 pint, liquid =	28.875 cubic inches
	0.473 litre
1 U.S. quart, dry =	67.201 cubic inches
	1.101 litres
1 U.S. quart, liquid =	57.75 cubic inches
	0.946 litre
1 British quart =	69.354 cubic inches
	1.032 U.S. quarts, dry
	1.201 U.S. quarts, liquid

ANSWERS TO REVIEW QUESTIONS

Chapter 1

1. **d.** micronutrients.
2. **d.** all of the above.
3. **c.** contain 370 kJ (90 kcal) of energy.
4. **d.** "A high-protein diet increases the risk for porous bones" is an example of a hypothesis.
5. **b.** Water-soluble vitamins can never be toxic.
6. **c.** are all primary sources of energy.
7. **d.** Recommended Dietary Allowance
8. **c.** Produce energy.
9. **d.** Fats are insoluble in water.
10. The difference between a trace and a major mineral is in how much we need to consume daily. We need to consume 100 milligrams or more of major minerals each day, but trace minerals are required in amounts less than 100 milligrams per day.
11. Both the EAR and RDA refer to the average daily nutrition intake levels for healthy individuals in a particular life stage and gender group. However, the EAR levels will meet the requirement of half while the RDA will meet the requirements of most (97%–98%) of these people.
12. When looking for nutrition information, you have to be wary of supposedly "expert" sources of information. Trustworthy experts are educated and credentialed. In Canada, look for registered dietitians (RD, RDN, PDt, or RDt) for reputable nutrition information. Registered dietitians are professionals who have completed an accredited undergraduate program and dietetic internship.

    In addition, government sources of information are also trustworthy. For example, Health Canada is the federal agency that protects the health and safety of Canadians. Governments will provide health information that is both trustworthy and reputable.

    The internet is full of nutrition-related information, but you have to be careful when choosing dependable sources of information. Look for website extensions .org, .edu, or .gov for organization, educational institution, and government sites. You should be wary of the information on sites ending with .com.
13. A chocolate study funded by the chocolate industry may have different results from the same study funded by a health research organization (e.g., Heart and Stroke Foundation), as each have different agendas and interests.
14. The characteristics of the study sample are very different from those of your mother. Your mother is younger, more active, and has lower blood pressure than the study's sample population. Moreover, half of the study's sample are smokers, which could influence the results of the study since data is averaged across participants. Meanwhile, your mother is a non-smoker. These two issues could cause you to doubt the study's relevance to your mother.

    In addition, the study was only based on 12 participants. It is difficult to apply the results of this study to everyone based on so few study participants.

Chapter 2

1. **d.** The % daily values of select nutrients in a serving of the packaged food.
2. **b.** provides enough of the energy, nutrients, and fibre to maintain a person's health.
3. **d.** Protein and iron
4. **a.** meets a set of criteria by the Canadian Heart and Stroke Foundation for a "heart-healthy" choice.
5. **b.** Foods with a lot of nutrients relative to their energy content, such as fish, are more nutritious choices than foods with fewer nutrients, such as candy.
6. **c.** If omega-3 polyunsaturated fats are listed, omega-6 polyunsaturated fats must be listed as well.
7. Eating out can be a part of a nutritious diet, but careful choices need to be made. Suggestions include choosing smaller-sized items, ordering grilled or broiled meats, avoiding fried foods, choosing steamed vegetables, avoiding rich appetizers and desserts, and eating half of the meal and taking the rest home.
8. The Percent Daily Values show how much one serving of food contributes to the overall requirement for various nutrients. By comparing the %DV of a nutrient (e.g., iron) in one product with a similar product, you can determine which of the two products is a better choice for that nutrient.
9. Different people need different amounts of food. Everyone has different dietary needs, preferences, and limitations. For example, a petite woman who is lightly active will require different energy and nutrient intakes compared to a highly active man.
10. A traditional Mediterranean diet includes olive oil as the main dietary fat, moderate amounts of meats and eggs, and sweets a few times each week. In addition, this diet is high in fibre, vitamins, and minerals due to the regular consumption of bread, pasta, grains (couscous, bulgur, and beans), legumes, nuts, vegetables, cheese and yogurt, and fish.
11. Do not agree. With child obesity on the rise, it is not a surprise to find that Canadian youth are reported to consume less than 5 servings of fruits and vegetables a day. While vending machines are important for extra school income, their presence and food offerings do not encourage a nutritious diet with plenty of fruits and vegetables, and "empty calorie" snacks may contribute to overweight and obesity.
12. Agree. All food offerings in schools should be aligned with the nutrition education in the curriculum taught. To combat child obesity, it is important to encourage healthy eating and physical activity behaviours from a young age.

    Disagree: Schools that run on already-tight budgets will be concerned with the removal of vending machines and thus the loss of extra income. The funds generated from these machines are used to purchase much-needed items for the school. Lack of income may compromise the quality of education the school can offer. Moreover, children need to learn to choose wisely for themselves. Outside of school boundaries, vending machines and low nutrient foods will not be hidden.

Chapter 3

1. **c.** atoms, molecules, cells, tissues, organs, systems
2. **d.** emulsifies fats.
3. **c.** hypothalamus.
4. **a.** seepage of gastric acid into the esophagus.
5. **c.** small intestine.
6. **b.** hunger, a physiological response.
7. **c.** Stomach
8. a) Joyce first experienced digestion when she stopped to choose from all the different breakfast foods. During this process, her brain prepared her digestive organs for the consumption of food.

    b) Vitamins and minerals are small compounds that are mainly absorbed in the small intestine.

    c) To protect herself from traveller's diarrhea, Joyce should avoid fruit that has been prepared and cut up (pineapple rings, honeydew chunks, grape clusters). She should choose fruit with peels intact such as bananas and oranges.
9. **a.** wheat, rye, and barley.
10. Aside from medications to relieve constipation, stress management, regular physical activity, eating smaller meals, avoiding

foods that exacerbate symptoms, eating a higher-fibre diet, and drinking at least six to eight glasses of water each day can also help with prevention or relief.

11. The lining of the small intestine is heavily folded so that there is a greater surface area for nutrient absorption. If the lining of the small intestine was smooth, fewer nutrients would be absorbed because there would be less surface area for absorption. As a result, it would be more difficult for us to meet our requirements for all the nutrients we need for daily living.

12. Heartburn. Some people may at times secrete too much HCl or have their gastroesophageal sphincter open up too soon (especially after lying down). The result is that gastric juices that contain HCl seep back up into the esophagus and cause a burning sensation in the chest area.

Chapter 4

1. **b.** potential of foods to raise blood glucose and insulin levels.
2. **d.** carbon, hydrogen, and oxygen.
3. **d.** sweetened soft drinks.
4. **a.** monosaccharides.
5. **a.** phenylketonuria.
6. **c.** glucagon.
7. **b.** glucose + galactose
8. **d.** Speeds up movement of contents in the large intestine
9. **c.** Sugar causes diabetes
10. **c.** Bloating and cramping are common symptoms they experience.
11. **a.** gluconeogenesis.
12. Soluble fibre absorbs water and forms gels that slow down the movement of food through the small intestine.

    Insoluble fibre does the opposite. It attracts and clings to water and thus speeds up the movement of food through the large intestine.

13. High fibre intake may help prevent hemorrhoids, reduce the risk of diverticulosis and heart disease, enhance weight loss, lower the risk of type 2 diabetes, and promote regular bowel movements. Recent research on the association between dietary fibre intakes and colon cancer is mixed, and it is no longer clear if high fibre intakes are associated with a reduced risk of colon cancer.

14. Complex carbohydrates break down slowly, helping you to sustain satiety (or that "full" feeling). This may help to prevent overeating, which increases the risk of obesity and heart disease. Simple carbohydrates include most commercial bakery products, sugary soft drinks, sugary cereals, white bread, and white rice. They break down quickly in the body, leaving you feeling hungry sooner. Moreover, simple carbohydrates are blamed for many health problems such as tooth decay and high levels of blood triglycerides, and they may have a role in obesity.

15. Cells of many obese people are less responsive to insulin and thus these people are said to have "insulin insensitivity." The pancreas tries to fix this by secreting more insulin. With time, the pancreas will have to secrete more and more insulin for normal blood glucose levels. Eventually, the pancreas will be incapable of secreting more and the beta cells reduce or stop production of insulin, leading to type 2 diabetes.

16. i) Sonomi's meal is high in simple carbohydrates (e.g., apple juice) and in complex carbohydrates in the form of starch (e.g., spaghetti, bread, pudding). Starch molecules are long chains or branched chains of molecules of glucose, and when starch is completely digested, the end product is glucose. In this sense Matthieu is correct in declaring that the meal was made of mainly carbohydrates.

    ii) At the mouth, salivary amylase works to break down some of the starch into disaccharides that will be further digested later on in the small intestine. The stomach's acidic environment turns off all carbohydrate digestion. In the small intestine, pancreatic amylase enters to digest any remaining starches into disaccharides. In the microvilli,

maltase, sucrase, and lactase further digest the sugars into the monosaccharides glucose, fructose, and galactose. After the heavy carbohydrate meal, the liver converts these monosaccharides into glucose, which enters the blood and elevates her blood sugar levels. Insulin is released and it works to help the glucose leave the blood and enter the cells, where it is used for energy. Any excess glucose is converted to glycogen and stored in the liver and muscles for later energy use.

   iii) Sonomi could add in some protein in the form of meats or legumes in her pasta. Instead of the apple juice, she could have milk for a serving of dairy products. Because there is plenty of starch in her pasta, she could replace her piece of bread with a side of steamed vegetables or salad. For the same reasons, her pudding could be replaced with fruit for dessert.

Chapter 5

1. **d.** found in leafy green vegetables, flaxseeds, soy milk, and fish.
2. **b.** exercise regularly and watch portion sizes.
3. **a.** lipoprotein lipase.
4. **b.** consume a diet high in industrial *trans* fats.
5. **a.** monounsaturated fats.
6. **c.** Sterols are lipids containing a single ring structure.
7. **c.** Bile breaks fat into small droplets.
8. **b.** Low-density lipoproteins
9. Both *trans* and saturated fatty acids, because of their straight, rigid shape, can pack tightly together. Other fatty acids that contain one or more double bonds have bends or kinks in their shape, and tend to be more fluid at room temperature. Research over 20 years has shown that diets high in saturated fatty acids increase blood cholesterol and risk of heart disease. They appear to change cell membrane function and the way cholesterol is removed from the blood.

10. This is not particularly good advice for someone doing a walk-a-thon. Fat is a primary source of energy during rest and during less-intense exercise. In addition, we use predominantly more fat as we perform longer duration exercise. This is because we use more carbohydrates earlier during the exercise bout, and once our limited carbohydrate sources are depleted during prolonged exercise, we rely more on fat as an energy source. Although carbohydrates are an important source of energy during exercise, loading up on carbohydrates is typically only helpful for individuals who are doing longer duration exercise at intensities higher than those experienced during walking. As the primary goal of this walk-a-thon is to raise money and not to finish in record time, you can walk at a pace that matches your current fitness level. Thus, it would be prudent to consume adequate carbohydrates prior to and during the walk-a-thon, but loading up on carbohydrates is not necessary.

11. Your father probably had a blood test to determine his blood lipid levels, including total cholesterol, LDLs, HDLs, and triglycerides. Unfortunately, switching to cottage cheese and margarine will not necessarily improve his blood lipid values. Many types of margarine are high in *trans* fatty acids, and these increase our risk for heart disease. In addition, cottage cheese made from full-fat milk contains saturated fatty acids, which also increase blood lipid levels. Lower fat (skim, 1%, and 2%) cottage cheese would be a better choice, but there's no reason to exclude lean meats, skinless chicken, and fish from his diet. In fact, the omega-3 fatty acids in fish could possibly reduce your father's risk for some health problems.

    A non-dietary lifestyle choice that might improve his health is regular physical activity. Regular physical activity can help people maintain a more healthful body weight, can increase HDLs, and can also cause other changes that reduce our risk for heart disease.

12. Total energy needs = 8400 kJ or 2000 kcal per day
    Maximum AMDR for fat = 35% of total energy intake
    = 0.35 × 2000 = 700 calories

Saturated fat = 7% of total energy intake
= 0.07 × 2000 = 140 calories
Linoleic acid = 10% of total energy intake
= 0.10 × 2000 = 200 calories
Alpha-linolenic acid = 1.2% of total energy intake
= 0.012 × 2000 = 24 calories
Trans fatty acids = 0 calories

Chapter 6

1. **d.** mutual supplementation.
2. **a.** Rice, pinto beans, acorn squash, soy butter, and almond milk
3. **c.** protease.
4. **b.** amine group.
5. **c.** carbon, oxygen, hydrogen, and nitrogen.
6. **c.** Edema
7. **c.** Most enzymatic digestion occurs in the mouth
8. **d.** Amino acid bonding and attraction determine protein shape
9. **c.** 0.87
10. Adequate protein is needed to maintain the proper balance of fluids inside and outside of the cells. When a child suffers from kwashiorkor, the protein content of the blood is inadequate to maintain this balance. Fluid seeps from inside of the cells out to the tissue spaces and causes bloating and swelling of the abdomen.
11. In general, only people who are susceptible to kidney disease or who have kidney disease suffer serious consequences when eating a high-protein diet. Consuming a high-protein diet increases protein metabolism and urea production. Individuals with kidney disease or those who are at risk for kidney disease cannot adequately flush urea and other by-products of protein metabolism from the body through the kidneys. This inability can lead to serious health consequences and even death.
12. i) Proteins are critical for cell growth.
    ii) Proteins are critical for cell repair.
    iii) Proteins are critical for maintenance of cells.
    iv) Proteins are needed to make enzymes, which speed up chemical reactions and allow our bodies to function optimally.
    v) Proteins are used to make certain hormones, such as insulin. These hormones are important chemical messengers in our bodies.
    vi) Proteins assist in the maintenance of fluid and electrolyte balance.
    vii) Proteins assist in the maintenance of acid-base balance.
    viii) Proteins are critical for the development of antibodies, which are necessary for our immune system to work effectively.
    ix) Proteins can serve as a source of energy during times of low carbohydrate intake or starvation.
13. Listed here is one possibility.
    Breakfast: 250 mL (1 cup) skim milk, 2 slices whole wheat toast, 30 mL (2 Tbsp) peanut butter (on toast), 1 medium banana, 250 mL (8 fl. oz.) water
    Mid-morning Snack: 250 mL (1 cup) raw baby carrots, 30 mL (2 Tbsp) walnuts, 375 mL (12 fl. oz.) water
    Lunch: 250 mL (1 cup) low-fat flavoured yogurt with 125 mL (½ cup) sliced strawberries, vegetarian sandwich (2 slices 9-grain bread, ¼ of an avocado, 3 slices tomato, 3 leaves of spinach, and 50 grams (2 oz.) Swiss cheese), 1 medium orange, 375 mL (12 fl. oz.) water
    Afternoon Snack: 250 mL (8 fl. oz.) cranberry juice, 8 whole wheat crackers, 1 hard-boiled egg, 250 mL (8 fl. oz.) water
    Dinner: 375 mL (1½ cups) cooked whole wheat spaghetti noodles, 250 mL (1 cup) meatless spaghetti sauce (includes tomatoes, broccoli, onions, and chopped spinach), 250 mL (1 cup) green salad (with red leaf lettuce, chopped green onion, 2 tomato wedges, shredded carrots, and sunflower seeds), 30 mL (2 Tbsp) low-fat Ranch salad dressing, 1 slice sourdough bread, broiled with 5 mL (1 tsp) butter and 15 mL (1 Tbsp) parmesan cheese, 375 mL (20 fl. oz.) water

Evening Snack: 250 mL (1 cup) skim or soy milk, 65 mL (¼ cup) dried apricots
Note: More water would be consumed throughout the day as needed.
14. See Figure 6.3.
15. I would inform Stuart's mother that while high-protein, low-carbohydrate diets are extremely popular, these "extreme" diets should be supervised by a qualified physician who knows the individual's health status. These diets also rely on high-quality protein foods, and can be expensive.

    The primary key to weight loss is to consume fewer calories than you expend. Thus, the individual on a high-protein diet needs to consume fewer calories than he/she expends to achieve weight loss.

    I would also inform Stuart's mother that a high-protein diet is synonymous with a low-carbohydrate diet, since carbohydrate foods are replaced by protein foods. However, the high-protein diet is also typically high in fat, especially saturated fat (in this situation, the foods consumed were steak, scrambled eggs with butter, and ice cream with nuts). Given the family history of heart disease, and the fact that Stuart's mother has high LDL cholesterol, a diet high in saturated fat could further add to her risk of heart disease.

    When the body receives inadequate amounts of dietary carbohydrates to use for energy, it will break down glycogen stored in the liver and muscle: this process is necessary to maintain blood glucose levels and to provide energy to the brain.

    Because water is stored along with glycogen, using stored carbohydrate for energy results in a loss of water from the body, which registers on the scales as rapid weight loss. Moreover, the deamination of excess protein results in an increased production of urea, a diuretic, and so more water is lost.

    The Acceptable Macronutrient Distribution Ranges for adults recommend that individuals consume 45%–65% of total daily energy as carbohydrate foods, and 10%–35% of total energy intake from protein foods.

    I would, however, advise Stuart's mother that the current safest, most sustainable method for healthy weight loss is a diet that is moderately reduced in energy, that contains ample fruits and vegetables and whole grains, adequate carbohydrates and protein, moderate amounts of total fat, and relatively low amounts of saturated fats. And coupled with that, I would suggest she increase her activity level.
16. Vegetarian diets can be somewhat of a challenge, particularly vegan diets. The vegetarian diet can be healthful; however, by limiting consumption of animal flesh and dairy products, there is potential for inadequate intake of certain nutrients. Since Haley is a vegan, she will need to monitor vitamins B_{12}, riboflavin, and D, as well as iron, calcium, and zinc. There are many excellent non-animal food sources that will provide these nutrients, and so meat is not truly essential in an athlete's diet, and Rabyah's claims about the role of meat are not really valid. Research does indicate that a sign of disordered eating in some female athletes is the switch to a vegetarian diet, because some athletes may use vegetarianism as an excuse to restrict many foods from their diets.

    The challenge for the vegan is to plan a well-balanced diet, and in developed countries it is quite easy to find adequate protein sources for a person who doesn't eat animal products. The emphasis should be upon balance and adequacy of the diet, and so the vegan must eat complementary proteins and would likely benefit from taking a multivitamin and a mineral supplement. Therefore, Haley's vegan diet can be a healthy diet if she takes the time to become informed about adequacy and balance in her food consumption.

Chapter 7

1. **b.** It can be found in fresh fruits and vegetables.
2. **d.** A healthy infant of average weight.

3. **a.** extracellular fluid.
4. **d.** It is freely permeable to water but not to solutes.
5. **d.** all of the above.
6. **a.** Substances that increase urine output and therefore increase fluid loss.
7. **c.** Baked ham
8. **d.** Baked potato
9. Chronic diarrhea in a young child can lead to severe dehydration very quickly due to his or her small body size. Diarrhea causes excessive fluid loss from the intestinal tract and extracellular fluid compartment. This fluid loss causes a rise in extracellular electrolyte concentration, and intracellular fluid leaves the cells in an attempt to balance the extracellular fluid loss. These alterations in fluid and electrolyte balance change the flow of electrical impulses through the heart and can lead to abnormal heart rhythms and death if left untreated.
10. One possible cause of these symptoms is dehydration. You most likely lost a significant amount of fluid during the cross-country relay race. In addition, you consumed a few beers after the race. Beer is a diuretic, which causes you to lose even more fluid. The "pins and needles" feeling in your extremities is consistent with a fluid loss of about 3% to 5% of body weight. To maintain your health and support optimal performance, it is critical that you consume enough fluid (preferably water, a sport beverage, or some other beverage that is not a diuretic) to regain any water you have lost due to your athletic efforts.
11. Although there are many things to consider when consuming foods prior to exercise, one important factor is consuming an optimal balance of fluid and electrolytes. In this case, lunch (b) would be the better choice. Lunch (a) is very high in sodium. While our bodies need adequate sodium to function properly, lunch (a) is filled with very high sodium foods, such as chicken soup, ham, and tomato juice. It is likely that consuming lunch (a) will lead to excessive thirst due to a rise in blood sodium levels. This excessive thirst could cause distraction or even lead to consuming so much fluid that you feel nauseous during practice. Lunch (b) has a more desirable balance of sodium and fluid, should not cause excessive thirst, and should provide ample energy for hockey practice.
12. Many over-the-counter weight loss pills are diuretics, which means that they cause fluid loss from the body. Your cousin should avoid diuretics, as she needs to maintain her fluid levels at a higher than normal level while breastfeeding. If she becomes dehydrated, she may not produce adequate milk for her infant. In addition, it is possible that the substances in the weight-loss pills could be passed along to her infant in her breast milk, which could have adverse effects for the infant.
13. It is true that the human body needs to replace fluids, and that we obtain the fluids we need each day from beverages, foods, and the production of metabolic water by our bodies. We do not have the capacity to store water, and so we must replace it daily. However, fluid requirements are very individualized. The DRI for adult women aged 19–50 years is 2.7 L of total water daily: this includes about 2.2 L (9 cups) as total beverages, such as drinking water. In general, most people should consume 8 glasses of fluid per day. Fluid intake needs depend upon age, body size, physical activity, health status, and environmental conditions.

    Some of the choices that Cheyenne is making are diuretics; these include the skim milk lattes and tea. Diuretics are substances that increase fluid loss via the urine. The cranberry juice and water are wiser choices. She should be cautious about warm apple cider, as it may contain caffeine if purchased in a powder or mix format.

    Cheyenne has increased her fluid intake, and her kidneys will constantly be helping to maintain fluid balance. When she consumes more fluid than she needs, the kidneys will process the excess fluid and excrete it in the form of dilute urine. In addition, Manitoba's extremely cold weather can trigger hormonal changes that result in an increased fluid loss.

    Cheyenne would benefit from the following suggestions:
    i) continue to consume beverages that are excellent sources of fluid, such as water, clear broths, tomato juice, and lower fat milk;
    ii) many fruits and vegetables such as grapefruit, strawberries, tomatoes, cabbage, lettuce, celery, cucumber, broccoli, and squash are also good sources of fluids and electrolytes;
    iii) limit, or at least monitor, intake of common diuretics such as coffee, tea, cola, and other caffeine-containing beverages; and
    iv) if exercising, increase fluids due to loss via sweat and respiration.

Chapter 8

1. **d.** It is destroyed by exposure to high heat.
2. **b.** an atom loses an electron.
3. **a.** cardiovascular disease
4. **d.** all of the above
5. **a.** vitamin A
6. **b.** They destabilize our cells.
7. **b.** vitamin E.
8. **d.** Legumes
9. Elena should be careful with Vitamin E supplementation, as it has a negative interaction with aspirin. In taking both, she may risk hemorrhaging.
10. i) Yes, William should be worried since beef liver contains large amounts of preformed vitamin A and pureed pumpkin contains large amounts of beta-carotene, which can be converted to vitamin A in the body. Taking too much vitamin A may cause serious birth defects and spontaneous abortions.
    ii) Vitamin A toxicity symptoms include loss of appetite, blurred vision, hair loss, abdominal pain, nausea, diarrhea, and liver and nervous system damage.
11. Free radicals steal electrons from the stable lipid molecules in our cell membranes. This stealing can destroy the integrity of the membrane and lead to membrane dysfunction and potential cell death.
12. There are three main steps in the development of cancer: initiation, promotion, and progression. During the initiation step, the DNA of normal cells is mutated, causing permanent changes in the cell. During the promotion step, the genetically altered cells repeatedly divide, locking the mutated DNA into each new cell's genetic instructions. During the progression step, the cancerous cells grow out of control and invade surrounding tissues. These cells then metastasize, or spread, to other sites of the body.
13. It is critical that individuals who take anticoagulants avoid vitamin E supplementation, as anticoagulants interact negatively with this particular vitamin. Anticoagulant medications are substances which stop blood from clotting excessively. Two examples of anticoagulants are aspirin and Coumadin. Vitamin E supplements may enhance the action of these anticoagulants, and may cause uncontrollable bleeding. Furthermore, there is recent evidence which suggests that in some individuals, the long-term usage of vitamin E supplements may cause hemorrhaging in the brain, leading to hemorrhagic stroke. Therefore, high doses of vitamin E can influence blood clotting times, and supplements must be used cautiously by individuals who are also taking anticoagulants.
14. Trace minerals such as selenium, copper, iron, zinc, and manganese are part of the antioxidant enzyme systems that convert free radicals to less damaging substances that are excreted by our bodies. Selenium is part of the glutathione peroxidase enzyme system. Copper, zinc, and manganese are part of the superoxide dismutase enzyme complex, and iron is a part of the structure of catalase.
15. Vitamin E protects LDLs from oxidation, thus helping to reduce the build up of plaque in our blood vessel walls. Vitamin E

may also help reduce low-grade inflammation. Vitamin E is known to reduce blood coagulation and the formation of blood clots, which will reduce the risk of a blood clot clogging a blood vessel and causing a stroke or heart attack.

Chapter 9

1. **a.** calcium and phosphorus.
2. **c.** has normal bone density as compared to an average, healthy 30-year-old of the same age, sex, and race.
3. **d.** It provides the scaffolding for cortical bone.
4. **c.** A fair-skinned retired teacher living in a nursing home in northern Manitoba.
5. **d.** structure of bone, nerve transmission, and muscle contraction.
6. **d.** taking high amounts of vitamin D in supplements.
7. **d.** large intestine.
8. As people age, their skin becomes thinner and fewer of the compounds needed for vitamin D synthesis are present in the skin. Moreover, we absorb less of the vitamin D from our food and supplements in our intestines as we age.
9. Osteomalacia (or soft bones) occurs in adults with bones that lack density and are prone to fractures because of low mineral content.

   Osteoporosis (or porous bones) occurs when there is less whole bone tissue. Soft bone matrix is lost and thus there is less surface area for minerals to be deposited. Bone density decreases since there is less bone matrix and less mineralization.
10. Treatment options for breast and prostate cancer may include the use of drugs to reduce levels of estrogen and androgen in the body. These treatments subsequently speed up bone loss and increase a cancer patient's risk of developing osteoporosis.
11. Because vitamins D and K are fat-soluble vitamins, they are absorbed with the fat we consume in our diets. If a person has a disease that does not allow for proper absorption of dietary fat, there will also be a malabsorption of the fat-soluble vitamins, which include vitamins D and K.
12. The two processes behind this phenomenon are bone resorption and bone formation. The combination of these processes is referred to as bone remodelling. To preserve bone density, our bodies attempt to achieve a balance between the breakdown of older bone tissue and the formation of new bone tissue. One of the primary reasons that bone is broken down is to release calcium into our bloodstream. We also want to break down bone when we fracture a bone and need to repair it. During resorption, osteoclasts erode the bone surface by secreting enzymes and acids that dig grooves into the bone matrix. Their ruffled surface also acts much like a scrubbing brush to assist in the erosion process. Once bone is broken down, the products are transported into the bloodstream and utilized for various body functions.

    Osteoblasts work to form new bone. These cells help synthesize new bone matrix by laying down the collagen-containing organic component of bone. Within this substance, the hydroxapatite crystallizes and packs together to create new bone where it is needed.

    In young healthy adults, the processes of bone resorption and formation are equal so that just as much bone is broken down as is being built. The result is that bone mass is maintained. At around 40 years of age, bone resorption begins to occur more rapidly than bone formation, and this imbalance results in an overall loss in bone density. This loss of bone density affects all bones, including the vertebrae of the spine, and thus results in a loss of height as we age.
13. Your friend only needs to expose his or her arms and legs or hands, arms, and face to sunlight for about five to ten minutes, two or three times a week in the summer, so that the skin can synthesize vitamin D with negligible risk of skin cancer. This is likely enough for a young person, and supplements may not be needed. The sunlight is not sufficient in Montreal during the winter, however, to provide adequate vitamin D for anyone. Thus, all people living in this climate in winter need to consume vitamin D in foods and/or supplements to meet their needs.
14. Sinead's risk factors for osteoporosis include her low calcium intake, her gender, and her age. She also has a "penchant" for diet pop. Since she is an older woman, she may be estrogen-deficient. One might also presume that, since Sinead lives by herself, she may not be preparing adequate meals for herself, and as such, her nutritional status may contribute to her risk for osteoporosis, especially since her children argue that she "rarely drinks milk." The lifestyle factors that are in Sinead's favour are that she "has always watched her weight" and "goes for walks at least three times a week."

    I would suggest that Sinead have a DXA test. The "dual energy x-ray absorptiometry" test is considered to be the most accurate assessment tool for measuring bone density. This test is simple, painless, safe, and non-invasive, and usually takes less than 30 minutes for a scan of the entire body. The DXA test is an important tool to determine Sinead's risk for osteoporosis, and the test is recommended for post-menopausal women because they are at the highest risk for osteoporosis and fracture. Given her documented risks, I would strongly encourage this test.

Chapter 10

1. **d.** thiamin, pantothenic acid, and biotin.
2. **b.** vitamin K.
3. **b.** Iron is a component of hemoglobin, myoglobin, and certain enzymes.
4. **c.** an amino acid.
5. **d.** Choline is necessary for the synthesis of phospholipids and other components of cell membranes.
6. **c.** Biotin
7. **a.** Sulphur
8. **d.** a B_{12} deficiency.
9. i) Foods that are good sources of folate include enriched breads, orange juice, and leafy green vegetables.
   ii) Jackie should have taken folate supplements before she was pregnant, since neural tube defects occur in the first four weeks of the pregnancy.
   iii) Folate is recommended for young women because folate requirements during pregnancy are substantially higher than usual. Inadequate folate intake during pregnancy is associated with fetus malformations such as neural tube defects. Since these defects occur during the first four weeks of the pregnancy, it is best for young women to intake 400 µg/day even if they are not planning for a pregnancy.
10. **b.** Wilson's disease.
11. Mr. Katz's doctor probably did not give him the vitamin in pill form because Mr. Katz is 80 years of age and it is more likely that he suffers from low stomach acid secretion. This is a condition known as atrophic gastritis, and it is estimated that about 10% to 30% of adults older than 50 years have this condition. Stomach acid separates food-bound vitamin B_{12} from dietary proteins. If the acid content of the stomach is inadequate, we cannot free up enough vitamin B_{12} from food sources alone. Because atrophic gastritis can affect almost one-third of the older adult population, it is recommended that people older than 50 years of age consume foods fortified with vitamin B_{12}, take a vitamin B_{12}-containing supplement, or have periodic B_{12} injections. Because Mr. Katz's condition was so severe, it was critical to treat him with a form of vitamin B_{12} that would be guaranteed to enter his system as quickly and effectively as possible; thus, his physician opted to use a vitamin B_{12} injection.
12. Cassandra is at a higher risk for iron deficiency anemia due to her menstrual status and the fact that she consumes only plant-based foods. Plant-based foods contain only the non-heme form of iron, which is more difficult to absorb. Consuming vitamin C enhances the absorption of iron from our foods;

thus it is imperative that Cassandra's parents encourage her to eat good plant-based food sources of iron with a vitamin C source to optimize her iron absorption and reduce her risk for iron deficiency anemia.

13. Loss of intrinsic factor → failure of intrinsic factor to bind with vitamin B_{12} in stomach → reduced absorption of vitamin B_{12} in small intestine → inadequate levels of vitamin B_{12} in body → destruction of nervous system cells (including central nervous system) → resulting symptoms include confusion, depression, paranoia, irritability, and other signs of dementia.

14. Based on this diet, Avery does not appear at risk for inadequate micronutrient intake. The foods he consumes contain all of the necessary micronutrients, and as long as he continues to eat a wide variety of foods from these groups, his risk for inadequate intake of micronutrients is very low.

15. i) Janine is of childbearing age. It is recommended that all women of childbearing age consume adequate folate even if they do not plan to become pregnant. This recommendation is made to reduce the risk for neural tube defects in the developing fetus in case a woman does become pregnant.

    ii) Janine is avoiding foods that are excellent sources of folate, including many vegetables and enriched grain products. Thus, it is likely that her intake of folate is inadequate.

16. No, the B vitamins do not increase or provide direct energy to the body. The primary role of the B vitamins is to act as coenzymes. As such, they activate enzymes and assist them in the metabolism of carbohydrates, fats, and amino acids. Simply put, the B vitamins play a critical role in ensuring that the body is able to *generate* energy from carbohydrates, fat, and protein. A B vitamin supplement would likely not help Monica. From the situation described (she doesn't get out of bed, seems disoriented and confused, cries a lot, does not enjoy exercise anymore, is always tired, and doesn't want to eat), it would appear as though Monica is suffering from pernicious anemia. Pernicious anemia is a special form of anemia that is the primary cause of a vitamin B_{12} deficiency, and it occurs at the end stage of an autoimmune disorder that causes the loss of various cells in the stomach. The most common cause of pernicious anemia is the lack of a protein called the intrinsic factor, which is normally secreted by these particular cells in the stomach. Pernicious anemia results in a reduction or complete cessation of intrinsic factor production and thus vitamin B_{12} cannot cross the intestinal lining.

    Additional advice that might be provided to Monica would include the following:
    1. Visit your doctor to obtain a blood test and to describe your symptoms.
    2. If pernicious anemia is determined, ensure treatment, such as vitamin B_{12} injections.
    3. Realize that even with treatment, some neurological damage may be permanent, but if left untreated, the condition could progress to Monica becoming more irritated, confused, depressed, and even paranoid.
    4. Monica should increase her consumption of foods containing vitamin B_{12}, which are found primarily in animal products such as meat, fish, poultry, shellfish, milk, cheese, eggs, and fortified cereals.

Chapter 11

1. **d.** body mass index.
2. **a.** basal metabolic rate, thermal effect of food, and effect of physical activity.
3. **b.** take in more energy than they expend.
4. **c.** all people have a genetic set point for their body weight.
5. **a.** hunger.
6. **b.** 3500 kcal.
7. **d.** More than 50%
8. **c.** Aim to lose more than 1 kg (approx. 2.2 lbs.) per week

9. i) Apple-shaped fat patterning, or upper-body obesity, is associated with risk of many chronic diseases such as type 2 diabetes, heart disease, and high blood pressure.

    ii) Sydney's dietitian has most likely advised him to exercise regularly to maintain aerobic fitness and muscle mass. Moreover, he was probably advised to eat a balanced diet with more energy than he planned to expend.

10. A weight that is appropriate for your age and physical development; a weight that you can achieve and sustain without restraining your food intake or constantly dieting; a weight that is acceptable to you; a weight that is based upon your genetic background and family history of body shape and weight; a weight that promotes good eating habits and allows you to participate in regular physical activity.

11. Dietary Recommendations for a sound weight-loss program include:

    i) Set reasonable weight-loss goals. Reasonable weight loss is defined as 0.25 to 1 kg (0.5 to 2 lb.) per week. To achieve this rate of weight loss, energy intake should be reduced by approximately 250 to no more than 1000 kcal/day of present intake. A weight-loss plan should never provide less than a total of 1200 kcal/day.

    ii) Eat a diet that is relatively low in fat and high in complex carbohydrates. Total fat intake should be 15% to 25% of total energy intake. Saturated fat intake should be no more than 10% of total energy intake. Carbohydrate intake should be around 55% of total energy intake with less than 10% of energy intake coming from simple sugars, and fibre intake should be 25 to 35 g/day.

    Physical Activity Recommendations include: Set a long-term goal for physical activity that is at least 30 minutes of moderate physical activity most, or preferably all, days of the week. Doing 45 minutes or more of an activity such as walking at least five days per week is ideal.

    Behaviour Modification Recommendations include:
    i) Shop when you are not hungry, only eat at set times in one location, refuse to buy problem foods, and avoid vending machines, convenience stores, and fast-food restaurants.
    ii) Take small food portions, eat foods on smaller serving dishes so they appear larger, and avoid feelings of deprivation by eating regular meals throughout the day.
    iii) Share food with others, learn appropriate serving sizes, plan healthful snacks, schedule walks and other physical activities with friends, and keep clothes and equipment for physical activity in convenient places.
    iv) Eat slowly, always using utensils, leave food on your plate, move more throughout the day, and join groups that are physically active.
    v) Reward yourself for positive behaviours with non-food rewards.
    vi) Use the "buddy" system by exercising with a friend or relative, and/or calling this support person when you need an extra boost to stay motivated.
    vii) Refuse to punish yourself if you deviate from your plan.

12. You can increase your basal metabolic rate by increasing your lean body mass or by using drugs such as stimulants, caffeine, and tobacco. Stress and certain illnesses can also increase BMR. The most healthful way to increase BMR is to increase your lean body mass by participating in regular strength training exercises. Attempting to increase your BMR using drugs or by increasing your stress is not wise and can be dangerous to your health.

13. i) Greater access to inexpensive, high-fat, high-calorie foods (for example, fast foods, vending machine foods, and snack/convenience foods).
    ii) Significant increases in portion sizes of foods.
    iii) Increased reliance on cars instead of bicycles, public transportation, or walking.

iv) Use of elevators and escalators instead of stairs.

v) Increased use of computers, dishwashers, televisions, and other time-saving devices.

vi) Lack of safe, accessible, and affordable places to exercise.

14. One important question for Misty is what her idea of her ideal weight is. It sounds as if Misty might have significant body image concerns. If this is the case, she could meet with a health-care provider or nutrition professional who can assist her with improving her body image perceptions.

Another question is what weight can she achieve and sustain without trying so hard (in other words, without restricting her food intake or constantly dieting). The fact that she must try so hard and is still not losing weight is an indication that she may already be at the weight that is healthy.

A third question is how her current weight and body shape compare to her genetic background and family history. If her body weight and shape are consistent with her genetic make-up and family history, she may have unrealistic expectations of reducing her body weight or significantly altering her shape.

A final question Misty might consider is whether she is able to maintain her current weight by being regularly active and by eating a healthful, balanced diet. If not, then this is another indication that her body weight goals are unrealistic.

15. There are some problems with Simon's food intake. From the meals described (bacon and eggs, ham sandwiches, hamburgers, and protein bars with no snacks in between meals), and with Simon being as active as he is, the following suggestions could be made to support safe and effective weight gain:

i) Eat a diet that contains 500–1000 calories per day more than is needed to maintain present body weight. This should result in a gain of 0.5–1 kg (1–2 lb.) of weight per week.

ii) Eat a diet that contains about 55% of total energy from carbohydrates, 20%–25% of total energy from fat, and 15%–20% of total energy from protein. At present, it would appear that most of Simon's calories come from fat and protein.

iii) Eat frequently, including meals and numerous snacks, throughout the day. Many underweight people do not take the time to eat often enough.

iv) Eat nutrient-dense snacks, such as apples, carrots, cheese, yogurt, smoothies, and milkshakes, to promote weight gain.

v) Pack lots of foods to take with you to school and for sports activities so that you enhance your opportunities to eat more often.

vi) Continue to exercise regularly and to incorporate weight-lifting or some other form of resistance training into the exercise routine. This form of exercise is most effective in increasing muscle mass. Aerobic exercise is also important for cardiovascular health.

Chapter 12

1. **c.** 55% to 90% of your estimated maximal heart rate.
2. **a.** 1 to 3 seconds.
3. **b.** Fat
4. **c.** seems to increase strength gained in resistance exercise.
5. **a.** 15% to 25% fat and 55% to 60% carbohydrates
6. **c.** Carbohydrate loading
7. **b.** Frequency, intensity, time
8. i) Since Catherine has just started training, this may be a case of sports anemia. Sports anemia is not true anemia. Rather, at the beginning of a challenging training period, the athlete's plasma volume increases but the amount of hemoglobin does not change. Therefore, iron content will be diluted and reported as low.

   ii) Catherine is at risk for iron deficiency because she is female, a vegetarian, an athlete, and an endurance runner. Females are at greater risk because of menstrual blood losses. Moreover, females and vegetarians may also consume less iron in their diets. Athletes lose iron through their excrement and

endurance runners lose more iron due to the red blood cell breakdown in their feet over time.

   iii) At this time, Catherine's hemoglobin content may increase as her training progresses. If her performance is not currently affected, supplements may not be needed until further testing is done. However, since Catherine is at high risk for iron deficiency, she may consider taking supplements under the advice of a health-care provider.

9. There are an infinite number of correct answers to this question. The plan outlined here is for a 40-year-old woman who is interested in maintaining a healthful body weight, optimizing her blood lipid profile, reducing her stress, and maintaining aerobic fitness, flexibility, and upper-body strength. She works full-time as a research scientist, and most of her occupational activities are sedentary in nature.

Monday and Wednesday: 60 minutes of fitness walking (including 5 minute warm up and 5 minute cool down)

Tuesday and Thursday: 75 minutes of Power/Ashtanga yoga (including warm up and cool down); 45 minutes of morning swimming (substitute with bicycling in the summer months)

Friday: 60 minutes of fitness walking (including warm up and cool down); 30 minutes of gardening

Saturday: 75 minutes of Hatha yoga (including warm up and cool down); 120 minutes of gardening

Sunday: 30 minutes of Hatha yoga (including warm up and cool down); 180 minutes of hiking with a light day pack.

10. To answer this question, you need to know the total energy that is required to maintain body weight and support the previously described activity/exercise routine. This value can be calculated using the simple equation provided in Chapter 11 in the You Do the Math activity.

If the woman described in Question 9 weighs 130 pounds:

Her weight in kg = 130 pounds ÷ 2.2 kg/pound = 59.1 kg

Her BMR = 59.1 kg × 0.9 kcal/kg body weight/hr = 53.19 kcal/hr × 24 hours/day = 1277 kcal/day

To estimate the amount of energy she expends to perform daily activities, you can again refer to the You Do the Math activity in Chapter 11. Based on the answer to Question 9, she is assumed to be moderately active, which means her daily physical activity needs are about 50% to 70% of her BMR.

1277 kcal/day × 0.5 = 638.5 kcal/day

1277 kcal/day × 0.7 = 893.9 kcal/day

She expends approximately 639 to 894 kcal/day doing physical activities.

To estimate her total energy needs for the day, add her BMR value to the estimates for physical activity needs previously calculated:

1277 kcal/day + 639 kcal/day = 1916 kcal/day

1277 kcal/day + 894 kcal/day = 2171 kcal/day

She expends approximately 1916 to 2171 kcal/day to support her current lifestyle.

This woman is not a competitive athlete and is exercising regularly to maintain health. Thus, it is recommended that she consume about 55% of her total energy as carbohydrates, 20% to 25% of her total energy as fat, and the remainder (20% to 25%) as protein. To simplify our calculations, let's assume that this woman requires 2044 kcal/day to maintain her present weight and physical activity level (the average of the two values calculated for her total energy needs). To calculate the number of grams that will come from each macronutrient:

For carbohydrates:

2044 kcal/day × 0.55 = 1124 kcal of carbohydrates per day

1124 kcal of carbohydrates/day ÷ 4 kcal/gram of carbohydrate = 281 grams of carbohydrates per day

For fat:

2044 kcal/day × 0.20 = 409 kcal of fat per day

2044 kcal/day × 0.25 = 511 kcal of fat per day

409 kcal of fat/day ÷ 9 kcal/gram of fat = 45 grams of fat per day

511 kcal of fat per day ÷ 9 kcal/gram of fat = 57 grams of fat per day

For protein:

2044 kcal/day × 0.20 = 409 kcal of protein per day

2044 kcal/day × 0.25 = 511 kcal of protein per day

409 kcal of protein/day ÷ 4 kcal/gram of protein = 102 grams of protein

511 kcal of protein/day ÷ 4 kcal/gram of protein = 128 grams of protein

Thus, the correct answer for the woman in question is 281 grams of carbohydrates, 45 to 57 grams of fat, and 102 to 128 grams of protein.

11. The most helpful strategy you might consider is the use of sports beverages. Sports beverages were designed for people who exercise for more than 60 minutes at a time and are specially formulated to replenish the fluid and micronutrients that are lost during intense, long-duration exercise. By consuming sports beverages during training for a marathon, you can ensure that you are maintaining adequate hydration levels and avoid hyponatremia by replenishing sodium.

12. Yes, I would encourage him to begin a planned exercise program of low to moderate intensity. Physical activity is any movement produced by muscles that increases energy expenditure, and it provides numerous health benefits, including reducing risks for heart disease, stroke, high blood pressure, obesity, type 2 diabetes, and osteoporosis. Physical activity also improves sleep patterns, improves immune function, and reduces anxiety and mental stress.

To be realistic and sustainable, the fitness program must:
* meet personal fitness goals
* be fun
* include variety and consistency
* appropriately overload the body, and
* include a warm-up and cool-down period.

The steps that should be taken before starting an exercise program include:

i) Change behaviour: the first step is to recognize the reasons for not exercising and to identify ways to overcome them, with the goal of gradually making lifestyle changes that increase physical activity.

ii) Start slowly.

iii) Make it fun.

iv) Set attainable goals.

v) Make exercise convenient.

vi) Include warm up and cool down.

vii) Challenge strength and endurance and do moderate workouts on other days.

viii) Don't overdo it.

ix) Record your progress as a motivator.

x) Listen to your body.

xi) Reward yourself (but not with food), and

xii) Consult with your physician to be sure that your plans are safe, considering your medical history.

13. Factors that assist Marisa in maintaining a normal, healthful weight include:
* walking to/from school each day;
* covering the lunch shift at her college's daycare centre, which requires that she be on her feet, walk, and perform light lifting two hours each day; and
* walking on the weekends

Factors that contribute to Conrad's weight gain include:
* driving to school each day;
* working an office job two hours each day; and
* going to the movies on the weekends instead of doing some form of physical activity

14. This woman's exercise routine is excessive, to say the least! Since she has not exercised in 10 years, she should start her exercise program slowly, after consulting her physician. The fact that she is able to run on the treadmill for 40 minutes is admirable, and indicates that she can still meet the "I" (intensity) and "T" (time) letters of the FIT principle. However, when she abruptly stops running, I would have cause for concern. I would wonder whether she had warmed up since she did not cool down. I would also wonder what had caused her to leave so abruptly: were her muscles fatigued, was she dehydrated, was she losing her breath, was she injured?

Suggestions I would make to her would include the following:

i) Remember to start slowly with your "new-found" exercise regimen—talk to your doctor—after all, it's been 10 years!

ii) Remember to warm up, to get muscles prepared for exertion and to cool down to prevent injury and muscle soreness.

ii) Always bring a water bottle while exercising to replace fluids and prevent dehydration.

iv) Don't overdo it when starting out again, and make sure you listen to your body.

v) Reward yourself for changing behaviours and returning to exercise to become physically fit.

Chapter 13

1. **d.** food, acid, time, temperature, oxygen, and moisture.

2. **c.** fungus used to ferment foods.

3. **b.** a flavour enhancer used in a variety of foods.

4. **b.** 48 hours.

5. **d.** Cooling, canning, pasteurization, irradiation.

6. **a.** *E. coli* 0157:H7 poisoning.

7. **c.** *Clostridium botulinum*

8. The safest choice is to select the pasteurized juice. Unpasteurized beverages such as juices and milk may contain a significant number of microbes that can cause food-borne illnesses. Pasteurization does not eliminate all microbes but significantly decreases the numbers of heat-sensitive microorganisms, which tend to be the most harmful. The amount of pesticides found in juice is most likely very low or zero, as the pesticides would have been applied to the trees and oranges with the peel on the fruit. It is highly likely that this juice contains none of the pesticides that may have been used because the peel is not used to make the juice.

9. There are a few different processes of pickling, but this process requires the use of vinegar and salt. The vinegar used works to destroy microbes that cause food-borne illness (particularly the *Clostridium botulinum* bacteria). The salt used not only adds flavour but also inhibits spoilage and the growth of harmful bacteria.

10. The cause of this disease was mercury poisoning from an industrial plant on Minamata Bay. Mercury, a naturally occurring element, is found in soil and rocks, lakes, streams, and oceans. It is also released into the environment by pulp and paper processing and the burning of garbage and fossil fuels. As mercury is released into the environment, it falls from the air, eventually finding its way into streams, lakes, and oceans. Fish accumulate mercury in their muscle tissue as they feed on aquatic organisms. This mercury is passed on to people when they consume the fish. As mercury accumulates in the body, it has a toxic effect on the nervous system. Mercury is especially toxic to the developing nervous system of fetuses and growing children. Thus, pregnant and breastfeeding women and young children are advised to avoid eating fish that may be contaminated with mercury.

11. i) Failure to wash your hands before you removed the chicken from the freezer. You touched the chicken when you placed it in the bowl to thaw in the refrigerator.

ii) Washing your hands in cold water without soap just prior to handling the breasts before you wash them. You should have washed your hands with soap and hot water.

iii) Failure to wash your hands with hot water and soap after handling the chicken breasts just prior to touching and rinsing the lettuce, red pepper, and scallions.

iv) Failure to check the temperature of the chicken breasts. Even though they were no longer pink in colour, they may not have been cooked to a high enough temperature to kill bacteria.

12. Food-borne illness is a term used to encompass any symptom or illness that arises from ingesting food or water that contains an infectious agent, poisonous substance, or protein that causes an immune reaction. Food-borne illness is commonly called food poisoning.

Many food-borne microbes are killed in the mouth by antimicrobial enzymes in saliva or in the stomach by hydrochloric acid. Any microbe that survives these chemical assaults will usually trigger vomiting and/or diarrhea as the gastrointestinal tract attempts to expel the offender. In addition, the white blood cells of the immune system will be activated, and a generalized inflammatory response will cause the person to experience nausea, fatigue, fever, and muscle cramps. Since Vakeesh was in the bathroom for a whole evening, and since he felt weak and exhausted the next day, there is the distinct possibility that he did experience a food-borne illness, as food-borne illness can affect anyone. Even though no other relative experienced this problem, the state of one's health, the precise microbe involved, and the number of microbes ingested will affect the severity of the illness.

In addition, Vakeesh had eaten two potentially hazardous foods: turkey casserole and potato salad. Perhaps these foods were not chilled properly, as this was a family picnic. Bacteria will rapidly multiply if the foods are left in the "danger zone" for an extended time frame. The foods he consumed could also have been cross contaminated. And perhaps Vakeesh had not washed his hands well enough: washing hands is one of the easiest and most effective ways to prevent food-borne illness.

13. Pesticides are used to help protect against crop losses due to weeds, insects, fungi, and other organisms, including birds and mammals. In addition, pesticides help reduce the potential for disease by decreasing the number of microorganisms on crops. They increase overall crop yield. The three most common types of pesticides used in food production are insecticides, herbicides, and fungicides. Many plants also naturally produce pesticides to help protect themselves from predators and disease, and farmers have been able to use naturally derived or synthetic analogues for agricultural use.

Contrary to common belief, many of today's pesticides are naturally derived, and/or have a low impact on the environment. Biopesticides are less toxic to humans and the environment. Many synthetic pesticides are petroleum-based products. Pesticides are, however, potential toxins, and can remain on food and affect immune system function, especially in people whose systems are already compromised. If pesticide residues are not effectively removed, they can damage body tissues. Others may affect the nervous system or endocrine system. Children may be more susceptible to pesticide residues. It is essential that all produce is washed carefully to remove pesticides.

Through the Pest Control Products Act, Health Canada's Pest Management Regulatory Agency is the government agency responsible for the registration of pesticides and assessment of the human health and safety aspects and environmental impacts of pesticides in Canada.

Louis' father is correct. Pesticides must be regulated and proven safe for usage, and there are regulations to enforce human health and safety aspects. However, Louis is also correct in his argument that while pesticides prevent or reduce crop losses, they remain potential toxins.

This situation could be resolved by having Louis take over the farm with the agreement that he will use biopesticides, which are primarily insecticides. Or Louis could eventually convert the farm to an organic farm. The term organic is commonly used to describe foods that are grown without the use of synthetic pesticides.

Chapter 14

1. **b.** Neural tube defects
2. **c.** Oxytocin
3. **a.** Fibre
4. **d.** women who begin their pregnancy at a normal weight.
5. **d.** iron-fortified rice cereal
6. **a.** 400 micrograms of folic acid
7. **c.** 7.0–11.5 kg (15–25 lb.)
8. **a.** 550 kcal
9. I would dissuade her from the "eating for two" thinking and guide her to speak to her doctor or dietitian about her recommended weight gain. For a normal-weight woman, expected weight gain is between 11.5–16.0 kg (25–35 lb.).
10. During pregnancy, the demand for red blood cells increases to accommodate the needs of the growing uterus, placenta, and the fetus itself. Thus, more iron is needed. Fetal demand for iron increases even further during the last trimester, when the fetus stores iron in the liver for use during the first few months of life. This increased need for iron in a pregnant woman means that women are often prescribed iron supplements during the last two trimesters. Iron supplements can cause constipation. Fluid needs increase in pregnant women, and consuming adequate fluid is critical to preventing the constipation that can occur with pregnancy and with taking iron supplements.
11. It is possible that your cousin is partly right and partly wrong. If she is very careful and consumes a wide variety of nutrient-dense foods, she is likely consuming adequate amounts of the macronutrients and many of the micronutrients she needs to support her pregnancy. However, there are some nutrients that are extremely difficult to consume in adequate amounts in the diet during pregnancy, as a woman's needs are very high for these nutrients. One of these nutrients is iron.

During pregnancy, the demand for red blood cells increases to accommodate the needs of the growing uterus, placenta, and the fetus itself. Thus, more iron is needed. Fetal demand for iron increases even further during the last trimester, when the fetus stores iron in the liver for use during the first few months of life. This iron storage is protective because breast milk is low in iron.

Because of these risks, the RDA for iron for pregnant women is 27 mg per day, compared with 18 mg per day for non-pregnant women. Even though your cousin feels her eating habits are sufficient, it is highly likely that she has low iron stores prior to pregnancy, as this is a common problem in many women. Women have a difficult time consuming 18 mg of iron per day in their diets; consuming twice this amount is extremely difficult if not impossible for most women. Thus, women of childbearing age typically have poor iron stores, and the demands of pregnancy are likely to produce deficiency. To ensure adequate iron stores during pregnancy, an iron supplement (often as part of a total prenatal supplement) is routinely prescribed during the last two trimesters. In addition, consuming vitamin C will enhance iron absorption, as will dietary sources of heme iron.
12. Based on this description, it is possible that Katie has a condition referred to as colic. Overstimulation of the nervous system, feeding too rapidly, swallowing of air, and intestinal gas pain are considered possible culprits, but the precise cause is unknown. If allergies are suspected and the colicky infant is breastfed, breastfeeding should be continued, but the parents should try to determine whether eating certain foods seems to prompt crying and, if so, eliminate the offending food(s) from the mother's diet. Formula-fed infants may benefit from a change in type of formula. In the worst cases of colic, a physician may prescribe medication. Fortunately, most cases disappear spontaneously, possibly because of maturity of the gastrointestinal tract, around three months of age. It is important

that Katie's parents discuss her condition with her pediatrician before making any decisions about changing her diet.

13. The primary information to share with this woman is that breastfeeding is recommended for all children up to at least two years (or 24 months) of age. Thus, a fourteen-month-old child is not too old to be breastfed. In addition, it is also possible that this woman is offended by seeing your sister breastfeed in public. If this is the case, it is important to point out that all women have the right to breastfeed in a public place. If this woman is offended, she can leave the area or choose not to watch your sister as she breastfeeds her child.

14. The foods that Mary's doctor has probably advised her to stay away from include refined carbohydrate foods such as crackers, cakes, and cookies. These foods are calorie-dense and nutrient-poor. These foods also have a high glycemic index, and have the tendency to cause sudden large increases in blood glucose and insulin levels. A strategy that may be suggested to help Mary control her cravings would be to incorporate fresh fruits and vegetables into her diet. Mary's food choices should be high in fibre and complex carbohydrates, and low in fat and sugar. By eating foods high in fibre and complex carbohydrates, she will feel fuller for longer periods of time.

If Mary is able to control her gestational diabetes, there should be no additional risk to the baby. However, if uncontrolled, gestational diabetes can result in pre-eclampsia, or in a baby that is too large, perhaps resulting in the necessity of a C-section to deliver the baby. In addition, there is also evidence that exposing a fetus to diabetes in the womb significantly increases the risk for type 2 diabetes during adolescence and adulthood. For most women who experience gestational diabetes, glucose tolerance usually returns to normal after pregnancy. However women with gestational diabetes and their children risk the development of type 2 diabetes later on in life, especially if they are overweight. Health-care professionals will closely monitor Mary and her baby, and medical attention should be sought if either one of them develops symptoms suggestive of diabetes. Strategies to achieve and maintain a healthy weight and to develop a regular exercise program should be implemented.

15. i) Breast milk contains the most complete nutrition for a baby. It is more digestible than formula and contains antibodies to prevent infection. Not only does breast milk encourage proper growth and development, it also changes to suit the infant's gestational age.

Breastfeeding also suppresses ovulation in the mother. This allows the mother to recover before becoming pregnant again. The very act of breastfeeding also encourages the development of an intimate bond between parent and child. Furthermore, breast milk is already ready, clean, at the right temperature, and available on demand. It is convenient and less costly than infant formula.

ii) Tera should speak to an experienced nurse, lactation consultant, or volunteer mother from La Leche League for advice in breastfeeding.

iii) When Tera returns to work, she can leave bottles of pumped breast milk for a caregiver to give the baby during the work day. It would be ideal if Tera's workplace had a breast pump and a room where Tera could express her milk during the day, and a fridge in which to store the milk. Alternatively, a caregiver could bring the baby to work and Tera could feed her on her breaks.

Chapter 15

1. **b.** Vitamin D
2. **c.** 45% to 65%
3. **d.** Dental caries
4. **a.** 125 mL (1/2 cup) of iron-fortified cooked oat cereal, 30 mL (2 Tbsp) mashed pineapple, and 250 mL (8 fl. oz.) whole milk
5. **a.** Cigarette smoking can interfere with the absorption of nutrients

6. Toddlers seem to have an innate ability to match their food intake with their needs. If a child does not want to eat all the food on his or her plate, the child should not be "forced" to finish it; the child might be feeling full. It is possible that too much food is on the child's plate, and smaller meals, interspersed with snacks, may be more appropriate to meet the child's energy needs. The concerns are: (1) forcing the child to eat everything might lead to weight gain; and (2) toddlers and children need to learn to stop eating when they feel full.

7. Older adults have lower energy needs due to their loss of lean tissue and decreased physical activity. Joe should consume a diet consisting of 20%–35% fat, 45%–65% carbohydrates, and 10%–35% protein, but with fewer calories than when he was younger. A BMI of 28 is in the overweight range, and is associated with an increased risk of health problems. It probably is a good idea for Joe to lose some weight to achieve a BMI closer to 25. Since most older people lose lean tissue, it would be ideal if Joe could lose some body fat and replace it with lean muscle tissue. Walking would be a good exercise, and strengthening exercises such as using hand and leg weights would also help to build lean tissue.

8. Advantages: Improved access to a wider variety of affordable fresh, healthful foods from around the world; improved access to nutrition and health information from a variety of sources, including television and internet sources; improved access to interactive nutrition and healthful lifestyle programs that encourage family participation.

Disadvantages: Reduced energy expenditure due to increased television viewing and computer use may be contributing to obesity; lower fitness levels and higher risk for chronic diseases due to the lack of physical activity; increased exposure to advertisements promoting junk foods and less healthful foods; failure to acquire important physical skills because not much time is spent engaged in physical activities; inhibition of imagination and creativity in young children because they do not have to develop skills necessary for creative play.

9. Toddlers are relatively picky eaters, and they can only consume small amounts of food at any given time. In consuming a vegan diet, the primary sources of quality proteins are restricted to legumes, meat substitutes, and various combinations of vegetables and whole grains. A vegan diet needs to be carefully planned to include enough high-quality protein for toddlers, as their protein needs are relatively high. Few toddlers can consume enough legumes and whole grains to provide sufficient protein, and many may not like the taste of vegetables and meat substitutes. In addition, certain staples of the vegan diet that are high in protein, such as wheat, soy, and nuts, commonly provoke allergic reactions in children. When this happens, finding a plant-based substitute that contains adequate protein and other nutrients can be challenging.

10. There are many correct answers to this question. The key to designing a menu for this age group is to keep in mind that these children need adequate fluid, and they do not eat large amounts of food. The foods should also look fun and attractive to encourage regular snacking and should be easy to eat when the children are active. Here are some foods you may want to offer to these children:
   - Ample water in small, coloured plastic cups
   - Whole grain crackers that are small and easy to eat
   - Small chunks of different colours and flavours of cheese to eat with the crackers (or you could make little peanut butter/whole grain cracker "sandwiches")
   - Baby carrot sticks
   - Melon balls and strawberries
   - 2% milk or yogurt

11. Here are three of many lunch choices that you could offer to these students:

i) Canadian Bacon and Tomato Pizza—made with whole wheat crust, low-fat mozzarella cheese, tomato sauce, Canadian bacon slices, and fresh tomato slices

ii) Vegetarian chili con carne—made with chili beans, black beans, kidney beans, onions, chopped tomatoes, and green bell peppers served over steamed rice

iii) California Cobb Salad—made with spinach and red leaf lettuce, turkey bacon, diced hard-boiled egg, feta cheese, and finely chopped broccoli and cauliflower served with non-fat salad dressing on the side

12. Based on this description, it sounds as if your grandmother has been living on her own for about one year. She was active and ate well while living with you and her family, but it is highly likely that she failed to maintain good nutritional intake after returning home to live on her own. She may be suffering from depression and social isolation, which can develop following the death of a spouse. These conditions not only contribute to poor nutritional status but can also cause her to become physically inactive, which results in muscular weakness and poor balance. These physical changes can increase the risk for falls and fractures. She has obviously not been consuming enough fluid, as she entered the hospital with significant dehydration. Her moderate dementia could be a result of a deficiency of vitamin B_{12}; deficiencies of other B vitamins could contribute to poor short-term memory, confusion, irritability, and also weakness and fatigue. Her dementia would have also contributed to her inability to properly shop for, prepare, and consume a healthful diet.

As your grandmother is aging, she is also losing her ability to smell and taste, and the loss of these senses most likely reduced her appetite, leading to lower food and nutrient intakes. It is also possible that she is struggling with a limited income, mobility or transportation problems, or concerns about neighbourhood safety. These factors may make food shopping difficult for her and may have contributed to her poor nutritional intake.

13. I would agree with Lillian that her parents should be taking vitamin-mineral supplements. Even though her parents enjoy a wide variety of vegetables and whole grains, the fact that they have never eaten dairy products regularly is cause for concern. There is an increased need for calcium and vitamin D in the elderly due to decreased bone density, decreased ability to convert vitamin D to its active form in the skin, and decreased absorption of dietary calcium. Lillian's doctor has advised calcium and vitamin D supplements, and these would be appropriate. There is no mention of meats and alternates in Lillian's parents' diets, and if they are not consuming foods from this group, they may also be at risk for deficiency of iron, zinc, and vitamins B_{12} and B_6. If this is the case, a multivitamin with iron would perhaps be the optimum choice if there were no contraindications with medications.

GLOSSARY

A

absorption The physiologic process by which molecules of food are taken from the gastrointestinal tract into the bloodstream or lymph system.

Acceptable Daily Intake (ADI) An estimate made by Health Canada of the amount of a food additive that someone can consume each day over a lifetime without adverse effects.

Acceptable Macronutrient Distribution Range (AMDR) The range of macronutrient intakes that provides adequate levels of essential nutrients and is associated with a reduced risk for chronic disease.

acetylcholine A neurotransmitter that is involved in many functions, including muscle movement and memory storage.

acidosis A disorder in which the blood becomes acidic; that is, the level of hydrogen in the blood is excessive. It can be caused by respiratory or metabolic problems.

added sugars Sugars and syrups that are added to food during processing or preparation.

adenosine triphosphate (ATP) The common currency of energy for virtually all cells of the body.

adequate diet A diet that provides enough of the energy, nutrients, and fibre needed to maintain a person's health.

Adequate Intake (AI) A recommended average daily nutrient intake level based on observed or experimentally determined estimates of nutrient intake by a group of healthy people.

alcohol Chemically, a compound characterized by the presence of a hydroxyl group; in common usage, a beverage made from fermented fruits, vegetables, or grains and containing ethanol.

alcohol abuse The excessive consumption of alcohol, whether chronically or occasionally.

alcohol hangover A consequence of drinking too much alcohol; symptoms include headache, fatigue, dizziness, muscle aches, nausea and vomiting, sensitivity to light and sound, extreme thirst, and mood disturbances.

alcohol poisoning A potentially fatal condition in which an overdose of alcohol results in cardiac and/or respiratory failure.

alcoholic hepatitis Inflammation of the liver caused by alcohol; other forms of hepatitis can be caused by a virus or toxin.

alcoholism A disease state characterized by chronic dependence on alcohol.

alkalosis A disorder in which the blood becomes basic; that is, the level of hydrogen in the blood is deficient. It can be caused by respiratory or metabolic problems.

alpha-linolenic acid An essential fatty acid found in leafy green vegetables, flaxseed oil, soy oil, fish oil, and fish products.

amino acids Nitrogen-containing molecules that combine to form proteins.

amniotic fluid The watery fluid contained within the innermost membrane of the sac containing the fetus. It cushions and protects the growing fetus.

anabolic The term applied to a substance that builds muscle and increases strength.

anencephaly A fatal neural tube defect in which there is partial absence of brain tissue, most likely caused by failure of the neural tube to close.

anorexia An absence of appetite.

anorexia nervosa A serious, potentially life-threatening eating disorder characterized by self-starvation, which eventually leads to a deficiency in energy and the essential nutrients the body requires to function normally.

antibodies Defensive proteins of the immune system. Their production is prompted by the presence of bacteria, viruses, toxins, allergens, and so on.

antioxidant A compound that has the ability to prevent or repair the damage caused by oxidation.

appetite A psychological desire to consume specific foods.

ariboflavinosis A condition caused by riboflavin deficiency.

atherosclerosis A condition characterized by accumulation of deposits of lipids and scar tissue on artery walls. These deposits build up to such a degree that they impair blood flow.

atrophic gastritis A condition that results in low stomach acid secretion; it is estimated to occur in about 10%–30% of adults older than 50 years.

B

bacteria Microorganisms that lack a true nucleus and have a chemical called peptidoglycan in their cell walls.

balanced diet A diet that contains the combinations of foods that provide the proper proportions of nutrients.

basal metabolic rate (BMR) The energy the body expends to maintain its fundamental physiologic functions.

beriberi A disease of muscle wasting and nerve damage caused by thiamin deficiency.

bile Fluid produced by the liver and concentrated and stored in the gallbladder; it emulsifies fats in the small intestine.

binge drinking The consumption of five or more alcoholic drinks on one occasion for men, or four or more for women.

binge eating Consumption of a large amount of food in a short period of time, usually accompanied by a feeling of loss of self-control.

binge-eating disorder A disorder characterized by binge eating an average of twice a week or more, typically without compensatory purging.

bioavailability The degree to which our body can absorb and utilize any given nutrient.

biopesticides Chemicals—primarily insecticides—that are derived naturally to reduce crop damage.

bleaching agents Chemicals used to speed the natural process of ground flour changing from pale yellow to white.

blood volume The amount of fluid in blood.

body composition The ratio of a person's body fat to lean body mass.

body image A person's perception of his or her body's appearance and functioning.

bolus A mass of food that has been chewed and moistened in the mouth.

bone density The degree of compactness of bone tissue, reflecting the strength of the bones. Peak bone density is the point at which a bone is strongest.

brush border The microvilli-covered lining cells of the small intestine's villi. These microvilli tremendously increase the small intestine's absorptive capacity.

buffers Proteins that help maintain proper acid–base balance by attaching to, or releasing, hydrogen ions as conditions change in the body.

bulimia nervosa A serious eating disorder characterized by recurrent episodes of binge eating and recurrent inappropriate compensatory behaviours to prevent weight gain, such as self-induced vomiting, fasting, excessive exercise, or misuse of laxatives, diuretics, enemas, or other medications.

C

calcitonin A hormone secreted by the thyroid gland when blood calcium levels are too high. Calcitonin inhibits the actions of vitamin D, preventing reabsorption of calcium in the kidneys, limiting calcium absorption in the small intestine, and inhibiting the osteoclasts from breaking down bone.

calcitriol The primary active form of vitamin D in the body.

calcium rigor A failure of muscles to relax, which leads to a hardening or stiffening of the muscles; caused by high levels of blood calcium.

calcium tetany A condition in which muscles experience twitching and spasms as a result of inadequate blood calcium levels.

Calorie 1 Calorie = 1 kcal = 4.184 kilojoules

cancer A group of diseases characterized by cells that reproduce spontaneously and independently and may invade other tissues and organs.

carbohydrate loading Also known as glycogen loading. A process that involves altering training and carbohydrate intake so that muscle glycogen storage is maximized.

carbohydrates One of the three macronutrients, a compound made up of carbon, hydrogen, and oxygen that is derived from plants and provides energy.

carcinogen Any substance capable of causing the cellular mutations that lead to cancer.

cardiovascular disease A general term that refers to abnormal conditions involving dysfunction of the heart and blood vessels; cardiovascular disease can result in heart attack or stroke.

carotenoid A fat-soluble plant pigment that the body stores in the liver and adipose tissues. The body is able to convert certain carotenoids to vitamin A.

cash crops Crops grown to be sold rather than eaten, such as cotton, tobacco, jute, and sugarcane.

celiac disease An autoimmune disorder characterized by an inability to absorb a component of gluten called gliadin. This causes an inflammatory immune response that damages the lining of the small intestine.

cell The smallest unit of matter that exhibits the properties of living things, such as growth, reproduction, and metabolism.

cell differentiation The process by which immature, undifferentiated stem cells develop into highly specialized functional cells of discrete organs and tissues.

cell membrane The boundary of an animal cell that separates its internal cytoplasm and organelles from the external environment.

Centers for Disease Control and Prevention (CDC) The leading federal agency in the United States that protects the health and safety of people. Its mission is to promote health and quality of life by preventing and controlling disease, injury, and disability.

cephalic phase The earliest phase of digestion, in which the brain thinks about and prepares the digestive organs for the consumption of food.

chronic diseases Diseases that come on slowly and can persist for years, often despite treatment.

chylomicron A lipoprotein produced in the mucosal cell of the intestine; transports dietary fat out of the intestinal tract into the lymphatic system.

chyme A semi-fluid mass consisting of partially digested food, water, and gastric juices.

cirrhosis of the liver End-stage liver disease characterized by significant abnormalities in liver structure and function; may lead to complete liver failure.

coenzyme A molecule that combines with an enzyme to activate it and help it do its job.

cofactor A mineral or other substance that is needed to allow enzymes to function properly.

colic A condition of inconsolable infant crying that lasts for hours at a time.

collagen A protein that forms strong fibres in bone and connective tissue.

colostrum The first fluid made and secreted by the breasts from late in pregnancy to about a week after birth. It is rich in immune factors and protein.

complementary proteins Two or more foods that together contain all nine essential amino acids necessary for a complete protein. It is not necessary to eat complementary proteins at the same meal.

complete proteins Proteins that contain all nine essential amino acids in sufficient quantities for protein synthesis. Proteins from animal sources are complete proteins. Soybeans are considered to be the only complete plant proteins.

complex carbohydrate A nutrient compound consisting of long chains of glucose molecules, such as starch, glycogen, and fibre.

conception (also called fertilization) The uniting of an ovum (egg) and sperm to create a fertilized egg, or zygote.

constipation A condition characterized by the absence of bowel movements for a time that is significantly longer than normal for the individual. When a bowel movement does occur, stools are usually small, hard, and difficult to pass.

cool-down Activities done after an exercise session is completed; should be gradual and allow your body to slowly recover from exercise.

cortical bone (compact bone) A dense bone tissue that makes up the outer surface of all bones as well as the entirety of most small bones of the body. It makes up 80% or our skeleton.

cretinism A form of mental retardation that occurs in children whose mothers experienced iodine deficiency during pregnancy.

cross-contamination Contamination of one food by another via the unintended transfer of microbes through physical contact.

cytoplasm The interior of an animal cell, not including its nucleus.

D

deamination The process by which an amine group is removed from an amino acid. The nitrogen is then transported to the kidneys for excretion in the urine, while the carbon and other components are metabolized for energy or used to make other compounds.

dehydration The depletion of body fluid that results when fluid excretion exceeds fluid intake.

denaturation The process by which proteins uncoil and lose their shape and function when they are exposed to heat, acids, bases, heavy metals, alcohol, and other damaging substances. Proteins must be denatured before they can be digested.

dental caries Dental erosion and decay caused by acid-secreting bacteria in the mouth and on the teeth. The acid produced is a by-product of bacterial metabolism of carbohydrates deposited on the teeth.

desiccants Chemicals that prevent foods from absorbing moisture from the air.

diabetes A chronic disease in which the body can no longer regulate glucose normally.

diarrhea A condition characterized by the frequent passage of loose, watery stools.

dietary fibre The indigestible carbohydrate parts of plants that form the support structures of leaves, stems, and seeds.

Dietary Reference Intakes (DRIs) A set of nutritional reference values for the United States and Canada that applies to healthy people.

digestion The process by which foods are broken down into their component molecules, either mechanically or chemically.

disaccharide A carbohydrate compound consisting of two sugar molecules joined together.

disease risk reduction claim A statement that links a food or a food ingredient with reduced risk of disease or a condition in the context of a total diet.

diseases of aging Conditions that typically occur later in life as a result of lifelong accumulated risk, such as exposure to high-fat diets, a lack of physical activity, and excess sun exposure.

disordered eating A variety of abnormal or atypical eating behaviours that are used to keep or maintain a lower body weight.

diuretic A substance that increases fluid loss via the urine. Common diuretics include alcohol, some prescription medications, and many over-the-counter weight-loss pills.

docosahexaenoic acid (DHA) Another metabolic derivative of alpha-linolenic acid.

drink The amount of an alcoholic beverage that provides approximately 17 mL or 13.5 grams of pure ethanol.

dual energy x-ray absorptiometry (DXA or DEXA) Currently, the most accurate tool for measuring bone density.

E

eating disorder A clinically diagnosed psychiatric disorder characterized by severe disturbances in body image and eating behaviours.

edema A disorder in which fluids build up in the tissue spaces of the body, causing fluid imbalances and a swollen appearance.

eicosapentaenoic acid (EPA) A metabolic derivative of alpha-linolenic acid.

electrolyte A substance that disassociates in solution into positively and negatively charged ions and is thus capable of carrying an electrical current.

electron A negatively charged particle orbiting the nucleus of an atom.

elimination The process by which undigested and unabsorbed portions of food and waste products are removed from the body.

embryo The human growth and developmental stage lasting from the third week to the end of the eighth week after fertilization.

emulsifiers Chemicals that improve texture and smoothness in foods; they stabilize oil-water mixtures.

energy cost of physical activity The energy that is expended on body movement and muscular work above basal levels.

energy expenditure The energy the body expends to maintain its basic functions and to perform all levels of movement and activity.

energy intake The amount of food a person eats; in other words, it is the amount of energy or number of kilocalories consumed.

enriched foods Foods in which nutrients that were lost during processing have been added back, so that the food meets a specified standard.

enteric nervous system The nerves of the GI tract.

enzymes Small proteins that act on other chemicals to speed up body processes but are not apparently changed during those processes.

epiphyseal plates Plates of cartilage located toward the end of long bones that provide for growth in the length of long bones.

ergogenic aids Substances used to improve exercise and athletic performance.

erythrocytes The red blood cells, which are the cells that transport oxygen in our blood.

esophagus A muscular tube of the GI tract connecting the back of the mouth to the stomach.

essential amino acids Amino acids not produced by the body that must be obtained from food.

essential fatty acids (EFAs) Fatty acids that must be consumed in the diet because they cannot be made by our bodies. The two essential fatty acids are linoleic acid (an ω-6 or n-6 fatty acid) and alpha-linolenic acid (an ω-3 or n-3 fatty acid).

essential nutrients Nutrients that must come from food or nutrient supplements because they are not manufactured by the body at all or in amounts sufficient to meet the body's needs.

Estimated Average Requirement (EAR) The average daily nutrient intake level estimated to meet the requirement of half the healthy individuals in a particular life stage or gender group.

Estimated Energy Requirement (EER) The average dietary energy intake that is predicted to maintain energy balance in a healthy adult.

ethanol A specific alcohol compound (C_2H_5OH) formed from the fermentation of dietary carbohydrates and used in a variety of alcoholic beverages.

evaporative cooling Another term for sweating, which is the primary way in which we dissipate heat.

exercise A subcategory of leisure-time physical activity; any activity that is purposeful, planned, and structured.

extracellular fluid The fluid outside the body's cells, either in the body's tissues or as the liquid portion of blood, called plasma.

F

famine A widespread severe food shortage that causes starvation and death in a large portion of a population in a region.

fats An important energy source for our body at rest and during low-intensity exercise.

fat-soluble vitamins Vitamins that are not soluble in water but are soluble in fat. These include vitamins A, D, E, and K.

fatty acids Long chains of carbon atoms bound to each other as well as to hydrogen atoms.

fatty liver An early and reversible stage of liver disease often found in people who abuse alcohol and characterized by the abnormal accumulation of fat within liver cells; also called alcoholic steatosis.

female athlete triad A condition characterized by the coexistence of three disorders in some athletic females: an eating disorder, amenorrhea, and osteoporosis.

fermentation A process in which an agent causes an organic substance to break down into simpler substances and results in the production of ATP.

ferritin A storage form of iron in our body, found primarily in the intestinal mucosa, spleen, bone marrow, and liver.

fetal adaptation The process by which a fetus's metabolism, hormone production, and other physiologic processes shift in response to factors, such as inadequate energy intake, in the maternal environment.

fetal alcohol spectrum disorders (FASD) A range of conditions that result from maternal intake of alcohol.

fetal alcohol syndrome (FAS) A set of serious, irreversible alcohol-related birth defects characterized by certain physical and mental abnormalities.

fetus The human growth and developmental stage lasting from the beginning of the ninth week after conception to birth.

FIT principle The principle used to achieve an appropriate overload for physical training; FIT stands for frequency, intensity, and time of activity.

fluid A substance composed of molecules that move past one another freely. Fluids are characterized by their ability to conform to the shape of whatever container holds them.

fluorosis A condition marked by staining and pitting of the teeth; caused by an abnormally high intake of fluoride.

food additives Substances intentionally put into food to enhance appearance, palatability, and quality.

food allergy An inflammatory reaction to food generally caused by an immune system hypersensitivity.

food insecurity Circumstances in which households are uncertain of having, or unable to acquire, enough food to meet the needs of all their members because they have insufficient money or other resources for food.

food intolerance Gastrointestinal discomfort caused by certain foods that is not a result of an immune system reaction.

food preservatives Chemicals that help prevent microbial spoilage and enzymatic deterioration.

food-borne illness An illness transmitted through food or water, either by an infectious agent, a poisonous substance, or a protein that causes an immune reaction.

fortified foods Foods in which nutrients are added that did not originally exist in the food, or which existed in insignificant amounts.

free radical A highly unstable atom with an unpaired electron in its outermost shell.

frequency The number of activity sessions per week you perform.

fructose The sweetest natural sugar; a monosaccharide that occurs in fruits and vegetables; also called levulose, or fruit sugar.

functional fibre The indigestible forms of carbohydrates that are extracted from plants or manufactured in a laboratory and have known health benefits.

fungi Plantlike, spore-forming organisms that can grow either as single cells or multicellular colonies.

G

galactose A monosaccharide that joins with glucose to create lactose, one of the three most common disaccharides.

gallbladder A tissue sac beneath the liver that concentrates and stores bile and secretes it into the small intestine.

gastric juice Acidic liquid secreted within the stomach; it contains hydrochloric acid, pepsin, water, and other compounds.

gastroesophageal reflux disease (GERD) A more painful type of GER that occurs more than twice per week.

gastrointestinal (GI) tract A long, muscular tube consisting of several organs: the mouth, esophagus, stomach, small intestine, and large intestine.

gene expression The process of using a gene to make a protein.

genetic modification The process of changing an organism by manipulating its genetic material.

gestation The period of intrauterine development from conception to birth.

gestational diabetes Insufficient insulin production or insulin resistance that results in consistently high blood glucose levels, specifically during pregnancy; the condition typically resolves after birth occurs.

ghrelin A protein, synthesized in the stomach, that acts as a hormone and plays an important role in appetite regulation by stimulating appetite.

glucagon The hormone secreted by the alpha cells of the pancreas in response to decreased blood levels of glucose; it causes the breakdown of liver stores of glycogen into glucose.

gluconeogenesis The generation of glucose from the breakdown of proteins into amino acids.

glucose The most abundant sugar molecule, a monosaccharide generally found in combination with other sugars; it is the preferred source of energy for the brain and an important source of energy for all cells.

glycemic index The system that assigns ratings (or values) for the potential of foods to raise blood glucose and insulin levels.

glycemic load The amount of carbohydrate in a food multiplied by the glycemic index of the carbohydrate.

glycerol An alcohol composed of three carbon atoms; it is the backbone of a triglyceride molecule.

glycogen A polysaccharide; the storage form of glucose in animals. Glycogen is not found in plants.

glycolysis The breakdown of glucose; yields two ATP molecules and two pyruvic acid molecules for each molecule of glucose.

goiter Enlargement of the thyroid gland; can be caused by either iodine toxicity or deficiency.

H

health A multidimensional, lifelong process that includes physical, emotional, social, occupational, and spiritual health.

healthful diet A diet that provides the proper combination of energy and nutrients and is adequate, moderate, balanced, and varied.

heartburn (gastroesophageal reflux [GER]) A painful sensation that occurs behind the sternum when hydrochloric acid backs up into the lower esophagus.

heat cramps Involuntary, spasmodic, and painful muscle contractions that are caused by electrolyte imbalances occurring as a result of strenuous physical activity in high environmental heat.

heat exhaustion A serious condition, characterized by heavy sweating, paleness, nausea and vomiting, dizziness, and moderately elevated body temperature, that develops from dehydration in high heat.

heat stroke A potentially fatal response to high temperature characterized by failure of the body's heat-regulating mechanisms; also commonly called sunstroke.

helminth A multicellular microscopic worm.

heme The iron-containing molecule found in hemoglobin.

heme iron Iron that is a part of hemoglobin and myoglobin; found only in animal-based foods, such as meat, fish, and poultry.

hemoglobin The oxygen-carrying protein found in our red blood cells; almost two-thirds of all the iron in our body is found in hemoglobin.

hemosiderin A storage form of iron in our body, found primarily in the intestinal mucosa, spleen, bone marrow, and liver.

herb A plant or plant part used for its scent, flavour, and/or therapeutic properties (also called a botanical).

hidden fats Fats that are hidden in foods, such as the fats found in baked goods, regular-fat dairy products, marbling in meat, and fried foods.

high-density lipoprotein (HDL) A lipoprotein made in the liver and released into the blood. HDLs function to transport cholesterol from the tissues back to the liver. Often called the "good cholesterol."

homocysteine An amino acid that requires adequate levels of folate, vitamin B_6, and vitamin B_{12} for its metabolism. High levels of homocysteine in the blood are associated with an increased risk for vascular diseases, such as cardiovascular disease.

hormone A chemical messenger secreted into the bloodstream by one of the many glands of the body, which acts as a regulator of physiologic processes at a site remote from the gland that secreted it.

humectants Chemicals that help retain moisture in foods, keeping them soft and pliable.

hunger A physiologic sensation that prompts us to eat.

hydrogenation The process of adding hydrogen to unsaturated fatty acids, making them more saturated and thereby more solid at room temperature.

hypercalcemia A condition marked by an abnormally high concentration of calcium in the blood.

hyperkalemia A condition in which blood potassium levels are dangerously high.

hypermagnesemia A condition marked by an abnormally high concentration of magnesium in the blood.

hypernatremia A condition in which blood sodium levels are dangerously high.

hypertension A chronic condition characterized by above-average blood pressure readings—specifically, systolic blood pressure over 140 mm Hg or diastolic blood pressure over 90 mm Hg.

hypocalcemia A condition characterized by an abnormally low concentration of calcium in the blood.

hypoglycemia A condition marked by blood glucose levels that are below normal fasting levels.

hypokalemia A condition in which blood potassium levels are dangerously low.

hypomagnesemia A condition characterized by an abnormally low concentration of magnesium in the blood.

hyponatremia A condition in which blood sodium levels are dangerously low.

hypothalamus A region of forebrain above the pituitary gland, where visceral sensations, such as hunger and thirst, are regulated.

hypothesis An educated guess as to why a phenomenon occurs.

I

impaired fasting glucose Fasting blood glucose levels that are higher than normal but not high enough to lead to a diagnosis of type 2 diabetes; also called pre-diabetes.

incomplete proteins Proteins that do not contain all of the essential amino acids in sufficient amounts to support growth and health.

inflammatory bowel disease (IBD) A term that includes two different autoimmune disorders with unknown causes that cause inflammation and swelling of the intestine: Crohn's disease and ulcerative colitis.

insensible water loss The loss of water not noticeable by a person, such as through evaporation from the skin and exhalation from the lungs during breathing.

insoluble fibres Components of plants that attract and cling to water, but do not dissolve in water. In humans, these substances speed up the movement of material through the large intestine.

insulin The hormone secreted by the beta cells of the pancreas in response to increased blood levels of glucose; it facilitates the uptake of glucose by body cells.

intensity The amount of effort expended during the activity, or how difficult the activity is to perform.

intracellular fluid The fluid held at any given time within the walls of the body's cells.

intrinsic factor A protein secreted by cells of the stomach that binds to vitamin B_{12} and aids its absorption in the small intestine.

ion An electrically charged particle, either positively or negatively charged.

iron-deficiency anemia A form of anemia that results from severe iron deficiency.

irradiation A sterilization process utilizing gamma rays or other forms of radiation, which does not impart any radiation to the food being treated.

irritable bowel syndrome (IBS) A disorder of the large bowel or colon that interferes with normal functions of the colon.

K

Keshan disease A heart disorder caused by selenium deficiency. It was first identified in children in the Keshan province of China.

ketoacidosis A condition in which excessive ketones are present in the blood, causing the blood to become very acidic, which alters basic body functions and damages tissues. Untreated ketoacidosis can be fatal. This condition is found in individuals with untreated diabetes mellitus.

ketones Substances produced during the breakdown of fat when carbohydrate intake is insufficient to meet energy needs. Ketones provide an alternative energy source for the brain when glucose levels are low.

ketosis The process by which the breakdown of fat during fasting states results in the production of ketones.

kwashiorkor A form of protein–energy malnutrition that is typically seen in developing countries in infants and toddlers who are weaned early because of the birth of a subsequent child. Denied breast milk, they are fed a cereal diet that provides adequate energy but inadequate protein.

L

lactase A digestive enzyme that breaks lactose into glucose and galactose.

lactation The production of breast milk.

lacteal A small lymph vessel located inside the villi of the small intestine.

lactose A disaccharide consisting of one glucose molecule and one galactose molecule. It is found in milk, including human breast milk; also called milk sugar.

lactose intolerance A disorder in which the body does not produce enough lactase enzyme to break down the sugar lactose, which is found in milk and milk products.

large intestine The final organ of the GI tract, consisting of the cecum, colon, rectum, and anal canal and in which most water is absorbed and feces are formed.

leisure-time physical activity Any activity not related to a person's occupation; includes competitive sports, recreational activities, and planned exercise training.

leptin A hormone, produced by body fat, that acts to reduce food intake and increase physical activity and energy, thereby leading to a loss of body weight and body fat.

leukocytes The white blood cells, which protect us from infection and illness.

limiting amino acid The essential amino acid that is missing or in the smallest supply in the amino acid pool and is thus responsible for slowing or halting protein synthesis.

linoleic acid An essential omega-6 fatty acid found in vegetable and nut oils.

lipids A diverse group of organic substances that are insoluble in water; lipids include triglycerides, phospholipids, and sterols.

lipoprotein A spherical compound in which triglycerides stay in the centre and phospholipids and proteins form the outside of the sphere.

lipoprotein lipase An enzyme that sits on the outside surface of cells and breaks apart triglycerides so that their fatty acids can be removed and taken up by the cell.

liver The largest auxiliary organ of the GI tract and one of the most important organs of the body. Its functions include the production of bile and processing of nutrient-rich blood from the small intestine, and detoxifying harmful substances.

low birth weight Having a weight of less than 2500 grams (5.5 lb.) at birth.

low-density lipoprotein (LDL) A lipoprotein formed in the blood from VLDLs that transports cholesterol to the cells of the body. Often called the "bad cholesterol."

low-intensity activities Activities that cause very mild increases in breathing, sweating, and heart rate.

M

macrocytic anemia A form of anemia manifested as the production of larger than normal red blood cells containing insufficient hemoglobin, which inhibits adequate transport of oxygen; also called megaloblastic anemia. Macrocytic anemia can be caused by a severe folate deficiency.

macronutrients Nutrients that our body needs in relatively large amounts to support normal function and health. Carbohydrates, fats, and proteins are macronutrients.

major minerals Minerals that must be consumed in amounts of 100 mg/day or more and that are present in the body at the level of 5 g or more.

malnutrition Any condition associated with under- or overnutrition.

maltase A digestive enzyme that breaks maltose into glucose.

maltose A disaccharide consisting of two molecules of glucose. It does not generally occur independently in foods but results as a by-product of digestion; maltose is also called malt sugar.

marasmus A form of protein–energy malnutrition that results from grossly inadequate intakes of protein, energy, and other nutrients.

maximal heart rate The rate at which your heart beats during maximal-intensity exercise.

meat factor A special factor found in meat, fish, and poultry that enhances the absorption of non-heme iron.

megadose A dose of a nutrient that is 10 or more times greater than the recommended amount.

metabolic syndrome A cluster of risk factors that increase one's risk for heart disease, type 2 diabetes, and stroke, including abdominal obesity, higher than normal triglyceride levels, lower than normal HDL-cholesterol levels, higher than normal blood pressure (greater than or equal to 130/85 mm Hg), and elevated fasting blood glucose levels.

metabolic water The water formed as a by-product of our body's metabolic reactions.

metabolism The process by which large molecules, such as carbohydrates, fats, and proteins, are broken down via chemical reactions into smaller molecules that can be used as fuel, stored, or assembled into new compounds the body needs.

metabolites The form that nutrients take when they have been used by the body. For example, lactate is a metabolite of carbohydrate that is produced when we use carbohydrate for energy.

micronutrients Nutrients needed in relatively small amounts to support normal health and body functions. Vitamins and minerals are micronutrients.

minerals Inorganic substances that are not broken down during digestion and absorption and are not destroyed by heat or light. Minerals assist in the regulation of many body processes and are classified as major minerals or trace minerals.

moderate-intensity activities Activities that cause moderate increases in breathing, sweating, and heart rate.

moderation Eating any foods in moderate amounts—not too much and not too little.

monosaccharide The simplest of carbohydrates, consisting of one sugar molecule, the most common form of which is glucose.

monounsaturated fatty acids (MUFAs) Fatty acids that have two carbons in the chain bound to each other with one double bond; these types of fatty acids are generally liquid at room temperature.

multifactorial disease Any disease that may be attributable to one or more of a variety of causes.

mutual supplementation The process of combining two or more incomplete protein sources to make a complete protein.

myoglobin An iron-containing protein similar to hemoglobin except that it is found in muscle cells.

N

National Institutes of Health (NIH) The world's leading medical centre and the focal point for medical research in the United States.

neural tube Embryonic tissue that forms a tube, which eventually becomes the brain and spinal cord.

neural tube defects The most common malformations of the central nervous system that occur during fetal development. A folate deficiency can cause neural tube defects.

night blindness A vitamin A deficiency disorder that results in loss of the ability to see in dim light.

night-eating syndrome A disorder characterized by intake of the majority of the day's energy between 8:00 p.m. and 6:00 a.m. Individuals with this disorder also experience mood and sleep disorders.

non-essential amino acids Amino acids that can be manufactured by the body in sufficient quantities and therefore do not need to be consumed regularly in our diet.

non-heme iron The form of iron that is not a part of hemoglobin or myoglobin; found in animal- and plant-based foods.

non-nutritive sweeteners Manufactured sweeteners that provide little or no energy; also called alternative sweeteners.

nucleus The positively charged, central core of an atom. It is made up of two types of particles—protons and neutrons—bound tightly together. The nucleus of an atom contains essentially all of its atomic mass.

nutrients Chemicals found in foods that are critical to human growth and function.

nutrition The science that studies food and how food nourishes our body and influences our health.

Nutrition Facts table The table on a food package label that gives the amount of energy and a minimum of 13 key nutrients in one serving of the food.

nutrition transition A shift in dietary pattern toward greater food security, greater variety of foods, and more foods with high energy density; associated with increased incidence of obesity and chronic disease.

nutritive sweeteners Sweeteners, such as sucrose, fructose, honey, and brown sugar, that contribute energy.

O

obesity Having an excess of body fat that adversely affects health, resulting in a person weighing substantially more than an accepted standard for a given height.

organ A body structure composed of two or more tissues and performing a specific function; for example, the esophagus.

organelle A tiny "organ" within a cell that performs a discrete function necessary to the cell.

organic A substance or nutrient that contains the elements carbon and hydrogen.

osmosis The movement of water (or any solvent) through a semi-permeable membrane from an area where solutes are less concentrated to areas where solutes are highly concentrated.

osteoblasts Cells that prompt the formation of new bone matrix by laying down the collagen-containing component of bone, which is then mineralized.

osteoclasts Cells that erode the surface of bones by secreting enzymes and acids that dig grooves into the bone matrix.

osteomalacia A vitamin D–deficiency disease in adults, in which bones become soft, weak, and prone to fractures.

osteoporosis A disease characterized by low bone mass and deterioration of bone tissue, leading to increased bone fragility and fracture risk.

overload principle Placing an extra physical demand on your body to improve your fitness level.

overnutrition A diet that has an imbalance of fats, carbohydrates, and proteins or simply too much energy.

overpopulated A term used to describe a region that has insufficient resources to support the number of people living there.

overweight Having a moderate amount of excess body fat, resulting in a person weighing more than an accepted standard for a given height, but not considered obese.

ovulation The release of an ovum (egg) from a woman's ovary.

oxidation A chemical reaction in which molecules of a substance are broken down into their component atoms. During oxidation, the atoms involved lose electrons.

P

pancreas A gland located behind the stomach that secretes digestive enzymes that break down proteins, carbohydrates, and fats.

pancreatic amylase An enzyme secreted by the pancreas into the small intestine that digests any remaining starch into maltose.

parasite A microorganism that simultaneously derives benefit from and harms its host.

parathyroid hormone (PTH) A hormone secreted by the parathyroid gland when blood calcium levels fall. Also known as parathormone, it increases blood calcium levels by stimulating the activation of vitamin D, increasing reabsorption of calcium from the kidneys, and stimulating osteoclasts to break down bone, which releases more calcium into the bloodstream.

pasteurization A form of sterilization using high temperatures for short periods of time.

pepsin An enzyme in the stomach that begins the breakdown of proteins into shorter polypeptide chains and single amino acids.

peptic ulcer An area of the GI tract that has been eroded away by the acidic gastric juice of the stomach.

peptide bonds Unique types of chemical bonds in which the amine group of one amino acid binds to the acid group of another to manufacture dipeptides and all larger peptide molecules.

Percent daily values (%DV) Information on a Nutrition Facts table that identifies how much a serving of food contributes to your overall intake of nutrients listed on the label; based on an energy intake of 2000 Calories (8400 kJ) per day.

peristalsis Waves of squeezing and pushing contractions that move food in one direction through the length of the GI tract.

pernicious anemia A form of anemia that is the result of either insufficient intake of vitamin B_{12} or the inability to absorb the vitamin B_{12} consumed. A primary cause of a vitamin B_{12} deficiency; often occurs at the end stage of a disorder that causes the loss of certain cells in the stomach.

persistent organic pollutants (POPs) Chemicals released into the environment as a result of industry, agriculture, or improper waste disposal; automobile emissions also are considered POPs.

pesticides Chemicals used either in the field or in storage to destroy plant, fungal, and animal pests.

pH Stands for percentage of hydrogen. It is a measure of the acidity—or level of hydrogen—of any solution, including human blood.

phospholipids A type of lipid with a glycerol backbone to which two fatty acids and another compound that contains phosphate are attached; unlike other lipids, phospholipids are soluble in water.

photosynthesis The process by which plants use sunlight to fuel a chemical reaction that combines carbon and water into glucose, which is then stored in their cells.

physical activity Any movement produced by muscles that increases energy expenditure; includes occupational, household, leisure-time, and transportation activities.

physical fitness The ability to carry out daily tasks with vigour and alertness, without undue fatigue, and with ample energy to enjoy leisure-time pursuits and meet unforeseen emergencies.

phytic acid The form of phosphorus stored in plants.

phytochemicals Compounds found in plants that are believed to have health-promoting effects in humans.

pica An abnormal craving to eat non-food substances such as clay, paint, or chalk.

placenta A pregnancy-specific organ formed from both maternal and embryonic tissues. It is responsible for oxygen, nutrient, and waste exchange between mother and fetus.

plasma The fluid portion of the blood; needed to maintain adequate blood volume, so that the blood can flow easily throughout our body.

platelets Cell fragments that assist in the formation of blood clots and help stop bleeding.

polysaccharide A complex carbohydrate consisting of long chains of glucose.

polyunsaturated fatty acids (PUFAs) Fatty acids that have more than one double bond in the chain; these types of fatty acids are generally liquid at room temperature.

preeclampsia High blood pressure that is pregnancy-specific and accompanied by protein in the urine, edema, and unexpected weight gain.

preterm The birth of a baby prior to 38 weeks' gestation.

prion An infectious, self-replicating protein.

processed foods Foods that are manipulated mechanically or chemically during their production or packaging. Processed foods may or may not resemble the original ingredients in their final form.

proof A measure of the alcohol content of a liquid; 100 proof liquor is 50% alcohol by volume, 80 proof liquor is 40% alcohol by volume, and so on.

pro-oxidant A nutrient that promotes oxidation and oxidative cell and tissue damage.

proteases Enzymes that continue the breakdown of polypeptides in the small intestine.

protein digestibility–corrected amino acid score (PDCAAS) A measurement of protein quality that considers the balance of essential amino acids as well as the digestibility of the protein in the food.

protein–energy malnutrition A disorder caused by inadequate consumption of protein and energy. It is characterized by severe wasting.

proteins The only macronutrient that contains nitrogen; the basic building blocks of proteins are amino acids.

protozoa Single-celled, mobile microorganisms.

provitamin An inactive form of a vitamin that the body can convert to an active form. An example is beta-carotene.

puberty The period of life in which secondary sexual characteristics develop and people become biologically capable of reproducing.

purging An attempt to rid the body of unwanted food by vomiting or other compensatory means, such as excessive exercise, fasting, or laxative abuse.

pyruvic acid The primary end product of glycolysis.

R

Recommended Daily Intakes (RDI) The amounts of vitamins and minerals used to calculate the % daily values.

Recommended Dietary Allowance (RDA) The average daily nutrient intake level that meets the nutrient requirements of 97%–98% of healthy individuals in a particular life stage and gender group.

reference standards The amounts of nutrients other than vitamins and minerals used to calculate the % daily values.

remodelling The two-step process by which bone tissue is recycled; includes the breakdown of existing bone and the formation of new bone.

residues Chemicals that remain in foods despite cleaning and processing.

resistance training Exercises in which our muscles act against resistance.

resorption The process by which the surface of bone is broken down by cells called osteoclasts.

resveratrol A potent phenolic antioxidant found in red wine as well as grapes and nuts.

retina The delicate, light-sensitive membrane lining the inner eyeball and connected to the optic nerve. It contains retinal.

retinal An active, aldehyde form of vitamin A that plays an important role in healthy vision and immune function.

retinoic acid An active, acid form of vitamin A that plays an important role in cell growth and immune function.

retinol An active, alcohol form of vitamin A that plays an important role in healthy vision and immune function.

rhodopsin A light-sensitive pigment found in the rod cells that is formed by retinal and opsin.

ribose A five-carbon monosaccharide that is located in the genetic material of cells.

rickets A vitamin D–deficiency disease in children. Signs include deformities of the skeleton, such as bowed legs and knocked knees. Severe rickets can be fatal.

S

saliva A mixture of water, mucus, enzymes, and other chemicals that moistens the mouth and food, binds food particles together, and begins the chemical digestion of carbohydrates.

salivary amylase An enzyme in saliva that breaks starch into smaller particles and eventually into the disaccharide maltose.

salivary glands A group of glands found under and behind the tongue and beneath the jaw that release saliva continually as well as in response to the thought, sight, smell, or presence of food.

saturated fatty acids (SFAs) Fatty acids that have no carbons joined together with a double bond; these types of fatty acids are generally solid at room temperature.

sensible water loss Water loss that is noticed by a person, such as through urine output and visible sweating.

set-point theory The theory that the body raises or lowers energy expenditure in response to increased or decreased food intake and physical activity. This action maintains an individual's body weight within a narrow range.

simple carbohydrate Commonly called sugar; can be either a monosaccharide (such as glucose) or a disaccharide.

small intestine The longest portion of the GI tract, where most digestion and absorption takes place.

soluble fibres Natural pectins, mucilages, and gums that absorb water and form gels. In humans, these substances slow down the movement of materials through the small intestine.

solvent A substance that is capable of mixing with and breaking apart a variety of compounds. Water is an excellent solvent.

sphincter A tight ring of muscle separating some of the organs of the GI tract and opening in response to nerve signals indicating that food is ready to pass into the next section.

spina bifida The embryonic neural tube defect that occurs when the spinal vertebrae fail to completely enclose the spinal cord, allowing it to protrude.

spontaneous abortion (also called **miscarriage**) The natural termination of a pregnancy and expulsion of pregnancy tissues because of a genetic, developmental, or physiologic abnormality that is so severe that the pregnancy cannot be maintained.

stabilizers Chemicals used to help maintain smooth texture and uniform colour and flavour in some foods.

starch A polysaccharide stored in plants; the storage form of glucose in plants.

sterols A type of lipid found in foods and the body that has a ring structure; cholesterol is the most common sterol that occurs in our diets. Plant sterols block the absorption of cholesterol.

stomach A J-shaped organ where food is partially digested, churned, and stored until it is released into the small intestine.

stunting Low height for age.

sucrase A digestive enzyme that breaks sucrose into glucose and fructose.

sucrose A disaccharide composed of one glucose molecule and one fructose molecule; sucrose is sweeter than lactose or maltose.

sudden infant death syndrome (SIDS) The sudden death of a previously healthy infant; the most common cause of death in infants over one month of age.

sustainable agriculture Techniques of food production that preserve the environment indefinitely.

system A group of organs that work together to perform a unique function; for example, the gastrointestinal system.

T

teratogen A compound known to cause fetal harm or danger.

texturizers Chemicals used to improve the texture of various foods.

theory A conclusion drawn from repeated experiments.

thermic effect of food (TEF) The energy expended as a result of processing food consumed.

thickening agents Natural or chemically modified carbohydrates that absorb some of the water present in food, making the food thicker while keeping food components balanced.

thirst mechanism A cluster of nerve cells in the hypothalamus that stimulate our conscious desire to drink fluids in response to an increase in the concentration of salt in our blood or a decrease in blood pressure and blood volume.

thrifty gene theory The theory that some people possess a gene (or genes) that causes them to be energetically thrifty, resulting in their expending less energy at rest and during physical activity.

time of activity The period of time that an exercise session lasts.

tissue A grouping of like cells that performs a function; for example, muscle tissue.

tocopherol The active form of vitamin E in our body.

Tolerable Upper Intake Level (UL) The highest average daily nutrient intake level likely to pose no risk of adverse health effects to almost all individuals in a particular life stage and gender group.

total fibre The sum of dietary fibre and functional fibre.

toxin A harmful substance; specifically, a chemical produced by a microorganism that harms tissues or causes adverse immune responses.

trabecular bone (spongy bone) A porous bone tissue that makes up only 20% of our skeleton and is found within the ends of the long bones, inside the spinal vertebrae, inside the flat bones (sternum, ribs, and most bones of the skull), and inside the bones of the pelvis.

trace minerals Minerals that must be consumed in amounts of less than 100 mg/day and that are present in the body at the level of less than 5 g.

transamination The process of transferring the amine group from one amino acid to another to manufacture a new amino acid.

transcription The process through which messenger RNA copies genetic information from DNA in the nucleus.

transferrin The transport protein for iron.

transgenic crops Plant varieties that have had one or more genes altered through the use of genetic technologies; also called genetically modified organisms, or GMOs.

translation The process that occurs when the genetic information carried by messenger RNA is translated into a chain of amino acids at the ribosome.

transport proteins Protein molecules that help transport substances throughout the body and across cell membranes.

triglyceride A molecule consisting of three fatty acids attached to a three-carbon glycerol backbone.

trimester Any one of three stages of pregnancy, each lasting 13 to 14 weeks.

T-score A comparison of an individual's bone density to the average peak bone density of a 30-year-old healthy adult.

tumour Any newly formed mass of undifferentiated cells.

type 1 diabetes A disorder in which the body cannot produce enough insulin.

type 2 diabetes A progressive disorder in which body cells become less responsive to insulin.

U

umbilical cord The cord containing the arteries and veins that connect the baby (from the navel) to the mother via the placenta.

undernutrition A diet that lacks energy or specific essential nutrients.

underweight Having too little body fat to maintain health, causing a person to weigh less than an acceptably defined standard for a given height.

urinary tract infection A bacterial infection of the urethra, the tube leading from the bladder to the body exterior.

V

variety Eating a lot of different foods each day.

vegetarian diet A diet that does not include meat (including poultry) or seafood, or products containing those foods.

very-low-density lipoprotein (VLDL) A lipoprotein made in the liver and intestine that functions to transport endogenous lipids, especially triglycerides, to the tissues of the body.

vigorous-intensity activities Activities that produce significant increases in breathing, sweating, and heart rate; talking is difficult when exercising at a vigorous intensity.

viruses A group of infectious agents that are much smaller than bacteria, lack independent metabolism, and are incapable of growth or reproduction apart from living cells.

viscous Having a gel-like consistency; viscous fibres form a gel when dissolved in water.

visible fats Fat we can see in our foods or see added to foods, such as butter, margarine, cream, salad dressings, chicken skin, and untrimmed fat on meat.

vitamins Organic compounds that assist in regulating body processes.

W

warm-up Activities that prepare you for an exercise bout, including stretching, aerobics, and movements specific to the exercise bout; also called preliminary exercise.

wasting Very low weight for height.

water-soluble vitamins Vitamins that are soluble in water. These include vitamin C and the B-vitamins.

Wernicke-Korsakoff syndrome A form of thiamin deficiency seen in chronic alcoholics that results in mental confusion and a loss of memory.

Z

zygote A fertilized egg (ovum) consisting of a single cell.

INDEX

Key terms and the pages on which they are defined appear in boldface; *t* denotes a table, and *f* denotes a figure.

CREDITS

PHOTO CREDITS

Note: Photos appearing in the Table of Contents are duplicates of chapter photos.

Chapter 1   p. 2, Valua Vitaly/Fotolia; p. 4, Richard Embery/Pearson Education/PH College; p. 5, Lester V. Bergman/Encyclopedia/Corbis; p. 6, Wrangel/Dreamstime; p. 7, Blazej Maksym/Fotolia; p. 11, Dragon_Fang/Fotolia; p. 12, Fotogiunta/Fotolia; p. 13 (top), Richard Embery/Pearson Education/PH College; p. 13 (middle), Warren Goldswain/Fotolia; p. 19, Monkey Business/Fotolia; p. 21, Dolgikh/Fotolia; p. 22, Robert Kneschke/Shutterstock; p. 24, Shock/Fotolia; p. 25, Randy L. Jirtle; p. 31, Ljupco Smokovski/Fotolia; p. 31, Kristin Piljay/Pearson Education/Pearson Science; p. 32, Michael Newman/PhotoEdit; p. 34 (top), Monkey Business/Fotolia; p. 34 (bottom), radarreklama/Fotolia; p. 35 (left), Science Photo Library/Photo Researchers, Inc; p. 35 (right), Martin M. Rotker/Photo Researchers, Inc.; p. 36 (top), Streissguth, A.P, Clarren, S.K., & Jones, K.L. (1985, July). Natural history of the Fetal Alcohol Syndrome: A ten-year follow-up of eleven patients. Lancet, 2, 85–91. Fetal Alcohol & Drug Unit (FAS); p. 36 (bottom), Alexey Klementiev/Fotolia.

Chapter 2   p. 38, Yuri Arcurs/Fotolia; p. 40 (top), Richard Embery/Pearson Education/PH College; p. 40 (bottom left), Photosani/Fotolia; (bottom right), jazavac/Fotolia; p. 41 (top), Sergejs Rahunoks/Fotolia; p. 41 (bottom), Michael Newman/PhotoEdit, Ian Dagnall/Alamy, Betacam/Fotolia; p. 42 (top), Courtesy of President's Choice®, www.presidentschoice.ca; p. 42 (bottom), Monkey Business/Fotolia; p. 50, Heart and Stroke Foundation; p. 54, Kristin Piljay/Pearson Education/Pearson Science; p. 55 (top), Sashahaltam/Fotolia; p. 55 (center), Ivonne Wierink/Fotolia; p. 55 (bottom), Kzenon/Fotolia; p. 57, PHB.cz/Fotolia; p. 58, Richard Embery/Pearson Education/PH College; p. 59, Image Source/Alamy, Envision/Corbis, F. Schussler/PhotoLink/Getty Images, Ragnar Schmuck/Getty Images; p. 61, Pearson Education; p. 62 (top), Joe Raedle/Getty Images News/Getty Images; p. 62 (bottom), Corepics/Fotolia; p. 63 (top left), Creative Digital Visions/Pearson Science/Pearson Education; p. 63 (top right), Creative Digital Visions/Pearson Science/Pearson Education; p. 63 (bottom), zech/Fotolia; p. 64, Pearson Education/Pearson Science; p. 68, Barbro Bergfeldt/Fotolia; p. 70, Southern Illinois University/Photo Researchers, Inc., Image Source/Getty Images, Joy Brown/Shutterstock, Pixtal/Age Fotostock, DJM-photo/Shutterstock; p. 71 (top), Rob Bartee/Alamy; p. 71 (bottom), HG Photography/Fotolia.

Chapter 3   p. 72 WavebreakMediaMicro/Fotolia; p. 74 (top), Deklofenak/Shutterstock; p. 64 (bottom), Maridav/Fotolia; p. 76, Jon Riley/Stone/Getty Images; p. 77, Richard Embery/Pearson Education/PH College; p. 81, Jonelle Weaver/Taxi/Getty Images; p. 87, Bon Appetit/Alamy; p. 89, Gino Santa Maria/Fotolia; p. 92, SPL/Photo Researchers, Inc.; p. 93, ene/Shutterstock; p. 94, Monkey Business/Fotolia; p. 95 (top), MedicalRF.com/Alamy; p. 95 (bottom), Dr. E. Walker/Science Photo Library/Photo Researchers, Inc.; p. 96, Hubert Heller; p. 97, Richard Embery/Pearson Education/PH College; p. 100, Annabella Bluesky/Margie Finchell/Photo Researchers, Inc.; p. 104, Springfield Gallery/Fotolia; p. 105, Richard Embery/Pearson Education/PH College; p. 106, Richard Embery/Pearson Education/PH College; p. 107, Cordelia Molloy/Photo Researchers, Inc.; p. 107, Monkey Business Images/Fotolia; p. 108, Stoonn/Fotolia.

Chapter 4   p. 100, JMB/Fotolia; p. 113, lightpoet/Fotolia; p. 115 (left), Richard Embery/Pearson Education/PH College; p. 115 (right), Richard Embery/Pearson Education/PH College; p. 116, Richard Embery/Pearson Education/PH College; p. 117 (top), Kristin Piljay/Pearson Education/Pearson Science; p. 117 (bottom), Zurijeta/Shutterstock, p. 118, Richard Smith/Masterfile, Doug Menuez/Photodisc/Getty Images, technotr/iStockphoto.com; p. 119, Stephen Kirschenmann/Fotolia; p. 120, Richard Embery/Pearson Education/PH College; p. 125, Richard Embery/

Pearson Education/PH College; p. 126, Richard Embery/Pearson Education/PH College; p. 127, lunamarina/Fotolia; p. 129, Richard Embery/Pearson Education/PH College; p. 130, Barbro Bergfeldt/Fotolia, Brett Mulcahy/Fotolia, JJAVA/Fotolia, M.studio/Fotolia; p. 132, Pearson Education/Pearson Science; p. 137, bayu harsa/Fotolia, p. 141, Dmitry Lobanov/Fotolia, p. 142, Scott Camazine/Alamy, p. 143 (left), hdcphoto/Fotolia; p. 143 (right), Lisa Svara/Fotolia; p. 145, Tim Mosenfelder/Getty Images Entertainment/Getty Images.

Chapter 5   p. 146, dream79/Fotolia; p. 148, erwinova/Fotolia; p. 148, Polina/Fotolia; p. 150, Richard Embery/Pearson Education/PH College; p. 150, Richard Embery/Pearson Education/PH College; p. 152, Parmalat; p. 160, Kurhan/Fotolia; p. 160, Radin Myroslav/Fotolia; p. 161, sylvaine thomas/Fotolia; p. 162, Jacek Chabraszewski/Fotolia; p. 163, Richard Embery/Pearson Education/PH College; p. 163, Steffen Sinzinger/Fotolia; p. 165, Richard Embery/Pearson Education/PH College; p. 165, Richard Embery/Pearson Education/PH College; p. 166, Richard Embery/Pearson Education/PH College; p. 167, Travis Amos/Pearson Education; p. 169, Dr. Alejandro Maragoni; p. 169, Dr. Alejandro Maragoni; p. 171, Helen Sessions/Alamy; p. 171, Richard Embery/Pearson Education/PH College; p. 171, Richard Embery/Pearson Education/PH College; p. 171, Richard Embery/Pearson Education/PH College; p. 171, Scott Karcich/Fotolia; p. 172, JB Reed/Landov; p. 176, Monkey Business Images/Fotolia; p. 177, Science Photo Library/Photo Researchers, Inc.; p. 177, Biophoto Associates/Photo Researchers, Inc.; p. 178, Alexander Raths/Fotolia; p. 179, Inger Anne Hulbækdal/Fotolia; p. 180, Jaroslaw Grudzinski/Fotolia.

Chapter 6   p. 184, kristajean/Fotolia; p. 186, iofoto/Fotolia; p. 191, Richard Embery/Pearson Education/PH College; p. 192, Andrew Syred/Photo Researchers, Inc.; p. 193, Creative Digital Visions/Dorling Kindersley, Ltd.; p. 193, Creative Digital Visions/Pearson Education/Pearson Science; p. 193, Creative Digital Visions/Pearson Education/Pearson Science; p. 193, Creative Digital Visions/Pearson Education/Pearson Science; p. 195, Falater Photo/Fotlia LLC; p. 195, Mediscan/Medical-on-Line/Alamy; p. 199, Richard Embery/Pearson Education/PH College; p. 200, Galina Barskaya/Fotolia; p. 201, Jupiterimages/Comstock Images/Getty Images; p. 201, Andrew Holbrooke/Corbis; p. 201, Rubberball/Alan K. Bailey/Getty Images; p. 204, Richard Embery/Pearson Education/PH College; p. 206, Richard Embery/Pearson Education/PH College; p. 207, BananaStock/Alamy; p. 208, Richard Embery/Pearson Education/PH College; p. 209, Richard Embery/Pearson Education/PH College; p. 210, ZUMA Press/Newscom; p. 210, Paul Almasy/Historical/Corbis; p. 210, Paul Almasy/Corbis; p. 212, Kalim/Fotolia; p. 212, ne_fall_photos/Fotolia; p. 216, Yasonya/Fotolia; p. 217, Richard Embery/Pearson Education/PH College; p. 217, Richard Embery/Pearson Education/PH College; p. 218, Paul Prescott/Fotolia; p. 220, Bradcalkins/Fotolia; p. 223, Richard Embery/Pearson Education/PH College; p. 223, Robert Lehmann/Fotolia; p. 224, Zkoritni/Fotolia.

Chapter 7   p. 226, MP2/Fotolia; p. 228, Monkey Business/Fotolia; p. 230, Lonescu Bogdan/Fotolia; p. 234, Suprijono Suharjoto/Fotolia; p. 234, Photo25th/Shutterstock; p. 235, Kzenon/Fotolia; p. 236, Warren Goldswain/Fotolia; p. 237, PhotoDisc/Getty Images; p. 237, Ted Levine/Fancy/Corbis; p. 239, Dreambigphotos/Fotolia; p. 240, Lorraine Kourafas/Shutterstock; p. 240, Richard Embery/Pearson Education/PH College; p. 240, Natalia Mylova/Fotolia; p. 240, Sassyphotos/Fotolia; p. 240, Barbara Dudzinska/Shutterstock; p. 241, spaxiax/Fotolia; p. 242, Kenishirotie/iStockphoto; p. 242, Tomalu/Fotolia; p. 243, Viktor/Fotolia; p. 244, Avesun/Fotolia; p. 244, Peter zijlstra/Shutterstock; p. 246, Owen Brewer/ZUMA Press/Newscom; p. 250, pkchai/Fotolia; p. 251, AGphotographer/Fotolia; p. 251, Rick Stewart/Getty Images Sport; p. 253, Pearson Education/Pearson Science.

Chapter 8   p. 254, Lidante/Shutterstock; p. 258, grynold/Shutterstock; p. 260, volff/Fotolia; p. 261, eyewave/iStockphoto; p. 261, Laks/Fotolia;